T0133129

SYSTEM-BASED VISION FOR STRATEGIC AND CREATIVE DESIGN

PROCEEDINGS OF THE SECOND INTERNATIONAL CONFERENCE ON STRUCTURAL
AND CONSTRUCTION ENGINEERING, 23–26 SEPTEMBER 2003, ROME, ITALY

System-based Vision for Strategic and Creative Design

Edited by

Franco Bontempi
University of Rome "La Sapienza", Rome, Italy

Volume 1

A.A. BALKEMA PUBLISHERS   LISSE / ABINGDON / EXTON (PA) / TOKYO

Copyright © 2003 Swets & Zeitlinger B.V., Lisse, The Netherlands

All rights reserved. No part of this publication or the information contained herein may be reproduced, stored in a retrieval system, or transmitted in any form or by any means, electronic, mechanical, by photocopying, recording or otherwise, without written prior permission from the publisher.

Although all care is taken to ensure the integrity and quality of this publication and the information herein, no responsibility is assumed by the publishers nor the author for any damage to property or persons as a result of operation or use of this publication and/or the information contained herein.

Published by: A.A. Balkema, a member of Swets & Zeitlinger Publishers
www.balkema.nl and www.szp.swets.nl

For the complete set of three volumes: ISBN 90 5809 599 1
Volume 1: 90 5809 600 9
Volume 2: 90 5809 601 7
Volume 3: 90 5809 630 0

Printed in the Netherlands

System-based Vision for Strategic and Creative Design, Bontempi (ed.)
© 2003 Swets & Zeitlinger, Lisse, ISBN 90 5809 599 1

Table of Contents

Preface	XXV
Acknowledgements	XXVII
Organisation	XXIX

Volume 1

1. Keynotes

Life-cycle maintenance strategies for deteriorating structures based on multiple probabilistic performance indicators   3
D.M. Frangopol & L.C. Neves

Culture in construction – "human reengineering"?   11
R.F. Fellows

Influence of the anchorage system and of the deck stiffness on the postcritical behaviour of suspended bridges   17
P.G. Malerba

2. Risk analysis and structural reliability

Codified design and reliability aspects of structural timber elements   25
T. Keskküla & L. Ozola

Uncertainties of the method of partial safety factors   31
A. Kudzys & E.R. Vaidogas

Prototype testing for reliability-based design   37
S.G. Reid

Microbiology risk and hydraulic of the hot water system   45
Z. Pospíchal & Žabička

A general framework for risk management of stable links   49
F. Petrilli

3. Construction planning and project management

Improving construction processes: experiences in the field of contact–contract–conflict   57
W. Tijhuis & R.F. Fellows

International procurement of construction materials for the Middle East   65
E. Koehn, H.J. Tohme & A.P. Shukla

Building design evaluation – facility manager's and designer's perspectives   69
K. Lueprasert & Y. Kanhawattana

Development of the logistics plans in building construction   75
S.M.B. Serra & O.J. Oliveira

A design/evaluation approach to building design and construction   81
T.H. Nguyen & S. Yazdani

Organisational and managerial attributes of innovation among firms in the construction industry
in the UK: why culture matters?   85
G. Zawdie, J. Abukhder & D. Langford

Lighting design for highway nighttime construction operations   93
K. El-Rayes & K. Hyari

Process analysis of interior finishing and building services works   99
N. Mine, T. Kunugi & N. Miura

Construction of super high-rise composite structures in Hong Kong   107
Raymond W.M. Wong

Design of a buried polyfunctional centre   117
A. Rago & P. Giura

Wall panels for industrialized housing method   123
S.P.G. Moonen

Development of a framework for valuing variations in concrete works   129
M. Sutrisna, K. Potts & D. Proverbs

An estimating system for construction and demolition waste management   137
A. Touran, J.Y. Wang, C. Christoforou & N. Dantata

Steel fabricator involvement in project design   143
M.J. Horman, M.H. Pulaski, C.M. Hewitt & J.P. Cross

Existing and emerging delivery system for construction projects   151
K.A. Tenah

Success factors of partnering in new project delivery models – experience in Switzerland   157
G. Girmscheid

Alternative courses of action for industrialized construction processes in small and
medium-sized enterprises   163
J. Bärthel

An industrialized foundation   169
S.P.G. Moonen

Applying the theory of constraints to construction scheduling   175
J.-B. Yang

Simplified simulation system of overlapping CPM networks   181
A.M. Odeh

Planning the installation of steel structures using simulation   189
G. Uzzi & J. Shi

Probability applications in the precedence diagram scheduling method   195
M.F. Samara & C.S. Putcha

The application of simulation modelling in identifying company's logistic system models   199
A. Sobotka

Resource scheduling of construction projects using a hybrid genetic algorithm model   205
A.B. Senouci & K.K. Naji

The importance of new information technologies in a concurrent design environment   211
P.J. Bártolo & H.M. Bártolo

IT tools for collaborative working in relationally integrated supply chains 217
O.O. Ugwu, M.M. Kumaraswamy, M.M. Rahman & S.T. Ng

Information technology training: aligning competence with corporate capability 223
J.S. Goulding, M. Alshawi & A. Alani

E-commerce in the construction industry in Lebanon 229
T. Mezher, M.A. Abdul-Malak & M. Ajam

Decomposition of data base – modulation for management of designing and construction of highways 237
M. Knezevic

4. Cost control and productivity management

A Bayesian approach for updating change order uncertainty 245
A. Touran

Study on the development of the curing system for concrete in construction site 249
T. Tamura, Y. Tominaga, O. Sakamoto, H. Ueno & H. Sumito

Methodological problems of productivity measurement in the construction industry 255
J. Iwamatsu & K. Endo

An expert system for construction cost indexing and forecasting 263
M.F. Samara

Driving down construction project labor cost 269
H.E. Picard

Production planning and cost optimization for prestressed concrete alveolar slabs 275
G. Greco, A. Rago & G. Iaconianni

Productivity management, improvement and cost reduction 283
L.H. Forbes, S.M. Ahmed, M. Hocaoglu & S. Azhar

Design team characteristics in aerospace, construction and product design for co-located and distributed projects 289
F.T. Edum-Fotwe, A. Thorpe, M.J. Gregory, P.J. Deasley, A.B. Wootton, A.N.W. North & R. Cooper

Advanced developments in semiconductor facility construction 299
S.J. Eibl

Construction productivity of multistory buildings in developing countries 303
E. Koehn, P. Shukla & H.J. Tohme

A life-cycle energy model of the UK steel construction sector 309
J. Ley, M. Sansom & A.S.K. Kwan

Robotics and the construction industry 315
N. Pires & T.D. Pereira

A review of capital procurement in the UK National Health Service 321
D.G. Proverbs, M. Sutrisna & G. Riley

Construction techniques for efficient and economical housing 325
R.K. Jain

Automating quantity takeoff and decision support for in-place reinforced concrete structures 329
R. Drogemuller, S. Foo, C. McNamara & J. Oliver

Analyses on the productivity of multi-skilled team in the reinforced concrete construction site of the residential buildings 335
K. Endo, H. Kanisawa & Y. Kimura

Comparative study of UK and Italian refurbishment sites involving demolition activities and structural instability: risk factors and Health & Safety management strategies 343
B.M. Marino Duffy, C.O. Egbu, C.J. Anumba, A. Gottfried & B. Neale

Integrated risk management for construction system providers 349
T.A. Busch

Cost and risk management utilizing an integrated master plan 357
A.R. Minter, D.W. Ebersole, P.D. Howorth, M. Plank, K. Raum & I. Henderson

Three missing elements of construction risk management: a conceptual exploration 363
C.-Yu Chang & M.-T. Wang

Developing benchmarks for project schedule risk estimation 369
F.T. Edum-Fotwe & Y. Nielsen

Practical cost management system for construction projects 377
K.A. Tenah

The cost caused by lack of interoperability in design 383
C.A. Jacoski & R. Lamberts

The choice of the rib thickness in the mass-production of ribbed R/C floors 389
L. Fenu

5. Human factor, social–economic constraints on the design process

Reciprocal model of construction safety culture 397
W.F. Maloney

Impossibility claims in construction projects 403
Y.M. Wong, T.W. Yiu, S.O. Cheung & C.H. Suen

Engineering the World Trade Center disaster recovery 409
D.A. Cuoco

Highest and best use of people 413
W.L. Kelly

Barriers to constructability in Saudi Arabian construction industry 419
S. Assaf, O. Jannadi & F. Al-Yousif

Ethics of surveyors – a study of Hong Kong SAR 425
R.F. Fellows & A.M.M. Liu

Organizational culture of the Chinese construction companies: towards a C-E model 431
A.M.M. Liu & S.B. Zhang

Environment friendly design of residential buildings in hot-dry climate 437
R. Ahuja & V.M. Rao

Claim analysis involving multiple compensable factors 443
A. Singh

How soccer results effects concrete cracking 449
S.P.G. Moonen

6. Structural optimization and evolutionary procedures

Identification of Strut-and-Tie mechanisms in reinforced concrete structures using the cell method and genetic optimization techniques 455
D. Baron, S. Noè & G.A. Rassati

Strut-and-Tie model of deep beams with web openings using optimisation technique 461
H. Guan & J. Parsons

Analysis and optimization of a cable stayed bridge with external prestressing 467
G. Agostino

Searching for innovative structural layouts by means of graph grammars and evolutionary optimization 475
A. Borkowski, E. Grabska, P. Nikodem & B. Strug

An overall approach to structural design of steelworks using genetic algorithms 481
N. Bel Hadj Ali, J.C. Mangin & A.F. Cutting-Decelle

Optimal arrangement of studded paving block system by multi-objective genetic algorithm 487
H. Furuta & T. Nishi

Optimal design of space structures with stability constraints 493
A. Csébfalvi

A design procedure for multi-component structures 499
Q. Li, G.P. Steven & Y.M. Xie

Discrete Lagrangian method for optimal design of truss structures 507
D.S. Junag, Y.T. Wu & W.T. Chang

The optimal topology of composite beams: analysis, design and experiment 515
B. Wethyavivorn & K. Atchacosit

Design optimization of tall steel buildings 521
L. Catallo, L. Sgambi & S. Tranquilli

Shape optimal design of skeletal structures 527
B. Harl, M. Kegl, D. Dinevski & M.M. Oblak

Multidimensional design and systemic vision in structural engineering 533
F. Biondini & A. Marchiondelli

On the design of optimised R/C sections in bending 543
L. Fenu

7. Shaping structures and form finding architectures

The design of structural systems for geometrically irregular buildings 549
M. Veltkamp & M. Eekhout

Integrating architectural and structural form-finding processes for free-form digital architectures 557
T. Kocaturk, C. van Weeren & M.W. Kamerling

An interdisciplinary approach to the design of free-form buildings 563
M.W. Kamerling & T. Kocaturk

Form finding research: development between empirical and numerical methods 569
D. Abruzzese & A. Tursi

On the shaping of cable-membranes by using "simulated annealing" 575
L. Fenu & S. Manca

8. Issues in computational mechanics of structures

Nonuniform torsion of bars of variable thickness 583
E.J. Sapountzakis & V.G. Mokos

From load path method to classical models of structural analysis 589
F. Palmisano, A. Vitone & C. Vitone

Algebraic method for sensitivity analysis of eigensystems with repeated eigenvalues 597
K.M. Choi, S.W. Cho, I.W. Lee & J.H. Lee

Expression of rotational motion on flexible body 603
K. Miura, T. Nishimura & T. Yamada

Modified modal methods for calculating eigenpair sensitivity of asymmetric systems 611
Y.J. Moon, I.W. Lee & J.H. Lee

Efficient eigensolution method of large structural systems with proportional and
non-proportional dampers 617
H.-J. Jung, J.-S. Jo, I.-W. Lee & M.-G. Ko

On static limit analysis using the *p*-version FEM 625
F. Tin-Loi & N.S. Ngo

Analysis of edge and corner column-slab connections with and without stud shear reinforcement 631
H. Guan & Y.C. Loo

Elastic–plastic large displacement analysis of thin-walled beam type structures 639
G. Turkalj, J. Brnic & D. Lanc

A strain based solid element for plate bending 645
L. Belounar, S. Benmebarek, M. Guenfoud & A. Charif

Study of full composite action in slab-beam systems 651
N. Chikh & J. Harrop

9. Advanced modelling and non-linear analysis of concrete structures

Modelling non-linear behavior of shear walls with damage 659
S. Yazdani

Non-linear analysis of reinforced concrete slabs 663
B. Belletti, P. Bernardi, R. Cerioni & I. Iori

Finite deformation analysis using natural strain (on anisotropy in yield surface under large
uni-axial tension and shear) 669
Y. Kato & Y. Moriguchi

The effective length factors for the framed columns with variable cross sections 677
S.G. Lee, S.C. Kim & Y.J. Moon

Development of a continuum-mechanics-based tool for 3D finite element analysis of reinforced
concrete structures 685
H. Hartl

Stringer Panel Method: a discrete model to project structural reinforced concrete elements 693
G. Tarquini & L. Sgambi

Design of reinforced structures with Strut-and-Tie model 701
S. Arangio, L. Catallo & A. Rago

Approximate methods for analysis of viscoelastic behavior of concrete structures 707
D.Veglianti & L. Sgambi

Studying of elastic–plastic behavior of concrete ceiling, joints, supports by live loading of
concrete ceiling 715
A. Turk

Crack width control in two dimensional reinforced concrete elements 721
G. Bertagnoli, V.I. Carbone, L. Giordano & G. Mancini

Effect of cracking and material non-linearities on the dynamic behavior of reinforced concrete beams 729
K.S. Numayr & S.K. Jubeer

Continuous-discontinuous failure analysis in a rate-dependent elastoplastic damage model 737
A. Simone & L.J. Sluys

10. Concrete and masonry structures

Cracking around the interface joint between masonry panels and their supporting reinforced
concrete beams in buildings 745
J.L.M. Dias

Restoration and repair of existing masonry structures 753
W.C. Bracken

Mechanical response of solid clay brick masonry reinforced with CFRP strips under eccentric loading 761
A. Brencich, C. Corradi, E. Sterpi & G. Mantegazza

On the numerical analysis of localized damage in masonry structures 769
J. Alfaiate, A. Gago & J.R. de Almeida

Load carrying capacity of masonry arch bridges 775
A. Brencich, A. Cavicchi, U. De Francesco, L. Gambarotta & A. Sereno

Limit analysis of masonry domes: two case studies 781
P. Foraboschi & M. Nart

ACI shear reinforcement for flat slabs 789
R.L. Vollum & U.L. Tay

Shear behavior of prestressed concrete beams reinforced by CFRP grids bonded on the web surface 797
A. Yonekura, H. Ito, U. Idehara, Y. Kawauti, K. Era, T. Mihara & K. Zaitsu

Rotation capacity in shear crack hinges of R.C. beams 803
S. Coccia, M. Como & U. Ianniruberto

Bond recovery in reinforced high strength concrete after post-fire recuring 811
R.H. Haddad & L.G. Shannis

Ultimate strength of rectangular CFT column 817
R.V. Jarquio

Bonded-in reinforcement for frame node connections 823
J. Kunz, F. Muenger, H. Kupfer & A. Jaehring

11. Steel structures

Minimum stiffness requirements of intermediate transverse stiffeners in plate girders 833
Y. Ogawa & K. Fujii

Experimental noise improvement and vibration attenuation of an old steel-bridge 839
R. Geier, P. Furtner, G. Magonette & F. Marazzi

Elasto-plastic response of a bar structure to oscillatory external agency 845
K. Hasegawa, T. Nishimura & N. Kayama

Water filled steel structures 851
J.P. Paoluccio

Moment-rotation relationships of single plate connections 855
X. Sun & T.H. Tan

Prestressed steel structures: historical and technological analysis 861
A. Masullo & V. Nunziata

Collapse and buckling of sheet piles, modification solution in Mared pump station, ABADAN 867
A. Turk

Effect of number of bay on sway of building frames 873
B. Ahmed & M. Ashraf

CFRP reinforcement design of steel members damaged by fatigue 879
P. Colombi

Buckling strength evaluation of corroded flange of plate girder 885
T. Kaita & K. Fujii

Testing equipment for fatigue and damage tests of steel cords 893
M. Kopecky, V. Cuth, I. Letko & J. Vavro

Performance of bolted semi-rigid connections under cyclic loading in steel portal frames 899
Y.M. Kim & C.M. Yang

Sway estimation of rigid frames using equation 907
B. Ahmed & M. Ashraf

Prestressed steel structures design: a new frontier for structural engineering 915
V. Nunziata

Development of criteria for using of bracing and shear walls in tall buildings 923
S. Azizpour, M. Mofid & M. Menshari

Linear stability bearing capacity analysis of pin-connected steel structures 927
S.J. Duan, H.M. Jia, S.Y. Li & Z.Y. Liang

Author index 933

Volume 2

12. Bridges and special structures

Croatian experience in design of long span concrete bridges 941
J. Radic, G. Puz & I. Gukov

Hydrogen embrittlement of suspension bridge cable wires 947
K.M. Mahmoud

An universal approach to analysis and design of different cable structures 951
V. Kulbach

The Maya suspension bridge at Yaxchilan 957
J.A. O'Kon

Roles of stiffening systems of steel plate girder bridges 965
E. Yamaguchi, K. Harada, S. Yamamoto & Y. Kubo

Continuity diaphragms in continuous span concrete bridges with AASHTO Type II girders 969
A. Saber, J. Toups & A. Tayebi

Modification of walking bridge into semi-heavy load bridge by new steel connection opener 975
A.A. Turk & B.P. Samani

Bridge deck analysis through the use of grillage models 981
G. Battaglia, P.G. Malerba & L. Sgambi

Hybrid truss and full web systems in composite bridges: the SS125 viaducts in Sardinia 989
M.E. Giuliani

Effectiveness of intermediate diaphragms in PC girder bridges subjected to impact loads 995
F.S. Fanous, R.E. Abendroth & B. Andrawes

Modelling aspects for the analysis of a box girder steel bridge 1003
L. Catallo, S. Loreti & S. Silvi

Structures for covering railways with real estate 1009
Th.S. de Wilde

Grain silos problem and solution 1017
F. Shalouf

Structural response characteristics of stack with hole 1023
T. Hara

Tendencies for solid structures in waterway engineering 1029
C.U. Kunz

Performance of a fibre-reinforced polymer bridge deck under dynamic wheel loading 1035
A.F. Daly & J.R. Cuninghame

Numerical simulation of steel and concrete composite beams subjected to moving loads 1043
N. Gattesco, I. Pitacco & A. Tracanelli

Ultimate and service load simulation of a masonry arch bridge scheduled for controlled demolition 1051
P.J. Fanning, V. Salomoni & T.E. Boothby

Comparison of methods to determine strengths due to mobile loads, in simply supported bridge beams 1057
H. Pankow

Design and construction aspects of a soil stabilized dome used for low-cost housing 1067
M. Gohnert & S.J. Magaia

The last mile – deployment of optical fibers through sewers 1075
S. Gokhale, M. Najafi & E. Sener

13. Precast structures

Nonlinear analysis of prestressed hollow core slabs 1083
B. Belletti, P. Bernardi, R. Cerioni & I. Iori

R.C. shell revival: the Malaga airport new control tower 1091
M.E. Giuliani

Building system with joints of high-strength reinforced concrete 1097
L.P. Hansen

Moment-rotation relationships of hybrid connection under monotonic and cyclic loading 1103
X. Sun & T.H. Tan

Mechanical response of pre-cast concrete wall panels to combined wind and thermal loads 1109
A. Brencich & R. Morbiducci

Strength of precast slab subjected to torsion 1115
S. Nakano

Column-foundation connection for pre-cast elements 1121
E. Dolara & G. Di Niro

14. Earthquake and seismic engineering

Modal damage of structures during earthquake 1129
H. Kuwamura

Architectural design influence on seismic building behavior: evaluation elements 1137
A. Gianni

Seismic retrofit of a historic arch bridge 1145
S. Morcos, A. Hamza & J. Koo

Effects of taking into consideration realistic force-velocity relationship of viscous dampers in the
optimisation of damper systems in shear-type structures 1151
T. Trombetti, S. Silvestri, C. Ceccoli & G. Greco

Rational estimation of the period of RC building frames having infill 1159
K.M. Amanat & E. Hoque

Experimental results and numerical simulation of a concrete sandwich panel system proposed
for earthquake resistant buildings 1165
O. Bassotti, E. Speranzini & A. Vignoli

Theoretical and experimental investigation on the seismic behaviour of concrete frames 1177
F. Biondini & G. Toniolo

Seismic effectiveness of direct and indirect implementation of MPD systems 1187
S. Silvestri, T. Trombetti, C. Ceccoli & G. Greco

A practical code for seismic risk mitigation of historical centers: the case of Umbria (Central Italy) 1195
F. Maroldi

Effect of column characteristics on its inelastic seismic behavior 1201
A. Khairy Hassan

Effects of building vibration to low intensity ground motion: towards human perceptions 1207
A. Adnan & T.C. Wei

Probabilistic hazard models: is it possible a statistical validation? 1211
E. Guagenti, E. Garavaglia & L. Petrini

Fixing steel braced frames to concrete structures for earthquake strengthening 1217
J. Kunz & P. Bianchi

15. Geotechnical engineering and tunnelling

Mechanical properties of steel-concrete composite segment for micro multi box shield tunnel 1227
I. Yoshitake, M.I. Junica, K. Nakagawa, M. Ukegawa, M. Motoki & K. Tsuchida

To an estimation of dynamic stresses around of the immersed body with a rectangular form 1235
L.V. Nuzhdin, A.O. Kolesnikov & V.N. Popov

Design of a railway junction in Palermo: underground structures and building damage risks 1241
D. Pelonero, A. Pigorini, E. Scattolini & E.M. Pizzarotti

Computational methods for deep tunneling design 1247
S. Francia, E.M. Pizzarotti, M. Rivoltini & C. Pecora

Life-cycle maintenance management of traffic tunnels – strategy assessment to develop new
calcification reduction methods in tunnel drainage system 1253
T. Gamisch & G. Girmscheid

Foundation design formulation: a process approach 1259
J.F. van den Adel, S.H. Al-Jibouri, U.F.A. Karim & M. Mawdesley

Relationships between soil conditions and construction costs 1263
J.F. van den Adel, S.H. Al-Jibouri, U.F.A. Karim & M. Mawdesley

A mathematical model for the analysis of the rectangular machine foundations on a layered medium 1269
M.Z. Aşık

Numerical studies of seepage failure of sand within a cofferdam   1273
N. Benmebarek, S. Benmebarek, L. Belounar & R. Kastner

Criterion of crack initiation and propagation in rock   1279
Y.L. Chen & T. Liu

16. Structural problems and safety devices of road and railways

Load-carrying capability of PC beam during shear destruction by impact   1285
N. Furuya, I. Kuroda, K. Shimoyama & S. Nakamura

Study on performance of aluminum alloy-concrete hybrid guard fence   1291
T. Hida, R. Kusama, B. Liu, Y. Itoh & T. Kitagawa

Dynamic actions on bridge slabs due to heavy vehicle impact on roadside barriers   1297
G. Bonin & A. Ranzo

The structural behavior of high strength aluminum alloy sections   1303
Y.B. Kwon, K.H. Lee, H.C. Kim & D.H. Kim

Vehicle-structure interaction modelling   1311
F. Giuliano

Criteria for airport terminal roadway analysis post 911   1319
H.W. Hessing

17. Structural damage assessment

Assessment of fire damage in historic masonry structures   1327
D.M. Lilley & A.V. March

Detection of crack patterns on RAC pre-stressed beam using ultrasonic pulse velocity   1333
E. Dolara & G. Di Niro

Structural failures: lessons for a brighter future   1343
K.L. Carper

Behavior of epoxy-coated reinforcement concrete beams with sodium chloride contamination   1349
M.M.A. Elmetwally

Damage analysis of masonry walls under foundation movements by distinct element method   1355
Y. Zhuge & S. Hunt

18. Materials, composite materials and structures

Ultimate strength of CFT columns – an analytical method   1363
R.V. Jarquio

Shear transfer mechanism of Perfobond strip in steel-concrete composite members   1369
H. Kitoh, S. Yamaoka & K. Sonoda

Delamination of FRP plate/sheets used for strengthening of R/C elements   1375
M. Savoia, B. Ferracuti & C. Mazzotti

The abrasion resistance of fiber concrete surface   1383
Y.W. Liu, T. Yen & T.H. Hsu

Calculation and check of steel-concrete composite beams subject to the compression
associated with bending   1387
G.P. Gamberini & G.F. Giaccu

Application of steel fibre reinforced concrete for the revaluation of timber floors 1393
K. Holschemacher, S. Klotz, Y. Klug & D. Weiße

Application of fiber composite materials with polymer-matrix in building industry –
new possibilities of structure durability rise 1399
L. Bodnarova, R. Hela, M. Filip & J. Prokes

Flexural design of steel or FRP plated RC beams 1405
P.M. Heathcote & M. Raoof

Design methods for slabs on grade in fiber reinforced concrete 1413
A. Meda

Economic aspects of steel composite beam stiffened with C-channel 1419
M.Md. Tahir, A.Y.M. Yassin, N. Yahaya, S. Mohamed & S. Saad

Deformation capacity of concrete columns reinforced with CFT 1423
K. Maegawa, M. Tomida, A. Nakamura, K. Ohmori & M. Shiomi

The deformability of hybrid (carbon and glass fibers) pultruded profiles 1431
S. Russo & G. Boscato

Comparison between BS5400 and EC4 for concrete-filled tubular columns 1435
A.K. Alrodan

A cohesive model for fiber-reinforced composites 1443
A.P. Fantilli & P. Vallini

19. Innovative methods for repair and strengthening structures

Heat straightening repairs of damaged steel bridge members 1453
K.K. Verma & R.R. Avent

Laboratory and field observations of composite-wrapped reinforced concrete structures 1459
E. Berver, J.O. Jirsa, D.W. Fowler & H.G. Wheat

Improving interface bond in pile repair 1467
G. Mullins, J. Fischer, R. Sen & M. Issa

Effectiveness of FRP strengthening of masonry systems of arches and columns 1473
U. Ianniruberto, M. Imbimbo & Z. Rinaldi

Uses of composite design for new and rehabilitated tall buildings 1479
J.P. Colaco

Structural repair of brick masonry chimneys 1487
B. De Nicolo, Z. Odoni & L. Pani

Replacement of Metro-North's Bronx River Bridge 1495
T. Henning & P. Pappas

20. Artificial intelligence in civil engineering

Joint stiffness estimation of thin-walled structure using neural network 1503
A. Okabe, Y. Sato & N. Tomioka

Integrating neural networks, databases and numerical software for managing early age concrete
crack prediction 1511
M. Lazzari, R. Pellegrini, P. Dalmagioni & M. Emborg

An ANN model for biaxial bending of reinforced concrete column 1517
M.E. Haque

Development of a high performance fully automated application system for shotcrete 1523
S. Moser & G. Girmscheid

A learning-based design computer tool   1531
H.M. Bártolo & P.J. Bártolo

Architectural reverse design through a biomimetic-based computer tool   1537
N.M. Alves & P.J. Bártolo

21. Knowledge management

Managing intellectual capital in construction firms   1545
S. Kale & T. Çivici

Process- and success-oriented knowledge management for total service contractors   1551
R. Borner

An intelligent cooperation environment for the building sector, why?   1559
I.S. Sariyildiz, B. Tunçer, Ö. Ciftcioglu & R. Stouffs

Knowledge acquisition for demolition techniques selection model   1567
A. Abdullah & C.J. Anumba

Supporting verification of design intent   1575
I. Faraj

Organization and decomposition of a complex structural project   1581
S. Loreti & M. Salerno

22. Quality and excellence in constructions

Creativity and innovation   1589
W.L. Kelly

Deploying and scoring the European Foundation for Quality Management Excellence
Model (Part One)   1595
P.A. Watson & N. Chileshe

Evaluation and improvement of public school facilities services using a TQM framework   1599
K. Jayyousi & M. Usmen

Warranty practices on DOT projects in the US   1607
Q. Cui, M.E. Bayraktar, M. Hastak & I. Minkarah

Why are some designs more interesting than others? The quest for the unusual, the
unconventional and the unique in design   1613
L. Kiroff

Improved design by progressive awareness   1621
S.P.G. Moonen

Deploying the European Foundation in Quality Management (EFQM) Excellence Model (Part Two)   1625
P.A. Watson & N. Chileshe

23. Sustainable engineering

Production of artificial fly ash lightweight aggregates for sustainable concrete construction   1631
C. Videla & P. Martínez

Sustainable buildings with the infra$^+$ space floor   1637
G.C.M. van der Zanden

Falling accident in the roofing work of residential houses   1641
Y. Hino

Fly ashes thermal modification and their utilization in concrete 1649
R. Hela, J. Marsalova & L. Bodnarova

Necessity of study on countermeasure for climate change to avoid possible disasters 1655
K. Baba

Sustainable bearing structures for (office) buildings 1661
M.J.P. Arets & A.A.J.F. van den Dobbelsteen

Recycled aggregate concrete for structural purposes: ten years of research 1993–2003 1667
E. Dolara & G. Di Niro

24. Life cycles assessment

Estimating the environmental aspects of an office building's life cycle 1685
S. Junnila

Quality and life cycle assessment 1691
J. Christian & L. Newton

Integrated life cycle design of structures 1697
A. Sarja

Towards lifetime oriented structural engineering 1703
A. Sarja

An approach to optimal allocation of transportation facilities on expressway 1709
A. O'hashi, A. Miyamura & A. De Stefano

An integrated computational platform for system reliability-based analysis of mixed-type
highway bridge networks 1717
F. Akgül & D.M. Frangopol

25. New didactical strategies and methods in higher technical education

Architects and structures: how much structure is (not) enough for an architect? 1725
D. Simic

Teaching creativity to undergraduate civil engineers 1729
T.M. Lewis

A WWW-based learning framework for construction mediation 1739
T.W. Yiu, S.O. Cheung, K.W. Cheung & C.H. Suen

Moving the university to the industry – a successful case study 1745
C. Cosma, Z.J. Herbsman & J.D. Mitrani

InfoBase: a multimedia learning environment to support group work and discourse 1751
R. Stouffs, B. Tunçer & I.S. Sariyildiz

26. Durability analysis and lifetime assessment

Impact of low sulfate metakaolin on strength and chloride resistance of cement mortar and
high strength concrete 1759
J. Suwanpruk, S. Sujjavanich & J. Punyanusornkit

Influence of environmental variables on moisture transport in cementitious materials 1765
M.K. Rahman, M.H. Baluch, A.H. Al-Gadhib & S. Zafar

Stainless clad reinforcing for greater durability of motorways and infrastructure 1771
A.G. Cacace & H.S. Hardy

Design models for deteriorated concrete bridges   1777
G. Bertagnoli, V.I. Carbone, L. Giordano & G. Mancini

A case study of a concrete bridge corrosion phenomenon   1783
A. Guettala & A. Abibsi

Estimation of the residual capability of existing buildings subjected to re-conversion of use:
a non linear approach   1789
H. Albertini Neto, L. Sgambi & E. Garavaglia

Natural ageing of earth stabilized concrete   1797
A. Guettala, H. Houari & A. Abibsi

Serviceability assessment of deteriorating reinforced concrete structures   1803
W. Lawanwisut, C.Q. Li, S. Dessa Aguiar & Z. Chen

Vulnerability assessment of deteriorating reinforced concrete structures   1811
C.Q. Li, W. Lawanwisut & Z. Chen

Influence of cover on the flexural performance of deteriorated reinforced concrete beams   1817
E.H. Hristova, F.J. O'Flaherty, P.S. Mangat & P. Lambert

Evaluation of atmospheric deterioration of concrete   1823
R. Drochytka & V. Petránek

Author index   1829

Volume 3

27. High performance concrete

Biaxially loaded high strength concrete columns for strength design   1837
I. Patnaikuni, A.S. Bajaj & P. Mendis

Testing eccentrically loaded externally reinforced high strength concrete columns   1843
M.N.S. Hadi

Helically reinforced high strength concrete beams   1849
M.N.S. Hadi

Time series modelling of high performance concrete column shortening due to creep and shrinkage   1855
C.Y. Wong & K.S.P. de Silva

An experimental study of basic creep of High Strength Concrete   1863
J. Anaton, S. Setunge & I. Patnaikuni

Double – tee prestressed unit made from high strength concrete   1869
E. Dolara & G. Di Niro

Efficiency of repair of HSC beams subjected to combined forces by GFRP sheets   1875
H.A. Anwar & W. El-Kafrawy

28. Concrete properties and technology

Three-dimensional quantitative simulation of flowable concrete and its applications   1883
M.A. Noor & T. Uomoto

Rheological properties of fresh concrete before and after pumping   1891
K. Watanabe, M. Takeuchi, H. Ono & Y. Tanigawa

The properties of lightweight aggregate concrete for pre-cast bridge slab   1899
H. Tanaka, I. Yoshitake, Y. Yamaguchi, S. Hamada, H. Tsuda & M. Kushida

Bond behaviour of reinforcement in self-compacting concrete (SCC)   1907
K. Holschemacher, Y. Klug, D. Weiße, G. König & F. Dehn

Self-compacting concrete – hardened material properties and structural behaviour   1913
K. Holschemacher, Y. Klug & D. Weiße

Shrinkage cracking and crack control in fully-restrained reinforced concrete members   1921
R.I. Gilbert

Properties of a self-compacting mortar with lightweight aggregate   1929
L. Bertolini, M. Carsana & M. Gastaldi

Durability of cement and cement plus resin stabilized earth blocks   1937
A. Guettala, H. Houari & A. Abibsi

Experimental investigation into the effect of fly ash on the fresh properties of self-compacting
concrete (SCC)   1943
M. Dignan & C.Q. Li

Potentialities of extrusion molded cement composites   1949
K. Yamada, S. Ishiyama, S. Tanaka & A. Tokuoka

Analytical modelling of rheology of high flowing mortar and concrete   1957
M.A. Noor & T. Uomoto

29. Innovative tools for structural design

A web-based control and management environment for interoperation of structural programs   1967
J. Wang & C.-Mo Huang

Attitudes to 3D and 4D CAD systems in the Australian construction industry   1973
S. Saha, M. Hardie & A. Jeary

The 4D-CAD: a powerful tool to visualize the future   1979
M. Barcala, S.M. Ahmed, A. Caballero & S. Azhar

Computer aided design of composite beams   1983
V.K. Gupta & R. Kumar

30. Issues in the theory of elasticity

Variable pressure arresting opening of internal and external cracks weakening a plate   1991
R.R. Bhargava, S. Hasan & P.K. Bansal

Vertical stress formulas for surface loads   1997
R.V. Jarquio

Stress fields for a semi-infinite plane containing a circular hole subjected to stresses from
infinite points   2003
T. Tsutsumi & K. Hirashima

Study of two-dimensional elasticity on Functionally Graded Materials   2009
T. Seto, M. Ueda & T. Nishimura

Equivalent shear modulus of Functionally Graded Materials   2015
T. Sakate, M. Ueda, T. Seto & T. Nishimura

31. Special session on "Structural monitoring and control"

Structural health monitoring based on dynamic measurements: a standard and a novel approach   2023
F. Vestroni, F. dell'Isola, S. Vidoli & M.N. Cerri

Control of vortex-induced oscillations of a suspension footbridge by Tuned Mass Dampers   2029
E. Sibilio, M. Ciampoli & V. Sepe

Active control of cable-stayed bridges: large scale mock-up experimental analysis — 2037
G. Magonette, F. Marazzi & H. Försterling

The implementation of a cable-stayed bridge model and its passive seismic response control — 2045
V. Barberi, M. Salerno & M. Giudici

Active control in civil engineering: a way to industrial application — 2055
M. Aupérin & C. Dumoulin

Modal control for seismic structures using MR dampers — 2063
S.W. Cho, K.S. Park, M.G. Ko & I.W. Lee

New development of semi-active control with variable stiffness — 2067
F. Amini & F. Danesh

Reducing damages in structures during earthquake using energy dissipation devices — 2071
K.K.F. Wong & D.F. Zhao

Economical seismic retrofitting of bridges in regions of low to moderate risk of seismic activity — 2079
M. Dicleli, M. Mansour, A. Mokha & V. Zayas

Electro-inductive passive and semi-active control devices — 2085
M. Battaini, F. Casciati & M. Domaneschi

Wireless communication between sensor/device stations — 2091
L. Faravelli & R. Rossi

A benchmark problem for seismic control of cable-stayed bridges: lessons learned — 2097
S.R. Williams, S.J. Dyke, J.M. Caicedo & L.A. Bergman

Interval expression of uncertainty for estimated ambient modal parameters — 2105
Y.G. Wang, H. Li & J.H. Zhang

32. Special session on "New didactical strategies"

Complex of thinking-development in IT-based education — 2113
P. Toth & P. Pentelenyi

When less is more: a practical approach to selecting WWW resources for teaching IT hardware — 2119
N.N. Berchenko & I.B. Berezovska

Evaluation of higher educational services by means of value analysis — 2123
M. Gyulaffy, R. Meszlényi & F. Nádasdi

Bigbang: a web-learning portal in education — 2127
G. Luciani, P. Giunchi & S. Levialdi

An investigation on the students' learning styles in an advanced applied mechanics course — 2129
A. Matrisciano & N.P. Belfiore

MIPAA, Multimedia Interactive Platform for an Appropriate Architecture: a prototype of dissemination and education — 2137
M. Nardini

Algorithmic approach in engineering educational process — 2143
P. Pentelenyi & P. Toth

A methodology for teaching "Computer Aided Design and Drawing": a didactical experience — 2149
E. Pezzuti, A. Umbertini & P.P. Valentini

E-learning and university teaching: a virtual, interactive, distance, learning course — 2155
C. Bucciarelli-Ducci, F. Fedele, R. Donati, R. Mezzanotte, D. Mattioli & C. Grisoni

Vocational guidance on the net: a pilot survey — 2159
P. Spagnoli & G. Tanucci

On some new emerging professions in the higher technical education 2163
N.P. Belfiore, M. Di Benedetto, A. Matrisciano, C. Moscogiuri, C. Mezzetti & M. Recchioni

Increasing competitiveness by means of value analysis in higher education 2171
R. Meszlényi, M. Gyulaffy & F. Nádasdi

33. Special session on "Information and decision systems in construction project management"

Evaluation of risks using 3D Risk Matrix 2179
D. Antoniadis & A. Thorpe

Modelling change processes within construction projects 2185
I.A. Motawa, C.J. Anumba, A. El-Hamalawi, P.W.H. Chung & M.L. Yeoh

Improving performance through integrated project team constituency 2191
D.R. Moore, A.R.J. Dainty & M. Cheng

An integrated information management system for the construction industry 2197
S.P. Sakellaropoulos & A.P. Chassiakos

Public–private partnerships for infrastructure development in Greece 2203
F. Striagka & J.P. Pantouvakis

A Microsoft Project add-in for time-cost trade off analysis 2209
K.P. Anagnostopoulos, L. Kotsikas & A. Roumboutsos

Perspectives' investigation of a systematic implementation of PPP/PFI model in Greece 2215
F. Striagka & J.P. Pantouvakis

A computer-based feedback model for design/build organizations 2221
G.O. Alptekin & A. Kanoglu

A model for forecasting public risks created by large urban infrastructure construction projects 2227
W. Korenromp, S. Al-Jibouri & J. van den Adel

A risk management model for construction projects 2233
S. Smit, S. Al-Jibouri & J. van den Adel

Multicriteria decision support systems in engineering planning and management 2239
O.G. Manoliadis & J.P. Pantouvakis

Integrated project management information systems in construction: a case study implementation 2245
P. Stephenson & I.C. Scrimshaw

Multi-project scheduling in a construction environment with resource constraints 2251
P. Stephenson & Y. Ying

Workflow technology and knowledge management in construction process 2257
M. Masera, A. Stracuzzi & S. Mecca,

34. Special session on "Innovative materials and innovative use of materials in structures"

Flexural strengthening of RC members by means of CFRP laminates: general issues and
improvements in the technique 2267
A. Nurchi & S. Matthys

Experimental and numerical study of buckling glass beams with 2 m span 2275
J. Belis, R. Van Impe, M. De Beule, G. Lagae & W. Vanlaere

Torsional behaviour of laminated glass beams with a varying interlayer stiffness 2281
M. De Beule, J. Belis, R. Van Impe, W. Vanlaere & G. Lagae

Confronting non-linear and evolutional numerical analyses of horizontally loaded piles
embedded in soils with experimental results and the concept of safety 2285
R. Van Impe, J. Belis, P. Buffel, M. De Beule, G. Lagae & W. Vanlaere

Hyperbolic functions for modelling the elasto-plastic behaviour of soils in the evolutional,
non-linear analysis of slurry walls and sheet-piling structures 2293
R. Van Impe, J. Belis, M. De Beule, G. Lagae & W. Vanlaere

Innovative aluminium structures 2301
G.C. Giuliani

35. Invited session on "Recent advances in wind engineering"

Some experimental results on wind fields in a built environment 2309
C. Paulotto, M. Ciampoli & G. Augusti

Active control of a wind excited mast 2317
M. Breccolotti, V. Gusella & A.L. Materazzi

Representation of the wind action on structures by Proper Orthogonal Decomposition 2323
L. Carassale & G. Solari

A model for vortex-shedding induced oscillations of long-span bridges 2331
P. D'Asdia, V. Sepe, L. Caracoglia & S. Noè

Stochastic characterization of wind effects from experimental data 2337
M. Gioffrè

Inclined cable aerodynamics – wind tunnel test and field observation 2345
M. Matsumoto & T. Yagi

Database-assisted design, structural reliability, and safety margins for building codes 2353
S.M.C. Diniz & E. Simiu

Wind action and structural design: a history 2359
P. Spinelli

Performance of buildings in extreme winds 2369
K.C. Mehta

Flutter optimization of bridge decks: experimental and analytical procedures 2375
G. Bartoli & M. Righi

A wind tunnel database for wind resistant design of tall buildings 2383
C.-M. Cheng, C.-T. Liu & Po-C. Lu

36. Special session on "Geomechanics aspects of slopes excavations and constructions"

Identification of soil parameters for finite element simulation of geotechnical structures:
pressuremeter test and excavation problem 2393
Y. Malécot, E. Flavigny & M. Boulon

Displacements of river bridge pier foundations due to geotechnical effect of floods 2401
F. Federico & G. Mastroianni

A study of the microstructure to assess the reliability of laboratory compacted soils as reference
material for earth constructions   2409
C. Jommi & A. Sciotti

Stability of motion of detrital reservoir banks   2417
A. Musso, P. Provenzano & A.P.S. Selvadurai

37. Special session on "Fastening technologies for structural connections"

Hybrid structural steel beam – reinforced concrete column connection   2427
J.C. Adajar, T. Kanakubo, M. Nonogami, N. Kayashima, Y. Sonobe & M. Fujisawa

Semi-rigid composite moment connections – experimental evaluation   2431
A. Fernson, K.S.P. de Silva, I. Patnaikuni & K. Thirugnanasundaralingam

Analysis of waffle composite slabs   2437
A.M. El-Shihy, H.K. Shehab, M.K. Khalaf & S.A. Mustafa

Structural efficiency of waffle floor systems   2447
J. Prasad, A.K. Ahuja & S. Chander

38. Special session on "Advanced conceptual tools for analysis long suspended bridges"

A conceptual framework for the design of an intelligent monitoring system for the Messina
Strait Crossing Bridge   2455
S. Loreti & G. Senaud

Conceptual framework for the aerodynamic optimization of the long span bridge deck sections   2461
F. Giuliano & D. Taddei

Aspects for the determination of the complex stress states in suspension bridge for the
fatigue-analysis   2471
L. Catallo, V. Di Mella & M. Silvestri

A hybrid probabilistic and fuzzy model for risk assessment in a large engineering project   2479
F. Petrilli

General aspects of the structural behaviour in the Messina Strait Bridge design   2487
L. Catallo, L. Sgambi & M. Silvestri

Strategy and formulation levels of the structural performance analysis of advanced systems   2495
M. Silvestri & F. Bontempi

Evaluation and results' comparisons in dynamic structural response of Messina
Cable-Suspended Bridge   2503
V. Barberi, M. Ciani & L. Catallo

A reference framework for the aerodynamic and aereoelastic analysis of long span bridges with
Computational Fluid Dynamic   2511
D. Taddei & F. Bontempi

Author index   2517

System-based Vision for Strategic and Creative Design, Bontempi (ed.)
© 2003 Swets & Zeitlinger, Lisse, ISBN 90 5809 599 1

Preface

The present Proceedings collect over 360 papers that will be presented during ISEC-02, the 2nd International Conference on Structural and Construction Engineering, hold in Rome, Italy, on September 23–26, 2003.

The Theme of the Conference, *System-based vision for strategic and creative design*, includes the following concepts:

- *systemic framework*: it includes the capacity to see all the aspects and the connections of any problem and its solution;
- *creative work*: the tension to develop something new;
- *design*: one of the methods to improve the world and make it better.

The current practice and research in structural and construction engineering is characterized by increasing levels of complexity and interaction.

This is due to several reasons. First, the transition to a global, high technology environment demands sound safety requirements in all aspects of human life and activities. With respect to what concerns buildings, structures and infrastructures, a century of continuous progress in knowledge, materials and technology should have reduced occurrences of damage, failure, and misconception by large magnitudes. In spite of this expectation, small and large structural and construction deficiencies are still common episodes. This is, probably, due to the more ambitious objectives our society intends to pursue. But, without doubt, there are still problems and mismatches along the engineering path from concept development to practical realization. Secondly, there is special attention being paid in the world today to the interaction, full of uncertainties and constraints, of the structure with the environment. In this sense, competitiveness and sustainability require a systems approach in which research activities support the development of coherent, interconnected and ecologically-efficient civil engineering structural systems, responding to both market and social needs. Finally, there is the necessity to answer to socioeconomic needs, by stimulating holistic approaches and heuristic techniques, by strengthening the innovative capacity, and by fostering the creation of businesses and services built on emerging technologies and market opportunities. Research will turn into environmentally and consumer friendly processes, products, and services and will contribute to improve the quality of life and working conditions.

With this point of view, the main objective of the Conference will be to define knowledge and technologies needed to design and develop project processes and produce high-quality, competitive, environment- and consumer-friendly structures and constructed facilities. This goal is clearly connected with the development and reuse of quality materials, excellence in construction management, and reliable measurement and testing methods.

Franco Bontempi

Professor of Structural Analysis and Design,
Faculty of Engineering, University of Rome "La Sapienza", Rome (ITALY)
Postgraduate School of Reinforced Concrete Structures "F.lli Pesenti",
Polytechnic of Milan, Milan (ITALY)

Acknowledgements

The Editor gratefully acknowledges the promotion, the sponsorship, and the endorsement of the following organizations:

Promoting Association:
– CTE, Italian Association for Building Industrialization

Co-sponsors:
– AICAP, Italian Association for Reinforced and Prestressed Concrete
– CIB, International Council for Research and Innovation in Building and Construction
– ACI, American Concrete Institute
– ASCE, American Society of Civil Engineers
– IABMAS, International Association for Bridge Maintenance and Safety

Endorsers:
– Faculty of Engineering of the University of Rome "La Sapienza"

From an institutional point of view, the following persons will be gratefully remembered: Giandomenico Toniolo, President of CTE, Emanuele Filiberto Radogna, President of AICAP, Giselda Barina, Executive Secretary – CTE, Vivetta Bianconi, Executive Secretary of AICAP, Tullio Bucciarelli, Chairman of the Faculty of Engineering of the University of Rome "La Sapienza", Fabrizio Vestroni, Head of the Department of Structural Engineering, Amarjit Singh, Chair of ISEC-01.

The specific financial support of University of Rome "La Sapienza", Ministry of Instruction, University and Research (MIUR), Societa' Stretto di Messina S.p.A. and HILTI Italia S.p.A. are gratefully recognized.

The scientific framework of the Conference finds its origin within interesting discussions with Remo Calzona, Fabio Casciati and Pier Giorgio Malerba, whose experience and advices are, for the Editor, of the utmost importance.

The conceptual organization and the operative development of such a complex and large international conference couldn't have been possible without the outstanding commitment of several people. Specifically, the Editor wants to recognize the contribute, always made with efficacy and positive tense, of the following persons, at the same time friends and colleagues: Fabio Biondini, Luciano Catallo, Pier Luigi Colombi, Ezio Dolara, Elsa Garavaglia, Cristina Jommi, Simone Loreti, Giuseppe Parlante, Flavio Petrilli, Paola Provenzano, Luca Sgambi, Maria Silvestri, Angelo Simone, Maria Laura Vergelli, Paola Tamburrini.

The Proceedings are dedicated to Professor Francesco Martinez y Cabrera.

Rome, September 2003

System-based Vision for Strategic and Creative Design, Bontempi (ed.)
© 2003 Swets & Zeitlinger, Lisse, ISBN 90 5809 599 1

Organisation

International Scientific and Technical Committee:

Franco Bontempi, Chair, University of Rome "La Sapienza", Rome, Italy

Amarjit Singh, Chair of past ISEC Conference, University of Hawaii, USA
Hojjat Adeli, the Ohio State University, USA
Chimay J. Anumba, Loughborough University, UK
Ghassan Aouad, the University of Salford, UK
Larry Bergman, University of Illinois at Urbana-Champaign, USA
Fabio Casciati, University of Pavia, Italy
John Christian, University of New Brunswick, Canada
Richard Fellows, the University of Hong Kong, Hong Kong
Dan Frangopol, University of Colorado at Boulder, USA
Ian Gilbert, New South Wales University, Australia
Paul Grundy, Monash University, Australia
Takashi Hara, Tokuyama University of Technology, Japan
Makarand Hastak, Purdue University, USA
Osama Ahmed Jannadi, King Fahd University of Petroleum & Minerals, Saudi Arabia
Vladimir Kristek, Czech Techinical University in Prague, Czeck Republic
In-Won Lee, Korea Advanced Institute of Science and Technology, Korea
Anita Liu, The University of Hong Kong, Hong Kong
Pier Giorgio Malerba, Technical University of Milan, Italy
Giuseppe Mancini, Technical University of Turin, Italy
Indu Patnaikuni, RMIT University, Australia
Takahiro Tamura, Tokuyama University of Technology, Japan
Francis Tin-Loi, New South Wales University, Australia
Ali Touran, Northeastern University, USA
Richard N. White, Cornell University, USA
Frank Yazdani, North Dakota State University, USA

Local Scientific and Technical Committee

Nicola Pio Belfiore, University of Rome "La Sapienza"
Remo Calzona, University of Rome "La Sapienza"
Claudio Ceccoli, University of Bologna
Carlo Cecere, University of Rome "La Sapienza"
Mario Como, University of Rome, "Tor Vergata"
Antonio D'Andrea, University of Rome "La Sapienza"
Bruno Della Bella, Precompressi Centro Nord S.p.A, Novara
Alessandro De Stefano, Technical University of Turin
Valter Esposti, ICITE Director, CIB Treasurer, S.Giuliano Milanese
Roberto Guercio, University of Rome "La Sapienza"
Luigi Annibale Materazzi, University of Perugia
Antonino Musso, University of Rome "Tor Vergata"
Emanuele Filiberto Radogna, University of Rome "La Sapienza", AICAP President
Alessandro Ranzo, University of Rome, "La Sapienza"

Luca Romano, Consultant Engineer, Albenga
Franco Rovelli, Gecofin Prefabbricati S.p.A, Verona
Marco Savoia, University of Bologna
Renato Sparacio, University of Napoli, "Federico II"
Paolo Spinelli, University of Florence
Franco Storelli, University of Rome "La Sapienza"
Giandomenico Toniolo, Technical University of Milan, CTE President

Local Organizing Committee

Giselda Barina, (Executive Secretary), CTE
Fabio Biondini, Technical University of Milan
Fabio Bongiorno, CTE
Luciano Catallo, University of Rome "La Sapienza"
Francesco Chillè, ENEL Hydro, Milan
Pier Luigi Colombi, Technical University of Milan
Ezio Dolara, University of Rome "La Sapienza"
Elsa Garavaglia, Technical University of Milan
Claudia Gomez, Consulting Engineer, Milan
Simone Loreti, University of Rome "La Sapienza"
Corrado Pecora, Consulting Engineer, Milan
Flavio Petrilli, Consulting Engineer, Rome
Paola Provenzano, University of Rome "Tor Vergata"
Luca Sgambi, University of Rome "La Sapienza"
Maria Silvestri, University of Rome "La Sapienza"
Angelo Simone, Delft University of Technology
Maria Laura Vergelli, University of Rome "La Sapienza"
Paola Tamburrini, University of Rome "La Sapienza"
Giuseppe Parlante, Content Manager and Web Master

1. Keynotes

System-based Vision for Strategic and Creative Design, Bontempi (ed.)
© 2003 Swets & Zeitlinger, Lisse, ISBN 90 5809 599 1

Life-cycle maintenance strategies for deteriorating structures based on multiple probabilistic performance indicators

D.M. Frangopol & L.C. Neves

Dept. of Civil, Environmental and Architectural Engineering, University of Colorado, Boulder, CO, USA

ABSTRACT: The highway networks of most European and North American countries are now completed or close to completion. As a result, the need in funding changed from building new structures to repair, rehabilitate, and replace the existing ones. In this paper, a model for analyzing the evolution in time of probabilistic performance indicators of existing structures, in terms of condition, safety, and cost under no maintenance, preventive maintenance, and essential maintenance, is presented. With this model, the results of visual inspections (condition), structural analysis (safety), and economics (cost) can be integrated during life-cycle of existing structures. Therefore, the cost-effectiveness of various life-cycle maintenance strategies for deteriorating structures can be evaluated. The probabilistic characteristics of the performance indicators of deteriorating structures are considered by using Monte-Carlo simulation to compute the resulting condition, safety, and cost profiles. Examples based on data gathered in the United Kingdom are presented.

1 INTRODUCTION

The highway networks of most European and North American countries are completed or near completion. However, a growing number of highway bridges are deteriorated and, in the United States alone, as much as one half of the 600,000 bridges in the national inventory are deficient and must be repaired, upgraded or replaced in the short term. This increase in the number of deteriorated structures enhanced the need for probabilistic methods that can help bridge managers in making rational decisions on maintenance strategies in order to keep structures serviceable and safe with limited maintenance funds (Frangopol et al. 1997, Thoft-Christensen 1998, Frangopol 2002).

Existing bridge management systems are based on visual inspections to assess bridge safety. However, visual inspections, and the resulting condition classification, do not accurately measure the safety of structures, as they do not consider the initial safety of the structure, the influence of deterioration on the reduction of safety of an element, and the relevance of each element to the safety of the overall structure.

In this paper, a model for predicting the deterioration of structures, under no maintenance, preventive maintenance, and essential maintenance, considering performance measured in terms of condition (obtained from visual inspections), safety (obtained from structural analysis), and cost (obtained from economic studies) is presented. Parameters defining condition and safety under no maintenance as well as the effect of maintenance actions are considered as random variables. Uncertainties in the initial condition and safety and their respective deterioration processes are also considered. Furthermore, the effects of maintenance actions on condition and safety, as well as their times of application and costs are considered nondeterministic.

The proposed model allows the consideration of interaction between condition and safety by including correlation between random variables and by defining deterministic relations between one performance indicator (such as condition) and the deterioration rate of the other (such as safety). With this model, the results of visual inspections (condition), structural analysis (safety), and economics (cost) can be integrated during life-cycle of existing structures.

As an example of application of the proposed model, a bridge element (reinforced concrete crosshead) is analyzed based on data obtained from the United Kingdom. The condition and safety indices of such elements under no maintenance and under various maintenance strategies are evaluated along with their associated costs.

2 SAFETY, CONDITION AND COST PROFILES

Both condition and safety profiles under no maintenance are assumed to be bilinear:

$$C(t) = \begin{cases} C_0 & \text{if } t \leq t_{ic} \\ C_0 - \alpha_c (t - t_{ic}) & \text{if } t > t_{ic} \end{cases} \quad (1)$$

$$S(t) = \begin{cases} S_0 & \text{if } t \leq t_i \\ S_0 - \alpha (t - t_i) & \text{if } t > t_i \end{cases} \quad (2)$$

where $C(t)$ and $S(t)$ are the condition and safety profiles, respectively, C_0 and S_0 are the initial condition and safety indices, α_C and α are the deterioration rates of condition and safety, respectively, t_i and t_{ic} are the times of initiation of damage of condition and safety, respectively, and t is time.

The effects of maintenance actions on condition and safety are modelled using superposition (Neves et al. 2003a). Each maintenance action can lead to one, several or all of the following effects: (a) increase in the condition and/or safety index immediately after application; (b) elimination of the deterioration in condition and/or safety index during a time interval after application; and (c) reduction of the deterioration rate of condition and/or safety index for a time interval after application.

These effects are modelled through several random variables such as: (a) increase in condition and safety index immediately after application, γ_c and γ, respectively; (b) time interval during which the deterioration processes of condition and safety are eliminated, t_{dc} and t_d, respectively; (c) time during which the deterioration rate in condition and safety are eliminated or reduced, t_{pdc} and t_{pd}, respectively; and (d) deterioration rate reduction of condition and safety, δ_c and δ, respectively, where $\delta_c \geq 0$ and $\delta \geq 0$. The meaning of each of these random variables is presented in Figures 1 and 2 for condition index and safety index, respectively (Neves et al. 2003a).

The parameters defining the profiles under no maintenance and the effects of maintenance can be either deterministic or probabilistic. Depending on the definition of the time of application, maintenance actions can be classified in: (a) time-based; (b) performance-based; and (c) time- and performance-based.

The profiles under no maintenance obtained from Equations 1 and 2 are combined with the profiles defining the effects of maintenance actions by using superposition. In Figure 3 the superposition of the effects of two maintenance actions, denoted by 1 and 2, is presented (Neves et al. 2003a).

Time-based maintenance actions are those for which the time of first application and the time interval between subsequent applications are defined by

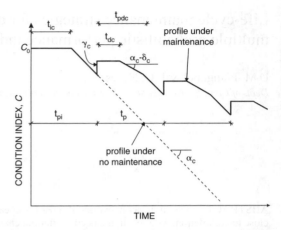

Figure 1. Condition index profile without and with maintenance.

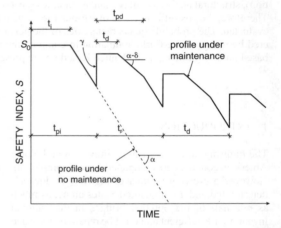

Figure 2. Safety index profile without and with maintenance.

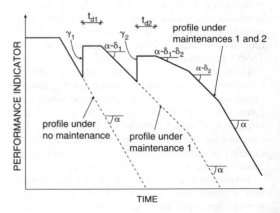

Figure 3. Superposition of effects of two maintenance actions.

4

random variables independent of the performance indicators. Performance-based actions are those for which maintenance is applied when a condition and/or safety threshold is violated. Time- and performance-based actions are those for which the times of applications are defined by a condition and/or safety threshold and by a random variable independent of the performance indicators.

Preventive maintenance actions are usually time-based, as these actions can be scheduled in advance. Essential maintenance actions are usually performance-based or time- and performance-based actions, since they are usually applied when the performance of the structure is not satisfied.

The cost of a maintenance action can include cost at time of application, user cost, and yearly cost after application. The cost at time of application can be defined as a random variable or random function of the effects of maintenance (Neves et al. 2003b). These costs must include both the direct costs and user costs (Chang & Shinozuka 1996).

The effect of time on the value of money must be taken under consideration. As a result, the cost of each action must be converted to an equivalent value at a certain instant. This can be achieved through the discount rate, v. The equivalent cost today, C_0, of spending a certain amount of money, C_t, at a given time t in the future, can be expressed by the present value of cost, given as:

$$C_0 = \frac{C_t}{\left(1+v\right)^t} \tag{3}$$

The discount rate is difficult to predict, since it depends on the economical conditions during the lifetime of the structure. In the United Kingdom, for bridge investments, this value is 6% (Tilly 1997).

Monte-Carlo simulation is a powerful tool to analyze the probabilistic characteristics of structural systems. The computation of the probabilistic characteristics of the resulting profiles (e.g., mean, standard deviation) can be obtained using the flowchart presented in Figure 4.

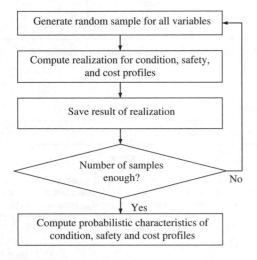

Figure 4. Basic flowchart of Monte-Carlo simulation process.

3 EXAMPLE

The model previously described was implemented in a computational platform and used to analyze data compiled by Denton (2002) for bridge elements in the United Kingdom. This data describes in a probabilistic manner the deterioration of reinforced concrete crossheads and the effects of five different maintenance strategies on the condition and safety of these elements. The parameters defining the condition and safety profiles under no maintenance are presented in Table 1.

The five maintenance strategies considered are: (a) minor concrete repairs; (b) silane; (c) do nothing and rebuild; (d) cathodic protection; and (e) replacement of expansion joints. Of these, silane and replacement of expansion joints are time-based, minor concrete repairs and rebuild are performance-based, and cathodic protection is time- and performance-based.

Table 1. Data for defining condition and safety profiles under no maintenance.

Condition index profile			Safety index profile		
Initial index C_0 (1)	Time of damage initiation T_{ic} (years) (2)	Deterioration rate α_c (year^{-1}) (3)	Initial index S_0 (4)	Time of damage initiation T_i (years) (5)	Deterioration rate α (year^{-1}) (6)
Min = 0.00	0.0	Min = 0.00	Min = 0.91	0.0	Min = 0.00
Mode = 1.75		Mode = 0.08	Mode = 1.50		Mode = 0.015
Max = 3.50		Max = 0.16	Max = 2.5		Max = 0.035

Table 2. Data for defining condition profiles under cyclic maintenance.

| Maintenance strategy | Time of application of first maintenance T_{pi} (years) | Time of subsequent applications T_p (years) | Effect on condition index | | Deterioration rate during effect $\alpha_C-\delta_C$ (year^{-1}) | Duration of maint. effect T_{pdc} (years) | Cost (k£) |
			Improv. γ_C	Delay in deterioration T_{dc} (years)			
(1)	(2)	(3)	(4)	(5)	(6)	(7)	(8)
Minor concrete repair	when $C = 3.0$	when $C = 3.0$	2.0 2.5 3.0	0.0	–	–	16 3605 14437
Silane	0.0 7.5 15.0	10.0 12.5 15.0	0.0	0.0	0.00 0.01 0.03	7.5 10.0 12.5	0.30 39.0 77.0
Do nothing and rebuild	when $S = 0.91$	when $S = 0.91$	to 0	10 15 30	–	–	247 7410 28898
Cathodic protection	when $C = 2.0$	7.5 10.0 12.5	0 0	12.5 12.5	–	–	19 2604 5189
Replace expansion joints	0.0 20.0 40.0	20.0 30.0 10.0	0	0	0.00 0.04 0.08	10.0 15.0 30.0	0.7 15 39

All random variables have a triangular distribution, characterized by their minimum, mode and maximum values.

Table 3. Data for defining safety profiles under cyclic maintenance.

| Maintenance strategy | Time of application of first maintenance T_{pi} (years) | Time of subsequent applications T_p (years) | Effect on condition index | | Deterioration rate during effect $\alpha_C-\delta_C$ (year^{-1}) | Duration of effect maint. T_{pdc} (years) | Cost (k£) |
			Improv. γ_C	Delay in deterioration T_{dc} (years)			
(1)	(2)	(3)	(4)	(5)	(6)	(7)	(8)
Minor concrete repair	when $C = 3.0$	when $C = 3.0$	0	while $C < 1$	–	–	16 3605 14437
Silane	0.0 7.5 15.0	10.0 12.5 15.0	0	0	0.00 0.007 0.018	7.5 10.0 12.5	0.30 39.0 77.0
Do nothing and rebuild	when $S = 0.91$	when $S = 0.91$	1.00 1.25 1.50	while $C < 1$	–	–	247 7410 28898
Cathodic protection	when $C = 2.0$	7.5 10.0 12.5	–	12.5	–	–	19 2604 5189
Replace expansion joints	0.0 20.0 40.0	20.0 30.0 40.0	0	0	0.00 0.007 0.018	10.0 15.0 30.0	0.7 15 39

All random variables have a triangular distribution, characterized by their minimum, mode and maximum values.

In Tables 2 and 3 the effects, time of applications and costs of the aforementioned five maintenance strategies are presented. All random variables are characterized by triangular distributions defined by their minimum, mode and maximum values (Denton 2002).

Condition index is numerically defined as follows (Denton 2002):

0 – no chloride contamination;
1 – onset of corrosion;
2 – onset of cracking; and
3 – loose concrete/significant delamination.

The safety index is defined by the load capacity, S, whose minimum acceptable threshold is 0.91 (Denton 2002).

The minor concrete repair strategy is characterized by an improvement in condition without an increase in safety. Safety deterioration is delayed until condition index is higher than 1.

The second maintenance strategy (silane) is time-based. It is applied at probabilistic time intervals, reducing the deterioration rates of both condition and safety.

The third maintenance strategy (do nothing and rebuild) is safety-based and is characterized by a significant increase of both condition and safety.

Cathodic protection is a time- and performance-based strategy, as the first action is applied when condition index reaches 2.0, but subsequent applications are separated by time intervals defined by a triangular distribution. This strategy delays the initiation of deterioration after application of maintenance and, if applied according to the prescribed distribution, can delay the deterioration processes for both condition and safety, indefinitely.

The last maintenance strategy (replace expansion joints) is also time-based and reduces the deterioration rates for both condition and safety.

The costs of the five maintenance actions show a great dispersion. However, it is clear from the data in Tables 2 and 3 that essential maintenance actions, due to the need to interrupt bridge traffic, have a much higher cost than preventive maintenance actions.

The results obtained for the first maintenance strategy (minor concrete repairs) are presented in Figures 5, 6, and 7, for condition, safety, and cost, respectively.

The results presented in Figures 5, 6, and 7 show that the minor concrete repair strategy has a much higher impact on condition than on safety. In fact, the mean and standard deviation of the condition index are almost constant during the lifetime of the structure. However, there is a significant reduction of the mean safety during the lifetime. For both performance measures, the thresholds defined ($C_{target} = 3.0$ and $S_{target} = 0.91$) are not violated by the mean indices during the time horizon of 50 years.

The analysis of the probability density functions (PDFs) at different time intervals shows that the condition index has a zero probability of violating the threshold, $C_{target} = 3.0$, since maintenance is applied when condition reaches this target value. On the other hand, results presented in Figure 6 show that there is a significant probability of having a safety index lower

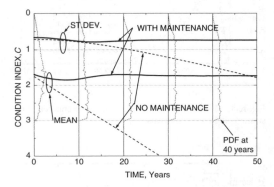

Figure 5. Mean, standard deviation, and PDF of condition index under no maintenance and under minor concrete repair strategy.

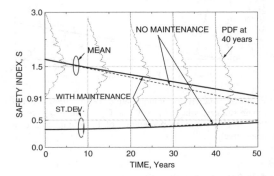

Figure 6. Mean, standard deviation, and PDF of safety index under no maintenance and under minor concrete repair strategy.

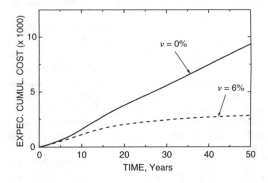

Figure 7. Mean profiles of cost under minor concrete repair strategy considering 0% and 6% discount rates.

7

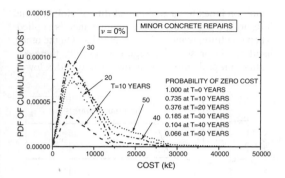

Figure 8. PDFs of cumulative cost of minor concrete repair strategy at 10-year intervals.

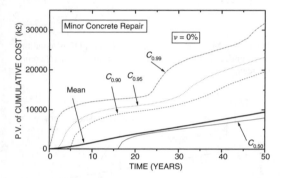

Figure 9. Percentiles of cumulative cost of minor concrete repair strategy, where $C_{0.99}$, $C_{0.95}$, $C_{0.90}$, and $C_{0.50}$ are the 99-, 95-, 90-, and 50-percentiles of the cumulative cost, respectively.

than 0.91. This probability is increasing significantly with time. Therefore, the analysis of the mean profile alone is not enough to decide on a maintenance strategy and the PDFs of the condition and safety indices must be used to make rational decisions on maintenance strategies.

In Figure 7 the expected cumulative costs of minor concrete repair strategy is presented. The expected cost is a useful tool to compare the cost-effectiveness of different maintenance strategies but is not always the most appropriate measure. The bridge manager is usually more interested in knowing what are the necessary funds to be spent, given a certain level of confidence (say, 95%). In fact, the cumulative cost has a very significant dispersion as shown in the PDFs in Figure 8.

As a result, the percentiles of the cost profiles for each maintenance action were computed. The corresponding results for minor concrete repair strategy are shown in Figure 9.

From this figure it is clear that if the decision policy consists in using the cumulative cost that is not exceeded in 95% or 99% of the times (i.e., $C_{0.95}$ or $C_{0.99}$), a cost two or three times higher than the mean cost must be used.

4 CONCLUSIONS

In this paper, a probabilistic model for predicting the deterioration of structures, under no maintenance, preventive maintenance, and essential maintenance, considering performance indicators in terms of condition (obtained from visual inspections), safety (obtained from structural analysis), and cost (obtained from economic studies) is presented. Parameters defining condition and safety under no maintenance as well as the effects of maintenance actions are considered as random variables. Uncertainties in the initial condition and safety and their deterioration processes are also considered. Finally, the effects of maintenance actions on condition and safety, as well as their times of application and costs are considered nondeterministic.

The proposed model allows the consideration of interaction between condition and safety by including correlation between random variables and by defining deterministic relations between one performance measure and the deterioration rate of the other. With this model, the results of visual inspections (condition), structural analysis (safety), and economics (cost) can be integrated during life-cycle of existing structures.

As an example of application of the proposed model, a bridge element (reinforced concrete crosshead) is analyzed based on data obtained from the United Kingdom. The condition and safety indices of such elements under no maintenance and under one maintenance strategy considering also its cost are evaluated.

The results presented show a significant difference between condition and safety indices, making it clear that these two measures of performance, although related, are usually not perfectly correlated. Furthermore it was shown that a probabilistic model for bridge maintenance cannot only be based on the expected profiles of the performance indicators, due to significant dispersions in condition, safety, and/or cost.

ACKNOWLEDGMENTS

The first author gratefully acknowledges the partial financial support of the UK Highways Agency and of the US National Science Foundation through grants CMS-9912525 and CMS-0217290. The opinions and conclusions presented in this paper are those of the writers and do not necessarily reflect the views of the sponsoring agencies.

8

REFERENCES

Chang, S.E. & Shinozuka, M. 1996. Life-cycle cost analysis with natural hazard risk. *Journal of Infrastructure Systems*, ASCE, 2(3): 118–126.

Denton, S. 2002. *Data Estimates for Different Maintenance Options for Reinforced Concrete Cross-Heads*. (Personal communication for Highways Agency, U.K.). Parsons Brinckerhoff Ltd., Bristol, U.K.

Frangopol, D.M. 2002. Reliability deterioration and lifetime maintenance cost optimization. Keynote lecture in *Proceedings of the First International ASRANet Colloquium on Integrating Structural Reliability Analysis with Advanced Structural Analysis,* July 8–10, 2002, Glasgow, Scotland.

Frangopol, D.M., Kong, J.S. & Gharaibeh, E.S. 2001. Reliability-Based life-cycle management of highway bridges. *Journal of Computing in Civil Engineering*, ASCE, 15(1): 27–47.

Frangopol, D.M., Lin, K.-Y. & Estes, A.C. 1997. Life-cycle cost design of deteriorating structures. *Journal of Structural Engineering*, ASCE, 123(10): 1390–1401.

Neves, L.C., Frangopol, D.M. & Hogg, V. 2003a. Condition-reliability-cost interaction in bridge maintenance. *Proceedings of the Ninth International Conference on Applications of Statistics and Probability in Civil Engineering, ICASP9,* San Francisco, California, July 6–9 (in press).

Neves, L.C., Frangopol, D.M. & Cruz, P.S. 2003b. Cost of reliability improvement and deterioration delay of maintained structures. *Proceedings of the Second MIT Conference on Computational Fluid and Solid Mechanics*, Massachusetts Institute of Technology, Cambridge, Massachusetts, in *Computational Fluid and Solid Mechanics 2003*, Edited by K.J. Bathe (in press).

Thoft-Christensen, P. 1998. Assessment of the reliability profiles for concrete bridges. *Engineering Structures*, 20(11): 1004–1009.

Tilly, G.P. 1997. Principles of whole life costing. *Safety of Bridges*, London: P.C. Das (ed.), Thomas Telford, 138–144.

Culture in construction – "human reengineering"?

R.F. Fellows
Department of Real Estate and Construction, The University of Hong Kong, Hong Kong

ABSTRACT: This paper discusses the rationale, work to date and programme of current work of the CIB task group, TG-23 "Culture in Construction". The paper proceeds to outline definitions of culture, levels of cultural consideration and dimensions used to "measure" cultures. The paper proceeds to examine the role of goals in cultural contexts and impacts of culture on realisation within the construction industry. The impacts of norms are discussed in shaping cultures, levels of performance and potentials for change. The dynamics of people constantly "doing culture" are explored leading to consideration of culture as a tool or as a method in the current vogue of reengineering with potential for "human reengineering" (managing culture) as the focus. Conclusions revolve around the remaining paucity of understanding of the nature of culture and cultural adaptation and the problems and potential which ensue.

1   INTRODUCTION

Some years ago, at a conference organised by the Association of Researchers in Construction Management (ARCOM), held on the Isle of Man, David Seymour and Richard Fellows, were concerned at the number of occasions on which "culture" was being identified as an important variable but, then, left unexplored. That experience was not limited to the ARCOM conference by any means and so, with invaluable support from CIB, a tentative research agenda was developed, leading to the inauguration of the Task Group (TG-23) at a meeting in Cambridge in September, 1997.

The original scope and objectives of TG-23's work were:

- To identify and define concepts of culture in the international construction industry and to carry out research into their manifestations and effects.
- To discuss and develop appropriate methodologies for the study of culture in construction.
- To determine and, where appropriate, adopt methodologies used in other disciplines, with special reference to the Social Sciences, for researching culture in the international construction industry.

Those original objectives were pursued by members of the task group through individual and collaborative studies, the progress and findings of which were presented and discussed at the group's numerous meetings around the world. Two specific publications, in addition to proceedings of the meetings, have been produced – "Culture in Construction – Part of the Deal?" (Tijhuis 2001) and "Perspectives on Culture in Construction" (Fellows & Seymour 2002). The former comprises papers and discussions of a group workshop held at the University of Twente, The Netherlands during May 2000. The latter constitutes a major collection of papers from members of the task group and includes reports of studies into a wide variety of aspects of culture from various countries – as such, it includes considerations of appropriate research methods, examinations of theories and manifestations of cultures in industry practices and procedures.

In 2002, David Seymour, retired as Joint coordinator and, shortly afterwards Wilco Tijhuis, a managing partner in WT/Consult BV and part-time assistant professor at the University of Twente was appointed joint coordinator.

In 2002, CIB extended the mandate of TG-23 for a further three years. The objectives of the task group have been revised to reflect what has been achieved and to progress studies of theoretical and practical import; the current objectives are:

- To extend the studies of TG-23 to research cultures existing in the construction industry world-wide from societal and organizational perspectives.
- To stimulate and facilitate international exchange and collaboration for studies into reengineering processes adopted by construction organizations to examine their culturally-dependent consequences.

- To research cultural facets of the construction industry to determine feasibilities of changes to improve performance.
- To assemble a "Cultural Inventory" to assist organizations in adapting to new cultural situations across construction industry sectors and countries.

The updated objectives also reflect current research themes of CIB and, of course, the broader construction world perspective.

These are interesting times to be researching culture within the construction industry. Not only are practitioners and academics ever more aware of the important impacts of cultures (e.g. Construction Industry review Committee 2001) but there is much debate over what were widely regarded as seminal studies – notably the work of Geert Hofstede (1980, 2001) (see, e.g. Smith 2002; McSweeney 2002).

Recently, much attention has been devoted to desires to improve performance of the industry – a great deal of attention, and advocacy, has been directed at employing different procurement approaches and forms of contract with the objective of "changing culture" to invoke teamwork/partnering/relational contracting to overcome the negative consequences of fragmentation and conflict. However, the mechanisms advocated concern behaviour modification – a temporary change but which could, if sustained, lead to cultural change. Further, the approaches usually ignore any benefits potentially resulting from some, well managed, conflict (as is fundamental in competition theory). Finally, it is common for fragmentation to be identified as a major problem – Adam Smith (1995), and subsequent economists, advocates division of labour to yield benefits of specialisation, as do the proponents of scientific management (e.g. Taylor 1964) which led Lawrence and Lorsch (1967) to determine that the issue really concerned the twin factors of differentiation and integration – appropriate balancing of which results in effectiveness and efficiency.

2 CULTURE

2.1 Definitions

Defining culture has proved highly problematic. In the early 1950s, Kroeber and Kluckhohn (1952) noted 164 definitions! However, it is important to recognise that culture, and its manifestations, are not static. The cultural dynamics model proposed by Hatch (1993) successfully encapsulates the processes of manifestation, realisation, symbolisation and interpretation to provide a framework within which to understand the dynamism of organisational cultures. The dynamism comes from the continual construction and reconstruction of culture as contexts for setting goals, taking action, making meaning, constructing images and forming identities.

Such perspectives are implicit in Hofstede's (1980) notion of culture being "… the collective programming of the mind which distinguishes the members of one category of people from another". Clearly, culture is a collective construct and may be articulated simply as "how we do things around here". Perhaps the most informative definition is that of Kroeber and Kluckhohn (1952) "… patterns, explicit and implicit of and for human behaviour acquired and transmitted by symbols, constituting the distinctive achievements of human groups, including their embodiment in artefacts; the essential core of culture consists of traditional (i.e. historically derived and selected) ideas and, especially, their attached values; culture systems may, on the one hand, be considered as products of action, on the other as conditioning elements of future action".

If we follow the definition of Kroeber and Kluckhohn, it seems that more enduring societies enjoy advantages of cultural development and stability. That perspective accords with the notion of indexicality in sociology (see, e.g. Clegg 1990) in which interpretation of messages and, thence, comprehension of meaning is recognized to be dependent upon socialization; including education and training.

2.2 Dimensions

Culture is manifested through facets of behaviour. Behaviour is dependent upon values and beliefs, whether any behaviour is determined by conscious thought/evaluation or "instinctive". In the latter case common survival mechanisms are likely to govern and so, be relatively common amongst humans whilst, in the former case, cultural influences will be stronger. That leads to models of culture with physiological instincts and beliefs at the core (survival imperatives; religion, morality etc.) values as the intermediate layer (the hierarchical ordering of aspects of beliefs, perhaps with visions of trade-offs) and behaviour at the outer layer (as in language, symbols, heroes, practices etc.).

It is, then, the observable outer layer which must be employed to secure measurements indicative of culture through first, identifying and defining suitable dimensions – exhaustive in scope and exclusive in content. In studying national cultures, Hofstede (1980) determined four dimensions: Power Distance; Collectivism/Individualism; Masculinity; Uncertainty Avoidance – a fifth dimension of Long-Termism/Short-Termism was added later (Hofstede 1994) following studies in Asia which detected important impact of "Confucian Dynamism" (The Chinese Culture Connection 1987). Trompenaars and Hampden-Turner (1993) advanced five value-oriented dimensions of culture which, they suggest, "… greatly influence our ways of doing business and managing as well as our responses in the face of oral dilemmas". Those dimensions are:

Universalism–Particularism (rules-relationships)
Collectivism–Individualism (group–individual)
Neutral–Emotional (feelings expressed)
Diffuse–Specific (degree of involvement)
Achievement–Ascription (method of giving status).

Hofstede (1994) proposed six dimensions for analysis of organisational cultures:

Process–Results Orientation (technical and bureaucratic routines {can be diverse} – outcomes {tend to be homogeneous}
Job–Employee Orientation (derives from societal culture as well as influences of founders, managers)
Professional–Parochial (educated personnel identify with profession(s)–people identify with employing organisation)
Open–Closed System (ease of admitting new people, styles of internal and external communications)
Tight–Loose Control (degrees of formality, punctuality etc., may depend on technology and rate of change)
Pragmatic–Normative (how to relate to the environment, n. b. customers; pragmatism encourages flexibility).

Scrutiny of the various dimensions used to analyse both national and organisational cultures, essentially, indicate a high level of conceptual commonality. Further, Hofstede's dimensions of organisational culture align with the human-task schools of management thought (such as Herzberg, Mausner & Bloch Snyderman 1967 – theory X and theory Y).

3 GOALS AND REALISATION

3.1 *Goals*

Goals for construction projects are often confused with targets; goals, or objectives, are performance variables for which desired directions should be expressed and any limitations (such as keep cost as low as possible and within an upper limit of a specified sum). Targets represent anticipated/required levels of performance (on continua) consequent upon examination of goals in the context of constraints, including practicalities (such as the construction period stipulated in tender and contract documents).

The notion of "project goals" is both popular and mistaken as it is commonly considered. Newcombe (1994) aptly describes a construction project as a shifting, multi-goal coalition based around a fluid power structure. Coupling that perspective with participants' likely pursuit of self interest (to varying degrees) and opportunistic behaviour, project performance targets emerge from protracted struggles between powerful participants for which early decisions tend to be most

influential and direct and constrain subsequent actions. The degree of influence of the client (employer) operates within that structure.

A noteworthy aspect is the way in which targets are expressed – most frequently as single figures with no indication of inherent variability. The understandable consequence is that employers perceive such targets (forecasts) to be exact and accurate. That is also a widespread view of those in the industry, as manifested in how such targets are used in examining performance achievements, if not as a real belief! The problem is encapsulated by Reugg and Marshall (1990) who characterise construction project price forecasts as "best-guess", conglomerate estimates of input variables but which are treated as certain estimates with results presented in single-figure deterministic terms. Fortunately, there are signs (anecdotal evidence) that the industry is changing and beginning to provide measures of variabilities with forecasts thereby, potentially, enfranchising decision makers through encouragement of "what if?" questions. That should foster appreciation of what factors bring about changes in performance and to what degrees as well as appreciation of relationships between performance variables and measures.

Locke, Latham and Erez (1988) isolated four main links between goals and outcomes – (1) legitimate authority of the goal setter, (2) peer and group pressure towards goal achievement, (3) participants' expectations (effort leads to performance), (4) incentives and rewards (via "valence", to enhance commitment to the goals). Liu (1995) notes that goals must be challenging and, further, that participants must accept the goals for them to be effective performance incentives. That goals often remain uncommunicated and subject to fluctuations in power-based dominance of individual participants, extends the problems, potentially invoking detrimental conflicts. References to norms of performance may do little to alleviate the situation because such norms are, themselves, products of the same processes and so, contain elements of self-fulfilling prophesies.

3.2 *Realisation*

Particularly during the last fifteen years, focus has returned to integration as a performance enhancing mechanism; teamwork remains but in adapted guises. Management contracts, the British Property Federation (procurement) system and (subsequent) contract, followed by the New Engineering Contract (now in an extended second edition) sought to enhance project performance by improving relationships through fostering cooperation. But the method was "top-down" – change the formal system components and the informal system will adapt and accord immediately. None have been wondrous successes; some behaviour modifications have occurred but the underpinning cultures remain largely unaltered – claims and conflict still abound.

Partnering and relational contracting represent alternative approaches but tend to suffer from lack of implementational conviction, piecemeal use and contextual difficulties. Opportunism in market economies seems to be deeply entrenched and is unlikely to be overcome by participation in a 40-hour "workshop". Green (1999), for example identifies continuous improvement as "management by stress" and that powerful employer organisations which are major proponents of construction partnering behave quite contrary to the principles of partnering in their own core activities.

Popularly, partnering is founded upon trust – but what is trust and what is necessary to foster trust? Trust is a relational construct in which one actor is sure about the behaviour of another; generally, it is regarded as a positive behavioural attribute – that the other will not do anything to harm the actor. Trust results from respect for the self and for others leading to behaviour according to appropriate morals; hence, may be regarded as reliable, ethical (and positive) behaviour. Trust may be an initial stance, one found by Axelrod (1984) to be highly successful in the context of the "prisoner's dilemma" – trust and only cheat if cheated – "tit-for-tat".

However, it is apparent that the normal approach is the converse – to employ legal regulation (contracts) to endeavour to prevent (constrain) opportunism; enforcement is a further complicating issue. So, unless trust is used as the initial approach (tactic?) by participants, it must be actively fostered and earned by refraining from both cheating and opportunistic pursuit of self-gain. Partnering workshops operate to achieve trust as the initial stance and to demonstrate the advantages of maintaining the approach throughout. Could it, then, be countermanding to require a partnering charter/agreement (contract) to be executed by the participants? The perspective that partnering is founded on trust emerged from examination of Japanese industry but Womack, Jones and Roos (1990) assert that Japanese industry operates upon recognition of interdependencies between organisations, as reflected in Green's (1999) discussions.

4 NORMS

Cultures are manifested through norms of behaviour and, as such, also reflect morals through ethics of practices. Whilst norms imply averages, they also imply variability. There are no imposed "upper limits" of behaviour but bottom limits of acceptance are specified in laws, codes of conduct etc. Of course, issues of detection, enforcement and sanction then arise. A further complexity is due to social dynamism and the essential for appropriate changes to be incorporated to accord with modifications in societies' value structures. Globalisation might suggest that social differences are reducing – that convergence is occurring. However, studies (e.g. World Bank 2001) indicate that,

on various measures, evidence for divergence is just as robust as evidence for convergence.

In practice, economic considerations indicate upper limits of behaviour in businesses operating in market economies. In command economies, the norms and parameters are prescribed by State organisations in their regulation of economic activity. In the public sector of mixed economies (which tend to have been much reduced over recent years), although the state determines what will be purchased, the purchasing is done form the private sector and so, is dependent upon market forces. In construction, public sector activities have not only declined (commonly, through privatisation) but also have changed in their nature to reduce capital expenditure by government by use of concession-based procurement. That has placed significantly different investment and financing requirements on construction organisations; amending the traditional role of construction being a cash generating activity, the speed and effective management of which leads to generation of profit. Understandably, construction businesses are exploring mechanisms to adapt concession arrangements to align more closely with their more familiar financing of activities.

Thus, it seems clear that businesses are resistant to imposition of changes and, although changes may occur, responses tend to involve reversion towards the previous status quo.

Within an existing paradigm of business behaviour, the positioning of a firm is dependent on its influential personnel through their determination of the organisational culture. Clearly, such positioning varies but, within limits, is determined by the society. Further, organisational cultures tend to be self-perpetuating through recruitment, induction, training, operating procedures etc. – any recruits who do not fit with the culture (if, mistakenly recruited in the first place) tend to leave the firm quickly; others, perhaps less remote from the culture, may adapt. The greater the tolerance of the society in which an organisation operates and the more self-contained the organisation's activities are, the more diverse the spectrum of organisational cultures, and behaviour, will be.

Fragmentation, a widespread and long standing criticism of construction means that, at any stage of a project, there is a distinct, if transient, power hierarchy. The independence of individual specialist organisations, the inputs from which are vital for the realisation of the project, facilitate that situation. It should be unsurprising, therefore, that coordination proves to be so problematic and that real and extensive cooperation is rare. There are always others to blame for faults and room for manoeuvre is extensive. Thus, claims are widespread, litigation is common, innovation is low and performance suffers.

There seems to be two polar approaches to cultural awareness – one which focuses on similarities and the other which focuses on differences. Whilst cognisance of both similarities and differences is important for understanding, appreciation and adaptation of behaviour – i.e. to achieve compatibility; there are potential negative aspects also. Focus on similarities may induce complacency and lack of sensitivity to important differences whilst focus on differences may encourage incompatibility through ethno-centrism, "jokes" about differences etc., thereby enhancing alienation. Unfortunately, the negative aspects of differences focus is ascendant in construction leading to participant's behaviour generating a culture of mistrust and disrespect in interpersonal/interorganisational dealings to compound the other negative perspectives which abound. To overcome such problems, change initiatives must be enormously robust and be high in valence of expected benefits with evidence of realisation. More commonly, periodic power of shifting market forces lead to (temporary) changes.

5 DOING CULTURE

Culture is the constant practise of daily existence. We all "do culture" all the time which, of course, yields the dynamics, norms and variability of such human group measures. From a managerial perspective, culture can be regarded as a process or as a tool. Certainly, culture is about communication of meaning and, as with any communication mechanism, is subject to distortion, noise etc. resulting in lack of and mis-understanding. Thus, we may view manifestations of cultures as "signifying systems" through which collections of signals are given which the sender believes will invoke understanding by the receiver and, thence, lead to behaviour (such as an element of project performance).

Problems of communicating meaning (messages) are well known and addressed in detail in the social sciences through conversation analysis (e.g. Potter 1997), discourse analysis (e.g. Heritage 1997) etc. Again, the construction industry has long known of its extensive communication problems (e.g. Higgin & Jessop 1963) but little seems to have been achieved towards their resolution. Dismissive statements, abrogating responsibility to act ("it's the culture of the industry") remain common. We respond to communications relating to their contents and contexts, the presence and importance of each of those elements depending on the nature of the society (culture) and the language used. Sensitivity to relevant others influences our communications, interpretations of meaning and consequent action within a power hierarchical context of who those relevant others are (in a business context, at least).

Thus, we may accept culture as a contextual variable or we may believe that we can mould culture for change; the latter is much more likely to constitute behavioural modification, in the short term/initially, at least.

6 "HUMAN REENGINEERING"?

Hammer and Champy (2001) define reengineering as, "... the fundamental rethinking and radical redesign of business processes to achieve dramatic improvements in critical, contemporary measures of performance, such as cost, quality, service and speed" (35). Whilst such, apparently, customer-oriented performance measures seem laudable, they are also subject to potential abuse and the criticisms cited by Green (1999), above. Given a perspective of culture as a tool of management whereby behaviour and, thence, performance may be altered and shaped according to the manager's desire, the human is reduced to another category of passive business resource rather than being the active participant in the business processes.

A number of "reengineering" initiatives have been attempted in the construction industry – partnering, JIT, lean construction etc. – over recent years. Others, such as the New Engineering Contract (as noted, above) have, overtly, sought to change "the" culture of the industry; in the case of NEC, beyond the domestic national borders – an endeavour of no small bravado! Such initiatives serve to indicate the deep and widespread view that culture is a tool which managers can manipulate readily at their will to obtain changes in performance. Such a view belies the fundamental and complex nature of human cultures and so, necessarily, those initiatives are doomed. Only insofar as people affected recognise and accept merits in the change attempts will such changes be incorporated into those cultures.

Thus, it appears that, in reengineering, Adam Smith's "hidden hand" has far from decreased in its sinister apparitions. The desires of and opportunities for the (transiently) powerful to manipulate the less powerful may, in fact, have become enhanced!

Reengineering organisations – essentially, revisiting organisational design, structuring etc., is heavily value (and, thus, ethically) laden. Whose values are pursued and to what degrees of vehemence, with what effects on others are essential issues in which opportunism may play no small role. On the international level, such a struggle is articulated by Hutton (2002) in his analysis of the global role of USA.

So, reengineering constitutes radical organisational change – but how, what is involved and with what consequences? In adopting reengineering and endeavouring to apply it to people – as "human reengineering" – the perspective of culture as a tool which may be manipulated by management at will is apparent. That perspective raises value judgements – for whose benefit and at whose cost?

7 CONCLUSIONS

Culture constitutes an essential field of understanding for all managers but one which remains poorly understood. Too often, researchers and practitioners seek to attribute what they cannot explain readily to "culture". Others seek to effect "cultural changes" but endeavour to do so rapidly and by superficial mechanisms. Cultures are deep seated, fundamental phenomena governing human behaviour and have an (almost) infinite number of constantly evolving variants. Thus, it should be no surprise that (inter-) cultural understanding is fraught with difficulty and requires great patience and inter-personal sensitivity.

CIB, through task group, TG-23, is endeavouring to gain, foster and disseminate both more understanding of what culture is (or what cultures are), their variants in the world's construction industry, and how knowledge of cultures and cultural variants may be researched appropriately. The work programme of TG-23 remains unashamedly ambitious but, realistically so for, only through such studies can knowledge and understanding leading to cultural sensitivity and tolerance in a rapidly globalising environment be advanced.

REFERENCES

Axelrod, R. 1984. *The evolution of cooperation*, New York: Basic Books.

Construction Industry Review Committee 2001. *Construct for Excellence*, (the Tang Report) Report of the Construction Industry Review Committee, The Government of Hong Kong SAR.

Fellows, R.F., Seymour, D.E. 2002. *Perspectives on Culture in Construction*, CIB Publication #275, Rotterdam: CIB.

Green, S.D. 1999. Partnering: the propaganda of corporatism? In Ogunlana, S. O. (Ed.) *Profitable partnering in construction procurement*, London: E & FN Spon, 3–14.

Hammer, M. & Champy, J. 2001. *Reengineering the corporation (new edn.)* London: Nicholas Brealey.

Hatch M.J. 1993. The dynamics of organisational culture. *Academy of Management Review*, 18 (4), 657–693.

Heritage, J. 1997. Conversation analysis and institutional talk, In Silverman, D (Ed.) *Qualitative research: theory, method and practice*, London: Sage, 161–182.

Herzberg, F., Mausner, B. & Bloch Snyderman, B. 1967. *The motivation to work (2 edn.)*, New York: Wiley.

Higgin G. & Jessop N. 1963. *Communications in the Building Industry*. London: Tavistock Institute.

Hofstede, G.H. 1980. *Culture's consequences: international differences in work-related values*, Beverley Hills, Calif.: Sage Publications.

Hofstede, G.H. 1994. *Cultures and organizations: software of the mind*, London: Harper Collins.

Hofstede, G.H. 2001. *Culture's consequences: comparing values, behaviours, institutions and organisations across nations*, Thousand Oaks, Calif.: Sage Publications.

Hutton, W. 2002. *The World We're In*, London: Little, Brown.

Kroeber, A.L. & Kluckhohn, C. 1952. Culture: a critical review of concepts and definitions, In *Papers of the Peabody Museum of American Archaeology and Ethnology*, Vol. 47, Cambridge, MA.: Harvard University Press.

Lawrence, P.R. & Lorsch, J.W. 1967. *Organization and environment: managing differentiation and integration*, Boston: Division of Research, Graduate School of Business Administration, Harvard University.

Liu, A.M.M. 1995. *Evaluation of the outcome of construction projects*, PhD Thesis (unpublished), The University of Hong Kong.

Locke, E.A., Latham, G.P. & Erez, M. 1988. The determinants of goal commitment, *Academy of Management Review*, 13, 23–29.

McSweeney, B. 2002. Hofstede's model of national cultural differences and their consequences: a triumph of faith – a failure of analysis, *Human Relations*, 55 (10), 89–118.

Newcombe, R. 1994. Procurement paths – a power paradigm, In Rowlinson, S.M. (Ed.), *East meets West: Proceedings of CIB W-92 Procurement Systems Symposium*, The University of Hong Kong, CIB Publication 175, Rotterdam: CIB.

Potter, J. 1997. Discourse analysis as a way of analysing naturally occurring talk, In Silverman, D (Ed.) *Qualitative research: theory, method and practice*, London: Sage, 144–160.

Reugg, T.T. & Marshall, H.E. 1990. *Building economics: theory and practice*, New York: Van Nostrand Reinhold.

Smith, A. 1995. *An inquiry into the nature and causes of the wealth of nations*, Playfair, W. (Ed.) London: W. Pickering.

Smith, P.B. 2002. Culture's consequences: something old and something new, *Human Relations*, 55 (1), 119–135.

Taylor, F.W. 1964. *Scientific management : comprising Shop management; The principles of scientific management; Testimony before the Special House Committee*, New York: Harper & Row.

The Chinese Culture Connection (a team of 24 researchers) 1987. Chinese values and the search for culture-free dimensions of culture, *Journal of Cross-Cultural Psychology*, 18 (2), 143–164.

Tijhuis, W. 2001. Culture in Construction – Part of the Deal?, *Proceedings, CIB TG-23 Workshop*, CIB Publication #255, Rotterdam: CIB.

Trompenaars, F. & Hampden-Turner, C. 1993. *Riding the waves of culture: understanding cultural diversity in business (2 edn.)*, London: Nicholas Brealey Publishing.

Womack. J.P., Jones, D.T. & Roos, D. 1990. *The machine that changed the world*, New York: The Free Press.

World Bank 2001. *Global Economic Prospects and the Developing Countries 2001*, http:// www.worldbank. org /prospects/gep2001/ sumeng.htm, 17 May 2001.

System-based Vision for Strategic and Creative Design, Bontempi (ed.)
© 2003 Swets & Zeitlinger, Lisse, ISBN 90 5809 599 1

Influence of the anchorage system and of the deck stiffness on the postcritical behaviour of suspended bridges

P.G. Malerba
Department of Structural Engineering, Politecnico di Milano, Milan, Italy

ABSTRACT: The influence of the anchorage system and of the stiffness of the main structural elements on the postcritical behaviour of suspended bridges is studied through a numerical model suitable to deal with large displacements and large strains.

1 INTRODUCTION

The design of a new structure starts from basic criteria which, in essential form, resume its overall behaviour and allows us to define a first set of dimensions and of thickness.

Such criteria derive from the capacity of perceiving and of highlighting the flow of the force vectors, which convey the applied loads to a fixed reference system ("to the earth"), as well as from specialised theories, which focus the main factors characterising the response of the structure to given loading conditions. Usually these criteria are presented as the "conceptual design" of that type of structure. So, for instance, a single span deck bridge, having rigid transversal section, can be treated as a simply supported beam with rotational restraints at the ends; while a bit more complex system, like a slender arch bridge, having span l, rise f and which is loaded by the loads per unit of length p (dead load) and q (live load), is known to have a thrust $H \cong (p + q)l^2/8f$ and, for the live load q, maximum and minimum moments at the quarters of the upper deck, which equal approximately $M_{min}^{max} \cong \pm ql^2/60$. Something similar can be given for the cable stayed and for the suspended bridges.

These specialised theories introduce simplified hypotheses, suitable to reduce the full stress behaviour to a rational and more essential scheme and to translate the structural problem into analytical linear and non linear algorithms, which can be frequently solved in closed form. In conclusion these theories frame in essential schemes the suggestions of the intuition and of the experience and classify, in this way, well defined and known behaviours.

From this point of view, the design based on consolidated schemes can only continue to reproduce the same forms with great or little variants. For new and unconventional schemes we can't dispose of similar references. Nowadays it isn't a real problem, because the computational structural analysis can help us to solve any kind of structure. The numerical solutions, however, give us particular results, linked to that particular structure. Parametrical studies can be developed for a wide variety of configurations, but they are not able to synthesize with the same efficiency of the classical theories, the essence of the structural behaviour. Furthermore the usual parametric studies are carried out in the field of the linear problems. The linear behaviour can describe only a limited range of the overall behaviour of a structure. For instance one can deduce satisfactory results and measure equivalent performances even for very different typological configurations and, at the same time, ignore fundamental differences which can develop along the path to the collapse. In particular, the elastic analysis cannot allow us to measure how one is near to the limit or to collapse conditions and how the collapse mechanism is reached.

Systems which exhibit marked non linear behaviours are those suspended by cables. In particular, the structural response behaviour of long span suspended bridges is strongly influenced by the characteristics of the anchorage system.

In this work the influence of the anchorage system and of the stiffness of the main structural elements on the postcritical behaviour of suspended bridges is studied.

2 ANALYSIS OF EARTH ANCHORED AND SELF ANCHORED SUSPENSION BRIDGES

In suspended bridges, the forces acting on the main cable, can be transferred to the earth directly through anchor blocks at the end of the side spans or can be

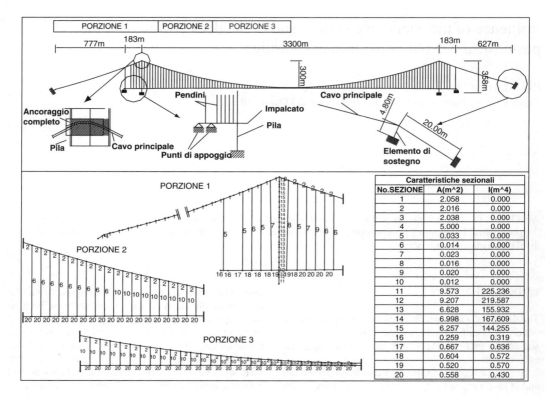

Figure 1. Model of the Messina Strait bridge.

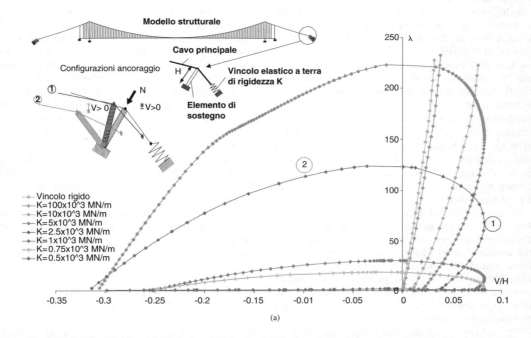

(a)

Figure 2. Messina Strait bridge: (a) Vertical and (b) horizontal displacements of the point at the top of the anchorage lever divided by the lever length (V/H), in function of a scalar multiplier λ of the uniform live load applied to the deck.

18

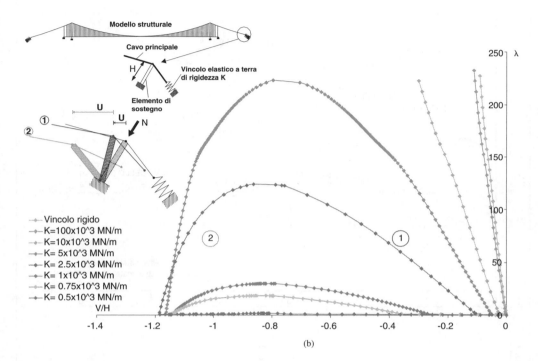

Figure 2.   (*Continued*).

self-contained by the longitudinal action of the deck (self-anchored systems). The self-anchored systems don't require the volumes of the anchor blocks. On the other hand the stiffening girder, heavily compressed, will require a larger cross section.

By taking into account the large amount of geometrical, topological and stiffness characteristics which influence the actual behaviour of the bridge, a systematic structural analysis can be carried out only through numerical methods.

A numerical model suitable to deal with large displacements and large strains, typical of these system, has been developed. Through the principle of virtual works, developed according to the Updated Lagrangian formulation, a truss and a beam element have been introduced.

The extension of such a formulation to complex structures gives a central role to the numerical techniques for solving non linear problems in presence of singular points and of unstable behaviours. As known, the classical Newton Raphson Method allows us to follow the equilibrium paths working by a load increments, but it is not able to follow the postcritical behaviours. In order to extend the analysis to the post-critical field, the arc length method has been used. The method has been improved by specific procedures, able to detect the bifurcation points and the paths which depart from the these points.

Table 1.   Cases studied.

Model	Description
0	Real case: suspended bridge earth anchored (stable).
1	The bridge of Model 0, but self-anchored (Area and inertia of the deck are A = 0.5 m², J = 1.66 m⁴).
2	The bridge of Model 1 with increased deck stiffness (A = 0.9 m², J = 3.32 m⁴).
3	The bridge of Model 1 with increased deck stiffness (A = 1.4 m², J = 4.98 m⁴).
4	The bridge of Model 1 with height pylons increased from 257.6 m to 277.6 m, but maintaining the sag of the cable f = 180 m.
5	The bridge of Model 4 with increased deck stiffness (A = 0.8 m², J = 4.0 m⁴).
6	Equal to Model 1, but having a truss hanger net.
7	Equal to Model 1, but with hangers having a variable slope along the side spans.
8	Equal to Model 7 with increased deck stiffness (A = 0.8 m², J = 3.32 m⁴).

This numerical approach has been tested through many benchmarks. An example of application regards the influence of an elastic connection between the main cable and the anchor blocks of the Messina bridge. Figure 1 shows the model of the bridge. Figure 2 shows

19

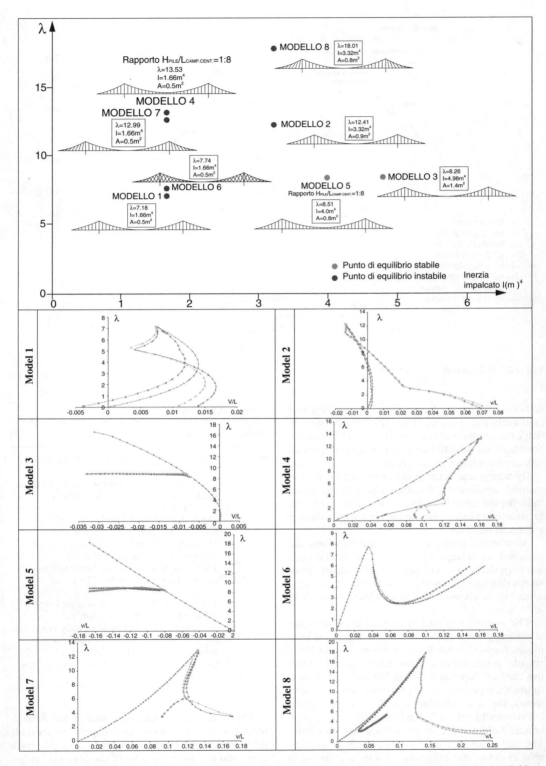

Figure 3.   Great Belt bridge: critical loads and load–displacement paths for the models 1–8 described in Table 1.

two families of curves, corresponding to different stiffness of the elastic connection, which show how the vertical (Fig. 2a) and horizontal (Fig. 2b) displacements of the point at the top of the anchorage lever divided by the lever length (V/H), varies in function of a scalar multiplier λ of the uniform live load applied to the deck.

3 COMPARATIVE STUDIES

With reference to the basic dimensions of the Great Belt bridge, which has a central span length $s_c = 1624$ m, two lateral spans lengths $s_l = 535$ m, height of the pylons $h = (180 + 77.6) = 157.6$ m, sag of the cable $f = 180$ m, a comparative study by varying some fundamental characteristics is carried out. The different cases listed in Table 1 have been examined.

The results are shown in Fig. 3. The first diagram present the values of the load multiplier at the limit point in function of the inertia of the deck. The little circles used to mark the limit points allow us to recognise if a limit point is stable or if it is followed by unstable branches.

4 CONCLUSIONS

The conclusions of these comparative studies can be synthesised as follows:

– the suspended and earth anchored systems are generally stable.
– the behaviour of the suspended and self-anchored systems is sensitive to the action of the deck and to the slackness of the hangers.

Furthermore, for the suspended and self-anchored systems we can observe that:

– there are limit and bifurcation points which lead to post critical and generally unstable response, with snap back effects.

– the limit load multiplier can be augmented by stiffening the deck, but having a look to the increasing of the weight which can transfer the critical behaviour from the deck to the pylons, due to increasing of the axial forces.
– an increment of the pylon height involves a greater slope of the main cables which reduce the axial component of the cable loading the deck, with an increase of the singular point.
– The increase of the deck inertia together with the eight of the pylons don't produce relevant positive effects, because the critical behaviour depends on the pylons again and the piers are higher and more stressed.
– Particular slope of the hangers induces market improvements in the system stability. In fact by sloping the vertical cable of the lateral span one can obtain a relevant increment of the limit load without increasing costs and dead loads.

REFERENCES

Bonet J., Wood, R., *Nonlinear continuum mechanics for finite element analysis*. Cambridge University Press, 1977.

Bontempi, F., Malerba P.G., The control of the tangent formulation in structural non linear problems, *Studies and Researches*, **17**, Graduate School for Concrete Structures "F.lli Pesenti", Politecnico di Milano, Milan, Italy, 1996, (in Italian).

Bontempi, F., Malerba, P.G., The Role of Softening in the Numerical Nonliner Analysis of Reinforced Concrete Frames, *Structural Engineering and Mechanics*, **5**(6), 785–801, 1997.

Di Domizio, M., *Geometrical non linear analysis of cable stayed and suspended structures*. Thesis, Politecnico di Milano, Milan, Italy, 2003, (in Italian).

Gimsing, N.J., *Cable supported bridges*, John Wiley & Sons, 1988.

Riks, E., An incremental approach to the solution of snapping and buckling problems, *Int. J. of Solids Structures*, **15**, 529–551, 1979.

2. Risk analysis and structural reliability

Codified design and reliability aspects of structural timber elements

T. Keskküla
Estonia Agricultural University, Tartu, Estonia

L. Ozola
Latvia University of Agriculture, Jelgava, Latvia

ABSTRACT: The objective of this paper is the consideration on the uncertainties involved in the design procedure of structural timber elements. The discussed qantities of timber refer to measured variability of: wood resistance values in compression, buckling factor values for simple supported elements, geometric characteristics of structural element sections. The probability calculations are carried out and the distributions of predicted load bearing capacity values are presented. The values of reliability indexes are calculated. The classification system as related to safety is presented for structural timber elements.

1 INTRODUCTION

Structural design codes reflect the recent level of investigations in the related science branch. The unknown fields are covered by the decisions from experience, judgement and intuition. As regards the timber structures the uncertainty of material characteristics and insufficient knowledge to describe the complexity of interrelationship by mathematical equations are the items of research and discussion for dozens of years. The design codes for timber structures have reached the top level of development as Eurocode 5. Eurocode 5 is the most advantageous limit state design code document which is drafted out on the bases of the results from serious investigations. Eurocode exhibits considerable improvements due to more sophisticated analyses of wood and structural timber elements.

Nevertheless the complex relationship of the strength and load in the wood cause higher or lower uncertainty to any design condition. The uncertainties arise from inherent variabilities in loads and timber strength and stiffness properties, dimensions, model uncertainty, natural and man-made hazards, as well as from the insufficient knowledge and human error in design and construction.

Any realistic reliability study of structures requires an assessment of uncertainties as related to the properties of structural elements being used. In this study the focus is the uncertainties referred to the variability of strength properties, behaviour of wood in longitudinal buckling and variability effects of section sizes.

In this study the reliability calculations of structural timber elements is presented based on experimental data. The reliability index for axially loaded elements in longitudinal buckling and beams in pure bending is calculated using the empirical data samples obtained while inspection of timber frames and from the tests of wood.

At the last chapter the proposal for classification system of timber structures is presented.

2 STATISTICAL DESCRIPTIONS OF SOME AFFECTING QUANTITIES

2.1 Inherent uncertainty of wood strength in compression

In the last few years we have stored up some large data samples on compression strength values of clear wood (*Pinus silvestris*) standard specimens (20 × 20 × 30 mm) subjected to a short-term static loading. During testing moisture content of wood was from 6 to 8%. Strength values are reduced to 12% moisture content using the reduction factor 0.04 per 1% of moisture content.

The statistical characteristics of strength-density data samples (A, B, C) are presented in Table 1. Large data samples mentioned are divided into subgroups as related to certain density ranges. The following symbols are used in Table 1: n – sample size (number of tested specimens), f_{mean} – the mean value of compression strength; ρ_{mean} – the mean value of wood density

Table 1. Statistical characteristics of tested samples.

Sample	n	f_{mean} N/mm^2	V_f kg/m^3	ρ_{mean}	$V\rho$
A	717	54.8	0.143	502	0.113
A1 ($\rho < 500$)	365	49.9	0.120	460	0.066
A1_1 ($\rho < 450$)	144	45.7	0.096	430	0.053
A1_2 ($\rho = 450–500$)	210	52.3	0.096	482	0.037
A2 ($\rho > 500$)	363	59.8	0.101	543	0.084
A2_1 ($\rho = 500–550$)	248	58.3	0.107	521	0.038
A2_2 ($\rho > 550$)	115	63.3	0.061	589	0.083
B	692	41.7	0.189	502	0.128
B1 ($\rho < 500$)	294	47.5	0.124	441	0.081
B1_1 ($\rho < 450$)	180	44.7	0.083	416	0.045
B1_2 ($\rho = 450–500$)	114	52.1	0.113	481	0.030
B2 ($\rho > 500$)	398	57.9	0.108	546	0.071
B2_1 ($\rho = 500–550$)	267	57.8	0.110	527	0.025
B2_2 ($\rho > 550$)	131	58.2	0.094	586	0.075
C	122	52.3	0.240	474	0.140
C1 ($\rho < 500$)	80	45.7	0.201	433	0.095
C1_2 ($\rho = 400–500$)	61	48.9	0.166	451	0.065
C2 ($\rho > 500$)	42	64.8	0.118	550	0.043

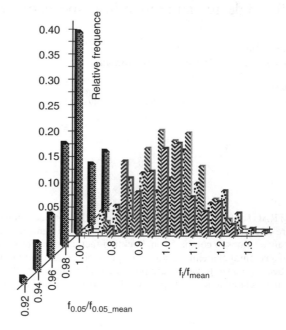

Figure 1. Distributions of relative values of strength data for different samples.

in dry condition; V_f, V_ρ – coefficient of variation for strength and density data samples correspondingly.

The characteristic 5-percentile values ($f_{0.05}$) for each of strength data set was calculated assuming good fitting with lognormal law of distributions and correspondingly using a standard procedure for the calculations of characteristic 5-percentile values (EN14358). The result in the strength data sample of characteristic values was obtained in size of 68. Approximately the notion on probability distributions of 22 data sets is shown in Figure 1.

2.2 Variability of geometric characteristics

While inspecting the timber framings after longterm service (12–17 years) in livestock buildings a large quantity of cross section measurements were made on beams and studs. In total 3515 of real cross section dimensions for bending members (22 data samples) and 530 sections (5 samples of data) for free supported column elements were fixed. The statistical description of geometric data samples are presented in relative terms – as distributions about mean value and graphically displayed in Figures 2 and 3.

The variability of geometric characteristic relative values are characterised by the coefficient of variations: $V_{A/Amean} = 0.033$ for data set of section area values of studs and $V_{W/Wmean} = 0.052$ for data set of section modulus values of beams and girders.

2.3 Variability of buckling factor values

The data groups of buckling factor values were obtained by testing series of free supported softwood

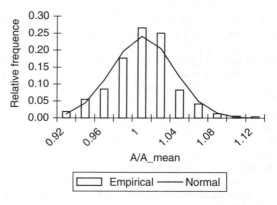

Figure 2. Histogram of relative area values with normal distribution curve superimposed.

timber specimens ($20 \times 20 \times 300$ mm) in axial compression (longitudinal buckling). The stress value after that the loss of linear proportionality between the longitudinal force and transversal displacement values was observed, was assumed as a critical stress (σ_{cr}). After that the standard samples were cut out and tested in compression to obtain the ultimate limit stress σ_u value. The buckling factor values were estimated as ratio $k_c = \sigma_{cr}/\sigma_u$ (see distribution in Figure 4).

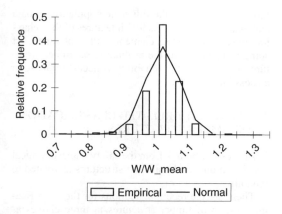

W/W_mean

Empirical ☐   Normal ——

Figure 3. Histogram of relative section modulus values with normal distribution curve superimposed.

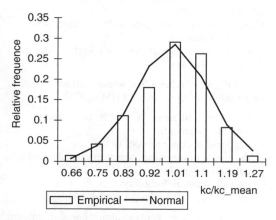

kc/kc_mean

Empirical ☐   Normal ——

Figure 4. Histogram of relative buckling factor values with normal distribution curve superimposed.

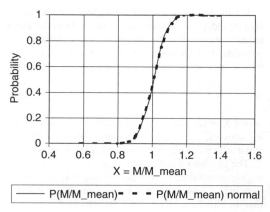

X = M/M_mean

—— P(M/M_mean) - - - P(M/M_mean) normal

Figure 5. Probability distribution (cumulative) of relative load bearing capacity values in pure bending with cumulative normal distribution curve superimposed.

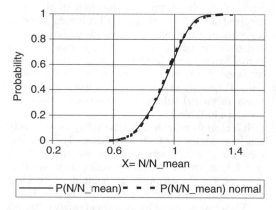

X= N/N_mean

—— P(N/N_mean) - - - P(N/N_mean) normal

Figure 6. Probability distribution (cumulative) of relative load bearing capacity values in longitudinal buckling with cumulative normal distribution curve superimposed.

3 PROBABILITY CALCULATIONS AND ASSESSMENT OF SAFETY

All variables tested in probabilistic meaning is assumed as mutually independent events. The predicted probability of load bearing capacity for structural elements is calculated according to multiplication rule of probability. The probability of each load bearing capacity value is calculated by multiplying of probabilities of influencing factors as follows:

$$P(y) = P(x_1) \times P(x_2) \times P(x_3) \qquad (1)$$

where $P(y)$ = the probability of load bearing capacity characteristic values; $P(y) = P(N_k/N_{kmean})$ for elements in longitudinal buckling (studs) and $P(y) = P(M_k/M_{kmean})$ for beams in pure bending; $P(x_1)$ = the probability of material resistance minimal (5-percentile) value, $P(x_1) = P(f_{0.05}/f_{0.05mean})$; $P(x_2)$ = the probability

of geometric characteristic value, $P(x_2) = P(A/A_{mean})$ for studs and $P(x_2) = P(W/W_{mean})$ for beams; $P(x_3) = $ the probability of buckling factor for studs, $P(x_3) = P(k_c/k_{cmean})$. Distributions of predicted load bearing capacity values for beams and studs are shown in Figures 5 and 6. The distributions are described by the following characteristics:

- mean values (expectations): $\mu_N = 0.98$ for elements in longitudinal buckling; $\mu_M = 1.04$ for bending elements;
- standard deviations: $\sigma_{yN} = 0.133$; $\sigma_{yM} = 0.07$;
- coefficients of variation: $V_{yN} = 0.136$; $V_{yM} = 0.067$;
- 3-rd and 4-th moments about sample means: $m_{3yM} = -0.11$; $m_{4yM} = 4.15$; $m_{3yN} = -0.27$; $m_{4yN} = 2.87$.

27

Let us assume that the load factors are characterised by independent constant value ($=1$) as the loads are not measured in this study. Therefore the task may be reduced to one component case and the limit state is described by the following equation:

$$g = X - 1/\gamma \qquad (2)$$

where X = load bearing variable; γ = the safety factor between loading and resistance part. Function g constantly increases with increasing of X values.

The obtained distributions (Figs 5, 6) of load bearing capacity values have a good fitting with the normal distribution law. For these conditions the probability that the structural element will not fail is

$$P(g > 0) = \Phi\left(\frac{\mu_X - 1/\gamma}{\sigma_X}\right) = \Phi(\beta) \qquad (3)$$

where Φ is the distribution function of the standardized normal distribution (Christensen (1996)); μ_X = mean value and σ_X = standard deviation of resistance variables; β = reliability index. Using Partial Safety Factor Method's solutions (Ditlevsen & Madsen (1996)) the reliability index (β) and probability P ($g > 0$) values are calculated for different safety factor (γ) values. The results of calculations are given in Table 2.

It is clear from Table 2 that the safety factor is very sensitive to number of affecting factors. For beam elements it is satisfactory to adopt the safety factor $\gamma = 1.3$ to ensure reliability index approximately $\beta = 3.9$. For the elements in longitudinal buckling the value of $\gamma = 1.8$ relates with value of $\beta = 3.26$.

When making consideration about safety of timber structures it is essential to appreciate that the analysis of large data samples nevertheless does not really reflect the essence of the matter of such complicated structural material as timber.

The knowledge of wood as a structural material continues to improve every dozen of years. Nevertheless time is too far when the full scale population of data and mathematical models for all features of the behaviour of structural timber elements will be obtained. Yet some mechanism for the evaluation of timber structures as related to the reliability is necessary as soon as possible.

4 RELIABILITY RELATED CLASSIFICATION OF TIMBER STRUCTURES

It is necessary both – from the safety and economical considerations to classify the structures as related to reliability.

There are the recommendations for the classification system of timber structures in three classes as related to reliability:

Class 1: structures with lowest designed degree of reliability;
Class 2: timber structures with medium designed degree of reliability;
Class 3: timber structures with highest designed degree of reliability.

The degree of reliability of a timber structure should be assessed taking account of (ISO 2394):

– the cause and mode of failure of a structure or structural element;
– the possible consequences of failure;
– the choice of the values of action variables and calculation parameters;
– consideration of durability;
– the accuracy of the design models used.

Let us have some considerations based mainly on design practice and professional judgement.

The prediction of possible failure mode in the limit state is a very significant factor. The structural element which would be likely to collapse suddenly without a previous warning must be defined as brittle and should be designed for a higher degree of reliability than one for which the collapse is preceded by some kind of warning (deformations etc.) in such a way that measures can be taken to limit the consequences. Degree of reliability may be assessed by the following criteria (see Table 3):

1 point – elements with trend towards a brittle failure (tensile elements, elements with sections stressed in shear up to design resistance value, glue joints with high concentration of shear stress and the like);

3 points – elements with trend towards a plastic failure mode and possibility of brittle failure mode is low (bended elements, compressed elements and elements in longitudinal buckling with slenderness ratio more than 70, nailed and bolted joints, nail plate joints and the like);

Table 2. Results of reliability calculations.

γ	$1/\gamma$	ν_x	σ_x	β	P ($g > 0$)
1.2	0.833	0.98	0.13	1.128	0.8686
1.2	0.833	1.04	0.07	2.952	0.9984
1.3	0.769	0.98	0.13	1.621	0.9474
1.3	0.769	1.04	0.07	3.868	0.9999
1.4	0.714	0.98	0.13	2.044	0.9793
1.4	0.714	1.04	0.07	4.653	1
1.5	0.667	0.98	0.13	2.410	0.9920
1.6	0.625	0.98	0.13	2.731	0.9968
1.7	0.588	0.98	0.13	3.013	0.9987
1.8	0.555	0.98	0.13	3.265	0.9994

Table 3. Proposed criteria for differentation of timber strucures as related to reliability.

Condition	Minimum of criteria for classes		
	1	2	3
Predicted failure mode	1	3	6
Risk, possible consequences of failure	2	4	6
Checking of action variables	1	2	3
Checking of material properties and of elements geometric uncertainties	1	2	3
Durability and maintenance	1	2	3
Design models used	2	4	6
Quality control level	1	3	6

6 points – elements with trend towards a plastic failure mode (bended elements, compressed elements and elements in longitudinal buckling with slenderness ratio less than 70, nailed and bolted joints prevented from a brittle failure through shear planes, joints with toothed rings and the like).

The possible consequences of failure may be measured in terms of risk to life, injury, potential economic losses and by social inconveniences taking place after failure. Degree of reliability may be assessed according to the consequences of failure by the following criteria:

2 – risk to life high, social inconveniences very great. This criteria is satisfactory for temporary structures and buildings without human activities;
4 – risk to life medium, social inconveniences considerable (for livestock buildings, warehouses and the like);
6 – risk to life low, social inconveniences small or negligible (for public buildings).

The degree of reliability is closely pertained with checking of an appropriate values in really possible combinations of actions on the structure. In this relation the criteria are selected as follows:

1 – the structure is checked on permanent and variable actions in fundamental combinations using decreased values of partial safety factors;
2 – the same using normal values of partial safety factors;
3 – the structure is checked on permanent, variable and accident actions in all possible combinations using normal or increased values of partial safety factors. The complete action models are considered.

Effects of uncertainty of the material matter itself showing up the fluctuations of the physical properties and geometric characteristics of elements from sample to sample is assessed by the following criteria:

1 – materials are selected by visual grading method;

2 – materials are selected by mechanical grading method and geometric sizes are controlled;
3 – materials are selected by mechanical grading method or testing, geometric sizes are controlled, safety factors for material and elements are involved according to observed distributions of values.

The durability of the timber structure and the structural elements in their environment should remain fit for use during their design lifetime under appropriate maintenance. The criteria of durability are choosed as follows:

1 – the structure satisfy the required performance criteria and system integrity is ensured;
2 – the structure is manufactured and erected with confirmity to design requirements, the service conditions correspond with the same as designed and the necessary protective measures are realised;
3 – the structure is manufactured and erected with confirmity to design requirements using testing machines and special instruments for quality control; the environmental conditions correspond with the same as designed; the necessary protective measures are realised and periodical inspecting of structures is ensured during the service.

Design models shall describe the timber structure and its behaviour up to the limit state under the consideration, accounting for relevant actions and environmental influences. Simultaneously calculation model always represents the real structure as a simplified system in which more decisive factors are obligatory and the less important ones are neglected. Actually the design consumption on timber structure includes as a minimum three models: action model, structural model (definition of elements and connection types as regards to degree of freedom), and resistance models by which wood resistance values corresponding to the action effects (duration of load, moisture content, direction of grains, effects of plastic behaviour of the material, geometrically linear versus geometrically nonlinear response) are determined.

The criteria for the assessment of fitting the design model with the real structure are selected as follows:

2 – simplified loading and design models are used for determining internal forces, load duration and effects of service conditions are encountered in resistance model;
4 – the correct design model is used for determining internal forces, load duration and service effects are encountered, the time-dependent behaviour (creep) of elements is considered;
6 – the correct design model is used and geometrically nonlinear response of structure is considered, load duration and service effects are encountered, the time-dependent behaviour (creep) of elements is

29

considered, the experimental verification of original models are carried out.

The appropriate quality control policy must be adopted and implemented with purpose to achieve an adequate confidence that the designed and erected structure fulfil the specified requirements. The criteria are selected as follows:

1 – the code requirements are considered in design and construction; general visual inspecting and quality control is carried out;
3 – the review of design documents is carried out by expert commission; the manufacturing and erection processes are followed by control measures including sampling and testing procedures detailed in the structural design standards; the control of service conditions and appropriate maintenance regime of structures is provided;
6 – both quality control and compliance control of materials and structures are realised, for example, proof tests of real structures are performed, every produced unit is inspected.

5 CONCLUSIONS

The probabilistic calculations of timber elements based on the tested variables proved that the considerable decrease of reliability is expected for elements in longitudinal buckling the capacity to resist external forces for which is affected by much more factors than in bending. It means that the safety factor for structural elements should be determined not only for materials.

The system for the classification of timber structures should be developed. It is very important in the current situation when different building codes exist in East European countries.

REFERENCES

Christensen R. 1996. *Analysis of variance, design and regression. Applied statistical methods*. London: Chapman & Hall.
Ditlevsen, O. & Madsen, H.O. 1996. *Structural reliability methods*. Chichester: John Wiley & Sons.
EN 14358. *Structural timber – Calculation of characteristic 5-percentile values.*
ISO 2394: 1998(E). *General principles on reliability for structures.*

Uncertainties of the method of partial safety factors

A. Kudzys
Institute of Architecture and Construction, Lithuania

E.R. Vaidogas
Vilnius Gediminas Technical University, Lithuania

ABSTRACT: Shortcomings, conditionality and incorrectness of the conservative method of partial safety factors are discussed. Principles of structural safety assessment of load-carrying members for pre-use and use working life is analyzed. The recommendations for the safety analysis of members subjected to short term variable action-effects distributions of which obey Gumbel and exponential laws are presented. Uncertainties of the conservative method and probability-based safety assessment and verification of steel and reinforced concrete cross-sections under compression are illustrated by numerical examples.

1 INTRODUCTION

Some reasons of unexpected failures, damage and dangerous accidents in buildings and construction works can be caused not only by irresponsible behavior of designers and erectors but also by conditional recommendations and directions of design codes based on the method of partial safety factors (PSFM) in Europe or the method of load and resistance factors (LRFM) in the USA. Many structural engineers and researchers doubt on universality of PSFM because of some principled conditional and questionable approaches. It is difficult to assess various peculiarities of structures subjected to time-variant non-stationary actions using PSFM.

Any increase in structural quality of load-carrying members and their joints can be carried out by updating design codes and skilled analysis on safety and durability of structures. A disregard of effect of uncertainties and time-dependency of calculation models which give member resistance and action-effect values on the performance and safety degree of systems and their components can not be justified.

It is well-known that a wide range of structural design issues can be neither formulated nor solved within the deterministic analysis methods. Probability-based analysis is inevitable in the assessment and verification of a response of structures to extreme loading caused by short term episodic and reiterated time-variant variable actions.

This paper is devoted to turn attention of some civil and resident engineers being convinced of PSFM perfection and to encourage them to introduce probability-based methods into design and erection practice.

2 DETERMINISTIC AND PROBABILITY – BASED ANALYSIS

2.1 Structural safety margin

The present design codes of load-carrying structures of buildings and construction works are based on the conservative method of partial safety factors (PSFM). It is difficult and sometimes inconceivable to define enough accurately the performance and action-effects of structural members by deterministic approach analysis. Usually, so called, the universality of PSFM leads to overestimation of design performance and safety of high-reliability structures and their members (components) the resistances and action-effects of which are time-dependent fixed or non-stationary functions.

Many members of load-carrying structures belong to auto-systems representing multicriteria failure mode because of variety of behavior situations at pre-use t_{pre} and use t_u periods. Therefore, both deterministic and probability-based design methods must take into account not only working life actions but also erection-construction ones.

A negative influence of the action-effects caused by erection-construction loads is double. There exists probability of failure of members and systems through overloading with irreversible consequences and because of presence of latent defects. Usually, autosystem model consists of some stochastically dependent performance functions as conventional member elements connected in series.

It is very pity that Eurocode 1, International Standard ISO 2394 (1998) and JCCS (2000) are passed in silence all problems and specific features of life cycle safety assessment of structural members including their safety analysis for the pre-use period.

The safety margin of structural members may be defined as the performance function M_{pre} for the period t_{pre} and as the performance process $M_u(t)$ for the period t_u and may be expressed as:

$$M_{pre}=g(X, \Theta)=\Theta_{R,pre}R_{pre}-\Theta_{ge}S_{ge}-\Theta_{qe}S_{qe} \tag{1}$$

$$M_u(t)=g[X(t), \Theta(t)]$$

$$=\Theta_{R,u}(t)R_u(t)-\Theta_g(t)S_g(t)-\Theta_q(t)S_q(t) \tag{2}$$

Here X, Θ and $X(t)$, $\Theta(t)$ are the random vectors and processes of basic X_i and additional Θ_i variables; R_{pre}, S_{ge}, S_{qe} and $R_u(t)$, $S_g(t)$, $S_q(t)$ are the resistance and action-effect functions and processes in the member critical section at pre-use and use periods. The random functions $\Theta_{R,pre}$, $\Theta_{R,u}(t) \approx \Theta_{R,u}$ and Θ_{ge}, Θ_{qe}, $\Theta_g(t) \approx \Theta_g$, $\Theta_q(t) \approx \Theta_q$ represent uncertainties of calculation models for member resistance and action-effects. The model uncertainty functions may be represented by probability density functions or simply as the means and standard deviations of the random variables Θ_R, Θ_g and Θ_q.

According to the approaches of PSFM, the safety margin can be written as follows:

$$M_d = R_d - S_{gd} - S_{qd} \tag{3}$$

where the components R_d and S_{gd}, S_{qd} are the design values of resistance and action-effects. Thus, the design criterion of member load-carrying capacity may be written as: $R_d - S_{gd} - S_{qd} = 0$.

2.2 Shortcomings of deterministic analysis

The analysis of the safety margins (1), (2) and (3) allows to enumerate main shortcomings of PSFM:

- a disregard of an effect of the working life and probability distribution law peculiarities of safety margin components on the performance and safety of high-reliability load-carrying members;
- an incapability to take account of unfavorable deviations and inaccuracies in calculation models and the same to safeguard the rational design solution for members or their joints for usual and complicated systems;

- an inconceivability to calculate the performance and long term safety values of members taking into account behavior differences in statically determinate and indeterminate systems;
- a carelessness to assess and guarantee the structural safety and sustainability of members exposed to short term non-stationary action-effects using some ordinary partial safety factors;
- an impossibility to estimate the durability of structures or their parts in spite of the random processes of member resistances and environment actions, reparability and replaceability peculiarities of structural components;
- a disregard of pre-use defects and failures upon the serviceability, durability and safety of load-carrying structures or components for their working life cycle.

2.3 Probability-based analysis

The long term probabilistic safety index for member life cycle t_r may be introduced as:

$$P\{T \geq t_r\} = P\left\{ \bigcap_{i=1}^{m}(M_{ei} > 0) \right\} \times$$

$$P\left\{ \bigcap_{j=1}^{n}(M_{uj}(t) > 0) \middle| \bigcap_{i=1}^{m}(M_{ei} > 0) \right\} \tag{4}$$

where m and n are the number of failure criteria of members at the pre-use (erection) and use periods. According to ISO 2394 (1998), JCSS (2000) and Vrouwenvelder (2002) recommendations, the Gaussian and log-normal distributions may be used for member strength and permanent or long term variable actions. The Weibull, gamma, exponential and extreme value distributions may be convenient for short term episodic and reiterated variable gravity or side (lateral) forces. Overloading of structural members can be associated with actions of a natural character, human activities and technological disturbances.

When the vectors R, S_g and S_q are stochastically independent, then it is expedient to simplify mathematical models by establishment of the conventional resistances. For erection and working life periods their values may be written, respectively, in the forms:

$$R_{pre} = \Theta_{R,e}R_e-\Theta_g S_g \tag{5}$$

$$R_u(t) = \Theta_{R,u} R(t)-\Theta_g S_g(t) \tag{6}$$

The bivariate probability distributions of the joint junctions (5) and (6) are close to the normal ones.

Reiterated transient time-variant action-effects are caused by wind gusts, snow pressures, earthquake motions and wave slams. The probability distribution of reiterated actions obeys the Gumbel extreme value one. In this case, the long term safety index can be calculated using the following equation:

$$P\{M_u(t) > 0\} \approx \prod_{k=1}^{r} \int_{0}^{\infty} f_{R,u}(R) F_S(R) dR \qquad (7)$$

Here k is the cut of the random sequence consisting from r cuts; $f_{R,u}(R)$ is the bivariate normal density function of the resistance (6);

$$F_{S,q}(R) = \exp\left[-\exp\left(\frac{S_{u,m} - R}{0.7994 \, \sigma S_u} - 0.5772\right)\right] \qquad (8)$$

is the Gumbel distribution function of the action-effect $S_u = \Theta_{qu} S_{qu}$ with the mean $S_{u,m}$ and standard deviation σS_u.

Episodic short term action-effects are caused by random erection, explosion and impact forces, the probability distributions of which are close to the exponential ones. If the conventional resistances (5) and (6) are stationary functions, the safety indices of members for pre-use and use periods can be calculated, respectively, by the formulae:

$$P\{M_{pre} > 0\} = \int_{0}^{\infty} f_{R,pre}(R) F_{S,pre}(R) \, dR \qquad (9)$$

$$P\{M_u(t) > 0\} = \int_{0}^{\infty} f_{R,u}(R) F_{S,u}(R) \, dR \qquad (10)$$

The generalized structural safety index may be presented as follows:

$$\beta = \Phi^{-1}(P\{M > 0\}) \qquad (11)$$

where $\Phi^{-1}(.)$ is the inverse of the standard normal distribution. This index is used as a tentative target value related to relative costs of safety measures and minor, moderate or large consequences of failure.

3 NUMERICAL EXAMPLES

3.1 Steel cross-section analysis

The H-shape cross-section ($A = 295 \times 10^{-4}\,\mathrm{m}^2$, $W_y = 4481.8 \times 10^{-6}\,\mathrm{m}^3$) of the Class 3 steel member is exposed to the eccentric compression by the force $N = N_g + N_q$ with eccentricity $e = 0.14\,\mathrm{m}$ (Figure 1).

The characteristic and design values, mean and coefficient of variation of the steel yield strength are: $f_{yk} = 235\,\mathrm{MPa}$, $f_{yd} = 235/1.1 = 213.64\,\mathrm{MPa}$, $f_{ym} = 260.7\,\mathrm{MPa}$ and $\delta f_y = 0.06$. According to

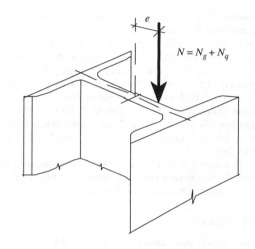

Figure 1.   Steel cross-section under eccentric compression.

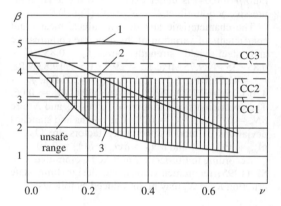

Figure 2.   Safety index β versus factor $\nu = N_{qm}/(N_{gm} + N_{qm})$ when variable action distribution is normal (1), Gumbel with $r = 50$ (2) and exponential (3).

Eurocode 3 directions, the design limit state criterion $R_d = N_d$ may be introduced as follows:

$$R_d = f_{yd} \bigg/ \left(\frac{1}{A} + \frac{e}{W_y}\right) = 1.35 N_{gk} + 1.5 N_{qk} \qquad (12)$$

The criterion (12) is in force for various values of the compressive components N_{gk} and N_{qk}. The probabilistic safety index of the cross-section for working life t_u was calculated taking into account of the coefficients of variation $\delta N_g = 0.10$ and $\delta N_q = 0.20$, the normal, Gumbel and exponential distributions of short term variable actions.

The curves presented in Figure 2 corroborate the shortcomings of the method of partial safety factors enumerated in substitution 2.2. The target β-values 3.1, 3.8 and 4.3 correspond to the failure consequence classes CC1, CC2 and CC3, respectively, as it is recommended by Calgaro & Gulvanessian (2001) and ISO 2394 (1998). Thus, the failure probability $P_f = \Phi(-\beta)$ of steel members designed by Eurocode recommendations can exceed the target values, respectively, $P_f = 0.000967$, $P_f = 0.000072$ and $P_f = 0.0000085$ many hundreds of times. Therefore some efforts made by Ellingwood & Tekie (1999) to improve PSFM with the specified partial safety factor $\gamma_q = 1.6-1.7$ instead of $\gamma_q = 1.5$ could not very effective.

The curve 3 in Figure 2 shows that short-term episodic actions are very dangerous and should call a special attention of structural engineers.

3.2 Concrete cross-section analysis

The reinforced concrete section ($A_c = 0.1\,\text{m}^2$, $\delta A_c = 0.03$, $A_s = \Sigma A_{s1}$, $\delta A_s = 0$, geometrical steel ratio $p = 0.04$) is under exposure to the axial compressive action-effect $N = N_g + N_q$ (Fig. 3).

The characteristic and design values, means and coefficients of variation of the concrete compressive and steel yield strengths are: $f_{ck} = 0.85 \cdot f'_{ck} = 0.85 \cdot 35 = 29.75\,\text{MPa}$, $f_{cd} = 29.75/1.5 = 19.83\,\text{MPa}$, $f_{cm} = 41.78\,\text{MPa}$, $\delta f_c = 0.175$; $f_{sk} = 420\,\text{MPa}$, $f_{sd} = 420/1.15 = 371.7\,\text{MPa}$, $f_{sm} = 466\,\text{MPa}$, $\delta f_s = 0.06$. The coefficients of variation of forces N_g and N_q are $\delta N_g = 0.10$ and $\delta N_q = 0.20$. The means and standard deviations of model uncertainty factors are $\Theta_{Rm} = \Theta_{gm} = \Theta_{qm} = 1$ and $\delta\Theta_R = \delta\Theta_g = \delta\Theta_q = 0.10$.

According to Eurocode 2 and ACI Committee 318-89 (1995) recommendations, the design limit state criterion $R_d = N_d$ may be introduced as follows:

$$R_d = A_c(f_{cd} + p\,f_{sd}) = 1.35\,N_{gk} + 1.5\,N_{qk} \qquad (13)$$

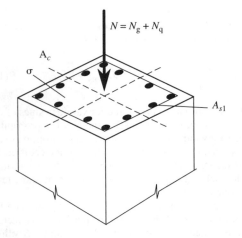

Figure 3. Concrete cross-section under axial compression.

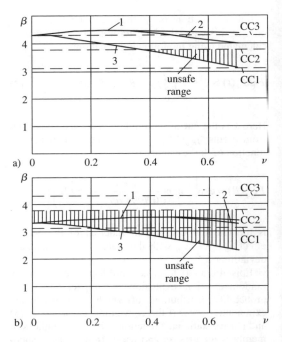

Figure 4. Safety index β versus factor $v = N_{qm}/(N_{gm}+N_{qm})$ when model uncertainties are neglected (a) and heeded (b), variable action distribution is normal (1), Gumbel with $r = 1$ (2) and $r = 50$ (3).

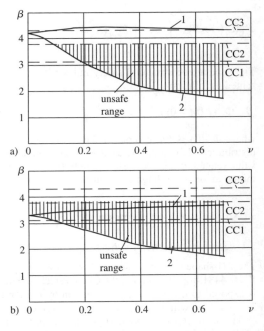

Figure 5. Safety index β versus factor $v = N_{qm}/(N_{gm}+N_{qm})$ when model uncertainties are neglected (a) and heeded (b), variable action distribution is normal (1) and exponential (2).

The criterion (13) is in force for various values and nature of the action-effect components N_{gk} and N_{qk}.

The results presented in Figures 4 and 5 show that the failure probability of reinforced concrete members designed by Eurocode 2 directions may exceed the specified target values hundred times and more. However, reinforced concrete members are less sensitive to the uncertainties of PSFM as steel structures. It is not difficult to be convinced of dangerous loading of building structures by short term episodic actions (Fig. 5).

Besides, the calculation model uncertainties must be estimated in any case of pre-use and use loadings in spite of presence or absence of variable actions. The uncertainty factors as additional random variables must be taken into account in spite of a probability distribution law of basic variables.

Analogical data are characteristic for other types of structural members and their systems.

4 CONCLUSIONS

It is impossible to ensure sufficient structural safety of load-carrying members designed by the method of partial safety factors for building structures exposed to intensive short term episodic or reiterated time-variant variable actions. Therefore, the universal deterministic values of partial safety factors for variable actions must be used in design practice with great caution. At any case, these variables must be related to an intensity of extreme variable and episodic actions.

REFERENCES

ACI Committee 318. 1995. Building code requirements for reinforced concrete. American Concrete Institute. Detroit.

Calgaro, J.A. & Gulvanesian, H. 2001. Management on reliability and risk in the Eurocode system. Safety, Risk and Reliability – Trends in Engineering, March, 155–160.

Ellingwood, B.R. & Tekie, P.B. 1999. Wind load statistic for probability-based structural design. *Journal of Structural Engineering*, April, 453–463.

Eurocode 1, CEN. 2002. Basis of design and actions on structure – Part 1: Basis of design. ENV 1991-1.

Eurocode 2, CEN. 2002. Design of concrete structures – Part 1: General rules and rules for buildings. ENV 1992-1-1.

Eurocode 3, CEN. 2002. Design of steel structures – Part 1-1: General rules and rules for buildings. ENV 1993-1-1: 2002 E.

ISO 2394. 1998. General principles on reliability for structures. Second edition. Switzerland.

JCSS 2000. Probabilistic model code. 12th draft. Joint Committee on Structural Safety.

Vrouwenvelder, A.C.W.M. 2002. Development towards full probabilistic design codes. *Structural Safety*, Vol. 24, 417–432.

System-based Vision for Strategic and Creative Design, Bontempi (ed.)
© 2003 Swets & Zeitlinger, Lisse, ISBN 90 5809 599 1

Prototype testing for reliability-based design

S.G. Reid
University of Sydney, Sydney, NSW, Australia

ABSTRACT: Several prototype load-testing procedures for the determination of structural design strengths are described and evaluated with regard to statistics of the resultant design strengths, the associated safety indices β and the nominal probabilities of failure. Results are presented for structures with lognormal and Weibull strength distributions. The prototype load-testing procedures are also evaluated with regard to efficiency (characterized by the variability of the design strengths) and dependability (characterized by an entropy-based measure which accounts for the uncertain distribution of the probability of failure). It is shown that statistical load-testing procedures based on conservative estimates of characteristic strengths (for high levels of statistical confidence) can produce very conservative design outcomes. Also it is shown that the use of "sample variance correction factors", to account for sampling uncertainty, reduces the efficiency of probabilistic methods. The dependability of all the procedures is shown to be affected by the strength distribution type, although results based on the sample mean strength are more stable than results based on the minimum strength. It is concluded that efficient probabilistic methods should be calibrated to achieve the target level of dependability, and different methods should be used for different strength distribution types.

1 INTRODUCTION

Prototype testing can be used to assess the strength of structural elements or structural systems which are not amenable to codified structural analysis and design, and such testing can be particularly useful in the assessment of innovative designs involving novel types of structural elements or structural systems. However, for the purposes of reliability-based design, prototype test results must be assessed using rational (statistical or probabilistic) procedures to determine dependable strength levels appropriate for comparisons with the design action levels specified in design codes. The results of prototype load testing can be used to estimate characteristic strengths (associated with particular levels of statistical confidence), or they can be used to obtain direct estimates of reliability-based design strengths (related to particular levels of structural reliability).

Structural design procedures based on load testing must account for the effects of sampling variability (especially for small samples). In statistical load-testing procedures, sampling variability is taken into account with regard to the statistical confidence attached to the derived estimates of characteristic strengths, whilst in probabilistic load-testing procedures, sampling variability may be taken into account using "sample variance correction factors".

The paper describes some statistical and probabilistic procedures (with particular reference to an AISI Standard and Australian Standards) that have been developed to determine design strengths. The procedures are discussed with regard to their efficiency and their dependability, using an entropy-based measure of overall uncertainty that accounts for the variability (from sampling) of the notional probability of failure. Conclusions are presented concerning efficient and dependable procedures that can be used to determine reliability-based design strengths based on prototype testing of small samples.

2 LOAD-TESTING PROCEDURES

2.1 *AISI procedure for probabilistic design*

The AISI specification for cold-formed steel structures (AISI 1990) includes reliability-based load testing provisions for determining structural performance where strength calculations cannot be made in accordance with the AISI specification. To determine structural performance without theoretical strength calculations, load tests must be carried out on at least four identical specimens.

The design load carrying capacity of the tested elements R_d is given by the product of the sample mean capacity R_p and a capacity reduction factor ϕ:

$$R_d = \phi R_P \tag{2}$$

$$\phi = 1.5 M_m F_m \exp(-\beta_o V_o) \tag{3}$$

where M_m and F_m denote the mean values of a material factor and a fabrication factor, respectively; β_o is the target reliability index; and V_o is the coefficient of variation of the safety margin, given by

$$V_o = (V_M^2 + V_F^2 + C_P V_P^2 + V_Q^2)^{0.5} \tag{4}$$

where V_M, V_F V_P and V_Q denote the coefficients of variation of the material factor, the fabrication factor, the sample strengths and the relevant load effect, respectively; and C_P is a "sample variance correction factor" dependent on the sample size n (i.e. the number of test results):

$$C_P = (n-1)/(n-3) \tag{5}$$

The expression for the resistance factor ϕ (Equation 3) is obtained from reliability calibration studies based on lognormal distributions of the random variables, including approximations that apply when the coefficients of variation are small.

The sample variance correction factor C_p (Equation 5) is based on an assumption that strengths are log-Student T distributed and the factor C_p is set equal to the variance of the standardised Student T distribution with $m = (n - 1)$ degrees of freedom (Pekoz & Hall 1988).

2.2 Australian standards

2.2.1 Australian standard procedure for semi-probabilistic design

Several Australian Standards include statistical procedures based on proof load tests of one or more prototype test specimens. The strength of the population of structures of the type tested is deemed to comply with design requirements if no prototype test specimen fails on the application of a specified proof load. The proof load is normally specified as the product of the ultimate design load and a proof load factor PLF that is given as a function of the specimen type (structure, member or connection) and the size of the test sample (possibly as small as one).

The proof load factors PLF are based on the factor $k(p, c, n)$ that relates the minimum sample strength $R_{min,n}$ (from a sample of size n), to the characteristic strength estimate $R_{p,c}$ (for a particular characteristic strength fractile p and statistical confidence c that the

true value of the characteristic strength R_p is not less than the estimated value $R_{p,c}$).

$$R_{p,c} = R_{min,n} / k(p,c,n) \tag{6}$$

Based on a result obtained for a Weibull distribution of strengths (Leicester 1987), the factor $k(p,c,n)$ is taken to be

$$k(p,c,n) = \{\ln(1-c)/[n\ln(1-p)]\}^{V_R} \tag{7}$$

where V_R is the coefficient of variation of the resistance.

In order to obtain proof load factors related to a target reliability index β_o, the factors $k(p, c, n)$ are multiplied by the relevant capacity reduction factors ϕ_p related to the characteristic strength R_p (Leicester 1987). Hence, the design strength R_d is related to the minimum sample strength $R_{min,n}$ by means of a Proof Load Factor (PLF) such that

$$R_d = R_{min,n} / PLF \tag{8}$$

where

$$PLF = k(p,c,n) / \phi_p \tag{9}$$

For the purposes of determining proof load factors for the Australian Standards, the factor $k(p, c, n)$ has typically been evaluated for $p = 0.05$ and $c = 90\%$, and the coefficient of variation of the resistance has been assigned assumed values dependent on the structural type.

For the purposes of this discussion, Table 1 shows theoretical Proof Load Factors PLF for a Weibull distribution of strengths with a coefficient of variation of 0.224, based on concrete shear strengths (Reid 1995). The factors are based on confirmation of the characteristic strength $(p = 0.05)$ with statistical confidence

Table 1. Proof load factors, PLF.

Sample size n	Proof load factors, PLF	
	c = 50%	c = 90%
1	3.00	3.92
2	2.57	3.36
3	2.34	3.07
4	2.20	2.88
5	2.09	2.73
6	2.01	2.63
7	1.94	2.54
8	1.88	2.46
9	1.83	2.40
10	1.79	2.34

levels c of 90% and 50%, and with a capacity reduction factor ϕ_p related to the theoretical design point (for a lognormal distribution of loads with a coefficient of variation of 0.3, and a target safety index β_o of 3.0) (Reid 1995, 1998b).

The ultimate strength design requirements are deemed to be satisfied for design loads corresponding to the lowest values of the peak test loads divided by appropriate prototype proof load factors LF (where LF is the product of the relevant proof load factor PLF and a strength enhancement factor SF that relates the anticipated strength of the test specimen to the anticipated strength of a production unit).

2.2.2 Australian standard procedure for probabilistic design

An alternative probabilistic procedure given in an Australian Standard for reinforced concrete culverts is based on strength statistics obtained from prototype failure load tests (Reid 1995). The design strength (load capacity) R_d for a particular load combination and failure mode is

$$R_d = \phi_T (m_L / m_{SF}) \tag{10}$$

where ϕ_T is a test capacity reduction factor, m_L is the sample mean failure load and m_{SF} is the relevant mean strength enhancement factor (relating the anticipated strengths of test specimens to the anticipated strengths of production units).

The test capacity reduction factor ϕ_T is dependent on the sample size n, the coefficient of variation V_L of the test results and the type of sampling (either concentrated or dispersed). Dispersed sampling is defined as sampling that is dispersed with respect to manufacturing locations or time of manufacture, whilst concentrated sampling denotes sampling that is concentrated in time or location of manufacture.

The test capacity reduction factors have been determined for a target reliability index β_o equal to 3.0, consistent with the alternative procedures for design by calculation or prototype proof load testing. (Also, the capacity reduction factors have been calibrated for a reference load that is lognormally distributed with a coefficient of variation of 0.3 and for a reference load factor corresponding to the "design point" value for a lognormal resistance with a coefficient of variation of 0.2.)

Resistances are assumed to be lognormally distributed with a mean value m_R corresponding to the sample mean m_L and with a coefficient of variation V_R such that

$$V_R^2 = C_n V_L^2 + V_S^2 \tag{11}$$

where V_S^2 is a term to account for the type of sampling (with V_S equal to 0.1 or zero, for concentrated or

dispersed sampling, respectively) and C_n is a factor to account for statistical sampling uncertainty (related to the sample size n). The sampling uncertainty factor C_n is based on an approximate result that accounts for the variability of the sample mean (Reid 1995):

$$C_n = 1 + \frac{n-1}{n(n-3)} \tag{12}$$

Hence the specified test capacity reduction factor ϕ_T (based on lognormally distributed resistances) is:

$$\phi_T = 2.115 \exp[-V_R^2/2 - 3\sqrt{V_R^2 + (0.3)^2}] \tag{13}$$

2.3 Alternative probabilistic load-testing procedures

The probabilistic procedures specified in the AISI specification for cold-formed steel structures and the Australian Standard for reinforced concrete culverts differ mainly with regard to the sample variance correction factors used to account for the statistical sampling uncertainty. The AISI specification uses a sample variance correction factor given by Equation 5, whilst the Australian Standard uses a sample variance correction factor given by Equation 12.

Two other variations of the Australian Standard procedure are considered in this paper, using alternative values of the sample variance correction factor. One of the alternative factors has been calculated to account for the variance of the sample mean (Reid 1998a), giving:

$$C_n = \frac{n+1}{n} \tag{14}$$

The other alternative factor gives a procedure which simply ignores sampling uncertainty (so that the resistance mean and variance are approximated by the sample statistics). Accordingly,

$$C_n = 1 \tag{15}$$

The probabilistic procedures described above have been derived from results for strength distributions that are lognormally distributed. An alternative procedure has also been developed for the design of structures with Weibull-distributed strengths (Reid 2000b), using a different test capacity reduction factor ϕ_T as shown in Figure 1.

The test capacity reduction factor ϕ_T for Weibull-distributed strengths (Figure 1) has been determined for a target reliability index β_o equal to 3.0 (consistent with the other procedures described above) and it has been calibrated for a reference load that is lognormally

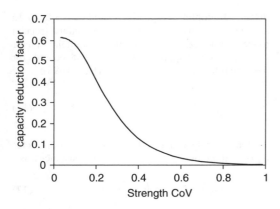

Figure 1. Test capacity reduction factor ϕ_T for Weibull-distributed strengths.

distributed with a coefficient of variation of 0.3 and for a reference load factor corresponding to the "design point" value for a Weibull resistance with a coefficient of variation of 0.224.

3 EVALUATION OF LOAD-TESTING PROCEDURES

Simulated load-testing results have been obtained for typical populations of structures with lognormal and Weibull distributed strengths. As assumed in the derivation of the proof load factors and test capacity reduction factors, the coefficient of variation of the strengths was taken to be 0.224, the load-effects were taken to be lognormally distributed with a coefficient of variation of 0.3 and the target reliability index was $\beta_o = 3$. Also it was assumed that the design load factor was calibrated to match a reference "design point" for a lognormal resistance and a load (of relevant distribution type) with respective coefficients of variation of 0.2 and 0.3. Results for the Australian Standard procedure for probabilistic load testing were calculated for dispersed sampling (Equation 11).

The simulation results have been evaluated with regard to statistics of the resultant design strengths R_d, values of the safety index β, the nominal probabilities of failure p_f, and an entropy-based measure of uncertainty which has been proposed as a measure of dependability based on the uncertain distributions of the nominal probabilities of failure p_f, as described below (Reid 1998a).

3.1 *Entropy*

In accordance with Bayesian probability concepts, the total uncertainty is characterized by the expected value of the probability of failure. In practice,

however, the consistency of the nominal probabilities of failure associated with uncertain outcomes of the design process is also important. In order to provide a quantitative measure of uncertainty that reflects not only the expected probability of failure but also the variability of the probability of failure (over all uncertain design outcomes) an entropy-based measure of uncertainty has been proposed (Reid 1998a).

Entropy ε is a measure of uncertainty associated with a range of possible (discrete) outcomes o_i with probabilities of occurrence p_i:

$$\varepsilon = -\sum_i p_i \ln p_i \qquad (16)$$

In the context of structural reliability analysis, there are only two possible outcomes of interest: failure or non-failure. Accordingly, it has been proposed that the entropy associated with a particular probability of failure p_f should be defined as follows:

$$\varepsilon(p_f) = -[p_f \ln p_f + (1 - p_f) \ln(1 - p_f)] \qquad (17)$$

Furthermore, for a range of designs with various nominal probabilities of failure p_f, the entropy of the design process is characterized by the expected value of $\varepsilon(p_f)$. This has been evaluated for the various load testing procedures.

3.2 *Results for lognormally-distributed strengths*

Simulation results for lognormally-distributed strengths are shown in Figures 2–6, based on the load-testing procedures given in the AISI specification and the Australian Standards. Results based on the Australian Standards include the proof-loading results (AS proof) and probabilistic results including the standard specified procedure (AS) and alternative procedures (AS* and AS**) with sample variance correction factors given by Equations 12, 14 and 15, respectively.

The expected values of the design strengths R_d, (normalized with respect to the "true" reliability-based design strength) are shown in Figure 2. Clearly, the proof-loading procedure is much more conservative (on average) than the probabilistic procedures. The least conservative probabilistic procedures are, of course, those that use the least conservative "sample variance correction factors".

Figure 3 shows the coefficients of variation of the design strengths. The proof-loading yields a CoV which is relatively small (but this is based on an assumed value for the population CoV, whereas the probabilistic procedures are based on the sample statistics). The most consistent probabilistic procedures (with small CoV) are those that use the least conservative "sample variance correction factors".

40

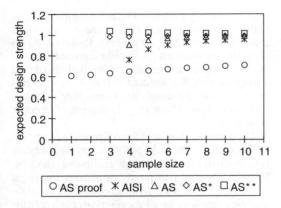

Figure 2. Expected (mean) design strength for structures with lognormally-distributed strengths.

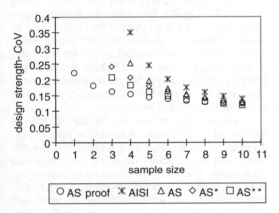

Figure 3. Coefficient of Variation (CoV) of design strength for structures with lognormally-distributed strengths.

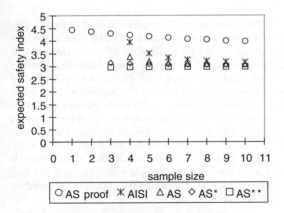

Figure 4. Expected (mean) Safety Index β for structures with lognormally-distributed strengths.

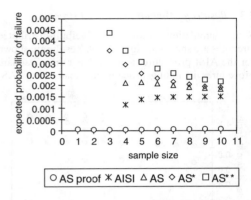

Figure 5. Expected (mean) probability of failure p_f for structures with lognormally-distributed strengths.

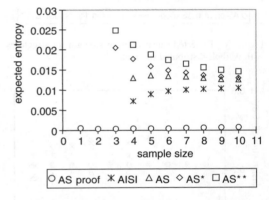

Figure 6. Expected (mean) entropy for structures with lognormally-distributed strengths.

Figure 4 shows the expected values of the safety index β which should be compared with the target safety index $\beta_o = 3$. The AS proof-loading is again shown to be relatively conservative on average (as expected for a procedure based on a conservative estimate of the characteristic strength).

Figure 5 shows the expected values of the nominal probabilities of failure p_f which should be compared with the target value $p_{fo} = 0.00135$ (corresponding to $\beta_o = 3$). Clearly, the AS proof-loading is very conservative whilst the least conservative probabilistic procedures are shown to be very unconservative for small sample sizes.

Figure 6 shows the expected entropy $\varepsilon(p_f)$ which should be compared with the reference value of $\varepsilon(p_{fo})$ = 0.0103 (corresponding to $\beta = \beta_o = 3.0$ and $p_f = p_{fo} = 0.00135$, exactly, for all designs). The relative values of the expected entropy are similar to the relative values of the expected probability of failure, but the entropy is an increasing function of both the expected value and the variance of the probability of failure.

3.3 Results for Weibull-distributed strengths

Some simulation results for Weibull-distributed strengths are shown in Figures 7–9. Results are shown for the AISI procedure, and the Australian Standard procedures including probabilistic loadtesting (AS)

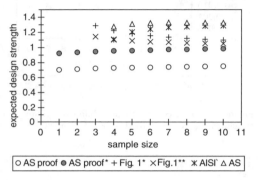

Figure 7. Expected (mean) design strength for structures with Weibull-distributed strengths.

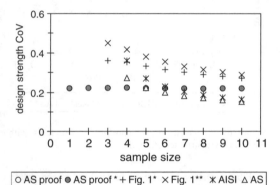

Figure 8. Coefficient of Variation (CoV) of design strength for structures with Weibull-distributed strengths.

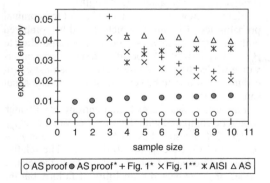

Figure 9. Expected (mean) entropy for structures with Weibull-distributed strengths.

with ϕ_T given by Equation 13, and also proof loading (Table 1) with statistical confidence $c = 90\%$ (AS proof) and $c = 50\%$ (AS proof*). Results are also shown for the alternative probabilistic procedure using ϕ_T from Figure 1 (derived for Weibull-distributed strengths) with the standard deviation of strengths estimated from the sample assuming either n degrees of freedom (Fig. 1*) or $(n - 1)$ degrees of freedom (Fig. 1**).

These results show that the AS proof-loading procedure with $c = 90\%$ (AS proof) is very conservative (as expected) even for Weibull-distributed strengths, but with $c = 50\%$ (AS proof*) it matches the target entropy ($\varepsilon(p_{fo}) = 0.0103$). On the other hand, the probabilistic procedures are all unconservative and only the procedures derived specifically for Weibull-distributed strengths approach the target entropy (and only for large sample sizes).

The consistency (and efficiency) of the procedures is indicated in Figure 8. The CoV of the design strengths based on proof-loading is simply the CoV of the population strengths (regardless of sample size), whilst the CoV of the design strengths based on the probabilistic procedures decreases as the sample size increases. Contrary to expectations, the most consistent results were given by the probabilistic procedure derived for lognormallydistributed strengths.

Comparing the results for Weibull-distributed strengths (Figs 7–9) with the results for lognormally-distributed strengths (Figs 2–6), it is clear that the efficiency and dependability of all the procedures are significantly affected by the strength distribution type. However, it should be noted that results based on factored sample means are less sensitive to the strength distribution type than results based on sample minima (Reid 2000a).

4 CONCLUSIONS

It has been shown that statistical load-testing procedures based on conservative estimates of characteristic strengths (for high levels of statistical confidence) can produce very conservative design outcomes, whilst a statistical confidence level of 50% was sufficient to achieve the target level of dependability. Also it has been shown that the use of "sample variance correction factors", to account for sampling uncertainty, reduces the efficiency of the probabilistic methods. The dependability of all the procedures has been shown to be affected by the strength distribution type, although results based on the sample mean strength are less sensitive to the distribution type than results based on the minimum strength.

It is concluded that the most efficient prototype testing procedures (with the most consistent results) are the probabilistic procedures based on the sample mean strength and without "sample variance correction factors". These procedures should be calibrated to achieve target levels of dependability, but different (recalibrated) procedures should be used for structures with different strength distribution types.

REFERENCES

AISI 1990. Load and Resistance Factor Design Specification for Cold-Formed Steel Structural Members, *Research Report CF 90-1*, AISI, Washington, DC, USA, 1990.

Leicester, R.H. 1987. Load Factors for Proof and Prototype Testing, *First National Structural Engineering Conference, IEAust., Melbourne, Australia, 1987*, pp. 546–550.

Pekoz, T. & Hall, W.B. 1988. Probabilistic Evaluation of Test Results, *Proc. Ninth Inter. Specialty Conference on Cold-Formed Steel Structures, Rolla, USA, 1988*, University of Missouri-Rolla, USA.

Reid, S.G. 1995. Load Testing for Reliability Based Design of Culverts, *Seventh International Conference on Applications of Statistics and Probability in Civil Engineering (ICASP7), Paris, France, 1995*, pp. 903–909.

Reid, S.G. 1998a. Prototype Load Testing Procedures for Structural Design, in *Structural Safety and Reliability, Proc. ICOSSAR'97, Kyoto, Japan, 1997*. N Shiraishi et al, eds, Balkema, pp. 573–580.

Reid S.G. 1998b. Prototype Load-Testing Procedures for Probability-Based Limit States Design, in *Structural Engineering World Wide 1998*, N K Srivastava, ed., Paper T 104-3, Elsevier.

Reid, S.G. 2000a. Reliability-Based Design Strengths Based on Prototype Testing of Small Samples, *Eng. Found. Conf. on Composite Construction in Steel and Concrete IV (CCIV), Banff, Canada, May-June 2000, Proc., Vol. 2, NSF Symposium - Session 2*, United Engineering Foundation, pp. 1–12.

Reid, S.G. 2000b. Load Testing for Design of Structures with Weibull-Distributed Strengths, in *Applications of Statistics and Probability, Proc. ICASP8, Sydney, Australia, 1999*. R Melchers & M Stewart, eds, Balkema, pp. 705–712.

System-based Vision for Strategic and Creative Design, Bontempi (ed.)
© *2003 Swets & Zeitlinger, Lisse, ISBN 90 5809 599 1*

Microbiology risk and hydraulic of the hot water system

Z. Pospíchal
Technical University of Brno, Brno, Czech Republic

Z. Žabička
Žabička company, Brno, Czech republic

ABSTRACT: The calculation flow in distribution pipeline is in Czech Republic assessed according to Czech regulation CSN 73 6655 and depends on the type of building, on a kind and number of at the same time used water outlets and other technological equipments and need of fire water. The system of indoor pipeline has to be designed to secure, that circulation of water in the indoor hot water pipeline is steady and demanded service – supply of hot water of demanded temperature and quantity to distribution places – water outlets and also bacteriological risks are kept down.

1 THEORETICAL BASIS

The calculation flow in distribution pipeline is in Czech Republic assessed according to Czech regulation CSN 73 6655 and depends on the type of building, on a kind and number of at the same time used water outlets and other technological equipments and need of fire water. To assess the calculation flow for dimensioning of inner water pipeline the buildings are divided to a three groups:

- residential buildings
- other buildings with equable water consumption
- other buildings with collective and peak water consumption

There is an equation for each group of buildings or their parts. According to this equation calculation flow Q_d [l.s^{-1}] can be assessed in factual part of distribution pipeline

a) residential buildings

$$Q_d = \sqrt{\sum_{i=1}^{m}(q_i^2 . n_i)} \qquad (1)$$

b) other buildings with equable water consumption

$$Q_d = \sum_{i=1}^{m} q_i \sqrt{n_i} \qquad (2)$$

c) other buildings with collective and peak water consumption

$$Q_d = \sum_{i=1}^{m} \varphi_i \cdot q_i \cdot n_i \qquad (3)$$

where Q_d calculation flow [l.s^{-1}]; q nominal outflow from particular kinds of water fittings [l.s^{-1}]; n number of same kind water fittings; m number of kinds of water fittings; φ coefficient of contemporary water consumption.

By dimensioning of parts of inner water distribution pipeline which at a time serves for building water supply same as for fire pipeline, there is assumed that when there is some fire water usage the building supply water is not consumed. Bigger of both flows in these parts of pipelines is considered as the calculation flow.

If the pipeline serves collective for technological purposes together with building supply water and fire water it is necessary that contemporarity of consumption is based on technological conditions of operation.

Calculation flow for hot water circulation is assessed under presumption that there is not hot water consumption at water outlets. By such a operating conditions of hot water pipeline there has to be guaranteed flow which ensures economical operation (no wasting of water and energy) and minimization of microbiological risks during operation of system.

The Colebrook–White equation is used for determining of hydraulic terms, which is mentioned in proposal PrEN 806.

Calculation flow in circulation pipeline is based on heat losses of supply pipeline. The heat losses in circulation pipeline are not considered by calculation of flow.

In correctly projected hot water system feedback of water in circulation pipeline is not allowed and therefore water temperature in circulation pipeline do not have effect to maintain above mentioned condition.

Calculation flow in one part of hot water distribution pipeline is assessed:

$$Q = \frac{q_1 \cdot L}{c \cdot \rho \cdot \Delta t_1},$$ (4)

where

$$\Delta t_1 = t_{beg} - t_{end}$$ (5)

and

$$t_{mn} = \frac{t_{beg} + t_{end}}{2},$$ (6)

where: q_1 is linear heat loss of definite section of supply pipeline [$W \cdot m^{-1}$]; L length of supply pipeline [m]; c heat capacity of water [$kJ \cdot kg^{-1} \cdot K^{-1}$]; ρ water density [$kg \cdot m^{-3}$]; t_{beg} temperature at the beginning of section [°C]; t_{end} temperature at the end of section [°C]; t_{mn} mean temperature in section [°C].

By assessing of linear heat loss for Equation 6 there is not covered up effect of heat losses of fittings, connection parts and place of pipeline, therefore it is recommended to rise counted heat losses of 15%.

Now only systems with forced circulation of hot water are projected. These systems guarantee demands on hot water at all water outlets.

Economical projection of system extent, isolation and circulation flow can help us to operate systems without huge waste. Inner pipeline systems of hot water with forced circulation should be equipped with automatical thermoregulation valves which ensure hydraulic and termic balance of system.

Inner systems of hot water have to be operated in way that the difference of water temperature on top floor during normal water consumption (full outflow 60 sec) is smaller than 4 K. So there is requirement to good pipe isolation and to keep calculation flow of circulation water in complete system.

Drop of water temperature caused by unfitting project or operation conditions have big effect on user demanded service.

The main factor that determinate reliability of water supply to consumer is flow velocity in pipeline. This factor has also effect on acoustic conditions, life service and also on microbiological quality of water.

Water flow in inner pipeline with its value near to calculation flow have turbulentar character. Noise arise from water flow through pipes. Cause of their existence are miscellaneous and they depend on different factors.

In the first place it's mainly the pressure and the speed of water stream in the pipe and particularly in the fitting, a way of attachment of pipe, material of pipe and not least the quality of water and it's ability to form an incrustation in the pipe. In places where a change of speed of water stream and thus change of pressure occur, a chaotic motion of water happens and that's why there is a different speed of water stream in single section of the pipe. Incipient water twists are increasing emission of noise from the pipe and simultaneously cavitations occurs which is the reason of lowering lifetime of metal pipe, especially copper pipe. In case of incrustation in irregular shapes, the cavitations shows also in places of straight pipelines where no water twists exists. Due to increasing incrustation in the pipeline the clear section of pipe is decreasing and thus the speed of water stream is increasing. Increase of the speed partly increases the noise in pipeline, partly increases cavitations.

Arguments mentioned above could form an idea that's very useful to decrease speed to the minimum and get for a calculation flow rate laminar water stream in the pipe. Reduction of speed in the indoor pipeline mainly in pipeline for drinking water and also in pipeline for hot water could increase lifetime of the pipeline, on the other hand it would bring serious problems with the water quality. Slow motion of water helps production of drifting sediments and thus to support chance of reproduction of microorganisms. In the same time decrease of concentration of active biocide in the drinking water occurs. Increase of temperature of cold water and decrease of temperature of hot water helps to this conditions. Cold water, which is in contact with a warmer environment, gets warmer and thus organoleptic characteristics are changing.

Concurrently the temperature between 25°C and 40°C is optimal, while intensive reproduction of microorganisms in the water occurs, increased by a fact, that it's mainly the end part of pipelines with a low concentration of residual biocide. Too low design speed (thus bigger diameter of pipe) deteriorates the whole process, while it excessively increases volume of water in the pipeline and extends the delay of water in the pipeline.

2 DESCRIPTION OF ORIGINAL STATE

Monitored dormitory part of hospital with rehabilitation in Ivancice (Czech Republic) was built in 70. of the last century. It is a long six-story building. There was established a hydrotherapy in the ground floor. Heating of the water is central with a calorifier room by the near gable of the building. Pipeline is situated to a technical floor under the building. After putting to service problems with regular water supply occurred, especially with the hot water. Direct connection of hydrotherapy from the pipeline ascending conduction even caused cut-off of water supply of the higher floors during filling up the bathtubs. Another problem was that during a pressure loss an overflow of cold water to the hot water and vice versa occurred in dependence on water demand.

The temperature of hot water in the outermost areas of indoor pipeline regularly was falling below 35°C.

Additionally there was connected a house for night service (30 m from the main building) to the hot water system. The doctor was unable to get water hotter than 30°C during the night. The problem was resolved by adding circulative pump to the connection place.

Through this conditions a detailed survey and recalculation of hydraulic ratio of present pipelines, simultaneously there was a microbiological survey. The suggested changes were made under these circumstances.

3 DESIGN AND IMPLEMENTATION ADJUSTMENTS

There was carried out a reconstruction of the indoor pipeline in the whole building on the basis of the survey results. The basis of the technical solution was a hydraulic calculation of the complete system.

Because of the survey results a new connection for the hydrotherapy was made directly from the calorifier room.

All the main pipelines of the indoor pipelines were dismantled and replaced by new ones. The water is distributed from the distributor through polypropylene and galvanized steel pipe through the building.

The preparation of hot water is central and was maintain without changes. The circulation is secured by circulatory pump (Parameters of the main pump: $Q = 1$ l/s, $H = 3.8$ m, $N = 300$ W/400 V).

For regulation of the circulation on 21 risers are used thermoregulatory valves to balance the circulation system.

To secure circulation in the night service building there is installed auxiliary circulatory pump on the far gable of the building (Parameters of the auxiliary pump: $Q = 1$ l/s, $H = 2.3$ m, $N = 50$ W/230 V).

Two hot water risers including circulation were dismantled in comparison with original state. These risers were supplying WC in the hallways for visitors – almost no hot water was used there thus all horizontal pipelines contained "dead" water.

Mud-charge valves were installed on main pipelines of cold, hot and circulation water on both sides of the pipeline in the technical floor. Centrifuge was simultaneously installed on circulation pipeline before entering back the heating system. These pipelines and the centrifuge are at least once a week decanted, simultaneously with decanting of the heaters (alternately on both sides).

Table 1. Detected amount of undissolved materials.

Place	Amount of undissolved materials in mg/10 l (by above mentioned methodic)
Heating	1406
Main pipeline cold water	287
Main pipeline hot water	427
Main pipeline circulation pipeline	1039
Centrifuge (tangential separator)	1060

Decanting is under way systematically for allowing check of the pipelines and heaters: in the exact place are in the first 10 l discharged into a white bucket, then continues the discharge for 1 minute.

After mixing this amount of water a specimen is taken for determine water haze and after this the whole amount of 10 l is left to sediment for 24 hours. Clear water is after this put out and the approx. 2 l from the bottom is then put into a sample bottle. This specimen is filtrated and after drying out contents of undissolved materials are determined from this specimen.

After a week – with a week consumption about 70 m³ – following amount of undissolved materials is detected (see Table 1).

These measurements shows that for securing the quality of distributed water there is a need of removal of detected sludge from the circulation pipeline and heating equipment.

4 CONCLUSION

The system of indoor pipeline has to be designed to secure, that circulation of water in the indoor hot water pipeline is steady. The speed of water stream in the circulation pipeline has to be such to eliminate sedimentation of the sludge in the pipeline. A trapping sludge device has to be installed in the system while this device is equipped with fitting for easy dismantling. Decanting has to be allowed in every place where we can expect big production of sludge, consequently the water heating devices and mains. As a result of all changes, arrangements and improvements was providing of demanded service – supply of hot water of demanded temperature and quantity to distribution places – water outlets but also ensured smaller bacteriological risk.

REFERENCES

ČSN 73 6655, Výpočet vnitřních vodovodů.
PrEN 806, Specifications for installations inside buildings conveying water for human consumption.

System-based Vision for Strategic and Creative Design, Bontempi (ed.)
© 2003 Swets & Zeitlinger, Lisse, ISBN 90 5809 599 1

A general framework for risk management of stable links

F. Petrilli
Structural Engineer, Rome, Italy

ABSTRACT: Recent hazards affecting strategic structures such as stable links led to large economic losses, thus showing the necessity to develop a new approach for the design of such structures. In this context, a risk-oriented framework may be used in order to include in the design not only technical considerations but also societal and economical expectations. This document describes and summarizes the conceptual framework for risk management of stable links.

1 INTRODUCTION

The large economic losses in several recent natural hazards, e.g., the Lota Prieta and Northridge earthquakes and Hurricanes Hugo and Andrew, show the deficiency of the current structural design approach and the need for new concepts and methodologies especially for the design of large structures. The performance of structures designed by traditional methods during these disasters has been a topic of public and professional criticism. Although loss of life was relatively low, economic losses from just these four natural disasters were approximately $50 billion. Moreover, the climate of structural engineering practice has changed in recent years, with increasing levels of attention paid to economic and social as much as technical issues (Ellingwood, 1998). In such a context, a performance based approach is gaining momentum both in the academic and the professional world.

Consequently, many countries are moving toward performance-based codes in order to couple the performance, societal expectations, and design requirements more closely than is possible in a prescriptive code, to ensure that hazards are treated consistently and that design conservationism is appropriate to required functions, and to move beyond the occupant safety focus of present building codes to address financial losses associated with failure to perform according to expectations.

Structural loads from users, the natural environment, and accidents, and structural strength and stiffness variables are random in nature. Differentiated levels of performance cannot be achieved consistently without considering the role played by uncertainties in building performance (Ellingwood and Harris, 1977). The field of structural reliability provides a framework for the rational evaluation on uncertainties. Design for explicit levels of performances requires a connection between performance level, structural limit state and probability of occurrence. This, in turn, requires an explicit assessment of reliability levels associated with existing or proposed construction.

For exceptional and strategic structures, such as stable links, the target reliability level should be determined according to broader social-economical considerations.

This optimization approach allows striking a balance between the possible high initial cost and potential large losses over the structure's lifetime.

2 DEFINITION OF RISK MANAGEMENT

As aforementioned, this reliability-based view of structural design has to deal with uncertainties, both of epistemic and aleatoric nature.

These considerations lead to the necessity of developing a general framework capable to treat and quantify all risks affecting the structure over its lifetime.

This purpose can be achieved by the systematic use of techniques, procedures and tools conducted on probabilistic bases, identifying and quantifying all possible hazard scenarios and their consequences on the structure and on users, expressed in terms of fatalities, financial losses and environmental damage.

At this extent, the following definitions can be generally applied and are not particularly related to transportation links.

– *"Danger"* should be defined as an attribute of substances or processes, which may potentially cause harm;

– "*Hazard*" is a danger that has a nature and magnitude that is directed to objects, people, assets, etc.;
– "*Risk*" should be defined as a measure under uncertainty of the severity of a hazard.

The risk is a function of the frequency of an undesired event or accident F, and its pertinent consequences C, i.e.

$$Risk = f(F, C) \qquad (1)$$

While in principle, there is no exact definition for the function combining F and C, in practice, risk is commonly formulated as the product of F and C, i.e.:

$$Risk = R = F \times C \qquad (2)$$

Risk analysis consists of the systematic hazard identification and in the estimation of the two components of the risk, the likelihood and the consequence.

Finally, the risk is evaluated against some acceptance criteria.

Risk quantification allows developing a rational and general way to assess economic losses within a lifecycle cost approach to the design and to define acceptable reliability levels.

In order to ensure that risk analysis achieves the Quality standards required to the design, it is necessary to frame the assessment process in a formal approach.

This formalism consists of a set of procedures and documents defined by the project team in order to suit the needs of the particular case under development; in such a context, risk analysis will be one of the steps in a more articulated and systematic procedure (Fig. 1).

The first step in the abovementioned procedure is the *Risk management planning* is the process of deciding how to approach and plan the risk management activities for a project. The output of this phase is the *Risk Management Plan* which documents how risk identification, assessment, quantification, response planning, monitoring and control will be structured and performed during the project life cycle. It includes: 1) Methodology; 2) Roles and responsibilities; 3) Timing; 4) Thresholds; 5) Reporting formats.

In the second phase the *object of the analysis should be defined*. The system definition is very important for identification of hazards and scenarios. The object of the analysis can be defined modelling the structure as a whole (Global System), as a sub-system (Local System) or as a system evolving during construction phases (Temporary System).

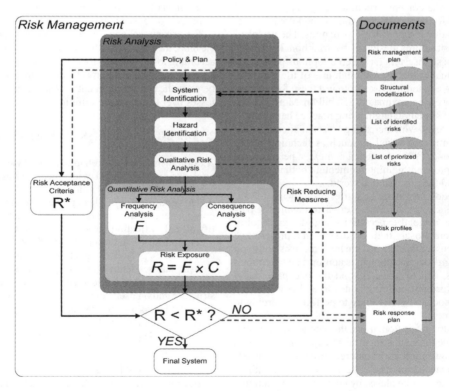

Figure 1.   A general framework for risk management: required activities and documents.

Risk identification is the third step. It involves the identification of risks which might affect the project and the documentation of their characteristics. Often hazards are identified in an iterative approach, where different methodologies (brainstorming, what-if analyses, Delphi questioning) are applied in succession.

The forth and fifth phases are the analytical procedures to assess risk. Namely, *qualitative risk analysis* is the process of performing a qualitative analysis of identified risks. This process is intended to prioritize risks according to their potential effect on the project performances.

The *quantitative risk analysis* process aims at analyzing numerically the probability of each risk and of its impact on project objectives, as well as the extent of overall project risk.

The last step in risk analysis is *risk monitoring and control*. Risk monitoring and control is the process of keeping track of the identified risks, monitoring residual risks and identifying new risks, ensuring the execution of risk plans and evaluating their effectiveness in reducing measures.

It is an ongoing process for the life of the project. Risks change as the project matures, new risks develop or anticipated risks disappear. Good risk monitoring and control processes provide information which assist in taking effective decisions in advance of the risks occurring. The purpose of risk monitoring is to determine if:

- Risk response has been implemented as planned;
- Risk response actions are as effective as expected;
- Project assumptions are still valid or strongly held;
- Risk exposure has changed from its prior state;
- Have occurred or arisen risks that were not previously identified.
- Risk control may involve choosing alternative strategies, taking corrective action, or replanning the project.

3 ACCEPTANCE CRITERIA

In order to evaluate whether the goals stated in the risk plan have been achieved, a comparable risk measure and acceptance criteria have to be established and documented in the Risk Response Plan.

This comparable risk measure might be defined, for example, as the average fatality risk on common motorways and railways, for one billion passages for a stretch corresponding to the total length of the link.

Supplementary to the risk acceptance criteria for the individual risk also social risk acceptance criteria should be specified. Often it is claimed that Society regards one accident with 100 fatalities much worse than 100 accidents each with one fatality. Such an attitude toward risk aversion can be introduced in the risk

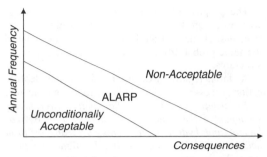

Figure 2. ALARP acceptance criteria.

policy and in the risk acceptance criteria. The aversion against large accidents can also be modelled with aversion factors that are multiplied on the consequences of accidents with many fatalities: the more fatalities, the higher the factor.

In order to strive for a balance between risk levels on the one hand and technically feasibility and economically reasonability on the other hand, one of the most common acceptance criteria is the ALARP, which is briefly described in the following.

Two limits given, three areas are specified. Below the lower limit, the risk is considered to be broadly acceptable or even negligible. Above the upper limit, the risk in considered unacceptable. Between the two limits the risk may be considered tolerable if risk reduction is impractical or if the costs of risk reduction exceed the improvements gained. The region between the two limits is sometimes called the ALARP region referring to the principle of reducing the risk to a level being As Low As Reasonably Practicable.

If the risk is found to be non-acceptable, risk-reducing measures shall be introduced. If the risk profile is in the ALARP area, the risk reduction measures shall be introduced as long as these are cost effective.

Reducing frequencies or consequences or both of them can reduce the risk. A reduction in frequency can be obtained by requirements in the operational procedures, e.g. restrictions on traffic, restrictions on the transportation of dangerous goods, various train systems, etc. Reduction in consequences can be obtained by changes in the overall layout of the link or in the determination of accidental design loads, e.g. fire loads, train derailment loads, etc.

4 RISK AFFECTING STRUCTURAL RELIABILITY

The general framework exposed in the previous section will be applied to the specific cases of risk assessment for transportation links. The proposed methodology will be firstly illustrated in the specific cases of *Structural Reliability Analysis*.

The purpose of the *Structural Reliability Analysis* is to ensure that the probability of failure of any structural element of the link is less than or equal to the same probability for similar large and important structures.

As far as regards structural reliability, the identification processes should include the following hazards: *1. Earthquake; 2. Wind; 3. Tsunami; 4. Aircraft/vessel impact; 5. Sabotage; 6. Explosions; 7. Fire; 8. Geological and hydrological events; 9. Transportation accidents; 10. Volcanic activity; 11. Weather conditions; 12. Incorrect assembly or erection.*

Natural hazards such as earthquakes, tornadoes and hurricanes, and accidents such as explosions could impose severe loads on some or all of the structural elements of the link. Such loads could increase the structural failure probabilities significantly. The quantification of risk due to events that impose severe loads consists of the following five steps (Sundararajan, 1995):

1. Determine the annual probability of the event as a function of its magnitude (*hazard analysis*);
2. Determine structural failure probabilities at different magnitudes of the event (*structural fragility analysis*);
3. Determine the system failure probability at different magnitudes of the event (*system fragility analysis*);
4. Determine the annual system failure probability due to all possible magnitudes of the event (*system reliability analysis*);
5. Determine the annual system risk due to the event (*system risk analysis*).

The sum of the risks of all undesired events associated with the system gives the total system risk.

The described assessment procedure is the same of the Level 1 PRA (Probabilistic Risk Assessment) of the Nuclear Regulatory Commission (1983). In Level-1 PRA, one analyses the system and focuses the attention on the paths, which can lead to failure, on their causes and their probability of occurrence. For this purpose, hazard and fragility analyses are combined into a risk assessment procedure. The result is the probability of reaching the failure by any given path. The quantification of the associated system damage is pursued at this stage, too. However, two other levels of analysis are required for complex and interdependent systems (nuclear or chemical plants, infrastructural systems) (Casciati et al., 1991).

Level-2 analysis deals with the seriousness of the failure event according to technical schemes. The main objective is to establish whether or not that failure will lead to an interaction with the world outside the system. The results are then integrated with the ones of the previous step in order to assess the probability of occurrence of different categories of interaction.

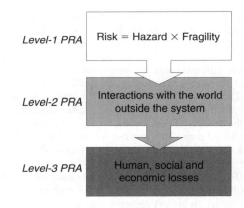

Figure 3. PRA: different levels of analysis.

Level-3 analysis, finally, assesses the social, human and economic consequences of the failure. The output of this level is the "complementary cumulative distribution function" (CCDF), which is a graph providing the probability of a selected nonstructural damage index (e.g., fatalities, repairing costs per year…).

Each of the five steps of Level-1 PRA is described briefly in the following sections.

4.1 Hazard analysis

Generally speaking, the objective of the hazard analysis is to calculate the probability of the exceeding, in given periods, different intensities of the undesired events. A graphical plot of this relationship provides the so-called hazard curve.

Examples of intensities are: the peak-ground acceleration of earthquakes, the site wind speed for tornadoes, the size (weight) of aircraft, and the peak pressure in the case of explosions.

In principle a family of hazard curves should be developed, each with its probability, in order to include the uncertainties in the hazard-parameter values. Hazard analysis is based on historical data, mathematical models and/or expert opinion.

Seismic hazard analysis, for example, is usually expressed in terms of the frequency distribution of the peak value of a ground motion parameter (e.g., peak ground acceleration) during a specified time interval (e.g., 30, 40, or 100 years). The different steps of this analysis are as follows:

1. Identification of the sources of earthquakes, such as faults;
2. Evaluation of the earthquake history for the considered region in order to assess the frequencies of occurrence of earthquakes of different magnitudes;
3. Development of attenuation relationships to estimate the intensity of earthquake inducing ground motion at the site;

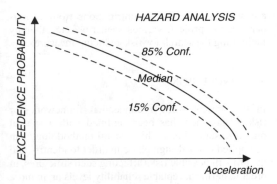

Figure 4. A typical hazard curve for seismic analysis.

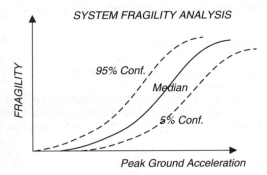

Figure 5. Fragility curves for seismic analysis.

4. Integration of the above information to estimate the frequency of exceedance for selected ground motion parameters.

Several parametric or non parametric methods are used in the hazard analysis to include uncertainties affecting attenuation relations, upper bound magnitudes and the geometry of the postulated sources (see Fig. 5).

4.2 Fragility analysis

The probabilistic risk assessment of a structural system consists of the combination of the results of the hazard analysis with the understanding of the system weakness and of its possible poor performance (fragility analysis).

Structural fragility is the probability of failure of a structural element (or of the structure as a whole) conditional on a specific hazard intensity. Results are commonly presented in the form of structural fragility curves. The horizontal axis of the curve represents the event magnitude while the vertical axis represents the conditional probability of structural failure given that an event of intensity I has occurred.

Structural fragility curves are developed through structural reliability analysis and expert opinion. Structural fragility is needed to estimate the frequency of occurrence of initiating events and to quantify the fault trees to obtain the event-induced accident sequence frequencies.

Seismic fragility, for example, is described by means of a family of fragility curves reflecting the uncertainty in the parameter values and in the models. It is customary to show the median fragility curve and the 95% and 5% confidence fragility curves (see Fig. 6).

4.3 System risk analysis

Once computed the structural fragility of an element, it is necessary to assess the probability of failure of the whole system. Event trees and fault trees are the basic tools to develop such system analysis.

System reliability analyses are conducted at different magnitudes of the event: for example, in the case of hurricanes, system reliability analyses are conducted at different wind speed. System failure probability or undesired event probability is determined at each of these wind speeds. The output is again a conditional probability. The unconditional probability can then be obtained by integrating over the entire range of hazard intensities (system reliability analysis).

Probabilistic risk analysis is completed by the system risk assessment. The product of the undesired event probability and the corresponding consequences (economic losses and fatalities) is the risk due to the undesired event. The sum of the risk of all undesired events associated with the system gives the total system risk (see Fig. 7).

5 RISK AFFECTING SAFETY

For a transportation link, besides structural reliability one of the main issues is to guarantee the safety of users in all service conditions. In particular, the purpose of the *Safety Risk Assessments* is to ensure that the risk of the users of the link is reasonable and comparable to other similar traffic installations. Furthermore, also the risk for third parties and the risk of disruption have to be analyzed.

As far as regards Safety Risk Analysis, the previous methodology leads to the following steps:

1. System description and establishment of basic information;
2. Hazard identification;
3. Calculation of frequencies and consequences;
4. Determination of individual risk and risk profiles;
5. Comparison with risk acceptance criteria and risk-reducing measures.

The system description and the establishment of basic information are prerequisites for dealing with project changes and new information throughout the project. This description is based on project documents as drawing, design reports, etc. Examples of basic information are the data on rail traffic, dangerous goods, ship traffic, etc.

The hazard identification gives a picture of all foreseeable hazards and the result of the hazard identification is a definition of a set of hazard scenarios that are entering the analyses of frequencies and consequences. For a transportation link, the following hazards should be analyzed:

1. Derailment; 2. Transportation accidents; 3. Collision; 4. Fire; 5. Explosion; 6. Toxic spill/release; 7. Corrosive spill/release; 8. Overhead line equipment failure.

For all kinds of hazards, a number of accident scenarios should be identified, describing the different possible accident situations, as large release of ammonia from a road tanker following an ordinary accident, fire in a car or train, etc.

These accident scenarios have to be analyzed with respect to the frequency of occurrence (or return period) and the consequences for road and rail passengers.

Risk contributions from hazards are calculated by product of frequencies and consequences. Frequencies can be evaluated using probabilistic models utilizing available statistical information and engineering judgments.

Concerning the safety of users, the calculations of consequences are calculations on the fatalities in the various hazard scenarios.

These calculations are based on:

- Basic information/assumptions, e.g. period between passenger trains;
- Physical models, e.g. collision models, fire models, gas dispersion models, etc;
- Assumption/information on the fatality rates given certain impacts, e.g. fatality rates in train collisions, etc.

The results of the Safety Risk Analyses are presented in risk profiles and in bar charts. It is customary to show in the risk profile graphs also the acceptance criteria in order to make possible a direct comparison. Bar charts are used to present risk contributions from various parts of the project, various scenarios, etc., thereby facilitating the search for risk-reducing measures.

6 CONCLUSIONS

In the present work a conceptual framework for risk management has been outlined with a special regard to stable links. This general methodology can be applied in the design phase in order to identify and quantify all possible risks affecting such structures, in order to define acceptable reliability levels or, in more general terms, to acceptable performance levels. The conceptual methodology has been then illustrated in the two specific cases of structural reliability analysis and safety risk assessment of a transportation link.

ACKNOWLEDGEMENTS

The financial support of *Stretto di Messina Spa* is acknowledged.

Anyway, the opinions and the results here presented are responsibility only of the Authors and cannot be assumed to reflect the ones of Stretto di Messina Spa.

REFERENCES

Casciati, F. & Faravelli, L. 1991. *Fragility analysis of complex structural systems*. New York: Wiley.
Ellingwood, B.R. & Harris, J.R. 1976. Reliability-based performance criteria: load factors and load combinations. *Structural Safety* 1: 15–26.
Ellingwood, B.R. 1998. Reliability-based performance concept for building construction. *Structural Engineering World Wide*.
Karlson, M. 1995 *Risk modeling of the Oresund link railway tunnel*. International Workshop on Stochastic Risk Modelling. Zurich, 1995.
Ostenfeld, K.H. & Hommel, D.L. & Olsen, D. & Hauge, L. Planning of major fixed links. In: Chen, W.F. & Duan, L. 2000. *Bridge Engineering Handbook*. CRC Press.
Sundararajan, C. 1995. (ed.) *Probabilistic Structural Mechanics Handbook*. Houston: Chapman and Hall.

3. Construction planning and project management

System-based Vision for Strategic and Creative Design, Bontempi (ed.)
© 2003 Swets & Zeitlinger, Lisse, ISBN 90 5809 599 1

Improving construction processes: experiences in the field of contact-contract-conflict

W. Tijhuis

Department of Construction Process Management, University of Twente, School of Business, Public Administration and Technology, The Netherlands, Joint Co-ordinator (Culture in Construction)

R.F. Fellows

Department of Real Estate and Construction, The University of Hong Kong, Joint Co-ordinator (Culture in Construction)

ABSTRACT: Modern construction industry represents a growing approach for modernization. This is e.g. visible in the field of equipment, materials, communication, ICT, etc. These developments are quite controllable. However, one important factor still stays quite uncontrollable and maybe even unpredictable: The human behaviour of people, e.g. involved in construction. Therefore it is one of the important reasons, causing failures in international construction industry.

This paper focusses on the relationship between *culture, project-organisation* and *technology* within the context of a management-tool, which connects *contact, contract* and *conflict*. These three dimensions play an important role in the management of national and international projects, focussing on the control of (cultural) differences between the stakeholders involved. Process-experiences with specifically the use these dimensions in a recent project are described, combined with short analyses of the experiences and theoretical backgrounds.

Results are in the field of the need for growing awareness of the fact that due to e.g. differences in roles, mainly as a result of the basic project-contract, the behaviour of the different parties can seriously lead towards conflict-situations. Thus, taking more care in establishing project-teams and to "match" it with its environment, looking more into detail towards the basic behaviour (culture, reputation, etc.) of the stakeholders involved, can reduce the risk of unsatisfied contracts and even avoid conflicts. Especially such an approach may lead to a serious improvement of construction processes.

1 INTRODUCTION

In the past decades several developments could be described, related to improvement of construction industry. As some main themes can be mentioned the improvement and development of e.g. (Habraken 1961, Bats 1994, Erkelens 1991, EEIG 1999, Halberstadt 1996):

- New materials, like e.g. high-strenght concrete, carbon-fiber, etc.;
- New building methods, like e.g. open-building, fast-tracking, etc.;
- New training methods for improving on-site productivity, etc.;
- New working regulations, like e.g. safety and health, etc.;
- New communication technology, like e.g. internet, e-mail and mobile phones, etc.
- Etc.

And a lot of other developments can still be mentioned, although e.g. the use of new technologies in general should be introduced quite carefully. As Van der Schaaf mentioned, they could be leading to cost-overruns in the first phases of introduction (Schaaf Van der 1987). We think a change of approach to new technolgy in such situations seems to be necessary then, e.g. not only looking to the opportunities (although maybe a "hype"), but also and especially looking to the threats of it.

However, another important issue is the fact that people involved also have been changed. They develop themselves often by improving and training their experiences, adapting their skills, etc. Not only in the modern industrialized communities, but also and especially training in developing regions, although it not necessarily may be really effective on improving people's skills (Bajracharya et al. 2002). But, as another point of view, training as a fact should at least be incoporating local habits, values, etc. in the respective training-programmes (Tijhuis 2002).

Nevertheless, despite the things mentioned, the people involved in construction still stay the main factor of production, although productivity itself can differ (depending e.g. on the degree of training and skills, etc.). Therefore, as construction industry still is "the ultimate peoples" business', this paper focusses especially on the human behaviour of people, involved in construction projects; not trying to find an "utopia" nor an "arcadia" (Medawar 1972) but primarily trying to get more understanding of reality.

2 RESEARCH OF HUMAN BEHAVIOUR IN CONSTRUCTION PROCESSES

As human behavior is an important issue in construction processes, it also introduces the big problem: While human beings are no robots, their behaviour in construction industry (and not only there …) still stays quite unpredictable. Therefore, when investigating human behaviour in general, and especially in construction industry more specific, this implies the need for more or less continuous investigation like (partly) participative research practice during e.g. the realization of real-life projects (Spradley 1980). And added to this, the analysis of practical situations should preferrably be related to investigation of groups of people involved, as construction business ist still a dynamic people's business, but then also trying to eliminate the effect of "following the leader" of a group (Zeisel 1984). Therefore, the focus on the most prominent roles (i.e. parties) in projects should give satisfying results.

However, this approach incorporates some difficulties, which can be listed as follows:

1. The researcher should have good access to the project-situation and data;
2. The researcher should stay apart of the project;

Ad 1:
This implies the possibilities for (partly) involvement in the real-life projects, from which the research data should be derived.

But this first point bears the risk for not fulfilling the second one, as e.g.:

Ad 2:
Being "close" to project environments introduces the risk for too much involvement, possibly leading to false results.

Joint together, these difficulties both can lead to a dilemma. But, related to e.g. Sanders, these are the day-to-day problems of anthropological researchers, especially in industries' environments. Therefore, this so called "third-culture" (Sanders 1995) of the researcher involved should at one hand be trained to be able to stay analyzing "from a distance", but on the other hand still stay close enough to get "the feeling of the situation". Due to e.g. earlier training and excercising within more-year research-projects on the basis of a partly-participating research approach (Tijhuis 1996), this dilemma was handled seriously.

3 A FRAMEWORK FOR SPECIFIC CASE-STUDY ANALYSIS

An often used management-tool for investigating (behavioural) experiences into construction projects and processes is the so called "3C-Tool", developed in a long-year investigation and research in real-life projects, consisting of the following three aspects with their respective connections (Tijhuis 1996 & 2001):

- Contact – Culture;
- Contract – Project Organisation;
- Conflict – Technology.

These items are related on the the the basis of "levels of influence", as presented schematically in Figure 1 (Tijhuis 2001). In this model, the "drivers for change" of project-organisations and their processes mainly proved to be culture (contact) and technology (conflict).

On the basis of this developed model, we already described in earlier publications the importance of the personal relationships in construction industry, despite of actual modern developments related to "dot.coms", etc. This viewpoint is also being supported by several research-outcomes in "culture-related" research in e.g. CIB-Task Group TG 23 (Fellows & Seymour 2002). The results of this paper therefore try to add more insight-information and (practice)-experiences to especially this research-field, related to different human behaviour in construction processes.

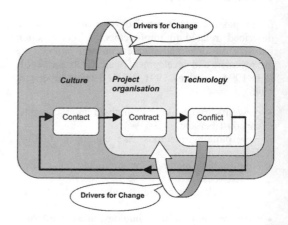

Figure 1. Tool for investigating (behavioural) experiences in construction processes (Tijhuis 2001).

4 THE CASE STUDY

As an example of several different views and roles, incorporated into one real-life construction project, there has been selected a full documented case-study. It consists of a quite small but actual project in The Netherlands, on which Dutch as well as German parties have been involved.

5 PROJECT DESCRIPTION

The projects consists of two main types of building:

- Two shops and/or offices on the street level;
- Six appartmens, divided into three appartments on two storeys.

As it is located into an old city centre of a mid-sized Dutch town, it has not only some difficulties in logistics, but also in legislation procedures. The location is represented in Figure 2 (Straetement 2002).

The building itself is a modern contemporary style design, based on a concrete structure with outer walls of masonry in different colours and styles. It has three storeys, with offices/stores and parking-facilities on the 1st floor and appartments with terraces on the 2nd and 3rd floor [Straetement, 2002].

6 STAKEHOLDERS INVOLVED

In the project, several stakeholders were involved. The following are mentioned, including their roles:

- *Land-owner*
A private party, who sold the site to the developer.
- *Developer*
A professional partnership between a developer, experienced in developing this kind of projects, together with the architect who knew the land-owner.

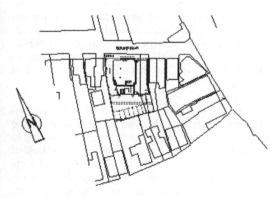

Figure 2. Schematic situation of the project (Straetement 2002).

- *Contractor*
The building company, without any influence in the development-risks.
- *Architect*
Design and also partner at risk within the development-combination.
- *Consultants/Engineers*
Professional advisors in legal, financial, organizational and technical issues.
- *Clients/Investors*
Non-professional and professional parties, buyers, owners and end-users of the building.
- *Municipality/City Council*
Public party, proceeding the legislation-procedures.
- *Neighbours*
Private parties, being afraid for the influences in their living environments.

7 DIFFERENCES IN BEHAVIOUR OF THE STAKEHOLDERS INVOLVED

Although it is quite often occurring that projects are getting disturbed within their running process, one can never find fully acceptance of this aspect in construction. As time is money, parties want to proceed as quick as possible. Time-management plays an important role in such situations, but especially related tot legislation-processes, one can not use other means than just wait and hope the local governments do proceed the procedures right. Other than inside project teams on e.g. sites, one can not use incentive programs here for increasing procedures' speed (Laufer et al. 1992), as it is a way of unallowed influencing of public parties, as e.g. the so called governmental "Commissie Vos" described in a recent investigation of certain branches in the Dutch construction industry (Vos et al. 2002). So, one can only be waiting for the governmental/municipal action, being proceeded as described and organised in national, regional or local regulation-framworks.

Looking to the Dutch situation, this mainly introduces the large influence and degree of participation of parties in the immediate physical neighbourhood of the site, given them the official opportunity, based on the applicable procedures, for complaining within the legislation-process of a building project. And this really can take some time, or even can stop and or block a whole planning and/or realisation-process of a project.

Within the legislation-procedure of this project, the neighbours were seriously complaining against the plans. Especially, while they expected already for years now that no one would ever build a project opposite their appartment-buildings opposite of the street. And that was just the problem: The project as described opposites immediately their existing appartment-building, being realized about circa seven years earlier.

However, in those days the municipality also pointed out in their official town-planning documents that the extension of appartment-buildings along this street would fit into their plans. So, from public side there were no complaints, only from private site, although there were also some neighbours which could be interesting parties for the developer to extend the project into the near future. But they also had typical behaviour, being described more into detail, and are numbered here as "neighbour-groups" according Figure 3, mainly representing the non-professional parties involved in the process (Straetement 2002).

Especially the following groups of neighbours with their respective behaviour were "part of the process":

- Group (A): they were complaining due to the unexpected building project opposite their appartments;
- Group (B): although they were satisfied while they sold the site for the project to the developer,they still were a little difficult, while their remaining home just beside the project needed an extra parking-place in the garden, with an entrance from the new building-site; and that was quite difficult to handle due to the less space left;
- Group (C): they were fully satisfied, while they got e.g. a new garden-wall into their backyard, and also had sold a small piece of land to the developer of the project;
- Group (D): a rather "difficult" party, while they did not complain at one hand, but on the other hand were quite "difficult" during construction of the project. They did (and did not ...?) and did (and did not ...?; yes, this was really going "on and on") want to sell their site to the developer, so a party with whom one hardly could discuss and/or negotiate. However, their site was still interesting for the developer as a possiblity for extension of the planned project in the near future.

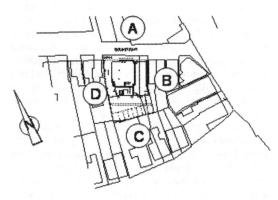

Figure 3.   Groups of neighbours within this project, as parties involved in the process (Straetement 2002).

As should be clear, a good dialogue between developer/team and the neighbours involved should still be taken care of seriously, as also Van Riemsdijk described in his research on large-influencing projects/companies and events in society (Riemsdijk Van 1994). This could at least reduce the fear by the neighbours for such projects and disturbance of their neighbourhood.

Besides these parties as more or less "non-professional", the professional parties involved in the project represented in general the following behaviour:

- *Land-owner*
As a private party, he was quite clearand strictly in the willingness of selling the site: As he knew the local architect, the architect got a "controlling position" in a certain way and claimed a co-development position when the developer bought the site;
- *Developer*
Due to the position of the architect, the developer hardly could do anything other than making a joint-venture with the architect in the buying of the site;
- *Contractor*
After a tender-procedure, he got awarded a normal traditional building contract, based on the tender-documents. And in this case he acted as a reliable party;
- *Architect*
As he had a dual position in the project (co-developer and architectural designer), he continuously moved between these two key-issues: (positively) Improving profit by the developer or (negatively) increasing salary for more design-tasks by the architect. And that resulted into a quite difficult way of handling;
- *Consultants/Engineers*
Due to the long delay in legislation (while the neighbours used their right of complaining/influencing the procedures -see above-) they had to adapt their plans several times. However, they kept their behaviour according their professional attitude, and were willing to collaborate within the team.
- *Clients/Investors*
As these parties were not involved during the legislation-procedure and preparation-phase of the project, they hardly were influencing the process. However, there were of course different wishes for the definitive interior-designs etc., but that was not really a problem due to the process;
- *Municipality/City Council*
As a public party, they were proceeding the legislation-procedures. And although this sometimes lead to difficulties in the process, they were quite willing to accept the plans. Only a small complaint in the field of the architectural style of the first designs caused some problems. However, further on in the legislation procedure, the official accepted complaints of the neighbours of the site were really leading to delay of the legislation-procedures.

It became clear that the behaviour of specifically two main parties were the main reason for disturbing the running process:

- *Architect*; mainly due to his dual interests from development and design;

Comment:
As member of the project-team, his behaviour should be stimulating instead of disturbing the running-process. Therefore, his behaviour was felt by the other team-members as really frustrating, and acted more or less as an "internal block".

- *Neighbours*; mainly due to their legal right of complaining against legislation.

Comment:
While they were no members of the project-team, their behaviour could not be expecte specifically positive or negative, and therefore acted more or less as an "external block".

Based on the scheme of figure 1, one can represent the above situation as "types of behaviour", being:

- positive; i.e. for behaviour, stimulating the speed of the running process;
- negative; i.e. for behaviour, disturbing the speed of the running process.

In Figure 4 this is represented schematically:
And so this quite small project got a serious delay due to specific differences in behaviour of parties involved, which had not been recognized seriously when establishing the project-team into its specific environment.

8 CONCLUSIONS & RECOMMENDATIONS: LESSONS LEARNED

The differences in behaviour could at one hand be seen as "just differences", but, on the other hand

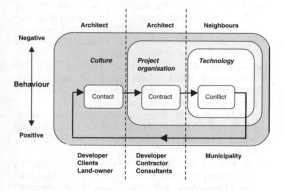

Figure 4.   Types of behaviour (positive and negative) of the parties involved.

(mainly from a viewpoint of improving processes in construction) they implicitly represent some lessons, which are described below, based on the frameworks of figure 1 and 4:
Contact (Culture):

Lesson 1:
As the architect was already from the first beginning member of the project-team, he should behave within the same goals of the team, i.e. "keeping the running process going". Therefore as lesson 1 we mention:

- A serious attention toward the culture (behaviour, reputation, etc.) of possible parties involved when establishing the project-team, should therefore be recognized within this selection process. And the "match" with its project-environment should be taken seriously then. Trying to understand team-member's "hidden agendas" as well as their "official agendas" is of great importance then.

Lesson 2:
The neighbours were only coming into the process when legislation started, i.e. after signing contracts by the team-members, etc. Therefore they were at one hand no "part of the deal", but were on the other hand still in the position to disturb the whole project, due to their official right of influencing the process. This had lead to the following lesson 2:

- A good communication at the front-end of the process, involving all the stakeholders, would possibly have improved the acceptance of the project. At least, when the architect and developer would have accept their influence in an early stage.

Contract (Project-organisation):

As the general accepted and assumed role of an architect is a neutral one, as a design-specialist, he should not take more roles within one and the same project.

Lesson 3:
Despite of his generally assumed "neutral" role, the architect had obviously within this project two main -separate- roles (designing and co-developing). This lead to a really difficult situation in the way that he had more than one goal: working on an attractive design with high fees for himself, and realizing a high-profit project. As lesson 3 we mention:

- Keeping a clear separation of the several roles within projects, divided over the parties involved, is always possible. However, when deciding this in the contract, each of the separate parties should have roles, being related to maximum one side of the "three sides of the table" (i.e. or client/developer-related; or neutra-based; or contractor/subcontractor-related).

Lesson 4:
A joint-venture between the developer and the architect lead to differences in behaviour. Not only by their differenct "agendas", but also by differences between their field of experiences and "branch-culture". Lesson 4 is therefore:

- Choosing and deciding about team-members for a (building-) contract should not only be based on legal or financial basis, but also on experiences and "culture" of the parties involved.

Conflict (Technology):

Lesson 5:
The neighbours were complaining about the plans presented to the municipality during the legislation procedure. Although in the end their complaints were not awarded, one can not be sure their behaviour during the use and "life-cycle" of the realized project will still be nice. So, the communication with them should still be organized in an effective manner by informing them about the technical aspects, levels of expected noice and nuisance during construction realization, etc. This should take away or at least reduce their fear for the "new" situation, especially during the construction process. As lesson 5 it is defined as follows:

- Apart from the project team-members, an open and structurized communication (a "dialogue") during the total construction process is an effective instrument for taking away certain fears of stakeholders (with active and less active roles) in projects. This certainly can reduce the risk of disturbing projects in an early stage, although it could take extra attention and energy of the team-members. But that's worth it.

9 RESUME

Working in construction processes generally implies that the parties involved should have the same goals: Or initiating, or designing, or realizing, thus delivering a project within the basic conditions negotiated between the public and private parties. However, as main results of the experiences, described into this paper, one should be aware that there is a need for growing awareness of the fact that due to e.g. differences in roles, mainly as a result of the basic project-contract, the behaviour of the different parties can seriously lead towards conflict-situations. Thus, taking more care in establishing project-teams and to "match" it with its environment, looking more into detail towards the basic behaviour (culture, reputation, etc.) of the stakeholders involved, can reduce the risk of unsatisfied contracts and even avoid conflicts. Especially such an approach may lead to a serious improvement of construction processes.

ACKNOWLEDGEMENTS

The data-collection of the case-study was made possible by the collaboration of the projectmanagers, WT/Consult (www.wtprojects.com). Therefore the author thanks them for their willingness to share their experiences for studying these within this research-project.

REFERENCES

Bajracharya A., S.O. Ogunlana & N.L. Bach 2002. *Why training does not work in developing countries and how to make it work?*; CIB-W107 Report no.282, "Training for Construction Industry Development"; pp.193–206; Ed. S.O. Ogunlana; AIT, Bangkok and CIB, Rotterdam.

Bats J.O. 1994. *Een Industrieel Wonongbouwsysteem op Basis van een Draagstruktuur van Demontabele Staalplaat-Elementen*; Report of "BKO-Researchdag 1994"; pp. 93–104; Eindhoven University of Technology; Eindhoven.

EEIG 1999. *EITO – European Technology Observatory 1999*; European Economic Interest Grouping (EEIG); Frankfurt am Main.

Erkelens P.A. 1991. Self-help building productivity – A method for improving house building by low-income groups applied to Kenya 1990–2000'; *Ph.D.-thesis*; Series "Bouwstenen", Nr. 20; Eindhoven University of Technology; Eindhoven.

Fellows R. & D.E. Seymour -Ed.- 2002. *Perspectives on Culture in Construction*; CIB-Publication no. 275; Task Group TG23, "Culture in Construction"; September 2002; University of Hong Kong & University of Birmingham; CIB-Rotterdam; ISBN 90-6363-030-1

Habraken N.J. 1961. De *Dragers en de Mensen – Het Einde van de Massawoningbouw*; Scheltema & Holkema Publishers; Amsterdam.

Halberstadt, H. 1996. *Demolition Equipment*; Motorbooks International, Osceola.

Laufer A., E. Raviv & E. Stukhart 1992. *Incentive Programmes in Construction Projects – The Contingency Approach*; article in: "Project Management Journal"; Vol.23, Nr.2; pp.23–30; Israel Institute of Technology, Haifa; Texas A&M University, College Station, Texas.

Medawar P.B. & J.S. Medawar 1972. *Some reflections on science and civilization*; paper in: "Civilization & Science – In Conflict or Collaboration?"; Ed. Ciba Foundation; pp. 9–22; Elsevier – Excerpta Medica – Associated Scientific Publishers; Amsterdam

Riemsdijk Van M.J. 1994. *Actie of Dialoog – Over de betrekkingen tussen maatschappij en onderneming*; Ph.D.thesis; University of Twente, School of Business, Public Administration and Technology; Enschede.

Sanders G.J.E.M. 1995. *Being "a third-culture man"*; article in: "Cross Cultural Management: An international Journal"; journal, Vol. 2, Nr. 1; pp. 5–7; MCB University Press.

Schaaf Van der T. 1987. *The Scheldt Barrier*; paper in: "Managing Construction Worldwide"; Vol. 3, "Construction Management and Organisation in Perspective"; pp.41–66; Ed.: Peter R. Lansley and Peter A. Harlow; E&F.N. Spon; London, New York.

Spradley J.P. 1980. *Participant Observation*; Holt, Rinehart and Winston; New York, Chicago.

Straetement 2002. *Data of project Bouwstraete*; RT Bau GmbH; Düsseldorf.

Tijhuis W. 1996. Contractors in projects or in conflict? – Lessons from international collaboration (published as a book in Dutch: Bouwers aan de slag of in de slag? – Lessen uit internationale samenwerking) *Ph.D.-thesis*; Eindhoven University of Technology, Faculty of Building and Architecture, Department of Building-Production, Eindhoven, The Netherlands; Berlin, Germany; WT/Consult BV, Rijssen (www.wtprojects.com); The Netherlands.

Tijhuis W. 2001. Construction Industry, E-Business and Marketing: Are the Dot.Coms pushing aside Personal Relationships?; *International Journal for Construction Marketing*; Oxford Brookes University; Vol. 3, Nr. 1; Oxford; ISSN 1463-7-189 (web) and ISSN 1463-770 (hard copy); also published on the internet: *http://www.brookes.ac.uk/other/conmark/IJCM/*

Tijhuis, W. 2002. *Training skills and productivity on site in construction industry in developing regions – focussing on practice, theory and culture in glocalizing construction business*; CIB-W107 Report no. 282, "Training for Construction Industry Development"; pp. 61–70; Ed. S.O. Ogunlana; AIT, Bangkok and CIB, Rotterdam.

Vos M. et al. 2002. *De bouw uit de Schaduw – Parlementaire enquête Bouwnijverheid – Eindrapport*; SdU-publishers; The Hague.

Zeisel J. 1984. Inquiry *by Design – Tools for Environment-Behavior Research*; Cambridge University Press; Harvard University, Cambridge, Massachusetts.

System-based Vision for Strategic and Creative Design, Bontempi (ed.)
© *2003 Swets & Zeitlinger, Lisse, ISBN 90 5809 599 1*

International procurement of construction materials for the Middle East

E. Koehn
Department of Civil Engineering, Lamar University, Beaumont, TX, USA

H.J. Tohme
Water Utilities Engineer, City of Beaumont Water Utilities Division, Beaumont, TX, USA

A.P. Shukla
Equipment International, Houston, TX, USA

ABSTRACT: Oil and petrochemicals, being in abundance in the Middle East, made the construction of refineries and related facilities a necessity of life. This paper is written, specifically, to analyze the process of estimating, negotiating and bidding that may lead to securing contracts for construction materials, especially steel. It was found that in the Middle East estimating depends on many factors such as the possibility of obtaining the steel from local mills, reputation of owner, the amount of steel to be provided, method of shipment, mode of payment, and special requirements or specifications. The time allowed for fabrication and delivery must also be taken under consideration. All these factors cumulatively affect the estimating process and appropriate bid price. It was found that the lowest bidder is not always awarded the contract. The findings of this investigation suggest that the reputation and history of the bidder also play an important role in the procurement process.

1 INTRODUCTION

The Middle East is a land of considerable wealth, trade and business. There are numerous oil refineries and related facilities that are constructed using large amounts of highly specialized structural steel.

Various regions in the Middle East have always been and continue to be important tourist destinations; many hotels have been built and the tourist industry is increasing. Hotels in the Middle East tend to be sophisticated in their architecture and constructed in full compliance with all aspects of international standards and specifications. A considerable amount of standard and specialized steel is utilized for both structural and decorative purposes. This paper discusses the bidding and estimating process for the procurement of the aforementioned facilities.

In this regard, the second writer of this paper has considerable practical experience and has worked for a consulting engineering firm in the Middle East. In addition, the third writer was employed by a company that represented European steel manufactures in the Middle East. The work required the organization to keep track of the new projects and contracts that were available for bidding on the open market. In addition, cost effective bids were developed and submitted to the proper agencies and owners. However, bids were also often reviewed and reduced in response to competitive pressures.

2 INVITATION TO BID

The contracting system in the Middle East tends to be traditional compared to other regions of the globe (Koehn & Ahmed 1999). In this regard there are different sources from which the "Invitation to Bid" for materials such as structural steel may originate.

2.1 *The owner*

Here, the contract will generally consist of a single package and, therefore, will be contracted either to a nominated supplier to the main contractor or to a direct supplier to the owner. In this case, the owner usually publishes the contract in the newspaper and invites companies to bid on the project. The owner generally has a team of engineers and consultants who review the bids to obtain the optimum price and recommend awarding the contract to a specific firm. The owner may invite firms to bid on the entire project, which may involve millions of dollars worth of work, and, also effectively limit the number of potential bidders.

The owner may also break the project into different sub-projects and invite companies to bid on various sections. This approach encourages small and medium companies to bid on different sub-projects. Since many small, medium and large firms may compete with each other, the total price of the entire project can possibly be reduced by a substantial amount. However, the disadvantage of such an approach is that the owner must maintain control and supervise numerous subcontractors.

2.2 The general contractor

Once the contract is awarded to a particular firm, that company invites numerous subcontractors to submit bids for the smaller sections of the project. This type of approach is common in the Middle East. There appear to be few turnkey projects since contractors generally do not have both in-house engineering and contracting expertise to perform the entire project (Koehn & Ahmed 2001).

Under this method of invitation, the successful general contractor would have received quotations and may have negotiated prices in the pre-bid stage of the main contract. If exclusivity was agreed upon at that state, finalizing the supply contract becomes a matter of ironing out details and fine tuning the contract.

However, if there was no exclusivity agreement, the successful general contractor may proceed in one of three scenarios (Wilson & Koehn 2000, Harper & Koehn 1998):

- Call for new bids with an open invitation especially to those organizations or firms who participated in the pre-bid phase of the main contract.
- Call for new bids with an open invitation to those organizations who participated and those who did not previously participate in the pre-bid phase of the main contract.
- Renegotiate prices with a short list of bidders representing various organizations.

3 COST ESTIMATING SYSTEMS

Estimating is a widely known and accepted practice, and has been utilized for many years in various business fields. In particular, cost estimating has been a primary but important step in almost every field of endeavor (Koehn et al. 2000). Estimation has played an equally important role in the third writer's work in the Middle East involving the procurement of steel.

It is known that every bid should involve the process of estimation. Unless there is thorough and detailed investigation concerning the cost, a realistic bid price cannot be developed. Also, an appropriate estimate may increase the chance of being awarded the bid (Kumar 2001). Estimation, especially in the Middle East, is a relatively complicated process that requires the estimation team to be very competent, experienced and fully aware of the following items.

3.1 The level of complexity of the structural steel in question should be considered. Numerous specific requirements or specifications will affect the cost estimate. Steel provided from a stockpile or production run generally has a standard set price. Conventional or stainless steel is in high demand in the Middle Eastern market and, hence, such material is generally produced in bulk and stocked. Any steel supplied from the stockpile, however, has a price that fluctuates with the international market. However, projects in the Middle East often require highly specified steel for the oil industry and offshore facilities. This steel is generally corrosion resistant and is required to be of high tensile strength. Depending on the type of project and use, different specifications may be required. There may be a few manufacturers and importers who stock certain specialized steels and hence the cost may not be very high. However, most steel members requiring special specifications are made-to-order and tend to be expensive. Companies do not usually stock highly specialized steel and only manufacture the product when demand occurs.

Another factor to be considered is the size of the steel members. As an example, the standard size of steel plates is 6 m × 4 m. This is the most common size of steel plates available in the Middle Eastern market. Although other plate sizes may be available in the market, the cost will be relatively higher.

During the manufacturing process, molten steel is poured into the molds of the size required and allowed to cool. The material is then subjected to brazing and grinding to produce a finished product that meets the specifications required. When a customer request a size other than that readily available, the manufacturer must change the mold and re-set the production schedule accordingly. This is a time consuming process, increasing overhead and other expenses, and delivers a final product at a higher price.

3.2 It may be feasible to propose an alternative design that may be less expensive but still satisfies the specifications. Involving structural steel designers as part of the estimating team is critical to the process. Such experts may be able to alter the design without reducing the load bearing capacity of the structure or changing its aesthetics while reducing the cost by utilizing standard structural steel elements or members with lighter weights.

3.3 The track record of all the competitors in similar bids is important. Construction companies in the Middle East tend to specialize in certain fields of the industry. Studying the bidding history of the competitors throughout the years on similar projects can assist the estimator with the information needed to be the successful bidder.

3.4 The possibility of procuring some, if not all, of the material from modern licensed factories in the Middle East should be investigated. In the last twenty years, as a result of accumulated wealth and high demand, the structural steel industry in the Middle East has become competitive with that of the industrialized nations. The advantage these steel mills posses is, the ability to produce steel members that meet international standards and specifications at lower labor cost. Such advantage is allowing the steel industry in the Middle East to compete on the international market.

3.5 The track record of the owner and/or the general contractor vis-à-vis reputation, honesty, and keeping business commitments must also be taken under consideration.

3.6 Effect of quantity of structural steel required may also be significant. One of the most important factors affecting the estimating process is the quantity of steel to be supplied. Historical data generally indicate that as the quantity of steel increases, the price per pound decreases. In this regard, as soon as an order is placed, the manufacturer sets the schedule for the production of the order. Large bulk orders tend to be manufactured and delivered faster and at a cheaper price than those involving small quantities.

3.7 Method of shipment should be considered. Orders in the Middle East are at times urgent and must be placed and processed in a minimum amount of time. This mainly occurs when a massive project is delayed during the preliminary construction stage. Steel may then be ordered without cost being an important factor, so that the final completion date of the project is not delayed. In such cases, for an extra cost, the manufacturer agrees to rearrange the production schedule, manufacturing, and shipping of the steel at the earliest date possible. This mode of delivery can be very costly and, therefore, it has generally been the practice to keep track of the inventory and plan the schedule in such a way as to avoid such circumstances.

Mode of shipping also affects the cost. Although it is a general practice to have all the material from overseas shipped by sea, there are times when an urgent order is shipped by air. Airfreight causes the price to increase at least 10 times compared to that by sea, however, these instances are very rare. When a bid is placed, the project is generally at the initial stage and, hence, there is time to have the material shipped by sea. Also, the schedule is rarely disturbed at the early stages of the project, and shipping by air is not often encountered.

3.8 Mode of payment may be vital to the constructor. The standard modes of payments are as follows:

3.8.1 *C&F (Cost and Freight)*

In this mode of payment, the manufacturer arranges for the shipping and pays the cost for freight. The cost is then added to the end user's bill. This method can be advantageous for the manufacturer as the firm can add the overhead associated with the cost of freight and increase the margin of profit.

3.8.2 *Cost only*

Here, the end user pays the manufacturer only the price of the steel. The payment for the cost of shipping is made by the end user without any involvement from the manufacturer. This can be profitable only if the end user has a separate department or section dealing with freight rates and shipping charges. Many companies have formed a department for handling shipping due to frequently placed orders. Since the Middle East is a land of trade, and many items are imported, companies who have not set up their own shipping departments have an agent handling these matters. It is not advisable, however, to use this mode of payment if a company has few orders from overseas. In such cases, it is always advisable to use the C&F mode of payment.

3.9 Special requirements, if any, must be taken under consideration. For example, time should allow for unusually difficult fabrication details and transportation. Another factor affecting the bid price is the date of delivery. Generally, delivery time of the standard and in stock steel bound for the Middle East from Europe is roughly 4–6 weeks. This takes into consideration the time for processing the order, billing, transportation from factory to port and time for shipping. If the order is at all special or made-to-order, the delivery time increases based on the manufacturing and fabrication time and various other factors.

4 NEGOTIATIONS

Negotiation may be the most difficult part of the whole process. To be successful, it takes wit and extensive experience in and knowledge of the potential actions of the negotiator on the other side of the table. In the Middle East, negotiating is a part of life and an excellent estimator without negotiating capabilities will have difficulties securing contracts.

5 AWARDING CONTRACTS

It is a common notion that the firm that submits the minimum bid is awarded the contract. However, it may also depend on the nature and complexity of the project. For example, a complex or large project may not be awarded to the lowest bidder. In this regard, the history of the bidder can play an important role in the decision making process. Large contracts may need greater quality and specialized work by experienced people. In such cases, even a low bid placed by a relatively small and inexperienced firm may be rejected. The bid may be awarded to a company that has submitted a higher bid, but promises and has a history of satisfactory performance. It has also been noticed that the reputation and previous experiences of the firm may also be a deciding factor. For example, a firm that has worked for a client in the past may be given preference in spite of a higher bid price (Ahuja 1980).

6 SUMMARY AND CONCLUSIONS

It has been mentioned in the paper that the price of steel in the Middle East depends on numerous factors. These include, in part, the complexity of the structural steel in question, the possibility of purchasing the steel from Middle Eastern steel mills, quantity of steel ordered, reputation and history of the user and contractor, specialized requirements, the mode of shipping, and the time allocated for fabrication and transportation. In addition, global competition plays a role in determining the worldwide price of steel. It is common knowledge that the law of "Supply and Demand" is always in effect. As an example, high demand in the international market causes the price of steel to soar. On the other hand, a recession or slack period forces the manufacturers to lower the prices in order to reduce the inventory of their stockpiles.

In any business, any trade, or any issue of life, the demand for "High Skills" is increasing due to competition. Estimators have found that "High Levels of Competency" have become a common work-place

requirement. In review, it can be observed that be it structural steel or any other material, be it the Middle East or any other part of the globe, there is a strong tendency towards perfection in all organizational endeavors.

ACKNOWLEDGEMENT

The authors wish to recognize Ms. Linda Dousay for her assistance with the production activities involved with the preparation of the paper.

REFERENCES

Ahuja, H.N. 1980. Successful construction cost control. John Wiley & Sons, New York.
Harper, R. & Koehn E. 1998. Managing industrial construction safety in Southeast Texas. *Journal of Construction Engineering and Management.* ASCE. 124 (6): 452–457.
Koehn, E. & Ahmed, M.U. 1999. Production rates for international projects in Asia. *Cost Engineering.* 41 (8):38–44.
Koehn, E., Ahmed, S.A. & Jayanti, S. 2000. Variation in construction productivity: Developing countries. AACE International: INT.04.1-INT.04.07.
Koehn, E. & Ahmed, F. 2001. Production rates for urban/rural projects in developing areas, AACE International Transactions, AACE International, www.accei.org.
Koehn, E. & Ahmmed, M. 2001. Quality of building materials (cement) in developing countries. *Journal of Architectural Engineering.* ASCE. 7 (2): 44–51.
Kumar, A. 2001. Deliverable based service contracts – a challenge for bidders. *Cost Engineering* 43 (5): 29–31.
Wilson, J.M. & Koehn, E. 2000. Safety management: Problems encountered and recommended solutions. *Journal of Construction Engineering and Management.* ASCE. 126 (1): 77–79.

System-based Vision for Strategic and Creative Design, Bontempi (ed.)
© *2003 Swets & Zeitlinger, Lisse, ISBN 90 5809 599 1*

Building design evaluation – facility manager's and designer's perspectives

K. Lueprasert
King Mongkut's Institute of Technology North Bangkok, Thailand

Y. Kanhawattana
King Mongkut's University of Technology Thonburi, Thailand

ABSTRACT: This study aimed to investigate the quality of the design in the view of facility managers in order to feedback the information from facility managers to designers, to improve the design to further meet the actual utilization and needs. Normally, designers do not received feedback and designed the building according to building's owners or investors. The design usually reflected the budget and objective of the investors. The integrated systems within the building were often overlooked in the design phase, thus, lessening the building performance. It is often that designers must use their own judgements and experience to integrate all the building systems together. Questionnaires were sent to designers and facility managers to assess their accounts of the building designs and the building performances respectively. Facility managers were asked to rate the building systems in terms of their maintainability. On the other hand, the designers were inquired regarding the building systems in terms of their maintainability as well. These evaluations were performed to compare the perspectives of both parties and to investigate if the design feedback were absent and should be defined in order to achieve a quality design that fit the user's needs in terms of maintainability.

1 INTRODUCTION

Facility and asset management is an essential part of the construction life cycle. It has direct impacts on the facility and asset performance. Carpenter and Oloufa (1995) stated that "postoccupancy evaluation is the assessment of the success of a project in meeting its design and service requirements." Lack of information from such assessment can lead to various problems. Building can be inaccurately and insufficiently maintained and preventive maintenance is unattainable. Lueprasert et al. (2000) found that lack of building maintenance was common in Thailand. Moreover, maintenance was not sufficiently budgeted. Thus, numerous long-term problems occurred in existing building facilities due to ineffective maintenance and improper utilization. However, design-caused problems had not been fully addressed.

1.1 *Building design and development in Thailand*

The procedure typically started with owner attained a design firm. When the design phase was finished, the owner may further employ the design firm to act as owner's representative to procure a qualified main contractor. The construction was normally executed independently and carried out without full monitoring or consultation from the designers but usually by another construction consultant.

1.2 *Building management services in Thailand*

There were two main practices of building management services, i.e., (1) manage by owner and (2) outsource to building management firms. Managing-by-owner was the preferred system (Lueprasert et al. 2000) due to its cost competency or lack of budget.

1.3 *Objectives*

Therefore, this study investigated whether the design feedback was absent and should be defined in order to achieve an effective design that fits the user's needs in terms of maintainability. The scope of this study was focused upon high-rise buildings (23 meters or over in height) in Thailand.

2 RESEARCH METHODOLOGY

Two sets of questionnaire surveys were developed. Each aimed to acquire information from facility managers and building designers. Two hundred and fifty buildings and one hundred and fifty design firms were randomly selected as the surveyed target. The surveys were designed to measure the various practices and perspectives from facility managers and designers. To measure the perspectives of building components' maintainability, the applied scale ranged from 1 to 5 or from "easiest," "easy," "moderate," "difficult," and "most difficult". Since these scaling data are nominal, meaning that the interval of each scale may not be equal, the median was reported instead of the arithmetic mean to demonstrate the central tendency. For other general data, simple frequencies in percentage format were applied. A non-parametric statistical analysis, χ^2 (chi-square) test was used to determine whether perspectives between designers and facility managers were different. χ^2 can be calculated as shown in the following equation.

$$\chi^2 = \sum \frac{(O-E)^2}{E} \tag{1}$$

where O is observed frequency and E is expected frequency. Simple χ^2 test can be used when the total number of observations of the two sets was the same. However, it was likely that the number of responded facility managers and designers were not equal. Thus, the expected frequency was calculated using the expected frequency percentage multiplied by the observation frequency (Lowry 1999). In this study, O represented the frequency gathered from facility managers, where E was calculated using frequency percentage of designer's perspectives multiplied by number of responded facility managers in the same question. Since they were 5-level scale questions, the degree of freedom 4, at 0.05 significant level was applied.

2.1 Hypotheses

To achieve the objectives, the following three hypotheses were proposed to determine whether the perspectives between the designer and facility managers were different with 95% confidence level.

1. Perspectives between designers and facility managers were different in terms of difficulty level of building component management.
2. Perspectives between designers and facility managers were different in difficulty level in identifying causes of building components problem.
3. Perspectives between designers and facility managers were different in view of repairing building components.

If the perspectives were found different, this indicated that designers did not design based maintainability feedback and the feedback link from facility manager to designers was weak.

3 SURVEYED TOPICS

In order to examine the assumptions, the data was collected in the following topics from facility managers and designers accordingly.

3.1 Facility manager survey topics

1. General information of the facility managers.
2. General information of the building.
3. Perspectives of building component's maintainability.

3.2 Designer survey topics

1. General information of the designer.
2. Perspectives of facility management.
3. Perspectives of building component's maintainability.

4 FINDING'S DISCUSSION

Out of 250 questionnaires sent to facility managers, only 51 responses were received. However, only 41 responses were complete for analysis. Respectively, out of 150 questionnaires sent to designers, 38 were replied but only 37 were complete for analysis. The low percentage on replies may occur from several reasons. For example, in facility management survey, some buildings may not have assigned facility managers. On the other hand, designers may not wish to give out design information or may think that the survey was not relevant or beneficial.

4.1 Facility manager survey

4.1.1 General information of the facility managers

From the survey, it was found that 80.5% of the respondents were males and the average age of facility managers was approximately 41 years. Average years of experience in facility management were 8.6 years, where 51.3% of all respondents had 1 to 5 years experience. Moreover, 84.2% had management experience of 1 to 5 buildings. Types of building managed were office buildings (56.1%), residential buildings (58.5%), and others (26.8%) such as hotel, department store, factory, hospital, etc. More than 78% of office and residential buildings managed were 11 floors or higher.

Most of the respondents hold a bachelor degree (70.7%), where 65.9% were responsible for building management and 34.1% simply handled technical services. Table 1 and Table 2 contain the summary of general information from the survey.

Table 1 indicated that there were quite a number of owners that managed their own buildings, while less preferred outsourcing to facility management firms. Furthermore, Table 2 confirmed that maintenance

Table 1. Facility manager's organization.

Facility management firm	Freelance	Owner	Others
19.5%	34.1%	24.4%	22.0%

Table 2. Scope of facility management services.

Maintenance/Repair	Cleaning	Security	Finance & Acct
100%	56.1%	58.5%	48.8%

Table 3. Characteristics of current building projects.

Characteristics	Min	Average	Max
Height (Floors)	7	19.7	34
Total space (m^2)	500	20,403	96,000
Occupied space (%)	10%	74.3%	100%
Building age (Years)	1	9.0	37

Table 4. General management practices.

Practices	Yes	Partly	No
Management system	65.9%	31.7%	2.4%
HR management	53.7%	41.5%	4.9%
Budget management	53.7%	39.0%	7.3%
Satisfaction Surveys	87.8%	–	12.2%

and repairs remained the main focus of facility management services in Thailand as indicated by earlier study of Lueprasert et al. (2000).

4.1.2 General information of the building
Responded facility managers indicated the characteristics of their current projects as shown in Table 3. It is found that 68% of these buildings were assigned to facility managers after the completion of construction. This may indicate lack of relationships between contractors, designers and facility managers.

In addition, about 85% of the building structures were reinforced concrete, which was the preferred type of building structure in Thailand. The most preferred external wall of the buildings was combination of glass and concrete wall.

In terms of current practices as indicated in Table 4, it was found that budget and human resource management was still deficient. Respondents indicated difficulties in assigning proper staff. This may indicate lack of qualified human resources in the services. When cross-checked, whether the deficiencies had impacted on building tenants, using satisfaction surveys, out of 87.8% of respondents that performed satisfaction survey, 63.9% get good results while 30.6% get moderate satisfaction.

Table 5. Design practices related to facility management.

Practices	Yes	No	Unsure
Satisfaction surveys to facility mgrs	64.9%	35.1%	–
Facility management related training	48.6%	40.6%	10.8%
Consulting with facility managers	24.3%	73.0%	2.7%

4.2 Building designer survey

4.2.1 General information of the designers
It was found that no female designer responded to the survey and the average age of the responded designers were approximately the same as the facility managers. This means that male still dominated this profession.

All of the designer respondents hold at least a bachelor degree. The academic backgrounds of the designers were engineering (54.1%) and architectural (35.1%). The rest hold a master degree in management on top of either engineering or architectural background. The result also indicated that 68% of the designer respondents were in management position and 32% were in operation position.

Approximately 59.1% of designers had building design experiences of 11 to 20 years with the average years of experience of 15.1 years and 94.6% indicated that they had previously designed office and residential buildings. It can be concluded that the responded designers were fully qualified for their experience in building designs. On the contrary, majority of responded facility managers had comparably less experiences in facility management.

As shown in Table 5, majority of the designers did not consult with facility managers in their design process (73%) and about 40.6% have not been trained in the subject.

4.3 Perspectives of facility management

Both facility managers and designers were asked regarding the practices to their counterparts. The questions to facility managers concern the design matters and vice versa for the designers as shown in Table 6. Furthermore, a question regarding whether there were inquiries from designers or feedback from facility manager was included to establish whether the communications between both parties existed.

4.3.1 Comparisons of general practices
The data in Table 6 indicated that there were communications between designers and facility managers. However, about 19.5% of facility managers and 10.8% of designers did not know their counterparts. When asked regarding contractors, only 5.4% of designers indicated that they did not know who the contractors

Table 6. Comparisons of general practices.

Facility Manager	%	Designers	%
1. Have designer's list.		1. Know the facility manager.	
– Have complete list	31.7	– Know all	8.1
– Have partial list	48.8	– Know some	81.1
– No	19.5	– No	10.8
2. Have contractor's list.		2. Have contractor's list.	
– Have complete list	39.1	– Have complete list	51.4
– Have partial list	34.1	– Have partial list	43.2
– No	26.8	– No	5.4
3. Designer asked for eval.		3. Fac. mgr. asked for eval.	
– Yes	22.0	– Yes	64.9
4. Feedback to designers.		4. Informed from fac. mgrs.	
– Yes	41.5	– Yes	78.4
– No	43.9	– No	10.8
– Unsure/don't know	14.6	– Unsure/don't know 10.8	
5. Get outside FM expertise.		5. Get outside design expertise	
– Yes	65.9	– Yes	88.9

Table 7. Comparison of general perspectives in management.

	Rank No.		
Questions	1	2	3
Top reasons to out-source	*Expertise*	*Quality*	*Time*
maintenance	**Expertise**	**Time**	**Material ctrl**
Systems that can be	*Electrical*	*Plumbing*	*AC*
maintained in-house	**Cleaning**	**Plumbing**	**Energy consrv**.
Most complained systems	*AC*	*Plumbing*	*Security*
	AC	**Plumbing**	**Electrical**
Highest maintenance cost	*Vertical trans.*	*AC*	*Plumbing*
	AC	**Vertical trans**.	**Electrical**
Cause of problems	*Poor Design*	*Lack of maint.*	*Lack of HR*
	Lack of maint.	**Construction**	**Lack of HR**
Designers should	*Maintainability*	*Durability*	*Efficiency*
emphasize on…	**Efficiency**	**Maintainability**	**Integration**

were, compared to 26.8% of the facility managers in the same subject. This reflected the fact that the contractors would contact designers in case of design changes.

When asked whether lesson-learned or feedback from facility managers were pass on to designers, only 41.5% of facility managers did, while 78.4% of designers indicated that there had been contacts by facility managers. The corresponding percentages of this subject were somewhat different. This may due to the fact that the responded designers had higher average years of experience (15.1 vs. 8.6 years). Therefore, the majority of responded designers were likely to be contacted by facility managers. Meanwhile, designers were more likely to consult experts in their design process than the facility management did.

4.3.2 Comparison of perspectives in management
In this part, both designers and facility managers were asked to rate several management issues as shown in

Table 7. The ranks indicated in *italics* were the ranks or priorities rated by facility managers, the ones in **bold** were selected by designers.

From Table 7, it is clear that one or two out of top three items ranked from facility managers and designers were identical. These results indicate that the designers were somewhat aware of the problems faced by facility managers.

4.3.3 Comparison of perspectives on building component's maintainability
Maintainability, in this study, denoted and influenced by the combination or all of the following three conditions:

1. The complexity of a system or building component that made the system difficult to manage,
2. The difficulty to determine the cause(s) of a problem in a system, and
3. The difficulty to repair such problem(s).

Thus, to establish if the perspectives of facility managers and designers were different in terms of maintainability, all three aspects must be measured. The list of building components was developed and both facility managers and designers were asked to rate the difficulty level of each system in all three perspectives using 5-level scale from easiest (1) to most difficult (5).

Table 8, Table 9, and Table 10 demonstrated the mode of difficulty level of the three components. The tables also indicated χ^2 values performed between facility managers' frequency data and designers' data. The conclusion whether the perspectives in each building component were different was determined using the χ^2 critical value at 0.05 level of significant with

degree of freedom equaled to four. If the calculated χ^2 was greater than the critical value of 9.49, then the perspectives were different. In some cases, the χ^2 was not applicable because there was no expected frequency. For example, no designers indicated that the elevator system was the most difficult (level 5) system to manage but some facility managers indicated that the system is the most difficult to manage, therefore, χ^2 value was divided by zero and the value cannot be calculated. This clearly demonstrated that the perspectives between the two parties were different at some level but cannot be statistically verified that it was different at 95% level of confidence.

From the results, it is apparent that majority of perspectives were different between the two groups as

Table 8. Comparison of perspectives in system management complexity level.

	Fac. Mgr. Mode	Designer Mode	χ^2	Comparison of Perspectives
Structural system				
Main structure	3	2	40.54	Different
Concrete shell	3	2	21.26	Different
Glass shell	3	3	12.01	Different
Electrical				
Lighting	2	2	13.98	Different
Emergency lighting	2	2	6.08	Same
Power	2	3	19.16	Different
Air Conditioning				
Cooling	2	3	21.05	Different
Heating	3	3	0.46	Same
Ventilation	3	3	3.42	Same
Plumbing and Piping				
Plumbing	3	3	4.53	Same
Hot water piping	3	3	3.58	Same
Drainage	3	2	12.80	Different
Sewage	3	3	5.83	Same
Waste water treatment	3	3	9.82	Different
Transportation				
Elevator	3	3	N/A	Different*
Escalator	2	3	N/A	Different*
Fire safety				
Alarm	3	3	N/A	Different*
Fire plumbing	3	2	N/A	Different*
Extinguish equip.	2	2	N/A	Different*
Lighting Protection	2	2	31.68	Different
Telecommunications				
Telephone	3	2	N/A	Different*
Sound	3	3	N/A	Different*
MATV	3	3	N/A	Different*
CATV/Satellite	3	2	N/A	Different*
Security system				
Intrusion alarm	3	3	N/A	Different*
CCTV	3	3	N/A	Different*
Building automation	3	3	9.17	Same
Interior decoration	3	3	7.18	Same

χ^2 critical value at 0.05 level of significant with df = 4 is 9.49.
* Perspectives were somewhat different (χ^2 was N/A).

Table 9. Comparison of perspectives in difficulty to determine cause.

	Fac. Mgr. Mode	Designer Mode	χ^2	Comparison of Perspectives
Structural system				
Main structure	3	3	10.76	Different
Concrete shell	3	2	N/A	Different*
Glass shell	3	3	14.91	Different
Electrical				
Lighting	2	2	6.68	Same
Emergency lighting	2	2	3.17	Same
Power	3	3	N/A	Different*
Air Conditioning				
Cooling	3	3	29.36	Different
Heating	3	3	N/A	Different*
Ventilation	3	3	1.63	Same
Plumbing and Piping				
Plumbing	3	3	4.45	Same
Hot water piping	3	3	N/A	Different*
Drainage	3	3	4.89	Same
Sewage	3	3	N/A	Different*
Waste water treatment	3	3	4.60	Same
Transportation				
Elevator	3	3	N/A	Different*
Escalator	2	3	N/A	Different*
Fire safety				
Alarm	3	3	N/A	Different*
Fire plumbing	3	3	N/A	Different*
Extinguish equip.	2	2	N/A	Different*
Lighting Protection	3	3	23.37	Different
Telecommunications				
Telephone	3	3	4.73	Same
Sound	3	3	N/A	Different*
MATV	3	3	N/A	Different*
CATV/Satellite	3	3	N/A	Different*
Security system				
Intrusion alarm	2	Moderate	N/A	Different*
CCTV	3	Moderate	6.41	Same
Building automation	3	Moderate	6.36	Same
Interior decoration	3	Easy	41.70	Different

χ^2 critical value at 0.05 level of significant with df = 4 is 9.49.
* Perspectives were somewhat different (χ^2 was N/A).

Table 10. Comparison of perspectives in difficulty to repair.

	Fac. Mgr. Mode	Designer Mode	χ^2	Comparison of Perspectives
Structural system				
Main structure	3	4	17.95	Different
Concrete shell	3	3	N/A	Different*
Glass shell	3	3	2.95	Same
Electrical				
Lighting	2	2	9.25	Same
Emergency lighting	3	2	4.01	Same
Power	3	3	N/A	Different*
Air Conditioning				
Cooling	3	3	20.48	Different
Heating	3	3	N/A	Different*
Ventilation	3	3	2.01	Same
Plumbing and Piping				
Plumbing	3	3	5.57	Same
Hot water piping	3	3	N/A	Different*
Drainage	3	3	19.74	Different
Sewage	3	4	12.83	Different
Waste water treatment	3	3	8.88	Same
Transportation				
Elevator	3	3	34.99	Different
Escalator	3	3	13.41	Different
Fire safety				
Alarm	3	3	2.01	Same
Fire plumbing	3	3	14.77	Different
Extinguish equip.	3	2	13.75	Different
Lighting Protection	3	3	6.61	Same
Telecommunications				
Telephone	3	3	19.44	Different
Sound	3	3	N/A	Different*
MATV	3	3	1.56	Same
CATV/Satellite	3	3	3.33	Same
Security system				
Intrusion alarm	3	3	N/A	Different*
CCTV	3	3	4.72	Same
Building automation	3	4	N/A	Different*
Interior decoration	3	2	6.55	Same

χ^2 critical value at 0.05 level of significant with df = 4 is 9.49.
* Perspectives were somewhat different (χ^2 was N/A).

suspected. The level of difficulty in all three components of each building system were ranging from easy to difficult (level 2 to 4), where most of the system were rated as moderate (level 3).

The systems with all three aspects of maintainability different at 95% confidence level were the main structural system and the AC cooling system. The systems with the same perspectives in three aspects were the emergency lighting system, the AC ventilation system, and the plumbing system.

5 CONCLUSION

Maintainability, in terms of complexity level of system management, difficulty to determine causes, and difficulty to repair, of high-rise buildings was assessed from facility managers and designers in this study. It was found that only three building components were rated the same level between two parties.

It was clear that majority of perspectives between designers and facility managers were different. This may result from various factors such as lack of feedback and the different experience of both parties. The feedback and lesson-learned from facility managers should be transferred to designers to enhance future designs to include more maintainability concerns, which will further improve living conditions of tenants, life cycle, and life-cycle costs of the building.

Building management in Thailand can be considered new and unrecognized by many involved practitioners in the industry. This leads to the sustainability of ever increasing facilities. Further efforts to raise the awareness should be done to increase building's life and reducing maintenance or renovation cost.

Future study in the building components rated as "difficult" in maintainability by facility managers should also be investigated to determine the way to prevent problems that may arise from the building systems.

REFERENCES

Carpenter, C.L. & Oloufa A. 1995. Postoccupancy Evaluation of Buildings and Development of Facility Performance Criteria. *Journal of Architectural Engineering*. 1(2): 77–81.

David, A. & Nawakorawit. 1999a. Designing Building for Maintenance: Designer's Perspective. *Journal of Architectural Engineering*. 5(4): 107–116.

David, A. & Nawakorawit. 1999b. Issues in Building Maintenance: Property Manager Perspective. *Journal of Architectural Engineering*. 5(4): 117–132.

Kanhawattana, Y. 2001. A study of high-rise building performance in terms of building managers' and designers' perspective. *Master thesis*. King Mongkut's University of Technology Thonburi, Thailand.

Lowry, R. 1999. Concepts and Applications of Inferential Statistics. Retrieved 5 January 2003, from http://faculty.vassar.edu/lowry/webtext.html

Lueprasert K., Lorterapong, P. & Tansatcha T. 2000. Building Maintenance Practices in Thailand: A Case Study in Air-Conditioning Maintenance: *Proceeding of the Brisbane 2000 CIBW70 International Symposium on Facilities Management and Maintenance*, Nov 2000: 589–596, Queensland University of Technology.

Sadi, A. 1995. The Effect of Faulty Construction on Building Maintenance. *Journal of Building Research and Information*. 23(3): 175–181.

Development of the logistics plans in building construction

S.M.B. Serra
Civil Engineering Department of São Carlos Federal University, São Carlos, SP, Brazil

O.J. Oliveira
São Paulo University, Professor of São Judas University, São Paulo, SP, Brazil

ABSTRACT: The main objective is to present a tool for the development and implementation of logistics plans in building construction. Firstly it shows a review of related concepts. These are followed by a study of the relationship of the logistic plan with the elements that conditions its success. These are considered as main requirements for correct plan formulation, such as simultaneity among external logistics (control of suppliers) and internal logistics (construction site management). In conclusion, this paper present the guidelines for formulation and implantation of logistics plans that will aid in the operational planning of the work, programming of the deliveries of materials and improvement in the conditions of the work. Application of the logistics guidelines cited is directly dependent on a change in the culture and structure of construction companies, which must perforce begin to use lean thinking to guide decisions and to execute activities in every organizational level, with special emphasis on top management.

1 INTRODUCTION

The new production philosophy (lean production) sees the productive system as a group of interconnected and interdependent conversions and flow activities that should, ideally, encompass broader concerns than a mere analysis of the productive process alone. The growing awareness of the importance of improving the flow of materials and information has given rise to the emergence of a new production paradigm that is generating auspicious results.

Seen from the standpoint of lean production, innumerable criticisms can be made of the traditional production model, which, by focusing solely on conversions, neglects the physical flow occurring between them, that is, the activities of transportation, storage and inspection. Because they add no value to the final product and are consumed time and expensive, these activities should be eliminated or reduced to a minimum.

Now that the concept of lean production has matured and it was implemented by the manufacturing industry, it has finally begun to arouse the interest of civil construction managers, originating what can be dubbed lean construction. Nonetheless, the application of this philosophy in the construction sector still requires experimentation and research aimed at adapting it to the sector's particularities, which are usually factors that hinder the implementation of new technical and managerial tools.

According to Vrijhoef; Koskela (1999), the supply chain has been defined as the network of organizations that are involved, through upstream and downstream linkages, in the different processes and activities that produce value in the form of products and services in the hands of the ultimate customer. The traditional way of managing is essentially based on a conversion view (or transformation view) on production, whereas supply chain management (SCM) is based on a flow view of production. Koskela (1998) mentions that the conversion view suggests that each stage of production is controlled independently, whereas the flow view focuses the control of the total flow of the production.

Thus, the optimal construction site management requires the identification of all the agents present on the site. Each phase of the construction involves a variety of suppliers and subcontractors who contribute to the production with a multiplicity of materials and services. Other agents in the productive chain also participate in the construction process. Edum-Fotwe et al. (2001) presents examples of different actors that participate in some of the phases of the supply chain. During the construction the most important agents are: main contractor, subcontractors, project manager, material suppliers, equipment suppliers, designers, financial institution, insurance agency and regulatory bodies.

2 LOGISTICS IN THE BUILDING CONSTRUCTION

Construction logistics is a multidisciplinary process applied to a given construction to ensure the supply, storage, processing and availability of material resources on the construction site, to dimension the production teams and to manage the physical flows of production. Silva & Cardoso (1998) state that the main support of this process, which occurs through planning, organization, management and control activities, is the flow of information prior to and during the productive process.

Cardoso (1996) presents a subdivision for logistics applicable to construction companies, classifying it, in terms of scope, as *supply logistics* (external) and *on-site logistics* (internal). This subdivision allows for a clearer identification of the main activities associated with construction site logistics.

2.1 *Supply logistics*

Supply logistics involves provision of the material and human resources required for the building production. Among the most important activities are planning and processing of purchased items, supplier management, transportation of resources to the site, and maintenance of the material resources foreseen in the planning.

Wegelius-Lehtonen (2001) presents two tools developed to measure the improvement potential of deliveries process. The tools measure costs and time of delivery chains. The first step is to identify all the activities from the supplier's production line to the final assembly of product on construction site. The second step is to calculate costs of each activity and finally to present the results in an informative way.

The detailed division of logistics costs both on the construction site and at the supplier's is present in Figure 1. The example illustrates how the activity and cost analysis results can be used on specific material supplier level as a basis for improvement. In this case example, construction firm and plasterboard supplier wanted to develop their material deliveries together.

According to Wegelius-Lehtonen (2001), the standard materials, like timber, mortar and plasterboard, have the biggest logistics costs of material flows as percentage of the purchasing price, because the logistics chain of standard materials consist of many movements and warehousing. The accuracy and delivery time analysis is most useful in the development of customized material deliveries, like windows, concrete elements and kitchen cabinets. With the accuracy and delivery time analysis, the improvement potential in information flows and co-ordination can be identified.

2.2 *On-site logistics*

On-site logistics involves the management of the physical flows and information flows associated with on-site activities, the most important activities are: management of the physical flows involved in the execution (detailed planning of the service flow and its control mechanisms), interface management between agents interacting in the construction process (information and interposition among the services), and physical management of the construction site (establishment of the site, internal movements, storage and prefabrication areas, and work safety requirements).

3 THE LOGISTICS APPROACH DURING THE DESIGN PHASE

Novaes (1998) highlights two design concepts: *static* – which refers to the design as a product constituted of graphic and descriptive elements, ordered and elaborated according to an appropriate language and with

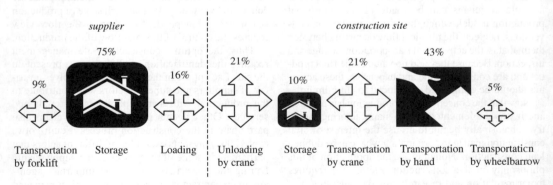

| supplier | | | | construction site | | | |

| 9% | 75% | 16% | 21% | 10% | 21% | 43% | 5% |

| Transportation by forklift | Storage | Loading | Unloading by crane | Storage | Transportation by crane | Transportation by hand | Transportation by wheelbarrow |

Figure 1. Division of the logistics costs in the plasterboard deliveries (Wegelius-Lehtonen 2001).

main objective to reach the requirements of the production phase, and *dynamic* – which gives the design a sense of process through which solutions are identified and adapted, assuming a technological and managerial character (production design). This latter concept (dynamic design) is the focus of our attention here, owing to its direct relation with the logistics activity in the construction site. From the beginning the concept of the design should include the building production with the integrated operation of all its constituents.

3.1 Production design

During the phase of construction work, the design's performance is largely dependent of the production team's interpretation and of the communication level used. A design that foresees good constructive techniques is useless if those techniques are not conveniently intelligibly by the work team (Nascimento & Formoso 1998).

The detailed operational planning should be carried out simultaneously with the product conception. In this stage it is very important the agents' participation that more influence, direct or indirectly, the production phase: designers and building companies.

In the words of Melhado (1994), production design is *"a set of design elements drawn up concurrently with the detailing of the execution design, for use within the scope of on-site production activities, containing the definitions of disposition and sequence of on-site activities and work teams, the use of equipments, and the arrangement and evolution of on-site work, among other resources connected with the construction company's characteristics and resources".*

According to Ferreira (1998) the production design should proceed the four great stages of the production planning: strategic production planning of the enterprise, production tactical planning, production operational planning and production operational planning detail.

3.2 Construction site design

The design of the construction site is possibly the design whose concept most strongly influences logistics. Several elements and areas must be considered, such as areas for the storage of materials, living areas for the workers, administrative areas and production areas.

To meet legal regulations and to reach the requirements of a highly demanding and competitive market, the companies have to design construction sites according to the current legislation and still allow improvements in the safety conditions on the on-site work, rendering the edifice's production system more efficient.

The *"on-site design is an integral part of the construction process, responsible for defining the size, shape and location of both permanent and temporary work areas and the circulation routes needed to develop the operations of support and execution during each phase of construction work, in an integrated and evolutive manner and in line with the enterprise's production design, offering specific conditions for the workers' safety, health and motivation, and for the rational execution of the services"* (Ferreira 1998).

The Systematic Layout Planning method (SLP) is a systematization tool for physical arrangement designs. According to Muther & Wheeler (2000), layout planning involves three essential conditions: the relations between the different functions or activities in the environment, the amount and type of space for each activity, and the adjustment of these two factors within the layout itself. The logistics approach and the development of management tools are important strategies for the success of the construction site design.

3.3 Influence of production design and site design on construction logistics

Oliveira (2001) states that production design and site design are the instruments that enable the constructor to plan and develop on-site logistics efficiently. The information they contain support the planning, operation and monitoring of the logistic activities of construction work (supply, storage, processing and availability of material resources), indicating when, where and how the production activities are to be performed and the amount of materials to be used in each phase, allowing for labor planning and aiding in the performance of the information system. These characteristics facilitate the development of supply logistics activities, allowing for the early identification of material and labor requirements, facilitating the planning and processing of purchased materials and optimizing the management of transportation to the site.

With regard to on-site logistics, multiple benefits accrue from the use of these designs, including visibly improved mapping and, hence, improved management of the physical flows relating to the execution of the work, smoothing out of the problems that usually appear at the interfaces between the different agents during the productive process, and a substantial reduction of wastage resulting from a well organized and signalized construction site. Finally, a schedule of the activities and another of materials movements are of inestimable value for the control of on-site logistic.

A well-implemented and managed logistic system, based on reliable information supplied by production and site designs, is expected to result in reduced rehandling, material shifting and losses, transforming the site into a creditable calling card, reducing the risk of accidents, creating greater worker motivation and providing a substantial increase in competitiveness.

4 CONSTITUENTS OF THE LOGISTICS PLAN IN BUILDING CONSTRUCTION

4.1 Logistics model of civil construction

In a study on logistics in construction, Agapiou et al. (1998) propose a logistics model developed to improve the aspects of the design and construction process. The project team identified several criteria for consideration, including:

- planning of site activities;
- deliveries of material to site;
- number of changes to the detailed design;
- re-work during the construction stages; and
- site work conditions.

According Agapiou et al. (1998), the basic components of the logistics model consisted of a number of management's tools, as it can be seen in the Table 1.

Because of the repetitiveness of this process and in order to reduce the managerial efforts of those

responsible for it, it is important to develop tools to aid in the administration and control of information transference. The examples proposed are: a schedule of the materials and components requirements, and a schedule of materials deliveries to the site. The latter is based on the logistics concept, knowledge of the conditions at the site, such as storage space, production pace and reduction of transportation flows. In addition to the need of distribution of efforts among the professionals or workers on the site, it is advisable that the delivery processes be well distributed. Figure 2 illustrates a schedule of materials deliveries to the site.

In addition, charts can also be developed to facilitate comparisons between proposed quotations, drafts in consonance with the negotiation phase, and to draw up guidelines for on-site materials storage.

The following guidelines seek to take into account the importance of the topics discussed here.

4.2 Logistics plan guidelines

The logistics approach should be considered throughout the development of the production cycle of the enterprise, this is, from its conception to its execution.

Table 1. Components of logistics management model (Agapiou et al. 1998).

Logistics management tools	Description
Materials coordinator	Responsible for managing the logistics model during the construction process.
Supply plan	Supply plan indicates the proposed delivery dates of units for the whole project. This plan is specified by the materials coordination in cooperation with each supplier/subcontractor.
Request schedule	A detailed version of the supply plan covering a three week period. The schedule is draw up by the coordinator in cooperation with each subcontractor.
Unloading plans	These plans indicated where daily supplies (units) would be delivered on site.
Unit specification	A unit is a package of materials required for one working operations within one craft at one location on the construction site. The whole project is divided into units. The content of each unit was specified by individual subcontractors. A unit plan is specified by the materials supplier in conjunction with the materials coordinator.

ACTIVITIES		Delivery	Week							
	material	Strategy	16	17	18	19	20	21	22	23
STRUCTURE										
	steel (ton)	month	5000							
	concrete (m3)	week		25		25		25		25
MASONRY										
	block (unit)	two week			10000		10000		10000	
cement (bag 50Kg)		month				146				525
whitewash (bag 20Kg)		month				548				1971
	sand (m3)	week				30		30		30

Figure 2. Gantt chart of deliveries of materials to the site.

Table 2. Logistics Production Plan Guidelines.

Production cycle	Guidelines and tools
Design	• Logistics guidelines for the conception • Analysis of technological alternatives • Definition of the plan of attack for on-site work • Production design • Site design • As-built design
Planning	• Gantt physical chart • Gantt materials consumption chart • Gantt equipment chart • Histogram of own labor • Gantt subcontractor chart • Gantt chart of implementation of work safety-related preventive measures
Supplies	• Materials specifications • Plans for materials deliveries to the site • Gantt chart of the startup of the purchasing process (quotations) • Materials/supplies purchasing rules • Materials and services supplier qualification • Guidelines for equipment purchasing or leasing • Use of indices of material losses and wastage
Execution	• Plan for the execution of work on the floors • Documentation, implementation and maintenance of the information system • Use of labor and equipment productivity indices • Work safety and health rules

All the agents participating in the enterprise should be integrated so that the logistics (supply and site) tools and instruments can be utilized systematically, aiming for synergic gains. Table 2 presents guidelines and tools for the preparation and application of logistics plans in building construction.

These tools should be prepared based on the principles for optimization of construction site efficiency through objective programming on the operational level of execution. It is important that feedback of the process be provided through critical analysis and reprogramming of the schedules and logistics plan, according to need. Experiences and information should be recorded and reused so as to ensure the continuous improvement of the construction site management process.

The logistics plans development and implantation request technical specialization and professional's managerial training. It is advisable to assure the logistics manager's qualifications for not overloading him with other functions. Moreover, the organization must have adequate computational tools for communication and information processing.

5 CONCLUSIONS

This paper, within its limitations, made an brief review of the main concepts directly related with the logistics in the construction. Based on these concepts, it was made a reflection on its importance and basic guidelines were proposed for the first steps on the logistics plans implementation and its utilization in the building construction.

Based on the precepts of the new production philosophy (lean production), the construction companies have been showing increasing interest in the implementation of integrated management tools of production, and are beginning to realize the importance of identifying and managing the different agents that participate in the enterprise.

The adoption of logistics plans may render these companies more competitive, enabling them to reduce activities that add no value to the product, such as stocks, inspections, movement of materials, etc.

The proposed subdivision between supply logistics (external) and on-site logistics (internal) allows for unequivocal identification of the main logistics-related activities in the building construction, thus permitting more detailed planning, in which the anticipation and adoption of modern instruments for control should be basic premises.

Also highlighted was the need for concern regarding logistic management starting in the design phase, including a discussion of the dynamic design concept and its constituents – production design and site design. These constituents supply a large part of the information required to carry out of the logistic plan and are therefore fundamental elements in the planning and implementation of such plans.

Application of the logistics guidelines and instruments cited in this text is directly dependent on a profound change in the culture and structure of construction companies, which must perforce begin to use the lean thinking to guide decisions and to execute activities at every organizational level, with special emphasis on top management.

Finally, the development and implementation of the logistics techniques and instruments in a simple and direct way are not enough for the logistics plans success.

Above all, it is necessary the development of a conscience and real commitment with the lean thinking on the part of all company's employees.

REFERENCES

Agapiou, A. et al. 1998. The role of logistics in the materials flow control process. *Construction Management and Economics*, v. 16, p. 131–137.

Cardoso, F.F. 1996. Importância dos estudos de preparação e da logística na organização dos sistemas de produção de edifícios. In: 1º SEMINÁRIO INTERNACIONAL LEAN CONSTRUCTION – A CONSTRUÇÃO SEM PERDAS. *Proceedings...* São Paulo, Brazil.

Edum-Fotwe, F.T. et al. 2001. Information procurement practices of key actors in construction supply chains. *European Journal of Purchasing & Supply Management*, v. 7, p. 155–164.

Ferreira, E.A.M. 1998. *Metodologia para elaboração do projeto do canteiro de obras de edifícios*. São Paulo, Brazil: Escola Politécnica da Universidade de São Paulo. (doctorate thesis).

Koskela, L. 1998. "Lean construction". In: VII ENCONTRO NACIONAL DE TECNOLOGIA DO AMBIENTE CONSTRUÍDO. *Proceedings...* Florianópolis, Brazil.

Melhado, S.B. 1994. *Qualidade do projeto na construção de edifícios: aplicação ao caso das empresas de incorporação e construção*. São Paulo, Brazil: Escola Politécnica da Universidade de São Paulo. (doctorate thesis).

Muther, R., Wheeler, J.D. 2000. *Planejamento sistemático e simplificado de layout*. São Paulo: IMAM, 50p. Brazil.

Nascimento, C.E. & Formoso, C.T. 1998. Método para avaliar o projeto do ponto de vista da produção. In: VII ENCONTRO NACIONAL DE TECNOLOGIA DO AMBIENTE CONSTRUÍDO. *Proceedings...* Florianópolis, Brazil.

Novaes, C.C. 1996. *Diretrizes para garantia da qualidade do projeto na produção de edifícios habitacionais*. São Paulo, Brazil: Escola Politécnica da Universidade de São Paulo. (doctorate thesis).

Oliveira, O.J. 2001. Influências do projeto de produção e do projeto de canteiro no sistema logístico da construção de edifícios. In: WORKSHOP NACIONAL DE GESTÃO DO PROCESSO DE PROJETO NA CONSTRUÇÃO DE EDIFÍCIOS. São Carlos, SP. 2001. *Proceedings...* São Carlos, Brazil. 5p.

Silva, F.B. & Cardoso, F.F. 1998. A importância da logística na organização dos sistemas de produção de edifícios In: VII ENCONTRO NACIONAL DE TECNOLOGIA DO AMBIENTE CONSTRUÍDO. *Proceedings...* Florianópolis, Brazil.

Vrijhoel, R. & Koskela, L. 1999. Roles of supply chain management in construction. In: CONFERENCE OF THE INTERNATIONAL GROUP FOR LEAN CONSTRUCTION (IGLC 7), 7th. 1999, Berkeley. *Proceedings...* Berkeley, USA: University of California, Jul., p. 133–146.

Wegeluis-Lehtonen, T. 2001. Performance measurement in construction logistics. *International Journal of Production Economics*, n. 69, p. 107–116.

System-based Vision for Strategic and Creative Design, Bontempi (ed.)
© 2003 Swets & Zeitlinger, Lisse, ISBN 90 5809 599 1

A design/evaluation approach to building design and construction

T.H. Nguyen & S. Yazdani
North Dakota State University, Department of Civil Engineering and Construction, Fargo, North Dakota, USA

ABSTRACT: This paper outlines a novel approach to building design and construction, in which the evaluation of design objectives is carried out during the design process to provide real-time feedback to project participants. One component of this research effort is focused on the overall project cost estimate, which can be done by means of an "engine", named cost analyzer, to be incorporated into the proposed computerized building design system. The engine contains several functions or methods responsible for performing cost analysis and enabling designers to consider cost-effective alternate designs while keeping track the effect of various designs on the overall cost of the project.

1 INTRODUCTION

Traditionally, design objectives concerning various performance aspects (e.g. energy efficiency, budget limit, constructability, code compliance, etc.) of a building at a particular design phase are not evaluated until all design works for the building have been completed. In the case that one or more of these criteria are not satisfied, for example the budget limit is exceeded, all project participants including designers, estimators, and/or project managers need to discuss and determine how to appropriately modify the design so that the project cost can be cut down to the expected budget limit. Another example involves the constructability issues of a building project within the constraints of a construction site. A lack of attention for selecting a proper structural system and its associated details could lead to change orders and reworks of structural design. This in turn is time-consuming and potentially expensive. In order to avoid such pitfalls, the manual evaluation of building designs is usually employed through numerous meetings. However, the manual evaluation often overwhelms meeting participants who come from many different disciplines and organizations with many diverse sources of knowledge and expertise. At present, with computer supports the performance evaluations can be handled with relative ease. An estimating software linked to a CAD (Computer-Aided Design) system can automatically generate the quantity take-offs needed for cost evaluation or estimates. However, the current computer software are unable to explicitly rationalize how building elements or systems selected by a designer could effect the overall design objectives

in general and the total cost of the project in particular. This shortcoming makes it difficult for the project participant to determine when and how to adjust the cost information in the case of design changes so that the cost estimate and project scope are in balance. This paper describe a framework underlying a computer-based building design system that is able to interface with project participants for how a designed component effects the overall design objectives concerning projects issues such as budget limits, constructability, code compliance, and energy efficiency. One component of this research effort is focused on the overall project cost estimate, which can be done by means of an "engine", named cost analyzer, to be incorporated into the proposed computerized building design system. The engine contains several functions or methods responsible for creating cost estimates and performing cost analysis enabling designers to consider cost-effective alternate designs while keeping track the effect of various designs on the overall cost of the project.

2 BACKGROUND

2.1 Cost estimate

Cost estimates of a building project usually evolve along with design changes in different phases of the building design and construction process. As a result, it is critical that cost estimates need to be maintained and monitored throughout the project life cycle. Traditionally, cost estimates of building projects at a particular design phase are not created until all design works have been completed. Such a traditional design process may result in more design changes and reworks and the overall cost may finally exceed the budget. Although current estimating computer applications assist estimators in expediting the estimating process by automatically generating take-off quantities, they are unable to help estimators to interact with other project participants during the design phase so that any changes in design affecting the overall cost will be identified in real-time. Hence, the proposed building design approach is that the evaluation of design objectives should be carried out during the design process to provide feedback to project participants (i.e. estimators) immediately.

Most of large projects designed by an A/E firm are usually completed with many changes in the original design causing budgetary problems and it would take multiple project meetings to resolve such problems. Through these meetings, project participants could not evaluate and predict the performance of alternatives in terms of design objectives with any reliability because:

- Access to project information and the determination of the impact of the proposed changes to the design are carried out manually.
- Graphical representations of the project are two-dimensional and they do not visually represent critical relationships between project information such as building performance, space, time, costs, etc. With this shortcoming, it is difficult to establish communication between project participants and to identify the element that has caused a design objective (project budget) to be violated.

2.2 Related research

Today, powerful CAD systems such as solid modelers or geometric modelers are able to describe 3D models. Several researchers (Eastman et al. 2002; Fischer et al. 2001; Haymaker et al. 2001; Griffis & Sturts 2000) have taken the advantages of the 3D solid modelling techniques to develop computer-based systems with emphasis on the integration of various design and construction applications. In addition, the integrated use of multidisciplinary design applications in the building design systems leads to a need for a standard data protocol to support interoperability among different AEC applications. As a result, the current major effort in developing a building data model is based on the Industry Foundation Class building model (IFC 2001), which has been developed by the International Alliance for Interoperability (IAI). The IAI mainly consists of a wide range of construction industry organizations who have come together to fund the development of the IFCs in response to the need for a standard data structure to support data exchange among different AEC professionals.

2.3 The previous work

Nguyen and Oloufa (2001) have outlined a computer-based building design framework with emphasis on an engine capable of automatically deducing topological information of building components. Such information support various aspects in building design such as constructability analysis, construction planning, and building code compliance checking (Nguyen & Oloufa 2001). In addition, an object-based programming application is used to develop mechanisms for extracting geometric data needed for the deduction. In this stage, the research effort to develop the computerized building design system is limited to the capability of automatically generating spatial relationships among building components.

3 CURRENT RESEARCH

3.1 Research objectives

The current research outlines the development of another component of the proposed building design framework, called Cost Analyzer. The Cost Analyzer is responsible for evaluating the overall cost of the project and for providing real-time feedback. The feedback concerning budget limits allows designers/estimators to identify the most cost-effective design alternatives.

The scope of the current research on cost estimate and analysis focuses on preliminary design because decisions made during this early design stage have a significant influence on the subsequent project phases as well as the overall project cost.

3.2 Selection of a CAD system

Recently, the emergence of solid modelers has offered solutions for the representation of 3D geometric information of design objects and has provided support for the addition of semantic attributes describing the design objects. Unlike traditional CAD systems, which are merely tools to graphically represent a design by means of primitives such as points, lines, and arcs, solid modelling provides various representation schemes using primitives such as vertices, edges, faces, cells, and loops. Such primitives are suitable for a complete and unambiguous description of design objects. Furthermore, using solid modelling, the objects observed in buildings can be quickly created as blocks, thus making it simple to perform calculations of volume and mass properties of the building objects. Such building information are necessary for different design activities (especially the task of cost estimate) throughout the design and construction process. There are many 3D geometric representation techniques including Boundary representation (Brep) and Constructive Solid Geometry, and Feature-Based Representation. This research makes use of 3D boundary representation or

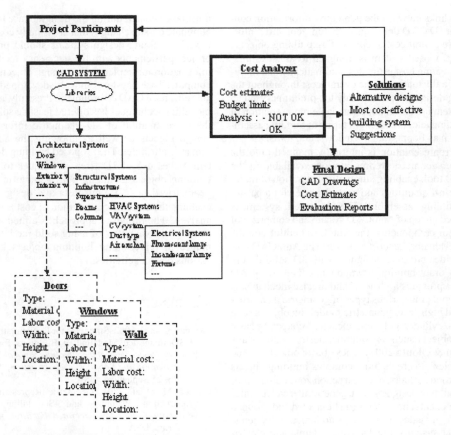

Figure 1. The proposed building design framework.

Brep of solid modelling for representing building objects. The representation provides both geometric and topological data necessary for deduction of spatial relationships between the building objects. In addition, the availability of Brep representation in a CAD software, such as AutoCAD, is useful for the development of the proposed building design system.

3.3 Programming environment

The main objective of this research is to develop the component of cost analyzer in the proposed system to perform cost analysis of a building project. This can be done by means of a new command "CostAnalyzer" to be developed and incorporated into the AutoCAD system. The command "CostAnalyzer" is implemented in an application development environment named ObjectARX. This development tool is an AutoCAD® Runtime Extension programming environment that includes a number of C++ dynamic link libraries (DLLs) that enable developments of AutoCAD applications (ObjectARX 2002). The main reason for selection of ObjectARX as a programming environment

for the implementation of this work is that the set of DLLs in ObjectARX can operate directly with core AutoCAD data structures and code, thus providing suitable mechanisms for accessing AutoCAD database to extract data of design objects that are necessary for generating cost estimate and analysis: the main subject of this research. In effect, the ObjectARX DLLs share AutoCAD's address space and make direct function calls to AutoCAD, thus avoiding the costly overhead of the Inter-Process Communication (IPC) that is usually required by other alternative AutoCAD Development System (ADS) applications and AutoLISP.

3.4 The proposed building design framework

Figure 1 shows the overall framework underlying the proposed building design system. As the proposed computerized system is developed in a solid modelling (Brep) environment, each building component is represented by a 3D object. Such 3D representations enable complete description of building objects by means of various attached attributes such as time, cost, design criteria, etc. The main research challenge is to develop links between the geometric information contained in 3D CAD drawings with non-geometric information (e.g. unit costs) representing building objects.

The proposed system is designed to assist estimators in creating cost estimates automatically and monitoring the fluctuation of the overall cost throughout the building design process, mainly the preliminary stage. The system uses a single, expandable representation of the building and its context in terms of building assemblies such as floors, walls, windows, and roofs.

This representation is internally mapped onto the computer geometric representations available in the 3D CAD tool, enabling automatic generation of material take-off quantities and cost estimates for a particular building assembly. The proposed system is developed on top of AutoCAD system and comprises of two major components: the AutoCAD editor and the design evaluator, i.e. cost analyzer. The AutoCAD editor provides building designers with 3D solid design tools to draw building components. The AutoCAD interface provides high-level and precise mechanisms for manipulating various types of geometric data structures and high-level geometric modelling objects such as prism, cylinder, polygon, line, etc. for creating basic design objects such as columns, beams, slabs, walls (Nguyen & Oloufa 2001). These basic objects can be "assembled" to create more complex building objects such as rooms, floors, or construction zones. In the proposed building design system, generic alternative building components and systems can be created and grouped into different categories such as architectural systems, structural systems, mechanical systems, and electrical systems, which contained in separate "libraries". These libraries of building systems allow designers to select the ones that support their own design intent. Once the designers have completed their designs for the building, the cost analyzer automatically extract information about cost estimate (e.g. take-off quantity of materials and unit costs) necessary for a cost analysis. This can be done by executing a new command, namely CostAnalyzer, which has been developed using an AutoCAD application development tool (e.g. ObjectARX) and added to the AutoCAD system. The final output including the generated cost estimate and analysis will be displayed in AutoCAD screen providing designers with a quick feedback on cost efficiency among different designed building systems.

4 CONCLUSION

Design objectives concerning various performance aspects (e.g. energy efficiency, budget limit, constructability, code compliance, etc.) of a building project must be evaluated during the design phase to avoid or eliminate on-site changes that are usually costly due to rework. Building design systems should provide the project participants with the necessary feedback and information for implementing design objectives. Such computer-based systems must be developed in a suitable advanced CAD environment. Presently, many solid modelling techniques has offered feasible solutions for the representation of 3D geometric information of design objects as well as allowing the addition of semantic attributes. The proposed building design system makes use of 3D Brep techniques to represent building objects including both geometric and non-geometric data (e.g. unit costs and design criteria), enabling the automatic generation of cost estimate and analysis. The proposed approach is aimed at demonstrating the feasibility of using solid modelling techniques in representing building objects to support various design activities.

REFERENCES

Eastman, C. et al. 2002. Strategies for Realizing the Benefits of 3D Integrated Modeling of Buildings for the AEC Industry. *Proceedings of the 19th International Symposium on Automation and Robotics in Construction*, Washington DC, 23–25 September, USA.

Fischer, M. et al. 2001. Geometric Representations for Construction Planning and Scheduling, Stanford University, *Center for Integrated Facility Engineering*, California, USA.

Griffis, F.H. & Sturts, C. 2000. Three-Dimensional Computer Models and the Fully Integrated and Automated Project Process for the Management of Construction, *Construction Industry Institute Report RR152-11*.

Haymaker, J. et al. 2001. Perspectors: Inferring Spatial Relations from Building Product Models. Stanford University, *Center for Integrated Facility Engineering, California*, USA.

IFC 2001. International Alliance for Interoperability. http://www.iai.org. Industry Foundation Classes IFC Release 2.X.

Nguyen, T.H. & Oloufa, A.A. 2001. Computer-Generated. Building Data: Topological Information. *Journal of Computting in Civil Engineering*, Vol. 15, No. 4, October 2001.

ObjectARX 2002. Software development Kit for AutoCAD 2002. *Autodesk Inc.*

System-based Vision for Strategic and Creative Design, Bontempi (ed.)
© *2003 Swets & Zeitlinger, Lisse, ISBN 90 5809 599 1*

Organisational and managerial attributes of innovation among firms in the construction industry in the UK: why culture matters?

G. Zawdie, J. Abukhder & D. Langford
University of Strathclyde, Glasgow, UK

ABSTRACT: How important is innovation to the construction industry; and what are the factors that explain the propensity and ability of firms to innovate? In addressing these questions, this paper looks into innovation as a source of sustainable competitiveness, and the issue of culture as a major influence on the innovation process through its impact on industrial organisation and management. Innovation is encouraged in a change-responsive culture but it is stifled in a culture such as that found in the construction industry which is characterised by the fragmentation of responsibilities. This has bred short-sightedness in planning, a lack of trust between firms and adversarial relations resulting in high cost transactions. In the UK the 1998 Egan Agenda challenged the traditional construction culture and sought to stimulate innovation and competitive performance through partnering. This paper argues that cultural change in the industry depends not only on the awareness of firms about Egan, but also on the performance of those institutional mechanisms which attempt to release the innovative potential of construction firms in the industry.

1 INTRODUCTION

Concern about innovation in the UK construction industry has grown since the recent government initiatives including, inter alia, the Latham Report (1994) and the Egan Report (1998) which argued for the promotion of cultural change and the stimulation of innovative activities through changes in the organisation and management systems. Also, they considered the implication of these changes for the competitiveness of industry performance and the design of the national, institutional and policy framework.

Whilst recognising the significance of innovation, construction firms vary according to their propensity and ability to innovate. Compared with firms in the manufacturing sector, construction firms are considered to be slow in generating innovations (Marosszeky, 1999). A survey of UK construction firms found that 80% of contractors were not actively involved in developing new ideas or in promoting research and development (R&D). Even when firms did engage in R&D, the majority of the ideas generated fail to materialise into innovations of commercial significance (Ross, 1992; Dulaimi, 1994; Lowe, 1997). This raises questions about the underlying cultural characteristics of the activities within the construction industry.

Set against this background, this paper aims to address the following propositions:

a) that innovation in construction has a cultural context which is reflected in the organisation and management of activities.
b) that differences in the ability and propensity to innovate at the level of the firm reflect the differences in attributes among firms.
c) that, as a dynamic socio-economic process, innovation requires cultural change and the provision of institutional mechanisms that facilitate interaction between firms on the supply chain, between firms and clients, and between firms, R&D agencies and other institutions, thus enabling individual firms to realise their potential to innovate and change.

This aim is expressed in four parts:

1. The innovation process is discussed in relation to its underlying cultural context.
2. The salient features of construction innovation are discussed, followed by a consideration of the implications of culture change for the firms' innovative potential.
3. A discussion of UK construction innovation examines the evidence for innovation performance and considers recent initiatives to promote a culture of innovation.
4. The paper concludes by examining those options which affect the organisation and management of firms and facilitate the innovation process.

2 THE INNOVATION PROCESS IN ITS CULTURAL CONTEXT

In this paper we argue that the significance of the complex innovation process is not only in the output of the renovated products or services but also in the innovation process itself and we aim to broaden the focus from the output to the innovation process itself. This involves a complex set of interactions among factors relating to the economic, social political and technical cultures. Why some firms are more innovative than others depends on how they manage the constraints arising from the wider cultural milieu. The study of innovation has evolved over time but the traditional linear approach does not capture the dynamic extent of the innovation process.

2.1 *The linear approach to innovation*

This concept of innovation was proposed by a pioneer of innovation theory, Joseph Schumpeter (1934). It assumed that the innovation process began with invention deriving from R&D or research which was then translated into innovation through design and pilot production processes. Then, the innovated products and services were diffused into the market. Although Schumpeter acknowledged the inherent dynamism of the innovation process in his tri-partite conceptualisation of invention, innovation and diffusion, he did not take into account market feedback and the development of incremental innovations. The linear approach fragmented the innovation process and so isolated it from the influences of the wider socio-economic and cultural milieu. Moreover, it took innovation out of its essential context which is to be surrounded by the interaction of all those active in the process. This is, as explained by Kozul-Wright (1995), a product of:

a series of simultaneous activities undertaken by a number of firms, often in close co-operation with the users of the innovation and with the collaboration of other institutions, such as universities and public research bodies.

Two further drawbacks of the linear approach are firstly that by precluding "incremental innovation" from the process it fails to take account of the learning and accumulation of knowledge which energise innovation. Secondly, as Schmookler (1966) explained, it assumes that the market remains at the receiving end and that all innovation results from "supply push" rather than necessity being the mother of invention.

2.2 *The non-linear systems approach to innovation*

The linear approach was based upon a division of labour between "knowledge search" and "knowledge use" whereas the radically different systems or non-linear approach is based on the understanding that knowledge cannot be independently produced in specialised research organisations and then transferred to passive users. As Douthwaite (2002) states, the complex process of the production and use of new knowledge requires technical, social and institutional changes which involve interaction among participants across the divide between the knowledge producer and the user. This approach places innovation and its producers/users in a socio-economic and cultural context and accounts for the groups of stakeholders and partnerships which influence the innovation process. Hall (2002) says that the institutional and organisational factors underlying the innovation process must evolve to suit the stakeholders perspectives and policy imperatives rather than remaining fixed.

The national systems of innovation approach was proposed by Freeman (1987) and developed by Lundvall (1992). It states that innovation emerges from evolving systems of participants in the generation and application of knowledge. The essential elements of the system are interactive learning as a socially embedded process in the cultural context of institutions. Therefore, according to Hall (2002), the innovation systems concept provides a framework for the following:

(i)   exploring patterns of partnerships;
(ii) revealing and managing the institutional context that governs relationships and processes;
(iii) understanding research and innovation as a social process of learning;
(iv) thinking about capacity development in a systems sense and linking the wide range of actors in a network with the view to promoting innovation.

According to Jorde and Teece (1990) and Morroni (1992), innovation is not merely a matter of output, instead it has many dimensions, directions, and causes which require linkages and feedback mechanisms among a variety of activities both within and outside the firm. A different approach which promotes the understanding of interaction between culture and the innovation process was put forward by Etzkowitz and Leydesdorff (1997) and Etzkowitz (2002). Represented as a "triple helix" network between the three institutional spheres of university, industry and government it recognised the market influences on the innovation process and the significance of incremental innovations as reflections of the dynamism in the learning process.

2.3 *The role of culture in the innovation process*

Social processes and cultural changes are the driving forces of innovation. They affect social relations and the economic activities of production and consumption which hitherto have reflected the dominant culture.

A theoretical framework for a culture of innovation began with the work of Schumpeter (1934) who emphasised the role of the individual genius or entrepreneur who achieves innovation through insight and intuition. This elitist view was amended by Usher (1954) who saw a culture of cumulative synthesis as generating innovation. This social process of innovation begins with a number of individual acts of insight which may develop into a series of relatively simple innovations. These acts converge over time culminating in a massive synthesis which then becomes a strategic innovation.

According to Usher, there are four steps in the process of innovation:

- *Perception of the problem*: in which an incomplete or unsatisfactory pattern of satisfying specific needs is perceived.
- *Setting the stage*: in which the elements necessary for a solution (e.g. skills) are brought together through some particular configuration of events or thoughts.
- *Act of insight*: in which the essential solution of the problem is found.
- *Critical revision*: in which the newly perceived relations become fully understood and worked out in their surrounding social and cultural context.

The wider social context of innovation was explored by Zghal (1995) who argued that societies with a minority culture encourage entrepreneurs and innovators and are more likely to change and Hall and Hall (1990) who studied what happened when local firms were exposed to the business culture of international companies. They identified three types of reaction on the part of the local firms which characterised them as *encapsulators, absconders* and *cosmopolitans. Encapsulators* withdrew from their local culture, identified with the expatriate organisations and learned uncritically from them thereby failing to connect the two cultures which could provide a springboard for sustainable innovation. The *absconders* totally reject the expatriate organisations and fail to learn from them so, if they become dominant, there is little scope for innovation. In contrast, the *cosmopolitans* learn selectively from the expatriate organisations and apply their knowledge to local conditions. The resulting cultural synthesis is beneficial for innovation.

Zawdie and Langford (2002) showed how the analyses of Zghal and Hall and Hall corresponded to the behaviours which arise when there is a meeting of two radically different cultures as in the case of international contractors working in developing countries in liaison with local firms.

At the level of the firm, culture influences innovation by interacting with the management of activities. Innovation is inhibited in a rigidly hierarchical firm because the scope for information flow and creativity is limited by the dominant vested interests. Similarly, in the market, monopoly cultures thrive where markets are fragmented, there is no coherent information system and no competition to stimulate change. Basil and Cook (1974) identified the following three types of management strategy according to their implications for innovation and change:-

- Tradition-based
- Reform oriented
- Change-responsive

Tradition-based strategy is closed, backward looking and dependent on centralised and hierarchical approaches to decision-making. Consequently, it is averse to reform and a *fortiori* to more radical changes. Reform-oriented strategy brings in some changes but these are reactive and marginal and it is still conservative because the dominant status quo is not challenged. However, the optimal change-responsive strategy is proactive and forward looking, thereby creating opportunities and encouraging the development of new ideas.

Therefore, cultural change requires the removal of those barriers which could constrain creativity and information flow. This removal calls for paradigm shifts at the level of the firm, in the culture of the organisation and in the wider cultural, institutional and policy environment surrounding business. How does this relate to the innovation process in construction?

3 CONSTRUCTION INNOVATION

The under-provision of the R&D effort in the construction industry compared with other sectors of the economy has meant that the industry has been slow in the uptake of innovation. Moreover, according to Egan (1998), the level of R&D carried out in construction is known to have dropped by 80% since 1981. This has begun to change since the construction industry in many countries, including the UK, has embraced new working practices similar to those found in the manufacturing sector. Even so, the pace of construction innovation has varied across countries and has been particularly slow in the UK industry which is resistant to innovation and change. For example, the UK industry was slow to adopt structural steel frames and reinforced concrete, in comparison with the experience in the USA, France and Germany (Bowley, 1966).

This slower rate of innovation reflects the cultural gap between the UK and other countries because the dominant culture in the UK industry has made contractors risk-averse, price conscious and reluctant, if not resistant to adopting new ideas. As Gann (1997) noted, the traditional tendency for UK firms to compete on price rather than on quality or technical competence explained the prevalence in the industry of an overdeveloped sense of price and an under-developed sense of value.

Similarly, as Lowe (1997) found, the reluctance of UK firms to take the long view meant that even when innovation was accepted – as in the case of non-traditional, system-built housing – the results were found wanting. Lorenz and Smith (1998) argued that the lack of vision in the organisation and management of business was due to a shortfall in the supply of skilled and experienced managers which stemmed from the consultancy-dominant industrial culture in the UK. Consequently, most managers never developed the self-confidence to work things out for themselves so they were often hesitant about change and opted for minimalist solutions. This was because the dominant culture in society was not concerned with the long term and was averse to risk and uncertainty in policy and planning processes. Not surprisingly, as Harvey and Ashworth (1993) pointed out, successive post-war governments in the UK systematically used the construction industry as an economic regulator thereby exposing it to the boom and bust effect of demand management policies and undermining any prospects of innovation.

In recent years, there has been increasing awareness at both government and industry levels about the significance of innovation for the competitiveness of the industry, and the need for a radical reorientation of policy and management practices to make innovation happen. This concern is reflected in a range of initiatives, including the following:

- The Construction Innovation Forum (CIF) at the Building Research Establishment.
- Innovation programmes sponsored by the Department for Environment, Transport and the Regions (DETR).
- The Construction IT Centre for Excellence.
- Government task force groups and reports (Latham 1994 and Egan 1998) which led to the establishment of the Movement for Innovation (M4I).

Innovation is important for the construction industry because:

- It improves value for money to clients through positively influencing cost, quality and delivery time.
- It enhances the competitiveness of firms. This is important for the UK industry because of the growing threat of competition to British construction and declining construction standards.
- It makes construction activities environmentally sustainable through the application of "lean construction"; and the development of "environmentally sound" materials.
- It minimises safety and health risks for users of construction, thereby reducing litigation and transaction costs.

Increased awareness has led to innovation in the two major forms of supply-chain management and value engineering. This has followed from the Latham and Egan initiatives which challenged the traditional, innovation-resistant culture and set out to promote teamwork and partnership in the industry.

3.1 Reconstructing the construction culture

The traditional adversarial culture led to the fragmentation of organisational and management responsibilities and hence to activities in, for example, the supply chain. leading to increased transaction costs and a failure to exploit the benefits of economies of scale. The outcome was limitations in the scope of innovation and improvements in "value for money" for clients Cultural fragmentation also meant a rigid differentiation of responsibilities along the procurement process, so that design, financing, building and managing were done independently of one another. Contractors, who were alienated from the design and management activities through working under tight completion schedules according to given designs, would not be interested in innovation. If contractors have no management responsibilities after delivery of the project, and if they are operating with generally low profit margins, they are unlikely to consider minimising the life-cycle cost of the project. From this comes the so-called "capital cost fallacy", i.e. the benefits of reduced costs over the life of the project are often ignored in favour of the identifiable and assessed savings accruing from reduced capital expenditure (Langston, 1999). This is the outcome of a supply-led procurement practice which ignores take clients' concerns about "value for money" and where contractors see building and construction projects as being a "one-off" experience, thereby shifting the burden of life cycle cost to the project users.

Over the last two decades the globalisation of procurement and the emergence of long-term clients has altered this culture. These developments found the traditional systems wanting so the industry is moving towards new working practices similar to those found in the manufacturing sector, including partnering or supply chain management and value engineering.

3.2 Shifts in supply chain management culture

West and Fletcher (1994) found that the traditional construction supply chain relied on adversarial contracts to procure materials and services. The oligopolistic relationship between supply chain firms led to sub-optimal and wasteful, decisions. The trend now is to phase out the system of sub-contracting based on competitive tendering in favour of partnering arrangements, involving target cost contracts (alternatively known as benchmarking). These contracts, based on previous benchmark data and cost reductions across the supply chain, are expected to encourage improvement by placing pressure down the supply chain. Thus, partnering shifts the emphasis from the lowest price tender to the "value for money" of the end product. It achieves this through agreed prices and schedules for the work and tendering through a quality selection process which leads to long term savings.

Trust between the parties in the supply chain makes it more efficient. This is reflected in increased transparency, low transaction costs and reduced wasteage of resources and there is greater scope for long term planning, including innovation.

Fellows (1997) conceptualises partnering along the supply chain as a joint venture involving long-term commitment between parties in order to achieve specific business objectives by maximising the effectiveness of resources available to each party. However, the benefits of synergy in the partnering strategy are largely contingent on the flexibility and orientation of the organisation within firms on the supply chain.

3.3 Shifts towards holistic value management and engineering culture

In the context of sustainable construction, value management is no longer about cost cutting, but about providing clients with the best "value for money". Reconstructing value management means establishing a culture which recognises the relation of value to all parties along the supply chain and encourages the planning and monitoring of value improvements. Value management means looking into objectives before providing solutions and identifying critical areas in management that influence innovative solutions to maximising "value for money" and the achievement of competitiveness and sustainability. Value engineering culture aims for the holistic maximisation of "value for money" which takes into account the whole life of projects and covers cost effectiveness, quality performance, product safety, environmental impact, competitiveness and sustainability.

Innovative efforts in construction cannot be sustained without major changes in the underlying fragmented and adversarial culture with its "supply-dominated" business strategy that ignores the interests of clients. Partnering and value engineering can change the culture and enhance the innovative potential of UK construction firms.

4 CONSTRUCTION INNOVATION INITIATIVES IN THE UK

Cultural change aimed at promoting construction innovation in the UK is emerging from concurrent initiatives at the levels of government policy, of the industry, and of the firm. Government policy, has provided the Egan agenda for "Rethinking Construction", set the scene for innovation and instigated the wider networking of those involved in the innovation process, namely government, university or research institutions and the construction industry. The issue for the industry and firms is awareness about the Egan agenda for change and the extent of its implementation.

4.1 Networking initiatives and construction creativity clubs

Following Egan, the government Construction Industry Task Force initiated the Movement for Innovation (M4I) to provide a network for the generation and dissemination of new ideas. The M4I developed a programme of demonstration projects to communicate innovative experiences to the construction sector through bodies like the Construction Best Practice Programme, the Housing Forum, regional clubs and by workshops and company visits. These Government bodies were responsible for informing and advising construction firms and client organisations to implement the Egan agenda and innovation programmes.

Other emergent forms of networking and knowledge dissemination include the university-led Network of Construction Creativity Clubs (NCCC) as described by Dimitrijevic et al. (2001). This offers construction innovators the opportunity to communicate their innovations to a wider audience from industry and client organisations by presenting them at events and publishing them on the NCCC web site. This Network created a culture of innovation by facilitating the interaction between innovators, users of innovation and research scholars. It has four regional clubs across the UK, each with strong links between universities and industry link:

- the Southern CCC, led by the University of Reading and South Bank University.
- the Midlands CCC, led by the Universities of Central England, Coventry and Wolverhampton.
- the Northern CCC, led by the Universities of Sheffield Hallam, Liverpool John Moores and Salford
- the North East and Scottish CCC, led by the Universities of Glasgow Caledonian, Strathclyde and Northumbria.

These regional CCCs organise up to six meetings a year in liaison with industry and public agencies which provide a forum for sharing information and stimulating firms' innovation effort by showcasing innovations and discussing reasons for their success. Dimitrijevic et al. (2001) noted that by 2001, a total of 50 innovations were showcased as a result of the NCCC exercise and argued that if three innovations were showcased at each meeting, a total of 72 industry-led innovations a year would be documented across the UK network of CCCs.

Although both the government and university initiatives recognise the need for radical change in industrial and research cultures, so providing a framework for innovation, it is still not clear how far these initiatives have succeeded in breaking the innovation stifling culture within construction. The Egan agenda is only five years old so it is perhaps too early to evaluate the effectiveness of networking initiatives at regional and national levels. These initiatives have yet to evolve, and, as discussed earlier in this paper, their effectiveness depends not only on the quantity of output deriving from innovations, but also on the sustainability of the interactions between the elements that comprise the innovation process. The responsiveness of individual firms to the Egan agenda is also significant for innovation because it reflects the extent of the recognition of cultural change and restructuring as preconditions for innovation.

4.2 Reaction of construction firms to the Egan agenda

The targets of the Egan agenda are to promote innovation and change, thereby enhancing the sustainability and competitive performance of the industry and its implementation requires an overhaul of the firms' management ethos. This ethos is embedded in national cultures and institutions so that change in the construction culture cannot be fully realised in isolation from the national and institutional contexts. Egan challenged construction firms to reduce costs and time by 10 per cent and waste by 20 per cent on annual basis. In order to achieve these targets, firms need to address the following points:

- Creating an integrated project process based on the principle of partnering the supply chain.
- Using techniques for eliminating waste and increasing value for the customer based on the principles of value management and engineering.
- Designing projects that make maximum use of standard components and processes, thus enhancing the "value for money" objective of construction activities.
- Replacing the conventional competitive tendering with target cost construction contracts based on long-term relationships arising from partnerships along the supply chain.

The evidence that the Egan agenda been received by individual firms is fragmentary and anecdotal. A more comprehensive picture requires additional surveys to be conducted across UK firms. Meanwhile, the evidence the authors have suggests that not all firms in the construction industry are aware of the Egan agenda or are keen to implement it. This is due to both the rigidity of the prevailing culture and the limited impact to date of the networking initiatives for information and innovation.

A survey by one of the authors of 17 Scottish main and sub-contracting construction firms studied cultural change. About 30% of these firms were aware of the main aspects of the Egan Report and had fully adopted its recommendations; 35% were aware of the Egan agenda, having heard or read about it, but they had not implemented it; and another 35% said they were not aware of Egan at all.

This sample survey shows that the Egan agenda still has a long way to go before it is fully implemented in the UK industry. However, the sample size used in the survey was too small to provide a representative profile so the conclusions drawn can only be tentative. Even so, the survey has highlighted some salient features about how firms respond to the challenge of innovation. Most of the firms which are unaware of Egan are small sub-contractors who are, as a rule, highly risk-sensitive and therefore reluctant to learn about the Egan agenda as the way forward. However, this does not mean that all small firms are inherently averse to innovation: one of the small "unaware" sub-contracting firms won contracts on competitive tenders because the innovative designs of its heating system helped the main contractor to save on costs and reduce delivery time. Also, the survey showed that most of the firms implementing the Egan recommendation were large, main contractors. Only one such firm was unaware of Egan but it had been in business for more than one hundred years. Egan aware firms also showed evidence of partnering, which they considered to be beneficial to all on the supply chain.

Most of the firms covered in the survey recognised the need for cultural change in the industry, but perceived it to be an evolutionary process. They were also aware that this evolutionary and complex process could be accelerated by the development of network systems such as links between government, the universities and industry, partnerships between firms on the supply chain, and links between contractors and clients.

5 CONCLUSION

At the beginning of this paper, we discussed how culture affects construction innovation through its influence on the organisation and management of activities in the industry. We have also looked at how interventions in the industry influenced the cultural and institutional environments, which shape perspectives and the propensity and ability of firms to innovate. The Egan agenda has now been widely adopted as the way forward for the UK industry and the university-led networking initiative has aimed to promote innovation through the regional creativity clubs. However, these networking initiatives for the generation and dissemination of innovation would be ineffective if the culture at the level of the firm remained resistant to change.

Therefore, the promotion of innovation at this level should begin by developing strategies to make the organisational systems forward-looking and responsive to change. A progressive approach to organisation would replace the culture of fragmentation with flexible systems that allowed firms to interact with minimum friction and transaction costs. Within the firm, innovation-inhibiting structures which encourage the persistence of bureaucracy and the entrenchment of vested interests need to make way for systems which promote co-operation rather than conflict and for the building of capacity rather than empires. For innovation to thrive, it is important that the organisation of the firm is integrated rather than fragmented, and is flexible enough to adjust to changes in the markets and industry. Strategies for promoting innovation at this level need to provide the conditions for a progressive and proactive stance by the management system. However, this type of management culture takes time to evolve through the process of learning both from the experiences of others and one's own failures and successes in dealing with problems in industry and the market.

A pro-innovative management culture would encourage open communication between management and labour and envision change and support schemes for the training of employees. This would create in them feelings of ownership and commitment to the firm and provide an environment conducive to creativity and risk-taking. Rather than feeling threatened by new ideas, progressive managers would both champion and defend new ideas, so ensuring that the required funding for their development is made available to the firm. If R&D cannot be undertaken in-house, they would subcontract it to universities or research centres either individually or in concert with other firms. Moreover, they would ensure that the firm has its own "gatekeepers" who would keep it abreast with innovation and development activities that take place elsewhere (Basil and Cook, 1974; Akintoye et al., 1999).

If construction firms lacked these managerial attributes they would neither be expected to be innovative and dynamic nor to be aware of or implement the Egan agenda for change. However, construction innovation is more than the mere awareness of Egan and in order for it to thrive, progressive management cultures should be complemented by the development of a wider network system. This would expose firms to the interactive relationships within the innovation process and would enable them to realise their full innovative potential.

REFERENCES

Akintoye, A., Zawdie, G. and Tookey, J. (1999), *Construction Innovations: Learning from Other Industries*, Glasgow: Centre for Built Environment.

Basil, D.C. and Cook, C.W. (1974), *The Management of Change*, London: McGraw Hill.

Bowley, M. (1966), *The British Building Industry*, Cambridge: Cambridge University Press.

Dimitrijevic, B., Langford, D. and Arnett, S. (2001), "Background and Profile of Innovations in the UK Construction," Paper No. 255, presented at the CIB World Building Congress held in Wellington, April 2001.

Douthwaite, B. (2002), *Enabling Innovation: A Practical Guide to Understanding and Fostering Technological Change*, London: Zed Books.

Dulaimi, M.F. (1994), "The Challenge of Innovation in Construction," in *Quality Management in Building and Construction*, Proceedings of the Vision Eureka Conference.

Egan, J. (1998), *Rethinking Construction*, London: Report of the Construction Task Force to the Deputy Prime Minister, DETR.

Etzkowitz, H. (2002), "Networks of Innovation: Science, Technology and Development in the Triple Helix Era," *Technology Management & Sustainable Development*, Vol. 1, No. 1, pp. 7–20.

Etzkowitz, H. and Leydesdorff, L. (Eds) (1997), *The University in the Global Knowledge Economy*, London: Continuum.

Fellows, R.F. (1997), "The Culture of Partnering," in C.H. Davidson (Ed.), *Proceedings of the CIB W-92 International Conference on Procurement*, Montreal, May 1997.

Freeman, C. (1982), *The Economics of Industrial Innovation*, London: Frances Pinter.

Gann, D. (1997), *Building Innovation: Complex Constructs in a Changing World*, London: Thomas Telford.

Hall, A. (2002), "Innovation Systems and Capacity Development: an Agenda for North-South Research Collaboration," *Technology Management & Sustainable Development*, Vol. 1, No., pp. 146–152.

Hall, E. and Hall, F. (1990), *Understanding Cultural Differences*, Sommerville, USA: International Press.

Harvey, R.C. and Ashworth, A.A. (1993), *The Construction Industry of Great Britain*, London: Butterworth-Heinemann Ltd.

Jorde, T. and Teece, D. (1990), "Innovation and Cooperation: Implications for Competition and Anti-Trust," *Journal of Economic Perspectives*, Vol. 4, No. 3, pp. 75–96.

Kozul-Wright, Z. (1995), *The Role of the Firm in the Innovation Process*, Geneva: UNCTAD Discussion Papers, No. 98.

Langston, C. (1999), "The Capital Cost Fallacy," in Best, R. and de Valence (Eds), *Building in Value*, London: Arnold.

Latham, M. (1994), *Constructing the Team*, London: HMSO.

Lorenz, A. and Smith, D. (1998), "Britain Fails to Close Competitiveness Gap," *Sunday Times*, 11 October (cited in Akintoye, A. et al. (1999)).

Lowe, J. G. (1997), "Technological Change and Construction," Glasgow: *BSR Research Paper No. 2*, Glasgow Caledonian University.

Lundvall, B. A. (1992), *National Innovation Systems: Towards a Theory of Innovations and Interactive Learning*, London: Frances Pinter.

Maosszeky, M. (1999), "Technology and Innovation," in Best, R. and de Valence (Eds), *Building in Value*, London: Arnold.

Morroni, M. (1992), *Production Process and Technical Change*, Cambridge: Cambridge University Press.

Ross, T. (1992), *Readers' Survey: Innovation*, London: Insight.

Schmookler, J. (1966), *Invention and Economic Growth*, Camb. Mass.: Harvard University Press.

Schumpeter, J. (1934), *The Theory of Economic Development*, Camb. Mass.: Harvard University Press.

Usher, A.P. (1954), *History of Mechanical Inventions*, Camb. Mass.: Harvard University Press, Revised edition.

West, M. and Fletcher, C. (1994), *Fostering Innovation*, Research Report of the Psychological Society, UK.

Zawdie, G. and Langford, D. (2002), "Influence of Construction-Based Infrastructure on the Development Process in sub-Saharan Africa," *Journal of Building Research and Information*, Vol. 30, No. 3, pp. 160–170.

Zghal, R. (1995), "Science, Technology and Society: What Makes the Culture of Innovation?" *Science, Technology and Development*, Vol. 13, No. 3, pp. 105–113.

Lighting design for highway nighttime construction operations

K. El-Rayes & K. Hyari
Department of Civil and Environmental Engineering, University of Illinois at Urbana-Champaign, Urbana, USA

ABSTRACT: This paper presents an automated model for lighting design of nighttime construction operations. The primary objective of the model is to provide proper lighting arrangements on site that satisfy multiple design criteria including: (1) providing adequate lighting levels; (2) improving uniformity of lighting conditions; and (3) minimizing glare to workers and road users. In order to satisfy these multiple criteria, the model can be used to provide a solution for all relevant design parameters including: number and type of lighting equipment; type of lamps; lamp lumen output; lighting tower positioning; luminaires light distribution; mounting height; aiming angle; and rotation angle. The design model consists of three major modules: (1) illuminance and uniformity module; (2) glare module; and (3) optimizer module. The illuminance and uniformity module performs design calculations to ensure the provision of adequate lighting levels and uniformity on site. The glare module calculates veiling luminance ratio in order to control glare on and near the construction site. The optimizer module is employed to optimize the design process and generate feasible designs that satisfy the required lighting design criteria. As such, the lighting design model should prove useful to contractors and transportation officials alike, and is expected to improve the safety and quality of nighttime highway construction operations.

1 INTRODUCTION

The application of nighttime construction in highway maintenance and rehabilitation projects has been increasing in recent years in order to reduce construction-related traffic disruptions (O'Malley 2002; Park et al. 2002; Hancher & Taylor 2001; Cottrell 1999). This increase in the volume of nighttime construction can be attributed to two main reasons: (1) roads are getting more congested and many roads are currently operating near capacity during daytime hours; and (2) the growing need for significant maintenance and rehabilitation projects due to the deterioration of the road network (Bryden & Mace 2002).

Highway nighttime construction is a practice that offers many advantages and suffers from a number of disadvantages. Highway officials should take the decision of performing nighttime work after a careful assessment to ensure that the advantages out weigh the disadvantages. The reported advantages for performing highway construction and repair operations during nighttime include: (1) reducing impact on the traveling public through reducing construction-related traffic disruptions; (2) decreasing project duration by enabling multiple shifts of work in construction projects (Hancher & Taylor 2001); (3) minimizing adverse economic impacts of traffic congestion and delay on

local commerce, particularly for shipping and delivery services; (4) decreasing air pollution from idle vehicles stopped near construction work zones (McCall 1999); (5) providing more freedom to construction personnel in planning lane closures with a greater possibility for enlarging work zones; (6) enhancing work conditions in hot climate zones due to lower night temperatures (Shepard & Cottrell 1985); (7) facilitating delivery of material to and from the work zone due to better traffic conditions at night (Price 1986); and (8) reducing equipment rental costs and allowing better utilization of available equipment (Hancher & Taylor 2001).

Despite the above advantages, nighttime construction suffers from a number of limitations including: (1) decreased visibility for both workers and motorist, causing decreased levels of safety and quality (Shepard & Cottrell 1985; Hancher & Taylor 2001); (2) problems in implementing quality control procedures, and decreased quality of workmanship; (3) increased number of drivers with insufficient sleep, vision problems and intoxication during nighttime leading to higher number of accidents at work zones; (4) adverse public reactions due to construction noise during nighttime; (5) difficulty in recruiting personnel in spite of the wage premiums that compensate for the inconvenience of nighttime work; (6) difficulties in material delivery, utility services and urgent equipment repairs during nighttime hours (Shepard & Cottrell 1985); and (7) increase in cost for nighttime operations due to labor premiums and overtime, additional traffic control devices, additional artificial lighting arrangements, and higher engineering inspection costs (Hinze & Carlisle 1990).

To maximize the advantages and overcome many of the above limitations, proper and adequate lighting arrangements need to be provided on nighttime construction sites. Lighting is a crucial factor in any nighttime work and was reported to be one of the most important factors affecting quality, safety, cost and productivity of nighttime construction projects (Kumar 1994; Bryden & Mace 2002). Providing proper lighting arrangements with adequate lighting levels for nighttime construction is essential for construction activities to be performed safely and with satisfactory quality. While several guidelines have been developed for special applications such as roadways and parking areas, little or no reported research has focused on establishing lighting design procedures for highway nighttime construction operations.

This paper presents an automated model for lighting design of nighttime construction specifically developed to satisfy the lighting requirements of nighttime construction operations. The development of the design tool is achieved in three main stages: (1) establishing design criteria; (2) identifying design parameters; and (3) implementing a robust design procedure.

2 DESIGN CRITERIA

Lighting design criteria for highway nighttime construction need to be established and fulfilled on site in order to ensure that proper and adequate lighting conditions are provided for nighttime work. Lighting design criteria include: (1) illuminance; (2) uniformity; and (3) glare (IESNA 1999; CIE 1986).

2.1 Illuminance

Illuminance represents the quantity of lighting and can be defined as the density of luminous flux incident on a certain surface. (Kaufman 1981). Illuminance is used as a design criterion for many exterior lighting applications (CIE 1986; IESNA 1999), and it can be measured in foot-candles (fc) or lux.

A recent study was conducted to identify the required illuminance levels for different highway construction tasks. In order to satisfy these levels, the study incorporated the findings of (1) a recent literature review; (2) an analysis of available standards for nighttime lighting; and (3) the results of a recent survey of highway contractors and transportation officials in USA (El-Rayes et al. 2002a). The required

illuminance levels for highway construction tasks were classified in three main categories of low, medium, and high which represents 5, 10, and 20 fc respectively (El-Rayes et al. 2002b).

2.2 Uniformity

Lighting uniformity criterion identifies how evenly light reaches different parts of a target area. It can be measured and quantified using one of two ratios: (1) an average-to-minimum ratio which represents the ratio of the average illuminance at all points to the minimum illuminance in the studied area; and (2) a maximum-to-minimum ratio which represents the ratio of the maximum illuminance at any point to the minimum illuminance in the studied area (IESNA 2000). The average to minimum ratio is selected and considered more practical for highway construction work areas because lighting tower luminaires are usually directed towards pavement surface to avoid causing glare to road users, which creates a high illuminated area under these light towers. These highly illuminated areas can lead to higher maximum to minimum ratios that do not practically represent the uniformity of lighting in nighttime construction zones. After comparing recommended values for exterior lighting applications, and considering the practical limitations usually experienced in positioning lighting equipment on site, this research recommends an average to minimum lighting uniformity ratio of 6:1.

2.3 Glare

Glare is a term used to describe the sensation of annoyance, discomfort or loss of visual performance and visibility produced by experiencing luminance in the visual field significantly greater than that to which eyes of the observer are adapted (Pritchard 1999). Disability glare is the most severe type of glare, and can be defined as the veiling effect produced by bright sources or areas in the visual field that result in decreased visual performance and visibility (Kaufman 1981). Disability glare is measured in terms of veiling luminance in units of candela per square meter. Veiling luminance can be used in order to control glare during nighttime hours. For example, in roadway lighting design, the Illuminating Engineering Society of North America (IESNA) has set the limits for glare in terms of the ratio of veiling luminance produced by all light sources to pavement luminance because the severity of glare depends on the adaptation of the eye to the prevailing background luminance of the pavement. Using veiling luminance ratio as glare control measure is based on the assumption that pavement luminance controls the level of driver adaptation (Bryden & Mace 2002). This ratio ranges from 0.3 to 0.4 depending on the category of road (IESNA 2000).

This veiling luminance ratio of 0.4 can be applied to control glare in highway work zones due to the similarities in design criteria, parameters, and designer concerns in both cases. It can also be slightly relaxed in order to account for the temporary nature of work zone lighting.

3 DESIGN PARAMETERS

Lighting design in highway nighttime construction requires the designer or field personnel to select eight major design variables that affect lighting. These design variables include:

Number and type of lighting equipment
The designer needs to decide on the number and type of lighting equipment to be used on site. Available alternatives of nighttime lighting equipment include: (a) ground mounted lighting towers; (b) trailer mounted towers; and/or (c) equipment mounted luminaires.

Type of lamps
The type of lamps needs to be selected from available alternatives of: (a) metal halide lamps; (b) high pressure sodium vapor lamps; and/or (c) halogen lamps.

Lamp lumen output
It represents the light and energy emitted from the lamp and influence visual comfort and illuminance (IESNA 1998).

Luminaires light distribution
This variable represents the candlepower distribution of the light in different directions, and determines the shape and area of the lighting contour diagram of the luminaire. A very wide selection of luminaires, each with somewhat different distribution characteristics is available. This variable has a significant impact on the glare produced by the lighting system.

Luminaires mounting height
It represents the vertical distance between the center of the luminaires and the pavement surface. Portable lighting towers are typically manufactured with adjustable mounting heights that can reach up to 9.14 m (30 ft).

Lighting tower positioning
This variable represents the horizontal location of lighting towers in the work zone in terms of their coordinates. Lighting positioning affects average illuminance and uniformity of lighting in the work zone.

Luminaires aiming angle
This represents the angle between the center of the luminaires beam spread and the nadir. This variable determines the directional distribution of lighting and

affects the coverage area as well as the glare produced by the luminaires.

Lighting tower rotation angle
This variable represents the rotation of the lighting tower luminaires around a vertical axis. A proper rotation angle enables the designer to direct the lighting intensity towards the intended area and to minimize light spillage to unnecessary directions, reducing light trespass that is a common source of complaints in nighttime construction in urban areas.

4 DESIGN PROCEDURE

Design procedures are needed to verify if a combination of design parameters produces adequate lighting conditions that satisfy the required design criteria. Currently, most contractors rely on experience and trial and error methods to figure the number of light towers they need and how it should be arranged on site (Brown 2002). A design tool has been developed in this research study to satisfy the earlier described lighting design criteria of: horizontal illuminance, uniformity, and glare. The design tool consists of three major modules: (1) illuminance and uniformity module; (2) glare module; and (3) optimizer module. The illuminance and uniformity module performs the necessary calculations to calculate illuminance and uniformity. The glare module calculates the veiling luminance ratio. The optimizer module seeks to achieve the best possible design for lighting arrangements.

4.1 Illuminance and uniformity module

The illuminance and uniformity ratio for nighttime construction are calculated in this module using the design procedure shown in Figure 1. The design procedure for both criteria starts with accepting the necessary input data including: (a) work zone layout information; (b) coordinates of the lighting equipment luminaires; (c) lighting configuration (luminaires mounting height, aiming angle, and rotation angle); and (d) photometric data files for the used luminaires. The photometric data files that determine the light distribution of each luminaire should be available in the standard format recommended by the Illuminating Engineering Society of North America (IESNA 1995).

This module utilizes the point-by-point method to calculate the average horizontal illuminance in the work area. This method consists of the following three main steps: (1) dividing the surface of the area that need to be illuminated into identical grid cells less than 5 meters wide; (2) calculating the horizontal illuminance at each grid point from all contributing luminaires; and (3) using the calculated lighting levels at all grid points to compute the average horizontal

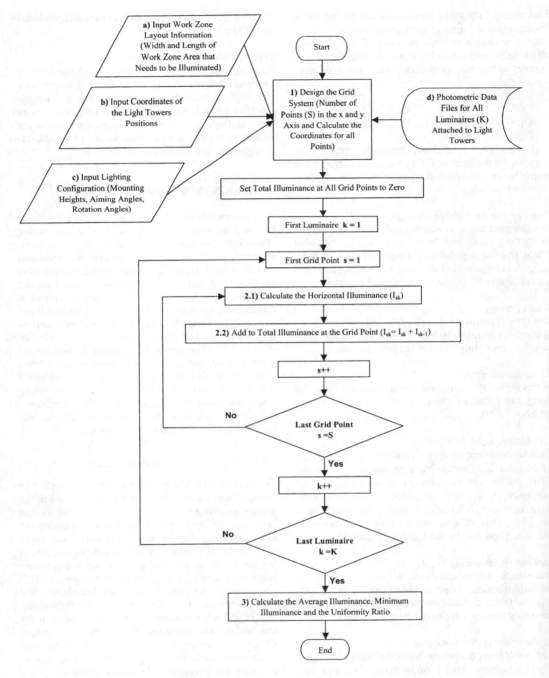

Figure 1. Illuminance and Uniformity Ratio Calculations.

illuminance for the whole work area and the uniformity ratio (i.e. the ratio of average horizontal illuminance relative to the minimum illuminance computed at any grid point. Illuminance level at each grid corner

is calculated using the inverse square rule. This rule states that illuminance at a certain point is directly proportional to the lighting intensity produced by the light source in the direction of that point and inversely proportional to the square of the distance between the light source and that point (Pritchard 1999).

The average illuminance in the work area is calculated by averaging the calculated illuminance levels at all grid points. The uniformity ratio is calculated by dividing the average illuminance over the minimum illuminance in the entire work area. It should be noted that the accuracy in lighting calculations improves with the increase in the number of grid points for the same area. However, this increase leads to higher computational requirements.

4.2 *Glare module*

This module calculates the veiling luminance ratio in order to control glare in the work zone. The module utilizes the same input data provided in the first module in addition to the type of work zone pavement surface in terms of its reflectance characteristics. Road pavements are classified into four categories according to their reflectance properties (IESNA 2000). Each pavement type has a data file that provides the reflectance coefficient as a function of luminaire location, observer location and observer line of sight. This module performs the following three main steps to calculate the veiling luminance ratio: (1) identify observer locations to represent possible drivers positions and lines of sight as they drive by the work zone; (2) compute the veiling luminance in the plane of the observers eye at each observing position considering all contributing luminaries; and (3) calculate average pavement luminance in the work zone using the same grid discussed in the first module. The veiling luminance ratio (glare) is then calculated by dividing the maximum veiling luminance calculated at any observer position over the average pavement luminance in the work zone.

4.3 *Optimizer module*

This module is used to eliminate the need for iterative solution procedures to satisfy lighting design criteria. It provides near optimum lighting design, and enables the optimization of multiple objectives including: (1) maximizing average illuminance to achieve the best value from the lighting equipment; (2) maximizing lighting uniformity by minimizing the ratio of the average horizontal illuminance over the minimum illuminance in the work zone; (3) minimizing glare in order to limit the visual impairments experienced by the traveling public and workers; and (4) minimizing the cost of the lighting system. The cost of the lighting system includes ownership cost (i.e. buy, rent, or lease), and operational cost (e.g. power consumption and maintenance of the lighting equipment).

The optimizer module utilizes a multiobjective genetic algorithm named the fast elitist nondominated sorted genetic algorithm (NSGA-II) (Deb et al. 2000). NSGA-II is a Pareto-based approach that handles multiobjective optimization problems through the nondomination concept. This algorithm was selected to optimize lighting design because of its competence in (1) providing the entire Pareto optimal front of non-dominated solutions in a single run; (2) handling design constraints effectively; and (3) handling any number of objectives (El-Rayes & Hyari 2002; El-Rayes & Hyari 2003). This module requires input data on the work zone layout, type of work to be performed, and characteristics of available lighting equipment. Lighting design criteria requirements are formulated and input as constraints. This module provides near optimum design solutions for design parameters (i.e. number and position of lighting equipment, luminaires aiming angle, rotation angle, and mounting height). This near optimum solution is obtained by randomly generating an initial population that evolves over a number of specified generations in order to obtain a set of feasible solutions. This set of solutions provides varying trade-offs among the optimized design objectives. Lighting design personnel can select one solution for implementation from these sets to satisfy the particular design problem at hand.

5 SUMMARY AND CONCLUSIONS

A practical lighting design tool has been developed for highway nighttime construction projects. The design tool incorporates three modules: illuminance and uniformity module to calculate average illuminance and lighting uniformity in the work zone; glare module to compute the veiling luminance ratio in order to control glare, and an optimizer module that seeks the best possible design for lighting arrangements. This design tool is capable of providing feasible solutions by satisfying the design criteria, and moreover advancing quality in lighting design through optimizing the design process. The developed tool is also capable of simultaneous optimization of multiple lighting design criteria including: maximizing lighting level and lighting uniformity in the work zone; minimizing glare to road users; and minimizing cost of the lighting system. The developed design tool can be utilized by contractors and transportation officials to ensure the delivery of proper lighting arrangements in nighttime work zones.

ACKNOWLEDGMENTS

The authors would like to acknowledge the financial support provided by the Illinois Transportation Research Center under grant number ITRC-02 VD-H1. The research team also wishes to thank the ITRC

97

technical review panel, all the survey respondents, and the Illinois Road Builders Association for their valuable information and constructive feedback.

REFERENCES

Brown, D. 2002. Temporary Project Lighting: Where Experience Matters Most, *Grading and Excavation Contractor.* Forester Communication, Inc. 4(1). January/February 2002. Santa Barbara, California, USA.

Bryden, J., & Mace, D. 2002. Guidelines for Design and Operation of Nighttime Traffic Control for Highway Maintenance and Construction. *NCHRP Report 476*, National Cooperative Highway Research Program, Transportation Research Board, National Research Council. Washington D.C. USA.

CIE Technical Committee TC-4.5. 1986. Guide to the Lighting of Exterior Working Areas. *International Commission on Illumination. Publication C.I.E.; No. 68.*, International Commission on Illumination, Vienna, Austria.

Cottrell, B.H. 1999. Improving Night Work Zone Traffic Control, *Final Report*. Virginia Transportation Research Council, Virginia Department of Transportation and the University of Virginia. Charlottesville, Virginia, USA.

Deb, K., Pratap, A., Agrawal, S., & Meyarivan, T. 2000. A Fast Elitist Non-dominated sorting genetic algorithm for multi-objective optimization: NSGA-II. *Proceedings of the Parallel Problem Solving from Nature VI Conference, 16–20 September 2000.* Paris: France. (pp. 849–858).

El-Rayes, K., & Hyari, K. 2002. Automated DSS for Lighting Design of Nighttime Operations in Highway Construction Projects. *Proceedings of the 19th International Symposium on Automation and Robotics in Construction, ISARC, September 2002*, National Institute of Standards and Technology. Washington: USA.

El-Rayes, K. et al. 2002a. A Survey of Current Practices in Lighting Highway Nighttime Construction. *Interim Report Two*, University of Illinois at Urbana-Champaign, USA.

El-Rayes, K. et al. 2002b. Development of Design Criteria for Lighting Highway Nighttime Construction. *Interim Report Three*, University of Illinois at Urbana-Champaign, USA.

El-Rayes, K., & Hyari, K. 2003. Lighting Design Requirements for Highway Nighttime Construction. *Proceedings of the ASCE Construction Research Congress 2003. March 19–21*. Honolulu, Hawaii: USA.

Hancher, D., & Taylor, T. 2001. Night-Time Construction Issues. *Paper presented at the Transportation Research Board 80th Annual Meeting, January 7–11, 2001.* Transportation Research Board. Washington DC: USA.

Hinze, J., & Carlisle, D. 1990. Variables Impacted by Nighttime Construction Projects, *Final Report TNW 90-07*, Transportation Northwest, University of Washington, Seattle: USA.

IESNA 1995. IESNA Standard File Format for Electronic Transfer of Photometric Data. *Report LM-63-95*. Illumination Engineering Society of North America. New York: USA.

IESNA 1999. Lighting for Exterior Environment an IESNA Recommended Practice. *RP-33-99*. Illuminating Engineering Society of North America. New York: USA.

IESNA 2000. IESNA Practice for Roadway Lighting. *ANSI/IESNA RP-8-00*. American National Standard/Illuminating Engineering Society of North America. New York: USA.

Kaufman, J.E. (Ed.) 1981. *IES Lighting Handbook, Reference Volume*, Illuminating Engineering Society of North America, New York: USA.

Kumar Kumar, A. 1994. Development of A Model for Determining Work Zone Illumination Requirements During Nighttime Highway Construction. *PhD thesis*, University of Florida. Florida: USA.

McCall, H.C. 1999. Report on the Department of Transportation's Administration of the Nighttime Construction Program, *Report 98-S-50*, State of New York Office of the State Comptroller. New York: USA.

O'Malley, P. 2002. Construction Work at Night: The View from Under The Lights. *Grading and Excavation Contractor*. Forester Communication, Inc. 4(5) July/August 2002. Santa Barbara, California: USA.

Park, S., Douglas, K., Griffith, P., & Haas, K. 2002. Factors of Importance for Determining Daytime Versus Nighttime Operations in Oregon. *Paper presented at the Transportation Research Board 81st annual meeting, January 13–17, 2002.* Transportation Research Board. Washington DC: USA.

Price, D.A. 1986. Nighttime Paving, *Implementation Report CDOH/DTP/R-86/6*. Colorado Dept. of Highways, Federal Highway Administration, April. Denver, Colorado: USA.

Pritchard, D.C. 1999. *Lighting*, 6th Ed., Addison Longman Limited, Edinburgh Gate, Harlow, Essex. UK.

Shepard, F.D. & Cottrel, B. 1985. Benefits And Safety Impact of Night Work-Zone Activities, *Report No. FHWA/RD-85/067*, US Department of Transportation, Federal Highway Administration. USA.

System-based Vision for Strategic and Creative Design, Bontempi (ed.)
© *2003 Swets & Zeitlinger, Lisse, ISBN 90 5809 599 1*

Process analysis of interior finishing and building services works

N. Mine
Department of Environmental Space Design, Faculty of Environmental Engineering, University of Kitakyushu, Kitakyushu, Japan

T. Kunugi
Institute of Technology, Shimizu Corporation, Tokyo, Japan

N. Miura
Department of Architecture, Faculty of Engineering, Kokushikan University, Tokyo, Japan

ABSTRACT: In the construction industry various kinds of trades work in the same place at the same time. This causes many problems on the construction site, reducing efficiency and increasing the construction duration. Finish and building services work are especially problematic. We conducted a field study to acquire finishing and building services work data in order to analyze a site's construction processes. Process analysis can indicate bottlenecks in field work. In this paper we explain current problems, the application of process analysis, and the results of our study.

1 INTRODUCTION

In the construction industry various kinds of trades work concurrently. This makes work more complex and less efficient, thereby increasing the construction duration. Interior finishing works ("IFW") and building services works ("BSW") in apartment building construction have especially complex work processes with many trades working concurrently in a confined space. We have identified few studies of IFW and BSW in the construction of multi-storied apartment buildings.

We carried out this study to obtain information to improve and develop a new construction scheduling method for IFW and BSW, to simplify complex work. This paper describes the results of our field study on a construction site. We first describe current problems in IFW and BSW in apartment building projects in Japan. Then we review former studies. The process analysis method is suitable to analyze complex problems, therefore we evaluate the adaptability of this method to construction works. Finally, we explain the results of the study.

2 CURRENT STATUS AND PROBLEMS

There are problems regarding labor allocation in IFW and BSW. Especially, in electrical work the electrician must various licenses to do wiring and other works.

In IFW different kinds of materials are used. As a result, many problems frequently occur such as delayed materials delivery slowing down work progress. In many cases these time wasting exist potentially. Such delays can cause unbalanced work progress between the trades. Progress control among trades: workers allocation, delay or misarranged material delivery creates inefficiencies in site work.

There are a many problems to be solved, the principal problems being:

(1) Various trades work concurrently causing more complex work processes and reducing efficiency.
(2) Small staging and storage areas make material delivery the source of frequent problems.
(3) Most IFW and BSW are carried out simultaneously at the end of the construction period creating a very busy and chaotic time.
(4) Sometimes trade arrangement becomes very difficult because of the work license problems.

3 PREVIOUS STUDIES ON WORK IN IFW AND BSW

Study of IFW and BSW began in 1960s. Wooden interior panel erection time data were acquired by a field observation of a public housing project. Then in the 1980s conventional IFW work was studied. A series of the papers provided analysis of complex interior works. However, the authors could not clarify the relationships among work processes.

As mentioned above, former studies of IFW in apartment building construction do not address the relations among complex work processes.

4 OBJECTIVES AND SCOPE OF THE STUDY

Under the currently depressed Japanese economy, the housing market faces especially stiff competition with cost reduction a top priority. We do not have enough information about IFW and BSW to improve productivity compared to structural works. The lack of work process data is crucial.

The study aims at balancing the IFW and BSW processes in apartment building projects. To this end we conducted a field observational study to clarify work processes and obtained the following data.

(1) work processes that are included in IFW and BSW phases
(2) work progress patterns
(3) man-hours for each work proess

In this paper, we report on item (1) and a part of item (3).

5 PROCESS ANALYSIS APPLIED TO BUILDING CONSTRUCTION

5.1 Application of process analysis method

To obtain the basic data for method improvement, activities must be distinguished into sub-activities such as transportation, inspection, and principal work such as operations. These must be expressed in a graphically different manner.

In the manufacturing industry process analysis is widely applied for work and method improvement. There are four work process categories. Each category has its own symbol so that it is easy to visually recognize work types. The relationships between processes are indicated with flow lines. By using the process analysis method for construction it is possible to visually describe multi-trade work processes.

5.2 Process analysis procedure

5.2.1 Process chart graphical symbols
The graphical process chart symbols are defined by the Japanese Industrial Standard (JIS). Process analysis is done with these symbols. In the analysis jobs are categorized into the four shown below.

(1) operation
(2) transportation

Table 1. Graphical symbols for process chart.

Processes		Symbol	Description
Operation		○	Process that provides figure change or transform to material, part, product
Transportation		○	Process that provides location change to material, part, product
Delay	Stock	▽	Status of stock material, part, product according to the plan
	Delay	D	Unexpected delay of material, part, product
Inspection	Quantity	□	Inspection of quantity of material, part, product and compare to plan
	Quality	◇	Inspection of quality of material, part, product and compare to standard

(3) delay (stock or idle)
(4) inspection (quantity or quality)

These four categories are represented by the symbols shown in Table 1.

5.2.2 Application of process chart symbols for a construction project

1) Process that contains inspection characteristics
Construction workers typically review their work results by themselves before the next process. Important processes also are subject to formal inspections. For example inspectors focus mainly on reinforcement work before concreting. Components such as door and partition frames are assembled along with marking on the concrete surface. Thus, these processes always contain inspection characteristics.

To analyze construction jobs that contain inspection characteristics, combined symbols are used according to the work characteristics. Following are examples of the combined symbols.

(1) marking (job that contains measurement and inspection)
(2) checking materials (inspection job quality and quantity are concurrently included)
(3) installing of door frame (door frame is installed at the proper elevation and location, plumb, level and in alignment.)

2) Symbolic representation of the trades
In construction, we can analyze IFW and BSW if we can properly express each trade's process. We tried to represent these by using graphical symbols. The most simple way is to put colors or patterns in each symbol for each trade. Table 2 shows symbol patterns for several trades. Hereafter, we will distinguish trades with a pattern inside the symbol for analysis.

3) Expression of relationships among processes
In normal process analysis, a connecting line between processes indicates the sequence. Thus, it is

Table 2. Examples of symbols for each trade.

Symbol	Description	Symbol	Description
●	Operation (Carpentry)	⊕	Operation (FC* fixer)
⊘	Operation (Board installer)	⊖	Operation (Wallpaper hanger)

*FC: Furring channel

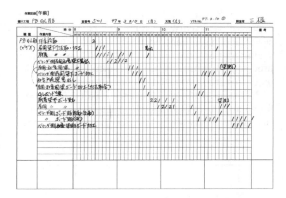

Figure 1. The sample of man-hour measurement sheet.

difficult to adquately express complicated relationships. For IFW and BSW we define the meaning of each connection line to express complicated relationships among processes. In this paper we define connection lines as follows.

(1) solid line: connection between same trade
(2) dashed line: connection between different trades
(3) arrow: sequence of processes

6 AN OBSERVATIONAL FIELD STUDY

6.1 Observation items and methods

6.1.1 Observation items
We conducted an observational field study on IFW and BSW in a medium sized apartment building project. We surveyed the following items.

(1) master schedule of the entire project
(2) the element work unit (an element such as work element is the basis of work done by single trade): EWP
(3) the unit work process (the group of EWPs to complete a unit work process): UWP
(4) man-hour for each EWP.

6.1.2 Analysis of the master schedule of the project
The site manager provided the master schedule of the project. Based on this we analyzed the entire workflow of the IFW and BSW in an apartment building project.

6.1.3 Analysis of the UWP
We first analyzed UWP by observing the furring channel frame installation, gypsum board fixing, finish carpentry, and wallpaper hanging work. We also analyzed bath unit (hereafter we call "UB" in this paper) assembly, electric wiring, water supply piping, and sewer piping as BSW.

6.1.4 Analysis of the EWP
The EWPs are analyzed with the flow process chart-man type. By watching workers we recorded worker's operations and man-hour on the recording sheet from start to finish. We also used a time-lapse video recorder to visually record a whole day's work. The symbols that we used are the same as the UWP analysis.

Table 3. The outline of the project.

Items	Description
Building use	Apartment house with retail shops
Location	Urban area in Tokyo
Structure	Steel reinforced concrete structure
N. of apartments	56 apartments
Stories	14 floors above ground, 1 basement
Site area	690 m^2
Building area	432 m^2
Total floor area	4,467 m^2
Apartment area	68 m^2–72 m^2 per apartment
Constr. period	15 months
Constr. method	Furring channel frame, gypsum board, and wallpaper partition wall

6.1.5 Measuring man-hours
We used the snap reading method (work sampling) to measure man-hours for each EWP. The snap interval was 5 minutes for one sample. In each snap the observer distinguished each worker's EWP and recorded it on the sheet. One observer measured one to three workers' time. One set of UWP was analyzed from start to finish, which includes various kinds of EWP. Figure 1 shows a sample of a man-hour measurement recording sheet.

6.2 Subject of the study

We studied a typical Japanese apartment building project with IFW and BSW method. Table 3 shows the outline of the project and Figure 2 shows the typical plan of an apartment.

6.3 The results of the study

6.3.1 UWP in a typical apartment

1) The work processes
The study was carried out on primary unit work process in a typical apartment. Figure 3 shows the

entire UWP in an apartment. For BSW, we separately expressed electricity, air conditioning, water supply, sewer, and gas. We included UB assembling as BSW. Transportation takes place before all the operation processes. To simplify, we expressed only the major processes and eliminated minor transportation.

As shown in the process chart, the unit work process for an apartment begins with structural work such as "stripping formwork", "transportation of stripped

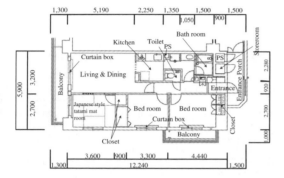

Figure 2.   A typical plan of an apartment (floor area: 72 m²).

form" and ends with "inspections" for completion of an apartment. As the unit work process level in an apartment represents the whole of the process sequences, most of the processes represent inspection operations such as adjusting and alignment.

In the subject apartment, the entire sequence of construction is as follows: installation of window and door frames, UB assembly, furring channel (FC) assembly, and finishing carpentry works (wooden door frames, hanging wallpaper, painting, laying flooring, closet fabrication), fixing baseboard, installing and adjusting doors. These are mainly architectural works. Among these, the BSWs such as electric, air conditioning, water supply, sewer, and gas piping are carried out.

2) The number of work processes
As shown in Figure 3 there are 87 processes at the unit works level. As mentioned above, when we eliminated these two structural works, 85 processes are IFWs and BSWs. We categorized these according to work processes and show them in Table 4. There are 74 operations, 3 transportations, 3 delays, and 5 inspections. 87.1% of total processes are operations. Architectural works versus BSW is 54 to 31. 63.5% of the total is architectural works. 59.3% of the BSWs are simple operations without inspection.

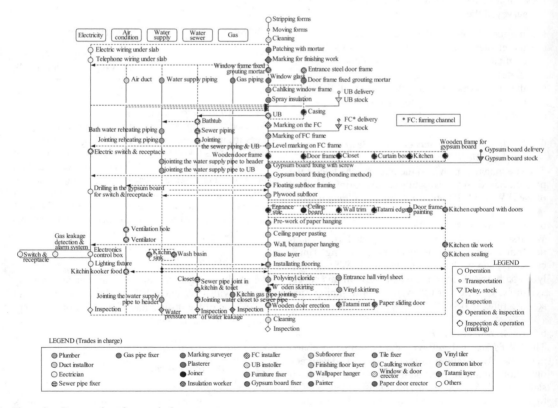

Figure 3.   Process chart for a typical apartment.

Table 4. Numbers of UWP in each category.

Process			Archi. work	UWP		TOTAL	
Operation	◎	Operation	22	16		36	
	◇	Marking	3	47	0	27	3	74
	⬡	Operation & Inspec.	22		11	33	
Transpor-tation	○	Transpor-tation	3	0		3	
Delay	▽	Material stock	3	0		3	
Inspec.	◇	Quality inspection	1	4		5	
TOTAL			54	4		85	

Table 5. The numbers of connection lines.

	Solid line	Dash line	Total
Connection line	40	87	127
Percentage (%)	31.5	68.5	100.0

However, in architectural works there are many operations that include inspections or inspection-like operations. In architectural works, the percentage of simple operations is 46.8%.

The reason is that architectural works are by achieved by checking dimensions, position, and alignment. On the other hand, most of the BSW are simple connection processs. This is because BSW mainly consist of industrialized production parts that are assembled without dimensional or positional adjustment.

3) Complexity of work process connections

In Figure 3 the architectural main processes are shown on the right side, patterns in the graphic symbols of each process are manifold. In the BSWs on the left hand side, there are many connection lines from the processes on the right side. Most of the connection lines are represented by dashed lines, which indicates the work progress with relations between different trades. When we asked the site engineer how many special contractors were working on the project, the answer was that there were 13 architectural-related trades, and 2 trades for building services works: electricity, water supply, and sewer. However, there were actually yet more trades. In this project there were approximately 20 architectural trades and more than 5 BSW trades.

Compounding this great number of trades, the same trade comes to the site several times. For example, the joiner first comes to the site to install window frames and casings, then works elsewhere. After that the joiner installs door frames, joinery work of closet, fixing kitchen counter, and waits again. Then, fixing gypsum board, install kitchen set such as sink and cooktop. The joiner then attaches wall trim, and fixes the tatami frame. Finally, after hanging wallpaper they install baseboard. Some of the trades mentioned above must come to the site several times.

To quantitatively express the complexity of work processes, we counted the number of connection lines, which is shown in Table 5. Therre are 40 solid lines representing the connection between the same

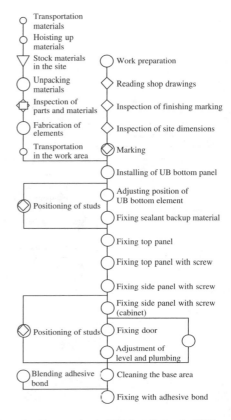

Figure 4. Process chart of UB installation In BSW.

trades; there are 87 dashed line representing the connection between different trades. These are, respectively, 31.5% and 68.5% of the total number of lines. More than two-thirds are connections between different work processes.

6.3.2 EWP that comprise a UWP

We conducted further observation at the level of the EWP to analyze the UWP in more detail. Here we show two examples: UB installation as a BSW and installing furring channel strip frames as an architectural work.

1) UB installation

Figure 4 shows EWPs in the UB installation. Three workers did the job. The trade in charge of the job is

Table 6. Number of processes in each category (UB installation).

	Oper.	Trans.	Delay	Inspc.	Total
No. of procc.	20	3	1	4	28
Percent (%)	71.4	10.7	3.6	14.3	100.0

Table 7. Numbers of processes in each category (installing furring channel frame).

	Oper.	Trans.	Delay	Inspc.	Total
No. of procc.	15	5	1	3	24
Percent. (%)	62.5	20.8	4.2	12.5	100.0

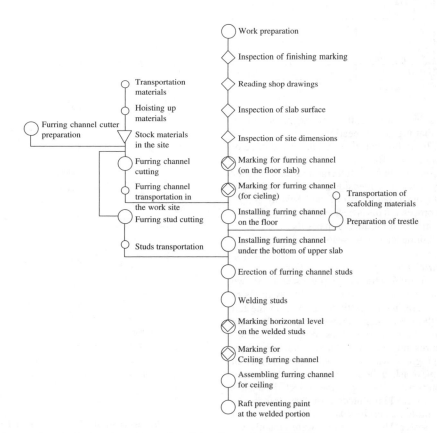

Figure 5. Process chart for furring channel frame installation for partition's EWP.

specially-trained UB installer. As shown in Figure 3, this work process was done after installing window frames; some BSW such as water, sewer, and gas piping on the slab have been completed.

Most parts are prefabricated in a factory and a set of parts for one apartment is arranged, packed, and supplied to the site. The jobs in the site are mainly parts assembly. In the side panel a mixing faucet passes through so there is some processing portion. Table 6 shows the numbers of EWPs in each category. The total processes are 28:20 operations (including marking), 3 transportations, 1 delay (material stock), and 4 inspections.

2) Furring channel frame for partition installation
Figure 5 shows EWPs in furring channel partition installation. This work becomes the reference point or the base line that successor are carried out based on the assembled furring channel frame. The workers fixed furring channel studs from slab top to slab bottom (floor height). Standard length materials are cut to adjust the floor height. The level lines are marked. The most important process is marking lines on the slab and on the bottom of the upper slab. Table 7 shows the numbers of EWP in each category. The total processes are 24 that include 15 inspection-related

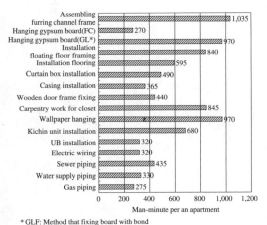

* GLF: Method that fixing board with bond

Figure 6. Man-hour of each UWP.

operations, 5 transportations, 1 delay (material stock), and 3 inspections.

6.3.3 Man-hour for each UWP
The man-hours for each process in an apartment are shown in Figure 6. In the total man-hours for one apartment, the largest is installing furring channel frame at 1,035 man-minutes. Next largest are two processes. Fixing gypsum board and hanging wallpaper are 970 man-minutes per apartment. Joiner's work for the closet is 845 man-minutes per apartment. Adjusting and fixing sub-floor is 840 man-minutes per apartment.

In the BSWs such as assembling the kitchen unit, installing UB, and gas piping, assembling the kitchen unit is most time-consuming at 680 man-minutes per apartment. The quickest is gas piping at 275 man-minutes per apartment.

7 CONCLUSIONS

We carried out an observational field study to obtain basic data for improving site productivity and develop the IFW and BSW construction method. Based on the analysis we clarify the work process in a typical multi-storied apartment building. We also pointed out some problems to be solved. Through the study, we confirmed that process analysis can be applied to construction.

And we proposed the modified process analysis method to analyze complex work. Based on the results of this study, we plan to develop a new IFW and BSW construction method.

REFERENCES

Nakamura H. 1964. An observation of construction site productivity of prefabricated interior finishing works for public housings, *J. Archit. Plann. Environ. Eng., AIJ, No. 103,* 49. Tokyo

Ohtake E. & Yamaguchi Y., et al. 1966. A study on medium height prefabricated apartment housing (Part 7 Interior building services works), *Proc. of AIJ Kanto annual conference, AIJ, No. 37,* 237–244. Tokyo

Nakamura Y. & Ando M., et al. 1985. A study on interior building elements of apartment house (Part.6 A consideration of standard of interior finishing and building services works), *Proc. of AIJ Annual Conference, AIJ,* 455–456. Tokuo

JIS. Symbols of Process Chart (JIS-Z 8206) 1982. Standard Association of Japan

System-based Vision for Strategic and Creative Design, Bontempi (ed.)
© 2003 Swets & Zeitlinger, Lisse, ISBN 90 5809 599 1

Construction of super high-rise composite structures in Hong Kong

Raymond W.M. Wong

Division of Building Science and Technology, City University of Hong Kong

ABSTRACT: Quite a number of Super High-rise buildings have been built in the recent years in Hong Kong. Majority of these buildings are in the form of composite structure, that is, they are built using reinforced concrete as the core and structural steel as the outer embracing frame.

This paper discusses how these structures are being constructed. Recent project cases including the 88-storey International Finance Center Tower II, the 62-storey Cheung Kong Center, the 50-storey Manulife Tower and a number of other similar projects of significance will be focused.

Typical construction processes starting from the foundation, basement construction and up to the completion of the superstructure will be reviewed. Features such as the structural arrangement, various kinds of composite elements, construction of the core wall and other major reinforced concrete components, erection of the steel frame and other stiffening systems, connection methods of the major elements, other related construction arrangement, as well as the commonalities and future trends for this kind of construction, will also be highlighted.

1 A GENERAL REVIEW OF THE STRUCTURAL FORM OF COMPOSITE BUILDINGS IN HONG KONG

There are not more than 10 super high-rise composite buildings being built for the past decades in Hong Kong, of which, 3 are of single-tower type (Manulife Tower, Cheung Kong Center and International Finance Center Tower 2), 2 are of multi-tower type (Shun Tak Center, office and hotel blocks for the Hong Kong Convention and Exhibition Center), 1 is of linear block type (Time Square). There are also a few composite structures which consisted portion of the building at lower floors constructed in reinforced concrete, while the upper structure being constructed in RC and structural steel composite (Citic Tower and International Finance Center Tower 1).

Buildings constructed in composite manner in Hong Kong are all very big in size. As a general reference, the building size of these buildings ranging from about 1800 to 2500 m^2 per floor with a total building area from 80000 to 200,000 m^2. There is no building example of significance smaller than the figure as quoted above being built in Hong Kong. All these structures bear a number of commonality in their structural form. Due to the height of the building and the tremendous wind load they are taking, these structures are all founded either on large diameter bored piles or directly seated on bed rock (Photo 1).

They all have a deep basement, for some cases reaching almost 30 m down into the ground. A RC core wall which is usually located in the center part of the building and serves to provide the rigidity to the entire building, is also a typical design. Other stiffening provisions used in the design include the transfer truss, belt truss and outrigger systems. However, large-sized bracing members on the external frame are seldom used due to the blocking of the valuable exterior views. Some other forms of composite design, such as the use of Steel/RC composite column

Photo 1.   Construction of the foundation cap for the core wall of IFC Tower 2.

Photo 6. Climb form used in the Manulife Tower.

Photos 2 and 3. Cheung Kong Center (left) and Manulife Tower during the construction stage.

Photo 7. A lapse of 12 floors between core wall and steel frame due to delay by the erection of the outrigger.

Photos 4 and 5. The IFC Tower 1, with portion above 23rd floor constructed in composite manner (left) and the IFC Tower 2 during the construction stage.

or concrete-filled steel column, are sometimes used as a further means to increase strength and rigidity of building. For floor structure, steel beams with RC topping is again a typical design.

Please refer to Photos 2–5 for general views of some of the quoted projects.

2 MAJOR ELEMENTS IN COMPOSITE BUILDING STRUCTURES

2.1 Core wall

Core wall is the major structural element in Hong Kong's composite buildings which serves as the major load taking element as well as to provide rigidity in particular to resist the deflection caused by strong wind. The size of the core wall ranges from 400 to 900 m^2, and sometimes with a thickness close to 2 m at its base. Inner walls cast at the same time with the main walls are also provided as a means to increase sectional stiffness. These load bearing walls serve mainly as fire resisting partitions for the lift or stair shafts or other servicing purposes.

Mechanical-lifted formwork systems, like the climb-form or the jump-form systems (Photo 6), are employed for the construction of the core wall. This formwork system usually can achieve a working cycle of 4 to 5-day per floor comfortably. Since the form can only cast the vertical wall elements, while the floor slabs, both inside and outside the core, are required to construct at a later stage. Due to the delay caused by other operations (such as the installation of the outrigger system), sometimes a lapse in the work phases with more than 10 floors between the core and the working floor structure is not uncommonly (Photo 7). Therefore, special access and safety arrangement to allow workers making access to the working level at the top of the core wall have to be provided.

Connection provisions such as anchor plate for steel beams, build-in bar couplers or starter bars for floor slab, or even an anchoring frame for the connection of the entire outrigger structure, are required to embed in the core wall during the casting process (Photos 8 and 9).

Photo 8. Anchor frame embedded in the core wall and cast in an in-situ manner.

Photo 9. Anchor frame formed in a retro-installation manner (core wall cast in two phases with the anchor frame installed in-between).

2.2 Structural steel external frame

The external frame mainly composes of the steel columns which is usually located at the building perimeter and steel beams that tie the columns onto the core wall. Steel column can be in the form of H-section, square, rectangular or circular section, sometimes infill or encased with structural concrete to improve rigidity as well as fire resistance (Photo 9a). For Hong Kong's super high-rise buildings, these columns can be as large as 3 m × 3 m in size, with a steel section up to 2 m² (Photos 10 and 11).

In order to cater for the differential shortening occurs between the RC core wall and the steel columns, adjustment devices (using packing shims) is sometimes provided in columns so that the observable shortening can be toned by hydraulic action (Photo 12).

To make use of standard sections as much as possible, floor beams are often designed in standard I-section, with span ranging from 8 to 14 m (Photo 12a). Small-section lattice truss is seldom used due to their insufficiency in strength. Edging beams of

Photo 9a. Concrete filled column used in the Cheung Kong Center project.

Photos 10 and 11. 2.5 m × 2.5 m column fabricated from 150 mm thick steel plate for the Manulife project (left) and the Mega columns in IFC Tower 2 with averaged weight of steel at 9.7 ton/m.

Photo 12. Devices in the belt truss for the adjustment of differential shortening between the core wall and external frame (at location encircled).

109

Photo 12a. Typical layout of floor beams using standard sections.

Photo 13. Starter bars in core wall for connection onto the floor slab.

larger section are often required to improve the rigidity of the columns. Connection of the beams to the core wall is made by cleats and further connected onto the built-in anchor plate by welding.

2.3 Floor plate

Floor plate is in the form of reinforced concrete topping composite to the steel beams by shear studs. In most cases, corrugated galvanized iron decking is used as a permanent form which placed on top of the beams for forming the slab (Photo 13). The floor plate is further connected to the core wall by starter bars which are already embedded in the wall. Thickness of the slab is around 180 to 200 mm which forms a very strong lateral restrain to provide additional stiffness to the entire building structure.

2.4 Transfer truss

This is a common design used in Hong Kong the purpose of which is to provide a roomy and spacious ground entrance to a building. Usually very few numbers of columns, sometimes 2 on a side of a building, are provided at the entrance level. While above the entrance, normal configuration with closer columns is resumed. The transfer truss system is thus used to transfer the building loads carried from the upper columns down onto the main columns (sometimes called the super or mega columns). This structure is often in the form of a very huge truss that has a height equivalent to 2 to 3 normal floors (Photos 14 and 15). In some cases, the transfer truss is also connected to the outriggers, which serves to tie the external frame onto the core wall and provide the rigidity required on the lower section of the building.

2.5 Belt truss and outrigger

They are provided to the building frame at interval every 20 to 25 floors to allow the building to regain its

Photos 14 and 15. Transfer truss used in the Cheung Kong Center project.

stiffness after a significant drop occurs in typical floors. Again, the belt truss and outrigger system is a very huge structure and stretches 2 to 3 floors in height, which involve amount of steel sometimes as much as 10 times that is required for equivalent typical floors (Photos 16a–c).

Photos 18a and b. Anchor frame for connecting the outrigger as used in the Manulife Tower and IFC Tower 2.

Photos 16a–c. Belt truss used in the Cheung Kong Center (above) and the Manulife Tower projects.

Photo 17. Outrigger frame used in the Cheung Kong Center (the set located on the top of the tower).

Photo 19. Forming the floor slab inside the core wall using manual type formwork.

Outrigger is often in the form of inclined bracings, which tilts outward, inward, or in both directions forming a cross or Y-shaped brace frame (Photo 17). Occasionally, it can be replaced by large-sectioned beams in order to reduce the obstruction caused by the braces. Due to the very strong pulling out tendency, the outriggers are connected by welding to the anchor frame which is embedded inside the core (Photos 18a and b).

2.6 Other structures inside the core wall

Minor structures inside the core such as floor slabs of the lift lobby or other utilities areas, fire resisting wall or normal partitions for services rooms or toilets, are formed at an elapsed time by manual formwork method (Photo 19). However, these inner wall systems are sometimes replaced by dry walls due to the omission of wet works during the forming process (Photo 19a).

111

Photo 19a. Dry wall system for minor partitions within the core wall (can be of fire resistant purpose as required).

3 PRODUCTION CONCERNS FOR THE CONSTRUCTION OF COMPOSITE STRUCTURE

The construction of large-sized composite structures is not an easy task, in particular in most cases where a gigantic and deep basement is part of these projects. The construction period usually takes more than 3 years, excluding the time for the foundation and other works in an advanced phase.

On the production side, a number of practical problems should be noted in the construction process due to the unique nature and tremendous amount of activities involved, such as:

3.1 Site layout to cater for very congested site environment

To handle activities which work simultaneously with reinforced concrete and structural steel, together with the installation of other building services and fitting out works for very large and complicated building projects in a congested site is indeed very difficult, in particular to have all these essential things being carried out in close proximity in term of time and space (Photos 20 and 21). Problems like how to provide for the delivery and storage of the bulk and heavy materials, circulation and movement of materials and plants; locating the waste and environmental control equipment, administration and logistic areas; or provision of access and safety routes etc, should be catered for carefully and efficiently and to eliminate double handling as far as possible.

3.2 Simultaneous works

There are situations where a number of major construction works are constructed simultaneously with the main building structure, such as:

a) working at the same time with a basement, which is constructed usually using top-down arrangement (Photo 22),

Photo 20. Layout situation of very large and complicated site as seen in the IFC project.

Photo 21. Actual layout at the early stage of the IFC project to cater for material storage, equipment and other circulation requirements.

Photo 22. Superstructure and basement construction was carried out simultaneously in the Manulife Tower project.

b) with a very large-sized podium structure (Photo 23),
c) with other ancillary works such as pedestrian/vehicular linking structure or other external works.

These works are often very large-scale by themselves and cause significant coordination problems to the main structure in terms of scheduling, resources allocation, access to works, storage and site facilities etc.

Photo 23. Podium structure working at the same time with the IFC Tower 20.

Photo 25. Four tower cranes were provided in The Center project for the hoisting of all the required materials.

Photo 24. 65-ton steel column section forming the column cluster for the 80-storey tower of The Center.

Photo 26. A temporary truss was erected in the Cheung Kong Center project for the erection of the transfer truss.

3.3 Cranage requirements

There are countless heavy items for super high-rise composite buildings. These items come from 3 main activities, such as reinforcement bars and formwork shutters for constructing the core wall, individual or assembled structural steel members, and other plants and equipment for the building services installation. Some of these items are extremely heavy, such as in the case of THE CENTER, an assembled member for a section of the column cluster (there are more than 10 pieces of this) weighs more than 60 tons (Photo 24). While the number of other smaller members is enormous, sometimes it calls for more than 50000 pieces with average weight close to 1 ton each. For the 88-storey International Financial Center, the tower crane takes 8 minutes to make a delivery from ground level to the roof. Sufficient carnage provision will guarantee the project be completed efficiently and on time (Photo 25).

3.4 Temporary works

A number of temporary works and related provisions are often required during the construction period. These works mainly are provided to facilitate the erection of some very heavy, complicate-shaped or difficultly positioned structural components such as:

a) supporting trusses (Photo 26),
b) falsework for long-span components,
c) falsework for structures with very high headroom,
d) temporary work platform to store or support very heavy materials or plants (Photo 27),
e) temporary pier along seawall to allow barges to unload structural steel components and members,
f) provision of slot openings in the main structure for the entrance of very big assembled components (Photo 28).

These works are very costly both for the erection, dismantling or making good afterward. They also affect the critical path of the main program and should therefore be planned very carefully in the overall building schedule.

3.5 Height and headroom problems

When talking about super high-rise buildings we refer to those with 200 m or above in height. Besides

Photo 27. A temporary platform erected for the storing and handling of the steel components.

Photo 28. A 25 m wide slot was formed in the RC core wall for the delivery of a roof truss module (Hong Kong Convention and Exhibition Center, 1996).

human (workers) psychology and safety, quite a number of practical problems will accompany when the working position is at height. For example, the access for both human workers and materials to the upper part of the building becomes more difficult and time consuming, more access provisions or safety measures are needed when working at height, the rate of work done is getting smaller, or, there is stronger wind and more severe climatic environment when reaching higher altitude.

3.6 Works at peak period

In terms of cash flow, value of works to be completed during the peak period can be up to US$10 million per month. There may be more than 2000 workers

from more than 50 trades working inside the site every day. Daily consumption of building materials can be in the region of 500 to 600 tons. How to manage all these activities orderly and have the resources arrived to the right place and on time under a coordinated manner is a great challenge in these projects.

3.7 Controlling rain water getting into building during construction period

The construction of super high-rise building practically sub-sectioned into a few logical phases. Counting from the top level working in advance is the construction of the core wall. Follows sometimes with a lapse of as much as 10 floors or more, is the erection of the structural steel building frame. Further downward with a lapse of some 15 to 20 floors starts the fixing of the curtain walls, and with other interior fittings that are catching up from below. As seen from this sequential arrangement of works, the building at the initial stage can hardly be water sealed. The exposing vertical and horizontal openings of the still in-completed upper structure are convenient access for rain water. There are examples that the installed dry wall partitions on the lower floors are being wetted after a thunderstorm. Rain water runs down from the lift shaft and services ducts from the upper level have damaged more than 40 storey of internal dry wall below the leaking point. The replacement of the damaged walls will be costly and may delay the final completion of the project.

4 FUTURE TRENDS

The way how Hong Kong is using structural steel to construct buildings is far beyond what can be described as efficient and cost feasible for common projects. The use of structural steel or composite structure in building construction at present only limited to super high-rise or projects with exceptionally large size. The adaptation of technology that is supposed to be economical, such as the use of structural steel in construction, has not happened in Hong Kong as it is in most of the developed world.

The past decade is an important era for Hong Kong in the searching of new and cost effective technology in construction. It is, on one hand, the experience gained in the recent projects working with structural steel or composite design and construction, is significant. More and more architects, engineers, contractors and workers begin to master the skill and experience in the design and handling of this kind of construction method. They are by now feeling more confident and competent to procure a project using structural steel or composite design. What they need to do in the future is to find a way to make the work more diversify and adaptive, so that it can be able to apply to various scale and natures of projects more effectively and economically. From the view point of the author, this can be achieved by the following means.

4.1 From the design point of views, instead of using composite design, more straight-forward design like the using of simpler steel frame structure with columns and beams layout in more regular spacing and shorter span, could be adopted.

4.2 Similarly, more standardized components such as the use of universal sections, simple lattice trusses or prefabricated standard sections, could be used in order to cut cost and make installation easier and economical.

4.3 Applying the design to buildings of various types, nature and scale, such as for hotel, hospital, school, office and commercial buildings, or even for residential buildings of medium-rise nature. These are areas that structural steel can be made use of more effectively.

5 CONCLUSION

With the limited composite building cases being executed in Hong Kong, the rate of development and technology transfer is still unsatisfactory. One of the consequences is that this form of construction technique is still not be able to make use of in a more popular manner for other possible types of buildings.

At present, majority of these projects are designed by one or two leading consultant firms. Experienced contractors and operatives are also insufficient. This may discourage developers to select this construction option due to its relatively higher cost resulted from unpopularity in its application. At the same time, other related factors such as the adopting of more composite design with the use of in-situ reinforced concrete, pre-cast elements and structural steel at the same time in a project (Photo 31); the familiarization in the using of other finishing options other than solid external walls or traditional cladding systems; or the development of better and more adaptive building codes in the area of structural design or fire and safety requirements both by the engineers or the approving authorities, may also help in the technological evolution process. Otherwise, methods to construct buildings will remain traditional and cannot get advancement as the same pace with the rest of the modern world.

REFERENCES

Gibbons C., Lee A.C.C., MacArthur J.M. & Wan C.W. 2002. The Design and Construction of Two International Finance Center Hong Kong Station. Advances in Building Technology. *Proceedings of the International Conference on Advance Building Technology*. Elsevier.

Gibbons C., Ho G., MacArthur J.M. & Horsfield J.N. 1999. Development in High-rise Construction in Hong Kong. Symposium on Tall Building Design and Construction Technology.

Wong W.M. Raymond 1998. Fifteen Most Outstanding Projects in Hong Kong. Hong Kong, China Trend Building Press.

Wong W.M. Raymond 1998. Battle within the Ground – Experience learned from the Lee Garden Hotel Redevelopment (Manulife) Project. *Proceedings from the 5th International Conference on Tall Building*.

Wong W.M. Raymond 2001. Redevelopment of Hilton Hotel – Construction of the 62-storey Cheung Kong Center. *Technical Review in the Newsletter of The Chartered Institute of Building (HK)*, February 2001 issue.

System-based Vision for Strategic and Creative Design, Bontempi (ed.)
© 2003 Swets & Zeitlinger, Lisse, ISBN 90 5809 599 1

Design of a buried polyfunctional centre

A. Rago & P. Giura
"P.&A S.R.L.", Rome, Italy

ABSTRACT: The introduced design is relative to the realization of a trade space and of a multiscreen inside a zone destined to be a park, subordinated to environmental restrictions. For this reason the structure is totally thought integrated with the environment, being realized by a single level on the ground. It is also necessary the realization of a public square and a walk to access the park covered with laminated wood structure.

1 STRUCTURE'S AIM

The adopted planning criteria were developed by the conviction that the urban parks and gardens must be faced like integrated functions with the other categories of services and not like a single arrangement of residual areas. The site of a mix of functions in this area is proposed like an element of a total revitalization of the place.

The base planning idea is to give a total formal definition to the actual order of the park, in order to respect the pre-existences vegetational, with the insertion of several integrated functions in the plan of the park's arrangement.

2 PROJECT'S DESCRIPTION

2.1 *Altimetric and planimetric organization*

The site in object is situated in the northern part of the city of Rome, North of the confluence between two rivers: Tevere and Aniene.

The site is characterized, from an environmental point of view, by the presence of the Fosso della

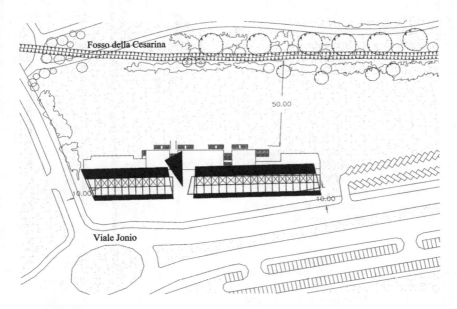

Figure 1. Planimetric placement of the poly-functional centre.

Cesarina: the zone is subordinated to environmental restrictions. In order to not disturb this park it has been chosen therefore to bury the structure of the multi-screen, leaving by the ground floor the only access to the multiscreen and to the commercial areas.

The project has to be realized in parallel with an important road axis of the Quartiere Talenti: Viale Jonio. Once defined the altitude of the street, the escarpment of the same one comes down until level −4.50 on the high part of the park, in order than to slip slowly towards the bottom of the valley to the level −10.00, at approximately 50 m of distance, where the deep furrows of the Fosso della Cesarina are.

2.2 Contextualization of the construction and architectural description

The access at the multiscreen happens at level 0.00 from the road along which there is the covered walk; the route is emphasized from a portico realized with slender metallic pillars and from a penthouse realized with a laminated wood structure and a copper roofing. This course shows towards the park and the commercial spaces, which are accessible from the portico that has shop windows also on the main road.

The route of the land and the presence of the road allow the project to never exceed the concurred maximum height of 4.00 m and to bury at the back of the street all the auditoriums. Behind the building, the auditoriums have roof gardens that follow the slanted course of the land and they do not obstruct the view of the portico and of the public square. At the level of the public park there are the escapes realized along the side of the building.

The longitudinal building, at the middle of the covered walk, is interrupted to create a little public square covered with a wooden lamellar structure, a place where rest and relax that through a great open perron concurs a comfortable and evocative access to the park.

The public square shows the income zone to the cinema where ticket office is and from which it is possible to reach the underground level through two escalators and a panoramic lift, at level −7.00, where there is the distribution hall to the auditoriums. At the intermediate level −3.00 there is the area where are lodged technical projection rooms and premises. This level partially covers the plan of the building and so there is a large double width for the distributive zones of the cinema. At level −10.00 there is another floor principally destined to warehouse but also to technical premises and service.

The multiscreen complex is made up of six auditoriums and they are essentially distinguished in three typologies: two large ones for 400 seats each that exceed a difference in height of 4.5 m with a unique gradine that receives the places to seat; the two intermediate ones of 150 seats each that exceed a difference

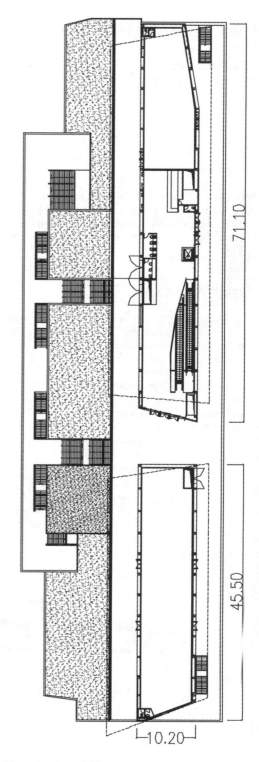

Figure 2.   Level 0.00.

118

in height of 3.00 m and finally the two most small both containing 100 seats with a difference in height of 2.00 m. Therefore, the multiscreen complex can approximately accommodate a total of 1296 persons.

2.3 *The realization of the digging*

The most problematic realization is that of the digging: in fact, the axis of the main development of the multiscreen structure is tilted of roughly 10° because it follows the course of the Fosso della Cesarina, on the bottom of the valley, from which it must have a minimal distance of 50 m, in respect of the environmental restrictions. That involves a variable distance between the designed structure and the axis of the road. It has become therefore necessary to realize a bulkhead of poles behind the road's edge, whose height and dimensions are variable along the development that in the complex is of approximately 60 m.

A similar problem has been found along the secondary road that develops along the short side of the multiscreen; in order to resolve this problem it has been necessary to realize another bulkhead of reduced dimensions regarding the previous one, arranged in parallel with the road for an approximate length of 25 m.

The remaining forehead of the digging is simply realized with a tilted wall of approximately 60°, interrupted to average height with an intermediate plan that has a width of 5 m.

Regarding level 0.00 of the road, the maximum depth of roughly 13.00 m is caught up on the bottom of the digging. At this depth it is possible to realize the indirect foundations on drilled poles. This type of foundations are necessary because the stratigraphy of the site previews that, under the vegetable land whose depth is of approximately 2.5 m, there is a layer of slimy clay of equal power to 7.00 m. The hypothesis of superficial foundations was discarded because of the excessive entity of the settlements that the structure would have endured in time. Under the argillaceous bench there is a much powerful layer of sandy gravel whose depth was not assessed because of its excessive compactness regarding the power of blots operating. The foundation poles go to attest themselves in the gravely bench.

Another problem has been checked out regarding the double water-bearing stratum that has been found in the project's area: one deeper and constant in its level (findable in the gravely bench) and a different one that slides above the argillaceous bench in the thickness of the vegetable land. This level is much variable in order to seasonal variations. The deepest stratum, connected to the Fosso della Cesarina, does not influence in a very important way on the project realization, while the most superficial one has been intercepted in proximity of the digging. So it is necessary to convey this stratum directly towards the bottom

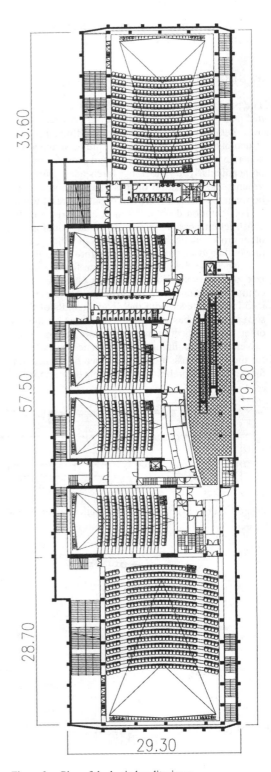

Figure 3.   Plan of the buried auditoriums.

119

of the valley so that it does not interfere with the realization of the structure.

3 STRUCTURAL FORMULATION

The project is articulated on the realization of three distinguished factory bodies, all buried, over hanged by a metallic structure at the ground floor. The construction of all the buried parts is previewed in armed concrete to form a series of resistant frames, arranged perpendicularly to the long foreheads against the ground; the realization of these frames acts as strut between the pushes of the two opposite breast walls.

This solution develops from a comparison of the construction costs between the actual solution and other proposed, like the one thought in which the fixture bulkhead was to be realized before the digging.

Connections between the opposite foreheads realized with passing frames has been univocal for the central projection rooms because they have been realized in coincidence with the dividing walls of themselves, but this has given some problems for the two other larger projection rooms that are located at the two ends of the building. It has been necessary to use, for those last ones, a close sequence of connections for the opposite foreheads with the help of prefabricated

beams disposed to a distance of approximately 3 m, whose span is of 20 m as so as to form a portal. The beams are supported from steel slabs realized on the head of the tapering pillars. The same beams have been used in order to realize a steel structure, mounting in false, for the wooden and steel structure at the ground floor. Between the prefabricated beams has been completed the auditoriums covering floor with prefabricated double tee slab disposed along the same direction of the beams. The determination of the reinforcing bars of the structure in the zones that act as support for the prefabricated beams and as joint for steel mounting has been made with a strut-and-tie calculation model.

In the central projection rooms, in order to support the mounting steel overhanging structure, became necessary to use locally precast beams inserted in the alveolar floor that acts like the cover of the same projection rooms: this floor is woven between the connection frames defined before.

The part of the projection rooms toward Fosso della Cesarina is partially covered from a roof garden, tilted towards the bottom of the valley, realized tilting the alveolar floor composed by hollow flat blocks in correspondence with the extreme projection rooms.

Along all the perimeter of the building it is necessary the realization of two types of control walls: the

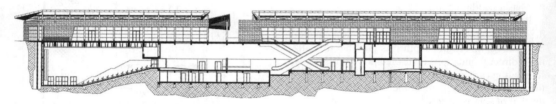

Figure 4. Longitudinal section: distributive area of the multiscreen.

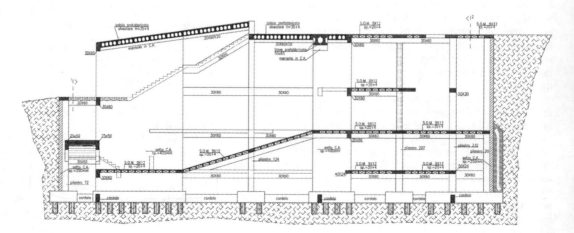

Figure 5. Structural transversal section.

first type of wall has a constant thickness equal to 25 cm modelled as a free plate on top and at the foundations level and laterally embedded on the pillars. This type of wall is subject to a variable rushing force that derives from the variable land's depth. The second type of wall has a variable thickness and it is used on the edge walls of the external projection rooms. This type of wall has a variable thickness from a minimum of 30 cm to a maximum of 55 cm and they are based on the two frames of edge of the projection rooms and on a central "T shaped" septum.

Calculation of the buried structure has been carried out into three distinguished blocks; everyone has been three-dimensionally studied in order to control the interactions with the surrounding land: it has been estimated the effect of the push assuming different levels of filling behind the wall on the two opposite foreheads, enveloping the turning out solicitations.

In order to estimate the correctness of the results of the elastic analysis it has been assumed to apply a series of distinguished cargo histories to a bidimensional model of the most stressed frame: it has been resolved a non linear analysis, in terms of materials and of geometry.

From the comparison of the results it is evident (about the turning out solicitations) a greater concentration of the solicitations in the walls of cut for non-linear analysis regarding the linear one.

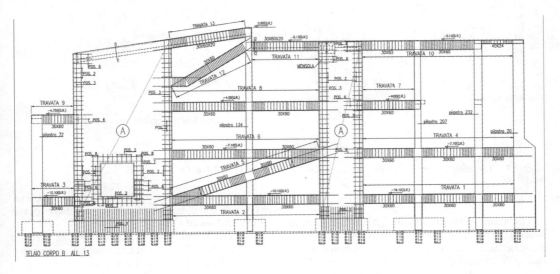

Figure 6.   Transversal connection frame.

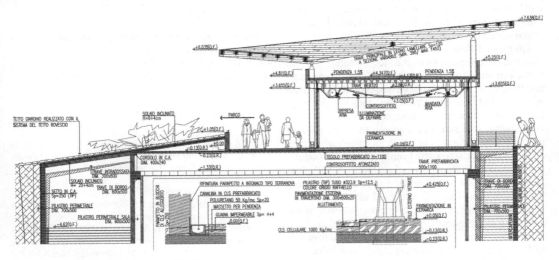

Figure 7.   Section and details at level 0.00.

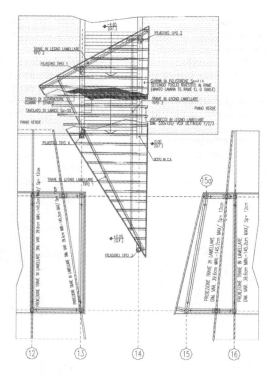

Figure 8. Covering structure of the public square at level 0.00.

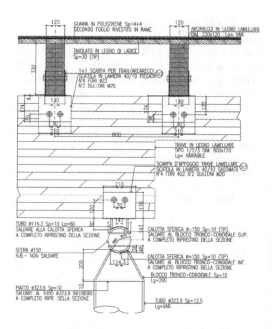

Figure 9. Detail of the lamellar wood penthouse.

The shear reinforcement design for the stressed walls come out from an elastic analysis with an ended elements bidimensional model of calculation and also basing on a model defined as "stringer and panel".

It has been obtained a good correspondence of the percentages of the turning out reinforcement bars with an over dimensioning of the turning out reinforcement bars derived from the elastic bidimensional ended elements analysis.

On ground floor part the building has been distinguished, for solicitations of the steel structure , in two parts: one destined to receive functions of commercial trades and cinema hall and a second one (realized in wood) destined to cover the passages and the large square. Steel structure has been considered embedded in the below structure and previews the realization of all the nodes in continuity while the lamellar wooden covers, various shaped, has been thoughts all isostatic.

Particular attention has been placed in the planning of the steel-wood connection nodes; they have been thought as three-dimensional elements for the extreme complexity of the connections between the mounting and the cover, both tilted.

Besides, particular attention was given also to points of less solicitation where steel connection nodes are placed in order to facilitate the realization.

4 CONCLUSIONS

The linear modelling of a buried framed structure, even in its complexity, is mainly representative of the efforts that speed it up.

The results confirm the actual planning practice even if engineers are not exempt from the comparison between different models of calculation.

ACKNOWLEDGEMENTS

Special thanks to "Petruccioli & Associati" S.r.l., in particular to arch. M. Prozzo, arch. L. Porcelli, arch. A. Perna, arch. M. Santandrea, ing. G. Greco for the helpful collaboration in the structural planning phase.

REFERENCES

Rago, A. 1999. Analisi probabilistica di strutture intelaiate in C.A. C.A.P. in campo non lineare, degree thesis, University of Rome "La Sapienza", Italy.

Simone, A., Malerba, P.G. & Bontempi, F. 1999. Modellazione di zone diffusive in elementi in C.A. mediante il modello a pannelli e correnti, in *A.I.C.A.P.days* 4–6 November 1999 Torino.

Biondini, F., Bontempi, F. & Malerba, P.G. 1998. Optimization of Strut-and-Tie Models in Reinforced Concrete Structures, in G.P. Steven, O.M. Querin, H. Guan, Y.M. Xie (eds) Structural Optimization, Oxbridge, Sydney, 285–292.

System-based Vision for Strategic and Creative Design, Bontempi (ed.)
© 2003 Swets & Zeitlinger, Lisse, ISBN 90 5809 599 1

Wall panels for industrialized housing method

S.P.G. Moonen
Eindhoven University of Technology, Eindhoven, The Netherlands

ABSTRACT: As part of the development of an industrialized housing method wall panels are designed and tested. The main objective is to develop wall panels that can be produced beforehand without knowing specific project requirements of the later use of the panels. The aimed industrialized housing method is an open way of building, suitable for irregular layouts. This paper describes the assembled components and the laboratory tests to study the ultimate load bearing capacity. Four wall panels (2028 × 2800 mm²) are tested. The total dead weight of a panel is 0,45 kN (= 7,1 kg/m²) and the average failure load is 486,7 kN. This is more than a factor 1000 times the dead weight of the wall. The found maximum load is sufficient for the wall panels to be used as load bearing structure in a two-story building with concrete floors and concrete tiles.

1 THIN SKIN SANDWICH WALL PANELS

Sandwich panels with a very thin skin such as roof sheets in Figure 1 are well known for their structural performances. In this use the structural strength is mainly determined by bending. In the Netherlands for

Figure 1. Cross-section of a roof sheet. This sandwich panel with a thin skin was also used in the preliminary tests to study the possibility of light sandwich wall panels.

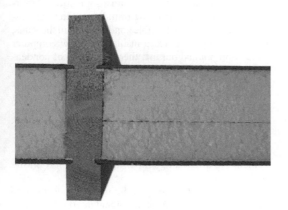

Figure 2. Top view of structural components. Four panels each with five studs are build for testing, see Figures 4–6.

example 3 mm chipboard glued to 120 mm rigid insulation is used in sloped roofs with a maximum span between purlins of 3-meter. But sandwich constructions with very thin skin can also be well used in walls where the strength is mainly determined by compression (and not to forget buckling). Figure 2 shows an appropriate use for a wall with a substantial saving in structural materials. This saving is made possible by the major structural contribution of insulation and skin. The cross-section of Figures 2–3 shows how insulation and 3 mm skin will obstruct a slender stud (28 × 148 mm²) to buckle in plane of the wall (in other words buckling sideward in the drawings is obstructed by the skin). Since the thin skin is forced in plane a tremendous buckling support is obtained. Because the skin is glued to rigid insulation (here for example EPS-expanded polystyrene) the very thin skin is not subjected to lateral folding.

2 DESIGN PROGRESS

Preliminary studies (Moonen & Fiege 2000) were primarily oriented on the width of the skin needed for buckling support. Several panels with a cross-section similar to Figure 1 were tested in the laboratory with an axial compression to the studs. The dimensions of the studs were 22 × 96 mm² or 22 × 120 mm² both glued to 3 as well as 8 mm chipboard. The outcome of the test was that the thinnest skin (3 mm) already can provide the required buckling support. Calculations based on the test results showed that a standard size in

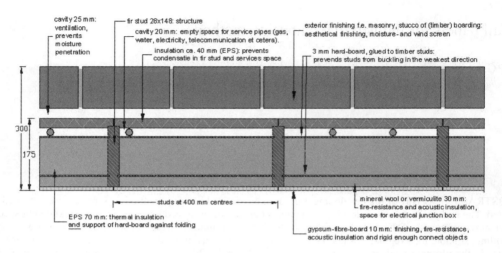

Figure 3. Horizontal cross-section of the industrialized housing method. (Here a wall with an exterior brickwork layer is shown). All materials of the wall with their main functions are given. Like in timber frame buildings the brickwork can be replaced by many other claddings.

dwellings of $48 \times 98\,\text{mm}^2$ can be reduced to $16 \times 98\,\text{mm}^2$ to bear the same axial load.

The preliminary tests proved on the one hand that a good composition of small structural elements is sufficient to be used as basis for an industrialized housing method but revealed on the other hand an unfavorable failure mode. Although all studs were forced to buckle out of plane, failure occurred when glue between skin and stud gave way after extended curvature of the panel. And since failure of the glued connection immediate effects in loss of buckling support, a very brittle failure mode was observed.

3 IMPROVED COMPOSITION

Based on preliminary studies the glued connection of skin and stud is changed, as shown in Figure 2. Instead of glueing 3 mm chipboard to both smallest sides of a stud, 3 mm hardboard is fed in longitudinal saw-cuts of the stud. This connection requires more thickness of the stud (28 mm instead of 16 mm) to leave enough material in between the saw-cuts but also creates a more simple and sound panel.

For making the panel two hardboard sheets are first glued to 70 mm expanded polystyrene (Figs 2–4). The hardboard sticks out on both sides and is fed in the longitudinal grooves. Because grooves in fir studs can be best located some 10–30 mm from the edges of the stud, cavities can be created on both sides of the wall. Cavities close to the interior side can be used to locate service pipes for water, electricity, telecommunication et cetera. These cavities are also used to place

extra insulation. Mineral wool or vermiculite is chosen to improve thermal effects, fire-resistance and acoustical performances. The width of the cavity to place mineral wool or vermiculite is chosen 30 mm so electrical junction boxes can be put in the cavity without weakening the hardboard. The interior finishing is 10 mm plasterboard or gypsum-fiber-board. This layer gives the same appearance as traditional build dwellings and provides the required fire-resistance of the wall. Preliminary tests also indicate that acoustic performance is improved by interior finishing of plasterboard.

Thermal calculations have indicated that condensation in the described cross-section will not occur. Therefore the wall panel does not need a vapor barrier as timber frame buildings do. Subsequently the complete composition is studied with a sophisticated thermal computer program. The initial computer calculation did demonstrate possible condensation in the studs. But by adding some extra insulation a new computer simulation pointed out that there is no risk of concensation. This added insulation creates extra cavities at the outside of the wall panel. Since the computer calculations showed no temperatures below freezing inside the cavities service pipes are also located here. By applying demountable insulation, fitting of the service pipes can be done from the outside after erection of the superstructure. This sequence looks convenient for a fast and simple implementation on the building site.

All kind of claddings can be used as exterior finishing. With a traditional exterior and interior finishing, the housing method will have the same appearance as traditional build dwellings.

Figure 4.   Production of test specimen. 28 × 148 mm² fir planks are used to make the structural part of the wall panels. Each plank has four longitudinal saw-cuts to feed in hardboard sheets. The hardboard sheets are glued to expanded polystyrene.

4   TESTING PANELS UNDER AXIAL LOAD

Figure 4 gives an impression of the method used to produce the test specimen. Because the test series are meant to study structural behavior of the wall panels under axial compression only structural materials are applied (stud, skin and insulation). The main goal of this laboratory test is to prove whether the slender studs were forced to buckle in the strongest direction; this is out of plane of the panel.

Each panel consists of five studs with a length of 2800 mm. This length is chosen because buckling length in dwellings is about this length. The width of the panel is chosen 2028 mm (5 studs at centers 400 mm and two sandwich elements of 200 mm as sideward support of the outer studs).

The panels are horizontally produced and left for about a day for the glue to harden. Then the panels are put upright. Because the weight of a panel is only 450 N, laboratory personnel wanted to put the panel in the test setup by hand. The test setup is shown in Figures 5–6 and consists of a heavy steal frame (made of HEA300). Above a panel two 500 kN hydraulic jacks are used to apply compression in the wall panels. The hydraulic jacks are linked and a rigid steel beam (HEA300) is put on top of the panel in order to get an almost uniform distributed load in the five studs. Underneath the panel there are five 150 kN load cells to measure the reaction of every stud. These five load cells register possible load distribution by the hardboard. The horizontal deflection of every stud (indicating

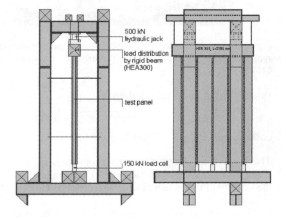

Figure 5.   Test setup for wall panels. Left: side-view, right: front-view. A steel beam is put on top of the panels to distribute the load from the hydraulic jacks to the individual studs. Underneath each stud a load cell is put to measure load distribution.

buckling) is measured at mid span by electronic potential meters. The vertical deflection (shortening) of the panel is measured at both short sides of the panel.

The average failure load of the four panels is 486,7 kN with a standard deviation of 12,8% (62,5 kN). This ultimate failure load comes to an average stress in the studs of 23,8 N/mm² (neglecting the load bearing capacity of hardboard). This stress is an extremely high

Figure 6. All four tested panels showed clear out of plane buckling, indicating that the 3 mm hardboard is appropriate to support slender studs. The average failure load of the panels is 486,7 kN. The maximum measured load in a load cell is 118 kN.

value for a fir stud with slenderness in-plane:

$$\lambda: l_{buc}/i = 2800/\sqrt{(^1/_{12}*28)} = 1833$$
out-of-plane $\lambda: l_{buc}/i = 2800/\sqrt{(^1/_{12}*148)} = 65$

The high value combined with the observed out-of-plane buckling of all four panels (Fig. 6) substantiate the validity of hypothetical structural scheme and calculation method.

The difference of the measured force in the five load cells of a panel varied up to 50% of the maximum force. This means that hardboard is able to redistribute the applied load if the stiffness of a stud is less or if a stud is partially broken. This is also a reason for the extreme high stress in the fir studs.

When considering the average failure load with standard deviation, and assuming that these values are valid for a large test series, one find the 5% confidence interval at approximately 190 kN/m. As a reference, the intended combined dead and live load of a wall panel used in a traditional house supporting two concrete floors with a span of 6 meter and a roof covered with concrete tiles is approximately 80 kN/m. These test results confirm that the panels can be used as starting-point for any industrialized housing method.

Figure 7. Composed photo of different stages in a trial project. The scope of this project is to test possibilities of connecting doorframes, window frames, sloped roof, terrace roof, et cetera to panels with little vast materials. Existing roof sheets substitute for the intended sandwich wall panels.

5 FIXING WINDOW FRAMES TO A VOID

Now the structural principle is resolved conclusively by these small-scale laboratory test other aspects of the industrialized housing method deserves attention. One of the major problems to be hold up to the light is how to connect all required arrangements such as doors, windows, roofs, gutters et cetera to a panel with only 5% vast material from which the most massive part is merely 28 mm in thickness. In order not to build castles out of air this aspect is studied simultaneously with the laboratory tests (Moonen 1998, 2001b).

Since the proof of the pudding is in the eating the developed details had to be put in practice. Two trial projects were realized simultaneously with the structural laboratory tests. Therefore the structural reliability of the wall panels shown in Figure 3 was not available at the time of implementation. So instead of the developed wall panels existing roof sheets (cross-section in Fig. 1) were used. The structural reliability of roof sheets in compression was established in preliminary studies mentioned before so the roof sheets could substitute the intended wall panel regarding the analysis of connections. Figure 7 gives an impression of the first trial project to test architectural details by practical experience. In this workshop several details to connect window frames, door frames, roofs, floors, gutters, et cetera were considered in real. The workshop has a predetermined layout so also possibilities to adapt fixed panels to a wall with a predefined length were tested. Photos and details of the second trial project can be found in Moonen (1998).

Based on these practical experiences various details are available to be used for building a dwelling. These details lay the foundation of a solid, light and sustainable housing method that can be applied for a two-story building. The details developed so far are directed towards concrete floors. Whether this is a optimal combination will be studied subsequently.

6 INDUSTRIALIZED HOUSING METHOD

Since 1, laboratory test validated the structural scheme, 2, the composition shown in Figure 2 looks convenient

for a fast and simple housing method and 3, the required details did substantiate in practice, the center of attention is currently focused on industrialization aspects of the building method. From the start the housing method is arranged as an industrialized system. Not as an industrial system where a volume is made by combining standard components. Since all developments are focused on an open way of building, suitable for irregular predefined layouts, an industrialized system is preferred. The idea of an industri- alized building is copied from the steel industry. Steel components are always based on fully industrial produced elements, meaning that the elements are all produced beforehand without knowing any project specific requirements. But in a steel workshop industrial elements (such as I-beams) can be treated, adapted, processed, resulting in high quality prefabricated components that need very little work on the building site. Steel skeletons show that tailor made structures can be well made with strictly standardized elements.

The triplet: *industrial production – prefabricated components – simple assembled structure* is called an industrialized system (Moonen 2001a). To further optimize an industrialized system one must first try to transfer as much activities as possible from assembling to prefabrication then from prefabrication to industrial production.

The composition of the elements in the cross-section of Figure 3 is geared to a panel with theoretical infinite length. Fir studs can be made "endless" by finger joints, all other elements can be fed in a manufacturing setup consecutively, as long as the connections don't mutually coincide. Like this an industrial panel with a length of for example 18 meter can be made. The idea is to have a limited choice in width, for example 400, 800 or 1200 mm.

The industrial panel can be cut to required lengths and assembled in a workshop. Two tongues, fed with glue in the longitudinal grooves will connect two panels (Fig. 8). Also a special connection-strip is developed that can be placed in between two panels (Fig. 9). The connection-strip is sawn from a composite plate

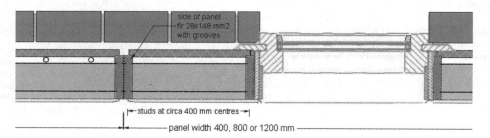

Figure 8. One of the possible ways to mount a window frame. On the left of the drawing a possible connection between two standard panels is shown. Two tongues made of plywood are placed in the longitudinal grooves of the studs and fixed with glue.

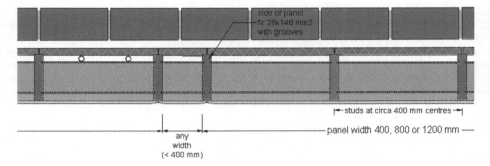

Figure 9.   A connecting-strip is developed to make a wall following a predefined layout. The connecting-strip is sawn up from a composite plate. On both sides insulation material is partially removed by a fraise, so the hardboard strip can be fed in grooves. With this principle any dimension of compound wall that can be transported can be made. By combining connecting-strips and standard panels cut to specific length any predefined wall with random located windows and doors can be made.

to a specific length and width. By combining connection-strips and panels with different width almost any façade-layout can be assembled. One of the advantages is that there is little waste in constructing prefabricated walls.

Transportation limitations will merely set the dimensions of the prefabricated wall that are assembled on site. The work on site is significantly reduced, since the ready-made walls can be easily connected. In order to further reduce work on site as well as waste during production, the height of the prefabricated walls is not determined by the height of floors but by the distance between top of foundation and edge of roof (as can be seen in the front façade of Figure 7). The consequence is that floors are suspended to the walls. So far several solutions have been developed to solve this (structural) issue. Preliminary laboratory tests look hopeful.

7   CONCLUSIONS

This paper describes the development so far of a solid and light industrialized building system made of planks, hardboard and insulation material. The basic structural principle of the wall is that studs will not buckle sideward if thin skins obstruct studs from bending in this direction. The thin skin itself will not fold because of the support of a rigid insulation. Laboratory tests substantiated this hypothesis.

The overall contribution of solid material in the test specimen is less than 5% of the wall volume, leaving 95% of the volume for immobile air. Still these wall panels can bear a substantial load. Details to connect

standard window and doorframes are tested in real and gave favorable indications.

At present the attention is focused on industrialization aspects of the building method. The scope is to optimize industrial production with full ability to realize predefined irregular layouts.

REFERENCES

Moonen, S.P.G. 1998. Integral building concept using large sandwich Panels *In proc. intern conf. WCTE'1998 – 5th world conference on timber engineering vol. 1, Montreux, Switzerland, 17–20 August 1998*. ISBN 2-88074-380-X. Lausanne: Presses polytechniques et universitaires romandes.

Moonen, S.P.G. & Fiege, M.A. 2000. New method for timber-frame houses based on integrated stud-theory. *In proc. intern. conf. WCTW'2000 – 6th world conference on timber engineering, Whistler, Canada, 31 July-3 August 2000*.

Moonen, S.P.G. 2001a. Ontwerp van een geïndustrialiseerde funderingswijze (Developing an industrialized foundation). *thesis, in bouwstenen 59*. ISBN 90-6814-559-2. Eindhoven: Universiteitsdrukkerij TU/e.

Moonen, S.P.G. 2001b. Roof sheeting as a primary structural element *In proc. intern IABSE Conf. Innovative wooden structures and bridges vol. 85, Lahti, Finland, 29–31 August 2001*. ISBN 3-85748-1003-X. Zürich: ETH Hönggerberg.

Moonen, S.P.G. & Tan, M.N. 2002. Extremely light and solid wall panels developed for an industrialized building method. *In proc. intern. Conf. 7th World Conference on Timber vol. 2, Shah Alam, Malaysia, 12–15 August 2002* ISBN 983-9414-36-4 (v.2). Malaysia: Perpustakaan Negara Malaysia Cataloguing-in-Publication Data.

System-based Vision for Strategic and Creative Design, Bontempi (ed.)
© 2003 Swets & Zeitlinger, Lisse, ISBN 90 5809 599 1

Development of a framework for valuing variations in concrete works

M. Sutrisna, K. Potts & D. Proverbs
Built Environment Research Unit, School of Engineering and The Built Environment,
University of Wolverhampton, Wolverhampton, West Midlands, United Kingdom

ABSTRACT: There has been much evidence that valuing variations in construction projects can lead to conflicts and disputes with many disadvantages such as loss of time, efficiency, effectiveness and productivity. One way to minimise these conflicts and disputes is to develop a robust mechanism for valuing variations. Focusing on the development of such a mechanism, essential issues and factors are identified and discussed. Since project activities are highly complex, the development presented focuses on a discrete construction activity, namely concrete work. A framework for analysing and valuing variations in concrete works is presented to enable a fair valuation scheme for both employers and contractors. The FIDIC Conditions of Contract for Construction 1999 are used as a platform in the development of the framework, thus making the framework internationally acceptable and applicable.

1 INTRODUCTION

In construction project management research, the subject of variations has attracted considerable attention and further study (Hibberd 1980 & Akinsola 1997). Variations have become an almost inevitable part of the construction process. It has been argued that it would be almost impossible to construct the project in a totally identical way to the original design used for the tender (Thomas 2001).

In most cases, variations will lead to conflict between the parties involved. Lack of effort in managing these conflicts can result in disputes (Fenn et al 1997). In the event of disputes, resolutions will be required. If the involved parties cannot resolve the disputes, then third party intervention, such as an adjudicator, will be necessary for a decision (Latham 1994). This obviously will also involve additional direct and indirect costs derived from the delays, and the time and expense incurred in preparing the delay claims document itself, which could be substantial (Alkas et al 1996). Furthermore, variations have been reported to significantly reduce the labor efficiency by up to 15.24% on electrical constructions (Hanna et al 1999b) and between 5–8% on mechanical construction projects (Hanna et al 1999a). One of the main causes of disputes is in the valuation of the variations (Seeley & Murray 2001). The current traditional approach to valuation, whilst being favored by many clients, has failed to provide an adequate scheme of compensation to contractors for any delay or disruption involved due to variations.

As variations and their valuation are obviously potential problems in the construction industry, they deserve significant attention and attempts to develop a robust methodology in order to avoid disputes. However, a construction project comprises many complex activities. This paper focuses on one activity, namely concrete works.

2 VARIATIONS

A variation was defined as an agreed alteration or modification by the parties of a pre-existing contract (Wallace 1995). FIDIC Conditions of Contract for Construction 1999 specified the range of this alteration or modification to be subjected to changes to quantities, quality and other characteristics of any item of work included in the Contract. It also includes changes to levels, positions and/or dimensions of any parts of the works, omission of any work (unless to be carried out by others), any additional work, Plant, Materials or services necessary for the Permanent Works or changes to the sequence or timing of the execution of the Works.

Variations can also be considered in the case of mistakes in the tender documents, or waivers by owners and the promise to pay (Wallace 1995) and also by a contractors proposal in the case of emergency works regarding safety and/or compliance with statutory regulations (Twort & Rees 1995) or simply for a contractors own benefits i.e. cheaper solutions and/or impracticality (Hibberd 1986). Whether a particular work can be treated as a variation or should be included in the original scope of works, will depend on the clauses contained in the contract documents. Standard forms of contracts have been designed to standardise the duties of contractors, employers and engineers and to distribute fairly the risks (Abrahamson 1956). Therefore, it is considered crucial to assess the treatment of variation events under these standard forms. As previously indicated, the standard form of contract to be assessed is the FIDIC Conditions of Contract for Construction 1999 that is intended for and widely used on international projects.

3 VALUATION OF VARIATIONS

Variations and their valuation have long been recognized as one of the commonest sources of disputes in the construction industry (Potts 1995). There are several ways to value variations, and different circumstances will require different valuations. Problems normally occur when there are different perceptions between the parties involved regarding the circumstances of the variations that require different methods of valuation. As argued by Hibberd (1986), the valuation in many cases depends upon a high degree of personal opinion or judgment.

On traditional contracts the rates and prices in the bill of quantities represent the main financial control between employer and contractor (Skinner 1982). However, difficulties occur when prices, applied to make up the contract sum, appear not to be an accurate figure for individual work items, thus represent the price for the project in a collective manner. Therefore, contractors frequently claim that the measured quantities of permanent works priced at billed rates fail to represent the true value of the construction works (Seeley & Murray 2001). Therefore, it has been widely acknowledged that the rules of valuation should not be implemented in a loose way, especially due to the accuracy and appropriateness of the rates applied (Hibberd 1986). The rates and prices to be applied in the event of valuation should be the rate that the contractor would have inserted against that item had it been included at the time of tender (Haswell 1963). This is in recognition of the need for a robust mechanism for valuing variations (Winter 2001).

While the latest edition of FIDIC is subject to continuous improvement (Corbett 1999); there are three events that initiate variations, namely the Engineer issues an instruction for a variation under Clause 13.1, the Engineer requests the Contractor to prepare a proposal for variations under Clause 13.3 and the Contractor initiates variations by making a proposal under Clause 13.2. The flowchart for the valuation rules in the FIDIC Conditions of Contract for Construction 1999 is provided in Figure 1.

The first two events provide a mechanism for the Contractor to consider whether they are willing and able to comply with such an order and/or request. If the contractor decides that they are unable to comply with the order/request, detailed justification should be presented, allowing the Engineer to cancel, confirm or vary the instruction and/or request. In other words, variations are not binding if the Contractor promptly notifies that he cannot perform the variations with acceptable reason (Booen 2001). The confirmation from the Contractor to comply with the instruction and/or request leads to detailed preparation of the proposal just like the third scenario of variations when the variation is initiated/proposed by the contractor. The next step will be the approval from the Engineer to the proposal which establishes the rate and price quoted in the proposal to be the rate and price used for valuation of the variation. If the proposal is not accepted then the valuation of the variations will be based on the mechanism expressed in Clause 13 that relates to Clause 12 as well.

The first question in such evaluation to be addressed is to whether the Contractor has suffered any delay and/or additional works because of any changes in legislation. Any delay and/or additional works incurred from this would allow necessary adjustment to the original rate and price. The next question is whether the Contract recognizes the Table of Adjustment Data. If this is the case, the adjustment formula is provided in Clause 13.8. It is also used to assess whether there are any variations that results in a reduction of the contract value for the benefit of the Employer.

The value of all additional cost incurred from the omission involved is proposed by the Contractor, supported with detailed documents. The approval from the Engineer on this proposal establishes the rate and price in the proposal to be used in the valuation of the variations. If there is no approval, the Engineer is obliged to determine the additional cost incurred. If this additional amount satisfies the Contractor then the additional cost will be included in the Contract Price. If the Contractor is not satisfied with this determination, the Contractor may apply for a further claim under Clause 20.1.

Variations other than omissions will be evaluated mainly based on the proportion of changes on quantities compared to the bill of quantities. It is expressed that the variation works should be checked if the amount is greater than 10% of the work itself in the bill of quantities. The next check is whether the amount of varied work is greater than 0.01% of the total Contract Amount. Also to be checked whether the varied amount is greater than 1% of the cost per unit quantity of the

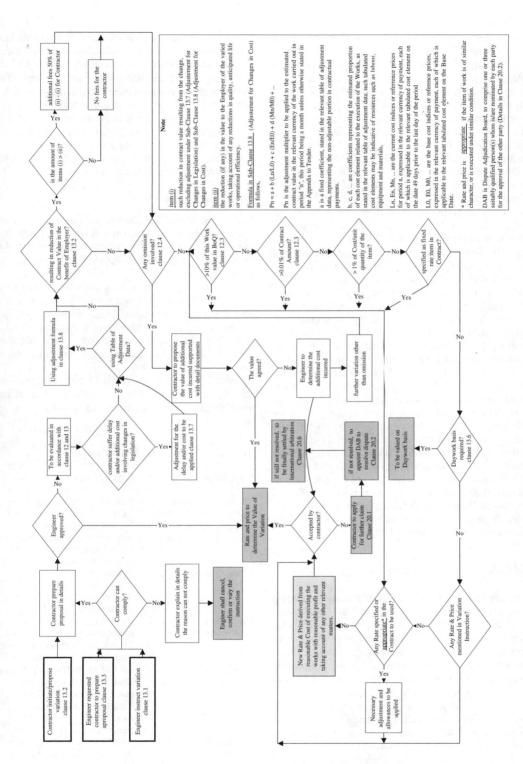

Figure 1. Caption of the rules for valuing variations in FIDIC for Construction, 1999.

131

related item. Another check is whether the varied amount is specified as a fixed rate item that will allow the valuation of the variations to simply use the fixed rate. If there is any necessity and/or requirement to value the varied works using the previously included daywork rates, the valuation of the variations will be based on daywork basis. If there is any rate and/or price mentioned in the variation instruction and accepted by the Contractor, the rate and/or price is to be used for the valuation of the variations.

Most of the processes in the given rules of the variations under FIDIC Conditions of Contract for Construction 1999 are fairly straightforward. However, there is one particular crucial process which may potentially incur disagreement, namely the appropriateness of any specified price and/or rate to be used in the valuation of variations. The rate and/or price is deemed to be appropriate for application if the item of work varied is of similar character, or is executed under similar conditions [Sub-clause 12.3 (b) (iii)]. This particular process is often prone to conflict and dispute. It is simply because of the ambiguity and subjectivity interpretation of the terms "similar character and similar conditions" of the varied works when compared to those included in the bill of quantities.

This point is important since if none of the rates and prices included in bill of quantity are of similar character or executed under similar conditions, then none of the rate and price in the bill of quantity is considered appropriate. This will require a new rate and price to be derived from costs associated to the execution of the varied works with regards to reasonable profit and taking account of any other relevant matters. The Contractor may perceive this as an opportunity to increase their return as new rates and prices in valuation will normally be more generous; while on the contrary, these new prices will increase the owners liabilities to the project (Wallace 1995).

4   CAST IN-SITU CONCRETE WORKS

Concrete work, forms the focus of this study, it being common in most construction projects and has attracted much international research (e.g. Proverbs 1998). Due to the level of difficulties and complexity in the execution, cast in-situ concrete work was selected for analysis towards developing an initial model. This shall provide a suitable platform on which to develop a robust mechanism for valuing variations in construction projects.

Cast in-situ concrete works are complicated operations involving several trades, materials and equipment. In order to be able to drive a fair and reasonable valuation of such varied works, a thorough analysis of all the involved factors has to be conducted. The analysis should assess whether the variation has resulted in any changes in the work character and condition and also

the extent of the resulting changes. The bottom line when considering whether a variation is executed under similar conditions necessitates consideration of all factors which should reasonably have been included at the tender stage and compare them to the actual conditions (Potts 1995). There are three major factors forwarded in this paper to be considered in distinction of the varied works to the ones in the bill of quantities through minor to major changes, including changes in the construction methods. These major factors are nature of the site, weather conditions and nature of the works.

4.1   Nature of the site

It has been argued that the site and its nature have an important impact on construction work. In-depth site investigations are standard practice to determine the suitability of the site for the intended construction works (Holmes 1983).

Furthermore, the site and its boundaries have been recognized as important when selecting construction equipment and methods, location of facilities and storage areas, sequences of operations and access. The site and its boundary conditions are also acknowledged as a major factor when identifying the temporary works needed (Illingworth 2000).

Table 1 provides a checklist to identify all alterations and changes within the nature of the site that affect and change the work character and/or work condition in the cast in-situ concrete works.

Table 1.   Changes in nature of the site.

Site changes	Details/examples
Changes in the transportation infrastructure	Resulting from changes of site location (roads, bridges, etc.)
Changes in natural and legislation restrictions	Natural preservation requirements (trees, rivers, etc.) Local legislation restrictions (height, weight, noise, etc.)
Changes in access to site	Degrees of site possession transfer from employer Accessibility to outsider (additional security, fencing, etc.)
Availability and distance from resources	Availability for resources (power, water, telephone, etc.) Distance from resources (labor, plant, material providers, etc.)
Changes in site lay out	Ease of site traffic coordination Available are for temporary material storage Ease of material loading Available working space to perform the work
Location & elevation of the work on site	Changes in spot of execution (horizontal difficulties) Changes in elevation of execution (vertical difficulties).

4.2 Weather condition

It is clearly expressed in Clause 4.12 that climatic conditions are excluded from the unforeseeable physical conditions that entitle Contractor to claim extra payment (Clause 20.1). However, there is a possibility that there are changes in the weather/climatic conditions to be encountered by the Contractor as the result of variations that necessitate execution at a time of the year. The Contractor may encounter different conditions, obstructions and productivity losses from the ones that were initially estimated in the tender due to executing the work at a different time of the year.

One slight possibility is a significant change in location that has also altered the climatic conditions to be encountered. However, this is rarely the case since such a significant change in location will normally result in modification or re-establishment of the contract itself.

The influence of weather conditions range widely from the effect on each concrete component (i.e. cement, aggregates, water, etc.) to the pouring of concrete, curing, striking and finishing through combinations of temperatures, humidity, frost, etc. (Blackledge 1992). The influence of direct weather effects such as snow and ice towards the loading on the formwork are also significant factors to be considered during the formwork design (The Concrete Society 1986).

Changes in weather conditions that may influence the work character and/or work condition for cast in-situ concrete works are listed in Table 2.

4.3 Nature of the works

Another factor to be assessed is whether there are any significant changes in the nature of the work itself. It is very obvious that changes in the nature of the work in most cases will lead the varied work to be executed under different work characteristics and/or conditions. However, the perceptions of the parties in interpreting these changes may not be the same. Therefore, a test or mechanism is required to ensure whether the varied work, if measured at bill preparation stage would have been lost among the items which went to make up the quantity of work described or would necessitate a separate bill description (Hibberd 1986). This mechanism will have to be able to incorporate all changes in every aspect of the nature of the cast in-situ concrete works.

However, in assessing concrete works, there are other related works that have to be taken into account, namely the formwork and the reinforcement works. The importance of formwork has been acknowledged as an essential part of the concrete works (Wynn 1951). Furthermore, formwork is now perceived as a technique rather than a material (Ricouard 1982). And the widely used term of formworks is deemed to include the actual material in contact with the concrete, known as the form face, and all necessary associated supporting structure (Brett 1988).

Another component of concrete works, namely steel reinforcement, has also been perceived critical to the success of concrete construction (Baker 1985). This is due to its positioning with regard to design, cover and rigidity of the cage in resisting the imposed weight and forces of fresh concrete during the pouring of concrete (Richardson 1977). Reinforcement steel bearing the tensile loads, together with the concrete that is bearing the compression load, provides an economical combination of reinforced concrete (Disney & Reynolds 1973). In some special circumstances such as heavy loading, the reinforcement has even been used to assist the concrete in compression bearing to reduce the effect of long term deflections (Nawy & Balaguru 1985).

Hence, formwork and reinforcement were included in the framework to assess the valuation of variations in cast in-situ concrete works as provided in Table 3.

5 PROPOSED METHODOLOGY FOR THE VALUATION OF VARIATIONS IN CONCRETE WORKS

Changes in these three major factors are argued to have significant impact to the work characteristic and/or work condition that can change the decision on valuing the variations.

From the contractors point of view, the rate and price included in the tender may contain low profits and/or high degrees of risk in order to make the tender competitive. Thus, if the contractor is paid such low rates and/or prices for further extensive amounts of similar works, the contractor may suffer significant losses. On the other hand, it is not fair for the employer if a variation, that is closely related and necessary for the completion of the main works, is valued at such a high rate and price. This may increase the liability of the employer and may cause significant discrepancies to the initial investment benefit analysis i.e. the project become unprofitable or less profitable due to extensive additional expenses for variations.

Table 2. Changes in weather conditions.

Weather changes	Details/examples
Changes in rainfall	Requirement for weather protection
Occurrence of snow	and increasing work difficulties,
Occurrence of ice/frost	Especially during the concrete pouring
Changes in temperatures	Mostly affecting concrete chemical reaction
Changes in humidity	Mostly affecting curing
Wind factor	Mostly affecting curing
Solar-ray	Mostly affecting concrete chemical reaction

Table 3. Changes in nature of works.

Works changes	Details/examples
Changes in the type of structure	Requiring completely different construction methods (slab, beam, column, etc.)
Changes in formwork	Panel material (timber/wood, metal, plastic, rubber, fabrics, cement base, etc.)
	Panel requirement (thickness, load bearing, water tightness, making on/off site, etc.)
	Panel surface (basic, plain, fine, superfine, etc.)
	Framework (scaffolding, clamp, struts, temporary supports, bracing, etc.)
	Accessories (void-formers, chamfers, form-liners, box-out, release-agent, etc.)
	Removal & re-usability (striking time, economical position & reusing sequences, etc.)
	Setting & erection (tolerances, erection methods, etc.)
	Additional requirements (construction joints, irregular shape & waste factor, permanent forms, etc.)
	Total area to be covered (m^2 of formwork required)
Changes in reinforcement	Re-bar type (plain, deformed, twisted, etc.)
	Re-bar diameter ($\varnothing 8$, $\varnothing 9$, $\varnothing 10$, D13, etc.)
	Accessories (mechanical couplers, spacers, ties, etc.)
	Construction joints (welded joints, splices, starter bars, dowel, etc.)
	Cutting & bending schedule, on/off site, etc.
	Positioning & fixing (tolerance, erection methods, etc.)
	Additional requirements (pre-stressing, water-stops, etc.)
	Total re-bar required (Kg of total re-bar weight)
Changes in concrete works	Design mix composition (cement, aggrecrete works gates, hydraulic binders, admixture, water etc.)
	Concrete mixing (site mixing or ready mix)
	Placing & compaction (protections, concrete pumps/bucket, tremie, internal/external vibrators
	Testing & sampling (slump test & sampling requirements)
	Curing (curing time, using membranes/compound/ponding/spraying, etc.)
	Finishing (intended usage & final surface, toppings/screed/exposed, etc.)
	Size attributes (length, width, thickness//height, etc.)
	Concrete volume (m^3 of concrete perpouring/total pouring)

However, the form of contract has been drafted to accommodate those risks and distribute them fairly to the involved parties; this requires the parties to look back to the forms of contract to make a careful assessment (Sutrisna & Potts 2002). In doing this, the appropriateness of the originally included rate and/or price requires an in-depth analysis that incorporates all changes in the nature of the site, weather conditions and nature of the works.

A further step to complete the framework is to analyse the factors presented in Tables 1, 2 and 3 by demonstrating the effect of each of these changes on certain parameters within direct operation activities as follows:

– Construction Schedule. Analysis of the implications of the listed changes to the construction schedule including changes in the on-cost, disruptions, delays, crash programme, etc.
– Assignment of Human Resources. Analysis of the impact of the listed changes on the human resources mainly labor including addition of human resources, loss of productivity, overtime cost, etc.
– Deployment of Plant. Analysis of the effect of the listed changes to the selection and deployment of the plant including extra time, standing charges, mobilisation and demobilisation, loss of productivity, etc.
– Material Ordering & Handling. Analysis of the effect of the listed changes to the mechanism of ordering and handling the materials including the ease of transportation and handling materials on site.
– Additional Prime Cost. Covers the possibilities of dealing with additional cost for specialists and/or services including sub-contractors, suppliers, local authorities, etc.

The presented checklists are incorporated with the direct operation activities described above as a new framework in valuing variations and presented diagrammatically in Figure 2. As shown in Figure 2, changes in nature of the works as the main driving force, reinforced by changes in nature of the site and weather conditions; are analysed against their impact on the direct operational effects. It is also shown that the nature of the site may affect the weather conditions and certain part of concrete works will be strongly depending on the weather conditions. The results of the analysis, i.e the consequences of all the listed changes towards the direct operational effects, are then being used to determine the valuation of the variations. The proposed framework provides a fair valuation scheme since the analysis must involve the contractors and employers. This involvement will accommodate both side opinions, point of views and purposes. Prior to the analysis, certain predetermined limits/values can be agreed between contractors and employers to establish which method of valuations to be taken for certain analysis result.

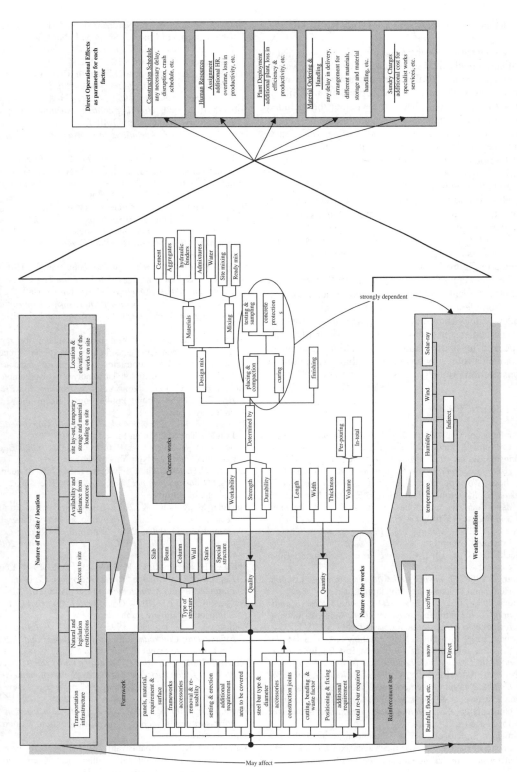

Figure 2. Caption of the proposed framework for valuing variations in concrete works.

6 CONCLUSION AND FURTHER RESEARCH

In valuing variations, there is one particular issue that is critical, namely the establishment whether the varied works are similar to the work character and/or work conditions with those that described in the Bill of Quantities. This will determine whether the included rates and prices in the Bill of Quantities can be directly applied or whether a new rate and/or price is necessary. This new rate and/or price should be derived from cost associated to the execution of the varied works with regards to reasonable profit and taking account of any other relevant matters.

However, as the activities within a project are very complicated; at this stage, a framework to assess concrete works including embedded works, formworks and reinforcement works, has been developed and proposed as a starting point. The framework is represented in Figure 2.

Further stages should develop a similar framework for other typical activities within a construction project and then blend and combine them with the expertise and practical know-how from many practitioners in this particular area to discover the association of certain type and level of changes to valuation decision to establish a robust mechanism in valuing variations in construction projects.

REFERENCES

Abrahamson, M. W. 1965. *Engineering Law and the I.C.E. Contracts*. London: C R Books Ltd.

Akinsola, A. O. 1997. *An intelligent model of variations' contingency on constructions projects*. Unpublished PhD thesis. Wolverhampton: University of Wolverhampton.

Alkas, S., Mazerolle, M. & Harris, F. 1996. Construction delay analysis techniques. *Construction Management and Economics* 14: 375–394.

Baker, T. 1985. *Making and Placing Concrete*. Essex: Longman Group Ltd.

Blackledge, G. F. 1992. *Concrete Practice*. Slough: British Cement Association.

Brett, P. 1988. *Formwork and Concrete Practice*. London: Heinmann Professional Publishing Ltd.

Booen, P. L. 2001. *The Four FIDIC 1999 Contract Condition: Their Principles, Scope and Details*. www.fidic.org/resources/contracts/booen_j.asp. Viewed: 30/08/02.

Corbett, E. 1999. FIDIC's New Rainbow – An overview of the Red, Yellow, Silver and Green Test Editions. *International Construction Law Review 16 Pt.1 39–46*.

Disney, L. A. & Reynolds, C. E. 1973. *Reinforcement for Concrete*, London: Cement and Concrete Association.

Fenn, P., Lowe, D. & Speck, C. 1997. Conflict and dispute in construction, *Construction Management and Economics* 15: 513–518.

Hanna, A. S., Russell, J. S. & Vandenberg, P. J. 1999a. The impact of change orders on mechanical construction labour efficiency. *Construction Management and Economics*. 17: 721–730.

Hanna, A. S., Russell, J. S., Nordheim, E. V. & Bruggink, M. J. 1999b. Impact of Change Orders on Labor Efficiency for Electrical Construction. *Journal of Construction Engineering and Management* 125 (4): 224–232.

Haswell, C. K. 1963. Rate Fixing in Civil Engineering Contracts. *In: Proceeding of Institution of Civil Engineering, February 1963 24: 223–234*.

Hibberd, P. R. 1980. *Building contract-variations*. Unpublished thesis. Manchester: UMIST.

Hibberd, P. R. 1986. *Variations in Construction Contracts*, London: Collins.

Holmes, R. 1983. *Introduction to Civil Engineering Construction*. Reading: College of Estate Management.

Illingworth, J. R. (2nd ed.) 2000. *Construction Methods and Planning*. London: E & FN Spoon.

Joint Committee of the Concrete Society and The Institution of Structural Engineers 1986. *Formwork: A guide to good practice*. London: The Concrete Society.

Joyce, M. D. 1982. *Site Investigation Practice*. New York: E & FN Spoon.

Latham, M. 1994. *Constructing The Team*. London: HMSO.

Nawy, E. G & Balaguru, P. N. 1985. *Reinforced Concrete: A Fundamental Approach*. London: Prentice-Hall.

Potts, K. F. 1995. *Major Construction Works: Contractual and Financial Management*. Essex: Longman Scientific & Technical.

Proverbs, D. G. 1998. A best practice model for highrise in-situ concrete construction based on French, German and UK contractor performance measures. PhD thesis. Wolverhampton: University of Wolverhampton.

Richardson, J. G. 1977. *Formwork Construction and Practice*. Slough: Viewpoint Publication: Cement and Concrete Association.

Ricouard, M. J. 1982. *Formwork for Concrete Construction*. London: The MacMillan Press Ltd.

Seeley, I. H. & Murray, G. P. (6th ed.) 2001. *Civil Engineering Quantities*. New York: Palgrave.

Skinner, W. H. 1982. The Contractor's use of bills of quantities. *Occasional Paper No.24*. Ascot: The Chartered Institute of Building.

Sutrisna, M. & Potts, K. 2002. Analysing Typical Project Factors for the Early Prediction of Variations. In: Greenwood, D. (ed.); *Proc. 18th Annual ARCOM Conference 1: 391–401, New Castle, 2–4 September 2002*, Reading: ARCOM.

Thomas, H. R., Smith, G. R. & Wright, D. E. 1991. Legal Aspects of Oral Change Orders. *Journal of Construction Engineering and Management* 117 (1): 148–162.

Thomas, R. (2nd ed.) 2001. *Construction Contract Claims*. Hampshire: Palgrave Publisher.

Wallace, I. D. (11th ed.) 1995. *Hudson's Building and Engineering Contracts: including the duties and liabilities 1*. London: Sweet & Maxwell.

Winter, J. 2001. *Valuations of variations under the ICE Conditions of Contracts-the Thrills & Spills of tendering*. www.bakerinfo.com/documents/837_tx.htm, viewed: 22/01/01.

Wynn, A. E. (4th ed.) 1951. *Design and Construction of Formwork for Concrete Structures*. London: Concrete Publications Ltd.

Yogeswaran, K. & Kumaraswamy, M. M. 1999. To instruct or not? The engineer's dilemma, *Construction Management and Economics* 17: 731–743.

An estimating system for construction and demolition waste management

A. Touran, J.Y. Wang, C. Christoforou & N. Dantata
Northeastern University, Boston, Mass., USA

ABSTRACT: This paper describes an estimating system that determines quantities of designated construction and demolition waste (C&D) for residential projects in Massachusetts. C&D waste comes from the following sources: new construction, demolition, and renovation. The C&D waste generated from new construction correlates well with the number of new building permits issued during a given period. A certain percentage of building permits involves demolition of existing structures. The quantity of waste generated from any new building or demolition project can be estimated by knowing the building type and size. We have estimated the quantities of four target materials (wood, gypsum wall-board, carpet, and asphalt shingles) for a variety of dwelling types (such as one-storey, two-storey, etc.) commonly built in Massachusetts as a function of the gross enclosed area of each building (in terms of square feet). These four target materials constitute most of the C&D waste stream (except concrete, brick, and asphalt) and their fate is of great interest to State regulators. In addition, a methodology is presented for estimating the waste generated from renovation/remodeling activity by considering renovations statistics reported by the U.S. Census Bureau.

1 BACKGROUND

Managing solid waste has challenged cities and governments in the past decades. Limited landfill capacity coupled with the difficulty of developing new landfills, especially in the face of environmental concerns and public opposition, has caused regulators to set plans for reducing the disposal of solid waste in landfills. In the United States, the major component of non-municipal solid waste consists of Construction and Demolition (C&D) debris. As an example, in the State of Massachusetts, it is estimated that 95% of non-municipal solid waste is C&D debris. Although C&D waste is generally inert, and therefore, may not pose an environmental threat as great as hazardous waste or typical municipal solid waste, still its large volume results in a major problem for many communities due to the diminishing disposal capacity. In order to respond to this concern, the State of Massachusetts has set a goal of reducing the non-municipal waste by 88% by the year 2010 (Executive Office 2000). In order to reach this goal, the State has proposed to increase the recycling of the C&D debris by banning the disposal of unprocessed C&D waste in the year 2003. While large quantities of C&D debris including concrete, asphalt, brick, and metals are routinely recycled, the State is now focusing on items such as wood, asphalt shingles (used in roofing), plastic films, cardboard, carpet and

gypsum wall-boards as prime targets for recycling. A major problem is that the quantities of specific recyclable material generated by construction activities are not known. While some aggregate data is available from waste management facility's records, this data typically does not provide information regarding the source of generation and the type of waste material. Having an effective means to estimate the quantities of each material type (such as wood, gypsum wall-board, *etc.*) is important for identifying viable recycling alternatives and performing cost and benefit analyses for such alternatives.

As part of a research project funded by the Department of Environmental Protection of the Commonwealth of Massachusetts, the authors have developed an estimating system that determines quantities of designated C&D waste for residential projects at the city and state level.

Residential C&D waste originates from three main sources: new construction, renovation and demolition. The C&D waste generated from new construction correlates well with the number of new building permits issued during a given period. A certain percentage of building projects involve demolition of existing structures. The quantity of waste generated from any new building or demolition project can be estimated based on the building type and size. We have estimated the quantities of four materials (wood, gypsum wall-board, carpet, and asphalt shingles) for a variety of dwelling types (such as one-storey, two-storey, *etc.*) commonly built in Massachusetts. The material generation for each dwelling type is calculated as a function of the gross enclosed area of each building (in terms of square feet). These four target materials constitute most of the C&D waste stream (except concrete, brick, and asphalt) and their fate is of great interest to the State regulators. In the case of new construction projects, the amount of waste as a percentage of the volume or weight of new material is estimated by referring to various industry sources. With regard to the generation of demolition waste, basically all materials in the building contribute to the volume of C&D debris. By knowing the number of building permits in a certain municipality (which identifies building type and estimated cost), our approach is to estimate the number of demolition projects and calculates the quantity of waste generated from new construction and demolition for the four material types indicated (Touran et al. 2003).

This estimating system works as a front-end to a comprehensive systems analysis tool, developed at Northeastern University, that would allow analysts to assess the financial consequences of certain proposed C&D waste management policies on the construction industry. The model is developed as an Excel® spreadsheet file. An overview of the system is illustrated in Figure 1. The systems analysis model includes major components of the C&D waste management system – beginning with generation, through source separation, processing, recycling (if the market exists), and final disposal. Based on the mass balance principle, the model accounts for any residual quantities generated at every intermediate stage. The link between any two modules in Figure 1 represents transportation activity, which is also a cost-incurring management activity and is included in the model simulation. A Visual Basic®

user interface has been developed to guide the user through the input process in an interactive environment. This paper describes the highlighted portion of the system (Fig. 1).

2 METHODOLOGY

Our objective is to estimate the quantity of the following four C&D materials: wood, drywall (gypsum wall-boards), roof asphalt shingles, and carpet generated in the Commonwealth of Massachusetts, USA. The source of C&D debris resulting from building construction can be traced back to the following activities: (1) new construction, (2) demolition, and (3) renovation and repair projects. These projects can be classified as residential or commercial. In this paper we focus on debris generated from new construction, renovation and demolition in residential projects. One can find the Commonwealth of Massachusetts building permit statistics at the following website: *http://www.danter.com/ STARTSWATCH/*. In this website, the number of building permits issued every year in various cities and towns is reported. Building permits are broken down into single unit, two-unit, three or four-unit, five or more units. Each of these potential construction projects generates C&D debris. As an example, an estimator factors in around 10% of wood to account for possible waste (Reiner 1981). A waste factor of 5% for drywalls and 5% to 8% for asphalt shingles has been suggested (Dagostino & Feigenbaum 1999). Values of 5% to 15% waste have been suggested as estimates of construction material waste in new projects.

In the case of demolition projects, without source separation efforts, one can consider 100% of material as C&D debris. Massachusetts does not report data on demolition permits. State of Connecticut, however, reports demolition permit statistics on an annual basis. We analyzed Connecticut demolition permit data and compared it with Massachusetts.

The general trend in building permits in both states is similar. Furthermore, both of these neighboring states seem to be affected by the same economic factors. This allowed us to use Connecticut data for estimating the number of demolition permits in Massachusetts.

For renovation and repair projects, no data is available at the State level but American Housing Survey of the U.S. Census Bureau (2002) lists extensive statistics on building renovation and remodeling data on the internet. We have used these data to estimate the tonnage of waste resulting from repairs and renovation for Massachusetts.

2.1 Estimating waste quantities in new construction

We have used R.S. Means (1999) data for estimating the quantity of wood, drywall, asphalt shingles, and

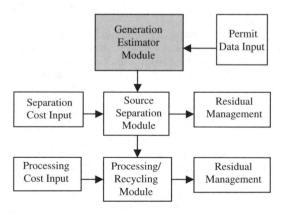

Figure 1. Overview of the C&D waste management systems analysis model.

carpet in various residential and commercial projects. R.S. Means is a company that specializes in publishing construction cost and productivity data. An example of factors used for estimating these quantities are shown in Table 1.

Using these factors, number of building permits reported for various towns and cities, and type of residential buildings (number of units per building permit), we estimated quantities for the five items mentioned in Table 1. Then by assuming a waste factor of 10 to 12%, we estimated the volume of waste generated from new construction projects. Assumptions with regard to construction types and multi-unit permits are described in Christoforou (2002). Although the U.S. Census Bureau estimates that only 98% of all building permits are actually built, we did not adjust our estimate because of other uncertainties involved in the analysis.

2.2 Estimating waste quantities in demolition

In order to estimate quantities of demolition waste for Massachusetts, we resorted to Connecticut's demolition permit data. The ratio of the number of demolition permits over the number of new construction was calculated for the past few years. We assumed that the average ratio for Connecticut is valid for Massachusetts as well.

This assumption is reasonable because the housing style in two states is very similar. The economic drivers for building construction appear to have impacted both states in a similar manner. As an example, Figure 2 shows variations in housing permits in Massachusetts and Connecticut during 1995–2000. It can be seen that these numbers closely follow each other. The correlation coefficient between the housing permits in these two states during this six-year period was calculated as 0.93.

Since both states are more or less similar in terms of population density and number of older residences, it seems plausible that the number of demolition permits may vary in similar ways. We used an average ratio of 19% (demolitions over new construction projects), which was calculated based on Connecticut's permit statistics, to estimate the number of residential demolition projects for the Commonwealth of Massachusetts.

3 ESTIMATING SYSTEM

The system for estimating the waste tonnage from new construction and demolition is developed using an Excel® spreadsheet. By entering the appropriate housing statistics, the system first calculates quantities of each of the specified material. Using appropriate unit weights for the four building materials and the number and types of residential projects reported in building permit statistics data, we then estimated the total tonnage of C&D debris for Massachusetts for 2000 (Table 2).

Because the housing permit data is reported according to towns and cities, one can generate a spatial distribution for the C&D debris generated. This becomes an effective planning tool for siting of processing plants, allocating resources to C&D recycling effort, and conducting economic analysis for the C&D recycling activities. We have done this by developing a Geographic Information Systems (GIS) interface that

Table 1. Typical factors used in the estimating system.*

	1-storey average residence	2-storey average residence
Wood (fbm/ft^2)	3.21	3.18
Plywood (ft^2/ft^2)	3.27	3.01
Drywall (ft^2/ft^2)	3.29	5.57
Shingles (ft^2/ft^2)	2.49	1.25
Carpet (ft^2/ft^2)	0.4	0.4

* Based on R.S. Means Residential Cost Data (1999) and converted to quantities per square foot of gross enclosed area of the building.

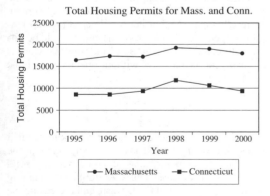

Figure 2. Number of housing permits in Connecticut and Massachusetts.

Table 2. Estimates of residential C&D for Massachusetts in 2000.

	Construction (tons)	Demolition (tons)	Total (tons)
Wood	30,800	56,300	87,100
Drywall	20,100	38,000	58,100
Shingles	5,800	11,300	17,100
Carpet	500	900	1,400
Totals	57,200	106,500	163,700

maps C&D quantities to towns and cities in Massachusetts (Touran et al. 2003).

3.1 Estimating the waste from renovation activity

Renovation waste includes materials from construction and demolitions activities during improvements and repairs to existing buildings. Renovation waste quantities vary widely based on the type of renovation project. Some projects are small (e.g. cabinet replacement) while others are extensive remodelling work (e.g. additions to buildings). Also, some projects generate only one type of material waste such as wood when cabinets are replaced and other jobs generate multiple material wastes such as room additions. Therefore, renovation waste estimates are more complex than that of construction and demolitions.

The U.S. Census Bureau provides the number of renovations for owner occupied units according to job type. These are available on the Internet at http://www.census.gov/hhes/www/ahs.html. Our analysis only considers those jobs that produce wood, gypsum, asphalt shingles, and carpet wastes. These jobs are listed in the website under carpeting, roofing, kitchen remodelling, bathroom remodeling, other remodeling, and additions. Jobs not considered include heating remodeling, and driveway replacements. The amount of waste may be an overestimate for the four materials of interest because other materials are likely wasted especially in the remodeling jobs. Furthermore, the data lacks sufficient specificity that is needed to arrive at an accurate estimate. For example, in a kitchen remodeling project, one may be dealing with metal cabinets or tiles removal.

The amount of waste generated for each job type is estimated using the estimates from the report by Franklin Associates (1998). This report provides a methodology for estimating the volume/tonnage of construction and demolition debris. It also gives average waste estimates for various renovation/remodeling jobs. As an example, according to the Franklin report, a typical room addition generates 0.75 tons of waste.

Using the Census Bureau statistics and the Franklin report waste estimates, the total C&D waste in the U.S. was estimated. These statistics are for the year 2001, which is the latest renovation data available from the U.S. Census Bureau. The data from the Census Bureau represent only owner-occupied units. Owner-occupied units represent 66% of total occupied units. Estimated values were adjusted accordingly to arrive at an estimate for the total residences in the U.S. In order to get the estimate for Massachusetts, the percentage of houses in Massachusetts is used. According to the U.S. Census data, as of 2001, there were 105.5 million houses in the U.S. of which 2.32% or 2.44 million are in Massachusetts. The total waste estimates for the U.S. were multiplied by 2.32% to get the estimates for

Table 3. Estimated residential renovation waste for Massachusetts (2001) (Wood, Gypsum, Asphalt Shingles, and Carpet).

Category (tons)	Waste
Carpeting	26,071
Asphalt roofs	195,220
Wood roofs	60,703
Kitchen remodelling	63,678
Bathroom remodelling	59,668
Other remodelling	10,726
Additions	45,139
Total	461,205

Table 4. Estimate of C&D waste in Massachusetts.

	Waste (tons)	Percent
New construction: Year 2000	57,200	9.15%
Demolition: Year 2000	106,500	17.04%
Renovation: Year 2001	461,205	73.80%
Total	624,905	100.00%

Massachusetts. Table 3 shows the results of the renovation waste estimates by individual job category.

3.2 Total C&D waste

Combining the data from Tables 2 and 3, one can estimate the total C&D waste in Massachusetts for the four items of interest. Please note that renovation data is from 2001 while construction and demolition data is from 2000. The main reason is that the Census Bureau did not report the renovation statistics for the year 2000. Table 4 gives the summary of results.

One word of caution is necessary. In Table 4, the share of renovation waste relative to new construction and demolition waste appears to be large. Part of the reason is that the renovations estimate may contain items other than the four items of interest (wood, shingles, carpet, and gypsum drywall), but it would be difficult to correct this because of the way that Census Bureau reports the data without specifying all the needed information.

4 CONCLUSION

Managing solid waste in the face of shrinking landfill capacity is a challenging task for many states in the U.S. The major component of non-municipal solid waste consists of C&D debris. A problem in planning for the management of C&D waste and increasing the recycling rate is that the quantities of specific recyclable material generated by construction activities are not known. While some aggregate data is available, this data typically does not provide critical information such as the source of generation and the type of material. Having an effective means to estimate the quantities of recyclable materials is critical for any effort in developing a successful recycling program. In this paper we presented an estimating system for four C&D items: wood, asphalt-shingles, gypsum dry-wall, and carpet. We also presented a methodology for estimating waste volume generated by renovation projects. Our approach also facilitates the development of a spatial distribution of C&D waste generation. These estimates can be used as input to the system analysis tools that will help planners in market development, economic analysis, and planning for C&D recycling efforts.

ACKNOWLEDGMENT

This project is funded by a grant from the Massachusetts Department of Environmental Protection. This support is gratefully acknowledged. We are also indebted to James McQuade and Peter Allison for their advice and contribution to this endeavor.

REFERENCES

Christoforou, C. 2002. *A Systems Analysis Tool to Assist Decisions in Construction and Demolition Waste Management.* MS Thesis. Northeastern University, Boston.

Dagostino, F.R. & L. Feigenbaum. 1999. *Estimating in Building Construction.* Prentice-Hall. p. 256 & 291.

Executive Office of Environmental Affairs. 2000. *Beyond 2000 – Solid Waste Master Plan.* Department of Environmental Protection, Commonwealth of Massachusetts. December.

Franklin Associates. 1998. *Characterization of Building-related Construction and Demolition Debris in the United States.* Prepared for the United States Environmental Protection Agency.

Reiner, L.E. 1981. *Methods and Materials of Residential Construction.* Prentice-Hall. p. 156.

R.S. Means 1999. *Residential Cost Data.* 18th Ed., R.S. Means Co., Kingston, Mass.

Touran, A., J. Wang, C. Christoforou & N. Dantata. 2003. A System for Estimating Residential Construction and Demolition Debris. *Proceedings, 11th Rinker International Conference on Deconstruction and Materials Reuse.* Gainesville, Florida.

U.S. Census Bureau. 2002. American Housing Survey. http://www.census.gov/hhes/www/ahs.html.

Steel fabricator involvement in project design

M.J. Horman & M.H. Pulaski
Penn State University, University Park, PA, USA

C.M. Hewitt
American Institute of Steel Construction (AISC), Chicago, IL, USA

J.P. Cross
AISC Marketing, Chicago, IL, USA

ABSTRACT: The involvement of specialty contractors in project design has been proven to benefit the schedule, quality, and cost of delivery for construction projects, but quantification of the impact that steel fabricators have on the project is minimal. This paper presents and analyzes data collected by the American Institute of Steel (AISC) on the patterns and roles of steel fabricators in project design. The analysis quantifies how deeply steel fabricators are presently involved in building projects. A model of the levels of steel fabricator involvement is used to classify the data collected. The results suggest that steel fabricators are involved in the early stages of the design process, but do little to quantify the impact that their involvement has on the successful outcome of a project. The paper proposes further research to identify and measure the impact of steel fabricators on project design so as to improve the effectiveness of their contribution.

1 INTRODUCTION

The involvement of specialty contractors in the design of a project has been proven to benefit the schedule, quality, and cost of delivery for construction projects, but quantification of the impact that steel fabricators have on the project is minimal. Specialty steel contractors can provide important fabrication and construction advice at the points in the design where initial decisions about structural system characteristics are being made. While good designers and engineers have a sound general knowledge of the issues involved in project delivery, specialty contractors can provide advice on project-specific issues and concerns. Advice may include cost estimates, advice on material selection, value engineering suggestions and design detail recommendations. Often systems need to be tailored to the design requirements of a specific building. Fabricator insights can be used to address these types of construction and design coordination issues in the most effective and efficient manner possible. Despite the intuitive benefit that this expertise can provide, there has been little critical analysis to quantify and understand the impact that early involvement of steel fabricators has on project performance.

Data has been collected by the American Institute of Steel Construction (AISC) on the patterns and roles of steel fabricators in project design. This paper presents and analyzes the data. The analysis shows how steel fabricators are presently involved in building projects and provides a measure of the penetration of steel fabricators into project design activities. A model of the levels of steel fabricator involvement is presented to classify the data collected.

2 ROLES FOR STEEL FABRICATORS IN DESIGN

The role that steel fabricators play in design can be substantial and might include any of the following.

- Develop creative solutions to complex architectural challenges through access to the most innovative structural steel technologies.
- Articulate space needs for construction processes.
- Address fabrication and construction capabilities in the design process.
- Ensure the most economical use of material through standardization of beam and connection sizes.

- Make sure design decisions that utilize the different abilities and strengths that different fabrication shop set-ups allow.
- Indicate supplier lead times and reliabilities based on accurate projections of material availability.
- Suggest member alternatives based on material availability and project erection phasing.
- Work with the architect to agree upon the building geometry and column locations early in the process, with the expressed need for all designers to maintain them as agreed upon, to permit pre-ordering of material.

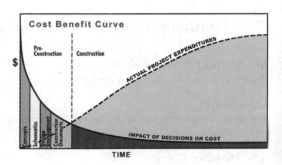

Figure 1. Level of influence on project costs. Source Haskell Company, after Paulson (1986).

3 LITERATURE REVIEW

The involvement of steel fabricators in design has received limited attention in the published literature. The ability of subcontractors to influence the performance of a project by being involved early has been the subject of much broader interest. There is some published research about the impact that mechanical and electrical contractors have on project design, but little specific research has been published on steel fabricator involvement in design.

A number of authors have studied the significant amount of specialty steel contractor expertise relevant to conceptual and schematic design as well as to the detailing phases of the project (Tommelein & Weissenberger 1999, Cross 2001, Ricker 2000). Holesapple (1982) argued that projects that take advantage of fabricator capabilities should observe an increase in the overall performance of the project. Moreover, he suggested that the best way to utilize these capabilities is to bring the fabricator on the project at the outset.

3.1 Contractor involvement in design

Early involvement in projects was first studied by Paulson (1976) who showed that the ability to influence a project, its progress and outcomes diminished as costs were expended in the project (refer Fig. 1). Although relatively generic, this was a seminal piece of work that has formed the basis for greater involvement of construction expertise in the design phases of projects. A substantial advantage of early involvement in projects is the opportunity to improve design constructability. Russell et al. (1992) showed that a structured constructability program implemented early in the project could generate 10.2% savings in project time and 7.2% savings to cost. Other researchers have reported similar savings to the project due to early contractor involvement (CII 1993, Jergeas & Van der Put 2001, Eldin 1988, Tatum 1990, AbulHassan 2001). While highly relevant to the involvement of the steel fabricator

in design, most of the research concerning early involvement addresses the general contractor and construction manager.

Some work has investigated the early involvement of specialty contractors in project design. Sanvido & Konchar (1999) reported in a study of over 300 design-build projects, the largest single difference between the top 25% of projects and the bottom 25% of projects was how well the subcontractors were involved and used in the project, especially their contribution to design. One important finding was that specialty contractors involved at least before 20% of the design is complete had the best performance (Sanvido & Konchar 1999). This study focused on mechanical and electrical contractors. The early involvement in projects is not only impacting project performance, but is flowing through to the specialty contractor profitability on these projects (Rowings et al. 2000). Gill et al. (2002) showed how specialty contractor knowledge used in design led to improvements in process efficiency and quality. Beyond these studies, no attempts were found in the literature to quantify the impact of specialty steel contractor involvement in early design.

A study by Thomas and Sanvido (2000) quantified the impact the steel fabricator has on construction performance. In that study, the loss of steel labor productivity on three projects was calculated to be 16.6%, 28.4% and 56.8%. Problems encountered on the project were due to late vendor deliveries, fabrication errors and out of sequence deliveries. The correlated schedule slippage for the projects was estimated to be between 50% and 129%. All three projects were built using a multiple-prime delivery system and design was complete before procurement. This study provides some measure of the negative consequences of selecting the fabricator late in the project. Importantly, the literature review found no attempts to quantify the positive impact fabricators can have on project performance when introduced early in the project.

Figure 2. Five levels of involvement. Source: American Institute of Steel Construction

3.2 Levels of steel fabricator involvement in design

Projects in the AEC (Architecture, Engineering, Construction) industry are strongly design and engineering driven. Cross et al. (2001) were interested in a more holistic approach to steel building design and construction and developed a model to classify and explain different level of steel fabricator involvement. In large part, this model was developed to encourage the use of design-build in steel projects. As shown in Figure 2, this model has five levels of involvement.

The first level, *PROVIDER*, represents involvement no different than that of bidding work on a traditional design-bid-build project. A design-build team performs the design work and coordinates construction, but the steel is still let out to bid.

At the second level, *RESOURCE*, the fabricator provides comments on the design drawings before they are released for bid. The comments may include a review of the completeness of the drawings and suggestions for value engineering. No guarantee exists that the fabricator investing time in the process will be the fabricator selected to perform the work.

At the third level, *ALLY*, the fabricator meets with the project team and evaluates the project. The fabricator works closely with the project team and has the opportunity to influence design choices, suggest cost saving alternatives and tailor the final design to the efficiencies of their particular shop. The steel on the project is still a bid item.

At the fourth level, *PARTNER*, the steel fabricator works with a structural engineer to provide preliminary framing options and a conceptual estimate. Involvement may begin at as early as 10% design completion. The conceptual estimate forms the basis of the fabricator's negotiated fee for the project. The steel fabricator has sole responsibility for all of the steel related activities on the project and controls all the risks associated with project performance by designing to a price rather than pricing a design.

At the fifth level, *MEMBER*, the fabricator is a member of team before the proposal stage of the project. Advantages and responsibilities are the same as they are in the Partner role, but include even earlier involvement, closer contact with the project owner and control of the structural system selection. In some cases the fabricator may bring the project to the design-build team. As a member of the team, the fabricator focuses on the relationships between team members and successful project completion.

There is a growing body of research on the early involvement of specialty contractors in design, but the research has not yet examined the impact of steel fabricator involvement in the design process. There is still much to learn about the specific advantages of steel fabricator involvement in design and their roles. An important question to be addressed at this early stage is how extensively steel fabricators are involved in project design.

4 METHOD

A survey of steel fabricators was performed using the above framework to determine their levels of involvement in projects. The survey was conducted by AISC in June of 2002. Surveys were sent by mail to a total of 704 AISC-member fabricating firms and their subsidiaries. Responses were received by mail and tabulated. The following questions were included in the survey:

- As a general estimate, what percentage of your design-build work *by dollar volume* would fall into each of the 5 levels: provider; resource; ally; partner; member?
- What percentage of your current work involves some form of design-build project delivery?
- Have you seen the opportunity for design-build work increase in the past year?
- Have you seen your involvement in design-build project increase in the past year?
- Are you using electronic data interchange (EDI) to accelerate your ability to detail your design-build projects?
- What is the biggest challenge you face performing design-build work?

5 RESULTS

Fifty-seven surveys (8.1%) were returned. The results to the question concerning the levels of involvement are shown in Figure 3. Most responses received were at the lowest level of involvement on the scale (Provider) at 27%. A slightly smaller proportion of responses (19%) were provided at the Resource level. The proportions at Ally and Partner continue to decrease (13% and 9% respectively). Responses at the highest level of involvement, Member, slightly increased to 12%. Clearly, and as might be expected, most responses were provided at

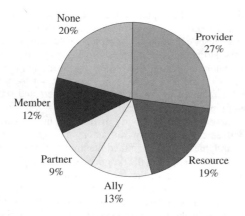

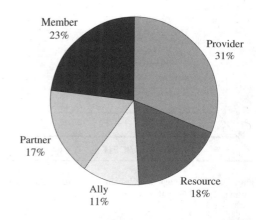

Figure 3. Levels of involvement distribution for 2002, measured by dollar volume of design-build work (n = 57).

Figure 4. Levels of involvement distribution for 2001, measured by dollar volume of design-build work (separate study).

lower rather than higher levels of involvement. Also, worthy of note is that 20% of the responses did not indicate involvement in any of the categories.

A similar study was performed in 2001 as a precursor to this study. These results are provided in Figure 4. Care is needed in closely comparing the results between these studies, but it can be seen that the proportional level of involvement at Member, Partner, and Provider level were greater in the survey for 2001 than in the 2002 survey. All respondents to the 2001 survey indicated some level of involvement. However, the None category was added to the 2002 survey to allow respondents to indicate that they did not perform any design-build work. There seem to be changes in levels of involvement. However, it is not clear from this general comparison whether there is a trend away from greater levels of involvement or whether there is a proportional increase in lower level involvement.

Design-build projects provide the greatest opportunities for steel fabricators and other constructors to be more involved in the early phases of the project and respondents were asked about the volume of work they performed that was design-build. Figure 5 shows that 16% of respondents were involved in some form of design-build project. DBIA estimates that 35% of all projects are delivered using design-build (ZweigWhite 2002). If this is accurate then the 16% involved in design-build projects represent a 46% steel market share for design-build projects. This compares with a national market share of 51% for structural steel (AISC Marketing 2003).

Correlation was analyzed in the data between levels of involvement and percentage of design-build work. It was hypothesized that contractors who do more design-build work would have higher levels of involvement in their projects—this being a typical reason for adopting design-build project delivery. Statistical correlation analysis was used to compare the percentage of work

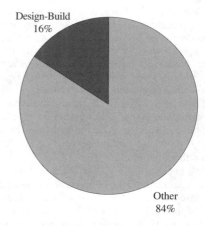

Figure 5. Percentage of work that is design-build.

allocated to Member status by the respondents to their percentage of work that was design-build. A very weak correlation was found with a value computed at 0.1494. (Correlations above 0.8 are typically regarded as strong and correlations around 0.5 are regarded as moderate. Correlations below 0.4 are not usually regarded as significant.) Work allocated to both Member and Partner status was combined and then compared to percentage of work that was design-build. A slightly more significant correlation value of 0.1900 was computed. The most significant value computed was when Member, Partner and Ally categories were combined (0.2117). Correlation was also assessed between the group of classifications of None, Provider and Resource and the proportion of work that was design-build. A correlation was computed to the value of −0.2567. It seems that there is only a marginal correlation between contractors who do more design-build projects and having higher levels of project involvement.

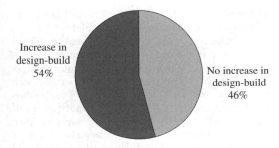

Figure 6.   Increased opportunity for design-build work.

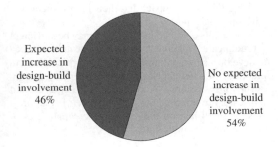

Figure 7.   Increased involvement in design-build work.

In the same line of questioning about the perceived correlation between design-build projects and higher levels of involvement, the future of design-build was explored. Figure 6 shows 54% of respondents saw design-build work increase in the past year. Figure 7 shows that the expectation for the future is slightly less optimistic with 46% of respondents expecting there to be a future increase in design-build involvement.

The survey also probed the level of electronic data interchange (EDI) use by steel fabricators. It was found that 46% of respondents used EDI on their projects. This was not a surprising result, but what was of greater interest was the potential correlation between levels of EDI use and levels of project involvement. It was hypothesized that contractors who have higher levels of involvement in their projects would be more likely to use developed forms of information exchange like EDI. Again, statistical correlation analysis was used to compare the percentage of work allocated to Member status by the respondents and their use of EDI. A correlation was found with a value computed at 0.2500. Work allocated to both Member and Partner status was then compared (together) to the use of EDI. A slightly more significant correlation value of 0.2951 was computed. The most significant value computed was when Member, Partner and Ally categories were combined (0.3357). Correlation was also assessed between the group of classifications of None, Provider and Resource and the use of EDI. A correlation was computed to the value of −0.3362. This is consistent

Table 1.   Challenges for steel fabricators to design-build.

Challenge	Tally
Shopping work after input	6
Early marketing leads	6
Still treated as a commodity	4
Understanding what it is	3
Cost to enter	3
Time to meet schedule	3
Communication	3

with the other results obtained. These results show a slightly moderate correlation between higher levels of project involvement and use of EDI.

Respondents were also asked about the challenges they faced to the increased involvement of projects. Table 1 shows the top seven ranked responses. The tally method was used to rank responses. This method simply totals the number of responses for each challenge. The equal top challenges seen by fabricators to greater involvement concern how fabricator expertise is used in design. The third ranked issue concerns how fabricator expertise is perceived by the project design team. The four equal fourth ranked issues concern the strategies and obligations that early involvement brings. There are two themes to the challenges identified. The first is how the design team (architect, consulting engineers, and owner) uses the expertise of fabricators, and the second concerns the ways fabricator expertise is best utilized in design. These are both important insights.

6   DISCUSSION

The results of the survey indicate a small penetration of steel fabricators into the design of projects. Although the involvement is not extensive, the results seem to indicate changes in levels of involvement. However, it is not clear whether there is a trend away from greater levels of involvement or whether there is a proportional increase in lower level involvement. The latter might be expected in circumstances where new companies were just beginning to pursue greater levels of design involvement and were starting at the "bottom of the ladder". A booming construction market may be the reason for the higher 2001 results. Broader data reported by DBIA suggests there is an industry-wide decline in design-build projects and this would suggest a short term variation.

The results concerning the insignificant correlation between design-build projects and higher levels of design involvement is noteworthy. A moderate to strong correlation between these two variables was expected. It is not clear why the low correlation result was returned, but the result may relate to the inadequacy of practices used to integrate fabricators into the design process.

It could also mean that design-build project delivery in the case of steel fabricators does not increase design involvement. In any case, the results suggest the need for further research to understand what is happening.

The current and future prospects of design-build project delivery suggest a slight increase in this type of project delivery method.

The level of EDI use lacking correlation with higher levels of involvement is also interesting. It seems that technology is not a major component to the issue of greater fabricator involvement in design either because the technology levels are satisfactory or that this is not a significant issue. Certainly, there was no mention of it in the challenges analysis.

The challenges facing design-build related primarily to how the design team uses the expertise of fabricators, and the ways fabricators best inject their expertise in design. Clearly, research needs to examine how fabricator knowledge is best used in design and one place to contribute to this is to identify ways to overcome these challenges.

There has been minimal penetration of steel fabricators into the market. There are things still impeding this involvement and further, detailed research is needed to understand why and what can be done to improve it.

7 FURTHER RESEARCH

The results of this survey provide a good idea of where fabricators are getting involved in project design and what impedes them. This is important but does little to show what practices (if any) impact project performance. It has to be extrapolated from research on other specialty contractors that greater steel fabricator involvement earlier in design will benefit the performance of the project. Yet, other specialty contractors are faced with the same dilemma as steel fabricators: Where can we have the greatest impact in the project? Which of our actions most substantially benefit the project and the owner's goals for the project? Little is known about this. A detailed quantitative study showing the impact of actions, behaviors, activities, and practices on project performance is needed for steel fabricators. This is the only real way to develop robust behaviors in project participants (Sanvido 2002, Sanvido & Taylor 2000). Without this evidence, steel projects run the risk of losing a large part of their competitive edge over other projects. Scientific analysis will allow fundamental principles of sound practice to be established and permit steel projects to be designed, fabricated and constructed with greatest success.

8 CONCLUSIONS

This paper reported the results of a study into the patterns of steel fabricator penetration into project design.

The results indicate the involvement of steel fabricators in design is not extensive, but is notable.

While the results suggest that more steel fabricators are involved in the design process, questions remain about the impact of increased steel fabricator involvement in design. It is not clear at what point of the design process the greatest benefits accrue from early fabricator involvement, nor is it clear what specific type of design input is most beneficial. This paper outlined an agenda for future research to measure the impact of steel fabricators on project design. Research should provide guidance as to what level of involvement a steel fabricator should and should not be pursuing and indicate the likely impact that their involvement will have on project performance.

The results obtained in this paper may be sufficient for rudimentary arguments, but more research is needed to develop a stronger knowledge base of principles and practices of steel fabricator involvement in design. Further investigation would benefit both engineers and fabricators to improve the performance of steel projects, and will help to fully realize the capabilities of steel fabricators in design.

REFERENCES

AbulHassan, H. 2001. *A Framework for Applying Concurrent Engineering Principles to the Construction Industry*. Ph.D. Dissertation. The Pennsylvania State University, USA.

AISC Marketing. 2003. Construction Statistics – 2002 and Forecast for the Year 2003. *General Bulletin #2245*. Feb. Chicago: AISC Marketing.

Construction Industry Institute (CII) Constructability Task Force. 1993. *Constructability Implementation Guide*. Austin, TX: CII.

Cross, J. 2001. Design-Build and the Steel Fabricator. *Modern Steel Construction*, November.

Cross, J., Liddy, W. & Miller, B. 2001. Making Steel a Design-Build Asset: Integrating the Steel Fabricator into the Design-Build Project Team. In *Proceedings of the 2001 Professional Design-Build Conference*, DBIA, Boston, USA, October 24–26.

Eldin, N. 1988. Constructability Improvement of Project Designs. *Journal of Construction Engineering and Management* 114(4): 631–640.

Gil, N., Tommelein, I.D., Kirkendall, R.L. & Ballard, G. 1998. Contribution of Specialty Contractor Knowledge to Early Design. In *Proceedings of the Sixth Conference of the International Group for Lean Construction (IGLC-6)*, Sao Paulo, Brazil.

Holesapple, C.J. 1982. The Fabricator/Designer Connection. *ASCE Civil Engineering* 52(11): 64–98.

Jergeas, G. & Van der Put, J. 2001. Benefits of Constructability on Construction Projects. *Journal of Construction Engineering and Management* 127(4): 281–290.

Paulson, B.C. 1976. Designing to Reduce Construction Costs. *Journal of Construction Engineering and Management* 102(4): 587–592.

Ricker, D.T. 2000. Value Engineering for Steel Construction. *Modern Steel Construction*. April.

Rowings, J.E., Federle, M.O. & Rusk, J. 2000. *Design-Build Methods for the Electrical Contracting Industry*. Report to the Electrical Contracting Foundation (ECF). Bethesda, MD: ECF.

Russell, M., Gugel, J. & Radtke, M. 1992. *Benefits and Costs of Constructability: Four Case Studies*. Austin, TX: Construction Industry Institute.

Sanvido, V.E. 2002. *Selecting Specialty Contractors: Proposed document for the design build manual of practice*. Washington, DC: DBIA.

Sanvido, V. & Konchar, M. 1999. *Selecting Project Delivery Systems: Comparing Design-Build, Design-Bid-Build and Construction Management at Risk*. State College, PA: Project Delivery Institute.

Sanvido, V. & Taylor, C. 2000. *Selecting Design-Build Subcontractors*. Presentation at the 2000 Professional Design-Build Conference, DBIA/AIA, San Diego, USA, October 4–7.

Tatum, C.B. 1990. Integrating Design and Construction to Improve Project Performance. *Project Management Journal* 21(2): 35–42.

Thomas, H.R. & Sanvido, V.E. 2000. Role of the Fabricator in Labor Productivity. *Journal of Construction Engineering and Management* 126(5): 358–365.

Tommelein, I.D. & Weissenberger, M. 1999. More Just-In-Time: Location of Buffers in Structural Steel Supply and Construction Process. In *Proceedings of the Seventh conference of the International Group for Lean Construction: IGLC-7*. U. of Cal., Berkeley. 109–120.

ZweigWhite. 2002. *2002 Design/Build Survey of Design & Construction Firms*. Natick, MA: ZweigWhite.

System-based Vision for Strategic and Creative Design, Bontempi (ed.)
© 2003 Swets & Zeitlinger, Lisse, ISBN 90 5809 599 1

Existing and emerging delivery system for construction projects

K.A. Tenah
M.E. Rinker, Sr. School of Building Construction at Gainesville, FL, USA

ABSTRACT: The whole process of building projects, from need identification to completion, operation, and maintenance, has traditionally been a fragmented effort of the owner (who is or represents the user of the project, the architect/engineer (who are in charge of design), and the builder (who constructs the project). Since the early 1970s, there has developed an increased awareness of the need to improve the management of planning, design, engineering, construction and maintenance of projects due to costly budget overruns, inadequate quality control, excessive delay in project completion, and project complexities. As a result, many varied management roles have emerged to deal with these problems and issues. Although there are many types of contracts and organizational arrangements, these delivery systems can be roughly classified as traditional design-bid-build, design-build, professional construction management (CM), build operate and transfer (BOT), joint ventures, and variations or modifications of these forms. These basic forms of project delivery systems will be the focus of discussion in this paper. The paper defines these project delivery systems and discusses how they affect the construction industry.

It is important to define these project delivery systems and also understand how they affect the construction industry. The paper thus lists, defines and compares project delivery systems available to determine (a) how each system best meets the owner's goals and (b) the circumstances under which they are best used. After defining the project delivery systems, the circumstances under which each of them is used will be discussed. Advantages and disadvantages of each deliver system are given. The agents for changes in project delivery, their causes, goals and objectives are given. The findings of studies conducted in Florida to determine the delivery system preferred by the Florida contractors are given.

The paper concludes that (a) professional construction management (CM) is the preferred project delivery system because CM brings an outsider to assist in the project; (b) the new project delivery systems involve all team members working together and having the project as a common goal; (c) design-build works very well combining design and construction under one company; (d) joint ventures can work in many different ways to bring the separate entities together; and (e) BOT is fast gaining acceptance in many countries to bring major infrastructure projects to fruition (Cruz 1998, Kaufman 1997, Marshall 1997, Tenah 1985, Tenah & Guevara 1985, Williams 1989, United Nations ... 1996).

1 EXISTING PROJECT DELIVERY SYSTEM

Construction practices have been traditionally based on an owner identifying a need to build a project and proceeding to hire an architect to develop the design, plans and specifications in accordance with owner's needs. The design, once completed, would initiate the bidding process. Virtually mandated in the public sector, the lowest bidding constructor would be awarded the work. On private jobs, selected constructors are often asked to submit bids for the project or a single constructor might be asked to negotiate with the owner. This arrangement was thought to be most economic

means for an owner to obtain the desired project for the lowest price. This approach is called "design-bid-build" and it involves the owner, designer, and constructor in the "construction triangle" that has existed for many years (See Figure 1). This arrangement is structured so these entities work separately and often in adversarial manner and/or relationship (Tenah 1985, Tenah & Guevara 1985). Not surprisingly, legal disputes and other related problems have associated with design-bid-build. The problems are mostly disputes between parties regarding the extent of responsibility that each party has for different facets of the project (Tenah 1985). Several trade and national organizations

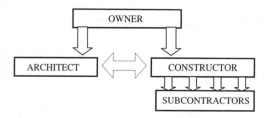

Figure 1.   Traditional design-bid-build relationship.

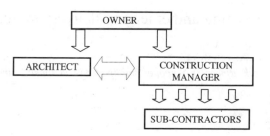

Figure 2.   Construction manager at risk.

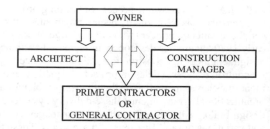

Figure 3.   Construction management as agent of the owner.

have developed contract languages designed to protect their respective constituents by shifting responsibility to other parties.

The advantages of the traditional design-bid-build process are: (a) it embodies a design in a set of substantially complete documents that are capable of transmitting all owner's wishes to the constructor; (b) the contractual relationships between the constructor and his/her subcontractors make it easy for the constructor to fire, replace, or take over from subcontractor in he/she defaults; and (c) owners are often guaranteed maximum price for completing the entire project.

The major disadvantage is that the whole process is sequential in nature, i.e., design comes first, then bidding, and finally construction (Tenah 1985). If any party fails to meet its obligation, the entire process is delayed. Another problem is that the owner does not really have control over cost of the project. The owner knows the expected cost of the project at the end of the bidding phase, but this may be not the lowest cost. The greatest deficiency in this process is the lack of continuity between the design and construction, as these phases are separate efforts. Another problem is the sacrifice of quality to increase profits by the general contractor. The general contractor and subcontractors often are encouraged contractually to cut corners to increase their profits. Furthermore, there are abuses of change orders, which often lead to unnecessary increases in the overall cost of the project in this process. There are also times where the designer is unfamiliar with the construction process and has difficulty in controlling costs. In essence, the traditional process does not create a unified team in which experience, feedback and new ideas are shared (Tenah & Guevara 1985). There is also no overall management or coordination. There is a distinct separation between design and construction, which are viewed as two isolated processes.

2   DEFINITIONS, CONCEPTS AND IMPACT OF EMERGING PROJECT DELIVERY SYSTEMS

2.1   Definitions, concepts and impact of construction management (CM)

The Associated General Contractors of America (AGC) defines construction management (CM) as a

process that " … treats the project planning, design, and construction phases as integrated tasks within a construction system" (Tenah & Guevara 1985). These tasks are assigned to a construction team consisting of the owner, construction manager, contractor, and the design professional. This team works together from the beginning or conceptual phase to the end of the project at the facility completion. Because of the CM's expertise, the CM works with the designer from the beginning of the design phase through to the completion of the project. The designer and the CM support each other during the construction phase of the project (Collier 1987). The CM, acting as an advisor, remains a third party that is not involved in the contracts of construction. The CM's contractual relationship with the owner is separate from the others and is limited to providing professional services. The CM usually manages and oversees the entire project with or without being at risk (see Figures 2 & 3). Even when construction management uses a team approach, each party still remains a separate entity (see Figure 2).

The construction management process has some noteworthy advantages. First is the incorporation of the experience of the construction manager during the design phase. "The objective of the combined and coordinated efforts of the owner, architectural-engineer, and the construction manager is to satisfy the owner's construction needs and interests right from the beginning of the planning to the completion of the project. The team works together and carefully examines the interactions between cost, safety, quality and completion schedule so that a facility of maximum value to the owner is realized in the most economic time frame" (Tenah 1985).

This delivery system integrates the owner's agent, with expertise in construction, into the design phase and gives to the owner greater control of the decisions that might influence time, cost, construction techniques, quality, safety and other variables in the construction process. This is the greatest advantage of the CM approach. The CM now becomes a fourth party in the traditional three party system. It can be argued that construction management approach is best suited for large projects because of the additional cost involved by bringing the construction manager on board. However, the savings realized from the addition of the construction manager outweighs the additional cost. Unlike, the traditional method, which is linear, the CM approach lends itself to concurrent design and construction. The CM and the rest of the team work in the owner's best interest to provide the owner with the desired project in the shortest time and within the budget. This fosters a reduction in problems within the industry.

2.2 Definitions, concepts and impact of joint ventures

The concept of joint ventures is to combine two or more entities for the purpose of constructing a project (see Figure 4). Joint ventures are created by agreements between the parties and do not include the owners. A joint venture is a new separate company that is temporarily formed; it is a special-purpose partnership (Tenah & Guevara 1985). Usually these entities enter a contractual relationship that defines the roles, responsibilities and duties of each of the parties. The entities will share, under agreed terms, all the profits and losses associated with the job. In addition, the written agreement will clearly delineate such matters as: the working capital, specific functions, responsibilities, and contribution of each joint venturer, supervision of accounting and procurement, and termination of the agreement (Tenah & Guevara 1985).

Joint ventures can be applied to any type of project delivery system. It can be used as a traditional, design-build, or construction management. Joint venture agreements also are created to meet project requirements such as mandated Minority Business Enterprise (MBE) participation. A small minority firm could team up with a large firm to get a project and benefit from the results of completing a large project for which the firm would otherwise not qualify. Figure 4 portrays a design-build joint venture where the constructor could be a joint venture with a separate design firm.

The major advantages of joint ventures are (a) the pooling of resources, assets, facilities, and skills of the participating firms and (b) spreading of risks

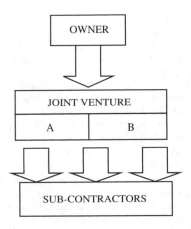

Figure 4. Joint venture entity.

(Tenah & Guevara 1985). Instead of having only one company's expertise, the project's resources are doubled or tripled. The companies entering into the joint venture can now combine their forces and collaborate on their strongest points. The greatest drawback of the system is the "ironing out," in a timely fashion, all the problems created by the relationship that now has emerged out of this joint venture. These joint venture partners will have to work out problems among themselves. This could be an issue especially when they do not agree on the percentage split or matters related to making decisions that all partners can honor. The contractual relationship that emerges is ultimately responsible for the project. The entities must work together to ensure a successful project.

2.3 Definitions, concepts and impact of design-build

Another project delivery method, receiving considerable attention in the last five to ten years, is the design-build approach (see Figure 5). This delivery approach focuses on the reduction of the number of contractual relationships. The owner contracts with a single firm, which provides both design and construction services. The design-build firm is known as an autonomous entity. The two previous methods described, traditional method and construction management, have their drawbacks in the number of contractual parties created and the division of responsibilities. The design-build process focuses on just two parties: the owner and the design-build entity. With fewer parties involved in the process of project delivery, the more efficient the process becomes. Design-build closely resembles its early predecessor, master builder, in the project formation and execution.

Design-build has enjoyed a considerable increase in popularity in the past 5 to 10 years. As a result, of the emergence of this delivery system, insurance companies such as C.N.A. Insurance, have begun to offer design liability insurance for contractors who assume primary responsibility for design-build projects. The contractor's design liability program provides direct coverage for design services performed by a contractor's in-house designers ("Design/build ... " 1996). Design-build's popularity has also reached Congress and the White House (Clinton Signs ... 1996). President Clinton signed a bill to allow the use of design-build by federal agencies. The design-build bill details how to proceed when federal agencies want to use this method as a project delivery system. Design and construction related associations are expected to have an input into the regulations of such a development (Clinton Signs ... 1996). In addition, other agencies are assisting in making the implementation of the process easier. The Construction Specifications Institute (CSI) and the Design-Build Institute of America (DBIA) developed a Master Guide Performance Specification System by the end of 1998. This was an ideal for design-build "because specifiers identify the end result (final level of quality and function) rather than the means (installation of individual materials and equipment)" ("CSI, DBIA ... " 1996). Other institutions such as the American Institute of Architects have published different documents that represent the different contractual relationships that exist in the design-build process.

The advantage of a design-build entity is the single contractual relationship that is involved in design and construction (see Figure 5). The concept allows for construction work to begin even when the design is not complete. For the owner, this means they can get a building in a much quicker time period. Also, problems are solved quicker since the designer and the contractor are both on the same team. One common drawback to this system is that there is no one in the design-construction team to represent the owner. The owner needs a representative in that arrangement. In addition, it is difficult to determine and/or control overall cost of the project, since design and construction are occurring at the same time.

2.4 Definitions and concepts of build, operate and transfer (BOT)

BOT is an intricate mechanism based on a relatively straightforward idea that allows governments to expand and improve the toke of infrastructure by tapping resources outside their budget allocations and dept commitments (United Nations ... 1996). Under a BOT arrangement, private investors, both domestic and foreign, build an infrastructure facility, operate it on a commercial basis for an agreed concessionary period and then turn it over to the government on pre-agreed terms. Some projects abandoned by governments due

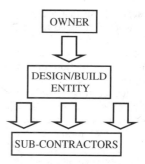

Figure 5. Design-build entity.

to lack of funds have been successfully completed under the BOT scheme. For a project to be undertaken under a BOT scheme, it must be financially and economically sound. It must also be feasible from a practical standpoint and affordable to the users. A BOT project, like any foreign investment, requires a stable political and economic environment. The BOT scheme is fast gaining acceptance in many countries to bring major infrastructure projects to fruition. This trend will continue far into the future, as governments with stretched out budgets look to private and foreign investors to provide the much-needed finances to meet increasing infrastructure demands.

There are, however, lots of risks associated with international BOT projects. These risks must be identified and structures put in place to mitigate their adverse effects on the success of the project. Some factors, which guarantee the success of BOT projects are: (a) the project must be financially sound, feasible and affording; (b) the country risks must be affordable; (c) there must be strong government support, (d) the legal framework must be stable; (e) the bidding procedure must be fair and transparent; (f) the sponsors must have sufficient financial strength; (g) the construction contractor must have sufficient experience and resources; (h) the project risks must be allocated rationally among the parties; (i) the financial structure must provide the sponsors adequate security and (j) the currency, foreign exchange and inflation issues must be solved (United Nations ... 1996).

3 AGENTS OF CHANGES FOR THE PROJECT DELIVERY SYSTEMS

3.1 Causes of the changes

The agents for the changes in the techniques for project delivery in the construction industry are the problems which have been caused in the construction community by the conflict of increasing expectations and the constraints of diminishing resources (Tenah 1985). The existing delivery processes and procedures were unable to ameliorate many of these problems. These problems include: (a) economic difficulties resulting from inflation, energy shortages, high interest rates, recession or depression, life-cycle costing, and rising COSTS; (b) changing world patterns and new society standards (e.g. ISO); (c) shortages of resources, including materials, equipment, skilled workers, and technical and supervisory personnel; (d) increasing governmental, social, and legal obstacles as well as environmental involvement and demands; (e) challenges of time, quality, safety and quality-time-cost tradeoffs; (f) challenges of high-level coordination and controls, including scheduling, resource allocation, and resource leveling; (g) challenges of labor, including jurisdictional disputes, strikes, productivity, and skills; (h) challenges of project complexity, size, and sophistication; (i) increasing technological complexity and more complex inter-dependencies and variations in relationships between organizations and institutions; (j) increasing owner involvement.

These problems accelerated and continued until the construction community, especially owners and users of construction facilities, became aware of the need to improve the management of project planning, design, engineering and construction.

3.2 Results, goals and objectives of changes

As a result of these problems, many different management methods or approaches emerged including those earlier discussed in this paper.

The major goals of the project delivery systems that emerged were to provide (a) efficient and high quality design and construction projects, (b) proper balance of economy, speed, quality and safety and (c) facilities of maximum value in the most economic time frame to their owners and/or users.

The objectives of these project delivery systems include the following (based on the United States General Services Administration (GSA), the Associated General Contractors of America (AGC) and the American Institute of Architects (AIA)) (Partnering Charter ... 1996): (a) promote design and construction excellence in all aspects of project construction program, thereby providing owners and/or project users with outstanding and cost-effective projects; (b) develop and support Qualification-Based Selection (QBS) for architect-engineer and construction management services in both public and private sectors; (c) develop and support open competitive and other bidding methods in the award of construction contracting services; (d) ensure the commitment to continuing education among such owners and professional organizations as GSA, AGC, and AIA at all levels; (e) share the construction industry and government best practices and new approaches to design and construction, including quality management, value engineering,

partnering and alternative dispute resolution (ADR); (f) foster a safe construction environment and instill pride in workmanship; (g) promote use of state-of-the-art and cost-effective design and construction practices; (h) promote environmental awareness in the conduct of all businesses; (i) promote uniform and effective procurement and contract administration practices that foster a fair, open, and competitive contracting environment; (j) advance team building among the participants in design and construction projects; and (k) promote good faith and fair dealings as the foundation of relationships among the participants in public design and construction projects.

4 CONCLUSIONS

After examining the roles of the parties involved in a typical construction project, it is clear that conflicts and disputes are caused by the lack of communication between the parties. Thus, communication is the key in the construction industry to successfully complete a project. Communication is not only important among the different employees within a company, but also among different disciplines, and parties involved in a construction project. Part of communication has to do with all parties fully knowing and understanding their role and responsibilities.

Several project delivery systems have been described. In addition, some of the advantages and disadvantages were very carefully examined. Each delivery system has conditions under which it works very well as well as conditions under which it is not suitable for. The agents of changes, their causes, goals and objectives, were also described.

The paper further concludes that (a) professional construction management (CM) was developed and is used as project delivery system because CM brings an outsider to assist in the project; (b) the new project delivery systems involve all team members working together and having the project as a common goal; (c) design-build works very well combining design and construction under one company; (d) joint ventures can work in many different ways to bring the separate entities together; (e) the BOT scheme is fast gaining acceptance in many countries to bring major infrastructure projects to fruition; and (f) this trend will continue far into the future, as governments with stretched out budgets look to private and foreign investors to provide the much-needed finances to meet increasing infrastructure demands.

REFERENCES

AGC 1996. Project Delivery Systems, *Conference Binder*, Oct. Article entitled "Design/build Contractors Offered Coverage," *Building Design & Construction*, September 1996, p. 12.

Article entitled "Clinton Signs Measure Authorizing Design/build," *Building Design & Construction*, April 1996, p. 29.

Article entitled "CSI, DBIA to Develop Performance-specifying System," *Building Design & Construction*, September 1996, p. 14.

Bentil, Kweku, 1989. *Fundamentals of the Construction Process R. S. Means Company*, Kingston, MA, p. 5.

Collier, K., 1987. *Construction Contracts*, Prentice-Hall, Inc., Englewood Cliffs, NJ, p. 42, 190.

Construction Management Association of America (CMAA), 1993. CMAA Documents A-1, A-2, A-3 & A-4: Standard Forms of Agreement Between Owner & CM, Owner & Contractor, General Conditions of Contract Between Owner & Contractor, and Owner and Design Professional, respectively, CMAA.

Cruz, J.C., 1998. *Evaluation of Project Delivery Systems*, Graduate Report, University of Florida.

General Services Administration (GSA) 1990 Construction Management Guide, US GSA, Washington, D.C.

Kaufman, D., 1997. *The Future of Design-Build*. Graduate Report, University of Florida.

Marshall, V., 1997. *Design/Build: The Project Delivery System of Choice*, Graduate Report, University of Florida, 1997.

Partnering Charter among the Unites States General Services Administration, the Associated General Contractors of America and the American Institute of Architects, March 4, 1996.

The American Institute of Architects, 1987. Document A201: The General Conditions of the Contract for Construction, Washington, DC.

The American Institute of Architects, 1991. Document A121/CMc: Standard of Agreement Between Owner and Construction Manager Who Is the Contractor, Washington, DC.

The American Institute of Architects, 1987. Handbook of Professional Practice, AIA, Washington, D.C.

The Associated General Contractors of America (AGC), 1993. AGC Document Numbers 400, 410, 415: Standard Form of Design-Build Agreement and General Conditions Between Owner and Trade Contractor (w/CM as Owner's Agent), Washington, D.C.

The Associated General Contractors of America (AGC), 1997. AGC Document No. 510: Standard Form of Agreement Owner and Construction Manager (w/ CM as Owner's Agent), Washington, D.C.

The Associated General Contractors of America (AGC), 1997. AGC Document No. 520: Standard Form of Agreement Owner and Trade Contractor (w/CM as Owner's Agent), Washington, D.C.

Tenah, K., 1985. The Construction Management Process, Reston Publishing Company, Inc., Reston, VA.

Tenah, K., & Jose M. Guevara, 1985. The Fundamentals of Construction Management and Organization, Reston Publishing Company, Inc., Reston, VA, pp. 50–51, 373, 333.

United Nations Industrial Development Organization (UNIDO), 1996. UNIDO BOT Guidelines, UNIDO publication, Vienna.

Williams, Stephanie, 1989. Hongong Bank: The Building of Norman Foster's Masterpiece, Little, Brown & Co., Boston.

Success factors of partnering in new project delivery models – experience in Switzerland

G. Girmscheid

Institute for Construction Engineering and Management, Swiss Federal Institute of Technology Zurich, Switzerland

ABSTRACT: Competition among contractors in the EU market is purely price-based. On the one side profit margins are dropping dramatically – mainly as a result of the traditional project delivery models – whilst on the other side a soaring number of claims by contractors is leading to considerable investment budget overruns on the part of the employers/investors. In consequence, investors are often not achieving their anticipated profit margins over the lifecycle use of the facility. The conference paper reports on case studies that investigated which kinds of project delivery systems are most cost effective for the owner. Moreover, the paper addresses the latest partnering models between employer/investor and total service contractor.

1 BARRIERS HINDERING CONVENTIONAL MODELS OF PROJECT DELIVERY

1.1 *Fragmentation of conventional construction processes*

The fragmented composition of construction processes no longer meets the requirements of today's socio economic conditions. The processes, which are still less than optimal, are, in part, based on the conventional methods of completing projects, which comprise fragmented phases and the subdivision of works, and on the increased outsourcing to subcontractors with project control lacking any direct system leadership.

This leads to unresolved interface problems, and to only parts of the project being optimized, instead of the overall project completion. Moreover, generally speaking, very few innovations are implemented that encompass the entire project and generate customer benefits across all works and phases; this is because of the fragmented interests of the various individuals involved in the project. The resulting product is frequently less than optimal for the customer in terms of return (maintenance, rentability), value conservation, etc. during the operation phase.

1.2 *Lifecycle orientation*

Our economic environment is undergoing dramatically dynamic changes. Market characteristics and corporate strategies are becoming ever shorter-lived. Invested capital has to produce a quick return. This situation is also placing new demands on the realization of construction projects.

Developers focusing on the return and long-term conservation of the value of their facilities have realized that the conventional approach to tackling projects often does not produce the desired results. The orientation towards return and value conservation can only be achieved using a lifecycle approach (Girmscheid 2000).

Unlike mass or consumer goods, lifecycle orientation cannot be achieved by comparing products. Instead, incentive systems need to be developed to ensure that traditional companies, which are only involved in certain phases of a construction project, take an interest in the commercial success of the subsequent phases. This could result in the following consequences for construction companies from both a customer and market perspective:

– less fragmentation of individual phases and works,
– a more innovative overall approach encompassing the planning, construction and – where possible – utilization/operation phases.

1.3 *New challenges and opportunities for companies*

This creates new opportunities for companies to develop new markets by offering lifecycle-oriented product and service innovations. By integrating planning and execution expertise, these develop into system products and services and generate new market shares by squeezing out the traditional suppliers of individual products and services (Girmscheid 2000).

New approaches to cooperation in the construction industry are needed to ensure that a construction's optimization and innovative potential, which is inherent in the overall system, is exploited across the entire spectrum of value creation phases. This includes both horizontal and vertical forms of cooperation with providers of complementary products and services on the one hand, and new approaches to partnering between developers and the providers of products and services in the construction industry on the other hand.

2 APPROACHES TO SELECTING PROJECT DELIVERY AND COMPETITION MODELS

2.1 Concept of risk-based analysis to determine the project-specific delivery model

This paper aims to discuss an approach to systematically identifying the optimal project delivery and competitive models using an analysis of the opportunities and risks (cost-benefit) as an aid to the decision-making process to ensure that the selection of the same is not based on subjective criteria ("We have always done it this way" or "We do not have sufficient basis for a decision").

In this case, risk must be defined from the client's perspective. Developers face the risk of not achieving their prioritized targets, such as value conservation and return, nor their secondary objectives in respect of the costs, deadlines, quality and functionality relating to the construction and utilization phases. The issue focuses on how to evaluate the project delivery and competition models to ensure the best possible target achievement.

This necessitates breaking down the target system into monetary and non-monetary goals, which can then be evaluated. Risk analysis using a Monte Carlo simulation is suitable for evaluating the monetary risks. Using cost-benefit analysis with appropriate weighting factors and sensitivity analysis, the monetary and non-monetary goals can be combined to produce a uniform overall evaluation of the opportunities and risks of the various project delivery and competition models (Girmscheid 2003b).

2.2 The risk-based decision-making process

Any approach to predicting future developments, opportunities and risks, is limited by the fact that we cannot anticipate every single opportunity and risk; as such, it is necessary to be aware of the limitations of such an approach to decision-making.

A decision-making process to determine the most suitable project delivery and competition model could be based on the flow pattern illustrated below (Fig. 1).

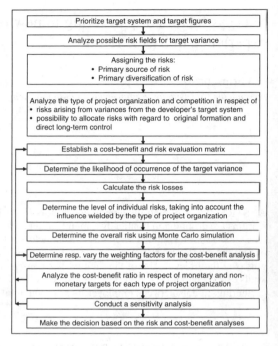

Figure 1. Flowchart analysis of the risks and cost-benefit ratio to determine the optimal project delivery and competition model (Cadez 1998).

2.3 Taking transaction costs into consideration when selecting the project delivery model

Surveys (Blecken & Gralla 1998) indicate that the delivery of projects using individual providers of products and services frequently does not result in the lowest overall investment costs, including ancillary costs, in spite of the "purely" price-based competition – although the proponents of this approach tend to make this claim. Often, the reasons for this are as follows:

– The danger of supplementary costs is more acute than with other project delivery methods offering a higher degree of integration (Girmscheid 2003a).
– The transaction costs (project management, measuring and billing expenses, no resp. few standard details, etc.) are higher than for other project delivery methods or, in positive terms, integrated project delivery models offer considerable potential for reducing transaction costs.

Transaction costs include those expenses incurred in initiating, agreeing, processing, controlling and retroactively adjusting work-related processes for the provision of products and services (Kleinaltenkam & Plinke 2000). In addition to the costs of the object of the contract, this concludes that even the process of selecting the appropriate project delivery model is dependent on and linked to costs and benefits for all parties involved.

For developers, the overall investment costs therefore comprise both the contracted price and the transaction costs.

Transaction costs, in particular, can be influenced by the various project delivery models, whereby we can assume that those project delivery models focusing on the provision of a complete product (general contractor, total service contractor, system provider) offer developers the following benefits in respect of transaction costs, compared with the provision of individual products and services, even if the developer is represented by a proficient project manager:

- Lower project management costs
- Lower planning costs
- Lower construction costs due to standard details
- Lower measuring and billing costs
- Lower costs for supplementary amendments
- Increased utilization value
- Increased risk premiums

3 PROJECT DELIVERY AND COMPETITION MODELS THAT SUPPORT PARTNERING

3.1 Definition of partnering

The term partnering is used to describe the largely symbiotic collaboration of the parties involved in the project to achieve the targeted performance goals by defining contractually agreed incentive systems. This partnership should encompass all phases of the project, where possible.

Whilst the partnership between developer and service provider is particularly important, the relationship between the service provider and his cooperation partners must, equally, be taken into consideration.

3.2 Partnering models

Partnership on the basis of competition can be attained using the following partnering models:

- Construction management (CM) combined with a guaranteed maximum price contract (GMP contract + value engineering)
- Public-Private-Partnership (PPP) models

Cost-conscious developers are increasingly also using target costing concepts, which have a close affinity to the GMP model.

In addition to the range of services and products focusing on the construction and renewal of facilities, professional developers – for whom securing the returns and conserving the value of their constructions are of foremost importance – increasingly expect the construction industry to offer products and services that not only include securing the operating contract for the utilization phase but also actually open these overall services to competition during the award phase.

3.3 Construction management (CM)

The construction management method has been gaining in popularity as a new form of project organization, especially in the USA, since the beginning of the 1970s. It is named after the construction manager (CM) who plays a decisive role within the project organization in shaping the success of the project (Halpin & Woodhead 1998). A distinction is made between two alternative forms of construction management in project delivery, which differ in terms of the contractually agreed assumption of the risks connected with adherence to the construction time and cost schedules.

In the USA construction management services are offered by firms of architects, engineering companies and construction companies. Construction companies who act as construction managers often have their roots in general contracting. Mostly they have been converted into specialized construction management organizations, or they continue to offer general and total service contracting in addition to construction management.

Generally, firms of architects and engineering companies offer construction management only in the form of management services, without assuming any of the risks, whereas construction companies offer construction services in addition to the management services: "Construction Management at Risk".

3.4 GMP and value engineering

The guaranteed maximum price (GMP) contract with or without "glass pockets" is a variation on the conventional global or lump sum contract. The GMP form of contract can be applied in one of the following alternatives:

- The top price or GMP is determined, i.e. billing takes place on the basis of the agreed unit prices and the products and services that have been supplied up to the maximum amount agreed. The entrepreneur bears the risk of these costs being exceeded. This type of GMP agreement is common for contracts awarded directly by the developer to the contractor.
- The top price or GMP is determined in line with the principle of billing by "glass pockets". It makes sense to apply this type of GMP agreement if the developer's contractor takes over the entirety of products and services at a very early stage in the construction process. In these early stages the optimization potential has often not yet been fully exploited, given the lack of any great planning depth, in spite of the competition surrounding the award of the overall products and services, nor has the real market price been fully evaluated. An agreement such as this enables the developer to secure a maximum cost guarantee at an early stage, whilst

at the same time an appropriate incentive system allows him to participate in the profits arising from the contract award and cost savings from optimization measures.

The fundamental concept of this second GMP form of billing by "glass pockets" makes it suitable for complex construction projects where the execution is planned parallel to the construction following the conclusion of the contract. Such a GMP agreement should be put out for tender in conjunction with a value engineering incentive agreement.

Value engineering distinguishes between at least two causes of cost savings:

- Planning savings from optimization measures
- Savings arising from the award process

3.5 *PPP-model*

The term Public-Private-Partnership (PPP) can be defined as follows: Construction and/or management of public assignments by private companies with control and/or investment by the public sector to guarantee the "political" quality and ensure adherence to public requirements.

For political reasons, and given the responsibility of the public sector for ensuring the availability of traffic routes, utilities and waste disposal, awarding purely private contracts or concessions without municipal involvement is frequently out of the question. Which is why the public sector wants to be involved in any privatization in order to influence or be a part of the decision-making process relating to the strategic objectives. The PPP project company then assumes responsibility for the operative realization.

Municipalities use such PPP-models, for example, for the following tasks:

- Urban development: for the rapid and financially interesting development and marketing of undeveloped land or for the redevelopment of existing buildings and industrial zones.
- Constructional maintenance of municipal traffic, supply and disposal networks.
- Operation of municipal traffic, supply and disposal facilities to lower costs and increase earnings.

4 CONCEPT OF THE CONSTRUCTION SYSTEM PROVIDER (SYSBAU) AS AN INTEGRATIVE FRAMEWORK

The implementation of the following three stages promises a better degree of achievement of both the partnership goals and the lifecycle orientation (Fig. 2):

The construction system provider research approach (SysBau)® of the Institute of Construction Engineering

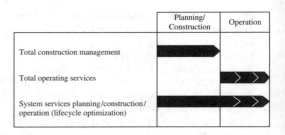

Figure 2.   Alternative approaches to partnering.

and Management at the Swiss Federal Institute of Technology in Zurich focuses on integrating both alternatives:

- Total construction management
- Integration of operating services (Performance)

The aim is to implement overall lifecycle-oriented optimization back in the planning phase that also includes the utilization/operation phase, whilst at the same time taking into consideration both appropriate incentive systems and attaining a win-win situation.

The term system provider (SysBau) is used in the construction industry to describe those companies that actively offer lifecycle-oriented all-round solutions from one source in a specific market segment. They are distinct from total service contractors in that system providers base their customer-oriented all-round solutions, which are tailored completely to the customer's needs, on both a functional and an optimally designed and/or engineered lifecycle-oriented system (Girmscheid 2000).

The system leader brings his core competencies to bear in the system concept and continues to develop the same (cross-project) on an ongoing basis. Since system providers focus on particular market segments, or even only offer specific constructions, they will succeed in developing innovative system concepts for these constructions. Such system concepts should aim to largely preserve the scope for architectural design.

5 SUCCESS FACTORS OF PARTNERING – RESULTS OF CASE STUDIES

The relevant success factors were identified on the basis of several case studies of projects executed on a partnership basis (Girmscheid 2003b), with explanation of the following practical examples:

- Case study 1: Project delivery with total services competition
- Case study 2: CM project delivery with GMP as a fast-track project
- Case study 3: Project delivery as a Public-Private-Partnership (PPP)

5.1 Case study 1: project delivery with total services competition

The developer of the project described below is a property profit center that forms part of an international conglomerate. This lean profit center is responsible for providing the core company with proprietary or rented office and work space.

In view of the strong growth of a new business unit in the conglomerate, the profit center drew up a forecast predicting the future requirement for desks in the relevant department. This forecast predicted that the developer was going to need 1000 new desks within about two and a half years. In addition to numerous other properties, the developer had also owned a cellar-like computer operations building for several years. This building was a low and massive construction offering a large floor space and, as such, was suitable for heightening.

Given the time pressure facing the project, the developer decided to run the project as a total services contractor model with total services competition.

For this case study the success factors illustrated as examples in Figure 3 were identified during the individual project phases.

5.2 Case study 2: CM project delivery with GMP as a fast-track project

The developer of this project is a technology company active in the chip industry. It needs a new production facility for its ongoing chip development. In view of the competition prevailing in the chip industry it is essential that the production facility be put into operation as soon as possible (time to market).

In order to ensure compliance with the tight schedule stipulated for the completion of this fast-track project, the developer decides to run the project as a construction management (CM) project and with a GMP contract.

As the contractor receives a share of any cost savings, he has a valid interest in optimizing the project (win-win situation). In order to reduce the overall duration of the project, schedule optimization and parallel triggering of the planning and execution measures (simultaneous engineering) are absolutely crucial.

For this case study the success factors illustrated as examples in Figure 4 were identified during the individual project phases.

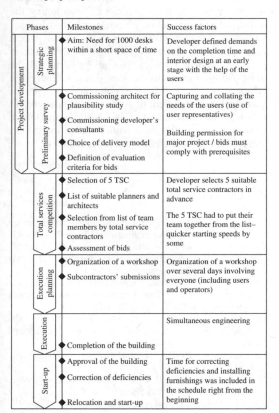

Figure 3.   Milestones and success factors on Project 1.

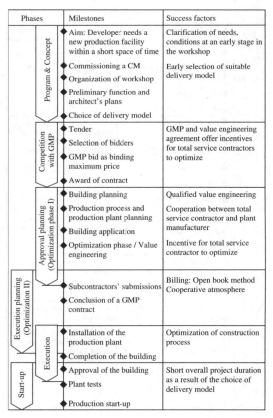

Figure 4.   Milestones and success factors on Project 2.

161

5.3 Case study 3: project delivery as a public-private-partnership (PPP)

In 2000, a Danish community decided to contract out the maintenance and repair of the municipal waste water network as a Private-Public-Partnership (PPP).

The community aimed to ensure that the public supply and sewage networks were rendered highly efficient in terms of cost minimization, supply and disposal reliability, and lifecycle-oriented maintenance. It was decided that a proprietary maintenance and repair department for investigations, planning and works was out of the question for reasons of efficiency and capacity. Moreover, experience of the conventional sequential execution using individual providers of products and services had not led to any synergies arising between the developer, planner and contracting company. In the field of repairs, in particular, innovative developments were storming ahead at such a speed that a single specialist planner for a town/community could not keep pace.

For this case study the success factors illustrated as examples in Figure 5 were identified during the individual project phases.

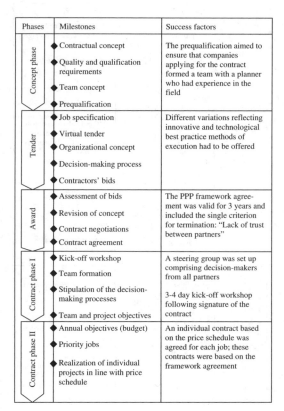

Figure 5.   Milestones and success factors on Project 3.

6   CONCLUSIONS

Processes of change, high operating costs and fragmented construction processes necessitate:

– Risk-based selection of the project delivery method, taking into account the investment, transaction, operating and maintenance costs
– New approaches to partnership
– Project delivery and competition models that support partnering
– Lifecycle integration, for example using the SysBau approach

Developers on the one side, and planners and entrepreneurs on the other, can secure sustainable advantages for themselves by selecting the most-efficient type of delivery and contract for a specific project and by applying professional project management and information logistics to control the processes in order to optimize the coordination between all parties involved in the project.

Developers, planners and entrepreneurs are understandably reticent when it comes to new approaches to project delivery. Everyone involved in the process is now faced with the challenge of abandoning the well-known project delivery models, role distributions and areas of responsibility with all their benefits and drawbacks and, instead, venturing into new and, in places, unknown territory. Not all projects will be immediately successful on this route to increased efficiency. Nevertheless the potential elements of success that are inherent in new forms of cooperation offering a fair distribution of risk should be exploited. Research and practice must work together to develop and test optimal conditions and process flows.

REFERENCES

Blecken, U. & Gralla, M. 1998. Entwicklungstendenzen in der Organisation des Bauherrn. *Bautechnik* 75, H. 7: 472–482.
Cadez, I. 1998. Risikowertanalyse als Entscheidungshilfe zur Wahl des optimalen Bauvertrags. *Fortschritt-Berichte VDI*, Reihe 4, Bauingenieurwesen Nr. 149.
Girmscheid, G. 2000. Wettbewerbsvorteile durch kundenorientierte Lösungen – Das Konzept des Systemanbieters Bau (SysBau). *Bauingenieur* 75, 1/2000: 1–6.
Girmscheid, G. 2003a. *Faires Nachtragsmanagement – Leitfaden für Bauunternehmen und Bauherren.* Bern: h.e.p. Verlag AG.
Girmscheid, G. 2003b. *Projektabwicklung im Bauwesen.* Berlin: Springer.
Halpin, D. & Woodhead, R. 1998. *Construction Management.* New York: John Wiley & Sons.
Kleinaltenkam, M. & Plinke, W. 2000. *Technischer Vertrieb – Grundlagen des Business-to-Business Marketing.* Berlin: Springer.

Alternative courses of action for industrialized construction processes in small and medium-sized enterprises

J. Bärthel

Institute of Construction Engineering and Management, Swiss Federal Institute of Technology Zurich, Switzerland

ABSTRACT: Industrialized construction is always put forward as a magic formula when problems in the construction industry reach life-threatening proportions. The use of computer-aided production technologies and standardised products is supposed to provide the solution to many problems, and yet the fact is ignored that the problems are due to fundamental structural deficits in the construction industry, which cannot be resolved so simply. The past has shown that attempts to apply industrialized techniques to construction have failed repeatedly, as production has always been placed at the forefront of these efforts. Therefore, the Swiss Contractors' Association and the Swiss Federal Institute of Technology Zurich have implemented a research project to study industrialized construction from the point of view of the contractor, and to use the term to encompass both process engineering and strategic approaches. This paper presents the developed alternative courses of action for industrialized construction in small and medium-sized enterprises as well as supplementary tools for the company-specific evaluation of the same and their implementation.

1 OBJECTIVES AND RESEARCH DESIGN

The quite practical goal of the research project was to develop alternative courses of action for industrialized construction in small and medium-sized enterprises (SME) and follows thereby the comprehensiveness of the science of business management in agreement with Ulrich (1984), according to which an application-oriented science should provide problem solving for practical acting by using findings of the theoretical or basic sciences as well as experiences of practice. According to the type of statements, the research project can be divided into a descriptive, normative or explicative project phase. Fig. 1 shows this classification, in addition to the overall research design.

The alternative courses of action were developed with reference to a model company with typical statistic characteristics in respect to the target group, the Swiss SME of the construction industry. The model company is based on the following statistically secured conditions:

- SME work above all in building and general construction, in particular in individual housing.
- SME usually have no or only a small budget for research and development at their disposal.
- The employees of SME have a very broad task spectrum and are no specialists.

- The demand for construction work is determined by the customers; the customers wish individual buildings and creative freedom.
- SME can exert influence on the working design only in case of a functional tender, which is a rare event for the projects in focus.
- SME usually do not possess a precasting plant, but even so components can be prefabricated on the work yard or on building sites to a certain extent. In addition, prefabricated components can be procured.

Due to the expounded reference of the alternative courses of action, the company-specific evaluation of the same is recommended and can be accomplished with selected systems engineering tools. The supply of aids for the implementation, such as checklists, flowcharts and summaries with key information, minimizes the costs for the enterprises and so facilitates the implementation.

2 DEFINITION OF INDUSTRIALIZED CONSTRUCTION

At first it is necessary to define what is actually meant by the term "industrialized construction". One of the task force members shaped a very concise definition during a workshop: "Robots are not the first step

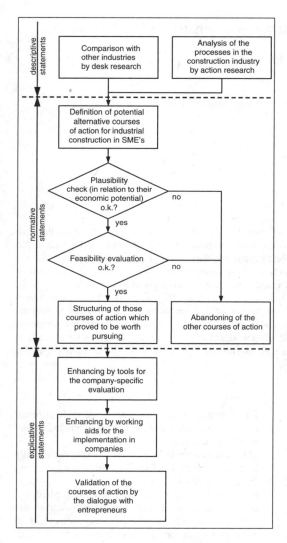

Figure 1. Project phases and overall research design.

towards industrialized construction but rather the possible final product of an organization with an industrially-oriented structure."

The approaches to identifying alternative courses of action in Figure 2, which were derived in the descriptive project phase (Fig. 1), illustrate the used definition of industrialized construction more in detail. The approaches' subjects correlate with the primary processes of the model company's value chain as shown (Fig. 2) and were explored in workshops with representative best practice companies. The workshops focused on examining the plausibility and the feasibility of potential alternative courses of action within the normative project phase. In Figure 2, the bold primary processes have more than one link and may be referred

to as key processes of industrialized construction in SME.

3 RESULTS

On the basis of the empirical findings, twenty-seven alternative courses of action for industrialized construction in SME were developed using theoretical support and logical thought processes. Due to the limited length of this paper, the alternative courses of action cannot be presented in detail here, but they can be assigned to four conceptual approaches (Bärthel 2002).

3.1 Conceptual approaches and associated alternative courses of action

3.1.1 Company-internal standardization of construction methods, building materials and components

Industrialized construction, as it is comprehended by the task force, does not intend to impair the individuality of our buildings, which we consider to be an achievement. The challenging aim is to standardize without constructing buildings which show indications of standardization. Thus the standardization must not cover the whole building but may cover the applied construction methods, the used building materials and even building components. It is a company-internal standardization. Its purpose is to reduce the complexity of all company processes so that defects are expected to be fewer and the advantages connected with the repetition of jobs (e.g. shorter adjustment periods and higher utilization degrees of special equipment) are generated. Company-internal standardization is about bringing certainty into processes that lack clarity and discipline. For example, company solutions for recurring technical problems are to be developed and documented.

Alternative courses of action:
1. Compare the construction costs due to the use of different brick sizes and masonry equipment for a company's typical building site (e.g. quantity of masonry, distance to the company's work yard) and inform all company's supervisors about the result.
2. Check, whether certain crafts are so often needed that a company's team of specialists would be remunerative. For this, a third-party performance benchmark must be set.
3. Compare the construction costs due to the use of alternative building materials and alternative technical details with the construction costs due to the use of the standard materials (concrete, bricks, timber) and the standard details. Compile estimation instructions for alternatives.

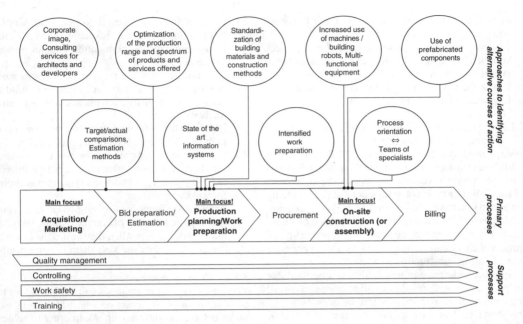

Approaches to identifying alternative courses of action

Corporate image, Consulting services for architects and developers	Optimization of the production range and spectrum of products and services offered	Standardization of building materials and construction methods	Increased use of machines / building robots, Multi-functional equipment	Use of prefabricated components	

Target/actual comparisons, Estimation methods	State of the art information systems	Intensified work preparation	Process orientation ⇔ Teams of specialists

Primary processes

| Main focus! Acquisition/ Marketing | Bid preparation/ Estimation | Main focus! Production planning/Work preparation | Procurement | Main focus! On-site construction (or assembly) | Billing |

Support processes

- Quality management
- Controlling
- Work safety
- Training

Figure 2. Approaches to identifying alternative courses of action and their correlation with the primary processes of the model company's value chain.

3.1.2 Prefabrication of building components

The prefabrication is of great importance in the context of industrialized construction, since it allows avoiding site conditions, which are unfavorable for industrialization (in particular changing project locations with the influence of weather). The fabrication can be mechanized and automated significantly more economically in a factory-based environment than on site.

Using prefabricated components also deconcentrates the construction process on site and reduces the time interference between trades. Prefabrication concepts can exceed carcass components; prefabricated integral components, which integrate several crafts (e.g. insulations, installations and surface finishing for concrete components) are possible. Some sophisticated designs and finishes (e.g. complicated formworks or high precision requirements) can be realized by prefabrication only.

The profitability of prefabrication rises with the number of similar components, so that the course for the use of prefabricated components should already be set during project planning. For this reason, SME must seek the contact to planners as soon as possible, otherwise the economic potential of prefabrication will be limited, because SME can suggest prefabrication only for certain components, e.g. stairs, columns and balcony slabs, then.

The only way out of the expounded dilemma is the consistent use of information technology in precasting plants. If the fabrication process is completely automated and a CAD-drawing which is compatible with

Figure 3. Example of the use of individual and automatically prefabricated components by Peter Bausysteme AG, Switzerland. The concrete wall units can contain, for example, door and window trims, windows, pipes, cables and thermal insulation – dimensioned with a CAD-drawing.

the CIM-system of the precasting plant is available, even the efficient prefabrication of individual (Fig. 3) and architecturally demanding components is conceivable.

Alternative courses of action:
4. Accumulate know-how concerning the construction methods with prefabricated components and their availability.
5. Examine the use of prefabricated components systematically within estimation and work preparation. Provide aids for estimating construction costs

as well as aids for the choice of fixing elements and other design features.

6. Use real cost elements in estimation and protect contractually against the consequential costs of unilateral project changes.

7. Check the claim management with customers and precasting plant in advance.

3.1.3 *Integration of project planning and construction planning*

Today's usual practice of calling in SME only in the actual construction stage is a handicap for industrialized construction. Accordingly neither the know-how of the SME nor their company-specific requirements for a cost-effective construction (e.g. due to existing resources such as employees, equipment and business relations) are taken into account during project planning, which is barely influenced by the experience gained during construction as a result.

In other industries in which also unique products are produced (e.g. shipbuilding and plant construction), the working drawings are prepared by or on behalf of the producer. The SME of the construction industry, which – in contrary to customers and planners – know the company-specific construction costs of the different construction methods, could and/or should be allowed to:

– develop company solutions including warranty for firmness, heat insulation, acoustic insulation and carrying capacity,
– decide whether building components should be prefabricated or constructed on site,
– alter a project planning insignificantly in order to enable repeated formwork use and large-size brick use,
– suggest alternative building materials and
– generally exert their strengths to benefit the customers.

The SME's influence on the working design is a condition for their willingness to invest in special equipment and information technology, in the associated employee training, in the development of company solutions and in the buildup of strategic alliances with planners and precasting plants.

Alternative courses of action:

8. Check, whether the market segments in which works are offered provide potential for construction cost reduction due to industrialized construction and are lucrative.

9. Establish credibility as being progressive and competent with customers and planners by references (projects, persons, other companies).

10. Establish credibility as being reliable and cost-conscious (concerning the contract value) by offering lump sum payment and using tools for cost monitoring.

11. Make tacit knowledge ("knowledge in people's heads") (cp. Nonaka & Takeuchi 1995) available to the company by nominating contact persons for certain subjects.

12. Structure projects in a recognizable way by partitioning them into jobs according to building components, construction phases or construction methods.

13. Define, what plans and data the company needs in digital form for accelerating processes.

14. Use electronic aids offered by building material suppliers (e.g. free software, interactive Internet pages and catalogues with smart query possibility) for work preparation.

15. Arrange deadlines for the completion of working drawings and the way of communication with customer and planners when they award the contract. Prefer digital data and save them systematically.

3.1.4 *Process improvement and automation*

There are construction methods and equipment for the automation of construction on site, which work well under optimal conditions (Fig. 4). In order to achieve their regular employment, it is essential to design buildings not only with regard to their use, but also with regard to automated construction methods. Building sites must be adapted to comply with the requirements for further mechanization and automation.

Besides the construction methods themselves, many work preparation and controlling processes are suited for automation, i.e. for the definition of standard procedures and their support by processing aids. Permanent improvements in the sense of the concept Kaizen are to be realized (e.g. Imai 1989).

Alternative courses of action:

16. Facilitate project-oriented work preparation by implementation of a modular cross-project work preparation system which provides project-independent information for frequently demanded works.

17. Compare the costs involved with equipment purchase and equipment rent (also for formworks).

18. Enlist company's supervisors and foremen in devising the functional specification of new equipment.

19. Establish credibility as being capable of punctual and careful execution with customers and planners by definition of processes in the sense of a quality management system.

20. Use the proper equipment for each work and do not use "all-round equipment".

21. Analyze the costs involved with the placement of concrete for the different possibilities, e.g. ready-mixed concrete vs. in-situ concrete and concrete pump vs. concrete bucket. Compile instructions.

22. Review the hours worked for a construction stage in the context of a target/actual comparison.

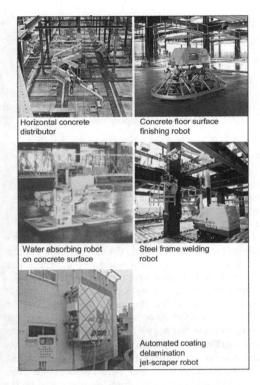

Horizontal concrete distributor

Concrete floor surface finishing robot

Water absorbing robot on concrete surface

Steel frame welding robot

Automated coating delamination jet-scraper robot

Figure 4.   Examples of construction automation on site by Takenaka Corporation, Japan.

23. Set up an information system for staff employment and equipment use and make the information available to all company's supervisors.
24. Analyze the construction costs after execution, detect weak points and update estimation instructions.
25. Record non-productive times, e.g. because of material handling, preparation, supervision and hold-up, for later analysis.
26. Track the further development of construction methods and building materials, e.g. self compacting concrete and fiber reinforced concrete.
27. Track the further development in the field of information technology and construction automation systematically and reappraise the use of theses technologies annually.

3.2   Tools for the company-specific evaluation of the alternative courses of action

The implementation of most of the alternative courses of action which were developed within the research project requires investments by SME, e.g. for new equipment, software or employee training. These investments can be classified as real investments (in contrast to financial investments – according to the acquired assets) and as rationalization investments (in

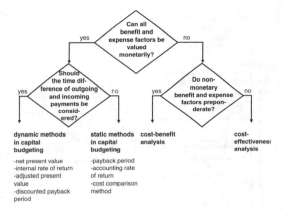

Figure 5.   Decision tree for choice of tools for the company-specific evaluation of the alternative courses of action.

contrast to formation, replacement and extension investments – according to the purpose) because they change company processes. The collective aim of the alternative courses of action is to increase the profitability of SME by reducing construction costs.

If all benefit and expense factors of an investment (due to an alternative course of action for industrialized construction in SME) can be valued monetarily, the well-known capital budgeting methods are suitable tools for the company-specific evaluation and the calculation of profitability (Fig. 5). The decisive advantage of the capital budgeting methods is that they result in a value with an explicit unit, e.g. CHF, EUR or years.

If not all benefit and expense factors can be valued monetarily, the benefit-cost analysis must be used, which can be divided into cost-effectiveness analysis and cost-benefit analysis (e.g. Thommen 2000). The cost-effectiveness analysis is very suitable for the evaluation of rationalization investments. Often a negative net present value results, since all expensive factors but not all benefit factors can be valued monetarily, so that the results of the cost-effectiveness analysis indicate what benefit (measured in points) is attainable at what expenses (negative net present value in CHF or EUR). Usually non-monetary benefit and expense factors preponderate in praxis only with decisions on plant locations. Therefore, the cost-benefit analysis must be used for rationalization investments rarely.

3.3   Implementation aids

The implementation aids which were compiled in the research project can be divided into checklists, flowcharts and summaries with key information.

Checklists are mnemonic devices, i.e. they reduce the chances of forgetting to do or to check something important; they reduce errors of omission. To assist

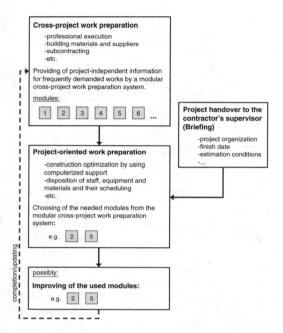

Figure 6. Interaction of cross-project and project-oriented work preparation.

the implementation of the developed alternative courses of action, reasonable application areas for checklists are for example:

– Determination of comparative market segment potentials for construction cost reduction due to industrialized construction.
– Preparation of installations of prefabricated components within work preparation.
– Inspection of building sites prior to installations of prefabricated components.

The purpose of a flowchart is to create a graphical or visual representation of a process. Thus it appears that flowcharts are suited for the documentation and explanation of new and modified company processes. In connection with industrialized construction, such new and modified company processes are for example:

– Initiating of the use of prefabricated components by SME and the information and material flow which arise from it.
– Selecting of prefabricated concrete floor and wall systems for a certain project.
– Interaction of cross-project and project-oriented work preparation (Fig. 6).

Summaries with key information are helpful to point out the essentials of a complex matter. Here, this tool was used for:

– Describing the characteristics of different electronic drawing types, e.g. object-oriented drawings.
– Describing the characteristics of self compacting concrete and fiber reinforced concrete.
– Compiling the cost elements which are necessary for the cost comparison of constructing on site and using prefabricated components.

4 CONCLUSION

Industrialized construction (in SME and also in bigger companies) is primarily a matter of a company's organization and process structure and only secondarily a matter of high-tech equipment.

The smaller a project the less industrialized is usually its execution on site and the more the work preparation and support processes must be industrialized. To SME which want to construct industrially, this means to focus their tenders on market segments where they can achieve the degree of industrialization which is necessary to become low cost producers. In doing this, the company's know-how, staff, equipment and market access as well as the customers' wishes and criteria for contract awards must be considered. Co-operation partners and potential subcontractors must be found for works which are uncovered by the company's own production range; these partners must heed the principles of industrialized construction, too.

The project findings assist Swiss SME in strengthening their competitive ability and are therefore being integrated in advanced training schemes as a logical consequence. They form the basis for a one-week training course, offered by the training center of the Swiss Contractors' Association and aimed at entrepreneurs and senior construction managers.

REFERENCES

Bärthel, J. 2002. Industrielles Bauen – Leitfaden für KMU-Geschäftsführer. Zurich: vdf Hochschulverlag.
Girmscheid, G. & Bärthel, J. 2002. Rationalisierungsmöglichkeiten im Wohnungsbau: Industrielles Bauen Die funktionale Ausschreibung als Voraussetzung. Der Schweizerische Hauseigentümer, 84(1), 11.
Girmscheid, G. 2003. Konzepte zur Generierung von Wettbewerbsvorteilen für Bauunternehmen: Markt- and ressourcenbasierte Perspektiven. Bern: hep (in prep.).
Imai, M. 1989. The Key to Japan's Competitive Success. New York: McGraw-Hill.
Nonaka, I. & Takeuchi, H. 1995. The Knowledge-Creating Company. Oxford: Oxford University Press.
Thommen, J.-P. 2000. Managementorientierte Betriebswirtschaftslehre. 6th ed. Zurich: Versus.
Ulrich, H. 1984. Management. Bern, Stuttgart: Haupt.

An industrialized foundation

S.P.G. Moonen
Eindhoven University of Technology, Eindhoven, the Netherlands

ABSTRACT: This paper describes a new foundation method for dwellings. At first this foundation method is developed as part of the authors study for a new industrial dwelling concept, also described in the proceedings of this conference (Moonen 2003a). Because an appropriate basis is essential to fully optimize benefits of any industrial building method an accurate foundation-system is needed. This foundation has to provide a smooth and level topside as a starting-point, instead of the excavating point of departure in traditional methods. Therefore a partial prefabricated foundation method was developed that promises to yield profit on various aspects when put into practice. Yet the several trial projects also revealed profits when applied to traditional building practice. As a result a universal foundation method is developed. This method is applicable for housing with irregular layouts as well as to workshops with regularities. The same system can be applied to reinforced strip foundations supported by piles as to grade beams. Both types can be combined with a structural slab as well as a slab on grade.

1 ACCURATE AND EFFICIENT FOUNDATION

At first an accurate foundation method has been developed. The basic principle of the designed foundation method is described in a thesis (Moonen 2001, in Dutch) and in proceedings (Moonen 1998, 2002). At the beginning the objective was to develop a foundation with a high degree of accuracy both regarding height and horizontal positioning. The aimed absolute deviation was set to less than 2 mm horizontally as well as vertically. From the start the foundation method was developed for strip foundations as well as pile foundations (Fig. 2) with minimal components. Two trial projects have demonstrated that the developed foundation principle is satisfactory technically. Yet the trial projects also demonstrated that, due to the designed operating procedure, the concrete floor could be poured at the same time as the foundation beams. This pays especially for small projects (Fig. 1).

On the basis of the trial projects the working details were re-adjusted (making an efficient foundation tailored to traditional building practice with masonry cavity walls). The most important boundary condition now became that the foundation work had to be done by a (specialized) subcontractor. For the building company this means that their activities can be limited to contracting the sub-contractor and placing building planks with dimensioning indicators.

After that, the specialized subcontractor takes over the work completely. When the subcontractor leaves the site after a few days the ground work is done, the foundation and ground floor is finished, the drainage and jacket pipes are in place, earth has been replaced and compressed, and the terrain is leveled. With the efficient foundation the entire foundation can be contracted out (as an extension to the groundwork, which is contracted out as a rule in any case).

The efficient foundation was tested in a large-scale trial project with the emphasis placed on organizational aspects. This trial project clearly demonstrated that an earth-moving company can construct the total foundation. Besides reducing the building time by removing intervals between separate activities, the trial project resulted in a substantial total labor reduction on the building site compared to the part of the same project, where a traditional foundation method was applied.

2 FOUNDATION PRINCIPLE

The basic principle of the designed foundation method is: After excavation, the soil is covered with a small plastic layer. On top of the plastic layer an adjustable (concrete) block is placed. The adjustable block holds three bolts to enable a precise leveling of the top surface of the block. Beneath the bolts a small brick or tile is put to spread the load. With these adjustable blocks the vertical positioning of all other accurate elements placed on top of the blocks is also fixed. A precasted plank is put upright on top of two adjustable

Figure 1. Impression of a small-scale trial project with 8 prefabricated concrete planks and 8 adjusting blocks. After excavating adjusting blocks are put on a plastic layer. By turning bolts in or out the top of each adjusting block is exactly leveled at an exact depth. A mini-excavator transports and assembles concrete planks on top of two adjusting blocks. These concrete planks are put upright and can still be horizontally moved in two directions, realizing an exact position of the top of the planks before the mini-excavator replaces earth. In the trial project concrete for ground floor and footing is poured simultaneously. Concrete completely fills the cavity in between and underneath the planks taking over the load bearing function of bolts in the adjusting blocks.

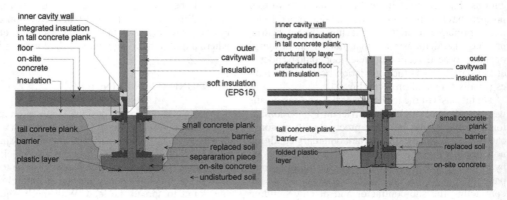

Figure 2. The foundation method only uses industrially produced elements produced beforehand. All elements (tall concrete plank, small concrete plank, adjusting block) can be applied in a strip foundation (shown left) and in a pile foundation (right). Both foundations can be combined with a slab on grade (shown left) or a prefabricated floor system (shown right).

170

blocks. A second plank is put parallel. These two planks are kept at a distance by small bars in between the planks. Two planks will be joined together to form the foundation beam by pouring concrete in between the planks on site. But before the concrete can be poured, side elements are placed at the bottom of the excavation so soil can be filled up first. The side elements form a cavity underneath the concrete planks. This cavity is also filled with in situ concrete, making the total foundation fit perfectly to the subsoil. After strengthening, the in situ concrete takes over the load bearing function from the bolts in the adjustable blocks. Soil filling gives the precasted planks the required horizontal support during pouring. Due to this operating procedure the concrete floor can be poured at the same time as the foundation beams.

3 LEARNING BY TRIAL PROJECTS

Since the foundation principle was especially developed as part of a new industrial building method the first small-scale trial projects were mainly focused on technical issues instead of commercial aspects. At that time it was clear that building companies would not immediately embrace such a foundation principle since the work method strongly deviated from customary foundation activities. The notion that the new foundation could also be made suitable for present building practice grew during work discussions with the building company of the trial projects. During work preparation it became clear that the building company was only actually involved in a very small part of the foundation work. And in discussions with the subcontractor for the groundwork, it was found that several activities of the building company could be smoothly transferred to the subcontractor. With minor changes of the foundation principle the excavating company can now carry out the digging of the foundation grooves, the application of foil, the setting of adjustable blocks, the placing of prefab elements lifted by a mini-excavator and the fill of earth. In the trial project the building company only had to pour concrete. By transferring activities from building company to excavating company less workers are involved on site. And unlike the traditional foundation these workers can carry out all activities sequentially (including earth replacement). Because of the sequence of all activities, the simultaneously pouring of foundation beam and concrete floor, the simplified organization and the reduced labor on site both building company and subcontractor expected substantial savings.

By changing the foundation principle the emphasis was shifted from accuracy to organizational aspects. The key question became whether the earthmoving company would be able to realize the entire foundation without the help of the building contractor. It was

Figure 3. In one trial project a steel skeleton is used with infill cavity walls in between the columns. A special adjusting block is needed to connect the steel column to the strip.

also important to know whether responsibilities could be defined clearly.

Since all trial projects before the alteration were small-scale projects, unsuitable to study organizational aspects, a new trial project was chosen with a reasonable size and complexity. The test was limited to a strip foundation, because previous trial projects were also realized as strip foundations.

4 LARGE-SCALE TRIAL PROJECT

In consultation with both building and earth-moving company an existing project on an industrial estate was selected. This project consisted of seven nearly identical, industrial complexes with a small block of two-story offices connected to each one (Fig. 3,4). In the project the new foundation was applied to four out of seven complexes. The foundation of the remaining three was made according to the traditional method. Hence, it was possible to gain an objective comparison (e.g. building costs) between the efficient foundation and a traditional foundation.

The trial project involved long straight walls of some 40 meters in length and small foundation strips (for toilets, corridors and entrances). Due to the specific shape of the building site there were various corners with angles 84.3°, 90° and 95.7°. All pipes for drainage and all connections for the meter cupboard had to cross the foundation beam. Approximately 155 prefab planks were necessary for the foundation with a total length of about 600 meters. The average length of a prefabricated plank was 3.85 meters. The smallest plank was 0.31 meter and the longest 6.63 meters. The foundation had to support both walls and a steel skeleton. The size and the complexity of the trial project made it particularly suitable for researching whether the theoretical advantages for the building organization could be realized in practice.

5 INDUSTRIALIZED FOUNDATION

The large-scale trial project clearly demonstrated that the earth-moving company can construct the total

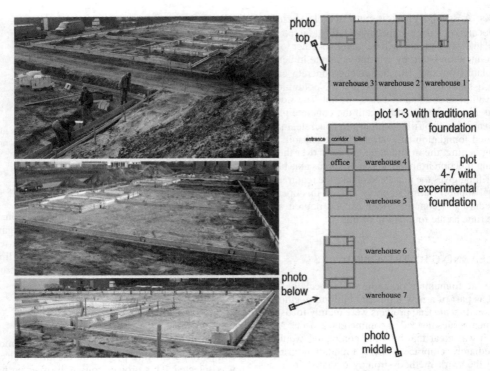

Figure 4. The foundation in this large-scale trial project is done by a specialized subcontractor. In warehouse 1, 2 and 3 a traditional foundation is applied as a reference for the experimental foundation in warehouse 4, 5, 6 and 7.

foundation. The activities carried out were comparable to those activities of this company found in road building. The organization for the building company is greatly simplified: only 1 participant needed guidance as opposed to over 20 separate participants for the traditional method. Besides this simplification the trial project resulted in a total labor reduction on the building site of some 30 to 45%.

But in evaluating the large-scale trial project it also became clear that the required time-consuming preparation period was a major handicap. Since prefab elements can only be produced after ratification of the final drawings, the work on site is delayed for about a month after receiving all permits. For this reason, another redesign of the foundation method was carried out. The objective was to combine the acquired advantages (simplification of the building organization, shorter building time, accuracy of work, higher quality and no thermal bridges) with the possibilities of industrially produced elements. This adaptation is called "industrialized foundation" since all elements to be used are produced beforehand and stored. When project requirements are confirmed the stored concrete elements are cut to the required specifications and work on the site can start immediately after.

In the presentation of this conference the possibilities of this industrialized foundation will be explained. In developing the industrially produced elements a high value was set by the possibility to create foundations for almost any irregular lay-out of dwellings. Since project specific requirements are unknown when producing the concrete elements, provisions should be made to cross pipes with a diameter up to 150 mm at an unknown point. The answer to this problem was found to provide the standard elements with weakenings at intervals of 250 mm. On site, before pouring concrete in between the planks, any weakening can be opened to enable passing through of a possible sewerage-pipe.

Another challenge in developing the standard elements was the requirement to cut a concrete plank and any unknown position under the express condition that upright concrete planks can be connected on site at any unknown angle.

6 CONNECTING PREFABRICATED CONCRETE ELEMENTS AT UNKNOWN CUT AND ANGLE

Figure 5 shows a possibility to connect two or more standard concrete elements at any unknown cut and at

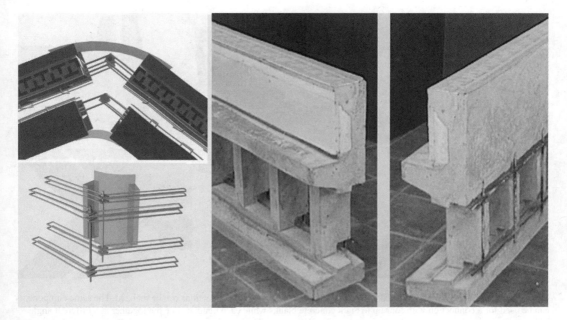

Figure 5.   Drawing on left is showing the longitudinal connection of two concrete planks at an unknown angle by feeding in a hairpin shaped reinforcement into a longitudinal groove of the plank. When all pieces are fed in, a peg is put in the holes of washer plates welded to the hairpins. The connection is achieved by solidifying of on-site concrete. Photos on right shows the prototype of the concrete plank with the two longitudinal grooves. In this photo the barrier (Figure 2) is not yet applied. The longitudinal grooves are present at every cross-section so the concrete plank can be produced in advance and cut down shortly before application. Accordingly, openings of 165 mm in width and 270 mm in height at intervals of 250 mm are prepared to enable almost any sewerage to pass through without influencing the production process.

any angle. During production two longitudinal grooves are realized so at any cut a hairpin shaped reinforcement can be slide in. When concrete in between the planks is poured on site a solid connection is established between hairpin shaped reinforcement and standard reinforcement of the industrial produced planks. On the other side of the hairpin shaped reinforcement a washer plate is welded. By entering a pin through the openings of several washer plates (and by pouring on site concrete) a solid connection is established, irrespective of the angle where two hairpin shaped reinforcements meet.

Figure 6 shows various examples of connections. The same connection can be applied to connect four up to eight concrete planks under different angles and with different lengths. This figure gives a good impression of the varied possibilities of the industrialized foundation. Since the standard concrete planks used can be cut at any length and these elements can be connected at any angle almost all layouts of dwellings can be realized.

The industrial produced concrete planks in Figure 5 require a rather complex formwork. Therefore the first impression is one of a very expensive foundation. However adjustments or modifications for specific projects do not occur, since all possible applications are already present. Hence the required formwork can be used many times, especially because aesthetics of the concrete finishing does not play an important part. When this frequently usable complex formwork is considered in a mass production the manufacturing of the concrete plank in Figure 5 is no more complex than the production of a linear rectangular beam. Calculations show that this complex form is well affordable if the industrial principles are kept strictly in hand.

7   CONCLUSIONS

With the composition of the industrial produced concrete planks and the hairpin shaped reinforcement fed in a longitudinal groove at an arbitrary chosen cut, almost any foundation of irregular layout of dwellings can be realized. With this method it is well possible to produce the concrete elements without knowing the project specific requirements. This foundation method can be used for strip foundations as well as pile foundations and will strongly simplify the building organization, shorten building time on site, improve accuracy of the superstructure and avoid thermal bridges resulting whether in almost equal costs or in a small saving.

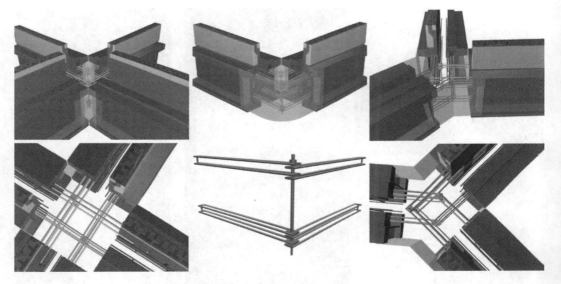

Figure 6. With the principle explained in Figure 5 various possibilities of connections can be realized. The same components can be used for a connection with four up to eight concrete planks while each plank can be put together at a different angle.

Figure 7. A mini-excavator is brought into action for transporting and placing of concrete elements as well as for digging grooves and refilling earth. Therefore the earthmoving company has a key role in this foundation method.

Because building methods tend to shift towards utilization of voluminous and close-fitting construction elements as well as to a larger extent of work contracted out, this foundation method will become more relevant in the near future.

REFERENCES

Moonen S.P.G. 1998. Simplified prefabricated foundation-concept. *In proc. intern. conf. XIII FIP on Challenges for concrete in the next millennium, Amsterdam, Netherlands, 23–29 may 1998*, Volume 1. ISBN 90 5410 945 9. Rotterdam: Balkema.

Moonen S.P.G. 2001. Ontwerp van een geïndustrialiseerde funderingswijze (Developing an industrialized foundation). *thesis, in bouwstenen 59.* ISBN 90-6814-559-2. Eindhoven: Universiteitsdrukkerij TU/e.

Moonen S.P.G. 2002. Fundamentals of Industrialization: developing an accurate foundation. *In proc. intern. conf. Challenges of concrete construction, Dundee, Scotland 5–11 September 2002.*

Moonen S.P.G. 2003a. Wall panels for industrialized housing. *In proc. intern. conf. ISEC-02 Second International Structural Engineering and Construction Conference, Rome, Italy, 23–26 September 2003.* Rotterdam: Balkema.

Moonen S.P.G. 2003b. Improved design by progressive awareness. *In proc. intern. conf. ISEC-02 Second International Structural Engineering and Construction Conference, Rome, Italy, 23–26 September 2003.* Rotterdam: Balkema.

TU/e 1999. Werkwijze voor het vervaardigen van een fundering en bij deze werkwijze toegepaste betonplaat (Method of producing a foundation with concrete plank for this method). *Dutch patent 12 January 1999.* Patent number 1006527.

Applying the theory of constraints to construction scheduling

J.-B. Yang

Institute of Construction Management, Chung-Hua University, Hsinchu, Taiwan

ABSTRACT: Schedule planning and control is the major task of construction project management. There are few studies on innovating new scheduling methodology as the popular Critical Path Method (CPM) and Program Evaluation and Review Technique (PERT) applied well. The Critical Chain Scheduling (CCS) method, derived from the Theory of Constraints (TOC) to project management domain and being popular in the industry engineering domain, can make schedule planning and control more effective than traditional CPM/PERT. The purpose of this paper is to attempt to adopt the CCS method to construction scheduling. A simple example is employed in demonstrating how CCS works and its differences between CCS and traditional CPM/PERT. The CCS method would be a good alternative for construction project scheduling.

1 INTRODUCTIONS

1.1 *Construction scheduling methods*

Schedule planning and control is the major task of construction project management. There are two general methods that are commonly used and embedded in commercial project management software: the Bar Chart (or termed the Gantt chart) and the Critical Path Method (CPM). A similar method to CPM, the Program Evaluation and Review Technique (PERT), provides probabilistic approach to scheduling. CPM, the most popular scheduling method, needs a deterministic duration for each activity. In general, the given duration for scheduling has much safety time and the produced schedule is uncertain and unreal. Furthermore, the duration in PERT is treated with three values, the optimistic, the normal and the pessimistic ones. This time estimate makes the project manager to control the project schedule more reliable and to finish the project on time more confident. However, the CPM and PERT methods do not consider the resource constraints in planning in advance. This makes the produced schedule be usually unreasonable.

Applying CPM scheduling on construction projects, Street (2000) criticized that unrealistic activity durations and failure to perform timely schedule updates are troublesome pitfalls. These vulnerabilities need to face against carefully. However, management approach on traditional CPM scheduling seems unable to deal with such circumstances. It is necessary to introduce new idea to construction scheduling domain.

1.2 *Theory of Constraints*

The Theory of Constraints (TOC) is an approach that is used to develop a management technique to continue to improve a system's performance. It was popularized by the novel, The Goal (Goldratt 1992), that introduced the principles to operation management to rescue a plant from closing. TOC considers that any system must have at least one constraint that affects system's throughput. Otherwise, its throughput would increase without bound, or go to zero.

TOC has developed five steps (Fig. 1) to improve a system's performance under elevating its constraints (Goldratt 1992, McMullen 1997, Rand 2000). The five steps could be regarded as a continuing strategy of self-improvement although TOC consists of a number of common-sense tools and processes. The ideas and principles of TOC have been employed in many domains especially in project management, the Critical Chain Scheduling (CCS) conducted.

1.3 *How TOC apply to project scheduling*

According to TOC's five procedures shown in Figure 1, some researches (Chesapeake Consulting, Inc. 1997, Leach 1999 and Steyn 2002) ever clarified TOC's application processes to project scheduling. These processes are summarized by author shown as follows.

1. Identify the system's constraint. The constraint of a project is the critical chain that dominates project's goal: to complete as soon as possible. The critical chain, not critical path that looks upon logical

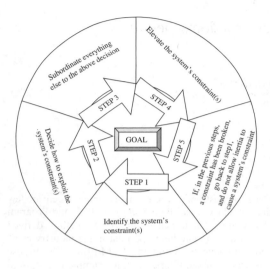

Figure 1. Application procedures of the theory of constraints.

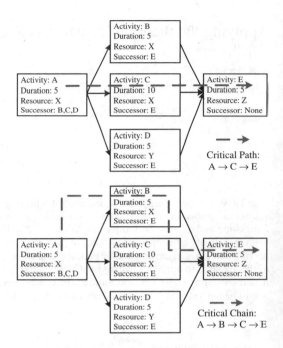

Figure 2. Critical path and critical chain.

dependences only, considers both resources contention and logical dependences in advance.

2. Decide how to exploit the system's constraint. The total duration of a project is the aggregation of the critical chain activities. CCS challenges traditional CPM estimating duration impractically and wasting project safety times. The basic weapon to shorten a project's total duration is to reduce individual activity's duration that makes the length of the critical chain shorter.

3. Subordinate everything else to above decision. Dr. Goldratt (1997) proposed the buffer concept to protect the critical chain and project execution. Detailed buffer meanings are illustrated in next section.

4. Elevate the system's constraint. Consolidating time estimate of individual activity and concentrating contingency management of whole project are incorporated in CCS.

5. If in the previous steps the constraint is broken, go back to step 1. Do not allow inertia to become the system's constraint. TOC insists on continuous improvement to meet system's global goal, not local. CCS allows scheduler to reschedule to satisfy the project target and hopes to update schedule information immediately, otherwise, to manage the project plan under control.

2 CRITICAL CHAIN SCHEDULING

2.1 Basic concept

The Critical Chain Scheduling (CCS) method, derived from TOC to project management domain and being popular in the industry engineering domain, can make schedule planning and control more effective. CCS has received much attention of researches in the project management domain especially in scheduling. In Goldratt's novel – Critical Chain (1997), he explained how to use TOC's concepts to solve project managers" desirable result of being to complete project as early as possible. The basic differences between CPM and CCS hinge on the treatment of resource constraints in the determination of "critical" activities, and in the use and placement of "safety" in a schedule network. A CPM network makes safety spread among all activities. A CCS network aggregates and concentrates safety in the form of buffers that are used in protecting project target date from variation in schedule performance, and in maintaining focus on the "critical" activities.

2.2 Critical chain

In CPM, the critical path (CP) is the longest chain from project start to finish that requires the longest time to complete the project that does consider only logical relationships among activities, ignoring resource conflicts. Goldratt (1997) defined the critical chain (CC) as the longest chain of dependent activities where the dependences are a result of considering resources usability in advance. Figure 2 shows a simple example to illustrate the differences between the CP and CC.

2.3 Buffer

In CCS, buffers are incorporated in project network to facilitate project contingency that could make the project behind its schedule. Basically, there are three buffers in CCS: the Project Buffer (PB) being used to protect project complete date to meet project target, the Feeding Buffer (FB) being used to protect critical chain from disruptions of other chains, the Resource Buffer (RB) being used to notify scheduler of a new resource on critical chain being employed. The relationships of these buffers and original networks are exhibited in Figure 3. How to decide an appropriate buffer size is complicated and is project-oriented and case-by-case. Many researches (Newbold 1998, Product Development Institute 1999, Herroelen & Leus 2001) and commercial software (ProChain Solution, Inc. 2003, Sciforma Corporation 2003, Realization Technologies Inc. 2003) provide some advisable options. A simple example of making buffers is exhibited in Section 3.

2.4 Application procedures

To apply the CCS method to develop a project schedule network, Newbold (1998) proposed a seven-step process summarized and explained as follows.

1. Clearly state the objectives of the project and of the project plan. It is necessary to build a project budget and completion target date according to client's requirements.
2. Determine the needs to be met and the activities needed to meet them. The Work-Breakdown-Structure (WBS) method is a proper means to clearly establish all required activities.
3. Determine the logical relationships between activities and needs. Four relationship, start-to-start, start-to-finish, finish-to-start and finish-to-finish, are usually employed to depict activity's execution sequence.
4. Estimate the resources requirements, activity durations and costs. A resource database is required to be built to collect resource's capability, historical data, and latest market information. Based on this database, an experienced estimator would accurately and quickly accomplish this task.
5. Calculate the critical chain schedule, including buffers. According to the CCSs methodology presented in previous section, a critical-chain-based project schedule would be built. The available, at least, three commercial software packages can aid to build the critical chain schedule network. Detailed information about how to build the schedule is explained in next section.
6. Evaluate the plan according to budget and timing restrictions. Owing to the scheduling results being the baseline for execution, it is necessary to compare them with objectives clarified in step 1.

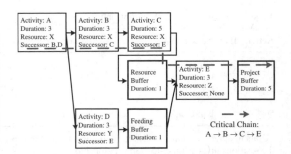

Figure 3.   Buffers in critical chain scheduling.

7. If necessary, go back to an earlier step and revise the plan. This step gives a concept of continuous improvement being a basic force to meet client's requirements.

3   CASE STUDY

3.1   Case information

A hypothetical example employed in this paper to explain how CCS works and the differences between CCS and traditional CPM. This example is a pipe installation project that includes five activities. Detailed information about each activity is summarized in Table 1. There are three resources of subcontractor X, Y and Z. Figure 4 shows the project network without considering resource contention. The project has a total duration of 19 days. After resource leveling, Figure 5 shows the project network of a total duration of 23 days.

3.2   Approaches and results

3.2.1   Tool employed
To demonstrate how CCS works, the commercial software – ProChain® version 6 under Microsoft® Windows XP Professional® with an Intel Pentium® IV 2.4 G processor and 256 MB of RAM is employed herein. ProChain® being collaborative with Microsoft Project® software, can translate Microsoft® Project (version 2002) network into a critical-chain-based network.

3.2.2   Processes
The following five steps show how to establish a critical-chain-based schedule network.

1. Establish project basic information. ProChain® is an integrated add-on of Microsoft Project®. Basic project information, including creating activities, resources and calendar, and assigning resources, is accomplished on Microsoft Project® platform.
2. Level resources. CCS schedules activity as late as possible to minimize work-in-process (WIP)

Table 1. Illustration example information.

Activity ID	Activity name	Activity duration	Successor	Relationship	Resource usage	Calendar
1	Excavate	5*	2	SS+3**	Subcontractor X	Working in everyday
2	Pipe	10	3, 4	SS+6,FS	Subcontractor X	Working in everyday
3	Backfill	5	5	FS***	Subcontractor X	Working in everyday
4	Test	3	5	FS	Subcontractor Y	Working in everyday
5	Landscape	3	None	None	Subcontractor Z	Working in everyday

*Units in duration is day; **Representing the relationship is a start-to-start relationship with 3 days lags; ***Representing the relationship is a finish-to-start relationship.

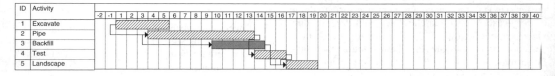

Figure 4. Project network without resource leveling.

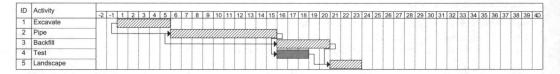

Figure 5. Project network after resource leveling.

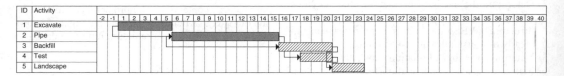

Figure 6. Project network on activity's late start mode.

activities of project which could decrease lead times. ProChain® pushes activities to late start times after resource leveling. "Test" activity shown in Figure 6 is scheduled to its late start time.

3. Identify critical chain. The critical chain is that set of activities which determines overall project duration under considering resource contention and logical dependences. ProChain® identify only one critical chain in which manager could always focus on the critical chain.

4. Create buffers. ProChain® provides customized buffer creation. Buffer size could be a fixed duration, a fixed duration plus a percentage of the critical chain, or a fixed duration plus a square root of the sum of square of the difference between low-risk and average activity durations. This demonstration uses 50% of critical chain length as project buffer,

50% of feeding chain length as feeding buffer and 1 day as resource buffer.

5. Insert buffers. After calculating all buffers, ProChain® could insert all buffer activity with finish-to-start logical relationship into project network.

3.2.3 Scheduling results

Figure 7 shows the critical-chain-based project network based on activities shown in Table 1 and processes depicted in previous subsection. The project has a total duration of 35 days, including a project buffer (dummy activity of ID of 9) of 12 days, a feeding buffer of 2 days (dummy activity of ID of 7) and two resource buffer of 1 day (dummy activities of ID of 1 and 6). The critical chain of this project is "Excavate"-to-"Pipe"-to-"Backfill"-to-"Landscape" without the dummy activities.

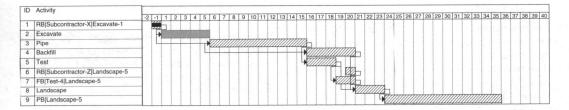

Figure 7.   Critical-chain-based project network.

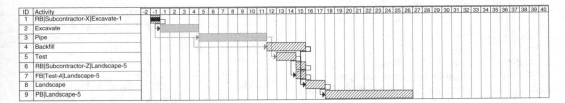

Figure 8.   Revised critical-chain-based project network.

Table 2.   Duration adjustment for critical chain scheduling.

ID	Name	Original duration	Revised duration
1	Excavate	5*	4
2	Pipe	10	7
3	Backfill	5	4
4	Test	3	2
5	Landscape	3	2

*Units in duration is day.

3.3   Refined project

Owing to the challenges of CCS on traditional CPM in estimating duration impractically and wasting project safety times, it is necessary to revise activity's duration in developing a critical-chain-based project network. Table 2 shows a revised data for each activity of hypothetical example. The durations are adjusted by the author arbitrarily. Based on this information, another critical-chain-based project network is developed as Figure 8 shown. The refined project has a total duration of 26 days in which a critical chain of 17 days and a project buffer of 9 days exist. The critical chain of this refined project is also the path of "Excavate"-to-"Pipe"-to-"Backfill"-to-"Landscape."

4   DISCUSSIONS

4.1   Standpoint and attitude

CCS, standing on the weakness of traditional CPM in time estimate, removes individual activity's safety time and inserts buffers instead of inflated duration to protect completion date of activity, of project. Comparing the project networks in Figures 6 and 8, it is clear that the project would finish inside 23 days and 17 days respectively, if all activities are on schedule. It proves that CCS could produce condensed schedule.

CCS also challenges traditional scheduling on human phenomena of "Student Syndrome (not taking action early until all floats or safety times consumed)" and "Parkinson's Law (works being completed in all allowed periods and even more)." In CCS, every achieved activity should be reported to carry on others. This means that a project would be finished when manager and performer realize the activity having no extra time for spending and achieving anything immediately. This changed attitude makes the project be completed ahead of schedule more reliable than traditional CPM.

4.2   Critical activity

Traditional CPM considers the activity with total float of zero being the CP. This approach makes a project could be not only one CP which confuses the focus of manager and performer and results in multitasking. CCS determines the CC in light of logical and resource dependences and the only one instead of multi-tasking. The critical activities in Figures 5 and 8 are exactly the same (by chance). It would be different if the project be complicated than demonstrated example. The critical activity (or termed as the critical-chain activity) CCS generated would be more practicable.

The CC is different to the CP of CPM not only in its dependences but also in management approach. While the CP is an index of delaying total project duration, the CC is a project success factor owing to its components determining the throughput of the project. It is necessary to manage the critical chain activities more active.

179

4.3 *Duration*

The elimination of estimating unrealistically makes CCS usually having a condensed normal total duration that excludes the project buffer. Mohamed (1996) ever claimed that 25% time saving is achievable in a typical construction work package without resources raised. That implies compressing activity's duration is a common dilemma. CCS provides a new concept of organizational behavior reform for solving duration unreality. The demonstrated example shows the CCS-based project being shorter than the CPM-based project.

5 CONCLUSIONS

This paper introduces the Theory of Constraints (TOC) and its application to project management – the Critical Chain Scheduling (CCS) method. A simple example is employed in demonstrating how CCS works and its differences between CCS and CPM/PERT. The CCS method would be a good alternative for construction project scheduling while project manager and performer realize the merits and pitfalls of CCS.

When adopting CCS to construction scheduling, it is necessary to figure out the following facts that need more studies conducted in the future.

1. Right standpoints and attitudes. Schedule manager and performer should realize that CCS is not just providing an alternative for scheduling. It needs a thought-breaking reform.
2. Solid duration estimates. In CCS, duration in schedule should be realistic and no any safety time in that. This makes the buffers functional and project completed fast.
3. Good scheduling tools. Most available commercial scheduling software packages do not provide the CCS method for use. To get a good one either purchasing or programming directly makes critical chain scheduling practicable.
4. Appropriate performance measurement. CCS has changed all components of a schedule network. To set a performance measurement system for construction project properly makes the scheduling system working.
5. Qualified education. It is absolute necessary to educate all project team members and allies that CCS provides overall benefits to share with. This is the way to success.

ACKNOWLEDGEMENTS

The author would like to thank the National Science Council, Taiwan, ROC, for financially supporting this research under Contract No. NSC91-2211-E-216-017 and the ProChain Solution Inc. for providing ProChain® software.

REFERENCES

Chesapeake Consulting, Inc. 1997. Goldratt's critical chain – a technical summary. (http://www.chesapeak.com/)

Goldratt, E.M. 1992. *The goal.* 2nd revised ed. Great Barrinton, MA: The North River Press.

Goldratt, E.M. 1997. *Critical chain.* Great Barrinton, MA: The North River Press.

Herrlelen, W. & Leus, R. 2001. On the merits and pitfalls of critical chain scheduling. *Journal of Operations Management* 19(5): 559–577.

Leach, L.P. 1999. Critical chain project management improves project performance. *Project Management Journal* 30(2):39–51.

Newbold, R.C. 1998. *Project management in the fast lane – applying the theory of constraints.* Boca Raton, FL: St. Lucie Press.

McMullen, T.B. 1997. *Introduction to the theory of constraints (TOC) management system.* Boca Raton, FL: St. Lucie Press.

Mohamed, S. 1996. Options for applying BPR in the Australian construction industry. *International Journal of Project Management* 14(6): 379–385.

Product Development Institute, 1999. Tutorial: Goldratt's critical chain method, a one-project solution (http://www.pdinstitute.com/).

ProChain Solution Inc. 2003. ProChain® software (http://www.prochain.com/).

Rand, G.K. 2000. Critical chain: the theory of constraints applied to project management. *International Journal of Project Management* 18(3): 173–177.

Realization Technologies, Inc. 2003. Concerto™ software. (http://www.realization.com)

Sciforma Corporation 2003. PS8™ software (http://www.Sciforma.com/).

Steyn, H. 2002. Project management applications of the theory of constraints beyond critical chain scheduling. *International Journal of Project Management* 20(1): 75–80.

Street, I.S. 2000. The pitfalls of CPM scheduling on construction projects. *Cost Engineering* 42(8): 35–37.

Simplified simulation system of overlapping CPM networks

A.M. Odeh
Jordan University of Science and Technology, Irbid, Jordan

ABSTRACT: This paper presents a resource-based simulation system of overlapping CPM networks. The system incorporates resource interactions and uncertainty inherent to construction operations into construction plans. For simplicity and acquaintance, the system retains the modelling elements and presentation as the CPM and CYCLONE networks of Activities, Queues, Forks representing probabilistic branching, Consolidation representing logical branching, and Links representing relationships among the activities and resources flow in the network. The system is capable of modelling finish-to-start and start-to-start relationships with probabilistic activity duration, lags, and branching. The activity may consist of many cycles that can be activated concurrently bending the availability of required resources, which may also flow in a cyclic manner. Cyclic activities and resource flows enables modelling of dynamic resource allocation and utilization policies. The system simulates the network and produces statistical reports pertaining to project duration; starts, finishes, durations, floats, and criticality of project activities; and the utilization of resources.

1 INTRODUCTION

Construction embodies the utilization of various resources to perform different activities and a successful planning for effective and efficient utilization of these resources is a primary managerial objective. Among the most known and widely used project planning techniques are the Critical Path Method (CPM) and the Program Evaluation Research Task (PERT). Various simulation models have also been developed and used to model resource interactions and the uncertainty associated with construction processes.

The CPM is the best known and most widely used formal scheduling technique (Tavakoli & Riachi 1990). Many of the shortcomings of the critical path method have been documented (Pritsker et al. 1989). In particular, the deterministic and static nature of CPM presents limitation in modelling a dynamic and stochastic system such as construction project. A CPM network is also constrained by the following modelling assumption: branching is done on a deterministic basis, no cycling or feedback are allowed in the network, project or portions of projects are always completed successfully as the concept of failure is nonexistent, no explicit storage or queuing concept are available, and resource handling is hampered with many assumption that limit its effectiveness in portraying an actual project.

The need to consider the uncertain event times were first addressed by PERT. Although the activities in PERT are assumed to have random distributions for their durations, PERT embodies basic assumptions that limit its applicability. First, it assumes that any path along which calculations are made contains many activities to make the central limit theory valid. Second, it ignores the variances of the distributions of the activities durations along the paths and may result in errors especially when the path lengths approach each other and the standard deviation of the merging paths increase (MacCrimmon & Ryavesc 1964).

Along with CPM and PERT, statistical discrete-event simulation has been used to model construction process and project-wide planning of both activities and resources. The major obstacles to its use by the construction industry are the complexity involved in constructing a model and the resulting time requirement (Shi & AbouRizk 1994 & 1997).

Simulation models allow a concise representation of repetitive activities and explicit formulation of resources flows. Despite these advantages, the model for a construction project using a general simulation technique is relatively complex. Another limitation of simulation techniques is that they do not provide allowable activity delay (float) and criticality, which many construction planners expect as part of the project scheduling information.

Several simulation techniques focus on the construction industry and attempt to simplify their model formulation. These techniques emphasize the analysis of resources and concentrate on analyzing construction processes more than on the project-wide planning of both activities and resources.

CYCLONE (Halpin 1977 & 1992) is probably the most known construction-specific process simulation techniques. It uses a small set of basic modelling elements, which contributes to its popularity in a construction context. The planning information provided by CYCLONE is comparable with that of other much more complex simulation techniques. It has been the basis for a number of construction simulation systems including INSIGHT (Kalk 1980) and STROBOSCOPE (Martinez & Ioannou 1994).

Although it is possible to translate a CPM network into a CYCLONE diagram (Senior 1995), the resulting CYCLONE diagram grows in size and complexity with the increase in the number of activities and with the presence of overlapping relationships among activities. Although additional modelling elements may be introduced for identifying the critical path, CYCLONE cannot provide activity float information. The level of connectivity between the two techniques has been limited to simple non-repetitive network.

Many researchers have attempted to correct and compensate for the limitations of CPM and simulation. Most of the work that has been done is of a hybrid nature. Generally, the model is CPM-based and a form of Monte Carlo simulation is utilized in evaluating the network performance under the imposed random processes (AbouRizk et al. 1992). Significant work in this area includes that done by Carr (1979), Ahuja & Nandakumar (1984), Ahuja et al. (1984), and Odeh et al. (1992).

The simulation system presented herein overcomes the limiting assumptions of PERT, the deterministic approach to uncertain event and branching as well as the limited resources interaction modelling capabilities of CPM, and the complexity and unsuitability of simulation systems for modeling CPM networks.

2 THE SIMULATION SYSTEM

2.1 Modelling elements

The system builds on the modelling construct of CPM and CYCLONE of Activities, Milestones, Queues, Links, Forks, and Consolidation elements. The graphical presentation of these elements and their functional parameters are shown in Table 1.

Queue (Que): Represents an idle state in which entities await the activation of any succeeding activity. It is also the element in which the initial resources are defined. A Que can only proceed and can only be preceded by activities. The Que parameters are: *ID* for the Que identification number, *Name* describing the

name or state of Que resources, and *IC* for the initial content or number of entities in the Que.

Activity (Act): Represents an active state in which entities interact to accomplish work. An activity can be preceded by a combination of other Activities, Milestones, Forks, Cons, and Ques. An activity cannot start until all the resources required for its activation are available – one entity in each preceding Que. For an activity to start, however, its precedence relationship(s) must also be satisfied. In this regard, the activity is a logical AND that can only start after all of its precedence relationships are satisfied.

Priority among activities competing for the same pool of resources is in a descending order of activities *PR* and in an ascending order of activities *ID* in case of equal *PR*.

The activity duration is determined by the cycle time (*CT*) and the number of cycles (*NC*) required to complete the activity. The cycle time (*CT*) can be deterministic or probabilistic as defined by a probability function and it's parameters. The probabilistic cycle time can be sampled from Discrete, Continuous, Uniform, Beta, Gamma, Poisson, Triangle, and Exponential probability distribution functions. The maximum number of concurrent cycles is defined by *MCC*.

Milestone: Represents an event being the start or completion of an important stage in the construction plan. Milestones consume no time and require no resources; as such they have zero duration and cannot be preceded by Ques.

Fork: Represents a probabilistic branching to one of the succeeding activities based on a specified discrete probability distribution (P_i). A fork does not require resources nor consumes time and thus cannot be preceded by queues.

Consolidate (Con): Represents a logical OR in the network in that it is activated upon the satisfaction of a limited number of precedence relationships as defined by the consolidation number (*CN*) parameter. A *CN* of 1, for example, means that the Con will be activated upon the satisfaction of any precedence relationship. A Con does not require resources nor consumes time and thus cannot be preceded by queues.

Resource flow: Represents the flow of resources from and to queues. The flow of resources can be cyclic represented by links with double arrowhead, or non-cyclic represented by links with single arrowhead.

Cyclic flow of resources involves the withdrawal of a resource entity from the queue at the beginning of each activity cycle and the subsequent release of the entity at the end of each cycle. The released resource becomes available for other activities of higher priority.

Non-cyclic resource flow involves the capture of the withdrawn resource entity in the activity for future cycles. A captured resource can be either busy or idle

Table 1. Graphical presentation of modelling elements and their parameters.

Element	Graphical presentation	Parameters
Queue (Que)	ID Name IC	ID = Identification Number. Name = Description. IC = Initial Content.
Activity (Act)	ID Name PR / NC CT MCC	ID = Identification Number. Name = Description. PR = Priority. NC = Number of Cycles. CT = Cycle Time. MCC = Max. Concurrent Cycles.
Relationship	Type + Lag →	Type = Type of relationship. Lag = Lag time.
Resource Flow: Non-cyclic Cyclic	→ ►►	
Milestone	ID Name	ID = Identification Number. Name = Description.
Consolidation (Con)	ID CN	ID = Identification Number. CN = Consolidation Number.
Fork	ID P1 P2 P3	ID = Identification Number. Pi = Probability of branch i.

awaiting the availability of other resources required to start a new cycle. A captured resource will be held in the activity as long as the number of captured resources is less than the number of remaining cycles. The number of resources held from a certain queue cannot exceed the maximum number of concurrent cycles (MCC).

Relationship: Represents the logical or precedence relationships among activities, milestones, forks, consolidate elements.

The system supports two types of relationships: Finish-to-Start (FS) and Start-to-Start (SS). The relationship is defined by its *Type* (i.e., FS or SS) and *Lag* time parameters. For a FS relationship, the *Lag* time can be deterministic or probabilistic. For SS relationship, the *Lag* time can be deterministic, probabilistic or number of cycles or percentage of the preceding activity.

2.2 Modelling capabilities

The simulation model of the construction plan is a network of activities, milestones, queues, forks, consolidate, and links describing the construction logic and resource utilization strategies.

The concepts of cyclic activities and cyclic flow of resources allow modelling of repetitive work and of complex yet realistic resource utilization policies such as enabling identical resources (e.g., crews) to work concurrently on a certain operation, reallocating resources to high priority tasks when several activities compete for the same pool of resources, and capturing of certain resources for the activity while allowing others to be reallocated to more important work.

Repetitive work can be modelled by cyclic activities as defined by *NC* and *MCC* parameters. The activity will be repeated for *NC* cycles and will be finished at the latest finish time of these cycles. Each cycle represents a unit of repetitive work such as m^3, 100 bricks, or column. The repetitive work can be performed one at a time or concurrently. The maximum number of concurrent cycles (*MCC*) represents technical, spatial or resource constraints.

Whereas limited resource availability is implied by *MCC*, resources involvement in an activity preceded by queues is explicit. The number of resource entities from a queue that can work concurrently in a cyclic activity is limited to *MCC*. Meanwhile additional resources available in the queue, if any, can be utilized to perform work in other activities.

Dynamic utilization of resources to competing activities can be modelled by the cyclic flow of the resources where a resource entity withdrawn from the queue at the beginning of a cycle will be released at the end of the cycle. Upon release, the entity becomes available for all competing activities and will be allocated to the one of higher priority (*PR*).

Forks with probabilistic branching model uncertain events such as the outcome of inspection. Forks and Consolidate elements, whose activation is conditional upon the satisfaction of a predefined number (i.e., *CN*) of precedence relationships, can be used to model inspection and rework. Forks and Consolidate may be preceded and/or succeeded by activities to model time and resource requirements.

These modelling capabilities will be illustrated and demonstrated through the forthcoming example.

2.3 *System implementation*

The system is implemented using The ACTOR® object oriented programming language. The implementation is user friendly with menus and input dialogs for defining, editing, saving, and simulating project plans. The system has been verified and the simulation output has been validated. Attempts to develop graphical interface (network) and graphical representation of the simulation output are ongoing.

2.3 *Simulation output*

The system simulates the network for a user-defined number of replications and produces the statistical data needed to plan, predict, and forecast the project duration and to optimize the project plan and the use of resources. It provides CPM like statistics regarding the project and activities times; and CYCLONE like statistics regarding the utilization of resources and areas of bottlenecks. In addition, the system provides statistics regarding the floats and the criticality of each activity.

CPM like statistics includes the minimum, maximum, average, and standard deviation of the project duration. For activities, the statistics include the minimum, maximum, average, and standard deviation of the cycle time and of the activities start and finish times, duration, and total and free floats. In addition, the statistics include the criticality index: the number of replications in which the activity is on the critical path (the longest path in the network) divided by the total number of replications. They also include the number of replications in which the activity did start and the number of cycles in each replication.

Similar statistics, excluding duration and cycle times, are reported for milestone, fork, and consolidate elements. For forks, branching statistics – the number of replications each branch was selected – are also reported.

CYCLONE like statistics include statistics of the queue output and input – number of departing and arriving resources, queue content – time weighted average and standard deviation of number of resources in the queue, and the percentage of time the queue content is above a certain number for the full range of minimum to maximum content.

3 NETWORK EXAMPLE

Consider the network shown in Figure 1 for the construction of reinforced concrete columns, staircase walls, and slab elements of a building floor. Each of these types of elements will go through the typical reinforcement, formwork, and casting of concrete. Work proceeds with the construction of the columns and the staircase walls and ends with the construction of the slab. The formed and reinforced slab shall be inspected and approved, with a possibility of rework, prior to concrete casting. The planning time unit for the cycle time and Lag is working hour.

The constraining resources under consideration are the steelworkers in Que 5 and the carpenters in Que 15. The availability and allocation of these resources to the competing columns and staircase walls activities have profound effect on the project duration and on the utilization of these resources. The number of available resources (initial content) in Ques 5 and 15 are IC5 and IC15 respectively.

The reinforce and form columns Activities 40 and 50 are cyclic with 16 cycles each corresponding to the number of floor columns. The cycle times, representing the time to reinforce and form each of the 16 columns, follow a Normal distribution with an average and standard deviation of 3 and 0.2 respectively for Act 40 and a Beta distribution with 5th, 50th, and 95th percentiles of 2, 2.5, and 3 respectively for Act 50.

The SS + 8C precedence relationship between activities 40 and 50 is a start-to-start relationship with a Lag of 8 cycles. Considering that each cycle corresponds to one column, this relationship in effect specifies that the form columns Act 50 can start after 8 columns have been formed in Act 40.

The staircase walls will be constructed as follows: form first side Act 10, reinforce wall Act 20, and enclose the forms: form side 2 Act 30. Act 10 has 2 cycles (*NC* = 2) each of which has a duration that follows a Normal distribution with an average and standard deviation of 7 and 2 respectively. These 2 cycles can be performed concurrently (*MCC* = 2) bending the availability of carpenters in Que 15.

The number of cycles for Activities 20 and 30 is limited to 1 each. This limits the number of resources

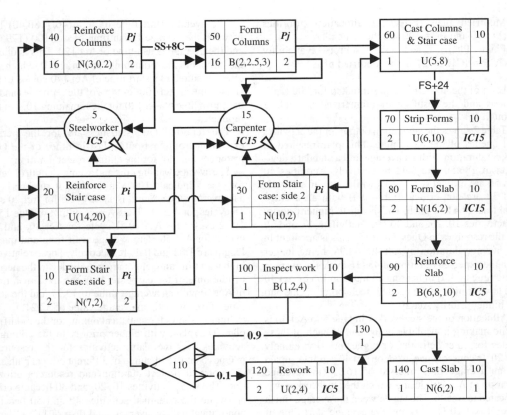

Figure 1. Sample problem – construction of reinforced concrete structure.

form a preceding Que that can be allocated to each of these activities to 1 thus allowing for the allocation of additional resources, if any, to other activities that compete for the same pool of resources; namely activities 40 and 50. The cycle time for Act 20 is Uniformly distributed between 14 and 20 while that of Act 30 is Normally distributed with an average and standard deviation of 10 and 2 respectively.

The cast columns and staircase walls concrete Act 60 starts after the columns and walls are formed and reinforced. Act 70, strip forms, starts 24 hours (FS + 24) after the casting of concrete in Act 60.

The final segment of the network pertains to the construction of the slab: form work Act 80, reinforcement Act 90, inspection Act 100, possible rework Act 120, approval Con 130, and casting Act 140. Fork 110 models the inspection result with two possible outcomes (branches): fail inspection and consequently rework Act 120 with a probability of 0.1, or pass inspection with a probability of 0.9. The approval Con 130, and consequently the cast slab Act 140, requires the satisfaction of only one precedence relationship ($CN = 1$) meaning that approval is achieved if the work passes inspection or after rework if the work fails inspection.

Explicit allocation of the steel workers and the carpenters in Ques 5 and 15 is limited to the overlapping activities that compete for them, namely the form-work and reinforcement activities of columns and staircase walls: activities 10, 20, 30, 40, and 50. Allocation of these resources to the slab's formwork and reinforcement activities (70, 80, 90, and 120) is implicit where each is performed in 2 cycles ($NC = 2$) with the maximum number of concurrent cycles being the number of carpenters (IC15) for activities 70 and 80 and the number of steelworkers (IC5) for Activities 90 and 120.

Utilization of available resources depends on the definition of the activities that compete for the resources, including number of cycles and maximum number of concurrent cycles, resource flow (cyclic/non-cyclic), and priority of competing activities over common resources. In this example, only the effect of the priority of the staircase activities (Pi) and the column activities (Pj) over the carpenters and the steelworkers is considered.

In particular the following plans are considered:

1. The basic plan with Pi = 100, Pj = 0, and IC5 = IC15 = 1.

185

2. Modified plan: Effect of allocation priorities ($Pi = 0$ and $Pj = 100$) on the basic plan.
3. Final Plan: Effect of resource availability ($IC5 = IC15 = 2$) on the modified plan.

Each of the above plans is simulated for 200 replications and the results are summarized in Table 2 through 4.

Table 2 shows the simulation output for the activities and queues of the basic plan. This plan resulted in project duration with an average and a standard deviation of 186.50 and 6.32 respectively. Activities 40 and 50 are critical ($CI = 1.0$) while activities 10, 20, and 30 are non-critical ($CI = 0.0$) with an average total float of 41.02 each. This is due to higher priority of activities 10, 20, and 30 over activities 40, and 50 for the resources in Ques 5 and 15. This is apparent in the average duration of Act 40, 64.95, being longer than the expected duration of 48 (16 cycles × average cycle time of 3.0) indicating an interruption of Act 40 due to allocation of the needed steelworker in Que 5 to the higher priority Act 20.

Allocation of the steelworker in Que 5 to Act 40 is cyclic making it available at the end of each of these cycles for other activities of higher priority; namely Act 20. In consequence, work on Act 40 was interrupted for an average time interval of 16.97 (the average duration of Act 20) during which the steelworker was allocated to Act 20. The lag between the average finish time of Act 10 (13.77) and the average start time of Act 20 (15.24), despite the FS + 0 relationship between the two activities, is due to involvement of the steelworker in Act 40.

The average start time of Act 140 (180.40) lies between the average finish time of Act 100 (179.64) and the average finish time of Act 120. This is due to the probabilistic branching at Fork 110 which, in effect, resulted in a start time of Act 140 equals to the finish time of Act 100 for 90% of the replicates and to the finish time of Act 120 for the remaining 10% of the replicates.

The reported Que statistics are for the period extending from first-out to last-in times of the Que resources and not for the entire project duration.

The average waiting time and average length of zeros for Que 5 indicate 100% utilization of steelworkers. The average Que output is 17, 1 cycle for Act 20 and 16 cycles for Act 40. The average output of Que 15 is 19; 2 cycles for Act 10, 1 cycle for Act 30, and 16 cycles for Act 50. The average wait time and queue length are 1.02 and 0.23 respectively. These relatively high wait time and length are mainly due to the period of idle time of the carpenter between the finish time of Act 10 with an average value of 13.77 and the start time of Act 30 with an average value of 32.21.

Table 3 shows the statistical output for the modified plan. This plan, with higher priority to the columns' activities over the slab's activities for the resources in Ques 5 and 15, resulted in different critical path and in improved project duration and resources utilization. The slab's activities 10, 20, and 30 became critical while the columns' activities 40 and 50 became non-critical with an average total float of 11.73.

Improvement to project duration is significant: shorter duration (drop in the average duration from 185.50 to 178.49) and less variation (drop in the

Table 2. Statistics for $Pi = 100$, $Pj = 0$, $IC5 = IC15 = 1$.

Activity	Average value				
	Start	Finish	Duration	TF	CI
a) Summary of activities statistics					
10	0.00	13.77	13.77	41.02	0
20	15.24	32.21	16.97	41.02	0
30	32.21	42.26	10.05	41.02	0
50	0.00	64.95	64.95	0.00	1
60	43.37	83.29	39.92	0.00	1
70–120	83.29	179.64	96.35	0.00	1
130	181.09	187.24	6.10	0.00	1
150	180.40	186.50	6.09	0.00	1

Que	Average				
	Output	First-out time	Last-in time	Wait time	Que length
b) Summary of Ques statistics					
5	17	0.00	64.95	0.00	0.00
15	19	0.00	83.29	1.02	0.23

Table 3. Statistics for $Pi = 0$, $Pj = 100$, $IC5 = IC15 = 1$.

Activity	Average values				
	Start	Finish	Duration	TF	CI
a) Summary of activities statistics					
10	0.00	13.77	13.77	0.00	1
20	48.04	65.01	16.97	0.00	1
30	65.50	75.61	10.11	0.00	1
50	0.00	48.04	48.04	11.73	0
60	23.10	63.89	40.79	11.73	0
70–120	75.61	172.04	96.43	0.00	1
130	172.94	178.35	5.41	0.00	1
150	172.53	178.49	5.96	0.00	1

Que	Average				
	Output	First-out time	Last-in time	Wait time	Que length
b) Summary of Ques statistics					
5	17	0.00	65.01	0.00	0 00
15	19	0.00	75.61	0.62	0 16

Table 4. Statistics for Pi = 0, Pj = 100, IC5 = IC15 = 2.

Activity	Start	Finish	Duration	TF	CI
Average values					
a) Summary of activities statistics					
10	0.00	8.23	8.23	3.30	0.3
20	9.52	26.63	17.11	3.30	0.3
30	27.52	37.44	9.92	3.30	0.3
50	0.00	33.30	33.30	1.60	0.7
60	14.50	39.14	24.64	1.60	0.7
70–120	40.74	108.04	67.30	0.00	1
130	106.40	110.08	3.68	0.00	1
150	108.41	114.18	5.77	0.00	1

Que	Output	First-out time	Last-in time	Wait time	Que length
Average					
b) Summary of Ques statistics					
5	17	0.00	33.30	0.08	0.04
15	19	0.00	40.74	0.91	0.42

standard deviation from 6.32 to 5.68). Improvement to carpenter's utilization is also significant in all aspects: last-in–first-out (from 83.36 to 75.61), waiting time (from 1.02 to 0.62), and Que length (from 0.23 to 0.16). This can be attributed to less idle time as a result of earlier average start of Act 50 (23.10 for the modified plan as compared to 40.98 for the basic plan). The carpenter idle time is limited to the times from the average finish time of Act 10 (13.77) to the average start time of Act 50 (23.10 on) and from the average finish time of Act 50 (63.89) to the average start time of Act 30 (65.01).

Table 4 shows the statistical output for the final plan. This plan, which differs from the modified plan in providing additional steelworker and carpenter, resulted a completion time with an average of 114.18 and a standard deviation of 3.76.

The results show probabilistic critical path: activities 10, 20, and 30 with probability of 0.3 and activities 40 and 50 with probability of 0.7. This can be explained by examining the proximate finish times of activities 30 and 50: the average and standard deviation of the finish time of Act 30 are 37.44 and 3.12 respectively while those of Act 50 are 39.14 and 3.28 respectively. These values indicate a probability for the finish time of Act 30 to exceed the finish time of Act 50. The average start time of Act 60 (40.74), being greater than the average finish times of its predecessors (activities 30 and 50), indicates that this time is controlled by Act 30 in some replicates and by Act 50 otherwise.

The Que statistics for the time interval between first-out and last-in indicate very efficient utilization of steelworkers with average wait time and length of

0.08 and 0.04 respectively, and less efficient utilization of carpenters with average wait time and length of 0.91 and 0.42 respectively.

4 CONCULSIONS

A simplified simulation system of overlapping precedence networks of construction plans has been presented. The system builds on and integrates the similar yet simple modelling construction of the well-known and widely used CPM networking technique and CYCLONE simulation system. By integrating the modelling capabilities of networking and simulation, the system overcomes many of the shortcoming of both CPM and CYCLONE and enables the modelling of repetitive work, probabilistic activity duration and branching, rework, as well as complex resource allocation policies that exist in real construction settings. The modelling capabilities of the system have been demonstrated.

The simulation output is extensive and instrumental to identifying bottlenecks and improving the construction plan. The output consists of CPM like statistics pertaining to start and finish times, floats, and criticality; as well as CYCLONE like statistics pertaining to resource utilization.

REFERENCES

Abourizk, S., Halpin, D. & Lutz, J. 1992. State of the art in construction simulation. *Proc., 1992 Winter Simulation Conf.,* 1271–1277.

Ahuja, H.N. & Nandakumar, V. 1984. Enhancing Reliability of Project Duration Forcast. *Transaction of American Association of Cost Engineering,* 25th Annual Meeting, Montreal, Canada.

Ahuja, H. Dozzi, S.P. & AbouRizk, S.M. 1995. *Project management techniques in planning and controlling construction projects.* 2nd Ed., John Wiley & Sons, Inc., New York.

Carr, R.I. 1979. Simulation of Construction Project Duration. *J. Constr. Div.,* ASCE, 105(June).

Halpin, D.W. 1977. CYCLONE: method for modeling of job site processes. *J. Constr. Div., ASCE,* 103(3), 489–499.

Halpin, D.W. 1992. *Microcyclone users manual, version 2.5.* Learning Systems, Inc., West Lafayette, Ind.

Kalk, A. 1980. INSIGHT – interactive simulation of construction operations using graphical techniques. *Tech. Rep. No. 238,* Constr. Inst., Dept. of Civ. Engrg., Stanford Univ., Stanford, Calif.

Martinez, J., Ioannou, P. & Carr, R. 1994. State and resource based construction process simulation. *Proc., 1st Congr. on Computing in Civ. Engrg.,* ASCE, Washington, D.C. 177–184.

McCrimmon, K.R. & Rayvec, C.A. 1964. *An analytical study of the PERT assumptions.* Operations Res., 12, 16–38.

Odeh A.M., Tommelein I.D. & Carr, R.I. 1992. Knowledge-based simulation of construction plans. *Proc., 8th Conf. on Computing in Civ. Engrg.,* ASCE, Va., 1042–1049.

Pritsker, A.A.B., Sigel, C.E. & Hammesfahr, R.D.J. 1989. *SLAM II: Network models for decision support*. Prentice-Hall Inc., Englewood Cliffs, N.J.

Sawhney, A. & AbouRizk, S.M. 1995. Simulations based planning method for construction project. *J. Constr, Engrg. and Mgmt., ASCE*, 121(3), 297–303.

Senior, B.A. 1995. Simulation and critical path method software. *Proc. 2nd Congr. on Computing in Civil Engrg., ASCE*, Atlanta, Go., 1412–1419.

Shi, J. & AbouRizk, S. 1997. Resource-based modeling for construction simulation. *J. Constr, Engrg. and Mgmt., ASCE*, 123(1), 26–33.

Shi, J. & AbouRizk, S. 1994. A resource-based simulation approach with application in earthmoving/strip mining. *Proc., 1994 Winter Simulation Conf.*, Inst. of Electr. and Electronic Engrs., Piscataway, N.J., 1124–1129.

Tavakoli, A. & Riachi, R. 1990. CPM USE in ENR top 400 contractors. *J. Mgmt. In Engrg., ASCE*, 6(3), 282–295.

Planning the installation of steel structures using simulation

G. Uzzi
E.D.IN. s.r.l.- Rome, Italy

J. Shi
Department of Civil and Architectural Engineering, Illinois Institute of technology, Chicago, USA

ABSTRACT: This paper describes modelling and simulation of a structural and miscellaneous steel erection project. It presents two schedules. One is the Experience Based Schedule (EBS). The second one is the Simulation Based Schedule (SBS), which is based on the simulation results using the ABC software. It shows how simulation technique can help project managers better plan this type of project.

1 INTRODUCTION

This paper describes modelling and simulation of a structural and miscellaneous steel erection project in which I was working as a project manager assistant and a structural engineer/detailer for the Pierini Iron Works, Inc. It shows how simulation technique can help project managers better plan this type of project.

This article presents and contracts two schedules. One is the Experience Based Schedule (EBS), which is prepared based on 35-year experience in steel erection of the project manager. The second one is the Simulation Based Schedule (SBS), which is based on the simulation results using the ABC software. The article then describes the actual construction progress, and contrast field results with the two schedules.

Finally, we will discuss our experience in this research and report some of the problems encountered and our observations on the general attitude toward new technologies in the industry.

2 PROJECT DESCRIPTION

2.1 *General overview*

Toyota-Leuxus chose Paris, Illinois to develop a new facility for producing and assembling the headlights for its cars in the Midwest market. Kajima was both the Architect and the General Contractor through a typical D/B (Design/Built) project delivery system. Pierini Iron Works, Inc. was the subcontractor for installation of all the miscellaneous and steel structures.

The building represents a classic production facility body with a rectangle shape running north/south, with 24 grid lines and flat roof. The columns placed along two lines in the middle of the facility create three bays which support the crane beams runways, the girders, the joists, and the roof.

The dimension of the building is $181 \times 49\,m$ ($593 \times 160\,ft$), with a total area of $8,815\,m^2$ ($94,880\,ft^2$). The roof height is $9.7\,m$ ($32\,ft$) on the West side and $7.6\,m$ ($25\,ft$) on the East side. The major steel components consist of 44 columns, 46 wide flange crane runway beams, 66 girders, 46 tie-joists, 621 joists, and 1,870 deck-sheets. The exterior walls are precast concrete panels. The concrete slab of $181 \times 49\,m$ is supported by concrete footings with one at each column.

2.2 *Steel erection detail and construction*

The project manager decided to install the structures by using one terrestrial crane to hoist all materials. The plan is to start four columns, starting from the very south side of the building and moving north. Doing so allows two grid lines of the building to be installed before moving the crane. Therefore, all of the necessary material – columns, beams, girders, joists, and deck between the two grid lines will be completed before the next cycle starts.

Like other steel erection process, the job characteristic is very repetitive. An item is picked, hoisted, and installed before the crane returns to starting point to pick up the next item. When all of the materials are installed for the location, the crane will move forward one step until the project is complete.

Table 1 shows the quantity takeoffs of the work items and corresponding production cycles.

Table 1. Quantity takeoff.

	Item per bay	Total bays	Total items	Item per cycle
Columns	2	22	44	4
Beams	2	23	46	4
Girders	3	22	66	6
Tie joists	2	23	46	4
Joists bundles	9	23	207	18
Deck bundles	–	23	115	1
Deck sheets	85	23	1955	170

Table 2. Resources.

Name	Number	Task	Type
Crane	1	Moving	Equipment
Operator	1	Crane operator	Labor
Crew1	2	Crane loading	Labor
Crew2	2	Setting	Labor
Crew3	2	Joist spreading	Labor
Crew4	2	Deck spreading	Labor
Crew5	2	Deck welding	Labor
Superintendent	1	Supervisor	Labor
Total	10 men		

The Table 2 shows the main resources used in construction. No driving resources are excluded such as welders, measuring tapes, measuring instruments, etc. As shown in the table a total of 10 men and one crane are used to perform the installation activities.

An operator operates the crane for all needed activities. Crew1 always stays at the loading point and helps move the crane at the end of every cycle of installation. The crane loads columns, joists bundles, girders etc. from the truck flatbed on the crane at the loading area. It then hoists the material to Crew2 that is responsible for setting the hoisted item. Crew 2 moves around on the site with their duty to detach and set the hoisted item from the crane. Columns, beams, girders and tie-joists must be completed set; but joist bundles and deck sheets are only needed to be placed. Crew3 spreads and installs the joist bundle. Usually joists come in bundles of three. After a bundle is placed, the ironworkers seating on the installed girder spread them by hand to the right place. Crew4 then spreads and sets the deck sheets. They walk on the installed joist, pick up a deck sheet, and place it at the right position. After finishing one sheet, they repeat the same process for the next sheet. Each bundle consists of 17 deck sheets. Crew4 must walk back and forth 17 times for each deck bundle. After the deck is set, Crew5 starts to weld each sheet to the underneath structural steel.

3 EXPERIENCE BASED SCHEDULING

The project manager prepared a schedule based on his 35 years experience on steel structures installation, and forecasted a project duration of seven or eight weeks with a production rate of 2.5 bays per week. Ten men are formulated in five crews plus a crane operator and a superintendent. The job was scheduled to start on the 9th of January and to finish at the end of March or the first week of April.

He explained to the project team of the construction process as described in section 2 without any further specification. Moreover, his experience was unable to tell the information such as resources idle time and production rate.

4 SIMULATION BASED SCHEDULING

4.1 *What is ABC*

ABC is an activity network-based modelling and simulation method (Shi 1999). Modelling a construction process is accomplished by using one single element, i.e. activity. In an ABC model, an activity may be either in an "idle" or "active" state. If an activity meets all required conditions for execution, the activity and involved resources are in active; otherwise, the activity is in idle and occupied resources are waiting.

Various functions needed for modelling a construction process are achieved by allowing activities carry attributes, including activity duration, operational conditions, resources, etc. Table 3 summarizes a contrast of ABC modelling and existing modelling approaches on some common functionality needed for modelling construction processes.

An ABC model is a static representation of the construction process under study. The dynamic behavior of the process is simulated by detailing status of activities, and movements and interactions of simulation entities over simulated time based on the activity based simulation algorithm. ABC simulation executes an ABC model by manipulating activities in three stages: a) select activity, b) advance simulation, and c) release entities. A detailed description of the ABC modelling and simulation method can be found in the reference (Shi 1999).

The differences between existing simulation systems lay in two major aspects: 1) modelling methods, and 2) functionality. All existing simulation systems require multiple elements from 5 to dozens with each element modelling a specific real world requirement such as resource waiting and collecting simulation results. Generally speaking, more elements bring in more functionality with the resulting problem of difficulty in use. From the end-user's perspective, the concern is whether a system has the needed functionality

Table 3. ABC versus existing simulation systems.

Functionality (1)	ABC-Model (2)	Existing simulation systems (3)
Generate entities	Entities can be generated by activity	Additional element for generating entities, e.g. CEATE
Terminate simulation	Simulation time or production cycle of selected activity	Simulation time or entity count on given nodes, e.g. COUNTER, TERMINATE
Idle state	An idle resource or entity waits at an activity	Waiting elements, e.g. QUEUE, AWAIT
Active state	Activity	Regular or service activity
Resource location	Activity or pool	Waiting location, activity, other elements, or pool
Multiply entity	Given number of entities to be released to a following activity	Specific modelling elements for splitting an entity, e.g. GENERATE, UNBATCH
Combine entity	Given iterations needed for the release of an entity	Specific element for combining multiple entities into one, e.g. COMBINE
Matching between resources	Directly specify matching units of resources	Split or combine entities to balance the matching
Matching between resources	Directly specify matching units of resources	Split or combine entities to balance the matching
Production	Count iterations of selected production activities	Elements for collecting production entity
Resource utilization	Trace the life cycle of a resource entity	Collect time at all idle states

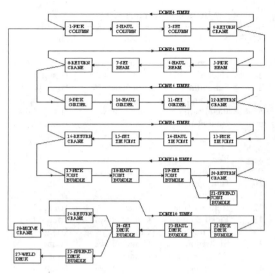

Figure 1. ABC network.

and Martinez 1999). Shi and AbouRizk (1997) identified the difficulty in use as one of the major obstacles, which are restraining the construction industry from adopting the simulation technology. With one single element, ABC has achieved ease of use as well as the same functionality as existing construction simulation systems have. Moreover, constructing an ABC model is similar to creating a CPM (critical path method) network so that practitioners can easily understand ABC with the popularity of CPM in construction industry (Shi 2000).

4.2 ABC simulation network

Figure 1 shows the ABC network the discussed construction process. The diagram clearly shows the logical sequences between the construction activities in the process.

Good communications with the project manager and the superintendent allow a simulation model to be created in a way similar how the real construction process operates.

As shown in Figure 1, the simulation model l allows some operations to repeat a number of times before going to the next operation. The construction cycle for columns starts from activity 1 to activity 4. They repeat 4 times before the simulation proceeds to the next cycle for setting the beams for crane runways, which comprises of activity 5 to activity 8. This cycle also repeats 4 times before the girder installation starts.

Table 4 lists all of the involved activities consisting of ID-number, name, resources, and duration. All activities are assigned with triangular distributions for modelling their durations in minutes. The project manager based on the projects conducted in the past or

for studying the given problem and whether it is easy to use. The results from different systems should be equivalent and comparable if these systems can model the problem at the same level of detail. In order to effectively use any simulation system, a user must go through an intensive technical training and a long experience-accumulating process (Shi 1999). Although construction simulation technology was created more than two decades ago with the development of CYCLONE (Halpin 1977), it remains as a research topic in academia with very limited industry applications (Halpin

Table 4. ABC activity summary table.

No.	Name	Resources	Time
1	Pick column	Crane, crew1	Triang[2,4,6]
2	Haul column	Crane	Triang[2,3,4]
3	Set column	Crane, crew2	Triang[9,11,3]
4	Return crane	Crane	Triang[2,3,4]
5	Pick beam	Crane, crew1	Triang[2,4,6]
6	Haul beam	Crane	Triang[2,3,4]
7	Set beam	Crane, crew2	Triang [9,11,13]
8	Return crane	Crane	Triang[2,3,4]
9	Pick girder	Crane, crew1	Triang[2,4,6]
10	Haul girder	Crane	Triang[2,3,4]
11	Set girder	Crane, crew2	Triang[7,810]
12	Return crane	Crane	Triang[2,3,4]
13	Pick tie joist	Crane, crew1	Triang[2,4,6]
14	Haul tie joist	Crane	Triang[2,3,4]
15	Set tie joist	Crane, crew2	Triang[4,5,6]
16	Return crane	Crane	Triang[2,3,4]
17	Pick joist bundle	Crane, crew1	Triang[2,4,6]
18	Haul joist bundle	Crane	Triang[2,3,4]
19	Set joist bundle	Crane, crew2	Triang[1,2,3]
20	Return crane	Crane	Triang[2,3,4]
21	Spread joist	Crew3	Triang [12,15,17]
22	Pick deck bundle	Crane, crew1	Triang[2,4,6]
23	Haul deck bundle	Crane	Triang[2,3,4]
24	Set deck bundle	Crane, crew2	Triang[1,2,3]
25	Spread deck bundle	Crew4	Triang [85,119,170]
26	Return crane	Crane	Triang[2,3,4]
27	Weld deck	Crew5	Triang [102,136,170]
28	Move crane	Crane, crew1	Triang [120,150,180]

Table 5. ABC duration and production output.

No.	Name	ABC duration	Action Count	Prod.
1	Pick column	3.43	16	16
2	Haul column	2.62	16	16
3	Set column	10.56	16	16
4	Return crane	2.57	16	
5	Pick beam	3.75	16	16
6	Haul beam	2.5	16	16
7	Set beam	10.50	16	16
8	Return crane	2.50	16	
9	Pick girder	3.45	24	24
10	Haul girder	2.45	24	24
11	Set girder	10.18	24	24
12	Return crane	2.41	24	
13	Pick tie joist	3.81	16	16
14	Haul tie joist	2.31	16	16
15	Set tie joist	5.31	16	16
16	Return crane	2.37	16	
17	Pick joist bundle	3.54	**64**	64
18	Haul joist bundle	2.5	63	63
19	Set joist bundle	3.42	63	63
20	Return crane	2.65	63	
21	Spread joist	14.31	62	186 joists
22	Pick deck bundle	3.66	30	30
23	Haul deck bundle	2.03	30	30
24	Set deck bundle	3.35	30	30
25	Spread deck bundle	117.81	29	493 sheets
26	Return crane	2.41	27	
27	Weld deck	129.19	26	442 sheets
28	Move crane	137.5	**3**	
	Total simulation time:	4001 minutes		

subjective judgments estimates the three-time parameter of a triangular distribution. The company did not have a database for its completed projects. However, talking to the superintendent, ironworkers and the project manager enabled us to obtain the needed activity durations. We had some hard time to determine durations for activities 21, 25, 27 because those activities were kind of unusual in this project. Some timing studies were also conducted on the site.

4.3 ABC results

After the model was created, the ABC simulation system was used to experiment with the model with the summary results as shown in Table 5.

Table 5 shows for the operating details of the activities including mean duration, operating cycles, and total operations. The crane was moved three times (i.e., at activity 28). The table also shows that the project duration is 4001 minutes.

Table 6 uses the ABC Immediate Report to aggregate the durations for major activities in order to generate a traditional bar chart schedule. Using Primavera Project Planner, Figure 2 can be obtained. The figure shows two cycles of installation. It clearly indicates the critical path and the controlling activity, i.e., Activity 25 – the deck sheets spreading. Welding of the deck sheets is close to being critical. Table 6 also shows that the last deck sheet is welded 2052,28 minutes after the construction starts.

Equation (1) can be used to calculate the total weeks needed to complete this project. The total time includes the first cycle – 2052,28 minutes and repeating spreading of the deck sheets – 1352,17 minutes, repeated for 10 times.

Table 6. Main activity duration per cycle.

Main activity	Start	End	Duration [min]	[hour]	[hour]
Columns	0	83,87	83,87	1,40	1
Beams	83,87	167,39	83,52	1,39	1
Girders	167,39	289,69	122,3	2,04	2
tie joist	289,69	356,48	66,52	1,11	1
joist bundles	356,48	615,93	259,45	4,32	4
spread joist bundle	615,93	636,81	267,82	4,46	4
deck bundles	615,93	744,62	121,24	2,02	2
spread deck bundle	626,32	1938,77	1352,17	22,54	23
weld deck	756,17	**2052,28**	1296,11	21,60	22
move crane	744,62	911,74	167,12	2,79	3

Table 7. ABC output resources usage time.

Resource	Usage time [%]	Task
Crane	100	Hoisting materials
Crew1	75.35	Loading the crane
Crew2	60.65	Set and install items
Crew3	21.94	Spreading joist bundles
Crew4	87.56	Spreading deck bundles
Crew5	83.95	Welding deck sheets

Table 8. The key dates of the project.

Start date	January 9th 2002
End date	March 15th 2002

	Weeks	Weeks of delay	Net time
Actual time	9.25	1.5	7.75

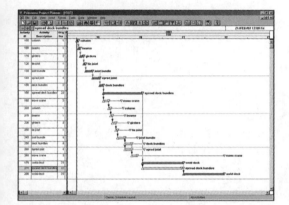

Figure 2. Gantt bar chart for two cycles.

$$\frac{(1352.17 \times 10) + 2052.28}{2100 \; minutes \; per \; week} = 7.416 \quad (weeks) \qquad (1)$$

2100 minutes per week are calculated based 60 minutes per hour, 7 hours per day of work and 5 working days per week.

Figure 2 and table 6, the ratio between the production rates of steel structures and spreading and welding of deck sheets can be calculated from Equation 2. The result shows that steel structures proceed about 48% faster than spreading and welding of deck sheets so they will be completed before the roof.

$$\frac{1352.74}{911.62} = 1.484 \qquad (2)$$

Table 7 shows the idle times of the resources obtained from the ABC reports. Those values are expressed in percentage of the total time for each resource. Bear the construction process (Figure 1) and the Gantt bar chart (Figure 2) in mind. It is possible to determine the bottleneck resource. An increase of a bottleneck resource would result in the most benefit in reducing the project duration. field results

The actual construction started as scheduled on January 9th 2002 with the first column on the South side of the building. The project completed on the 15th of March welding the last sheet deck with a total duration of 9.25 weeks.

It is usual in many D/B projects to see delays, which are frequently caused due to lack of information or change orders during construction. This job was no difference. A delay occurred because the layout of the roof openings was chanced many times. Because the structural steel interferes with the crane boom, everything was stopped while waiting for a new joist layout. At the end, there was a total of 11/2 week delay. Table 8 summarizes the actual key dates of the project. Although the actual total time was 9.25 weeks, it gives a net working time of 7.75 weeks after the 1.5 week delay is excluded. Therefore, the simulation results provide a very close to actual estimate.

The company attempted to collect actual activity durations. A spreadsheet was prepared for this task. The superintendent used a stopwatch to time starting and finishing times of every activity. Unfortunately, this time study did not last more than a week because the superintendent was involved in several activities and was unable to follow one operation for a long period of time.

5 CONCLUSION AND COMPARISONS

The study presented in this paper demonstrates that simulation provides an effective tool for us to better estimate the installation duration and the utilization of construction resources. Simulation results in this

Table 9. Comparison on the two schedules.

Schedule	Weeks	Percentage error
Simulation based scheduling	7.41	6%
Experience based scheduling	7	10%
Field results (net time)	7.75	

case helped us to improve the production rate and to shorten the total construction time.

Table 9 shows that the Simulation Based Scheduling estimated project duration with an error of 6% over the actual duration while the Experience Based Scheduling produced an error of 10%.

Because a simulation is consisted of basic activities, the data collected for activities can be used for future projects if these activities appear. The ABC system provides a user friendly network representation which help improve communications between team members in the project. When the superintendent was presented with the ABC network and the simulated progress, he could get a better idea on how the process should be conducted so that construction productivity and safety was improved accordingly.

System-based Vision for Strategic and Creative Design, Bontempi (ed.)
© 2003 Swets & Zeitlinger, Lisse, ISBN 90 5809 599 1

Probability applications in the precedence diagram scheduling method

M.F. Samara & C.S. Putcha
Department of Civil and Environmental Engineering, California State University-Fullerton, Fullerton, USA

ABSTRACT: The concepts of probability and statistics have been applied successfully to various branches of civil engineering for the past two decades. One of the areas of civil engineering, where these concepts are very useful is in the area of construction engineering dealing with project completion time where lot of uncertainties exist in the prediction of activity durations dealing with a project network. This results in uncertainty in completing the project. Weather, accidents, equipment failures, and similar occurrences are unpredictable random events that may alter the critical path of a project. This paper deals with application of Monte Carlo simulation techniques to predict the completion time of a project as no closed form solution exists when the input variables of activity durations are probabilistic variables. The work is based on the principles and applications reported in the literature (Putcha and Rao, 1991 and Putcha and Patev, 2000). The proposed method uses the precedence diagram to produce alternate critical paths with a predetermined probability of occurrence. For example, the probability of the critical path being shorter or exceeding a certain time period can be predicted using this method. An example is provided to illustrate the results.

1 INTRODUCTION

A construction project is a collection of activities with estimated durations and with certain dependencies that dictate a certain sequence of events. The dependencies could be due to logical considerations such as not being able to paint a wall until it is built, economic considerations such as performing certain tasks while the resources are readily available, and thus avoiding remobilization, or they could simply be the results of preferences and habits.

The project completion time is the result of combining the activity durations with the defined dependencies into a logical network. In general the estimated activity durations are predicated on the schedulers experience, the published productivity data, and availability of labor and materials. These activity durations are probabilistic in nature, and when combined with random occurrences such as weather, accidents, equipment failure, labor problems, and similar unpredictable random events the overall project completion time, and the critical path may be altered.

1.1 *Formulation of the problem*

In a construction project a manager is faced with a problem of completing the project within a given time T_1. The project completion time depends on the various activities which have uncertainties incorporated in them. Hence owing to the existence of such uncertainties affecting the activity durations these activities are treated as random variables.

Consider a general Precedence Diagram Method (PDM) network (Fig. 1) with n activities. Let the activity durations be D1, D2, ..., Dn in periods (Months, weeks, days, etc.) which are independent random variables. These variables are assumed to be uniform initially, distributed on the intervals $[L_{L1}, L_{U1}]$, $[L_{L2}, L_{U2}]$, $[L_{L3}, L_{U3}]$, ..., $[L_{Ln}, L_{Un}]$ where L and U represent the lower and upper limits of the activity duration.

The project completion time is a function of the activity durations D_i and can be expressed as

$$T = f(D_1, D_2 ..., D_n) \qquad (1)$$

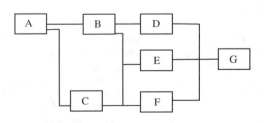

Figure 1. PDM Network.

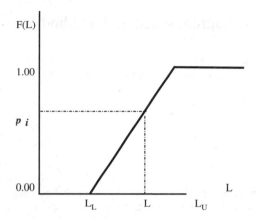

Figure 2. Graphic solution.

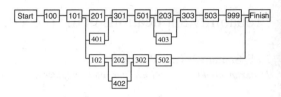

Figure 3. PDM network for example 1.

Since the project completion time will depend on the longest path through the network, the above equation may be rewritten as

$$T = Max(\text{All possible activity sequences}) \qquad (2)$$

The exact determination of the probability of the event $P(T > T_1)$ is a very difficult problem and certain methods such as Rosenblueth's (1981) "Two Point" scheme (Putcha & Rao 1991; Au et al. 1972) or a Monte Carlo simulation (Hart 1982; Rosenbleuth 1981) are used to determine the such a probability.

1.2.2 *Methodology*

A Monte Carlo Simulation is essentially a numerical method that uses random statistical techniques to estimate the value of unknown or uncertain quantities. It depends on the law of large numbers to obtain meaningful results.

The approach used in this study is a two-step procedure. The first step is to generate a random number, p_i for a uniform probability distribution function (PDF) with limits of 0.0 and 1.0, the second step is to transform such a random number to a new random number which corresponds to a uniform PDF over the range $[L_{Ln}, L_{Un}]$.

This procedure is illustrated mathematically as

$$L_i = L_{Li} + (L_{Ui} - L_{Li})p_i \qquad (3)$$

Figure 2 graphically illustrates equation 3.

This method indicates that it is necessary to integrate the PDF and obtain the corresponding probability distribution function, then successively solve this equation for each random number between 0.00 and 1.00. The value of the desired random number is then obtained by setting the distribution function equal to the 0.0 to 1.0 random number.

Table 1. Example 1 activity duration with selected simulation.

				Simulation number				
Task	Crit.	L_L	L_U	1	2	35	63	100
100	X	4	6	5.83	4.97	4.78	4.02	4 30
101	X	1	2	2.03	1.02	1.24	1.41	1 47
102		1	2					
201	X	4	6	4.33	6.52	5.89	5.52	6.48
401		1	2					
301	X	1	1	1.00	1.00	1.00	1.00	1.00
501	X	2	4	2.18	3.21	3.08	2.42	3.43
203	X	8	10	9.42	9.65	8.60	8.56	10.31
401		2	4					
301	X	2	3	2.61	2.32	2.14	2.28	2.51
503	X	11	15	11.09	11.02	13.49	13.09	12.93
201		2	5					
402		1	2					
302		1	2					
502		1	2					
999	X	0	0	0.00	0.00	0.00	0.00	0.00
Simulated project duration				38.48	39.71	40.22	38.30	42.44

2.1 *Examples*

Two examples are presented to illustrate this procedure. Both examples are adaptation to two projects presented by Suner (Hart 1982).

2.1.1 *Example 1*

Example 1 represents a wall foundation together with a cast in place basement wall. A total of 16 activities, excluding start and finish were identified the estimated completion time is 42 Days. Figure 3 illustrates the Precedence diagram for this project with the critical path highlighted. Activity names and description are omitted for brevity.

Table 1 shows the upper and lower bound estimated activity durations together with selected Monte Carlo simulations. 100 simulations were performed, and the probabilities were calculated based on these simulations.

Table 1 shows the upper and lower bound estimated activity durations together with selected Monte Carlo

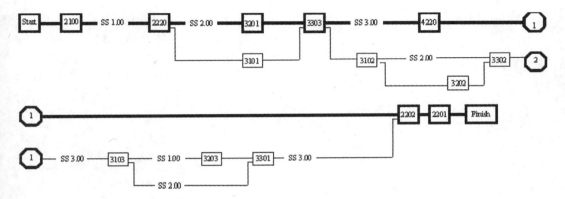

Figure 4.   PDM diagram for example 2.

Table 2.   Example 2 activity duration with selected simulation.

Task	Crit.	Lag	L_L	L_U	Simulation Number 1	4	18	72	100
2100	X	1	1	1	1.0	1.0	1.0	1.0	1.0
2201	X		2	5	2.0	2.4	4.8	3.8	4.9
2202	X		28	37	34.3	33.0	32.3	35.3	34.6
2220	X		20	24	22.2	20.6	20.3	21.1	20.1
3101			1	2					
3102			24	26					
3103			33	35					
3201	X	2	2	2	2.0	2.0	2.0	2.0	2.0
3202			14	16					
3203			11	14					
3301			18	19					
3302			14	18					
3303	X	3	3	3	3.0	3.0	3.0	3.0	3.0
4220	X		35	38	36.7	35.1	37.6	35.4	35.9
Simulated critical path.					101.2	97.0	101.0	101.6	101.5

simulations. 100 simulations were performed, and the probabilities were calculated based on these simulations.

Selected computations indicate that the probability of completion time will exceed 39 days is 83%, while the probability of completion within the 40 day estimated duration is 36%.

2.1.2   *Example 2*

Example 2 differs from example 1 in the sense that it involves PERT type estimates of durations as well as, lag between the activities.

The critical path length is 91 days. Figure 4 illustrates the Precedence Diagram for this project. Table 2 shows selected simulations as well as activity durations.

Probability calculations indicate that the probability of completing the project in 88 days is 8% while the probability of completing the project less than 91 days is 46%. The probability of finishing in more than 92 days is 87%.

3   CONCLUSIONS

This method provides the project planner with the probabilities of completing the project on time, ahead of time, or behind schedule. These probabilities should be used as a guide in determining schedule contingencies, and perhaps deciding on how to treat schedule incentives and penalties.

REFERENCES

Putcha, C.S. & Rao, S.J.K. Probabilistic network analysis for project completing time, *Civil Engineering Systems, 1991, Vol. 8.*

Rosenbleuth, E. Point Estimates for Probability Moments, *Proceedings of the National Academy of Sciences, October 1975,* 72(10) pp. 3812–4.

Au, T., Shane, R.M. & Hoel, L. "Fundamentals of Systems Engineering Probabilistic Methods", *Addison-Wesley, Washington, 1972.*

Hart, G.C. "Uncertainty Analysis, Loads, and Safety in Structural Engineering", *Prentice-Hall, Englewood Cliffs, NJ, 1982.*

Rosenbleuth, E. Two-Point Estimates in Probabilities, *Applied Mathematical Modeling,* **5**, *October, 1981, pp.329–35.*

Warner, R.F. & Kabalia, A.P. Monte Carlo Study of Structural Safety, *J. Stuct. Div. Proc. ASCE,* **94**, *1968.*

Suner, M.A. Precedence Diagramming Method in Planning and Scheduling of Construction Projects, *Report submitted to the faculty of Civil and Environmental Engineering in Partial Fulfillment of the Master of Science Degree, 1993.*

System-based Vision for Strategic and Creative Design, Bontempi (ed.)
© 2003 Swets & Zeitlinger, Lisse, ISBN 90 5809 599 1

The application of simulation modelling in identifying company's logistic system models

A. Sobotka
Faculty of Civil and Sanitary Engineering, Technical University of Lublin, Poland

ABSTRACT: Identification and optimalization of economic system models requires a lot of investigating. Simulation modelling is the method that allows such researches without of any danger of influencing the natural conditions, in which the real system works. Multiple simulations with various sets of input data allow to choosing the best solution. The paper presents simulation research that provides analytical model of a construction company's logistic system. Analytical solution allows concluding about system properties, and could be applied in practice for logistic management of a company, for example for choosing a controlling method of logistic processes and examining model's sensitivity to changes in parameters. The paper presents an example of investigation of logistic system by means of its analytical model. The identification of the model was done on the basis of modelling by means of simulator and complementary results of least square method. The received results were used to investigating model sensitivity to parameter and input variable changes in the model.

1 INTRODUCTION

Investigating economic systems to which logistic systems belong is carried out by means of simulation models and computer techniques, Hammeri & Paantla (1995), Kaplinski (1997), Prakash and Shannon (1985), Ulanicki (1993). A simulation model is understood as a mathematical model expressed by means of analytical and logic relationships for which there is no possibility of finding the solution in analytical way and so it is solved by means of computer simulation, Law & Kelton (1991). In these models independent variables are inputs, and dependent variables – output (output is univocal function of input). Formalization of simulation models description consists of the following stages, Sobotka (1998, 2000), Zeigler (1976), Rzemykowski (1994):

1. Verbal description of the system making the general description of its structure.
2. General mathematical model of the system structure.
3. Graphic model of the system. It presents flows of physical (goods) and information streams between particular elements of the system according to adopted symbols, Sobotka (2000).
4. Analytical–logical model. Relationships characterizing operations of transforming input quantities into state quantities in the logistic systems investigated in the present paper have a form of analytical

or logical relations. These relations and the description of the sets to which variables of the model belong, and the relation arranging the set of controlling variables that allows to compare elements of that set from the point of view of controlling goals (objective function), make analytic–logical model of the logistic system.

5. A computer program (simulator) which allows conducting simulation experiments.

In such models the form of the relation S "input X – output Y" is often unknown

$$S: X \to Y \qquad (1)$$

The knowledge of this relation (function, functional or operator, Gutenbaum (1992) enabling analytical solutions is indispensable from the point of view of obtaining possibilities for optimizing system quality coefficients, and drawing conclusions on system properties such as its sensitivity, stability, etc. The selection of the form of the model and estimating numerical values of its parameters (factors) called model parameter identification or model identifications can be done by means of various methods.

The present paper is a continuation of research presented in the article, Sobotka (2000). The simulation models described there are estimated by means of logistic costs described with the functions dependent on other output variables, which are generated by the simulator. That is why successive investigations of logistic systems lead to finding a directly conditioning costs function to input controlling variables.

The scope of research includes:

1. Description of simulation method identifying and optimization of logistic model. The basis of model's identification are results generated by means of a GPSS language programmed simulator and least square method.
2. The example of the simulation method application to examining the logistic model's sensitivity to changes in productions. The logistic cost is a measure of evaluation of the functioning model quality.

2 DESCRIPTION OF THE IDENTIFICATION METHOD OF LOGISTIC SYSTEM ANALITYCAL MODEL

The aim of investigating logistic systems is to explain mechanisms governing logistic processes, get to know these problems in their quality and quantity aspects, and employ the knowledge in practical actions of making decisions concerning the selection of logistic strategies in construction companies. A logistic strategy is a conception of action the implementation of which is to secure obtaining goals in the sphere of logistics, Pfohl (1996). The actions can be understood as controlling logistic system i.e. a decision-maker's affecting logistic system, which causes its desirable output reactions, Gutenbaum (1992). The aim of controlling is to secure a desirable course of a process (phenomenon) controlled in the system (in the present paper, this process is providing construction sites with materials). Estimating the course of controlled processes is done by means of controlling quality coefficient characterizing system reaction, in this case – logistic costs.

The identifying of the controlling quality coefficient is a kind of complex transformation in the method employed

$$S: X \to Y, \quad V: Y \to K, \quad F: X \to K. \qquad (2)$$

It results from the fact that during a simulation experiment carried out by means of the simulator, input quantities X are transformed into output quantities Y by relation S. Then quantities Y are transformed into the set K, whereas operator F transforms the set of input quantities X into the set of output quantities K. Logistic costs in simulation logistic models, Sobotka (2000), are a known function v of output variables $(y_1, y_2, \dots, y_n)$, but unknown function f controlling input variables $(x_1, x_2, \dots, x_n)$. In connection with this investigations should be supplemented with cost

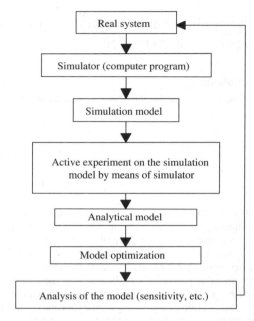

Figure 1. The order of investigations in the simulation method.

function f expressed by means of input controlling variables x_i

$$K = f(x_1, x_2, \dots, x_n), \qquad (3)$$

The order of investigations in the method employed is shown in Fig.1, and idea of identifying costs of the model and its optimization i.e. minimizing logistic costs is shown in Fig.2.

Fig. 2 should be interpret as follows:

1. Identifying and optimizing of the controlling quality can be done with two methods called here: indirect MB and direct MP.
2. In MB method analytical form of cost function v is expressed by means of output variables $(y_1, y_2, \dots, y_n)$, resulting from a simulation experiment. And optimization i.e. minimizing cost function which is the rate of controlling quality, depends in finding such values of input controlling variables $(x_1, x_2, \dots, x_n)$. where the value of costs function reaches minimum. Optimization is done by means of direct search method (this method and investigation results are described in Sobotka (2000).
3. In MP method, the basic problems are to find logistic costs analytical form i.e. function f which is a function of input controlling variables (formula (2.2)).

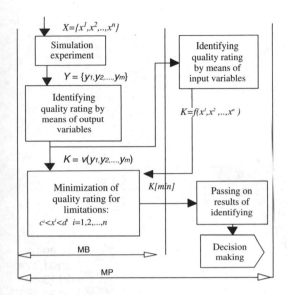

$X=\{x^1,x^2,...,x^n\}$

Simulation experiment

$Y = \{y_1,y_2,....,y_m\}$

Identifying quality rating by means of output variables

$K = v(y_1,y_2,....,y_m)$

Identifying quality rating by means of input variables

$K=f(x^1,x^2,...,x^n)$

Minimization of quality rating for limitations:
$c^i<x^i<d^i$ $i=1,2,...,n$

$K[min]$

Passing on results of identifying

MB

MP

Decision making

Figure 2.   The idea of minimizing quality rating.

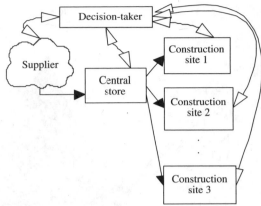

Decision-taker

Supplier

Central store

Construction site 1

Construction site 2

Construction site 3

Figure 3.   The outline of logistic system DSSL_6 structure.

To define analytical form of logistic costs model, the regression analysis method can be used because logistic systems models are stochastic models. Thus the basis for identifying a model are logistic system work costs seen in a simulation model ($K = v(y_1, y_2, ... y_n)$). Random sample to approximation of function costs is obtained by means of an active experiment, Lvovski (1982). Using active experiment decreases considerably labor consumption of research. The results of minimizing the quality coefficient are the basis to make logistic decisions in company.

3   AN EXAMPLE

3.1   Description of the model

The method of seeking explicit cost function, presented in Chapter 2, assumed to be the coefficient of estimating a logistic model, was employed to investigate a logistic system occurring in construction companies – called DSSL_6 model in the presented paper – which is controlled by the same method. The model presented is an example of how logistic service works in construction companies and other branches. The structure of this model is shown in Fig.3. Building companies provide themselves with materials being used up all the time, requiring safe storage and materials of the type "bottle neck" which should be maintained in stock.

In DSSL_6 model the order size is defined by Supplies Department on the basis of production planned i.e. planned consumption on construction sites. Transport conditions are also taken into account

(giving preference to load capacity and storage possibilities). The order is sent to suppliers on the basis of stock check in the central store or in cycles at regular intervals. The whole delivery is stored in the central store and then directed to sites according to site managers' orders. The size of delivery equals the order sizes or its part if there is not enough material in the central store. It is possible to lodge a complaint against faulty deliveries.

It is assumed that the examined model is controlled according to the following method:

1. An order placed by the central store Z_{mi} is defined on the basis of average consumption of material on sites at the planned period of demand with using the whole load capacity provided according to the following formula

$$Z_{mi} = \left(entier \frac{t_w \sum_{j=1}^{J} \overline{z}_j}{p_k} +1 \right) p_k \qquad (4)$$

where t_w = period of planning consumption; $\overline{z}_j$ = average daily consumption on j-th construction site; p_k = load capacity of lorry.

2. Time of sending the order by the central store t_{mi} is defined as follows

$$t_{mi} = k\,t_c \qquad (5)$$

where t_c = an ordering cycle of delivery.

3. Size of the order placed by construction sites Z_{bij}

$$Z_{bij} = \sum_{l=1}^{t_w} z_{lj} - s_{ij} \qquad (6)$$

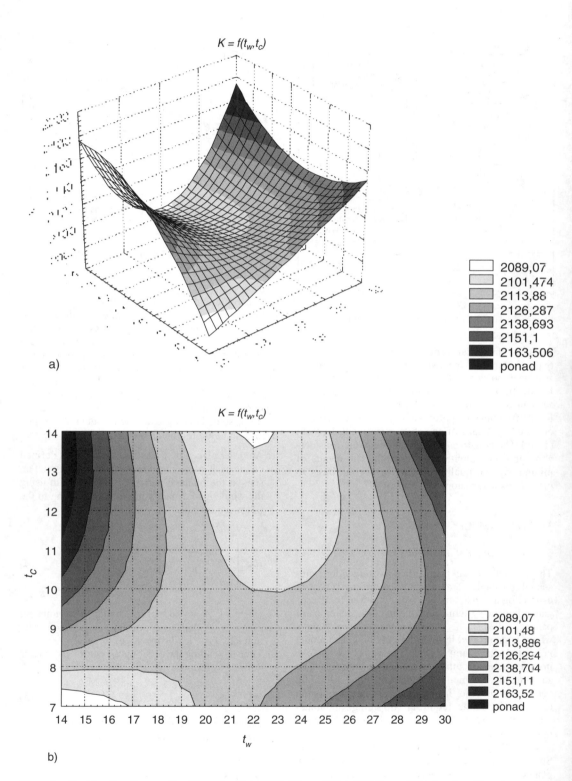

Figure 4. Cost function diagram $K = f(t_{wo}, s_m)$ with $t_w \in \{14, 15, \dots, 30\}$, $t_c \in \{7, 8, \dots, 14\}$: a) surface, b) contour area.

where z_{lj} = daily consumption of material on l-th day at j-th construction site; s_{ij} = stock level on i-th day at j-th construction site.

4. Time of sending the order t_{bij} is defined by the stock level when it falls below stock quantity equal to the sum of daily consumption during the period of planned consumption

$$t_{bij} = t_i \text{ when } s_{bij} \leq \sum_{l=1}^{t_w} z_{lj} \qquad (7)$$

where s_{bj} = safety stock at j-th site. The other denotations as above.

In this controlling method there are only two controlling variables: period of planning consumption t_w at the construction sites and ordering cycle t_c to the central store. The assumption of such controlling variables in this method differs from traditional supply models called stock controlling models.

The form of logistic costs function for the control according to variant as follows:

$$K = 669.750 + 95.700\, t_w + 237.945\, t_c -$$
$$+15.233\, t_w t_c - 1.307\, t_w^2 + 6.390\, t_c^2 \qquad (8)$$
$$+ 0.191\, t_w^2 t_c,$$

3.2 Description of investigations

To find a proper costs function f, the regression analysis method can be used. The investigations were conducted for controlling variables from the sets $t_w \in \{14, 15, \dots, 30\}$, $t_c \in \{7, 8, \dots, 14\}$.

The function obtained allows to optimize i.e. minimize costs and interpret results. Fig. 4 shows cost function variability diagrams.

1. The observed costs require to divide of chart into two areas because there are a big differences in the values of costs. It is depends from controlling variables value.
2. In the first area limited by $t_c = 9 \div 14$ days and in all variability range t_w, i.e. from 14 to 30 by increase t_w from 14 to 21 days, logistic costs decrease; by t_w from 21 to 24 have they the lowest level and next increase when t_w (the period of planning consumption) increase. In the area, limited by $t_w = 14 \div 21$ $t_w = 24 \div 30$ days are very sensitive for changes of values of this controlling variable.
3. In the second area, limited by $t_c = 7 \div 9$ logistic costs increase when t_w increase from 30 to 14 days and in the point $t_w = 14$ and $t_c = 7$ days K reaches minimum.
4. In this controlling method a logistic costs are sensitivity for the changes of controlling variables values

Table 1.   Elasticity $E_{xi} K$ and sensitivity w_i of logistic model.

Parameter x_i	Coefficients	
	$E_{xi} K$ [%]	w_i [%]
k_{tz}	0.072	14
k_{tw}	0.037	27
k_{id}	0.003	333
k_{kz}	0.009	111
s_o	0.012	83
c_j	0.88	1

t_w and t_c. But there is small range of their variability where logistic costs aren't sensitive for changes these variables. It concern $t_c \in \{12, 13, 14\}$ and $t_w \in \{21, 22, 23, 24\}$.

Graphic illustration of investigation results allows analyzing costs variability evolution according to changes in controlling variables.

3.3 Investigating model sensitivity to parameter changes in the model

In order to investigate sensitivity of the solution to parameters changes, which in the model represent conditions of building production i.e. unit costs of works transport k_{tz} and outer transport k_{tw}, costs of capital s_0, a goods price c and costs of loss k_{kz}, it is necessary to come back to the data observed in the simulator (simulation program). Table 1 presents results of calculating elasticity and sensitivity of logistic decisions for the optimum solutions obtained of method controlling examined. The meaning and methods for defining these coefficients were explained in the article Sobotka (2000).

In the physical interpretation of these rates:

1. Elasticity of function K in relation to a given variable x means that a change of the variable by 1% causes a change in value of function K by $E_x K$% (the more the value of elasticity rate, the more sensitive to changes the model is).
2. Sensitivity expressed with the reserve of elasticity coefficient denotes percentage of parameter $\times$ change which causes in logistic level costs by 1% (the bigger the value of coefficient w the less sensitive the model is).

The conclusions from sensitivity investigations of the model with the central store into changes in production conditions, controlled by the presented method, are as follows:

1. Very sensitive to changes on the level of prices (it is worth while to solicit discounts).
2. Sensitive to unit costs of outer transport and works transport.

3. Quite sensitive to costs of capita.,
4. Not sensitive to information-decision costs and to costs of loss because of demurrage charges caused by a lack of stock for the reason that in optimum solutions probability of such loss is inconsiderable.

4 SUMMING-UP

The presented methodology of creating and investigating a logistic model allows:

1. To conduct investigating models of systems, different variants without interfering with natural system.
2. To receive results those explain the rules of logistic system activity.
3. Seeking optimum solutions in the aspect of selected criteria consistent with company goals.
4. To recognize the sensitivity model to changes of production conditions.
5. Stating directions of re-engineering supply processes in a company.

The logistic systems models investigation and obtained results allow many conclusions on properties of systems, which can be used in the practice of logistic management.

REFERENCES

Gutenbaum, J. *Mathematical modelling of system.* Omnitech Press, IBS, Warsaw 1992 [in Polish].

Hameri, A. & Paantla, A. Multidimensional simulation as a tool for straategic logistics planning. *Computers in Industry,* No 27, 1995, pp. 274–285.

Kaplinski, O. Modeling of construction processes. A managerial approach. *Study of Engineering Scope,* No 43, KILiW PAN, IPPT PAN, Warsaw 1997.

Law, A.M. & Kelton, W.D. *Simulation modeling & analysis.* Mc Graw-Hill International Editions, Industrial Engineering Series, NY 1991.

Lvovskij, E. *Statistical method of empirical formula.* Izd. Wyzszaja Szkola, Moskwa 1982 [in Russian].

Poortman, E.R. & Bons, H.N.M. Information for the management of the building – materials flo ws. *Engineering, Construction and Architectural Management,* 1'2, 139–140, 1994.

Pfohl, H.CH. *Logisticsysteme. Betribswirtshaftliche Grunla-gen.* Springer-Verlag Berlin He idelberg 1996.

Sobotka, A. A decision support system for logistic management in a building company. *Statyba,* 4, 1, 64–71, 1998.

Sobotka, A. Identifying logistic system models in construction companies. *Archives of Civil Engineering,* XLVII, 1, 119–132, 2001.

Sobotka, A. Sensitivity of logistic strategies in construction companies. *Archives of Civil Engineering,* XLVI, 4, 663–679, 2000.

Sobotka, A. Simulation modelling for logistic re-engineering in the construction company. *Construction Management and Economics,* 18, 183–195, 2000.

Rzemykowski, Z. *Elements of economic cybernetics.* Economic Academy in Poznan Press, No 394, Poznan 1994.

Ulanicki, B. *The method of modelling and optimisation for simulation, controlling and designing water distribution nets.* Scientific Thesis, No 20, Bialystok Technical University Press, Bialystok 1993.

Zeigler, B.P. *Theory of modelling and simulation.* John Wiley & Sons Inc., New York 1976.

System-based Vision for Strategic and Creative Design, Bontempi (ed.)
© *2003 Swets & Zeitlinger, Lisse, ISBN 90 5809 599 1*

Resource scheduling of construction projects using a hybrid genetic algorithm model

A.B. Senouci & K.K. Naji
Civil Engineering Department, University of Qatar, Doha, Qatar

ABSTRACT: This paper presents an augmented Lagrangian genetic algorithm model for resource-constrained scheduling of construction projects considering precedence relationships, multiple crew-strategies, and time-cost trade-off. The proposed model, which considers both resource-constrained scheduling and project total cost minimization, uses the quadratic penalty function to transform the constrained resource scheduling problem to an unconstrained one. The algorithm is general and can be applied to a broad class of optimization problems. Three illustrative examples are presented to demonstrate the performance of the proposed method.

1 INTRODUCTION

Resource-constrained scheduling arises when limited amount of resources are available. The scheduling objective is to extend the project duration as little as possible beyond the original critical path duration in such a way that the resource constraints are met. In this process, both critical and non-critical activities are shifted.

Integer linear programming models have been used to formulate the resource-constrained scheduling problem (Nutdtasomboon & Randhawa 1996). Special algorithms have been developed for solving the resource-constrained problems such as the branch and bound and the implicit enumeration approaches (Christofides et al. 1987, Demeulemeester & Herroelen 1997).

This paper presents an augmented Lagrangian genetic algorithm model for resource-constrained scheduling of construction projects considering precedence relationships, multiple crew-strategies, and time-cost trade-off. An illustrative example is presented to demonstrate the performance of the proposed method.

2 PROBLEM FORMULATION

2.1 Total cost function

The total project cost, C_T, is the sum of the direct project cost, C_D, and the indirect cost, C_I:

$$C_T = C_D + C_I \tag{1}$$

The indirect cost, which represents the overhead costs, is assumed to be a linear function of the project duration, D:

$$C_I = C_o + b\,D \tag{2}$$

where C_o is the initial cost (such as mobilization cost) and b is the slope of the indirect cost line.

Each activity can be performed with a range of crew formations. Crew formations refer to all possible selections from different crew sizes or different acceleration strategies (e.g., overtime options or multiple shifts). For a given activity, each crew formation has an associated direct cost, a unique output rate (productivity). The duration of an activity n with a given crew formation C_n is represented by the component ActDur(n,C_n), where n = 1, 2, …, NAct; and C_n = 1, 2,…, NCrew(n). The number of type k resources associated with the crew formation C_n is represented by NRes(n,C_n,k).

The direct cost of an activity n using crew formation C_n will be denoted by ActCost(n,C_n). The project direct cost, C_D, is equal to the sum of the direct cost of all project activities.

The resource scheduling problem is now formulated as a constrained optimization problem in which the following total cost function is minimized:

$$C_T = C_D + C_I = \sum_{n=1}^{N} ActCost(n, C_n) + C_o + b\,D \tag{3}$$

Subject to the constraints presented in the following sections.

2.2 Precedence relationship constraints

Each activity n using a crew formation C_n is linked with its succeeding activities by satisfying one or more of the following precedence relationships:

1. Start-to-start (SS)

$$T(n, C_n) + L(n, n') \leq T(n', C_{n'}) \qquad n' \in \{S_n\} \qquad (4)$$

where $\{S_n\}$ = set of all the activities succeeding activity n, $T(n, C_n)$ = start time of activity n using crew formation C_n, $L(n, n')$ = lag/lead time between the activities n and n', and $T(n', C_{n'})$ = start time of the succeeding activity n' using crew formation $C_{n'}$.

2. Finish-to-start (FS)

$$T(n, C_n) + ActDur(n, C_n) + L(n, n') \leq T(n', C_{n'})$$
$$n' \in \{S_n\} \qquad (5)$$

3. Start-to-finish (SF)

$$T(n, C_n) + L(n, n') \leq T(n', C_{n'}) + ActDur(n', C_{n'})$$
$$n' \in \{S_n\} \qquad (6)$$

4. Finish-to-finish (FF)

$$T(n, C_n) + ActDur(n, C_n) + L(n, n') \leq T(n', C_{n'})$$
$$+ ActDur(n', C_{n'}) \qquad n' \in \{S_n\} \qquad (7)$$

2.3 Resource constraints

The total consumption of type k resource at any project time t must be less than or equal to the maximum number of available type k resources.

$$\sum_{n \in \{S_t\}} NRes(n, C_n, k) \leq RLimit(k) \qquad (8)$$

where $\{S_t\}$ is the set of all the activities in progress at time t and Rlimit(k) is the daily maximum number of type k resources.

2.4 Project duration constraint

The project duration must not exceed a given upper limit, D_{max}.

$$T(n, C_n) + Act(n, C_n) \leq D_{max} \qquad (9)$$

3 GENETIC ALGORITHMS

Genetic algorithms were originally developed by Holland 1975 and later refined by Goldberg 1989 and many others. They imitate the evolutionary processes with a particular focus on genetic mechanisms. As algorithms, they are different from traditional optimization methods in the following aspects: (1) Genetic algorithms operate on a coding set of variables and not with variables themselves; (2) they search for a population of solutions rather than improving a single solution; (3) they use objective function without any gradient information; and (4) their transition scheme is probabilistic, whereas traditional methods use gradient information (Goldberg 1989).

The standard genetic algorithm system has three major operators: reproduction, crossover, and mutation. These operators will be described later. Genetic algorithms operate on a population of chromosomes (bit-strings), which have two basic formats: binary (or true-valued) and ordering coding. When using a genetic algorithm model to solve resource-constrained scheduling problems, a character in a string (i.e., chromosome) stands for either a possible activity crew formation or a possible activity start time. The initial population can be manually prepared or randomly generated with the size between 30 and 500 individuals (Goldberg 1989), and consecutive generations are evolved by applying the operators of reproduction, crossover, and mutation.

The objective of the reproduction process is also the information stored in strings with good fitness values to survive into the next generation. Typically, each string in the population is assigned a probability of being selected as a parent string based on the string's fitness. However, reproduction does not change the features parent strings. The next generation of solution strings are developed from selected pairs of parent strings and the application of other explorative operators such as crossover and mutation.

Crossover is a procedure wherein a selected parent string is broken into segments and some of these segments are exchanged with corresponding segments of another parent string. The one-point crossover implemented in Goldberg's SGA breaks each string of a selected parent string of a selected parent string set into two segments and interchanges the second segment to create two new strings.

Mutation is usually used as an insurance policy (Goldberg 1989). Mutation allows for the possibility that non-existing features from both parent strings may be created and passed to their children. Without an operator of this type, some possibly important regions of the search space may never be explored.

Genetic algorithms develop solutions based on the payoff or quality of the fitness of solution strings. A scheme for properly evaluating the fitness is very important in a genetic algorithm. Traditional GAs are designed to work directly with maximum problems. Therefore, the minimum problem (minimum project total cost) will be converted to a maximum problem.

4 HYBRID GENETIC ALGORITHM FOR RESOURCE SCHEDULING

4.1 *Optimization formulation*

The resource scheduling problem is formulated as the following constrained optimization problem:
Minimize

$$C_T = f(X) \qquad (10)$$

subject to the following inequality constraints:

$$g_j(X) \le 0 \quad j = 1,...,J \qquad (11)$$

where $X = \{C_i, T_i | i = 1,...NAct\}$, g_j $(X) = j$th inequality constraint function, and J = total number of inequality constraints. The vector of decision variables, X, contains the crew formation number C_i and start time T_i for each project activity i. In the genetic algorithm model, each string (i.e., chromosome) corresponds to the vector of decision variables, X. Using the penalty function method, the constrained optimization problem is transformed to an unconstrained optimization problem by defining a pseudo-objective function, $P(X,\gamma)$, to be minimized (Adeli & Cheng 1994):

$$P(X,\gamma) = f(X) + \frac{1}{2}\sum_{j=1}^{J}\gamma_j\left[g_j^+(X)\right]^2 \qquad (12)$$

where $g_j^+(X) = \max\{0, g_j(X)\}$ and γ_j = positive real parameter associated with the jth constraint. The functions $f(X)$ and $g_j^+(X)$ are normalized in order to make the terms in the objective and penalty functions dimensionally consistent. In the GA terminology, Equation 12 is called the fitness function which is used in the reproduction phase in order to guide the genetic search.

4.2 *Optimization algorithm*

The optimization algorithm for resource-constrained scheduling is presented by integrating the genetic algorithm with the quadratic penalty function in a nested loop. The outer loop is used to update the penalty function coefficients. The inner loop performs the genetic algorithm to minimize the penalized objective function associated with the quadratic penalty function in the outer loop. The hybrid algorithm, which is summarized in Figure 1, has been implemented using a Visual Basic Program named "ProjectScheduler".

5 PROGRAM DESCRIPTION

ProjectScheduler is a Windows-based interface for resource-constrained scheduling of construction projects written using MicroSoft Visual Basic version 6.0. As shown in Figure 2, the program consists of a simple menu-driven interface with the following menu titles: Project, solve, display results, and chart. The project menu is used for the selection of the input data file through a typical Windows-based common dialog.

It is also used for the selection of the output file. The solve menu is used to activate the program to perform the analysis. The display results menu is used to display a text-based format of the analysis results. The last menu when activated displays a resource histogram chart as shown in Figure 3.

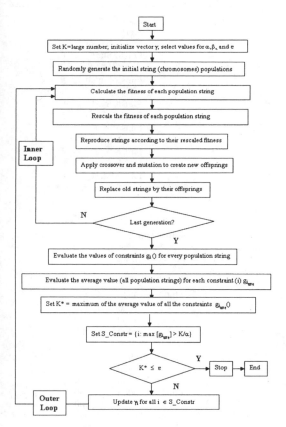

Figure 1.   Hybrid genetic algorithm flowchart.

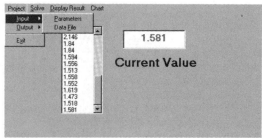

Figure 2.   Project menu-driven interface.

6 ILLUSTRATIVE EXAMPLE

A resource-constrained scheduling problem is presented in order to show the features of the proposed method and to illustrate the capabilities of the hybrid genetic algorithm computational model. The project, whose CPM planning network is shown in Figure 4, includes 12 activities labeled A to L. One resource type is available for each activity.

The activity durations, resources, and direct costs are given in Table 1. The precedence relationships between succeeding activities are given in Table 2. An initial cost of $6000 and a daily cost of $2500 are used as the indirect cost for this example. The rate of crossover and mutation were set equal to 0.8 and 0.005, respectively. The initial values of γ_i were set equal to 3, as suggested by Adeli & Cheng 1994.

A resource-constrained scheduling of the project was performed for a maximum resource usage of 11 resources. Table 3 summarizes the activity durations obtained by the hybrid genetic algorithm model in order to satisfy the constraints of: 1) minimum project total cost and 2) maximum resource usage. As shown in Table 3, project total cost is equal to $351500.

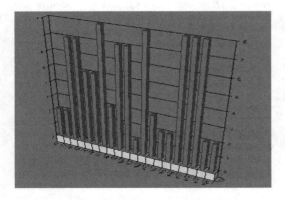

Figure 3. Resource histogram chart.

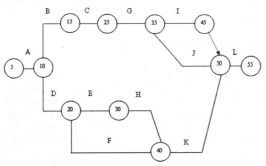

Figure 4. Example project CPM network.

Table 2. Activity precedence relationship information.

Activity name	Succeeding activity	Relationship type	Lag time (Days)
A	B	Start-Start	2
	D	Start-Start	2
B	C	Finish-Finish	3
C	G	Finish-Start	0
D	E	Start-Start	2
	F	Finish-Finish	5
E	H	Start-Start	1
F	K	Finish-Start	0
G	I	Finish-Finish	5
J		Finish-Finish	2
H	K	Finish-Start	2
I	L	Finish-Start	1
J	L	Finish-Start	0
K	L	Finish-Start	0

Table 1. Activity durations, resources, and direct costs.

Activity name	Activity durations			Activity resources			Activity direct costs		
	Crew1 (Days)	Crew2 (Days)	Crew3 (Days)	Crew1	Crew2	Crew3	Crew1 ($)	Crew2 ($)	Crew3 ($)
A	3	4	5	8	6	5	34000	30000	28000
B	2	3	4	5	4	3	13000	11000	10000
C	2	3	4	5	4	3	26000	23500	21500
D	10	11	12	9	7	5	75000	70000	65000
E	5	6	7	9	7	5	6000	5000	4000
F	1	2	3	3	2	1	32000	29000	27000
G	3	4	5	8	6	5	20000	18500	17500
H	4	5	6	9	7	5	24000	22000	21000
I	6	7	8	9	7	5	12000	10000	9000
J	1	2	3	5	4	3	7000	6000	5000
K	3	4	5	7	5	4	21000	19500	18000
L	3	4	5	7	5	4	25000	22000	20000

Table 3. Resource-constrained scheduling results.

Activity Name	Activity duration (Days)	Number of resources	Activity start time (Days)	Activity finish time (Days)	Activity direct cost ($)
A	4	6	0	4	30000
B	3	4	7	10	11000
C	2	5	17	19	26000
D	12	5	4	16	65000
E	7	5	0	7	4000
F	2	2	23	25	29000
G	4	6	19	23	18500
H	6	5	10	16	21000
I	8	5	20	28	9000
J	2	4	28	30	6000
K	5	4	25	30	18000
L	5	4	30	35	20000
			Project direct cost		257500
			Project indirect cos		94000
			Project total cost		351500

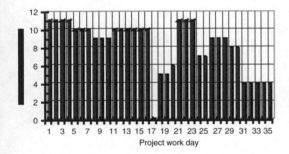

Figure 5. Example project resource histogram.

The activity start and finish times are also shown in Table 3. By summing the resources required by the activities that occur at any given day, the project resource requirements are determined as a function of time. The resource histogram for the project is shown in Figure 5. The resource requirement varies from a minimum value of 0 to a maximum value of 11.

7 CONCLUSION

A mathematical model for resource scheduling of construction projects was presented. Activity precedence relationships, multiple crew-strategies, and time-cost trade-off are considered in the model. An optimization formulation is presented for the resource-constrained scheduling problem with the objective of minimizing the total construction cost. The non-linear optimization problem is solved using an augmented Lagrangian genetic algorithm model. The proposed method provides features beyond what the existing software systems used by practitioners can do. It can handle large construction projects with a large number of activities. However, the solution execution time increases significantly with the size of the construction project. This problem is easily overcome with the availability nowadays of very fast and powerful computers.

REFERENCES

Adeli, H., & Cheng, N. 1994. Augmented Lagrangian Genetic Algorithm For Structural Optimization. *Journal of Aerospace Engineering*, ASCE 7(1),104–118.

Christofides, N., Alvarez-Valdes, R., & Tamarit, J.M. 1987. Project scheduling with resource constraints: a branch and bound approach. *Computers and Industrial Engineering*, 12(1), 227–242.

Demeulemeester, E., & Herroelen, W. 1997. New benchmark results for the resource-constrained project scheduling problem. *Management Science*, 43, 1485–1492.

Goldberg, D.E. 1989. *Genetic Algorithms in search, optimization, and machine learning*. Addison-Wesley Publishing Company, Inc., Reading, Mass.

Holland, J.H. 1975. *Adaptation in natural and artificial systems*. University of Michigan Press, Ann-Arbor, Mich.

Nudtasomboon, N., & Randhawa, S. 1996. Resource-constrained project scheduling with renewable and non-renewable resources and time-resources tradeoffs. *Computers and Industrial Engineering*, 32 (1), 227–242.

The importance of new information technologies in a concurrent design environment

P.J. Bártolo & H.M. Bártolo
School of Technology and Management, Leiria Polytechnic, Portugal

ABSTRACT: Concurrence in building design requires the simultaneous interaction of all design phases, together with the co-operation and commitment of all design participants. It is a collaborative process involving many sources of information that are often widely dispersed, enabling to shorten the time and costs of the design phase, as well an actual improvement of the quality of the design product. On the other hand, computer-aided design systems help designers to fully define the shape of their design concepts, while rapid prototyping techniques will allow the rapid creation of accurate physical models of these design representations. Its usage can particularly benefit concurrence in design, as physical prototyping will allow design participants to work with a three-dimensional hardcopy and use it for the validation of their design-ideas. To understand how effective these technologies and Internet facilities can be to enhance concurrence in design, design practitioners were asked to respond to a questionnaire survey. Its results suggest that design practitioners attitudes towards concurrence in design is positive but that any willingness is inhibited by a lack of knowledge in relation to the issue of rapid prototyping.

1 INTRODUCTION

Architectural design can be described as a social activity, involving the collaboration of many people with specialised knowledge, from many different fields (Nieuwenhuis & Ouwerkerk 2000). Bowen & Eduards (1996) emphasize the importance of effective communication between people during the design process, though a lack of communication is often mentioned as a characteristic of architectural design (Hatush & Skitmore 1997). Communication and collaboration plays a crucial part in reconciling different perspectives, and information sharing is a key requirement for collaborative work (Valkenburg 1998), though insufficient to establish a "shared understanding" among design participants (Austin et al. 2001). This process also involves a great amount of knowledge provided from different disciplines, resulting in a huge quantity of complex information often difficult to manage. Moreover, buildings are becoming more complex, not only in their forms and functions, but also in their infrastructures.

On the other hand, in today's architectural environment of market globalisation, the rise of competition and the increasing complexity of the relationships among clients, contractors and suppliers, drive organizations to form effective partnership with others if they are to successfully compete and remain profitable

(Egbu 1999). The process of decision-making is usually intuitive and based on experience where final decisions are often a compromise (Sariyildiz et al. 2000). Several authors (Ross & Von Krogh 1996, Egan 1998, Bennett 2000) highlight the importance of this co-operation and collaboration within the construction field.

Design must assimilate change and communication (Dyson 2000), using new computationally based approaches, as well developing new types of representation. This paper proposes a concurrent design approach based mainly on advanced modelling systems, network technologies and rapid prototyping processes. An exploratory web-based survey was used to understand how computer design aids are applied in real design situations, to investigate how design practitioners use the capacity of rapid prototyping machines to improve design synthesis.

2 CONCURRENT DESIGN

Concurrent design can be defined as an organisational and managerial strategy to bring together, from an early stage, designers, clients, constructors, etc., to participate in the design process. This strategy has been successfully applied in engineering design (Pham & Dimov 1998, Hindson et al. 1998), but is a

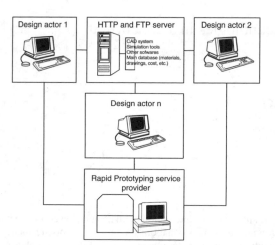

Figure 1. Network for concurrent design.

novel practice in architectural design. Considering the great complexity of architectural projects, three preliminary procedures should be considered to implement a concurrent design system:

- Shortening the design process
- The division of a project in several sub-projects
- Combining project phases.

Therefore concurrent design is a systematic approach to parallel development of a product and presupposes an enriched communication infrastructure that is unconstrained by geographical location and encourages right-first methods through cross-functional team working and consensus (Hanneghan et al. 2000).

In this research, an architectural concurrent design system has been developed using modern network communications, advanced modelling systems and rapid prototyping (Fig. 1). This system will enable the dissemination of ideas, the communication between design actors, the involvement of client/users and the validation of design solutions.

3   INFORMATION TECHNOLOGIES

In the past few years, the increase of distributed design teams and distributed work has been facilitated by the progress made in the computing world, particularly by the creation and growth of the Internet. Computer and networking technology can play a key role in distance collaboration. Costly and time-consuming travel and shipping of documents can be reduced, while still maintaining most advantages of the face-to-face interaction that is essential in creating a new building.

In the past, design information was exchanged primarily through face-to-face meetings, telephone conversations, physical delivery of drawings or other

data (Nielsen & Sayar 2001). Bjork (1999) describes IT as the use of electronic machines and programs for the processing, storage, transfer and presentation of information, involving the use of e-mail, computers, software, networks, videoconferencing, etc. IT is truly changing the architectural design process by improving communication and co-ordination and by acting as an enabler of change. Today, network technologies are stimulating a greater generalisation and globalisation of communication and information management as a result of near instantaneous information transfer.

4   ADVANCED MODELLING SYSTEMS

Computers were used initially in the building sector to perform administrative and repetitive tasks. Nowadays, computer software systems are becoming essential tools for the enhancement of creativity in building design, especially for technical design details, as well for the management of the entire design process (Sariyildiz et al. 2000). Geometric modelling systems have move forward in the last decade, as current CAD systems are now capable of handling sophisticated geometry. Computers now have huge memory capacity and high processing speed, besides using more user-friendly CAD systems. Moreover, several computer-assisted architecture design systems and three-dimensional (3D) animation software have been developed (Lee 1999). These systems can be used for the normal activity of two-dimensional (2D) drawings or, instead, to built and manipulate the corresponding 3D representation. It is now possible to generate photo-realistic images and render models according to elaborate shading algorithms (Lee 1999, Mäntylä 1988). In addition, current CAD systems have the possibility to store other information beyond geometric data (shapes and sizes), such as materials, electrical and heat components, different types of doors, windows, roofs, etc. This information is stored in libraries that can be easily accessed and used by designers. Moreover, the 3D design representation can be automatically generated and updated from the 2D drawings. This kind of software also enables anyone to "walk" inside the design and analyse different interior details.

Although CAD systems assist geometric modelling and analysis, they are not very helpful in conceptual design. First, they do not cope well with qualitative models or reasoning. On the other hand, these systems do not provide enough information about the physical aspects of the design object. Finally, clients/users usually do not have skills to understand computer rendered models. Consequently, to improve the design process and enhance creativity and reliability in design, computer models should be used together with other tools, such as rapid prototyping (to produce physical objects), simulation codes using the finite element method, etc.

5 RAPID PROTOTYPING

Rapid prototyping (RP) is a group of new technological processes where physical objects are quickly created directly from computer-generated models (Bartolo & Mitchell 2000). A RP system can be described as a sophisticated output device for computers, the three-dimensional analogue of a computer printer. RP techniques will allow the rapid creation of accurate physical models of design representations, as the geometry created during surface modelling or solid modelling is transformed into a physical three-dimensional model, by adding layers of material, one on top of another, until the complete model is built.

Through an accurate physical model of the design object, all members of an integrated design team can touch, feel, test, evaluate and make comments and suggestions to the several aspects of a design product, facilitating the communication among all the participants (Bartolo & Galha 2000, Bartolo & Bartolo 2001). Any changes resulting from this communication process can automatically be solved by upgrading the CAD database, enabling the generation of new physical representations of the design product and promoting further discussions and corrections of the design solution. Additionally, it will be possible to fully test and validate ideas enabling to get designs right first time. By using the latest rapid prototyping methods time to market and development risks can also be reduced.

6 SURVEY

A preliminary questionnaire was elaborated and sent to a geographically dispersed sample of design practitioners to understand how designers approach three-dimensional synthesis using the speed and accuracy of the computer coupled with physical models produced by a rapid prototyping machine, as well to perceive how useful these new technologies can be to make clear designers intent, to enable an effective participation of both the client/user and the constructor/supplier throughout the design process. This ongoing questionnaire was divided into four sections, concerning the following issues:

– personal details of the design practitioners and characterisation of the design firm
– to assess the effective usage of CAD technologies by design practice
– to identify the level of knowledge in relation to rapid prototyping technologies, the degree of its use and importance for the design process
– to understand the importance of the Internet tools for the design activity.

7 RESULTS

The findings report the analysis of 150 questionnaires received, from Australia, Brazil, Canada, France, India, Iran, Italy, Netherlands Portugal, Spain, South Africa, USA and UK.

On section 1, designers were asked for information on their academic degrees, professional skills and work environment, besides some personal details such as gender and age. From our sample of returned questionnaires, 75% are architects and 25% industrial designers, with a male percentage of 71%, distributed as following: 38% (aged from 25 to 34), 35% (aged from 34 to 44) and 27% (aged above 44). Most of the answers, 71%, came from small firms with less than 50 employees, while 18% work in companies with more than 100 employees. In Section 2, the design practitioners were asked to answer several questions on CAD systems, to understand how their organisations use them, to what purpose and what kind of difficulties were experienced.

The answers acknowledge a widespread usage of CAD systems. Designers currently use these systems to produce working drawings, prime presentations, design approvals, 3D renderings and animations. Most of designers (78%) use CAD to create both 2D and 3D design representations. It is apparent that the creation of 3D models in CAD is widespread, which is an important finding emerging from this exploratory study. If designers can easily create solid models, then they own the necessary skills to use RP systems. Consequently, RP systems could be integrated into the design environment just as conventional printers are used today. Though a large amount of designers, 81%, use frequently CAD systems as a tool to communicate with the client/user, a significant proportion of respondents, 63%, have experienced difficulties to communicate with the client/user, corroborating findings from other studies (NEDO 1983, Peng 1994 and Sonnerwald 1996). Clients/users major difficulty appears to be the understanding of design representations produced by CAD systems.

In section 3, the design practitioners were asked about their knowledge and usage of rapid prototyping technologies. They were also invited to express their views on potential benefits of these systems in terms of client/user involvement, quality of the design product, time to achieve a good design solution, costs, etc. Only 35% of the designers claimed to know RP technologies though, through their subsequent answers, it was found that the respondents (54%) perceived rapid prototyping and conventional CAD/CAM systems as similar systems. On the other hand, 81% of all respondents believed its introduction in the design process could be beneficial. This is an interesting finding, eventually acknowledging the need to divulge RP technologies among design practitioners, possibly through

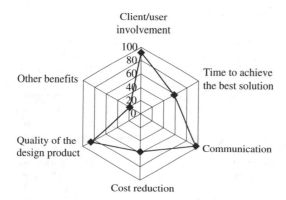

Figure 2. Main advantages of the use of RP technologies in architectural design studios.

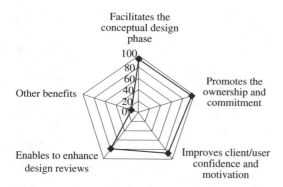

Figure 3. Main advantages of the use of RP technologies in terms of participant involvement.

its introduction in architectural curriculum similarly to what has already happened with the inclusion of RP issues in engineering curriculum. Moreover, it seems that the great majority of architectural firms frequently use model makers to produce their physical models, spending too much time and money in this process, between two and ten weeks, according to the complexity and size of the model. According to designers' answers (Fig. 2), the major advantages of the use of RP technologies in design practice are believed to be:

– Client/user involvement
– Time to achieve the best solution
– Communication between the design team, the client/user and constructor
– Cost reduction
– Quality of the design product.

Design practitioners also acknowledged quite a few advantages for the use of rapid prototyping technologies, as shown in Figures 3–5.

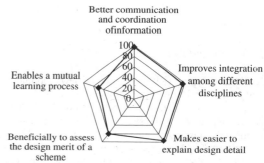

Figure 4. Main advantages of the use of RP technologies to facilitate communication.

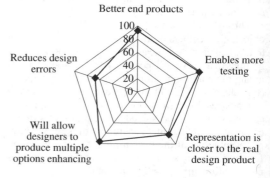

Figure 5. Main advantages of the use of RP technologies to improve quality of the design product.

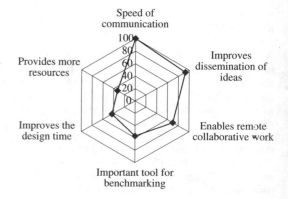

Figure 6. Main advantages of the use of Internet facilities in the architectural design environment.

Section 4 relates to the use of networking tools. The great majority of architectural firms (54%) frequently use both local and world network systems all through the design process. Moreover, most designers (82%) use the Internet facilities to communicate with clients/users. The main advantages and disadvantages

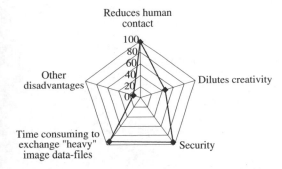

Figure 7. Main disadvantages of the use of Internet facilities in the architectural design environment.

of the Internet facilities in architectural design practices are indicated in Figures 6–7.

8 CONCLUSIONS AND FURTHER RESEARCH

A concurrent design approach, coupled with CAD and RP technologies, can expand design possibilities through the physical modelling of design ideas, and transform the design phase of architectural practice. Collaborative design requires the skills of many designers and experts, and each participant needs to create models or tools to provide information to other participants. The questionnaire results suggest a high level of agreement relatively to the importance of using innovative techniques to rapidly produce physical representations of the design idea, as it will enable designers to make physical models directly from CAD models, though a poor knowledge of RP technologies by design professionals is actually an obstacle for their actual usage. IT is widely used in design practice and plays a key role to over-come the barriers posed by distance and different levels of expertise. However, the Internet is understood by designers has a restriction to creativity due to its deficit in human contact.

This exploratory survey was important not only to identify the extent of the knowledge and effective application of rapid prototyping technologies by design practice, but also to use as a benchmarking tool for the next stage of the research. The next step involves the development of a computer network system using RP technologies towards the implementation of a concurrent architectural design environment.

REFERENCES

Ashworth, J.L. 1989. *The management of quality in construction*. London: Spon.

Austin, S., Steele, J., Macmillan, S., Kirby, P. & Spence, R. 2001. Mapping the conceptual design activity of interdisciplinary teams. *Design Studies* 22(3): 211–32.

Bartolo, P.J.S. & Mitchel, G. 2000. A Model for computer simulation and optimisation of stereolithographic processes. *Proc. European Conference on Rapid Prototyping and Manufacturing*. University of Nottingham.

Bartolo, P.J.S. & Bartolo, H.M. 2001. Concurrence in design: a strategic approach through rapid prototyping. *Proc. CIB World Building Congress*. Wellington.

Bartolo, P.J.S. & Galha, H.M. 2000. A concurrent design methodology through the use of rapid prototyping. Delft: University Press.

Bjork, B. 1999. Information technology in construction: domain definition and research issues. *Computer Integrated Design and Construction* 1: 3–16.

Bowen, P. & Edwards, P. 1996. Interpersonal communication in cost planning during the building design phase. *Construction Management and Economics* 14(5): 395–404.

Dyson, M. 2000. Determining extents of design determination. In A. Nieuwenhuis & M. Van Ouwerkerk (eds), *Research by Design*: 160-4. Delft: University Press.

Egbu, C. 1999. Mechanisms for exploiting construction innovations to gain competitive advantage. *ARCOM 1999; Proc. Annual Conference* 1: 115–123.

Emmitt, S., Gorse, C.A. & Jones, S.R. 1999. The housing site manager: changing roles and training needs. *ARCOM 1999; Proc. Annual Conference* 2: 551–558.

Hanneghan, M., Merabti, M. & Colquhoun, G. 2000. A viewpoint analysis reference model for concurrent engineering. *Computers in Industry* 41: 35–49.

Hatush, Z. & Skitmore, M. 1997. Criteria for contractor selection. *Construction Management and Economics*. 15: 19–38.

Hindson, G.A., Kochlar, A.K. & Cook, P. 1998. Procedures for effective implementation of simultaneously engineering in small and medium enterprises. *Proc Instn Mech Engrs* 212: 251–8.

Karloff, B. 1993. *Strategic precision – Improving performance through organisational efficiency*. John Wiley.

Lee, K. 1999. *Principles of CAD/CAM/CAE systems*. Reading, Massachusetts: Addison-Wesley.

Mäntylä, M. 1988. *An introduction to solid modelling*. Rockville: Computer Science Press.

Nielsen, Y. & Sayar, T. 2001. Web-based information flow modelling in construction. *ARCOM 2001; Proc. Annual Conference* 1: 219–229.

Nieuwenhuis, A. & Ouwerkerk, M. van. 2000. Architectural intervention. In A. Nieuwenhuis & M. Van Ouwerkerk (eds), *Research by Design*: 3. Delft: University Press.

Pham, D.T. & Dimov, S.S. 1998. An approach to concurrent engineering. *Proc Instn Mech Engrs* 212: 13–27.

Ross, J. & Von Krogh, G. 1996. *Managing knowledge: perspectives on co-operation and competition*. London: Sage.

Sariyildiz, S., Stouffs, R., Ciftcioglu, O. & Tuncer, B. 2000. Future ICT developments for the building sector. In T.M. de Jong, Y.J. Cuperus & D.J.M. van der Voordt (eds), *Ways to study architectural, urban and technical design*: 201-9. Delft: University Press.

Valkenburg, A.C. 1998. Shared understanding as a condition for team design. *The Journal of Automation in Construction*. 7(2/3): 111–21.

System-based Vision for Strategic and Creative Design, Bontempi (ed.)
© *2003 Swets & Zeitlinger, Lisse, ISBN 90 5809 599 1*

IT Tools for collaborative working in relationally integrated supply chains

O.O. Ugwu, M.M. Kumaraswamy, M.M. Rahman & S.T. Ng
Centre for Infrastructure & Construction Industry Development, Department of Civil Engineering,
The University of Hong Kong, Hong Kong

ABSTRACT: The pursuit of Value for Money (VFM) in construction projects requires a dual focus on optimizing the combination of whole life costs and quality in meeting the client's requirements. Relationally integrated supply chains (RISCs) have been proposed as a potential solution to achieving these VFM goals. However, an unambiguous understanding and knowledge of project-process interactions in RISC environments will underpin the success of such arrangements. It is essential that enabling IT tools and infrastructures be deployed to facilitate decision-making within a RISC framework. This paper analyzes the main characteristics of the targeted RISC environments and outlines the complexities of the interactions engendered by this new paradigms in construction project management. It then briefly summarizes the resulting data and information requirements at different decision points in the organizational structures, and identifies software systems requirements and suitable IT tools that would enhance the collaborative arrangements that are needed at these different decision points in the construction supply chain. Recommendations are formulated for achieving IT-enabled process innovations for accelerating the formation of relationally integrated construction supply chains.

1.1 INTRODUCTION & BACKGROUND

The pursuit of Value for Money (VFM) in construction projects requires a dual focus on optimizing the combination of whole life costs and quality in meeting the client's requirements. "Relationally integrated supply chains" (RISCs) have been proposed as a potential solution to achieving these VFM goals (Palaneeswaram 2003). Essentially RISCs were conceptualised to supplement transactional contract links in supply chains with more goal driven relational linkages based on advanced forms of partnering/ alliancing and teamworking. This paper discusses IT tools and system requirements for relationally integrated supply chains (RISCs) in construction. Previous papers have already identified the need for IT enabling tools and systems to facilitate decision-making in RISC environments (Kumaraswamy and Dissanayaka 2001, Rahman and Kumaraswamy 2002). The approach in identifying the IT tools and requirements involves simulating the procurement and operational decision-making processes in a virtual RISC environment to understand how and to what extent enabling Information Communication Technologies can be deployed and the required tools. The identified processes are then translated into sets of business use cases using the Unified Modelling Language UML (Rational 2003). By simulating decision-making in a virtual RISC environment, we are able to identify the IT tools that could aid in collaborative working and improve decision-support.

The work reported in this paper uses a combination of *goal driven* and *scenario-based* approaches to identify ICT tools and system requirements for RISC environments. By using the goal driven approach the aim is to model the RISC organisational objectives and relate them to the functions of the targeted system(s). This facilitates interpretation of requirements before transforming them into system level functional specifications, and helps in conceptualising the purpose of the system. The scenario-based approach is used to focus on the potential users' viewpoints in modelling the system usage and deriving the system functions. This hybrid approach facilitates delineation of supply chain process issues and system-specific functions in the targeted RISC system.

In the context of this paper a RISC information system (i.e. the system architecture) is viewed as an aggregation of different interrelated components including applications, hardware, networks, construction business processes, technology and data. By way of extrapolation, such a system (i) is a way of thinking and communicating ideas, and processes, and (ii) encompasses (or should encompass) everything that must be considered when describing how an organisation supports business processes in the

RISC environment. In this paper we use high-level data models to describe RISC and construction business data from a conceptual viewpoint independent of any current realisation by existing disparate systems that are used in construction organisations by the stakeholders (client, consultant, contractor, supplier). The data models comprise of (i) UML[1] class models of the business entities in RISC environment and their relationships, and (ii) a superset of attributes that define the business entities.

The outline of the paper is as follows: section 2 discusses the main characteristics RISC as they impinge on decision-making. These include communication and interaction patterns, and data/information requirements. Section 3 discusses the processes involved in RISC environment and maps these into sets of IT tools and system functional requirements. The methodology in knowledge acquisition for the domain is also discussed. Section 4 discusses the identified IT tools based on the preceding sections. The summary, conclusions and recommendations are given in section 5.

The main contribution of this paper is that it uses the UML approach to give an in-depth analysis of the inherent complexities (i.e. project-process interactions) engendered by the RISC paradigm, and then identifies the IT tools and requirements that are required for collaborative working in such an environment.

2 CHARACTERITICS OF RISC ENVIRONMENT

The ensuing sections discuss some characteristics of RISC as they impinge on collaborative working and decision-making. These can be summarised as follows: (i) there is a substantial amount of existing software currently in use by clients, designers, contractors and suppliers, (ii) the construction product development process is complex and requires many diverse types of activities and inputs from the stake holders, and (iii) a project team member is an integral part of the product development (or problem solving) group or community. The ensuing sections discuss interactions and data requirements that result from the above outlined characteristics, as a prelude to identifying the IT tools required.

2.1 Interactions and communication in RISC environment

This section discusses the patterns of interaction in a RISC environment, and highlights the complexities

[1] The decision to use UML is underpinned by the fact that it is de-facto industry standard that meets the real requirements for modelling complex systems and enterprises engendered by the RISC paradigm.

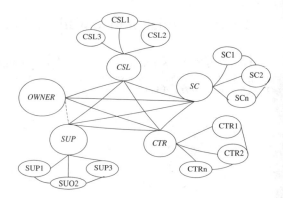

Figure 1. Communication in RISC environment.
Notes: CSL – Consultant, CTR – Contractor, SC – Sub-contractor, SUP – Supplier.

of communication engendered by the paradigm. This complexity has been captured from the knowledge acquisition process and is illustrated in the network diagram shown in Figure 1.

In Figure 1 the various stakeholders in RISC environment are shown in italics. The connections between different nodes show the possible interactions between the respective RISC participants. In practice, there is a complex web of interdisciplinary communication between collaborating team members in a RISC environment. The communication network highlights the following features and patterns of interaction (Kumaraswamy et al. 2003): (i) each contracting party will have its own network, which is not necessarily the same as others; (ii) a particular category of contracting party may have relationships among themselves (e.g. consultants with consultants, as in forming JVs), despite being potential "competitors"; (iii) the owner may also have relationships with other owners for some projects; and (iv) a requirement for a centralised databank where interested parties may enter and search for their potential partners. The communications are not necessarily bi-directional.

2.2 Data & information requirements – the object model

The data and information requirements are encapsulated in the static object model shown in Figure 2. The class diagram highlights only the attributes that define the project data structure and constitute inputs to a business rule (e.g. in choosing procurement route by an owner before assembling a relationally integrated project team – RIPT). This section only gives a snapshot summary due to space constraints. Details of some of the attributes required were identified in a previous research work reported fully in

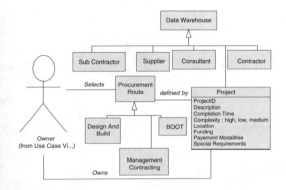

Figure 2. Objects & Classes in a RISC system.

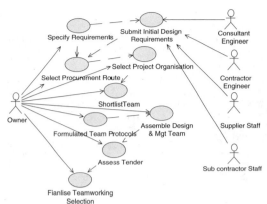

Figure 3. Use case view for a RISC system.

(Kumaraswamy & Dannasikaya 2001). Here we focus on a descriptive summary of the class model.

A typical class diagram is a structural representation of a domain showing the collection of objects, their attributes and operations that act on them to change the internal state of the object(s). It also shows the relationship between these classes. In the targeted RISC system, this translates to various class objects e.g., Projects, Consultants, Contractors, Subcontractors, System Users. Project and stakeholder information are stored in a data warehouse. The class diagram also incorporates other classes such as procurement route. The diagram depicts the relationships between them. For instance it shows that the owner selects a procurement route and that this decision is impinged upon by the project attributes such as complexity, payment modalities and other specific requirements. It also depicts instances of procurement routes such as design and build, BOOT, and management contracting arrangements. This level of abstraction would be useful in understanding the information model and system requirements irrespective of the design decisions and implementation path chosen to realise the system. The next section discusses the processes involved in RISC environments.

3 PROCESSES IN RISC ENVIRONMENT

3.1 Methodology for capturing data requirements & RISC processes

Previous research works identified different categories of project risks and some processes and activities required in procurement selection and assembling relationally integrated project team – RIPT (Rahman et al. 2003). The methodology includes literature review, questionnaire surveys and structured interviews with domain experts, initial model generation of the processes, and verification of the conceptual model with the domain experts. In order to formulate and identify the RISC processes such as procurement, two sets of semi-structured interview-based surveys were conducted in Hong Kong. The objectives were to; (a) collect information and expert opinion on present industry practice/trend of procuring construction projects and (b) seek guidelines in formulating a generic model for project procurement, including the relational integration among the potential project participants along the supply chain – clients, consultants, contractors, subcontractors and suppliers; and thereby meaningfully utilising the enthusiastic results obtained in the two previous questionnaire surveys. The interviewees were senior level executives from consultant, contractor, govt./public/private client organisations and independent bodies, and most of them were capable of influencing the policy of their respective working organisations. Details are described in (Kumaraswamy & Dissanayaka 2001, Kumaraswamy et al. 2003, Rahman & Kumaraswamy 2002).

Some of the identified processes and activities in a RISC environment (from the industry studies) include; specifying project requirements, selecting procurement route, selecting project organisation, short listing project team, formulating team protocols, assembling design and project management teams, assessing tender and finalising team selection, the outcome being a RIPT. The use case diagram in Figure 3 illustrates these processes from a system requirements perspective.

3.2 Model and requirements validation

The initial models generated from the knowledge acquisition exercise described in the preceding section were improved with feedback from six industry experts to whom it was presented. Its potential viability, usefulness, etc. was also tested with a total of ten local industry experts (including the above six), who have also positively ranked its various attributes, after

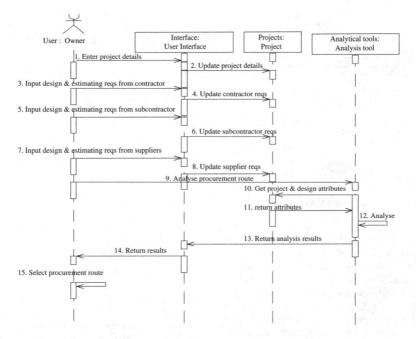

Figure 4. Sequence diagram/interaction model for the use case select procurement route.

thorough examination. The validation focused on seeking opinions of the experts who are actually engaged in analysing procurement options and team-building activities. The distribution of the 10 interviewees were: 2 – Govt. client, 1 – Public client, 3 – academia, 1 – consultant, 2 – contractor, and 1- partnering facilitator (Rahman et al. 2003). Current work involves mapping these identified project attributes, processes and functional requirements into sets of formal requirements specification for system level implementation. These aspects are discussed in the ensuing sections.

3.3   Functional requirements for a RISC system

Some of the identified processes and activities in a RISC environment (from the industry studies) include; specifying project requirements, selecting procurement route, selecting project organisation, short listing project team, formulating team protocols, assembling design and project management teams, assessing tenders and finalising team selection the outcome being a RIPT. The use case diagram in Figure 3 illustrates these processes from a system requirements management perspective.

The use cases are being mapped into functional requirements of the targeted RISC system. The next section uses interaction diagram to illustrate system level collaboration to realise a given use case.

3.4   System level collaboration

The sequence diagram and interaction model in Figure 4 simulates interactions between some of the components and subsystems within the integrated RISC environment. In this scenario, the user (i.e. Owner) specifies the project parameters including constraints through a user interface. This could be either a web-based interface or a single user interface for stand-alone applications. The model considers a scenario in which the analytical processing functions are performed using appropriate software components (e.g. spreadsheet tools) that are fairly commonly used in construction organisations as revealed by a recent study in Hong Kong[2].

4   IT TOOLS & SYSTEM REQUIREMENTS FOR COLLABORATIVE DECISION-SUPPORT

By simulating decision-making in a virtual RISC environment, some IT tools have been identified to aid in collaborative working and improve decision-support.

---

[2] Based on recent interviews and discussion conducted with major stakeholders (clients, and contractors) in the Hong Kong construction industry, January 2003. Report under preparation.

220

These include tools for; (i) data storage; (ii) friendly interfaces for user-machine communication; (iii) data extraction, analysis and report generation, and (iv) project management and visualisation. The next section discusses these tools in detail.

4.1 Data & information storage tools

The first IT tool is a data warehouse dedicated to "an orderly and accessible repository of known facts and related data that is used as a basis for making better (project) management decisions" (Price Waterhouse 1997). In a RISC context, it stores the different breadth and depth of information/knowledge associated with managing construction projects within a RISC environment, and it contains generic data and information on construction management domain objects such as projects, tasks, resources, task scheduling etc. (Ugwu & Tah 1999). The attributes and operations identified in the industry survey (that are suppressed in the presented static object model due to space constraints), define the various types of data and the depth and scope of information that is stored in the data warehouse. However, these sets of data can be broadly classified into "raw data", "knowledge data", and "process-engineering data".

4.2 User interfaces & communication tools

There are two levels of interfacing in the targeted RISC system: (i) at the physical level between the user and the system (i.e. the user interface) and (ii) at the application level between the system components/subsystems (i.e. application interfaces). At the physical level, the interfaces could be web-based or for stand-alone application. However, it should be designed with due consideration to various levels of user needs, knowledge and computing experience. Integration of components such as web based email systems (widely used in industry) would facilitate and/or automate data and information delivery and consequently improve collaboration between stakeholders.

4.3 Report analysis tools

Report generators and analysis tools are required to write data to and/or read data from data repositories including existing data storage systems. Examples of report generators include software components such as MS Excel that are fairly commonly used in industry.

4.4 Project management & visualisation tools

In order to facilitate collaboration, it is essential to be able to transfer data between components such as databases, project management and construction programming tools, so that project management plans and construction schedules can be generated and viewed by the appropriate users for subsequent operational decision-making and control. This capability ensures effective cross utilisation of data across the relationally integrated construction organisations.

As an illustration, a user working with a project management package (such as MS project) can request to load project schedule details from the data repository through a dedicated project management server. In this instance the MS project acts as a client, and triggers message(s) to the server. On receiving the triggered message(s), the server then executes the instruction (requests) using its own internal methods for accessing the appropriate data repository, extracting the necessary sets of data and information, and then creating instances of the task schedule objects. Finally, the results are presented to the user in a customised standard format. The user can also update scheduled details in the appropriate sections of the repository by using the services provided by the server (Ugwu 1999).

5 CONCLUSION AND RECOMMENDATIONS

This paper has discussed IT tools required for collaborative working in an integrated RISC environment. The requirements were summed up in section 4. The paper identified key features and the processes involved and virtually simulated procurement and operational decision making processes. Thus the main contribution of the paper is in providing in-depth analysis and understanding of requirements for a RISC system at the implementation levels.

The UML modelling approach used virtual simulations to provide a high level overview of the targeted RISC application(s). By so doing we have (i) supplied a view of the RISC system which could underpin its evolution into practical systems, (ii) helped in gathering and formalising requirements that could be used to initiate such system development, and (iii) used the interaction diagram to highlight the inherent complexity in such a system. The study shows that data and information modelling and database development will drive application of IT tools in the RISC environments envisaged, and that such systems are complex and will need to evolve over time.

Governments across the world are promoting the concept of a knowledge-based economy and are providing enabling infrastructures that underpin electronic deliveries and other forms digital communications (e.g. the Government of HKSAR 2003). The construction sector needs to harness such infrastructure and improve the new business processes engendered by the RISC paradigm, to achieve value for

221

money through IT-driven process innovation. Construction management research has pivotal roles in realising these objectives, by identifying and formalising these requirements, and this paper contributes towards realising these goals. Further developments in the RISC system implementation will be discussed in future papers.

REFERENCES

Government of HKSAR, 2003. Electronic Service Delivery Infrastructure, in http://www.info.gov.hk/digital21/eng/milestone/table02_esd.html (Last accessed on 24/02/03).

Kumarswamy M.M., Dissanayaka S.M. 2001. Developing a decision-support system for building project. *Building and Environment*, Vol. 36: pp. 337–349.

Kumarswamy M.M., Rahman M.M., Palaneeswaran E., Ng, S.T., Ugwu O.O. 2003. Relationally integrated value networks. *2nd International Conference on Innovation in AEC Sector, July 2003*, Loughborough University, UK (in press).

Palaneeswaran E., Kumarswamy M.M., Rahman M.M., Palaneeswaran E., Ng, S.T. 2003. Curing congenital industry disorders through relationally integrated supply chains. *Building and Environment*, 38, pp. 571–582.

Price Waterhouse. 1997. *Data warehousing – an overview of the business benefits and the system management methodology*, Price Waterhouse LLP.

Rahman, M.M., Kumarswamy M.M. 2002. Risk management trends in the construction industry: moving towards joint risk management. *Engineering, Construction and Architectural Management*, Vol. 9, No. 2: pp. 131–151.

Rahman, M.M., Kumarswamy M.M., Ng S.T. 2003. Re-engineering construction project teams, *ASCE Construction Research Congress*, Hawaii, March 2003 (in press).

Rational 2003: *UML*, Documentation on available from http://www.rational.com (last accessed on 24/02/03).

Ugwu O.O., Tah, J.H.M., 1999. A turnkey client-server decision support architecture for project management. *Journal of Decision Systems, Special Issue: Decision Support for Civil Engineering*, Vol 8(2): pp 223–247.

Ugwu O.O. 1999. *A Decision Support Framework for Resource Optimisation and Management Using Hybrid Genetic Algorithms – Application in Earthworks*, PhD Thesis, South Bank University, London, UK.

System-based Vision for Strategic and Creative Design, Bontempi (ed.)
© 2003 Swets & Zeitlinger, Lisse, ISBN 90 5809 599 1

Information technology training: aligning competence with corporate capability

J.S. Goulding & M. Alshawi
School of Construction and Property Management, University of Salford, UK

A. Alani
Department of Civil Engineering, University of Portsmouth, UK

ABSTRACT: The construction industry has witnessed a steady increase in the scope and complexity of information technology (IT) systems and applications in order to promote IT capability and help companies deliver core capability. However, developing corporate capability requires managers to fundamentally re-assess their approach to recruitment, performance appraisal and training policies (in order to maximise any benefits offered by IT). This is particularly important, as companies are now starting to build skills and competence (often termed "intellectual capital") into their capacity-building infrastructure in order to meet their current and future business requirements. Therefore, training, corporate culture, and organisational learning, are important facets of this process that therefore need careful consideration. This research identifies the key issues, requirements, deliverables and constraints associated with the deployment of IT training in a construction environment. A process protocol IT training model (GAPP-IT) is presented and discussed as an exemplar.

1 INTRODUCTION

The fragmented nature of the construction industry in the United Kingdom (Emmerson 1962, Banwell 1964, Latham 1994) has often been cited as a primary factor that can adversely affect performance and productivity. In this context, construction organisations are increasingly aware of the importance of linking their IT support infrastructure to the business strategy (BS) in order to maximise performance. However, care must be noted to ensure that IT resources are "in line" with business imperatives (Galliers & Sutherland 1991), as the process of aligning the information system (IS) strategy to the BS's key deliverables can often be difficult to achieve, especially where alignment is not in a steady state – reflecting a dynamic model of change (Burn 1996).

Advances in IT have had a significant impact on organisations' core business processes, and numerous companies are now using IT to deliver their BS in the quest of improving their overall competitiveness. However, many major management initiatives are needed to deliver these strategic objectives effectively (Rockart et al. 1996), and the subsequent alignment of the IS/IT strategy to the BS, is a crucial factor in this equation (Ward & Griffiths 1997). Thus, in order

to benefit from IT capabilities, organisations must carefully appraise their corporate training systems and infrastructure (Ahmad et al. 1995), the precursor of which however, requires the key decision makers in the organisation to fully understand the BS and its relationship with the IS/IT applications that help deliver it.

Progressive developments in IT can also often place increasing demands on personnel (Heng 1996). Therefore, training and development programmes are needed to facilitate and provide changes in organisational behaviour, which in turn can enhance the organisation's capability to survive (Kessels & Harrison 1998), as training is not only instrumental in addressing skill deficiencies (Krogt & Warmerdam 1997); it can also be used to integrate with the long-term needs of the company (Kumaraswamy 1997). Therefore, from an IT training perspective, managers should determine what IT skills and capabilities are required to bridge the gap between what currently exists, to what is needed (within a particular time corridor). These issues are already acknowledged and reflected in other industries (Mata el al. 1995, Rockart et al. 1996, Powell & Dent-Micallef, 1997); but the global precept however, must not focus specifically on addressing IT skills gaps per se, but should also concentrate on the key areas perceived to have the greatest impact on the BS.

Organisations should therefore aim to balance a range of skills and competence to meet business goals (Andrews 1987, Mintzberg & Quinn 1991), as "companies which are adapt at using their skillbase effectively are able to use and reuse ... these skills many times" (Klein et al. 1991). From a resource justification perspective therefore, construction organisations should endeavour to evaluate the "real net benefit/ cost of training" (Kumaraswamy 1997). However, justifying IT training expenditure can often be difficult to achieve, especially where benefits or improvements are intangible and unable to be directly measured. The difficulty therefore, is to determine a framework from which the justification process can be matched to (and measured against). From a business performance perspective, considerable research is therefore required to investigate the type of training (and competence requirements) needed to make an impact on organisational performance (Horwitz 1999).

From a process perspective, business benefits have been demonstrated by improving "process" (Hammer & Champy 1993, Davenport 1993), which can often lead to improved overall competitiveness (Chan & Land 1999); but, it is increasingly important that organisations should model their business processes before they try to automate and improve them (Soares & Anderson 1997). In construction therefore, this precursor requires process users to have a detailed understanding of their environment, organisational structure and subsequent relationship with their project environment (Shirazi et al. 1996), as " ... each individual produces an output ... which ... becomes the input for the next value adding process" (Cox 1996). One particular technique that successfully demonstrates the use of process is called Process Protocol (Kagioglou et al. 1998).

Process Protocol (PP) is a modelling tool capable of representing all diverse parties in a process, the flexibility and clarity of which allows generic activities to be represented in a framework encompassing standardisation. This need to represent process parties was reinforced by Morledge & Sharif (1996), Hibberd & Dejebarni (1996), Luck & Newcombe (1996), Franks (1990), Masterman (1992), Aouad et al. (1994), Mitchell (1991), Cooper et al. (1990, 1994). The PP approach was used in the development of this training model.

2 DEVELOPMENT OF A GENERIC ASSESSMENT PROCESS PROTOCOL MODEL FOR IT TRAINING

A Generic Assessment Process Protocol model for IT training (GAPP-IT) was developed with two major UK construction companies (one publicly-owned, and one privately-owned) to determine and "map" the key generic processes associated with IT, IT training, and the subsequent impact of these issues on the BS (Goulding 2000). The project participants consisted of 12 main contributors (representing a cross-section of skill areas), supported by several key domain experts. The remit of this team was to analyse the key sequential stages was to analyse the key sequential stages (processes) required to evaluate the impact of IT training on the BS. In this context, IT training issues and processes were categorised and placed in a framework for discussion and subsequent evaluation. Various iterations were assessed during the prototyping and testing stage to secure consensus, especially in the validation of processes (to achieve taxonomic understanding).

Training needs were divided into three discreet categories, specifically: operational, managerial and executive. These categories were chosen to differentiate between the different types of skills sets needed. For example, the operational category included staff predominantly engaged in functional activities. This group incorporated such roles as general support staff, clerks, secretaries, technicians, engineers, architects and planners. The managerial category however, included staff that had some degree of responsibility for subordinates (or had some input into staffing levels, e.g. recruitment, selection and appraisal etc.). Typical roles therefore incorporated line managers, section leaders and divisional managers. The final skill category involved executives; the remit of which included staff that had considerable influence on the way the company conducted its business i.e. the key policy and decision makers.

Seven key phases are offered for discussion in this paper, encompassing the initial preliminary stage (establishing the need for IT training), through to the final phase (steering committee) – the representation of which is shown in Figure 1. Each of these phases can be deconstructed to show lower level information, and subsequent analysis of this lower level detail will be discussed in later works.

The GAPP-IT model is divided into three horizontal levels (covering the operational, managerial and executive requirements). It is commenced in Phase ZERO, and exited in Phase SIX, after sequential progression through each phase has been achieved (if required). However, users can visit each phase independently without going through the whole model, subject to the constraints of each gate.

The gaps between each phase signify the presence of a physical boundary or barrier (termed stage gate). Stage gates can be either "hard" or "soft", the classification of which is determined by the requirements and conditions set by the preceding/succeeding phases (Kagioglou et al. 1998). Upon completion, users return to Phase ZERO through the feedback loop (via the

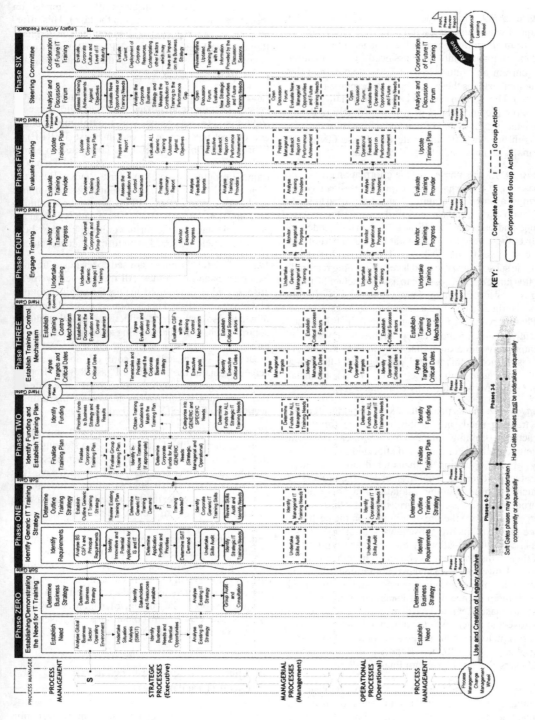

Figure 1. Generic Assessment Process Protocol model for IT training (GAPP-IT).

process wheel). A brief summary of each of these phases follows:

Phase ZERO: This is the initial opening phase, the remit of which aims to establish the need for IT training from an outline perspective. It is used to evaluate the existing and future business needs, contemplating the current and future IS and IT strategies (and the potential changes these may have on resource requirements). The BS is agreed and confirmed in this phase, the structure and drivers of which then help to determine the overall IS and IT demand. Users subsequently pass through a soft stage gate into Phase ONE – to formally identify and clarify these needs.

Phase ONE: This phase uses the information created in Phase ZERO to establish the processes involved in forming a generic IT training strategy. It is used to identify the BS deliverables, and to determine the precise scope and nature of the IS and IT demand needed to deliver these needs. A skills audit is used as part of this process to verify the existing skill levels, and to ascertain the subsequent type (and level) of training required. At this juncture, it is possible to assess whether IT training is needed. If training is not required, users exit this model through a decision icon into the stage gate, where a Phase Review Report is completed (which is subsequently stored in the Legacy Archive). However, if training is required, an outline generic IT training strategy is formed at this point. Users then pass through a soft stage gate into Phase TWO (as no financial resources have been formally committed yet).

Phase TWO: In this phase, the exact corporate generic IT training needs are established in the form of a structured training plan. This requires financial resources to be determined and allocated for the delivery of the operational, managerial and executive (strategic) generic IT training needs – the process of which requires training quotations to be sought. Corporate funds are then prioritised to those areas perceived to have the greatest impact on the performance gap. Groups are subsequently informed of this generic provision – allowing them to make appropriate arrangements for their specific IT training requirements. However, as a financial commitment is made during this phase, automatic progression is prevented due to the presence of a hard stage gate. In this context, a Phase Review board meeting is required to approve and sanction the anticipated resource expenditure, and to agree the scope and content of the training plan. A Phase Review Report is then completed, and users exit this phase into Phase THREE.

Phase THREE: This phase is used to establish the training and control mechanism needed to ensure the critical needs, deliverables, and deadlines are all met. All IT training needs generated from the BS are then matched to delivery dates – the process of which also requires the type of evaluation and control mechanism to be agreed (conscious of the impact on resources and appropriateness to the task). This information is then reported and sanctioned in a Phase Review board meeting (where a Phase Review Report is completed). Users then pass through a hard stage gate into Phase FOUR.

Phase FOUR: This phase is used to undertake the generic IT training identified, and to monitor and control training (in accordance with the training feedback and control mechanism agreed in Phase THREE). A Phase Review board meeting is conducted to assess and ratify all training achievements (and to record training progress to date). A Phase Review Report is then completed. Users subsequently pass through a hard stage gate into Phase FIVE, where these training outcomes are then evaluated. A hard gate is used at the end of this stage, as the formal training has now been completed (and will need to be formally documented).

Phase FIVE: This phase is used to evaluate training experiences and outcomes. All training achievements are assessed and measured against the original training objectives (established in the training plan), the process of which also evaluates the effectiveness of the training control mechanism. The existing training plan is subsequently updated at this point. The Phase Review board meeting is conducted to record all outcomes and achievements in the form of a Phase Review Report. Users then pass through the final hard stage gate (as this concludes the formal evaluation of the training section) into Phase SIX – the feedback stage.

Phase SIX: This is the final (and most important) phase of the GAPP-IT model. It uses a steering committee to overview and assess the whole process of IT training at both the corporate and group levels. It is predominately used to evaluate training achievements holistically and contextually – specifically against the performance gap. An "open" discussion forum is engaged to foster and stimulate discussion on training and development issues. Any new ideas or initiatives are then evaluated, contemplating the company's current deployment of resources, level of IT maturity, and prevailing level of organisational culture. All discussions and outcomes are documented in a Phase Review Report – the content of which also records process issues for improvement purposes. Users then exit the GAPP-IT model at this stage.

3   APPLICATION BENEFITS OF THE
     GAPP-IT MODEL

The GAPP-IT model can be used in construction organisations to assess the impact and "value" of IT training on the core business. The generic nature and architecture of this model is designed specifically to accommodate a range of organisational entities, from small to medium enterprises (SME's), through to larger construction companies. It is therefore possible to assess IT training's contribution to the "performance gap" using this model – and can help to justify training resources (which historically has often been difficult to achieve). Furthermore, it can additionally be used to improve process by capturing (and sharing) best practice in order to facilitate continuous process improvement. This philosophy is in keeping with the concepts of organisational learning (OL), as identified by Argyris & Schon (1978), Senge (1990), and Huber (1991). In this context, the principal tenet of OL (and GAPP-IT) is based on organisational development and organisational theory – whereby the collective actions of individuals are structured to improve organisational knowledge and performance.

4 CONCLUSIONS

The training framework presented in this paper enables process users to make important decisions at the end of each phase. The relationship between IT training and the BS can be better understood using the PP approach. However, certain limitations were noted with the PP approach, specifically regarding this techniques inability to "map" lower-level detail (which can make it difficult to determine process flow and connectivity below the first level). Furthermore, some restrictions and limitations were noted regarding process rules, conditions, and constraints. However, notwithstanding these issues, the seven-phase arrangement offered by GAPP-IT was considered "optimal" (in the trade-off between practicality and complexity); but the exact number of phases used in this model could be condensed (or expanded) to accommodate individual company requirements.

From an organisational performance perspective, construction companies are starting to benefit from a greater understanding of how skills can contribute to company performance – which from an IT standpoint, means aligning IT resources with business imperatives (to support the core business process). However, this procedure requires "appropriate" type and level of IT skills to be procured in order to deliver IT capability. The GAPP-IT model can be used to assess the need for (and impact of) IT training initiatives on the BS, moreover, investment decisions can be evaluated against the performance gap using targets that measure IT training's contribution to the delivery of BS key performance indicators. In this context, it can be used to enhance the decision-making process by enabling training resource expenditure to be justified (and IT training's contribution to

the performance gap can thereby be determined). However, it is important to note that the effectiveness of this IT training initiative is directly influenced by the prevailing level of organisational culture and the company's overall commitment to training.

REFERENCES

Ahmad, I., Russell, J. & Abou-Zeid, A. 1995. Information Technology (IT) and Integration in the Construction Industry, *Construction Management and Economics Journal*, Vol. 13, Part 2, pp. 163–171

Andrews, K.R. 1987. *The Concept of Corporate Strategy*, Irwin Inc, Illinois, USA

Aouad, G., Betts, M., Brandon, P., Brown F., Child, T., Cooper, G., Ford, S., Kirkham, J., Oxman, R., Sarshar, M., & Young, B. 1994. ICON Final Report, University of Salford, UK

Argyris, C. & Schön, D.A. 1978. *Organizational Learning: A Theory of Action Perspective*, Addison-Wesley, Massachusetts, USA

Banwell, H. 1964. Report of the Committee on the Placing and Management of Contracts for Building and Civil Engineering Works, HMSO, UK

Burn J. 1996. IS Innovation and Organisational Alignment – A Professional Juggling Act, *Journal of Information Technology*, Vol. 11, Part 1, pp. 3–12

Chan, P.S. & Land, C. 1999. Implementing Reengineering Using Information Technology, *Business Process Management Journal*, Vol. 5, No. 4, pp 311–324

Cooper, R.G. 1990. Stage-Gate Systems: A New Tool for Managing New Products, *Business Horizons*, 33:3, May/June

Cooper, R.G. 1994. PERSPECTIVE – Third Generation New Product Processes, *Journal of Production Innovation and Management*, Vol. 11, pp. 3–14

Cox, R.F. 1996. Understanding the Linkage Between Individual and Organizational Performance, *Proceedings of the CIB W89 Beijing International Conference*, Beijing, China.

Davenport, T.H. 1993. *Process Innovation: Reengineering Work Through Information Technology*, Harvard Business School Press, Boston, Massachusetts, USA

Emmerson, H. 1962. *Survey of Problems Before the Construction Industries*, HMSO, UK

Franks, J. 1990. *Building Procurement Systems: A Guide to Building Project Management*, 2nd Ed., Chartered Institute of Building, Ascot, UK

Galliers, R.D. & Sutherland, A.R. 1991. Information Systems Management and Strategy Formulation – the Stages of Growth Model Revisited, *Journal of Information Systems*, Vol. 1, Part 1, pp. 89–114

Goulding, J.S. 2000. GAPP-IT: A Generic IT Training Model for Construction, *PhD Thesis*, School of Construction and Property Management, University of Salford, UK

Hammer, M. & Champy, J. 1993. *Reengineering the Corporation: A Manifesto for Business Revolution*, Harper Business, New York, USA

Heng, L. 1996. The Role of IT Manager in Construction Process Re-Engineering, *Building Research and Information Journal*, Vol. 24, Part 2, pp. 124–127

Hibberd, P. & Djebarni, R. 1996. Criteria of Choice for Procurement Methods, *Proceedings of COBRA '96 Conference*, University of West England, UK

Horwitz, F.M. 1999. The Emergence of Strategic Training and Development: The Current State of Play, *Journal of European Industrial Training*, Vol. 23, Part 4/5, pp. 180–190

Huber, G.P. 1991. Organizational Learning: The Contributing Processes and the Literatures, *Journal of Organization Science*, Vol. 2, No. 1, pp. 88–115

Kagioglou, M., Cooper, R., Aouad, G., Hinks, J., Sexton, M., Sheath, D., 1998. Final Report: Process Protocol, University of Salford, UK, ISBN 090-289-619-9

Kessels, J. & Harrison, R. 1998. External Consistency: The Key to Success in Management Development Programmes?, *Journal of Management Learning*, Vol. 29, Part 1, pp. 39–68

Klein, J.A., Edge, G.M. & Kass, T. 1991. Skill-Based Competition, *Journal of General Management*, Vol. 16, Part 4, pp. 1–15

Krogt, F. & Warmerdam, J. 1997. Training in Different Types of Organisations: Differences and Dynamics in the Organisation of Learning at Work, *International Journal of Human Resource Management*, Vol. 8, Part 1, pp. 87–105

Kumaraswamy, M. 1997. Improving Industry Performance Through Integrated Training Programs, *Journal of Professional Issues in Engineering Education and Practice*, Vol. 123, Part 3, pp. 93–97

Latham, M. 1994. *Constructing the Team*, HMSO, UK

Luck, R. & Newcombe, R. 1996. The Case for the Integration of the Project Participants' Activities Within a Construction Project Environment, *The Organization and Management of Construction: Shaping Theory and Practice*, Vol. 2, E & FN Spon, London, UK

Masterman, J.W.E. 1992. *An Introduction to Building Procurement Systems*, E & FN Spon, London, UK

Mata, F.J., Fuerst, W.L. & Barney, J.B. 1995. Information Technology and Sustained Competitive Advantage: A Resource-Based Analysis, *MIS Quarterly*, Vol. 19, No. 4, pp. 487–505

Mintzberg, H. & Quinn, J.B. 1991. *The Strategy Process: Concepts, Contexts, Cases*, Prentice Hall International (UK) Ltd, London, UK

Mitchell, F.H. 1991. *CIM Systems – An Introduction to Computer Integrated Manufacturing*, Prentice Hall International, London, UK.

Moreledge, R. & Sharif, A. 1996. Client Time Expectations and Construction Industry Performance, *Proceedings of COBRA '96 Conference*, University of West England, UK

Powell & Dent-Micallef 1997. Information Technology as Competitive Advantage: The Role of Human, Business and Technology Resources, *Strategic Management Journal*, Vol. 18, Part 5, pp. 375–405

Rockart, J.F., Earl, M.J. & Ross, J.W. 1996. Eight Imperatives for the New IT Organization, *Sloan Management Review*, Vol. 38, Fall, pp 43–55

Shirazi, B., Langford, D.A. & Rowlinson, S.M. 1996. Organizational Structures in the Construction Industry, *Construction Management and Economics Journal*, Vol. 14, Part 3, pp. 199–212

Soares, J. & Anderson, S. 1997. Modelling Process Management in Construction, *Journal of Management in Engineering*, Vol. 13, Part 5, pp 45–53

Ward, J. & Griffiths, P. 1997., Strategic Planning for Information Systems, John Wiley and Sons, Chichester, England

E-commerce in the construction industry in Lebanon

T. Mezher, M.A. Abdul-Malak & M. Ajam
American University of Beirut, Beirut, Lebanon

ABSTRACT: The explosion of the Internet had a great impact on e-commerce in many different sectors including the construction industry. Many documents (BOQ, Specs, designs, tenders, etc.) are generated electronically but distributed on paper rather than using the virtual world. Some of the benefits of e-commerce in construction are increase efficiency, revenues, and quality of output. The objective of this paper is to investigate the status of the e-commerce in the construction industry in Lebanon. This is done in two-fold. First, a literature review on e-commerce and IT in construction in general is conducted. Second, a survey questionnaire is developed in order to determine the current status and readiness of the construction industry in Lebanon to engage in e-commerce. Results indicate that all the stakeholders in the construction industry in Lebanon are not making use of e-commerce in their core business functions. Finally, recommendations are given on improving the e-commerce use in construction industrial to the benefit of all stakeholders in the construction industry in Lebanon.

1 INTRODUCTION

Computers and IT has revolutionized the way we conduct our daily business, just as the mobile phone and fax dramatically altered the way we do business. E-commerce is considered the latest or one of the latest mutations of this IT evolution. E-commerce is also promising the construction industry many advantages, effectiveness and efficiency.

The world of e-commerce is huge and very complex, but what it can potentially provide is also overwhelming and very important to the construction sector. The most important of all is the integration of all the diverse and numerous players in the construction scene. The players, which represent the construction supply chain, are owners/developers, contractors/subcontractors, and architectures/engineers; in addition to lenders, merchants, and manufacturers. All these players will be affected by the e-commerce revolution. This paper starts by summarizing the literature on e-commerce in the construction industry in general. Then, a summary on the information technology infrastructure in Lebanon is given. Next, the impact of e-commerce on the construction industry in Lebanon is analyzed. This is done through a survey questionnaire distributed to main parties involved in the construction industry, mainly, owners/developers, contractors/subcontractors, and architectural/engineering firms (A/Es). Finally, closing with conclusions and recommendations to the local market on how to be more on

the cutting edge of the technology and possessing the required know-how to absorb any new mutations in the IT evolution.

2 E-COMMERCE AND THE CONSTRUCTION INDUSTRY

Construction projects can be considered quite complex undertakings. From an information technology (IT) perspective, these projects are challenging for several reasons. First data sets are large (BOQ, Specifications, Drawings etc.). Second these sets involve many types of unstructured, and interrelated data. Third the data is created and used by many types of users and software applications. During the last years, a large number of e-commerce companies are targeting the construction industry. These companies promise to create web-enabled process efficiencies that increase productivity, improve profitability, advance project completion schedules, and more efficiently deploy construction project resources (Aberdeen Group 2000).

The construction industry is becoming increasingly reliant on new electronic technology, ranging from project-specific web sites and online equipment auctioning to bid analysis software and negotiation tools. Although the construction industry has been slow to warm up to the technology, usage is increasing every day. However, the Internet is not without its problems. Hidden behind the technology's promise of greater efficiency, accountability and speed are traditional issues of contract formation and enforcement, project relationships and assessment of liability. Plus, new technology raises new concerns about security, reliability, and data integrity (Woodward 2000).

E-commerce depends heavily on electronic communications among the parties involved in the construction process. Such communication is considered the backbone of the new technology. The advent of what is called Extensible Markup language (XML) is considered vital to the construction sector for the integration and interoperability it provides. Many initiatives are underway in establishing specific XML schemas for the construction sector (aecXML 1999).

The Internet presents a novel opportunity to negotiate bulk prices with, purchase hard-to-find products from and sell surplus materials to a market that expands well beyond traditional regional boundaries. Many web sites provide contractors with real-time access to the inventories of suppliers. Ideally, the results are more opportunities for sellers and better selection and prices for consumers (Stoddard 1999).

Today's project web sites and extranets claim to provide more opportunities for consistent document review, multi-party collaboration and expanded communications, both on the site and in the office. With many programs (known as interactive collaboration), users can mark up documents online without changing the original drawings. Other online applications are more complex, combining the interactive collaboration features with a workflow tracker that posts and records communications and other documents between architects, engineers, contractors, and subcontractors. Furthermore, the web site or extranet becomes a common depository for communications, creating an accurate and comprehensive virtual paper trail for the project (Levin 2000).

For parties putting projects and requests out for bid, the world of e-commerce promises many advantages over traditional methods of procurement, such as real-time posting of requests and amendments, efficient dissemination of materials, and lower costs. Bid analysis applications also help parties on both sides formulate quotations and analyze proposals, again saving time and money. In all cases, the IT in general and e-commerce in particular is promising the construction industry a brighter future. However, this is not without costs, problems, and drawbacks. Many issues must be considered when transforming the construction sector into the electronic communication era. The most important problems are: security and reliability (Phair et al. 1997 & Hernandez 2000).

Many companies are still simply providing information about themselves and have not yet began to provide full-scale transactions for procuring, bidding, submitting BOQ/RFQ or even buying and selling online. This restraint is primarily the result of concern about network and transaction security. Information kept both on- and off-site is susceptible to user misuse and "spying" (Jones 1998).

In order for any study or survey to be comprehensive it must attempt to visualize the whole IT evolution and not only e-commerce technologies. Many surveys and studies were previously conducted in various countries over the last couple of years to determine the impact of information technology in the construction industries. Such surveys were conducted in New Zealand (Doherty 1997); Sweden, Denmark and Finland (Howard & Samuelsson 1998); Hong Kong (Futcher & Rowlinson 1998); Saudi Arabia (O'Brien & Al-Biqami 1999); and Canada (Rivard & Bjork 2000). The survey at hand took into consideration all the important issues in the previous surveys in addition to adapting it to local conditions and emphasizing on communications and electronic commerce use.

3 TELECOMMUNICATION INFORMATION TECHNOLOGY INFRASTRUCTURE IN LEBANON

After the end of the civil strife in 1989, the government of Lebanon (population 3.5 millions, GDP of 16 billions USD) started the reconstruction of the all the infrastructure including the telecommunication sector. The main projects included the rehabilitation and installation of new digital lines (including ISDN), the rehabilitation and modernization of the inter-office network which (SDH fiber-optic loops), and rehabilitation and upgrade of the international network. In addition to these projects, two private GSM networks currently exist and both have about 500,0000 subscribers. Since 1995 as many as 15 ISPs started operating in Lebanon and have about 52,000 subscribers and 135,000 users. Telephone and internet usage in Lebanon is considered expensive compared to USA and Europe (Raad 1999).

Today, Lebanon is facing many challenges. The biggest one is the national debt which is 200% of its GDP, therefore, government spending on upgrading the country's infrastructure is minimal. This is affecting the upgrading of existing infrastructure including construction projects. Other challenges include lack of government legislations in IT, non existence of communication between the different construction industry players including the government, and high cost of telephone and internet usage (Mezher 2000). These challenges are reflected in the results of the survey study in the next sections.

4 SURVEY'S SCOPE AND METHODOLOGY

The objective of the survey presented here is to reveal the current and planned use of computer-based and telecommunication technologies and their impact on construction field in Lebanon. To achieve this purpose, the survey looked at the availability and usage of computers, computer-aided drafting software, networks and Internet, and information technology among construction related firms. The results will provide directions in research, development, training, and strategies that will respond to the needs of this industry. In this paper we will give special emphasis on the network and electronic exchange sections of the survey.

The survey was sent at the beginning of April 2001 and answers were collected between the months of April and June 2001. The participants were among the biggest in the construction industry in Lebanon in terms of volume of work and their use of IT. The respondent rates were as follows: 3 out of 30 for owners/developers, 15 out of 30 for contractors, and 12 out of 30 architecture/engineering firms. The position of the respondents in their respective firms was 54% senior management, 20% in IT department managers, while the remaining 26% were senior technical engineers. The annual revenue of the firms was 30% between 10 and 100 millions USD, 20% between 1 and 10 millions USD, and the remaining 47% below 1 million USD. The geographic distribution of companies' operations was 60% in the Middle East and North Africa; 30% in Europe, USA, and Australia; and 10% in other countries.

5 SURVEY RESULTS

The main sections of the survey were: computer availability and usage; networks and communications; electronic services and data exchange; security awareness; and finally future trends and research areas. The details of some of the findings are discussed in the following paragraphs.

5.1 *Networks and communications*

The Internet is a global network of networks that uses a standard protocol for communication (called TCP/IP) that allows computers to be connected globally. The Internet has become ubiquitous in the industry as 87% of the company surveyed are connected to the Internet and the remaining 13% are planning to be connected soon. In terms of categories of firms, 89% of the consultant firms, and 81% of the contractors surveyed are connected to the Internet. All the firms surveyed have access to e-mail.

The most prevailing type of connections used is the modem (speed from 14.4 Kbps up to 56 Kbps). 76% of the firms surveyed that are connected to the Internet use modem connections. This is bound to change with the recent deregulation, since cable companies are now competing with telephone companies

in the domain of Internet connection and are offering an attractive and cheap alternative to modems. Cable modems are faster than modems with a speeds ranging from 500 Kbps to 10 Mbps. However, only 3% of the firms surveyed connected to the Internet have already adopted cable modems. The other two popular types of connections are Integrated Services Digital Network (3%) (ISDN) and T1/T3 (12%). ISDN has speeds ranging between 56 Kbps and 12 Kbps, while T1 is 24 ISDN circuits and has a data rate of 1.5 Mbps and T3 line is 30 T1 line and has a data rate of 45 Mbps (Levin 2000). Because of their associated high costs, ISDN and T1/T3 are mostly used in large firms. The other 6% use microwave link and DSL modems.

Another important aspect towards the existing of the virtual construction industry is the existence of a web page for the firms. Sixty three percent of the firms surveyed had an established web page. Sixty percent of these firms developed their own web page using their own IT human resources, while 40% outsourced their web page to an external party. Sixty two percent of the consultant firms, 63% of the contracting firms have a home page. All owner/developer firms have web pages but this is not indicative since the number is small and they are the most established.

Another important aspect of web page is the language of development and hence the awareness of the companies of the new language "XML". Unfortunately only 1 company (5.3%) has an XML web page. The majority of the firms (68.4%) having simple HTML web pages and only 26.3% of them having dynamic HTML web pages.

5.2 *Electronic services and data exchange*

This section investigates the use of the electronic commerce and Internet in general in the construction industry. However, the results were not encouraging. Only one of the companies surveyed rendered electronic services, most of its work is in USA and Europe, and its main office is not located in Lebanon. According to the survey 32% of the firms surveyed use separate software and e-mail but no integration into their core business functions. Twenty two percent of the firms are still using paper, fax, telephone to conduct their work. An equal percentage of them also use the document file transfer in their work. Eighteen percent use a shared databases system in conducting their tasks. Only 5% use application programming interfaces (API), and one company is in the process of implementing some e-commerce activities in its daily practice and again this company has operations in the Gulf region and Europe.

An important capability provided by information technology is the instant transfer of documents in electronic forms. A large portion of the documents in the industry are exchanged through a network.

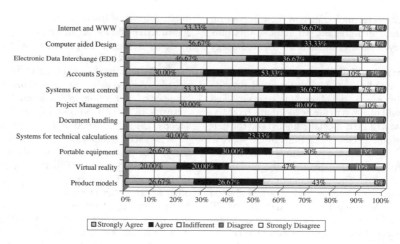

□ Strongly Agree ■ Agree □ Indifferent ■ Disagree □ Strongly Disagree

Figure 1.   Future plans regarding investments in information technology.

However, most of this exchange is done over closed networks inside the companies, that is to say LANs and not the Internet. Only 27% of the total exchange is done through the Internet. Based on these results, design documents are the type of documents with the highest probability (87%) to be exchanged often or always in an electronic form 33% of which is done over the Internet. With respect to textual documents, 77% of the minutes of meetings and 67% of the specifications are often or always exchanged digitally among the respondents, of which, 19% of the minutes of meeting and 22% of the specifications are exchanged over the Internet.

The main barriers to the widespread of the digital exchange of documents are: the slow Internet connections (the large majority of the respondents use modems); the lack of common standards that would permit the exchange of data among software applications; and the fact that this new mode of communication has still not been integrated into the core business functions of the construction industry. These proportions are bound to augment as more companies are switching to better connections and as more players in the construction industry are getting more accustomed to this mode of information exchange.

5.3   Security awareness

IT departments in the interviewed firms did not share a common method of learning about security. The results indicate that 27% of the firms get their security information from the web, 20% from other colleagues, 15% from computing magazines and newsgroup, 8% from security magazines, and 15% from other sources.

While it seems that there is a variety of sources for the IT people in the firms to update their information,

the application side of this new data is minimal in the construction sector. The survey showed that more than 65% of the respondents did not use any security measures. Half of them did not hear about any security standards. It is important to note that 55% of architects/engineers firms used security measures or are planning to use in the near future. Moreover, the number in the other categories is quite minimal. Further advanced question about the new markup security language S2ML becomes obsolete.

5.4   Future trends and research areas

The respondents were asked several questions regarding the future trends and research in IT. Figure 1 shows the results with respect to the firms' plans for investing in and using information technologies.

It is clear from these findings that the main area for future investments is computer-aided design (CAD) and the Internet. This is a major investment cost since almost every architectural and engineering firms surveyed depend on CAD to do their work. Internet on the other hand is a riskier investment since its use is still in its initial phases. Very little investments are planned in the areas of product models and virtual reality.

Figure 2 displays the main benefits achieved by the adoption of IT. The main advantages provided by a greater use of IT are work done more quickly, better communications, easier to use lots of data, and simpler and faster access to common data according to the respondents. Most respondents do not consider reducing and contentment of staff as important benefits.

The three main obstacles to greater use of IT in the firms surveyed are the continual demand for upgrading hardware and software, lack of standards and co-ordination, a greater know-how required from the

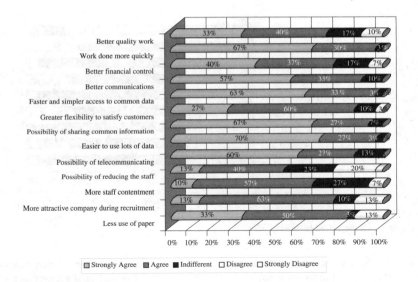

Figure 2. Benefits of information technology.

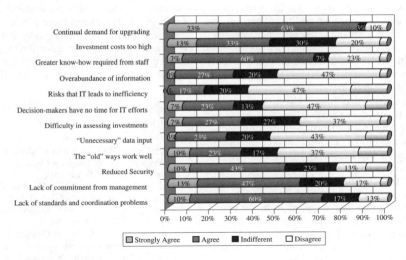

Figure 3. Obstacles to a greater use of information technology.

staff, and a lack of commitment from management. The investment costs problem is not considered that important obstacle to the use of IT. Figure 3 shows the respondents views on IT obstacles.

Figure 4 shows the respondents views on the important research topics in IT as it relates to the construction industry. According to the survey the most important areas of research are in computer-integrated design and construction, internet-based knowledge sharing, and standard format for the data exchange. On the other hand, many don't see the needs for robot-construction.

6 CONCLUSIONS AND RECOMMENDATIONS

Results indicate that all the stakeholders in the construction industry in Lebanon are not making use of e-commerce in their core business functions. Mostly, the internet is used for browsing and search for construction information, and for exchange of documents through intranet within firms. One reason for that is the Lebanese government, which is the biggest owner/ developer in the country, is not yet computerized and still functioning on paperwork. Therefore, firms are

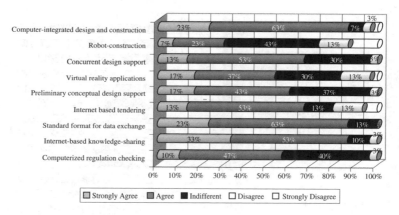

Figure 4.   Research needs identified by the industry.

not motivated to use the new information technology. Another reason is that telecommunication and Internet usage is still very expensive (twice as much) compared to other countries regionally and internationally. Slow connectivity, many firms are still using modems, and lack of standardizations are additional barriers to e-commerce. Finally, results showed that security measures are non-existing even though many firms have their own web pages. This could be due to that lack of awareness and security experts.

Regarding the future trends and research areas, findings have shown that future investments are in CAD and the Internet. The main advantages of using IT are: work is done more quickly, better communications, easier to use lots of data, and simpler and faster access to common data according to the respondents. The main obstacles to greater use of IT in the firms surveyed are the continual demand for upgrading hardware and software, lack of standards and co-ordination, a greater know-how required from the staff, and a lack of commitment from management. The last barrier is crucial because there is no change without top management commitment. The most important areas of research are in computer-integrated design, internet-based knowledge sharing, and standard format for the data exchange.

There is a need for the construction industry to start using e-commerce in order to stay competitive. The Lebanese government should start the computerization process in all its ministries and agencies. In addition, it should take the leadership role in encouraging the private sector to use e-commerce by controlling the public deficit, having a clear vision about the future of the direction of the country, updating the IT infrastructure and lowering communication costs, and by introducing innovative legislations. The construction industry players should start thinking about using e-commerce. This can only be done through the different professional syndicates and not just on individual basis. Another element important to this process is the educational sector represented by universities and training institutions. This sector holds the knowledge and know-how that can help ease the transition process of both government and construction industry. Therefore, there has to be a form of communication and collaboration between all the elements of the triangle; government, construction industry, and education sector; in order to ensure the success of e-commerce in the construction industry.

REFERENCES

Aberdeen Group 2000. *Integrating Process Productivity into the Engineering, Building, and Real Estate Industry Life Cycle*, An executive White Paper.

aecXML working groups 1999. *A Framework for Electronic Communications for the AEC Industries*. AecXML.org. Online, [available at www.aecxml.org/docs/aecwhite. doc]. pp. 3–9, December 1999.

Doherty, J.M. 1997. A Survey of Computer Use in the New Zealand Building and Construction Industry. *Electronic Journal of Information Technology in Construction*. 2:45–57.

Futcher, K.G. & Rowlinson, S. 1998. Information Technology Used by Hong Kong Contractors. In Bjork B.C. & Jagbeck A. (ed.), *The Life-Cycle of Construction IT Innovation: Technology transfer from research to practice; Proc. of the CIB-W78 Conference*. Stockholm, Sweden.

Hernandez, T.Jr. 2000. E-Commerce and AEC". *Building Design and Construction*, 6. Online, [available at www. bdcmag.com/archives/0600compcol2.htm.].

Howard, R. & Samuelsson, O. 1998. IT Barometer – International comparison of IT in building. In Bjork B.C. & Jagbeck A.(ed.), *The Life-Cycle of Construction IT Innovation: Technology transfer from research to practice; Proc. of the CIB-W78 Conf.* Stockholm, Sweden.

Jones, C. 1998. How Thin Client/Server Platform Solved One California Contractor's Computing Woes. *Construction Business Computing*, December Issue: 8–15.

Levin, P. 2000. Web-Based Project Controls. *Construction Claims Monthly,* 22(7): 6–15.

Mezher, T. 2000. Strategies for Industrial and Technological Development of Middle Eastern Countries. *International Journal of Environmental Studies,* 57(5): 543–562.

O'Brien, M.J. & Al-Biqami, N.M. 1999. Survey of Information Technology and the Structure of the Saudi Arabian Construction Industry. In Lacasse M.A. & Vanier D.J. (ed.), Information Technology in Construction, CIB-W78 Workshop *Proc. of the 8th Intern Conf. on Durability of Building Materials and Components*, Ottawa: Canada.

Phair, M., Powers, M., & Rubin, D. 1997. Buying and Selling Go On Line. *Engineering News-Record.* 239(17): 26–33.

Raad, H., 1999. The Internet – Policies, Analysis and Regulations Case Study: Lebanon. Masters Project Report. American University of Beirut, Beirut, Lebanon.

Rivard, H. & Bjork, B. 2000. A Survey on the impact of information technology on the Canadian architecture, engineering and construction industry. In Lacasse M.A. & Vanier D.J. (ed.), Information Technology in Construction, CIB-W78 Workshop *Proc. of the 8th Intern Conf. on Durability of Building Materials and Components*, Ottawa: Canada.

Stoddard, J. 1999. E-Commerce Boom or Bust? *Construction Business Computing.* November: 15–22.

Woodward, S. 2000. Firm Leaps into Web-Based Commercial Construction Management. *The Portland Oregonian*, August Issue.

System-based Vision for Strategic and Creative Design, Bontempi (ed.)
© 2003 Swets & Zeitlinger, Lisse, ISBN 90 5809 599 1

Decomposition of data base – modulation for management of designing and construction of highways

M. Knezevic
Civil Engineering Faculty in Podgorica, Montenegro

ABSTRACT: The concept of database has most important role in the project management. The development of the database in last decade is most important activities of computer usage in field of data processing.

In this paper bases for production of database in project management and highway construction are treated. In the paper the description of basic employer's activities while elaborating designing and highway construction is given that is: preparation and investigation works, designing phase, design approval and obtaining of building permit, solving of the real estate relations, issuing of the works to the designers and contractors, building survey, technical check up and work approval, guarantee period phase of the executed works and economical and financial activities.

1 INTRODUCTION

The concept of data base has more important role in the project management. The development of data base is in the past decade most important activities the usage of computers for processing of data.

In the paper, the usage of data base in project management and highway construction has been examined.

Designing and construction of highways is a complex process, which requires consumption of enormous material, environmental, and human resources.

For efficient and high-quality management of the highway designing and construction processes it is necessary to make reliable and timely decisions with a purpose of directing process toward optimum management in scope of chosen define number of criteria.

A necessary tool of management structures is data base, which is based on great number of useful data. It enables, with large percentage of probability, making reliable and timely decisions on the bases of detailed requirements, foreseeing possible consequences, actions and decisions.

Management of the processes of production of technical documentation and highway construction is essential activity in the realization of the project. Design Management has a goal to provide required level of quantity with lowest level of construction costs and traffic artery exploitation. Reduction and control of the costs and construction period, as well as quality

control, are basic target functions of highway Project management.

Influencing the price and quality in the phase of designing is effective in initial phase (production of General and Conceptual design). This influence falls once we approach physical realization of the structure.

For realization of the structure, the necessary works that has to be carried out are defined, quota of resource and budget of the project is forming. The management is performed in the defined time encirclement and in the scope of exterior imposed factors. Target function of the management is carrying out of the work within the deadline, with planed resources, finances and work quality control.

2 EMPLOYER'S BASIC ACTIVITIES

Here will be discussed design management and construction from Employer's point of view. Insufficient investigation of data base for designing management and highway construction, in specific conditions of economy development so far, leads to the management without reliable information, without recorded experiences for similar projects and creation of chaotic situation that leads to the irrational management.

Management of complex work processes, designing and highway construction, demands participation of numerous organization totalities, as well as series of activities that have to be carried out so that such project can be completed. Further it is given description of basic employer's activities while planing, designing and highway construction that is:

- preparation of investigation works,
- designing phase, design permission, and obtaining building permit,
- solution of real estate relations,
- issuing the works to the designers and to the contractor,
- construction supervision,

- technical survey and work approval,
- phase of warranty period for performed works and
- economic–financial activities.

3 DATA SOURCES

It is necessary that Employer predict expert personnel that shall be in contact with designers and which will take over , select, note and file data into the data base.

Table 1. Tabular review of entity within single module.

Ord No.	Module	Entity	
1	Preparation, investigation works	Approvals Expropriation Building book Building diary Reports Performance of works Financial construction Control of regulation application General practice Contact person Receiving and evidence of proposals	Bills Working order Solutions Concordance Certificates Certificate-leveling indexes Contracts Contract documents City plan – technical and other requirements Introduction into the work minutes
2	Designing and design approval, obtaining building permit	Approvals General design Main design Conceptual design Investment program Performance design General correspondence	Bills Working order Solutions Concordance City plan – technical and other Requirements minutes
3	Real estate relations	Expropriation General correspondence	Bills Working order
4	Issuing works to the designer and to the contractor	General practice Contact person Receiving and evidence of proposals Working orders Solutions	Certificate-leveling indexes Contracts Contract documents Introduction into the works Minutes
5	Construction supervision	Certificate of test Building book Building diary reports Performance of works Control of regulation application	General correspondence Bills Working orders Solutions Approvals
6	Technical survey and work approval	Permission Reports General correspondence Bills	Working orders Solutions Certificates Minutes
7	Warranty period phase for quality of performed works	General correspondence Bills Working orders	Solutions Minutes
8	Economic financial activities	Financial construction General correspondence Bills	Working orders Certificates

Also, it is necessary that all other employer's personnel, who are included into the following of designing and construction works (accounting, management structures etc), must inform data base operators about all information.

Data sources that can emerge in designing phase are:

- various contracts (about designing, consulting business, personnel training etc.),
- correspondence that is between employer–designer and employer–other organs and organizations,
- monthly and final certificate,
- bills,
- reports,
- minutes,
- contract documentation,
- city plan – technical and other requirements,
- design documentation,
- evidence about work participants,
- drawings and catalogs,
- visualization and simulation arise during the work on the project,
- personal designer's observation and/or employer's during work on the project.

Sources of data that can appear in phase of building are:

- various contracts (about designing, supervision, personnel training etc.),
- correspondence that is between employer–designer and employer–other organs and organizations,
- certificate-leveling index
- financial construction,
- monthly and final certificates,
- bills,
- advance payment,
- means for the expropriation,
- certificate of test,
- reports,
- minutes,
- contract documentation,
- building permit,
- permit for preparation works,
- performance design,
- design of performed situation,
- evidence about participants in the works,
- plans and catalogs,
- dynamic plans and work reports,
- guarantee deposit,
- personal observation of the designer's and/or employer's during the works on project.

4 DECOMPOSITION OF DATA BASE-MODULATION

Examined data base is consist of mutually linked segments or modules that are representing single logical totalities.

Modules are mutually liked with informational courses and with uniquely way of production.

Data base is consist of modules that are obtained with its decomposition. The decomposition is in concrete case done according to the processes that appeared in phases of designing and highway construction.

Each module represents logical and technological encircled totalities.

Modulation of the base was done to simplify real system, to describe its parts separately. Modules of the base represent firs level of decomposition of the base. The elements of module-entities are mutually overlapped so the defining of its limits is complex work. That's way to the same entities were described conditions in different modules. Quoted module multiplies with different types of data, from which are important to mention data with vector and raster graphics.

5 ENTITIES OF DATA BASE FOR DESIGNING AND HIGHWAY CONSTRUCTION MANAGEMENT

Within each module, the entities were analyzed by description of designing and highway construction.

Links between entities are established inside each logical module, and after that between modules as well.

Mentioned entities are presented in the table within modules as follows:

- module 1 entities that follows the procedure of designing and highway construction management in phase of preparation and investigation works,
- module 2 entities that follows the procedure of designing and highway construction management in phase of designing, design approval and obtaining the building permit,
- module 3 entities that follows the procedure of designing and highway construction management in phase of solving the real estate relations,
- module 4 entities that follows the procedure of designing and highway construction management in phase of issuing the works to the designers and to the contractors,
- module 5 entities that follows the procedure of designing and highway construction management in phase of survey of the construction,
- module 6 entities that follows the procedure of designing and highway construction management in phase of technical review and work approval,
- module 7 entities that follows the procedure of designing and highway construction management in phase of performed works warranty period,
- module 8 entities that follows the procedure of designing and highway construction management in phase of economic-financial activities.

Table 2. Tabular review of all entities.

1–8	<Main Subject Area>	Certificates of test	General correspondence
		Approvals	Contact persons
		Expropriation	Receiving and evidencing the proposals
		General design	Bills
		Main design	Working orders
		Building book	Solutions
		Building diary	Approvals
		Conceptual design	Certificates
		Investment program	Certification-leveling indexes
		Reports	Contracts
		Performance design	Contract documentation
		Performance of works	City plan, technical and other requirements
		Financial construction	Introduction into the work
		Control of regulation application	Minutes

- module 1–8 entities that follows the procedure of designing and highway construction management in all phases that are mentioned and for which it was obtained modular link of all phases.

Given review is very convenient as transitional step toward the way from real system to rational module data base.

Necessity of presentation data bases by modules, come from demands of participation of many users in the process of designing and highway construction management so that mutual exchange of useful information is possible as well as from demands of management of observed system in sense of reducing entropy on minimum. Further is given table 1 in which is given review of entities within single modules and table 2 in which is given review of all described entities.

6 SPECIFIC FUNCTIONS

In regard to the demands for specific functions, one should stress that data base has to be ready for dynamic exchange of data. Under the dynamic exchange of data hereinafter means that is necessary that data base is linked with some of the programs for dynamic planning. (PRIMAVERA, Microsoft Project etc.), so that on the bases of planed dynamic could give warnings to the users of data base when is necessary to complete some work. This is very important from following and management of whole project point of view. Also, important notice about conditions of completion of some work should be linked with dynamics of performed work from working order.

7 CONCLUSION

The employer has great interest to control all designers and contractors to whom it was entrusted production of technical documentation and highway construction, engineering construction and attached contents.

In this paper, the problem of modelling of data base for designing and highway construction management was discussed.

On the bases of exposed discussions can be proposed following conclusions:

- management of large investment project demands attached informational system, and the reasons are great number of stochastic factors which follows the construction of such major structures, as well as great money investment,
- numerous participants from different geographical localities can use information from data base, by which is improved efficiency of survey service function on distant design office and sites and theirs timely information,
- data base enables providing information based on which the realization of plan is done.
- data base enables usage of singular data.

Formed data base, after the construction of highways can be used for analyses of work effects. It is necessary to analyze work effects and on this bases make useful conclusions for closer and far future, which is almost neglected nowadays.

At the end, with effective usage of data base enables reduction of entropy of management system to the lowest point, reduction of data processing costs with reduction of time for system to answer and contribution to the efficient and timely information of participants in the management process, and all because of obtaining quality and prompt information.

REFERENCES

Alagic, S. 1984. *Relacione baze podataka, Svjetlost*, Sarajevo.
Andjus,V., Maletin, M. 1993. *Metodologija projektovanja puteva,* Gradjevinski fakultet u Beogradu, Beograd

Ivkovic, B., Popovic, 1993. *Faze realizacije investicionog projekta sa stanovista investitora*, Izgradnja br. 6.

Jankovic, M. 1992. *Uvod u informacione sisteme*, Tehnicka knjiga, Beograd.

Klepac, J., 1984. *Organizacija gradjenja*, Gradjevinski fakultet u Zagrebu.

Katanic, J., Andjus, V., Maletin, M., 1983. *Projektovanje puteva*, Gradjevinska knjiga, Beograd.

Knezevic, M., 1999. *Baza podataka kao dio informacionog sistema u organizaciji nadzora na izgradnji autoputeva*, Simpozijum Arandjelovac, 143–148.

4. Cost control and productivity management

A Bayesian approach for updating change order uncertainty

A. Touran
Northeastern University, Boston, Mass., USA

ABSTRACT: In this paper we present a probabilistic method that incorporates uncertainties in project cost based on the expected number of changes and the average cost of change. The model calculates the probability of cost overrun for a given contingency. The value of contingency calculated from the model will depend on the parameter of the Poisson distribution for the arrival of change orders. In other words, knowing the expected number of changes during a project is a deciding factor in calculation of contingency. We propose a Bayesian approach to directly incorporate the uncertainty in the estimate of the Poisson parameter (rate of occurrence of changes in this case) into the analysis. The method developed uses the appropriate conjugate distributions for the prior and posterior distribution of Poisson parameter's mean, and updates the value of the mean every time new data becomes available. The effect of this updating is the reduction of parameter variance and the increase in confidence for parameter estimate. A numerical example is presented that shows method application by using change order cost data from actual projects. The use of Bayesian approach is particularly appropriate because it can allow the systematic incorporation of new data into the existing database and further it can quantify the effect of new data in reducing the uncertainty associated with parameter estimate.

1 BACKGROUND

Owners of most large construction projects consider a reserve budget or contingency to cope with uncertainties during construction. The contingency should be sufficiently large to cover the potential cost overrun, however, the owner does not have a free hand in budgeting a large contingency because of the usual budget constraints and his desire to make the project seem attractive to sponsors or financiers. Contingency modelling and allocation has been the subject of research and various methods of contingency calculation and allocation have been described in several sources (Mak et al. 1998; Ranasinghe 1994; Yeo 1990).

One of the more common methods of budgeting for contingency is to consider a percent of estimated cost, based on previous experience with similar projects. A more detailed approach is to assign various percent contingencies to various parts of the budget. In this approach, the riskier sections of the project may get a higher percentage for contingency. As an example, consider a tunneling project. The contingency level for underground construction activities and tunneling (considered risky and hard to estimate accurately) may be set at 15% while the contingency level for the rest of the project may be established at 5%. Such deterministic approaches will not quantify the degree of

confidence that the contingency will provide against cost overruns.

This paper builds upon previous work by the author (Touran 2003a,b) and presents a methodology for updating contingency estimates based on performance in completed projects. The model incorporates uncertainties in project cost and calculates the contingency based on the level of confidence specified by the owner.

It is assumed that the total adjustment to project cost is the sum of all change orders approved by the owner. This is especially valid in the case of fixed price contracts where every deviation from original project scope has to be documented and executed through change orders. Assume that project change orders arrive according to a Poisson process with a rate of α (for example, average number of change orders per month). The mean and variance of arrivals would then be αT, where T is the original project estimated duration (for example, in months). The Poisson distribution for this rate of arrival of changes is given in Equation 1.

$$P[X = x] = \frac{e^{-\alpha T} (\alpha T)^x}{x!} \quad x = 0,1,2,... \quad (1)$$

where X is the number of change orders. Using this assumption, one can then establish a contingency for budget in such a way to limit the probability of cost overrun to pre-assigned values.

Using the following equation, we can calculate percent contingencies for budget (Touran 2003a). Note that changes are assumed to be identical and independent Gaussian variables.

$$P(O_{ch} \leq \eta) = \sum_{x=0}^{\infty} P[O_{ch} \leq \eta \mid X = x] P[X = x]$$

$$= \sum_{x=0}^{\infty} \Phi \left[\frac{\eta - \frac{x\mu}{C}}{\sqrt{\frac{xf^2\mu^2}{C^2}}} \right] \frac{e^{-\alpha T}(\alpha T)^x}{x!} \tag{2}$$

Equation 2 gives the probability of O_{ch} remaining below any assumed contingency percentage η. O_{ch} is the ratio of total cost of changes divided by the original project cost estimate, C. μ is the mean of a change order cost and f is the coefficient of variation of the change order cost.

One problem with this approach is that the value of contingency will depend on the estimate of α. If α is uncertain, then it will affect the rest of the analysis. A Bayesian approach is presented here that allows explicit treatment of uncertainty in the rate of change orders.

2 MODELLING THE UNCERTAINTY IN α

Because α is an uncertain parameter, we propose to model it as a random variable. This allows us to use a Bayesian approach for the process of analyzing the existing data and updating the parameters as new data becomes available (Ang & Tang 1975; Duckstein et al. 1978; Karaa & Krzysztofowitcz 1984). We assume that α is distributed according to a gamma distribution with parameters v and k (Equations 3–5). This is the prior distribution for the parameter of interest, i.e., mean of α. We choose gamma because gamma and Poisson are conjugate distributions. By selecting a prior distribution that is a conjugate of the underlying distribution (in this case the underlying distribution is the Poisson distribution that models the arrival of change orders), a posterior distribution is obtained that is gamma also (Ang & Tang 1975). Posterior distribution is a distribution that reflects new evidence (or data) describing the random variable and helps to refine our prior estimate of the random variable (in this case the mean of the Poisson distribution). A Bayesian approach allows us to update our information (in this case the value of α), as more information becomes available. Equation 3 gives the general form of the gamma distribution for α.

$$f_A(\alpha) = \frac{v(v\alpha)^{k-1} e^{-v\alpha}}{\Gamma(k)} \tag{3}$$

where v and k are distribution parameters. For the prior distribution, mean and variance are as follows:

$$E_{pri}(\alpha) = \frac{k}{v} \tag{4}$$

$$Var_{pri}(\alpha) = \frac{k}{v^2} \tag{5}$$

It can be proven that the posterior distribution for α is also gamma with the following parameters, where x is the new observed changes and t is the duration in months over which x changes have occurred (Ang & Tang 1975).

$$E_{pos}(\alpha) = \frac{k+x}{v+t} \tag{6}$$

$$Var_{pos}(\alpha) = \frac{k+x}{(v+t)^2} \tag{7}$$

In setting up a system for contingency modelling, the analyst can set goals with respect to the uncertainty of α. As a proposed methodology, one can accept contingency values only if the coefficient of variation (i.e., ratio of standard deviation over mean) for α remains below a certain value, say 0.15. The logic here is that in such cases, variation in α is sufficiently small and the probability of cost under-run (or the sufficiency of contingency) is estimated with acceptable certainty.

3 TYPICAL APPLICATION

We have collected change data from six projects executed by Army Corps of Engineers (Table 1; Touran 2002a). The data shows that the average rate of change per month for these projects is about 1.1 change orders per month (calculated as arithmetic mean of Column 5 in Table 2). Standard deviation of α is calculated as 0.50. Assuming that these values are reasonable estimates, we have

$$E_{pri}(\alpha) = 1.1 \tag{8}$$

$$Var_{pri}(\alpha) = 0.25 \tag{9}$$

Using Equations 4, 5, parameters of prior gamma distribution are calculated as follows:

$$v = 4.4 \tag{10}$$

$$k = 4.84 \tag{11}$$

Using Equation 3, the distribution of α can be obtained (Fig. 1).

3.1 Bayesian updating

Now let us assume that we get data from another project. Assume that in this project the total number of

Table 1.   Summary information on construction projects.

Project Code (1)	Description (2)	Original duration (cd) (3)	Original budget ($) (4)	No. of changes (5)	Cost of changes ($) (6)
DACA51-98-C-0033	Regional finance center	730	4,664,369	37	1,382,721
DACW33-00-C-0014	Concrete repairs	150	139,283	4	71,132
DACW33-95-C-0037	Replace gate system	360	1,127,000	12	172,320
DACW33-97-C-0018	Construct seepage control	730	16,360,130	10	712,761
DACW33-97-C-0019	Meadow brook restoration	120	413,954	7	364,456
DACW33-97-C-0021	Flood damage reduction	730	6,774,400	25	1,159,187

Table 2.   Statistics on change data.

Project Code (1)	Mean of change order ($) (2)	Mean of change as a ratio of original estimate (3)	Cost of changes as a ratio of original est. (4)	Rate of Changer per month (5)
DACA51-98-C-0033	53,400	1.14%	28%	1.5
DACW33-00-C-0014	62,800	45.1%	51%	0.8
DACW33-95-C-0037	21,200	1.9%	15%	1
DACW33-97-C-0018	72,800	0.4%	4%	0.4
DACW33-97-C-0019	52,100	12.5%	88%	1.8
DACW33-97-C-0021	43,000	0.6%	17%	1

changes is 20 for duration of 24 months. In light of this new information, we can calculate the posterior distribution for α using Equations 6, 7, and noting that $x = 20$ and $t = 24$.

$$E_{pos}(\alpha)=0.87 \qquad (12)$$

$$Var_{pos}(\alpha)=0.03 \qquad (13)$$

Using these new values, a posterior distribution can be calculated for α as shown in Figure 1. It is clear that the new information has helped in reducing the variance of α, hence reducing its uncertainty.

3.2   Calculation of contingency

Using Equation 2 probabilities of sufficiency of contingency (cost under-run) is calculated for various values of contingency for prior and posterior values of α. Because α is modelled as a random variable, probabilities calculated are random variables rather than fixed values. The results obtained in Table 3 have been obtained by Monte Carlo simulation (1,000 runs). The coefficient of variation of each probability value is also reported. It can be seen that the effect of the posterior observation has been to update the values of probability and reduce the uncertainty associated with these probabilities. Figure 2 shows this

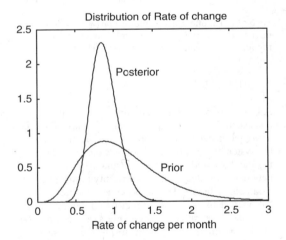

Figure 1.   Distribution of Rate of change and the Bayesian updating procedure.

graphically. By reviewing the results given in Table 3, one can see that the posterior distribution of α for contingencies of 15% and higher is reasonably reliable (small coefficient of variation). If a contingency of less than 15% is used, the effect of uncertainty in α is considerable and the probability of cost overrun will be subject to large uncertainty.

247

Table 3. Probabilities of cost under-run for various contingencies.

Contingency	Prior distribution			Posterior distribution		
	Mean	Std. Dev.	C.o.V.	Mean	Std. Dev.	C.o.V.
0.100	0.393	0.299	0.76	0.502	0.166	0.33
0.125	0.527	0.312	0.59	0.687	0.153	0.22
0.150	0.647	0.300	0.46	0.824	0.118	0.14
0.175	0.745	0.272	0.37	0.910	0.078	0.09
0.200	0.821	0.235	0.29	0.958	0.046	0.05

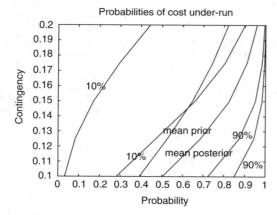

Figure 2. The effect of new information (posterior) on reducing uncertainty in the value of probabilities of cost under-run for various contingency values (simulation 1000 runs).

4 SUMMARY

A Bayesian model for calculating cost contingency in construction projects is presented. The use of Bayesian approach is particularly appropriate because it allows the systematic incorporation of new data into the existing database and further it can quantify the effect of new data in reducing the uncertainty associated with parameter estimate. The proposed methodology allows the analyst to assess the effect of uncertainty in the estimate of the rate of change orders (average number of change orders per month during the construction period). It can be used as a quality control measure in the process of estimating the rate of change orders by providing a system for establishing minimum data requirements from similar projects such that the probability of cost overrun can be calculated with certain reliability. A similar approach can be used to establish minimum data requirements for other critical factors in the original model such as the size of change orders.

REFERENCES

Ang, A.H.S., & Tang, W.H. 1975. *Probability concepts in engineering, planning and design*, Vol. I, John Wiley and Sons, New York.

Duckstein, L., Krzysztofowicz, R. & Davis, D., 1978. To build or not to build: a Bayesian analysis, *Journal of Hydrological Sciences*, Vol. 5, No. 1, 55–68.

Karaa, F. & Krzysztofowicz, R. 1984. Bayesian decision analysis of dam safety, *Applied Mathematics and Computation*, No. 14, 357–380.

Mak, S., Wong, J. & Picken, D. 1998. The effect on contingency allowances of using risk analysis in capital cost estimating: a Hong Kong case study, *Construction Management & Economics*, 16, 615–619.

Ranasinghe, M. 1994. Contingency allocation and management for building projects, *Construction Management & Economics*, 12, 233–243.

Touran, A. 2003a. Probabilistic model for cost contingency, *Construction Engineering and Management*, ASCE, scheduled for publication.

Touran, A. 2003b. Calculation of contingency in construction projects, *Transactions of Engineering Management*, IEEE, scheduled for publication.

Yeo, K.T. 1990. Risks, classification of estimates, and contingency management, *Journal of Management in Engineering*, ASCE, 6(4), 458–470.

System-based Vision for Strategic and Creative Design, Bontempi (ed.)
© *2003 Swets & Zeitlinger, Lisse, ISBN 90 5809 599 1*

Study on the development of the curing system for concrete in construction site

T. Tamura
Tokuyama College of Technology, Tokuyama, Japan

Y. Tominaga, O. Sakamoto, H. Ueno & H. Sumito
Yourin Kensetsu Inc., Tokuyama, Japan

ABSTRACT: This study aims the development of the curing system of the concrete in the construction site. To get the fundamental information, to develop the system that prevents a crack, an experiment was done. The parameters adopted herein are concrete strength, the height of the specimen, the existence of the reinforcing bars, and the structural restraint. Referring to the experimental result, the system that controls the temperature and the humidity analytically was developed. In spite of the change in the circumference temperature of the day and night, the developed curing system controlled concrete stress and strain, and it showed the effects for the actual construction site as well.

1 INTRODUCTION

1.1 Background

Temperature and humidity always changes in any construction site. Also, fever by chemical change occurs in the hardening concrete. Therefore, the hardening concrete is influenced by both inner and outer temperature and humidity.

In case of young age concrete, the problem of the effects of those environmental factors is important because of the small tensile strength of the concrete. Naturally, cracks form into the concrete members if the active stress exceeds the tensile strength of the concrete. Commonly the cracks are the unpleasant character of the concrete, so there are many investigations for the problems of the crack of the concrete.

The cure of concrete is the important countermeasures for those problems in the construction site. This study aims the development of the curing system of the fresh concrete in the construction site. In the experimental study, the relation between temperature change and concrete stress was measured day and night. From the results, it shows clearly that the curing system controls the concrete stress in comparison with the non-cure concrete. The system developed controlled the environmental temperature and humidity of the concrete member for good condition in any time. Finally, the curing system is applied to the practical construction site that constructs a water tank.

1.2 The factor of the crack occurrence

The engineers know that the cause of the concrete crack will be into the nature of the material, the loading condition, the environment condition and the construction technology and so on. Also, in the construction site the cause of the cracks that occurs in the early days is in temperature and the shrinkage mainly. The shrinkage is classified in the self-desiccation shrinkage and the drying shrinkage. Self-contraction occurs by the hydration reaction of the cement, and drying shrinkage is the phenomenon that cement paste shrinks after hardening or during hardening due to the evaporation of the water in the pore of cement gel. Then, if this phenomenon is obstructed some stress occurs in the member and when the stress exceeds the tensile strength of concrete, some cracks will occur. From such a thing, especially, the cure of concrete in the construction site is the very important point, i.e., the control of temperature and the humidity is very important point to prevent a crack.

2 EXPERIMENT

2.1 Fundamental experiment

A fundamental experiment was done to examine the factor of the cracks occurrence before the experiment that a curing system for concrete was used for. Table 1 shows mixture proportions of concrete, and Table 2 shows the parameters of the experiment.

Table 1. Mixture proportions.

Mix				Unit weight (kg/m^3)				
Series	Note	W/C (%)	S/A(%)	Cement	Water	Sand	Gravel	Admixture
No. 1	18-8-20(BB)	65	45.9	256	166	855	1045	4.86
No. 2	18-18-20(BB)	65	49.1	291	189	869	935	5.53
No. 3	27-8-20(BB)	50	42.8	332	166	769	1066	6.31
No. 4	27-18020(BB)	50	45.6	382	191	769	952	7.26

Note: required average strength – slump – maximum size of aggregate.
(BB): type of cement type: portland blast-furnace slag cement.
W/C = water-cement ratio.
S/A = absolute fine aggregate ratio.

Table 2. Parameters of the experiment.

Specimens No.	Mixture Series No.	Cure	Length (mm)	Width (mm)	Height (mm)	Rebar	Restraint
1	No. 2					RC	
2	No. 4					RC	Under
3	No. 2				1,000	C	restraint
4	No. 4					C	
5	No. 1	Non-cure				RC	
6	No. 3				300	RC	Without
7	No. 1		10,000	300		C	restraint
8	No. 3					C	
9						RC	
10						C	
11	No. 4	Normal cure			1,000	RC	Under
12						C	restraint
13		Systematic cure				RC	
14						C	

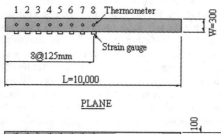

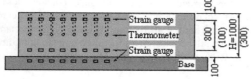

PLANE

ELEVATION

Figure 1. Specimen of the wall structure of the concrete or reinforced concrete.

Figure 1 shows the specimen of the wall structure of the concrete or reinforced concrete. The height of two types specimens are 1 m and 30 cm, respectively.

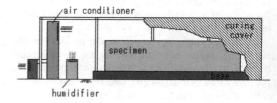

Figure 2. Cure apparatus including the specimen.

In each specimen, the inside temperature is measured at 1/2 of the height. Also, at 16 places of the top of specimen and the bottom, the surface strain is measured at regular intervals after concrete placing. Then, after the form is removed, the cracks conditions on the surface of the specimen are observed.

2.2 *Cure test*

Figure 2 shows the cure apparatus including the specimen. The system is composed of an air conditioner, the humidifier and the curing cover. The cure period is 10 days in accordance with the rule of JSCE.

Photo 1. Cure experiment.

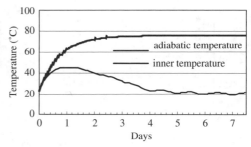

Figure 3. The analyzed amount of rise inner temperature and the adiabatic temperature rise.

Table 3. Q_m and γ.

		$Q_{(t)} = Q_m(1 - e^{-\gamma t})$			
	Temperature	$Q_m = aC + b$		$\gamma = gC + h$	
Types of	of fresh				
cement	concrete	a	b	g	h
BB	23.0 (°C)	0.10	15.0	0.0028	0.245

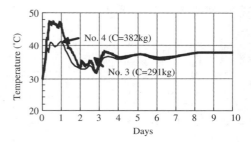

Figure 4. The progress of the temperature of the days (H = 1000 mm).

2.3 Analysis of the concrete temperature

Inner temperature of the specimen is analyzed by the following method in accordance with the process of JSCE. The material properties for the analysis are shown in Table 1.

(a) Adiabatic temperature rise
In the process of concrete hardening, the adiabatic temperature rise is calculated with the following equation.

$$Q_{(t)} = Q_m(1 - e^{-\gamma t}) \qquad (1)$$

Where,
$Q_{(t)}$: Adiabatic temperature rise of one day (°C)
Q_m: A coefficient on the adiabatic temperature rise
γ: A coefficient on a rise in temperature
t: day

Here, the standard value of the coefficient Q_m and γ shown in Table 3.

In the case of specimen No. 4, for example,

$Q_m = 0.10 \times 382.0 + 15.0 = 53.2$,
$\gamma = 0.0028 \times 382.0 + 0.245 = 1.315$.

Therefore,

$Q_{(t)} = 53.2(1 - e^{-1.315t})$.

Based on this numerical value, the inner temperature of the specimen is calculated with the following Syumitt method.

$$T_i = 1/2(T'_{i+1} + T'_{i-1}) + \Delta Q_{(t)} \qquad (2)$$

Where,
T_i = temperature of the point i
T'_{i+1}, T'_{i-1}: Temperature of both side of the point i, at the interval day (Δt) ago

Then, it is calculated that Δt and the width of the division of the structure (Δw) may satisfy the following equation.

$$\alpha \Delta t / (\Delta w)^2 = 1/2 \qquad (3)$$

Here, assuming that w = 0.3 m and thermal diffusivity $\alpha = 0.08 \, m^2$/day, Δt becomes 0.035. The analyzed inner temperature of the specimen and adiabatic temperature are shown in Figure 3.

2.4 Experimental results

About the concrete temperature, the strain on the surface, and the cracks, the results of fundamental and cure experiments are shown as follows.

2.4.1 Concrete inner temperature
Figure 4 shows the relationships between inner temperature and the cure day (H = 1000 mm). Also,

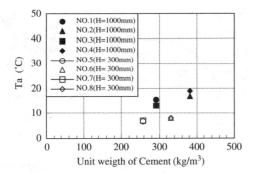

Figure 5. The relationships between inner temperature of specimen and the unit weight of cement.

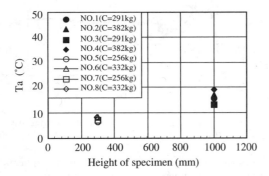

Figure 6. The relationships between inner temperature and the height of the specimen.

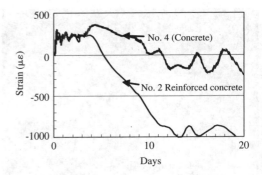

Figure 7. The progress of the strain of the surface of specimen of the days of the concrete specimen or of the reinforced concrete specimen.

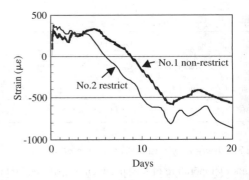

Figure 8. The progress of the strain of the surface of specimen of the days without restraint or of the surface of the strained one.

Figure 5 shows the relationships between inner temperature of specimen and the unit weight of cement. From both figures, it is clear that the inner temperature is high when the concrete includes much amount of cement. Also, Figure 6 shows the relationships between inner temperature and the height of the specimen. The temperature of inner concrete is influenced by the height of the structure, too.

2.4.2 Relationships between the strain and days

(1) Reinforced concrete and non-reinforced concrete
Figure 7 shows the relationships between the progress of the date and strain of the surface of the concrete specimen or of the reinforced concrete specimen. The strain of the surface of the specimen of the reinforced concrete is clearly bigger than the non-reinforced concrete one. In other words it shows the fact that cracks appear easily in the case of specimen of the reinforced concrete.

(2) Influence of restraint
When a structure is restrained, the stress due to the shrinkage of concrete occurs. Figure 8 shows the relationships between the progress of the date and strain of the surface of the specimen under restraint or of the specimen without restraint.

(3) Effects of the proposed curing system
Figure 9 shows the relationships between the progress of the date and strain of the surface of the specimen that used the curing system or covering sheet. Though the specimen was covered in the sheet covers, the strain of the surface reaches $1000\mu\varepsilon$.

However, within the period when a system was used, it goes to about 0 $\mu\varepsilon$ after that though distortion increases on schedule to $400\mu\varepsilon$ first. Furthermore, 10 days later, after the cured period, i.e., after the specimen was taken out from the system the distortion is kept in less than $200\mu\varepsilon$.

2.4.3 The state of the cracks
Typical figures of the cracks are shown in Figure 10. Here, these show the area of half of the length of specimen. The biggest width of the crack that occurred is 0.3 mm. These sketches of the cracks are expressed a little exaggeratedly in Figure 10.

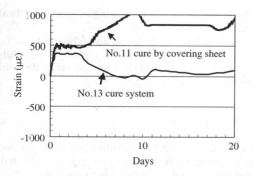

Figure 9. The progress of the strain of the surface of specimen of the days (used the curing system or covering sheet).

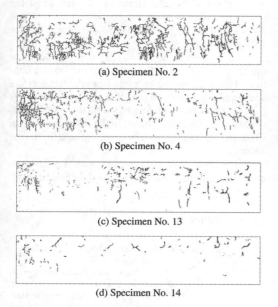

(a) Specimen No. 2

(b) Specimen No. 4

(c) Specimen No. 13

(d) Specimen No. 14

Figure 10. The state of the cracks of the typical specimen.

In the Figure 10, (a) and (b) are without cure of itself, and the condition for a crack is disadvantageous (See the Table 1). Also (c) and (d) are results that applied the curing system to them. It is clear that the system improved the occurrence phenomenon of the crack.

3 PRACTICAL USE OF THE PROPOSED SYSTEM

3.1 *Outline of the construction site*

The practical use of this system was tried in the following construction.

Figure 11 shows the plan of the water tank applied the curing system. Also, a photograph 2 is the state of the actual construction. As for the size of the water

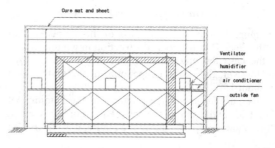

Figure 11. The curing system was applied to the construction of a water tank.

Photo 2. The practical use of the curing system.

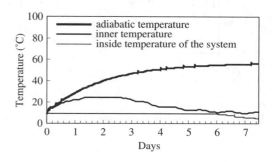

Figure 12. The analyzed amount of rise inner temperature and the adiabatic temperature rise.

tank, width, height, length and the thickness of the wall are 6 m, 4.0 m, 11.5 m, and 0.4 m, respectively. For the curing system the air conditioner and the humidifier used the same machines as the experiment. The season when construction was carried out is winter. Because the construction site was in the mountain, we supplied electric power by oil generator. In the application of the curing system, temperature in the system was controlled as shown in Figure 12.

3.2 Consideration on the practical use

Figure 13 shows the progress of the temperature of the days. Because it is construction in wintertime, by the case the outer temperature was less than 0°C. However, the inside temperature of the system kept about 15°C.

Figure 14 shows the progress of the humidity of outside and inside of the days. The humidity is aimed at maintaining 70%. From the Figure, it is understood that the amount of the change in the humidity is small in the system.

Also, it is clear that the strain of the surface of the concrete is small as shown in Figure 15. Naturally, cracks were hardly found on the surface of the completed structure.

4 CONCLUSIONS

For the development of the curing system for the concrete in the construction site, the experimental study and the practical use of the system was tried.

The behavior of the fresh concrete to hardening was examined in the fundamental experiment. Also, it was confirmed that the strain of the surface of the concrete is depended on the inside temperature that takes an influence by the amount of cement and the size of the structure.

Then, it could be confirmed in the experiment that the curing system was used for that the system controlled the stress of the concrete from the temperature and humidity. Furthermore, the curing system was used for the actual structure based on the result which could get it in the experiment. In the case of the actual structure, the curing system gave high quality to the concrete.

In the future, we will proceed with the development of the curing system controlled automatically.

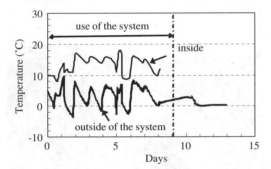

Figure 13.   The progress of the temperature of the days.

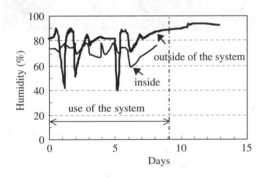

Figure 14.   The progress of the humidity of the days.

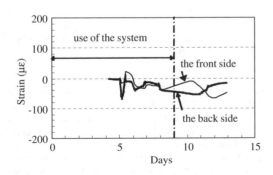

Figure 15.   The relationships between the strain on the surface of the concrete and the progress of the date.

REFERENCES

Allen, R.T.L., Edward, S.C., Shaw, J.D.N. 1993. *The Repair of concrete structure,* Capman & Hall.
Japan Society of Civil Engineers 2002. *Standard Specifications for concrete structure,* (Japanese).
Yosiga, T., Sogou, S. 1996. *The point for good concrete placing.* The Japan Federation of Construction Managing Engineers Association, (Japanese).
Architectural Institute of Japan, 2002. *Recommendation for Practice of Crack Control in Reinforced Concrete Structures (Design and Construction),* (Japanese).
Architectural Institute of Japan, 2000. *Recommendation for Practice of Hot Weather Concreting,* (Japanese).

System-based Vision for Strategic and Creative Design, Bontempi (ed.)
© 2003 Swets & Zeitlinger, Lisse, ISBN 90 5809 599 1

Methodological problems of productivity measurement in the construction industry

J. Iwamatsu
Sato Research Institute, Japan

K. Endo
Dept. of Architecture, Kogakuin University, Japan

ABSTRACT: As the infrastructure of Japan's economy should grow up on the total output of its construction industry, there should be a strong demand for its high productivity so that its national economy could stay healthy. Yet, the construction industry has been generally understood as one field where sizable improvement of the labour productivity can hardly be expected. From a microscopic viewpoint, meanwhile, the Japanese construction industry on its individual production scenes have done fairly well in remarkably boosting the productivity when they endeavored in introducing such management/control tools as prefabrication, mechanization, automation or "robotization" and other technologies. Also, the subject of productivity should be explored differently at each level of the industry. Therefore, it may be said that productivity indices need to be found for productivity measurement suitable at any levels of the construction industry. In this research, existing knowledge of productivity measurement methods have been summarized from a wide perspective. Firstly, existing problems of productivity measurement as being practically used in business or in economical research were analyzed. Secondly, taking up some typical examples of productivity measurement in the construction field, we discuss problems being faced in the actual stage of measurement. Then, it is necessary to distinguish the factor of stagnation of labour productivity; the distinction of "technical problems in measuring productivity", "what should be proper as the method of productivity measurement of the construction industry", "the problem of the industrial structure", etc. Also, we show various indices of productivity measurement that are being used in the actual business. Lastly, we discuss about what the significant productivity indices are for the construction industry and how it should be correctly evaluated.

1 THE BACKGROUND AND PURPOSE/OBJECTIVES OF RESEARCH

1.1 *The background*

In discussing about "Productivity," the inevitable focus is to clarify how it can be boosted up or improved. Generally, it always takes an assumption that productivity improvement should lead to a higher economic livelihood for the people in general. Particularly from the perspective of the entire industrial world, productivity trend in the construction industry seems to be actually being closely watched by other industrial circles, so that it will not serve as a bottleneck on the part of the entire national economy. It is because of the wide realm of the construction industry that inherently deals with the infrastructure essential to many other industrial areas.

However, the construction industry, with its labour-intensive nature, is being considered as an area where productivity improvement efforts cannot easily be made. Even it is so, a considerable amount of improvement efforts seems to be bearing fruits when we look at the first-line activities at individual construction sites.

We should note here that there are various levels of productivity measurement and evaluation, ranging from a microscopic level of measuring "unit productivity in man-hours" (man-hour productivity) or other data from respective construction sites to a higher macroscopic level of evaluation for the entire industrial world.

For instance, "productivity in man-hours" of first-line work-sites can be used to express productivity at a microscopic level. As preliminary forecasting of required amount of labour in observing the construction contract terms, some typical examples of "man-hour productivity" data are being developed according to specific work styles or technical project types. Such data is what the actual data accumulated by the contractors themselves has been standardized. In this process of standardization, the related quantity surveyors have taken the central role in collecting needed data, developing formats of classification, etc.

The data on the macroscopic level of productivity, on the other hand, is being used not only in the in-house historical benchmarking activities but also in such wider scopes as inter-industrial evaluation and international comparison of productivity. The aforementioned macroscopic level of evaluation for the entire industrial world is being made on this level.

It should be added here that individual general contractors, sub-contractors and related supplier-makers have each develop their own methods of productivity evaluation to be used for benchmarking purposes. There are cases where general contractors use the accomplished amount of contract work or project rather than the added value data, as they are related to the business models, methods of cost & profit control. These can be place in between the microscopic and macroscopic levels. Their productivity indexes will be discussed later in this paper.

1.2 The purpose and objectives of research

The main purpose of this research is to study the present state of productivity from a rather macroscopic viewpoint so that a more realistic direction of our present methodology of productivity measurement and evaluation can be predicted.

2 PRODUCTIVITY MEASUREMENT METHODS IN THE CONSTRUCTION INDUSTRY

2.1 Definition of productivity

Historically, productivity research as such can be dated back to the "Post WWI productivity movement" as triggered by the Marshall Plan (the European Recovery Program. In 1951, the Productivity Committee of the European Productivity Agency was formed, which was later absorbed into OECD. In Japan in 1955, the Japan Productivity Center – JPC (now renamed as the Japan Productivity Center for Socio-Economic Development – JPC-SED) was founded as the center of productivity research in Japan.

OECD definition of productivity is "Productivity is the numeral value of produced amount (or output) divided by one of the factors of production." This can be further expressed as follows:

Provided that Equation *Productivity = Output/Input* can be applied, and from the viewpoint of productivity measurement, the following four combinations can be possible, depending on whether its quantity is a numerical quantity or a numerical value:

① Quantity by Quantity

② Monetary Value by Quantity
③ Quantity by Monetary Value
④ Monetary Value by Monetary Value

Here, it can be said that ① and ② are measures of physical productivity and ③ and ④ are those of economic strength (or profitability).

There are a variety of specific definitions of productivity, some typical examples of which are shown below:

Multi-factor productivity
Amount produced/Total amount invested (labour, capital equipment, fuel for power generation, raw materials) – Because of the different units to express these different factors, conversion of stated values is necessary.

Labour productivity
Frequently used factor. Amount produced/Amount of labour input, Amount produced/labour cost. Only the factor of labour among all factors of production is used as the criteria of evaluation.

Capital productivity
Used in reviewing the degree of valid technical use of the invested capital amount. Amount produced/invested amount of tangible fixed assets, Amount produced/number of equipment units operated, Amount produced/number of hours of operation, Amount produced/number of horsepower, etc.

Intermediate inputs productivity
Most meaningful to the management pattern that heavily relies on the raw materials (such as iron & steel industry). If the denominator is amount of energy being used in the production process, this can be called Energy Productivity, and is one of the most up-to-date topics such as "global environment."

2.2 International comparison of construction labour productivity

For the purpose of knowing where Japan's construction labour productivity can be ranked in the international arena, the construction labour productivity by world nations, as easily obtained through the GDP statistics as published by OECD and labour-related KILM data base published by ILO, are graphically shown in the research. Labour productivity, as quoted here, is the product of the construction sector GDP (the total of the figures representing "Housing, Other Construction" from among OECD's GDP statistics) divided by Number of construction workers (the total of male/female labour populations under "Construction" category of the ISIC Industrial Classification by KILM) and further by annual total working hours (the weekly labour working hours by construction workers converted to annual working hours) from KILM's Labour Force Survey by nations), which merely represents a largely macroscopic view of the situation. Evidently,

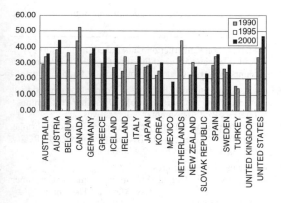

Figure 1. Nominal comparison of construction labour productivity by nations (conversion at current purchasing power prices).

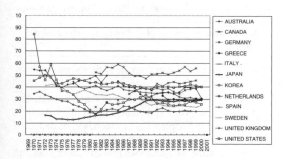

Figure 2. Transition of construction labour productivity in major nations (conversion at 1995 prices).

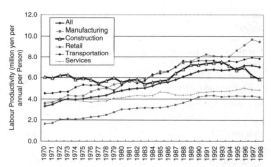

Figure 3. Labour productivity transition by major industry in Japan 1970–1998 (68SNA; Real 1995 price value).

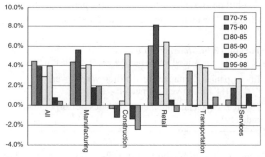

Figure 4. Average annual labour productivity rate by major industry in Japan.

any comparative survey on an international scale would end up with more or less different results as it depends on different rates used in the conversion of monetary data. Figure 1 was based on Average Purchasing Power Parities (PPP) in US Dollars. The unit used in the figure is US$/man-hour.

It can be said that the apparent figurative differences by nations can be traced back to various complicated factors inherent in the national differences such as in the basic built-up structures of respective construction industries. Figure 2 illustrates 30-year trend of labour productivity at 1995 market prices. Circumstantial changes affecting the construction industry in many countries over those years may be seen from the chart, where many countries are experiencing either sideway or declining changes with Japan as an exception as its labour productivity showed a remarkable growth during the 1980s.

2.3 Value-added productivity and related problems

Using Value Added notion to express Output or Amount Produced as the numerator, "Value Added

Productivity" is relatively well used in comparing productivity on an inter-industrial basis. Even in a rather simple comparison of productivity between the construction industry on one hand and all other industries on the other, Value Added Labour Productivity is used, as shown in Figures 3 and 4.

Figure 3 illustrates 30-year trend of Net Value Added Productivity by six major industrial groups and Figure 4 shows their growth rates by every 5 years, both are based on the product of the statistical data of Net Domestic Product by Industries (from SNA or system of national accounts by Cabinet Office of the government) divided by Number of Employees by Industries (from the "Labour Force Survey" by the Ministry of public Management).

These figures tell us that the growth rate of Japanese construction industry is lower than that of manufacturing and some other industries, a similar situation in other major industrialized countries.

Whereas the use of statistical data, as described above, can easily enable us to obtain needed productivity data, there are a few problematic inconsistencies involved, which are stated below in the rest of this chapter.

There are three different ways to calculate productivity or added value for the construction industry,

Table 1. Different formulas to calculate added value per person.

Formula 1 *by Ministry of Land, Infrastructure & Transport (the Construction Industry Information Center)*
– Amount of Construction Work Added Value per Person Engaged in Construction Business:

In companies capitalized at 1-billion yen or over
= 1.727 billion yen per person

(Source: "Management Analysis of Construction Business")

Formula 2 *by Japan Construction Surety Company*
– Amount of Added Value per Person = Total Added Value/Number of Personnel

In companies capitalized at 5-billion yen or over
= 1.063 billion yen per person
In companies capitalized at 1-billion yen up to 5-billion yen = 0.899 billion yen per person

(Source: "Financial Statistical Index for Construction Industry")

Formula 3 *by Ministry of Finance*
– Amount of Added Value per Person (Labour Productivity)

In companies capitalized at 1-billion yen or over
= 1.188 billion yen per person

(Source: Financial Statements Statistics of Corporations by industry)

Table 2. Different statistical definitions of the term "Value Added".

- Statistics on Construction Undertaken (annual survey)
  Added Value = Value of Finished Construction Work minus (Material Cost + Labour Cost + Supplier Cost)

- Financial Statements Statistics of Corporations by industry
  Added Value = Operating Cost (Operating Profit minus Interests Paid · Discounts) + Executives Remunerations + Employees Salary + Employee Fringe Benefit + Interests Paid · Discounts + Property · Realty Leases + Taxes & Other Public Imposts

- Census of Manufactures
  Added Value = Output Value minus Domestic Consumer Taxes minus Amount of Raw Materials Use minus Depreciation Cost

- Input-Output Tables
  Added Value = (Amount of Domestic Products minus Inter-mediate Input) minus Non-housekeeping Expenses

- National Accounts (Quarterly National Income Statistics News: QE & others)
  Added Value = Amount of Output minus Intermediate Input

Note: These are quotations from the statistical publications.

each being published and rather well known. For example (as shown in Table 1), you get three different answers as the amount of Added Value per Person as calculated for Fiscal Year 1999 (which happened to be the latest year when necessary data for the three modes of calculation was made available).

While it can be pointed out that above statistical formulas are applied to different organizational echelons, the problem to be rather noted here is that different definitions of "added value" as an economic term are being used among the users of those statistical formulas, as quoted in Table 2.

This means that nobody has ever clarified what "Value Added" should mean to everybody as a standard expression. A research book on productivity by H. Satomura (1971) argued on the following two points and more on the subject.

1. That Added Value consists of the two contradictory concepts together, that is, the concept of cost (such as wages, interests, rentals) and the concept of profit, and it can take an extreme argument that value added can be made larger even when profit becomes zero.
2. That the term Value Added is being wantonly used by everybody without knowing the definitive differences such as described in Table 2.

Similar contradiction can be seen also in the use of the denominator term "Amount of Labour."

One of the problems that can be pointed out about Value Added, as used in the statistics by the Ministry of Land, Infrastructure & Transport (such as Statistics on Construction Undertaken and some other data), is the way Outside Supplier Cost (which is to be deducted from Value Added) is being treated.

Supplier Cost data includes that of labour cost and that of materials cost. In measuring labour productivity, the labour cost is thought to be a factor that should also be somehow converted to a number of workers to be calculated as part of the denominator. In particular, the ratio of Supplier Cost against Work-completed Value (single construction) is so high at some 70% level, and so is Supplier Cost. Then, this factor should not be ignored in the measurement.

Added to above situation, the vagueness of Value Added definition is leading to wide spreading of ratios, such as in Supplier Cost ratios at 58.7% through 81.0% (up to March 1998) and in Labour Cost at 0.1% through 19.8%).

Another problem here is that Labour Force as used in Labour Productivity Index is treated as homogeneous data. In reality, however, some factors (such as skill levels, work potential and adaptability) are essentially varied by individual workers.

The competent ministry itself has pointed out a problem in this regard in its 1983 report saying that figures of construction workers in their data could be excessively counted mainly due to the fact that many construction workers are listed in plural groups (or under plural employment).

Above observations can lead to a conclusion that labour force figures as used in labour productivity index merely represent abstracted statistical concepts.

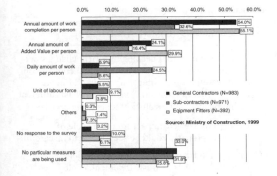

Figure 5. Labour productivity measures as used in the Japanese construction industry.

3 USE OF PRODUCTIVITY INDEX IN THE CONSTRUCTION INDUSTRY

3.1 Productivity indexes being practically used

Figure 5 is the result of a research of Productivity Measures as used in Japanese Construction Firms in three different groups. It is characteristic in that: 1) Gross Output per Person index and Value Added per Person index respectively revealed high percentages in the General Contractor group, and 2) Completed Construction Expenses per Person per Day index showed a high percentage in the Subcontractor group.

Then, A Furusaka/Endo research conducted in 1992 over 8 major general contractors and prefabricated housing products makers extracted 24 different productivity-related indexes, as shown in Table 3.

This table indicates that construction productivity and effectiveness at the major construction firm level mainly take up such measures as related to [completed work expenses], [working floor space], [profit], [schedule] and [cost].

3.2 Classification of productivity measures in the construction industry

As discussed in the above sections, there are a variety of productivity measures being used in the construction industry. Specific objects of productivity analysis relating to construction industry can be largely classified sequentially from microscopic through macroscopic levels.

This discussion is consistent with the 1993 research report by the Japan Federation of Construction Contractors (JFCC) which stated that productivity should not be judged by a single measure but rather generally by plural measures suitable at each of such unit levels as construction work, corporation, business type and the entire construction industry."

In 1999 the Ministry of Construction (now, the Ministry of Land, Infra-structure and Transport), reflecting on the above mentioned problem awareness,

Table 3. Types of measures for project evaluation.

Evaluation measures	No. of Firms
1. Amount of Accomplished Work per Employee	1
2. Amount of Accomplished Work per Engineering Person	4
3. Amount of Accomplished Work per Field Office Person	5
4. Construction Work Space per Employee	1
5. Construction Work Space per Engineering Person	1
6. Construction Work Space per Person	1
7. Number of Field Office Employees per Total Floor Space	1
8. Amount of Accomplished Work per Field Worker	–
9. Construction Work Space per Field Worker	3
10. No. of Field Office Workers per Total Floor Space	2
11. Scheduling Ratio (Ratio of a contract designated schedule against the standard schedule)	3
12. Operating Ratio	1
13. No. of Days as Scheduling Allowance	1
14. Work Combination Ratio	1
15. Design Efficiency	1
16. Quality Capability Index for Major Processes	1
17. Cost Ratio	3
18. Recovery Ratio	5
19. Profit Ratio	8
20. Estimation Efficiency	1
21. Composition Ratio of Project Cost	1
22. Quality Saving Ratio	1
23. Safety Saving Ratio	1
24. Value Added Labour Productivity	–

Source: Furusaka/Endo, 1992.

began reviewing the added value productivity theme only on the subject of "labour productivity." Table 4 summarizes the discussions as have been rendered in their 1999 report and on-going review to look over specific types and characteristics of productivity measures suitable to every phase of construction industry. This table lists up specific examples and their characteristics of productivity measures classified according to each category of comparison (from the entire construction industry down to the first line work sites).

In brief, we should bear in mind that labour productivity cannot be simply taken as an all-purpose term but it must be based on such awareness as which phase of industry is being dealt, what elements consist of the measure, and how it was calculated from what kind of source data.

4 SUMMARY AND FUTURE IMPLICATIONS

This paper first described the general trend of productivity research in the construction industry and

Table 4. Productivity indexes to fit the categories of Japanese construction industry.

Category	Example of productivity index	Notable characters [(O)Merits/(×)Demerit]
Construction Industry as a Whole	Average Annual Labour Productivity	O Suitable not only for checking historical changes but also for inter-industrial and international comparison. × Needs carefulness if comparing among different Industries because the term "value added" has different definition among the statistical tools being used.
Each of Industries & each of Construction groups	Total of Orders Received by Industry divided by total no. of employees	× Historically viewed, impact from the cycle of economic property could be seen. Need to be careful.
	Raw Materials Productivity (Energy Productivity, etc.)	O This is an index easy to perform evaluation from such aspects as waste treatment, ecology, etc.
Each company	Amount of Work Accomplished per Person	O Labour Productivity covering not only construction sites but also the clerical side of the industry can be known.
	Amount of Value Added per Person	× Impact from the cycle of economic prosperity is not avoidable.
Each Work-site	Amount of Physical Labour Productivity ... Yield: Labour Input per Project Construction Unit (or its reciprocal)	O Least vulnerable to the impact from the cycle of economic prosperity. O Reflects better effectiveness being caused by human efforts on work skills and technology.
	Original Unit of Labour Power ... Amount of Labour Input per every 1 million yen of the evaluation of total project cost	O Reflects better effectiveness being caused by human efforts on work skills and technology. × Since this is a comparison based on monetary values, it is vulnerable to the impact of economic prosperity, changes in material prices, etc.

Note: This table is a summary of the Ministry of Construction report, 1999, combined with the additional examples and a "Demerit line" added by the researchers.

various productivity measures that are being practically used elsewhere, then focusing on the productivity measures as practically used in the Japanese construction sector. The main points in these descriptions can be summarized as follows:

- As one aspect of the productivity measure is that the measurement uses some kind of actual data, it is necessary to have a sufficient understanding of the restraints imposed by the data being used and of the specific meanings of the measurement formulas to be used (so as not to be confused by more than one definitions of the term Value Added for one).
- In conducting productivity measurement, it is necessary that appropriate measures and data be selected and modified to suit the purpose of their use.
- There are some negative factors slowing down the construction business, such as technical problems in measurement methods, adequacy of measurement methods as applied in the construction industry, and pending issues in the industrial structure. So, it is necessary that such problems and factors be strictly discerned with each other.

As briefly touched on at the beginning of this paper, there have been cases of some positive improvements in productivity if on such microscopic levels

(work-unit or work-site levels). However, one characteristic of the construction industry is that such first-line improvements have not been perceived on the macroscopic levels (corporate or industry levels). Aside from the construction sites known for their higher productivity as being operated by major construction firms, such a corporate-level unawareness, as mentioned above, seems to be caused by some existing facts about Japanese construction industry, say, 1) the largest portion of construction investment is still being absorbed by medium/small construction firms where their productivity is generally low; 2) even including major corporations, cost control at their management level still remains to be of a budget-allocation type and cost-consciousness in its real meaning is not fully spread; 3) the nature of "build-to-order type industry" where cost competitiveness is not always considered as a merit on the part of both owners and contractors. It can be conclusively said that those abovementioned factors altogether may be contributing to the ambiguity of the real meaning of productivity measurement.

Future implication in our research on this theme should be for us to newly find out more suitable measures based on our findings about existing productivity measures and use more specific data so that productivity can be accurately measured. These efforts will meet the purpose of perceiving the characteristics of our construction industry as compared with other industries, and of using the findings in some sort of analysis within the construction industry. Further, it is hoped that our findings be used in comparing productivity on a global level, as was briefly touched on earlier in this paper.

REFERENCES

Construction Industry Development Foundation, 1995. *A survey Report on the Development of Productivity Measurement Index for Japanese Construction Industry.*

Ministry of Construction – Construction Technology Research Institute, 1962. *Productivity Measurement in the Building Industry*, 1966. Translated with comments from the same title by A. Fjosne & R. Remery.

Ministry of Construction, 1983. *A Survey on the Labour Productivity in the Japanese Construction Industry.*

Ministry of Construction, 1999. *A Research Proposal to Improve Labour Productivity toward an Age of More Elders and Fewer Children.*

Satomura, H. 1971. *Measurement of Productivity*, Toyo Keizai Shinposha.

Japan Federation of Construction Business Entities, 1993. *A Research for Higher Productivity of Japanese Construction Industry.*

Furusaka S. & Kazuyoshi 1992. *A Review of Evaluation Measures of Construction Projects*, in the Architectural Institute of Japan bulletin.

System-based Vision for Strategic and Creative Design, Bontempi (ed.)
© 2003 Swets & Zeitlinger, Lisse, ISBN 90 5809 599 1

An expert system for construction cost indexing and forecasting

M.F. Samara
Department of Civil and Environmental Engineering, California State University-Fullerton, Fullerton, USA

ABSTRACT: Project planners need to forecast the cost of construction for a future project in order to determine its feasibility. There are numerous approaches to performing such a task. This paper presents some of these approaches, and extends their validity by correlating, not only the inflation adjusted construction cost indices, but by generating a geographical correlation between indexed cities. The paper also provides a statistical confidence factor that gives an indication of the percentage prediction error based on the level of correlation between one city's historical price curve with another city's historical price curve. Two approaches are presented. The first approach is an inflation adjusted historical comparison of a project cost to another known project cost. The second approach is a regression analysis that compares project costs at different locations, and different time periods.

1 INTRODUCTION

Project cost estimating and forecasting are the most important aspects of project management. A cost estimate establishes the baseline of the project's cost at different stages of its development. In the planning stages of a project, various estimates reflect the progress of the design. At the very early stage, the estimate is usually made before the facility is designed and must therefore rely on the cost data of similar facilities built in the past. Such data, if available, is usually given in "old" dollars, i.e. not adjusted for inflation. Historical data do not guarantee that future costs will follow the same pattern. Therefore, predictions based on historical data are only a guide to making estimates. Additionally, the methods of correlating past and future cost data can lead to tremendous differences in the estimated costs of future projects.

Traditionally, estimators have used ten-year trends, and manipulated them in various ways to arrive at forecasts. Some take a simple ten-year average of escalation, others eliminate the lowest and the highest two years, and then take the average, and others have used variations, and combinations of these methods. The ultimate result of any prediction of a future occurrence is, at best, a gamble.

2 COST INDEX

Since historical cost data are often used in making cost estimates, it is important to study the trends in price levels over time. The construction cost indices reflect the price-level changes of labor and materials, as well as the changes in the productivity of construction. Construction cost indices are reported periodically in the Engineering News Record (ENR), and other periodicals and reports. ENR cost indices measure the effects of wage rate and material price trends; however, they are not adjusted for changes in productivity, efficiency, or competitive conditions. This Construction Cost Index is based on 200 hours of common labor, plus 1.25 tons of standard structural steel shapes at the mill price, plus 1.128 tons of Portland cement, plus 1,088 board-ft of 2×4 lumber at 20-city price. The base year is 1913(1913 = 100). It should be noted that any other cost historical database may be used.

The indexed cities are: Atlanta, Baltimore, Boston, Chicago, Dallas, Denver, Kansas City, Los Angeles, New York, and Seattle.

3 COST INDEX APPROACH

The traditional approach to utilizing published construction cost data is to take the cost of reference project, multiply that by a simple linear ratio of cost indices, and assume the new value is a good predictor of the cost of the proposed project. A "size multiplier" generally modifies this method. This is represented by the following relationship:

$$C_p = C_r \times \frac{CI_p}{CI_r} \times \left(\frac{S_p}{S_r} \right)^{\alpha} \qquad (1)$$

where,

C_p, C_r are the construction costs for the proposed project, and the reference project, respectively.

CI_p, CI_r are the cost indices for the proposed project, and the reference, project respectively.

S_p, S_r are the size or capacity of the proposed project, and the reference project respectively.

And α is the magnitude of the size exponent. Alpha provides a simple measure of the economy of scale associated with building extra capacity for future growth and system reliability present in the design of the project. The value of α generally varies between 0.5 and 0.9 in the construction industry, and varies by industry sector.

This approach is generally acceptable for getting order of magnitude estimates, or $\pm 30\%$ estimates. The problem reduces to determining the cost index for the proposed project. It is generally dependent on time, location, and type of construction.

4 NET FUTURE VALUE AND CONFIDENCE FACTOR

The investor looks to the possible rate of return from a project against what might be gained if the money were invested elsewhere. Profitability is measured by the *Net Future Value (NFV)*, which is the net return at the end of the planning period. The same concept applies to future costs by considering the rate of inflation in lieu of the rate of return. One can conclude inductively that an original investment P will increase after n periods to the sum S_n, given by:

$$S_n = (1+i)^n \times P \tag{2}$$

where,

n is the period in years,
i is the percentage rate change from the historical data,
S_n is the Net Future Value, or future cost as applicable.

And P is present value of the investment, or the past cost of known similar projects.

The value of i may be obtained from the minimum and maximum value of year-to-year percentage change in the index. This gives the historical range of inflation. Another method is to use a statistical approach to determine the minimum and maximum value within a confidence interval, say, 95% of the population mean (μ), so the range of confidence interval is:

$$P\left[\left(\bar{\chi} - 1.96 \times \frac{\sigma}{\sqrt{n}}\right)\langle\mu\rangle\left(\bar{\chi} + 1.96 \times \frac{\sigma}{\sqrt{n}}\right)\right] = 0.95 \tag{3}$$

Therefore we can get the minimum and maximum value of *i*:

$$i_{min} = \bar{\chi} - 1.96 \times \frac{\sigma}{\sqrt{n}}, \text{ and}$$

$$i_{max} = \bar{\chi} + 1.96 \times \frac{\sigma}{\sqrt{n}} \tag{4}$$

where χ is the mean, σ is the standard deviation and n is the number of data points.

There are several uncertainties in this approach due to the use of one city's historical data to forecast another city's data. However, if we consider the index ratios of the two cities, one can determine the linear correlation coefficient, (r), between them.

$$r = \frac{S_{xy}}{\sqrt{S_{xx} S_{yy}}} \tag{5}$$

where S_{xy} is the covariance, and S_{xx} and S_{yy} are the sample standard deviations for the X and Y axes.

The value of the linear correlation coefficient gives an indication of whether the data for the two cities are linearly related. When the absolute value approaches 1, the data is said to be perfectly correlated. When the data has little or no correlation the value tends to zero. Therefore, when the linear correlation coefficient is stated as a percent, it may be used as an indication of the confidence one has in extending historical data to predict future value.

Example 1:
Determine the confidence factor in comparing a project to be built in Chicago in 1996, with a similar project built in Baltimore in 1990 for $100,000? Assume the project sizes are the same. By using the ratio of the cost indices between the two cities one gets the correlation coefficient r, to be:

$$r = \frac{S_{xy}}{\sqrt{S_{xx} S_{yy}}} = |0.733765| = \mathbf{73.3765\%}$$

This suggests that one may forecast the future construction value in Chicago in 1996 based on the past construction value in Baltimore in 1990 with a confidence factor in the new project forecast of around 73%.

4.1 Predicting of future value by regression equation

To use the old city as a base to predict future costs in the new city, two regressions have to be used to make a comparison. The problem with this approach is that it will introduce two errors for the two values that are produced by the regression equation. One comes from the old city index, the other from the new one. The method used in this study to minimize the error of the regression calculation is to apply the regression to the year-to-year ratio. Using the previous example to illustrate this approach, we find that if C2/C1 is chosen as the y-axis, and Year is the x-axis, we get the slope (a), intercept (b) and correlation factor (r).

$$y\left(\frac{C2}{C1}\right) \quad a\left(\frac{C2}{C1}\right) = \frac{S_{xy}}{S_{xx}} = 0.015111,$$

$$b\left(\frac{C2}{C1}\right) = \frac{1}{n}\left(\sum y - a^* \sum x\right) = 1.291097$$

$$r\left(\frac{C2}{C1}\right) = \frac{S_{xy}}{\sqrt{S_{xx}S_{yy}}} = |0.733765| = 73.3765\%$$

$$= 0.015111\,x + 1.291097$$

where x = (1996-1985+1)

$$y\left(\frac{C2}{C1}\right) = 1.472429$$

Applying the same to Baltimore's data,

$$a\,(CI) = \frac{S_{xy}}{S_{xx}} = 103.0909,$$

$$b\,(CI) = \frac{1}{n}\left(\sum y - a^* \sum x\right) = 3174.4$$

$$r\,(CI) = \frac{S_{xy}}{\sqrt{S_{xx}S_{yy}}} = |0.968989| = 96.8989\%$$

$$y\,(CI) = 103.0909x + 3174.4$$

where x = (1996-1985+1)

$$y\,(CI) = 4411.49$$

$$y = y\left(\frac{C2}{C1}\right) * y(CI) = 1.472429 * 4411.49 = 6496$$

Therefore the index for new location in 1996 is 6496.

Using the old city index correlation coefficient r (C1) as a base, and then using the index ratio correlation coefficient r (C2/C1) a combined confidence factor is obtained. r (C1) * r (C2/C1) = 96.8989% * 73.3765 % = **71.10%** ç Confidence factor.

Accordingly the value of the new project in Chicago in 1996 should be:

$$\$100,000 \quad * \quad \frac{6496}{3884} * \left(\frac{800}{1000}\right)^{0.7} = \$143,055$$

dollars

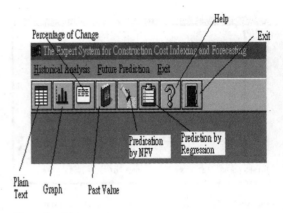

Figure 1.   Main menu.

5   EXPERT SYSTEM FOR CONSTRUCTION COST INDEXING AND FORECASTING

The Expert System (ES) presented is not a true rule based Expert System, it is however a cross between an Expert System and an event driven MS-Windows based application program. It can provide the future cost and confidence factor for a given project based on the data for a similar project. The two projects need not be of the same size or at the same location. By giving the location, time, and size of both construction projects, and the cost of the known project, one can get a forecast of the cost a similar project with some confidence that gives an indication of the percentage prediction error. Two prediction methods are utilized, Net Future Value and Regression Method. This system also includes a historical analysis capability, both numerical and graphical, to study the percentage change of the cost index from year to year at different locations, or within the same location.

The ES has two main menu items as shown in Figure 1, *Historical Analysis*, and *Future Prediction*. A brief discussion of these menu items, and of the corresponding sub-menu items follows.

5.1   *Historical analysis*

This function shows historical data by *Plain Text, Graphical* (Fig. 2), *Percentage Change*, and *Past Value*. The user selects a location from the list of indexed cities. An analysis of the index trends for that city can be viewed. The *Past Value* function is used to compare two different project sites in different years.

5.2   *Future prediction*

This ES will forecast a future cost estimate by one of two methods, *Net Future Value* (Fig. 3), or by *Regression* (Fig. 4).

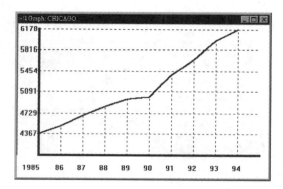

Figure 2. Graphical representation of historical data.

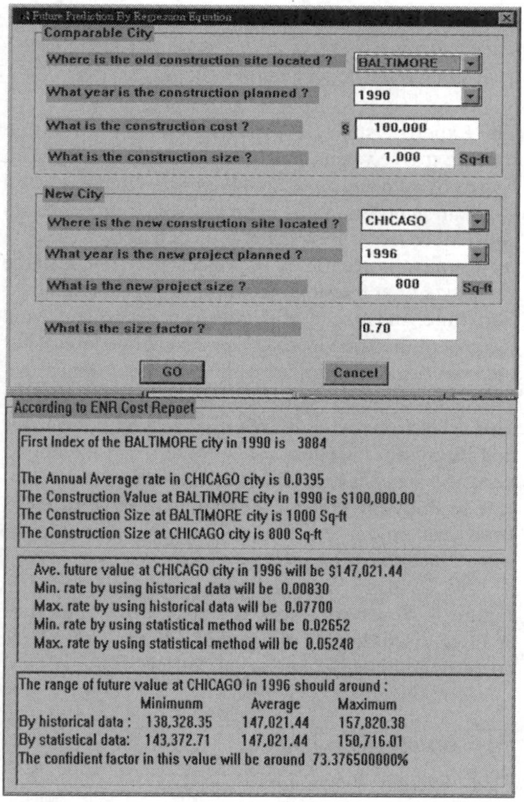

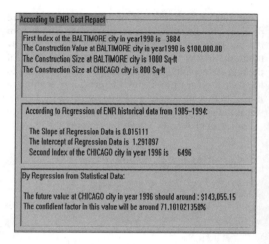

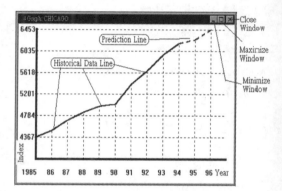

Figure 4. Regression analysis.

Figure 5. Regression analysis graphical representation.

Figure 3. Net Future Value method.

To use the *Net Future Value* method, one simply chooses the old construction location and the year of the old project by using the scroll bar, then input the old construction value, and the size of the project. Next choose the planned location, project size and year. Finally input the Size Exponent Factor. The expert system will calculate the future value of the comparable site. This method also provides the range

of predicted future cost by using the historical data and statistical equation together with the confidence factor for the forecast.

To use the *Regression* method, simply input the old construction location and the year of the planned project, then input the old construction value, and the size of the project. Next input the future location, project size and year. The expert system will calculate the future value of the comparable site by using the Regression equation. This system also provides a confidence factor predicted cost. A graph of the relationship between the past index and regression index is also available when using this method (Fig. 5).

6 CONCLUSION

Basically a simple concept has been molded into a pseudo-Expert System to help an estimator make a

266

prediction of future costs. The results can be viewed via text files, or optionally, via graphic representations. Historical data for the various indexed cities can be viewed and analyzed in a user-friendly graphic interface (GUI) application. Although ENR cost index is the basis of this Expert System, the user can input his own database by simply editing the database file.

REFERENCES

Hendrickson & Au 1989. *Project Management for Construction*, Prentice-Hall, INC.

Diamant & Tumblin 1990. *Construction Cost Estimates*, John Wiley & sons, Inc.

Weiss & Hassett, *Introductory Statistics 3rd Edition,* 1991, Addison-Wesley Co.

ENR, *First Quarterly Cost Report,* March 27, 1995, McGraw-Hill Co.

Pierce & David, *Project Planning and Control for Construction*, 1988, R.S. Means Co.

Driving down construction project labor cost

H.E. Picard
P+A Innovators, Corp., Cincinnati, Ohio, USA

ABSTRACT: Systemic inefficiencies in industrial construction projects can no longer be overlooked in a competitive industry operating at low profit margins. Major opportunity to improve construction productivity is available by gaining quantitative insight in the performance of the construction "production" process. Measurement of the efficiency of the construction work process during project execution provides metrics that differentiate non-value-added and wasted labor hours from productive activity. Continuous statistical monitoring of workforce activity is a useful, complementary management tool to continuously improve construction productivity and drive down costs without affecting quality or safety. Cases that demonstrate the importance of activity-based value analysis of the work process, and resulting significant cost savings are presented.

1 CONSTRUCTION PRODUCTIVITY

1.1 Declining US construction productivity

Challenging economic conditions have construction owners and managers looking for ways to reduce cost. The cheapest solution, however, is not necessarily the most cost effective. But how to tell the difference? Many executives do not trust their project performance measures enough to make confident decisions. Commonly used measurement systems are antiquated – not management tools to improve performance and reduce cost.

In spite of cost control, planning and scheduling, design practices, quality control, pre-fabrication, information technology, craft training and safety – which over the years have been believed by the industry to offer opportunities for productivity (Arditi & Mochtar 2000) – US construction productivity is on the decline (Teicholz 2003).

In fact, construction productivity has been lagging behind the U.S. economy for decades; see Figure 1. Construction labor costs per dollar of investment continue to increase. If construction would have achieved the productivity growth of the overall U.S. economy, labor requirements in 2001 would have been less than half what they were in 1964.

1.2 Importance of the construction work process

It's cliché that, if you don't know you have a problem, you won't solve it. During the execution of construction projects, systemic inefficiencies may go

Sources: U.S. Bur. of Labor Statistics, U.S. Dept. of Commerce, Paul M. Teicholz

Figure 1. US construction productivity trend vs. the economy, as measured in constant contract dollars per field labor hour. ("All Non-Farm Industry" includes Construction).

unnoticed – they are "transparent" to the participants because of their traditional organizational practices and long-standing field habits. Similarly, at the management level, entrenched inefficiencies may not be revealed with the usual performance indicators due to "buffers", embedded in historically based schedule and budget estimates.

As presented in this paper – based on field experience of applying systematic statistical value analysis on hundreds of industrial construction projects over more than two decades – managing and controlling the efficiency of the construction work process can significantly raise construction productivity.

Koskela (1992) pointed to the production-view of construction, which helps explain the possibility of applying inferential statistics to the construction process. Well-known in manufacturing and service industries, the process forms the basis of a management approach using statistical analysis to measure and improve process performance (Deming 1986). Process-based performance improvement includes:

- Measure level and variation of the process
- Identify and eliminate causes of variation
- Raise the level of process performance
- Identify events that could disrupt the process

Factors that cause construction process variability must be identified and constantly minimized. At the same time, the process must be brought to a higher level of productive performance. Any key events that can significantly interfere with the process must be identified, and action taken pro-actively to minimize their impact.

From time to time, productivity of skilled construction workers has been studied by so-called "wrench time" studies – often, regrettably, used in faultfinding rather than problem solving. Nevertheless, systematically applied statistical analysis of workforce utilization as a tool enables managers to steadily lower the amount of labor required on labor-intensive projects by as much as one-third, or more.

The premise is, that a competitive construction work process requires work activity that adds maximum possible value to resources – by converting them efficiently, effectively and safely into a completed project that satisfies the customer.

2 CONSTRUCTION PROCESS MANAGEMENT

2.1 A need for meaningful performance metrics

Among management's usual questions are: are we on schedule, are cost projections being met? Conventional construction management is focused on planning and controlling outcomes, not on the process. Project controls are typically set up to "manage the contract", and ensure schedule and budget expectations are met.

Feedback of results of planning and control is necessary for management to decide whether or not and which corrective action to take. But, alas, basic control data are accounting-based outcome measures that usually arrive too late for viable management action.

Project performance indicators conventionally used to determine performance are ratios of actual results to estimates, such as actual cost vs. budget or progress vs. schedule. But, if out-of-line, such estimate-dependent metrics provide little actionable information about the root causes of problems. A mix of performance drivers or "leading" indicators, such as efficiency, and "lagging", outcome indicators is needed for an improved management system (Kaplan & Norton 1996).

2.2 The "black-box" model construction process

The conventional construction management model emphasizes planning – "to do better, plan better" is often advocated. Consequently, the focus tends to stay too much on the planning process, and not enough on what happens once plans are put into action. No matter how "good" the planning is, construction projects are dynamic and complex with frequent unanticipated events, interferences, and constraints. Actually, the complexity of the execution process is sometimes so great that the production process is implicitly assumed indefinable and dealt with as a "black box" – to not be overwhelmed by its many details, uncertainties, and inefficiencies. Similar to a large construction project, a black-box has these elements: variable inputs, such as the amount of labor, a unique output, i.e., the completed project, and many internal interactions and relationships (Schoderbek, Schoderbek & Kefa-las 1990).

Valuable, new insight in what happens within the dynamic, complex "black-box" process can be obtained by operational monitoring of the efficiency of the work process. The proportion of productive activity, or: productive labor utilization is a useful, activity-based "leading" indicator of efficiency and a (partial) measure of productivity of the work process, as in:

Efficiency = Value Produced/Value Invested in Labor-Hours
= Productively Used Labor-Hours/
Total Labor-Hours = Productive Work Activity/All Activity + Non-activity

2.3 Variability of the construction process

It comes, perhaps, as no surprise that considerable variation in productive activity is not uncommon on a large job site. This variability and average level of productive utilization of the workforce can be measured to characterize the capability of the construction process supplied by a constructor. One of the tools of statistical analysis of the work process is a scatter diagram, which shows the relationship between the average percentage of productive labor utilization and the time of day.

Consider, for example, a Clean Air Act SCR (selective catalytic reduction) construction project at an existing fossil power plant with a workforce of an approximately 350. Productive labor utilization data collected on dayshifts over a period of months are represented in the scatter diagram of Figure 2.

Very high variability of labor utilization around the average or mean value was observed on this project, signifying poor ability to control the work process. The trend line, showing how the average productivity level of the process varies over the course of the shift, is created by regression analysis using basic statistical software. It suggests specific assignable causes, such

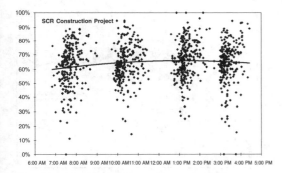

Figure 2. SCR construction process variability and average (trend) level of productive utilization of the overall workforce over the course of dayshifts. (Data points plotted are average workforce utilization measured vs. sampling tour start times. There were 3 breaks, when no data were gathered).

as slow starts due to schedule changes or lack of information, lack of tools, excessive socializing, absenteeism, etc., and slow-downs towards end of shift due to workers leaving work early, e.g., to return tools to central tool storage, or foremen leaving the work areas to fill out time sheets elsewhere. The average productive labor utilization was measured at 64.2%. The standard deviation, a common measure of variability, is calculated at 14.34% for this process (assuming a normal distribution).

2.4 Uncertainty and unpredictability

The uncertainty arising from high variability leads to unpredictability of the construction process, and sometimes risks unpleasant surprises, such as schedule delays and budget overruns. Often, the workforce is assumed at cause, but it is more likely a badly planned or controlled work process that causes below-par performance.

How can uncertainty be reduced? The answer is: through better information. Providing information about process performance reduces uncertainty and variability – one of the techniques of control that makes the system more predictable. The level of productive utilization in the work process must be raised and variability reduced by means of cause-and-effect analysis and corrective action on below-average results (Deming 1986).

2.5 A dynamic process model

The amount of labor hours required to complete tasks is minimized as productive utilization is maximized by eliminating obstacles that cause inefficiencies in the work process.

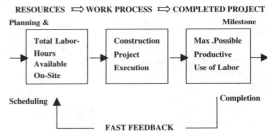

Figure 3. Dynamic feedback system for effective control of project execution by managing the efficiency of the utilization of the workforce.

Fast, dynamic feedback enables management and supervision to flexibly and pro-actively manage and control the efficiency of the work process. The feedback control system in Figure 3 illustrates the idea.

2.6 Implementing the process focus

Implementing this dynamic feedback system requires objective, statistical monitoring of field work activities. Throughout the workday, labor utilization is measured directly by activity sampling of the entire site and workforce. Expressed as percentages, the proportions of value-added productive activity, non-value-added, indirect activity, and lost or wasted time by the workforce are quantified. The percentage of productive utilization is an estimate-independent, real-time measure of productivity for which targets can be set.

The process focus complements the conventional project management approach. Starting in the project-planning phase with thorough analysis of the project scope, the process is planned and designed for efficient execution. To eliminate or minimize productivity constraints in advance as much as possible, optimal workflow and most beneficial site preparation are planned for the various stages of the execution phase.

2.7 Improving process capability

Continual random sampling measurement of workforce activity levels requires a disciplined, standardized procedure (such as described in DCAA Contract Audit Manual 2002). First, baseline labor utilization is measured; next, based on analysis of baseline results, project management sets challenging benchmark targets. Subsequently, daily measurement data are analyzed to determine systemic productivity roadblocks and their root causes. Management then decides on actions to further reduce variability and raise efficiency – there is always opportunity for further improvement in a process.

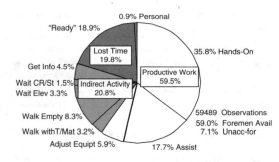

Figure 4. Sample format for daily feedback of labor utilization measurement.

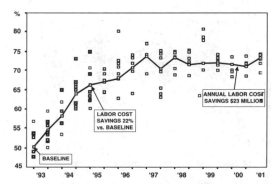

Figure 5. TVA Continuous improvement trend of productive contractor labor utilization percentage, from 1993 to 2001. Data points are averages plotted for measured in-plant construction projects, reported seasonally.

Communicating benchmark targets and feedback of measurement results, raises awareness of the requirements for efficient use of labor-hours at all organizational levels. For example, by widely distributing easy-to-understand daily pie chart reports, similar to the example in Figure 4. With management support, big changes can be introduced with little extra effort.

By allocating labor resources based on real-time, measured labor utilization, such as balancing the size of the workforce with actually available, do-able workload, the workforce will be staffed "lean". Crafts are hired "just-in-time" (JIT) instead of "just-in-case". Lost, wasted labor hours and variability of the work process can be greatly reduced, and the average level of productivity brought up by taking prompt corrective action, e.g., by minimizing non-value-added, indirect work activity, such as excessive "walking", or lost production time, such as "waiting" – activities for which the customer does not want to pay.

The daily labor utilization data enable management to effectively control the process, meet or beat project cost targets and schedules, and mitigate the risk of overruns. As a measure of efficiency, it promotes flexible, pro-active supervision. Foremen learn to work "smarter", ensuring crafts have all needed tools, supplies, information, facilities, and actually workable assignments at all times during work periods.

3 COMPETITIVE CAPABILITY

3.1 Successful construction process improvement

Experience on numerous industrial construction projects shows typical baseline productive utilization varies between 40% and 60%, with an average at about 50%. Work with the Tennessee Valley Authority (TVA) Fossil Group, a major electric power producer, is a representative case study (Seay 2000; Picard & Seay 1996).

As it became evident at TVA that its "partnering" approach of managing outsourced projects (involving some 3000 to 5000 craft workers) was not bringing construction costs down effectively, a strengthening of its performance-based contract with the two major constructors was sought. Implementation of third-party work process measurement and analysis was thus started in the spring of 1993 on in-plant maintenance outage and construction projects. A major feature in the contractual incentive is continuous improvement – continually "raising the bar" of expected, measured productive labor utilization.

3.2 Competitive benchmarks

The trend chart of Figure 5 shows baseline productive labor utilization, measured at several projects, was 50% on average. Subsequent process measurement, analysis and continuous improvement caused ever-increasing labor cost savings. Two years into the program, labor cost savings of 22% compared to baseline costs were generated. Productive labor utilization moved from a baseline of 50% to the 72–73% level, i.e., a 45% productivity improvement.

Our practice at TVA and other major US companies (Picard & Boehm 1996) demonstrates that effectively managed projects can be expected to perform at a 70%–75% level of average productive utilization with variability of 6%–9%, which can be considered a competitive level of capability for the industrial construction process.

In 2000, TVA Fossil Group reported saving $23 million annually in labor costs through construction work process improvement (Seay 2000).

4 SUMMARY

Why should we care about measuring efficiency of the work process? Because reliable and accurate data to support construction project productivity measures are needed. Determining how to measure the efficiency of the construction process is key to the productivity measurement problem.

A fundamental construction productivity problem is that projects customarily apply project control, but little or no systematic attention is given to controlling the "production" process. Project control focuses on project outcomes; process control complements project control by adding focus on efficiency and productivity of execution.

Production management can be seen as integral to the labor-intensive construction process. The process lends itself to helpful statistical analysis. Reduction of variability, and raising the level of performance are signs of an improving construction process.

While planning, estimating and project preparation are indispensable, measuring and analyzing the execution work process provides continuous daily feedback to continuously maximize the efficiency of the construction process.

New management insight can be obtained cost-effectively by objective statistical sampling of work activities in the field – and reduce labor-hour requirements by tracking costs back to work activities. Continuous improvement then minimizes or eliminates non-value-adding activities and wasted labor hours from the work process.

Competitive performance benchmarks for the industrial construction process are suggested.

The opportunity to significantly drive down construction time and cost by improving management of the construction process is real, cost-effective, and readily applicable.

REFERENCES

Arditi, D. & Krishna Mochtar 2000. Trends in productivity improvement in the US construction industry, *Construction Management & Economics*, Vol. 18 No. 1, Jan. pp 15–27.
DCAA 2002. Defense Contract Audit DCAAM 7640; *DCAA Contract Manual*, Vol. 2, January, Appendix 1.
Deming, W. Edwards 1986. *Out of the Crisis.* Cambridge, Massachusetts: MIT.
Kaplan, R.S. & Norton, D.P. 1996. *The Balanced Scorecard.* Boston, Massachusetts: Harvard Bus. School Press.
Koskela, L. 1992. Application of the New Production Philosophy to Construction. *Technical Report 72.* Center for Integrated Facility Engineering, Department of Civil Engineering, Stanford University.
Picard, H.E. & Boehm, R. 1996. Continuous Improvement of Power Plant Outage Cost Effectiveness, *Proc. 27th Annual Symp.,* Project Management Institute, Boston, Massachusetts.
Picard, H.E. & Seay, C.R. 1996. Competitive Advantage through Continuous Outage Improvement. Electric Power Research Institute Fossil Plant Maintenance Conference, Baltimore, Maryland.
Schoderbek, P.P., Schoderbek, C.G. & Kefalas, A.G. 1990. *Management Systems.* Homewood, Illinois: BPI/IRWIN.
Seay, C.R. 2000. Presentation at *Annual Conference of the Construction Industry Institute* re: TVA Fossil Group contractor work process improvement, Austin, Texas. www.construction-institute.org
Teicholz, P. M. 2003. Private communication.

System-based Vision for Strategic and Creative Design, Bontempi (ed.)
© 2003 Swets & Zeitlinger, Lisse, ISBN 90 5809 599 1

Production planning and cost optimization for prestressed concrete alveolar slabs

G. Greco & A. Rago
"P.&A. S.R.L.", Rome, Italy

G. Iaconianni
"Mabo2 Prefabbricati" Supino, Frosinone, Italy

ABSTRACT: With reference to outlines and procedures of design and building process planning inside a precasting plant, it has been analyzed valuation and cost optimization phases tied to the production of a particular precasted element. Important role has been given to the identification of variables necessaries in cost function determination. A calculation model has been proposed for cost optimization; this model has been applied in the comparison between two different technological solutions.

1 METHODS OF PRODUCTION PLANNING

The industrial planning and the management of an order takes up all those activities made to guarantee the realization of the aims fixed on the requests of the client: it can be divided in planning and production techniques.

Based to the ratio between production and disposition requested by the client, a series of production methodologies can be specified:

– Make to stock (MTS): the production orders are normally established on depots capacity.
– Assemble to order (ATO): the assembling of the different parts of the final product starts with the client order, while the different parts are manufactured with MTS methodologies.
– Make to order: the production operations start only after receiving the buyer orders.
– Engineer to order (ETO): production operations and those connected with design start only after having received the orders.
– Manufacture to order (M.T.O.): include both make to order and engineer to order.

Typical activities connected with planning are:

– Interpretation of the product model.
– Selection of useful instruments.
– Supplying determination.
– Expectation of the delivery time.
– Program generation.

Planning of the productive process includes two main phases:

– Analysis phase (study of different solutions);
– Executive phase.

2 PROCESS COST MANAGEMENT

When entering in the acquisition and development phase of a project, it's necessary to use methods for cost estimation and control essential to finish the work, paying attention to be inside the budged fixed on the commercial contract.

The production costs management is a sintex of four different phases of planning:

– Resource's planning;
– Cost's expectation;
– Cost's budget;
– Cost's control.

The planning of the design and of the production resources is connected to the costs of the resources needed for the different activities.

The planning of the resources needs a series of input:

– Work Breakdown Structure: identification processes needs of resources;
– Analysis of historical information;
– Evaluation of objectives and resources available;
– Estimate of the length of the activities needed.

In this way, it's possible to describe and to evaluate the resources necessary to different alternatives.

The resources planning must be strictly coordinated with cost forecast and cost budget.

During cost forecast must be analysed single resources costs necessary to the project.

Subsequently the cost's budget of the project can be prepared, this analyzes costs existing during the time necessary to develop the product, to monitor and measure the project performances.

During the realization phase the cost control must be executed.

3 PRODUCTION OPTIMIZATION AND COSTS REDUCTION

The aim of the manufacturer or of the client, is to obtain a safety and functionally construction, reducing at least the comprehensive costs during the production and utilization time.

The structural project must guarantee the ultimate tensile strength specified in the codes, avoiding collapse with an assigned probability.

Following terms play an important role in the global costs definition of the whole work:

– Investment's costs: planning, design, construction, quality assurance, quality control;
– Operation's costs: transportation, movement, assembly;
– Maintenance's costs: preventive and corrective maintenance.

4 OPTIMIZATION PROCEDURE

The building process of an alveolar slab can be represented as shown in the model on Figure 1, which summarize input and output variables.

The decision-making variables $X_d = \{x_1, x_2 \dots x_j\}^T$ are the project or production variables that can be optimised to minimize costs.

The vector $X_r = \{x_{j+1}, \dots x_k\}^T$ represents structural parameters that are not engineristic variables, but can influence on the failure probability or can represent bounds for the production process.

The vector $X_v = \{x_{k+1}, \dots, x_n\}^T$ is connected with external environmental parameters like temperature,

humidity, wind and snow loads, for whom project data are available, but that aren't under designer or manufacturer control.

The vector called noise $n = \{n_1, \dots n_l\}^T$ represents those parameters not controllable.

Finally, the vector $Y = (y_1, \dots y_m)^T$ is a vector that represent output variables and consider costs and structural behaviour that act as bounds for design.

The output variables Y can be evaluated in terms of X_d and X_r. A random component y_p of vector Y can be written in an approximate way under this shape:

$$y_p = F_p(x_1, \dots x_k) \quad p = 1, 2 \dots, m$$

In the choice of the function F_p it must be done an accurate and careful analysis of the whole process. A second order polynomial formulation can be chosen:

$$y = b_0 + \sum_{i=1}^{k} b_i x_i + \sum_{i=1}^{k} \sum_{l=1}^{k} b_{il} x_i x_l$$

b_i = first order coefficient, b_{il} = second order coefficient.

Costs minimization can be analyzing y function subjected to n bounds necessary to realize a certain performance level:

$$x_i^l \leq x_i \leq x_i^u$$

5 APPLICATION TO THE ALVEOLAR PRESTRESSED CONCRETE SLABS

An example of the cost optimization is presented below referring to the case of the production of an alveolar prestressed concrete slab.

Quantities that influence planning and production costs are:

– Concrete percentage;
– Water-concrete ratio;
– Reinforcement percentage;
– Plate height;
– Steel covering
– Edge distance;
– Methods and techniques for the industrial production.

These quantities constitute the project variables vector:

$$X_d = (x_1, x_2, \dots \dots x_j)^T$$

Some of the defined quantities must be aggregated in a unique project parameter like concrete strength function of concrete percentage, water-concrete ratio, granulometry.

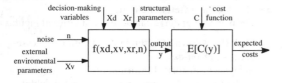

Figure 1. Building process.

Optimization task is searched to minimize production cost; the general scheme proposed for production costs in precasted elements quoted in expression (1):

$$C_T = C_D + C_P + C_C + P_{fs}\, C_{fs} + P_{fu}\, C_{fu} \qquad (1)$$

where:

- C_{fs}, C_{fu} are costs connected to the reaching of the service and ultimate limit state.
- P_{fs}, P_{fu} are the probability to achieve service and ultimate limit state.
- C_D is the design cost and includes payment to architects and structural engineers.
- C_P includes all the internal costs given by production and transportation, formed by fixed and variables costs. The variable cost include plant's workers, cost of parts to buy etc.; these can be estimated like a percentage of variable costs. General costs include capitals depreciation, inventory costs, etc. $C_P = C_m + C_w$; C_m is the materials cost; C_w is the cost connected with the salary of people taking part to the process.
- C_C are building costs. Depending on plate thickness, joint amplitude, concrete price needed for conjunction, based on unitary cost.

For the described costs up to now the sum is defined $y = C_D + C_P + C_C$; it represents the costs of the investments in the plan, it can be approximated with a polynomial model that assumes the following form (2):

$$y = P_1 l_h + P_2 {}^l A_s + P_3 {}^{lh}{}_n R_{ck} + P_4 l\frac{h_n}{R_{ck}} + P_5 l\frac{A_s}{R_{ck}^2} \qquad (2)$$

The definition of the various terms passes through a careful analysis of the production system.

Arranging this function with the other two terms that define the total cost total obtains:

$$C_T = y + P_{fs}C_{fs} + P_{fu}C_{fu}$$

In order to establish levels of acceptable performances for reinforced concrete slabs following limit states are considered (Figure 2):

In defining the optimization different bonds are applied to the project variables, following reasoning of practical type.

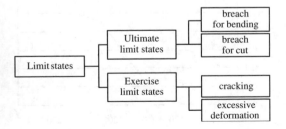

Figure 2. Limit states.

6 COST FUNCTION

At the beginning the function y has been analyzed obtaining some characteristics like the sensitivity coefficients of every member of the polynomial function.

The general shape of the function is (2), where $P_1 \ldots P_5$ indicates the fixed parameters entering in each member of the polynomial function.

The numerical values of these parameters, gained by European indications and referred to a typical precasting plant, are:

$$P_1 = 0.000455\,\frac{\text{\euro}}{m \times mm}\;;\; P_2 = 0.00035\,\frac{\text{\euro}}{m \times mm^2}\;;$$

$$P_3 = 0.00013\,\frac{\text{\euro} \times cm^2}{m \times mm \times kg}\;;\; P_4 = 0.0015\,\frac{\text{\euro} \times Kg}{m \times mm \times cm^2}\;;$$

$$P_5 = 0.012\,\frac{\text{\euro} \times Kg^2}{m \times mm^2 \times cm^4}\;.$$

An increment of 2% is assigned to every parameter (Table 1).

Table 1. Parameters variation.

Parameters variation (2%)	Final value assigned to the parameters
$\Delta P_1 = 0{,}0000091$	$P_1 + \Delta P_1 = 0{,}000464$
$\Delta P_2 = 0{,}0000007$	$P_2 + \Delta P_2 = 3{,}57E-05$
$\Delta P_3 = 0{,}0000026$	$P_3 + \Delta P_3 = 0{,}000133$
$\Delta P_4 = 0{,}00003$	$P_4 + \Delta P_4 = 0{,}00153$
$\Delta P_5 = 0{,}00024$	$P_5 + \Delta P_5 = 0{,}01224$

Obtaining the following sensitivity coefficients (Table 2):

Table 2. Sensitivity coefficients.

Final value of y	Variation of y function	Sensitivity coefficient
$y(P_1 + \Delta P_1 \ldots) = 210{,}5$	$\Delta y = 0{,}029$	$\Delta y/\Delta P_1 = 3200$
$y(\ldots P_2 + \Delta P_2 \ldots) = 210{,}5$	$\Delta y = 0{,}0106$	$\Delta y/\Delta P_2 = 15200$
$y(\ldots P_3 + \Delta P_3 \ldots) = 214{,}7$	$\Delta y = 4{,}16$	$\Delta y/\Delta P_3 = 16E05$
$y(\ldots P_4 + \Delta P_4 \ldots) = 210$	$\Delta y = 0{,}00019$	$\Delta y/\Delta P_4 = 6.4$
$y(\ldots P_5 + \Delta P_5) = 209{,}9$	$\Delta y = 1{,}46E-05$	$\Delta y/\Delta P_5 = 0{,}0608$

The first three parameters have more influence in the calculation of the y function.

Subsequently sensitivity coefficients have been calculated also for the four variables of the cost function following the same procedure.

Initial values:

- $l = 8\,\text{m}$;
- $A_s = 1900\,\text{mm}^2$;

- $h_n = 400\,mm$;
- $R_{ck} = 500\,Kg/cm^2$.

Increased values of the variables:

Table 3. Variables increment.

Variable increment (1%)	Final value assigned to the variable
$\Delta l = 0.008$	$l + \Delta l = 8.008$
$\Delta A_s = 1.9$	$A_s + \Delta A_s = 1901.9$
$\Delta h_n = 0.4$	$h_n + \Delta h_n = 400.4$
$\Delta R_{ck} = 0.5$	$R_{ck} + \Delta R_{ck} = 500.5$

Obtaining:

Table 4. Sensitivity coefficients.

Final value of y function	Variation of y function	Sensitivity coefficient
$(l + \Delta l...) = 210,2$	$\Delta y = 0,21$	$\Delta y/\Delta l = 26,25$
$(...A_s + \Delta A_s...) = 209,99$	$\Delta y = 5.4E-04$	$\Delta y/\Delta A_s = 0,00028$
$(...h_n + \Delta h_n) = 210,21$	$\Delta y = 0,208$	$\Delta y/\Delta h_n = 0,524$
$(...R_{ck} + \Delta R_{ck}) = 210,206$	$\Delta y = 3,216$	$\Delta y/\Delta R_{ck} = 0,416$

Thickness and characteristic resistance are the more sensitive variable of the model, while length is a variable tied to design choice of the precasted building. Tolerance account in the production of slabs has been kept in the final analysis of "y" cost variability.

The used tolerances have been estimated based on the acquired indications from the procedures of manufacturing control of MABO2 plant (Supino Italy, Frosinone).

The following table summarizes the adopted tolerances:

Table 5. Tolerances.

		Tolerance
Slab length	$l = 8\,m$	$t = \pm 10\,mm$
Slab thickness	$h_n = 400\,mm$	$t = +14, -13.4\,mm$
Characteristic resistance	$R_{ck} = 500\,Kg/cm^2$	$t = \pm 20\%$

With the adopted tolerances the ends for the calculation of the y function are gained.

Table 6. Variability limits.

	Max	Min
Slab length l	$8,024\,m$	$7,976\,m$
Slab thickness h_n	$414\,mm$	$386,6\,mm$
R_{ck}	$600\,Kg/cm^2$	$400\,Kg/cm^2$

7 VARIABLES GENERATION

Two different distribution functions have been assigned to every variable, in order to calculate the y function. A triangular and rectangular distribution have been studied, that concurs to confront values obtained with the assumed distributions and to estimate the more reliable one.

The calculation has been executed applying the "Montecarlo" method with the two distribution functions (triangular and uniform).

In conclusion, a number of terms of variable have been generated (l, h_n, R_{ck}) and for each term the correspondent value of the y function has been estimated.

8 CALCULATION OF THE COST FUNCTION

The following diagrams have been obtained generating 10000 random variables and calculating y function values for each term (reported diagrams are relative to triangular distribution).

9 CONVERGENCE OF THE MODEL

In order to analyze the convergence of the model, five cases have been studied, generating 500, 2000, 4000, 7000, 10000 term of values for each distribution function. Average and scrap(s) of investment cost have

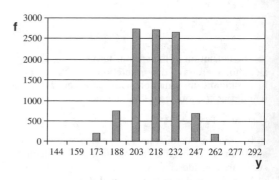

Figure 3. Frequencies diagram of the "y" values.

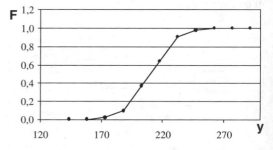

Figure 4. Cumulated probability diagram of "y" values.

278

been calculated with y function (as in the following table 7):

The following diagrams correspond to the Table7 values for triangular distribution function.

Strong variability for a low number of generated variable is noticed, while increasing the number of generations the model converge. In the next phases the number of random variables generated is assumed equal to 10000 and the distribution function used is the triangular one.

10 EFFECT OF REDUCTION OF THE R_{CK} TOLERANCE

In this phase the effect of reduction of the characteristic resistance tolerance has been studied. In order to proceed with analysis the values of the tolerance in the calculation model have been changed, and the various solutions have been confronted; Table 8 reassumes the 4 exanimate cases.

Figures 7 and 8 show the comparison between results obtained with the distribution functions and the cumulated probability functions.

Figures 9 and 10 show the variation of costs average and scrap caused from tolerance reduction.

As it can be noticed increasing the tolerance a reduction of average costs and an increasing of scrap (s) is obtained.

A cost parameter "P_c" has been assumed like meter to estimate formally the economic convenience to activate in the mixing plant the techniques that allow tolerance reduction.

P_c is defined like the costs average weighed with the scrap gained by the model.

Table 7. Convergence analysis.

| | Uniform distribution | | Triangular distribution | |
Number	Costs average	s	Costs average	s
500	208,93	24,35	209,674	14,01
1.000	209,97	24,17	210,212	14,27
2.000	210,216	24,07	210,263	14,31
4.000	209,99	24,18	210,126	14,17
7.000	209,694	24,19	209,989	14,13
10.000	209,754	24,27	209,95	14,25

Table 8. Tolerances reduction.

Case	Tolerance %		Average	s
1	25	−25	209,94	16,4
2	20	−20	209,95	14,25
3	15	−15	209,99	10,81
4	10	−10	210,01	8,1

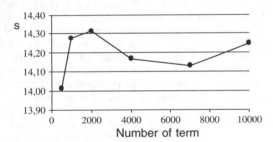

Figure 5. s for triangular distribution.

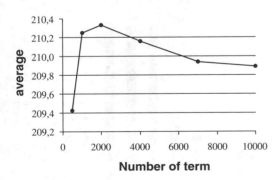

Figure 6. Cost's average in triangular distribution.

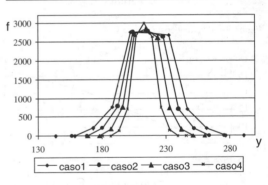

Figure 7. Comparison between the distribution functions.

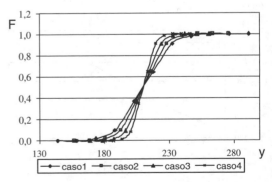

Figure 8. Comparison between the cumulated probabilities.

P_C assumes the following shape:

$$Pc = \frac{\overline{y} \times s}{\overline{s}}$$

where:

- $\overline{y}$ = cost average gained with the model.
- s = scrap (s).
- $\overline{s}$ = scrap average obtained with the four tolerance conditions.

The following course of P_C is obtained with tolerances varying.

From these results can be asserted that the reduction of the tolerance on the characteristic resistance

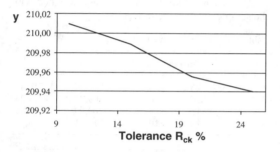

y

Figure 9.   Average costs course.

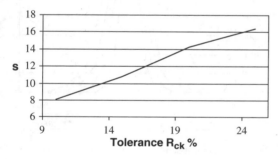

s

Figure 10.   s course.

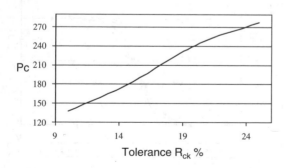

Pc

Figure 11.   Total appraisal of the effect of tolerance reduction.

generates for the precasting plant a lower cost of production of alveolar slab.

11   CASE OF STUDY: COMPARISON BETWEEN VARIOUS ALTERNATIVES

The case of study is the necessity, inside the plant MABO2 PREFABBRICATI of Supino, to catch up a greater concrete productivity level.

The impact that would have the purchase of a new concrete mixing system in the plant must be estimated.

11.1   Model characterization and comparison

Now it is necessary to characterize the calculation model in order to make it join with the productive abilities of the MABO2 plant.

The input is a population of 526 breaking tests at 28 days on the concrete produced by the plant.

Based on acquired input it is possible to proceed with calculation.

Table 9.   Inputs characteristics.

Tests number	Average R_{ck}	Scrap R_{ck} (%)
526	597,8	9,4

Scrap percentage is inserted like input representative of the characteristic resistance tolerance. The distribution found on the 526 tests has been translated in a triangular distribution that approximates it; Figure 12 shows the distribution function supplied by the model.

The next step is to modify the calculation model based on the representatives parameters of the new concrete mixing station, comparing results with previous one.

Values of production tolerance of the new plant have been supplied from the plant engineers based on similar concrete mixing station. Maintaining the same

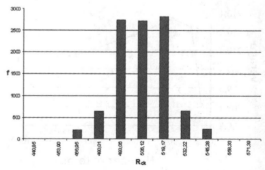

Figure 12.   Frequencies histogram of the input data's.

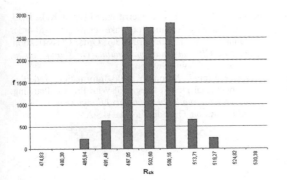

Figure 13. Distribution related with the new concrete mixing plant.

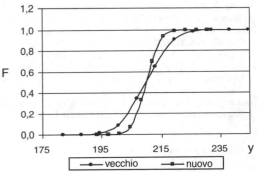

Figure 15. Cumulated probability comparison.

Table 10. Average/s comparison.

Plant	Cost average	s
Old	210,025	7,04
New	210,061	3,72

Table 11. Cost parameter.

Plant	Cost average	s	Pc
Old	210,025	7,035	274.7
New	210,061	3,72	145.3

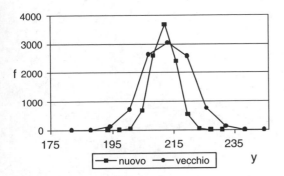

Figure 14. Distribution functions comparison.

design characteristic resistance, a tolerance of 4% has been adopted.

Figure 13 shows the distribution function obtained with this value.

Now it is proceeded to the comparison between the two alternatives.

Table 10 reassumes the values of the scrap and the costs average obtained.

Figures 14 and 15 show the comparison diagrams between distribution functions and cumulated probability.

The cost parameter defined in previous paragraph is taken like indicator for the comparison. In Table 11 is shown the final result of the model application.

The P_c parameter obtained with the old mixing station is considerably greater then the new one; the investment in purchasing the new mixing plant involves an effective economic advantage for producer in terms of production cost reduction.

ACKNOWLEDGEMENTS

Special thanks must be acknowledged to "MABO Prefabbricati" Society (Bibbiena Ar.), to Eng. Bittoni for the availability shown and to the job director of MABO2 plant, (Supino Fr.), for the productive collaboration finalized to the learning of production techniques and to the acquisition of input data's.

REFERENCES

MABO quality control procedure. MABO PREFABBRICATI Society Bibbiena (Ar), Italy.
Greco, G. 2002. Aspetti organizzativi di un impianto di produzione di elementi prefabbricati, con riferimento alla linea dei solai alvelari estrusi in C.A.P. Graduate thesis University of Rome "La Sapienza" Italy. (in italian)
Rago, A. 1999. Analisi probabilistica di strutture intelaiate in C.A./C.A.P. in camp o non lineare. Graduate thesis University of Rome "La Sapienza" Italy. (in italian)
Various authors 2000. A Guide To The Project Management Body Of Knowledge. Project Management Institute. Newton Square, Pennsylvania. U.S.A.
Griffis, F.H. & Farr, J.V. & Morris, M.D. 2000. Construction Planning For Engineers. McGraw-Hill New York. U.S.A.
Businaro, U.L. 1994. Il Progetto E Lo Sviluppo Dei Prodotti. Estalibri. Milano, Italy. (Italian edition)

Alunno Rossetti, V. 1995. "Il Calcestruzzo, Materiali E Tecnologia" McGraw-Hill Libri Italia. Milano, Italy.

Capuana, G. & Della Bella, B. & Della Bella, G. & Ghiottoni, P. & Moranti, P. 1998. *Il Solaio Alveolare Progettazione e Impiego.* ASSAP. Verona, Italy. (Italian edition)

Koskito, O.J. & Ellingwood, B.R. 1997. Reliability-Based Optimization Of Plant Precast Concrete Structures. *Journal of Structural Engineering.*

Ishikawa, K. 1986. Guida Al Controllo Di Qualità. Italian Edition, Franco Angeli Editore. Milano, Italy.

Giebels, M. & Hans, E.W. & Gerritsen, M.P.H. & Kals, H.J.J. 2000. Capacity Planning for Make- or Engineer-to-order Manufacturing: The Importance of Order Classification. *The 33rd CIRP International Seminar On Manufacturing System.* Stockholm, Sweden.

Shaw, C. & Feng, E. & Song, Y. 2000. Information Modelling of Conceptual Design Integrated With Process Planning. *The 2000 International Mechanical Engineering Congress and Exposition.* Orlando, Florida, U.S.A.

Productivity management, improvement and cost reduction

L.H. Forbes
Facilities Planning and Standards, Miami-Dade County Public Schools, Miami, Florida, USA

S.M. Ahmed & M. Hocaoglu
Department of Construction Management, Florida International University, Miami, Florida, USA

S. Azhar
Department of Civil and Environmental Engineering, Florida International University, Miami, Florida, USA

ABSTRACT: The management of productivity in construction is extremely difficult due to the labor intensive and diverse nature of the construction industry. A major obstacle is the issue of skill differentiation among construction workers which makes productivity measurement extremely difficult and uncertain. The objective of this paper is to investigate the factors (including costs) that affect productivity and propose a framework for total productivity measurement. The relationships between motivation, workers' abilities, technology, management and productivity are investigated in through literature review, and are included in a formalized approach that organizations may utilize when embarking on productivity measurement and improvement initiatives. Two case studies are also included in the paper to illustrate the use of the proposed framework for total productivity measurement.

1 INTRODUCTION

The construction industry accounts for a major portion of the Gross National Product of many industrialized nations, hence the levels of productivity that are reflected in that industry have a major impact at a national level. It is worthy of note that as the most heavily industrialized western nations increasingly shift their manufacturing base to countries that have lower wage rates, construction activity is relatively immobile. The sheer mass of typical building elements and the need to install them in place tend to confine most of the process to its final destination; although globalization has increasingly enabled foreign companies to compete for such contracts. The management of construction productivity is a major competitive factor that is not confined by geographic boundaries. Nevertheless, while the manufacturing and service sectors have long benefited from the cost reductions derived from productivity and quality improvement programs, the construction industry has been relatively slow to follow that example. Alfeld (1988) presents the view that construction promises a greater payback for performance improvement than any other industry because of its sheer magnitude.

By definition, *"Productivity is the measure of how well resources are brought together in organizations and utilized for accomplishing a set of goals.*

Productivity reaches the highest level of performance with the least expenditure of resources" (Paul 1978). Mali (1978), combines the terms productivity, effectiveness, and efficiency as follows:

$$\begin{aligned} \text{Productivity} &= \frac{\text{Output obtained}}{\text{Input supplied}} \\ \text{Index} &\\ &= \frac{\text{Performance achieved}}{\text{Resources consumed}} \\ &= \frac{\text{Effectiveness}}{\text{Efficiency}} \end{aligned} \qquad (1)$$

Therefore, productivity is the combination of effectiveness and efficiency. To increase productivity, the ratio(s) mentioned in Equation 1 must increase. This can be achieved by increasing the output, reducing the input or permitting changes in both such that the rate of increase in output is greater than that for input.

An increase in productivity can be achieved in five ways as follows (Gerald 1997):

(i) Reduced costs: $\frac{\text{output at same level}}{\text{input decreasing}}$

(ii) Managed growth: $\frac{\text{output increasing}}{\text{input increasing (slower)}}$

(iii) Reengineering : $\underline{\text{output increasing}}$
input constant

(iv) Paring-down : $\underline{\text{output down}}$
input down (faster)

(v) Effective working: $\underline{\text{output increasing}}$
input decreasing

These strategies often have unintended consequences – Cost reduction usually involves decreasing expenses, services, training, and advertisement. Management generally views people as a direct expense. Unless the respective costs are prioritized against the organization's objectives, this method may result in the wrong identification of cost cutting items and can become more defensive and contraction-oriented.

Growth management may involve an investment which yields a greater return than the cost of investment. It may be in the form of capital, technological improvements, system redesigns, training and/or organizational restructuring.

Increased productivity may also be achieved by reducing the cost of production inputs through a reengineering of the design and production processes.

Paring down means reducing both output and input amounts, with the input diminishing at a higher rate. This "sloughing off" seeks to improve marginally unproductive facilities. If an organization has a number of production facilities that vary in productivity, it would progressively eliminate the use of low-producing facilities.

Working effectively involves a total output increase with a decrease in input. This can be accomplished through a combination of changes in work and management procedures, and through proper training of workers. It also requires the motivation of all involved to "produce more with less", and to perform to high quality standards. Simply producing more may be detrimental to an organization if the increased outputs do not meet the quality expectations of its customers. Crosby (1979) points to the high costs of actions that involve not doing jobs right the first time.

2 TOTAL PRODUCTIVITY

Total productivity is a ratio of output to all inputs. All input resources are factored in this principle. Tracking the productivity changes that occur in different time periods is the most useful application of total productivity (Suite 1996). Sumanth (1984) points the limitations of partial productivity measures, which are measured by the ratio of output to one class of input such as labor productivity. Such measures, if used alone can be misleading, do not have the ability to explain overall cost increases, and tend to shift blame to the wrong areas of management control.

Total productivity (TP) may be defined as:

TP = $\dfrac{\text{Total sales or Value of work}}{\begin{array}{l}\text{Labor Cost }(M_1)\text{ + Materials Cost }(M_2)\text{ +}\\ \text{Machinery Cost }(M_3)\text{ + Money Cost }(M_4)\text{ +}\\ \text{Management Cost }(M_5)\text{ + Technology Cost }(M_6)\end{array}}$

or,

$$TP = \frac{T(s)}{M_1+M_2+M_3+M_4+M_5+M_6} \qquad (2)$$

Since $\quad P_i = \dfrac{T(s)}{M_i}$

$$Pt = \frac{1}{1/P_1+ 1/P_2+ 1/P_3+ 1/P_4+ 1/P_5+ 1/P_6} \qquad (3)$$

The above mentioned factors are expressed as constant dollars (or other currency) for a reference period To increase total productivity, it is necessary to determine which partial productivity factor (P_i) has the greatest short term and long term potential effect on total productivity.

2.1 Seeking for higher productivity

Productivity depends on both employees' performance and technology as shown in Figure 1.

Performance is determined by ability and motivation; ability may be native or it may be acquired through training. In the construction industry, training and experience are major determinants of workers' ability and their resulting performance. Motivation may be intrinsic or extrinsic, but the adversarial nature of most construction projects places the emphasis on extrinsic factors such as incentive pay. Management needs to select appropriate technology and to direct its use to complement and optimize workers' efforts. For example, workers may need to be trained on the use of computerized systems to ensure that they can use them effectively. But management must be actively able to influence the worker's ability, level of motivation and also be able to select and apply technology (Siegel 1994).

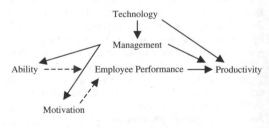

Figure 1. Factors affecting productivity.

3 CONCEPTUAL FRAMEWORK OF ORGANIZATIONAL PRODUCTIVITY

The most important conceptual view of any organization is the aggregation of resources to achieve desirable goals. The different resources and goals, in view of various authors, are as follows:

Resources used (Inputs)	Goals achieved (Outputs)
Monetary	Profit or Loss
Materials	Products
Equipment	Work Completion
Human	Role Behavior
Energy	Services
Space	Capacity

Once these goals are achieved, new goals are set, which may require new resources or a change in existing resources. The organization that experiences a continual series of goal achievement through resource use is a developing organization.

4 SETTING UP A PRODUCTIVITY MEASUREMENT PROGRAM

Productivity measurement is an important component of a construction organization's performance improvement. Deming (1994), advocates the importance of measurement to the PDSA cycle that is used for continuous improvement. The Plan, Do, Study, Act cycle utilizes measurement in the Study phase to gauge accomplishment, and as a basis for further improvements.

A successful productivity measurement program must consider the following.

1. The decision to measure costs and other indicators of performance.
2. The makeup of the measurement task force and its charter.
3. Program information and communication.
4. Inventory of data resources and skills.
5. Auxiliaries: consultants, trainers.
6. The design of the measurement system.
7. Installation and debugging.
8. Instructions for operation and recommendations for evolution.

The application of these procedures is shown in the following case studies.

5 CASE STUDIES

5.1 Case Study 1

In this case study, a *Productivity Linked Incentive Scheme* (PLIS) has been developed for a large engineering company. PLIS provides a methodology to measure the organization's productivity while simultaneously helping to improve it (Sahay 2001).

The main objective of PLIS is to motivate the employees of the organization. The motivation comes individually from each employee's recognition by company through awards, and collectively from increased team spirit among the employees. The following are the principal objectives of the program:

i. to help in identifying improvement opportunities.
ii. to identify gaps between actual performance and established goals.
iii. to provide a measure of performance of the organization as a whole.
iv. to encourage teamwork and human relations.
v. to encourage safe working conditions.
vi. to reduce the cost of production, and promote the improvement of quality and timely completion of work.

The methodology adapted to measure productivity is illustrated in Figure 2. The process starts with establishing organization goals that relate to the external and internal environment, in effect, establishing a strategic plan with vision and mission statements. Appropriate productivity measures must be selected to support corporate goals, and provide meaningful measures of work quality and efficiency.

The selected parameters for this study are as follows:

1. Key output parameters: measure outputs in terms of time and value.
2. Operational Efficiency Parameters: measure the efficiency of resource utilization.
3. Quality Parameters: measure the quality of product and process as perceived by the internal and external customers.
4. Developmental Parameters: measure improvements in systems and procedures.

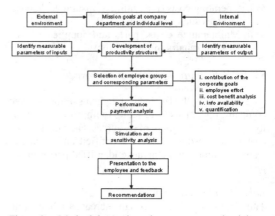

Figure 2. Methodology adapted to measure productivity.

These parameters were grouped into Unit; Department; and Individual levels and weighted according to their contribution to overall productivity.

Total productivity indices were computed as follows:

$$TPI = Wc \times Plc + Wd \times Pld + Wi \times Pli \qquad (4)$$

where

Plc: Productivity index at company level
Plc: Productivity index of individual employee
Wc: Weight for company level – 55%
Wd: Weight for department – 30%
Wi: Weight assigned at individual level – 15%

Productivity values were computed at each organizational level and compared to the values expected from the use of the application of a Management by Objectives model. This approach identified areas of opportunity for improving the productivity of the organization. The PLIS system was effective in monitoring productivity levels and providing improved accountability.

5.2 Case Study 2

This case study was based on a wholesale Marble Tile Company in Miami. The monthly sales and cost data were collected for a year, and total productivity tables were produced to analyze monthly company performance. The resources were evaluated for possible improvement, and suggestions were made to improve total productivity by managing resources.

Numerical values were extracted from the balance sheets and income statements as shown in Table 1.

$$\text{Total Productivity} = \frac{\text{Total Sales T(s)}}{M1+M2+M3+M4} \qquad (5)$$
$$(Pt)$$

where:

M1: Labor costs (salaries, wages)
M2: Material costs (cost of goods including freight)
M3: Operating costs (rent, utilities, insurance, license, services such as garbage, fuel)
M4: Maintenance costs (parts and supplies for the forklift, repairs of the forklift)

5.2.1 Setting up objectives to improve total productivity

After reviewing the financial statements of the selected company, objectives were set up to improve productivity through management of resources. Factors affecting cost items (resources) were identified and strategies were recommended to achieve identified performance goals.

Labor input: (salaries)
The hiring of a new salesman increased labor input, the resulting increase in sales led, in turn, to higher

Table 1. Productivity factor ratios in case study 2.

Months	OUTPUT Total sales	INPUT Materials cost	Labor cost	Operating costs	Maintenance costs	Total all inputs	Productivity factor ratios All inputs	Labor only	Materials only	Operating only
January	$ 187,556.00	$ 74,800.00	$ 14,885.00	$ 13,500.00	$ 1,756.00	$ 104,941.00	1.79	12.60	2.51	13.89
February	$ 243,598.00	$ 84,578.00	$ 17,940.00	$ 13,768.00	$ 1,290.00	$ 117,576.00	2.07	13.58	2.88	17.69
March	$ 147,896.00	$ 65,890.00	$ 17,940.00	$ 12,678.00	$ 557.00	$ 97,065.00	1.52	8.24	2.24	11.67
April	$ 143,567.00	$ 63,567.00	$ 17,940.00	$ 12,567.00	$ 789.00	$ 94,863.00	1.51	8.00	2.26	11.42
May	$ 144,560.00	$ 66,700.00	$ 14,560.00	$ 11,842.00	$ 1,923.00	$ 95,025.00	1.52	9.93	2.17	12.21
June	$ 235,100.00	$ 82,345.00	$ 14,560.00	$ 13,578.00	$ 876.00	$ 111,359.00	2.11	16.15	2.86	17.31
July	$ 151,200.00	$ 69,800.00	$ 10,660.00	$ 12,578.00	$ 1,214.00	$ 94,252.00	1.60	14.18	2.17	12.02
August	$ 112,429.00	$ 52,193.00	$ 10,660.00	$ 12,745.00	$ 1,043.00	$ 76,641.00	1.47	10.55	2.15	8.82
September	$ 115,932.00	$ 55,789.00	$ 10,660.00	$ 12,562.00	$ 1,478.00	$ 80,489.00	1.44	10.88	2.08	9.23
October	$ 146,960.00	$ 63,742.00	$ 10,660.00	$ 11,542.00	$ 825.00	$ 86,769.00	1.69	13.79	2.31	12.73
November	$ 98,490.00	$ 45,428.00	$ 10,660.00	$ 11,674.00	$ 1,149.00	$ 68,911.00	1.43	9.24	2.17	8.44
December	$ 113,786.00	$ 53,400.00	$ 13,220.00	$ 11,600.00	$ 968.00	$ 79,188.00	1.44	8.61	2.13	9.81

productivity. Each salesman worked on a commission basis, finding new accounts to generate additional sales. The showroom was also kept open on weekends in order to reach more homeowners; although overhead costs and salaries increased, the additional sales have compensated for these costs.

Material Input: (cost of goods including freight)
In the Marble industry, it is difficult to respond to increased business and maintain good quality control, because of the law of supply and demand. In the study, as demand increased at the source, prices drifted higher for first-quality material, initially reducing material productivity. However, as customer satisfaction increased with the improved quality, sales increased at a faster rate than overhead costs and productivity increased once again.

Although warehouse capacity was limited, buyers sought to reduce marble costs by agreeing to accept large quantities if the supplier guaranteed prices below the prevailing market conditions. With lower material costs, even with the same level of sales volume, the indices showed an increase in productivity.

On the other hand there are times when inventory may exceed warehouse capacity. Retailers then seek to reduce inventory-holding costs by lowering selling prices and profit margins. Customers typically respond to lower prices with improved sales, and total productivity increases once more.

Operating costs: (utilities, insurance, permits/ licenses, rent, etc.)
Warehouse management directly affects operating costs. With efficient management, unnecessary steps and activities are eliminated, and inefficient systems are replaced with more efficient ones. (e.g., the new manager decided to replace a gasoline-fueled with a more fuel-efficient propane-operated one. As can be seen from Table 1, each resource can be seen to have a different effect.

As the ratio of partial indexes increases, the effect on the level of productivity decreases. Therefore, the first task to reach higher productivity levels should be to focus work on lower ratio indexes, and come up with better productivity results.

6 TRANSITIONING FROM PRODUCTIVITY MEASUREMENT TO PRODUCTIVITY AND QUALITY IMPROVEMENT

The foregoing discussions emphasize the importance of productivity measurement as a component of the greater issue of performance and quality improvement. Construction organizations have a particular challenge to adopt this paradigm. As pointed out by Oglesby et al. (1989), traditional construction project management tools do not address productivity; they include schedule slippages and cost overruns. Forbes & Golomski (2001), observe that the construction industry as a whole measures performance in terms of completion on time, completion within budget, and meeting construction codes.

Code enforcement officials ensure that minimum standards are met for building reinforcement, mechanical and electrical systems that have life-safety implications, but these standards may be met while the quality of finish and workmanship can be below expectations. Owner/client satisfaction is rarely considered under this scenario. Contracts are often awarded on the basis of low bids; most construction activity is subcontracted, and as a whole there has been a tendency to offer minimally acceptable quality in order to be price-competitive.

Construction organizations (designers and constructors) would benefit significantly by establishing formal productivity and quality improvement programs that build on the knowledge gained from the measurement approaches that have been discussed above. This is best accomplished by dedicating a support staff function for one or more individuals certified in productivity and quality improvement techniques, such as industrial engineers or other disciplines that have undertaken relevant studies.

This function should report to top management, and should be versed in the construction process as well as in the use of such tools as Pareto charts, Cause and effect diagrams, activity sampling, time studies, histograms, and stratification. The function should also have experience with facilitating and leading team efforts such as assisting workers with brainstorming to identify process improvement approaches. Top management should empower this function to develop and conduct programs and activities that infuse productivity and quality thinking in the workforce from the lowest to the highest echelons. Productivity and quality reporting should become part of the organization's operating procedures, to the same extent as project progress and financial status reporting. These efforts can only succeed if management sets a clear example for the importance of productivity and quality and, very importantly, the use of measurement information to continuously improve the efficiency and effectiveness of procedures and activities.

7 CONCLUSIONS

The measurement of productivity both quantitatively and qualitatively is vital to the profitability of a construction company. The central task is the systematic collection of data based on measured levels of output of different workers performing similar tasks, across sectors and within a particular sector. This exercise will establish norms or average output rates. On each specific construction project, measurements should be taken and measured rates should be compared with norm rates. Management must keep up with technological innovations worldwide and seek to adapt as well as motivate employees with improved management systems.

To facilitate productivity measurement an improvement, constructors need to develop a culture of "building in" quality, and convey that philosophy to management and workers alike. They should begin to adopt Deming's fourth point "End the practice of awarding business on the basis of price tag alone.

Overall, as has been experienced in the manufacturing and other service industries, top management of all involved organizations – owners, designers, constructors, and construction management companies must be committed to the concept of productivity and quality improvement and must provide necessary funding and staff support to ensure success.

REFERENCES

Crosby, P. 1979. *Quality Is Free*. McGraw Hill Book Company, N.Y.

Deming, W.E. 1994. *The New Economics*. MIT Center for Advanced Engineering Study, MA.

Forbes, L.H., Golomski, W.A. 2001. A Contemporary Approach To Construction Quality Improvement. *The Best on Quality*, Ed. Sinha, M.N., ASQ Quality Press, Milwaukee, WI.

Gerlad, F. 1997. *Building a Strong Economy: The Economics of the Construction Industry*. Sharpe, Inc, MI.

Paul, M. 1978. *Improving Total Productivity*. John Wiley and Sons, NY.

Sahay, B.S. 2001. Productivity linked incentive scheme in a large Indian engineering company: A case study. In *Tenth World Productivity Congress*, India.

Siegel, Irving H. 1994. *Company Productivity Measurement for Improvement*.

Suite, Winston, H.E. 1996. *Measurement of Productivity in the Construction Sector*. Ph.D. thesis, University of the West Indies, Trinidad.

Sumanth, D.J. 1984. *Productivity Engineering and Management*, McGraw Hill, Inc.

Design team characteristics in aerospace, construction and product design for co-located and distributed projects

F.T. Edum-Fotwe & A. Thorpe
Department of Civil & Bldg Engrg, Loughborough University, Leicestershire, UK

M.J. Gregory & P.J. Deasley
Sch. of Ind. & Manuf. Sci., Cranfield University, Bedfordshire, UK

A.B. Wootton, A.N.W. North & R. Cooper
Institute for Social Research, Sch. of Art & Design, University of Salford, Salford, UK

ABSTRACT: Collaboration of physically co-located members making a team often presents considerable challenges. Where members making up the team are geographically remote from each other, this often results in a heightening of the potential challenges associated with such teamwork. Within the aerospace, construction and product design sectors, such teamwork challenges often characterize the design and development of products and infrastructure and the systems that make up or support their processes and operations. This paper provides a background to a current investigation focusing on how to enhance the effectives of engineering and design teams in distributed and virtual work environments. It also addresses teamwork characteristics associated with engineering design teams from three project related sectors with emphasis on *culture*, *project organisation* and *communication* based on a study undertaken to identify factors for enhancing performance of collaborating remote teams.

1 BACKGROUND

1.1 Introduction

The possibilities of remote working through virtual environments made available by IT and other technological solutions equally give rise to new ways of interaction for project teams. Within the aerospace, construction and product design sectors, such teamwork challenges often characterize the design and development of products and infrastructure and the systems that make up or support their processes and operations. The paper first provides a description of the TELEGENESIS project. This serves as a background to a current investigation focusing on how to enhance the effectives of engineering and design teams in distributed and virtual work environments. It also presents teamwork characteristics associated with engineering design teams from three project related sectors with regard to culture, project organization and communication based on a study undertaken to identify factors for enhancing performance of remote collaborating teams. The results from reviewing the teamwork characteristics in remote environments are contrasted

with the characteristics required of co-located teams. The analysis reveals a need for different set of skills to be deployed in working within such virtual and distributed environments. More significantly, it presents a need for a new set of social working rules and etiquette to be developed for designers who operate in such environments. The relevance of these factors to effective delivery of project objectives is highlighted and the significance of these factors to engineering and construction projects is discussed.

1.2 Telegenesis – creating designs from afar

TELEGENESIS is an EPSRC-IMRC project (www.telegenesis.org) that focuses on the characteristics of distributed design teams involved in complex products within aerospace, construction and product design sectors. Its primary object is to explore options and then make recommendations for innovation and improvement in the use of distributed design teams. Figure 1 illustrates the underlying concept of the project and the hierarchies of factors that are implicit on any cross learning that could transpire within the study.

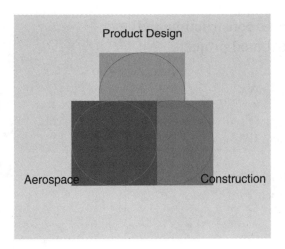

Figure 1. Degrees of cross learning in Telegenesis.

The *Telegenesis* project addresses these challenges through a series of scenarios on how the use of distributed design will evolve into the future, and more significantly how the principle of knowledge transfer can be employed to enhance design processes, practices and function across different sectors (Gregory & Deasley 2002, Edum-Fotwe & Thorpe 2002). The project involves three sectors, selected to ensure that any potential know-how transfers are not of limited application within a bi-sector context. The sectors bring together a diverse set of teamwork and design cultures that is often missed by focusing only on one sector.

2 DESIGN ORGANISATION WORK TRENDS

The intensifying trend in global economic competition has compelled many organisations to pursue a path of exploring all possible options for achieving greater effectiveness and efficiency in their working environment on a continuous basis (Drucker 1994). The availability of current technology and structured administrative systems for improving productivity, which is obtainable by all organisations, therefore shifts the emphasis for the required competitive improvement to the untapped potential of the workforce as the primary distinguishing factor in organisational performance (Cooper et al. 1998). Such a shift gives rise to the following *three* main imperatives for present and future design organisations and the environments in which designers work: namely, collaborative effort driven by high-intensity concurrency, growing emphasis on human skills and competencies, and enhanced corporate role for frontline designers. The relevance of each of the three imperatives for designers is briefly discussed below.

2.1 *Growing collaboration*

Recent workplace innovations of a general nature such as employee involvement and empowerment, has resulted in greater recognition that workers at all levels of the organisation are a significant source of creative thinking (Kotter & Heskett 1992). Consequently, the traditional division of work between *thinking* and *doing* is gradually melding, requiring all workers to become part of an organisation-wide collaboration process (Leimeister et al. 2001). This is because the development of design solutions for projects and products often involve complex processes, activities and resource inputs that demand participatory effort from several stakeholders. This is particularly the case for construction and the aerospace sectors.

The presence of project-oriented consortia and short-term alliances in most design communities often means projects must be carried out using a distributed work arrangement because of stakeholders who may be dispersed in different geographical locations.

On another level, this collaboration will have to be fostered between different organisations that contribute to distributed-teams for the design or manufacture of a specific product (Thompson 1967). This is largely due to the range of specialisation that is required for the design of products in aerospace and construction sectors, and for which it is rather uneconomic for any one company to retain the technical skills and organisational capabilities.

On a third level, similar collaborative effort can be identified within production-chains, value-chains, supply-chains and *design-chains* (Austin et al. 2001). Construction and engineering organisations are increasingly looking to their collaboration efforts to make design engineering more a part of the supply chain by doing away with design as a business-process silo and getting the company's engineers and its suppliers working together. For example many global manufacturers are trying to create an approach to design and manufacturing that can be described in terms of *design anywhere, build anywhere* in order to bring designers closer to the end-users of their products.

These collaborative efforts are often represented within organisations in the form of group-work or teamwork. There is ample evidence that the use of team-based problem solving, innovation, and product development is on the ascendancy and could accelerate to become the standard operating processes in aerospace, manufacturing and construction sectors (Morris et al. 2000). Some of the evidences for this changing trend towards team-based approaches in organising work include the following:

– Growing use of employee teams
– Re-design of workplace systems and physical space to enhance collaboration

- An increase in team-based education at primary, secondary and tertiary levels
- Evolution of team-centered software (e.g. Lotus Notes, Intranets, ERP)
- A re-definition of production away from functional to process models
- A growing awareness of deutero-knowledge as a key organisation asset.

2.2 Technical and human skills or competencies

Traditionally, designers are required to display a demonstrable level of high technical, some administrative, and decision-making abilities in the workplace. This orientation derives from the conventional thought that design engineers will be managed by a design manager who will provide the organisational leadership and where necessary, to control the behaviour of employees in design organisations and environments.

With increased competition many design organisations have had to rethink design management/design worker configurations significantly, as this paradigm of work is being challenged (Galbraith & Lawler 1993). The control mentality is being replaced by a commitment mentality as workers are being asked to take on more responsibility and accountability. Design engineers therefore, have to understand human behaviour and potential, as well as how to engender co-operation and collaboration, and stimulate creativity and innovation. The ability of designers to cope with this added new roles will be driven by the acquisition of requisite social and human skills and competencies to combine with their technical demands.

2.3 Enhanced frontline designer

Within the design environment no other role will be as affected by competition as that of the frontline design worker. As design management ranks thin out, more of the tasks formerly performed by these design managers will move to the front line design worker. These design workers, without day-to-day guidance, will depend more on themselves for direction and resources. They will also need multiple skills to accommodate shifting priorities and needs within the organisation (Thorpe et al. 1998). They will operate more as independent contractors within a team context, moving from team to team as the need arises. This will place a challenge on the design worker to take full responsibility for rapid development and renewal of their skills. Therefore, the design worker of the future will need to understand a full range of technical and administrative skills such as budgeting, planning and scheduling, quality control, performance measurement, vendor and customer interaction, hiring, purchasing, process improvement, problem solving, procedure development, and more. This will go hand in hand with the required authority to ensure that design processes proceed with the minimum redundant time and effort.

3 DESIGN TEAMWORK TECHNOLOGIES

Many design organisations are currently attempting to come to terms with the demands of collaboration in the form of distributed work environments by using group-enabled software products and collaborative strategies. The 1990s saw proprietary groupware packages increase in their usage by large organisations to aid communication and collaboration when operating in a distributed work environment. Currently, non-corporate network-based collaboration models, such as intranets and extranets, have started gaining popularity as alternatives to other proprietary systems. These internet-based alternatives bypass the need for corporate local area networks or wide area networks by using the Internet as their network infrastructure to connect remotely located, collaborating group members.

Equally, the transformation underway in the fields of data sharing and transmission, information processing, and telecommunication technology is opening up new possibilities in the way designers work. The dynamic nature of design processes in construction and aerospace, the interdependence of various participating entities, and the need for teamwork, flexibility, and a high degree of coordination suggest that IT systems should be profitably employed for effective design management in these sectors.

The distinctive features of construction and aerospace projects make the task of design management particularly appropriate for applications of IT tools. Some of these features and the roles IT can play regarding them are discussed below.

- The work atmosphere under which design projects are managed continually changes, requiring exchange of information in different forms. For this reason the design environment needs to be flexible to facilitate communication. IT systems can promote rapid communication, not only through voice media, but also by facilitating transmission of text and graphic information on a real-time basis.
- The design process is based on complex relationships between a variety of individuals, entities, and groups. Processes are often not well defined. The interdependence of process segments can be critical to the success of the whole development of a design solution. Interaction between design team members can be helpful in providing effective leadership and in motivating team members. IT can reduce the need for bureaucracy and hierarchy of interaction and can enhance integration of organisational activities from different corporate establishments.

In theory, the opportunities provided by such technology for collaborative work arrangements should provide a number of advantages, including a reduction in duplication of effort and wastage of resources. In practice, however, these advantages are often not realised due to limitations in current technology. For example Finley & Coleman (1999) provide analysis of a multi-participant, distributed project and identified a number of problems that are likely to be magnified in distributed environments. These include problems in communication, information movement, collaboration, project co-ordination, and management. The continued use of existing technologies will however, ensure their maturation and so influence the way designers undertake their work. Reaching a critical mass of adoption is especially important for design-collaboration software for one major reason: if your partners don't use it, it's a lot less useful to you.

4 COMMONALITY

The explosion of knowledge and information over the past three decades has helped to open up traditional disciplines, which have in the past been limited by the pigeon-hole of defined discipline boundaries. Attendant to this opening up of traditional disciplines has been the recognition of significant overlap in the way work patterns and practices in different professional areas and business sectors reflect considerable commonality in work environments. The establishment of commonalities in work and process practices and activities has fostered opportunities for bringing about considerable improvement in both engineering and commercial operations. For example, within the UK, these opportunities have included the consideration of *Construction as a Manufacturing Process* (CMP), under the public funded programme of *Innovative Manufacturing Initiative* (IMI). This orientation for construction has resulted in projects such as the process protocol (PP and PP2), and other schemes that have attempted to re-configure construction from a process viewpoint, as against the well-known and practiced functional approach. The limitations of the functional approach for organising production activities in construction industry has been given much consideration elsewhere and will therefore not be repeated in this paper (Galbraith & Lawler 1993). The process approach on the other hand offers potential opportunities for achieving a well-integrated production system for construction. A significant number of research projects have focused on the production side of the construction industry and exposed aspects where productivity improvements can be gained from the process approach.

While the design function in most engineering or technology based disciplines is well-appreciated by the designers who work in that domain, the benefits of developing crossover perspectives for designers from different backgrounds has often been hampered by a number of factors. These include:

– A commonly held view that activities of the design process cannot be modelled in the same way as production activities.
– Design concepts and solutions are often considered to be predominantly esoteric in nature. As such a rational approach is deemed to serve as a limitation on innovation and potential solution options.
– The notion that there are no common grounds in the work of designers from different disciplines as the products they generate are entirely different. Such an argument may be valid from the standpoint of a technical solution, but not the processes involved in the development of design solutions. It is essential to bear in mind that similar arguments had been addressed at the production side.

By focusing on the process and not the product it is possible for areas of commonality to be established for design activities in different sectors.

4.1 Design process introspection

Within this paper design is seen not as a single action, but is a translation of ideas into reality through a set of process activities (Cross 1989). The order in which these process activities are undertaken, and the interaction between the various process activities, can affect rate of progress in arriving at the design solution and also, more importantly, the quality of the eventual completed product. Some of the main process activities in design include:

– Requirements
– Analysis
– Concept
– High Level Design
– Design Embodiment
– Prototype
– Testing
– Production
– Maintenance

The traditional view of the design process is as a sequence of processes, where one process must be completed before the next one can be started. These design processes can apply not only to product design, but also to other domains such as software engineering. Within construction, there exists little scope for the prototyping and testing phases although it is known to exist on some major schemes for critical units (for example mock-ups on how a new orientation for integrated bed units within a hospital would fit into the delivery of in-patient services). The main characteristic of the design process is the large number of feedbacks or iterations. Such feedbacks and iterations emphasise considerable interaction and collaboration between individual designers and other participants involved in developing the design solution.

5 DESIGN TEAM INTERACTIVITY

In the recent past, engineers worked in centralized design teams, where individuals working on the same project sat in adjacent cubicles, often described as the *down the hall* work environment. Designers and other team members could easily meet with one another to compare notes, share information, iron-out problems and co-ordinate activities. However, in today's globally distributed product development environment, a company's various divisions and groups are often located around the world. To complicate matters further, critical aspects of product development such as analysis and manufacturing are now typically separated from the design group and are increasingly outsourced. This practice is aptly reflected by the construction sector, where the norm is for one organisation to design the facility and another to build it. It is not unusual for a design company and its partners to be many time zones apart (Thorpe et al. 1998). Situations whereby work on the same design project is undertaken in sequence round the globe to achieve a round-the-clock work regime have been known.

The benefits of the traditional style of collaboration that once occurred in hallways or in offices amongst engineers are being replaced by *virtual* interaction as the demands of time-to-market and the increasing pressure to cut development costs are complicated by greater fragmentation of the product development process. While e-mail, fax, and voicemail are valuable components of the design office environment, these make inadequate substitutes for simultaneous real-time collaboration.

Current technology in the form of *view and mark-up* solutions all claim to be collaborative but what they really provide is only a sequential view and mark-up process. Typically, electronic documents are routed by means of a workflow process to reviewers who view them at the desktop, add comments, and send the comments back to the designer. This is repeated in an iterative cycle until all changes have been processed, agreed upon, and the next revision of the document is signed off and released. This method may take quite some time and the process really involves very little personal collaboration. Many design companies are yet to develop sufficient capability on how to implement this simple *view and mark-up process*. Yet as designs become more complex and innovative products become more important in overcrowded markets, the added value of true collaboration cannot be overemphasised. When teams can easily share ideas

and information and work together in collaborative sessions, the right people make better decisions in a fraction of the time and information about these decisions is immediately available.

5.1 *Distributed design in aerospace*

Within the aerospace sector, the scale of investments required to support new product developments are often beyond the capacity of any one corporate organisation. This necessitates extensive collaboration between several organisations. Morris et al. (2000) identify a growing trend whereby new aircraft design is predominantly undertaken by a distributed team of engineers from different companies and in different countries and often collaborating *virtually*. Figure 2 depicts the nature of integration that such distribution often necessitates. This is presented as a *Core Team* (*CPT*) and a number of task-oriented *macro* teams (TPT) comprising human and information resources. Each task team equally comprises sub-task teams (STPT) as depicted in Figure 3. Morris et al. (2000) discuss the implications of such a structure from the viewpoints of organisation, culture, decision-making, the role of information technology and the interfacing of the various tasks to the overall project management. They need for addressing the human and work environment aspects of these distributed design teams in order for the technical activities associated with the actual design to be delivered efficiently.

5.2 *Distributed design in construction*

Designing a building or facility within the construction sector naturally represents a collaborative effort among

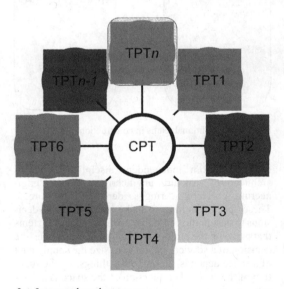

2. Integrated product teams.

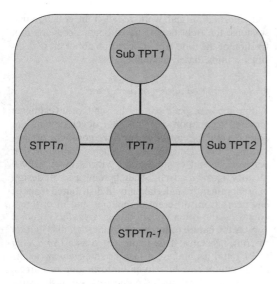

Figure 3.   Typical structure of task teams.

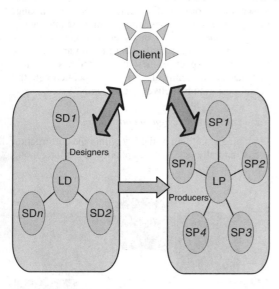

Figure 4.   Traditional teams in construction.

specialists from independent disciplines such as architecture, structure engineering, services engineering, cost engineering as depicted by Figure 4. These specialists have to make interdependent decisions to design the components of the various systems that make up the building or facility. For example, the decision of a services engineer to size the supply duct of a space depends, among other things, on the function of the space. The function of the space is a decision that is taken by another specialist, the architect.

It is not uncommon for these two specialists to be located in different corporate organisations. They thus collaborate in temporarily structured team organisations in a distributed fashion to realise the required design project. Traditionally, physical meetings during which design details are reconciled underpin this arrangement in construction. Designers and design engineers are therefore schooled with the art and know-how for managing in such team environments. In virtual environments, a lot of the skills required for physical meetings, are not directly applicable and different skills and work orientation is demanded.

5.3   Distributed design in product design

Product design is one of the historic roles of the design team within manufacturing and is becoming increasingly important in other sectors. Product design is now seen as an integral part of any manufacturing process and good design is highlighted as an important part of any sales and marketing campaign. While product design remains largely an in-house function in many industries, such as the car industry, the manufacture of consumer products is an area in which *product design* agencies are increasingly being used on a consultancy basis. This means working in harmony with other teams and specialist often in a distributed way.

6   EMERGING DESIGN TEAMS

The emergence of cross-functional teams has outpaced the understanding of how and why they work the way they do. Although cross-functional teams have improved new product processes in many organisations, not all work equally well, nor are all equally collaborative. A recent study of high technology-based industrial organisations showed that collaborative behaviours are difficult to learn, and seldom result from mere membership on teams (Pinto & Pinto 1990). Pinto & Pinto (1990) further opine that some teams consisting of representatives from R&D, production, marketing, and other functional groups transform and adopt collaborative behaviours and accelerate new product development processes. Issues of inter-personal interaction and committing to a common agenda present a daunting challenge to others.

The past ten years of furore over work teams have left managers and design professionals in a difficult situation. The need for and usefulness of teamwork (at least in certain process tasks including the design function) is clearly appreciated. But while the demands for high performance teams continue to increase, the ability to create and sustain them appears to have reached a peak (Perkins 1993; Varner & Beamer 1995).

Cross-functional teams, reflects distributed design environments, have emerged as a popular structural mechanism for managing new product initiatives in high-technology firms. It is argued that they hold the potential for better integration of diverse skills that exist in production, marketing, and other functional groups, required for new product development processes. According to Griffin & Hauser (1992), and Burgoon et al. (1995), building collaborative teams, even among highly qualified and technically people, is challenging because it requires participants to shed dated views, unlearn old habits, develop new theories of action, and adopt new behaviours. The rationale is that people thrown together into teams no more become collaborative in the short term than technology-driven firms become customer-focused overnight. As such ensuring that the collective capabilities of people across the organisation or in distributed teams are reflected in newly developed products will continue to represent a principal challenge to design teams.

The nature of learning that occurs and the development that characterise the process by which groups of individuals transform into collaborative new product teams are often context based (Gupta & Govindarajan 1991). However, there are generic issues from different sectors that can provide lessons and benchmarks for improving the design process and its management, as well as the environment and nature of work designers have to confront. These generic features are best captured through a commonality analysis.

7 CROSS SECTOR COMMONALITIES

The cross sector commonality analysis investigates different characteristics that reflect in design processes and the work environment of design teams in aerospace, construction sectors and product design. As an exploratory study, it is essential that basis for identifying such commonalities and their level of relevance is adequately structured to ensure that there is sufficient alignment in the outcome of the analysis.

7.1 Research approach and method of analysis

The research is conducted in close collaboration with industrial partners and is supported by the EPSRC-IMRC in the UK. The research agenda is driven by a steering group of practitioners and academics. The generic method for identifying and analysing commonalities adopted for the project is the *prioritisation matrix* (Edum-Fotwe et.al. 2002). The matrix approach is a technique that lies at the heart of many QFD methods. The technique is well established and interested readers are referred to other sources that provide a more comprehensive coverage (Checkland 1981; Cross 1989; Brassard 1994). The prioritisation matrix should allow team members in design environments to collectively define common options using a systematic approach to

Table 1(a–d). List of first and second order issues for analysis.

First order issue	Second order issue
(a) Type of tools	
(b) Team working	
Processes & activities	Design-related
	Organisation-related
Team characteristics	Type
	Culture and environment
	Selection criteria
	Nature of interaction
	Leadership
	Management
	Team skill development
	Performance assessment
	Team workplace and space
Core design teams	
Task design teams	
Supporting team	
(c) Info mgt & ICT	
Communication	
Information usage	
Data Management	
Tools	
(d) Working Medium	
Design medium	
General productivity medium	
Information generation & consumption	
Format of electronic documents	
Corporate IT system	
Other corporate IT facilities	

compare choices. This is achieved by selecting, weighting and applying a set of defined criteria to listed issues that are reflected in the design environment and processes.

7.2 Early indications

Early returns from the analysis provided the following factors, which have been organized into four broad areas.

7.2.1 Technology related

- 3D modelling
- Designing in 3D
- Interoperability issues
- Technology integration
- Push-pull approach to deploying IT tools for design
- Tools to support currently neglected aspects of design (conceptual design)

- IT as a design medium rather than a support tool for design
- Telematics.

7.2.2 Organisation related

- Flat organisations
- Team working
- Disappearance of command and control
- Distributed and virtual working
- Mobile and tele-working
- Virtual design organisations and networks.

7.2.3 People related

- Managerial skills
- IT skills
- Cyber social skills
- Multi-tasking.

7.2.4 Process related

- Integration across the design process chain
- A change in focus from the still dominant function approach to a process one for managing projects.
- The deployment of appropriate planning tools and standards to cover the conceptual phases of the design process
- Development of process management protocols for implementing projects in virtual/ distributed environments.

8 DISCUSSION

The use of distributed design teams is a well accepted principle for complex engineering systems producers where advantages accruing from concurrency can be realised, and also to overcome the impracticalities of co-location for large multi-functional or multi-organisational or in some cases multi-national teams. This approach to design is typified in the aerospace sector. The construction sector is more fragmented and dominated by complex, and a multiplicity of contractual arrangements. This feature of construction has often mitigated against the full exploitation of the principles and protocols required for operating in distributed environments. The use of dispersed, cross-functional development teams – typified by distributed design teams – involves a wide range of business, technical, social and knowledge-based challenges in the dispersed work. Understanding and appreciating these challenges are fundamental to the competitiveness of distributed design organisations.

Working in a distributed way presents a shift that gives rise to three main imperatives for present and future design organisations and the environments in which designers work. These are:

- collaborative effort driven by high-intensity concurrency,
- growing emphasis on human skills and competencies, and
- enhanced corporate role for frontline designers.

9 SUMMARY

This paper has focused on aspects that pertain to the way design teams will have to be organized in order to address the challenges presented in today's industry. Among these challenges is the influence of ICT tools in fostering a shift in the way designers will work into the future. Whilst their current skills would still be relevant in the emerging work environment, additional skills and know-how become apparent. These additional skills are predominantly human and social oriented. The paper has explored how technology is influencing the design environment of distributed teams including the use of groupware and extranet-based collaborative workspaces to aid designers operate in multi-participant, distributed projects. It explored a number of functionality issues involved in such a workspace and introduced an analytical framework for generating commonality factors from two sectors that could serve as support information for productivity improvement of designers who operate in such distributed environments. It has through a systematic prioritisation identified several factors that have significance for the team characteristic of designers in a changing industry environment.

REFERENCES

Austin, S.A., Baldwin, A., Hammond, J., Murray, M., Root, D., Thomson, D. & Thorpe, A. 2001. *Design Chains: a handbook for Integrated Collaborative Design*, Thomas Telford, London.

Brassard, M. 1994. *The Memory Jogger: A Pocket Guide for Continuous Improvement and Effective Planning*, GOAL/ QPC, Methuen, MA.

Burgoon, M., Hunsaker, G., & Dawson, E.J. 1995. *Human communication*, Sage Publications, Thousand Oaks, Calif.

Checkland, P., 1981. *Systems Thinking, Systems Practice*, Wiley, NY.

Cooper, R., Kagiogloul, M., Aouad, G., Hinks, J., Sexton M. & Sheath, D. 1998. The development of a generic design and construction process. *European Conference, Product Data Technology (PDT)*, Building Research Establishment, March, Watford, UK.

Cross, N. 1989. *Engineering Design Methods*, Wiley, Great Britain.

Drucker, P. 1994. The theory of business. *Harvard Business Review*, September/October, pp. 95–104.

Edum-Fotwe, F.T., Gregory, M.J., Thorpe, A., Cooper, R. & Deasley, P.J. 2002. Managing Distributed Design Teams and Processes: A Cross-Sector Study of Construction and Aerospace. In: Greenwood, D. (ed.) *Proceedings of the 18th Annual Conference of the Association of Researchers in Construction Management,* University of Northumbria, Newcastle, 2nd–4th September, pp. 87–98.

Edum-Fotwe, F.T. & Thorpe, A. 2002. *Current Practices and Future Directions in Design within the Construction Sector: General Considerations and Industry Perspectives,* July, T1 Construction Report No. E/IMRC/T1R-C/02/1, IMRC, Lough. University.

Finley, D.B. & Coleman, D.J. 1999. Introducing groupware to distributed geomatics production environments. *Journal of Surveying Engineering,* **125**(1), pp. 1–16.

Galbraith, J.R. & Lawler, E.E. 1993. *Organizing for the future: The new logic for managing complex organisations,* Jossey-Bass, San Francisco.

Gregory, M.J. & Deasley, P.J. (ed.) 2002. *Distributed Design Issues in the Aerospace, Construction and Product Design Sectors: Global Review,* August, T1 Report No. E/IMRC/T1R-G/02/1A, IMRC, Cranfield University.

Griffin, A. & Hauser, J.R. 1992. Patterns of communication among marketing, engineering and manufacturing – A comparison between two new project teams. *J. Mgmt. Sci.,* **18**(3), pp. 360–373.

Gupta, A.K. & Govindarajan, V. 1991. Knowledge flows and the structure of control within multinational corporations. *Academy of Management Review,* **16**(4), pp. 768–792.

Kotter, J.P. & Heskett, J.L. 1992. *Corporate culture and performance,* The Free Press, NY.

Leimeister, J.M., Weigle, J. & Kremar, H. 2001. Efficiency of virtual organisations: the case of AGI. *Electronic Journal of Organisational Virtualness,* **3**(3), pp. 13–36.

Morris, A.J., Syamsudin, H., Fielding, J.P., Guenov, M., Payne, K.H., Deasley, P.J., Evans, S., & Thorne, J. 2000. MACRO – A tool to support distributed MDO. In: *International Conference of Multi-disciplinary Optimisation,* Long Beach, CA, pp.

Perkins, D.N. 1993. Person-plus: A distributed view of thinking and learning. In G. Salomon (ed.), *Distributed cognitions,* pp. 88–110, New York: Cambridge University Press.

Pinto, M.B. & Pinto, J.K. 1990. Project team communication and cross-functional cooperation in new program development. *Journal of Product Innovation and Management,* **7**(3), pp. 200–212.

Thompson, J.D. 1967. *Organisations in Action – Social Science Bases of Administrative Theory,* New York.

Thorpe, A., Edum-Fotwe, F.T. & Mead, S. 1998. Managing construction projects within emerging information-driven business environments. In: Fahlstedt, K. (ed.), *Construction and the Environment, Proceedings of the CIB World Congress, Symposium D: Managing for Sustainability- Endurance Through Change,* 7–12 Gavle, Sweden, pp. 1901–1910.

Varner, I., & Beamer, L. 1995. *Intercultural communication in the global workplace,* Irwin, Chicago.

System-based Vision for Strategic and Creative Design, Bontempi (ed.)
© 2003 Swets & Zeitlinger, Lisse, ISBN 90 5809 599 1

Advanced developments in semiconductor facility construction

S.J. Eibl
Rumfordstrasse, Munich, Germany

ABSTRACT: The paper presents certain aspects of structural design and construction management for semi-conductor facilities. The state-of-the-art wafer fabrication illustrates future challenges and opportunities in engineering practice. The impact from the enhanced semiconductor high tech industry provides above that significant cost-effective benefit for related facilities in pharmaceuticals and life science.

1 INTRODUCTION

The high innovative and complex wafer technology requires a more integrated approach of structural components and process functions. For instance the lithographic process with steppers demands extreme dynamic conditions for the inner structure. Particularly, the structural dynamics of the entire waffle table induced by the soil-structure interaction, operator and hook-up are quite sensitive to the wafer process. The identification of integrated approaches will improve the key performance of the construction process, optimizes the cost and reduces the technical risk potential.

2 PROCESS TECHNOLOGY

2.1 Cleanroom characteristics

The cleanroom forms the heart of each semiconductor process. The filtered quasi-laminar air flow has a velocity of approximately 0.40 m/sec. The climate conditions are limited to a temperature of approximately 21 degree Celsius, a humidity of 50% and an over-pressure of about 30 Pa.

The measure for the cleanroom quality is defined by its cleanroom class according to US standards. The used class 1000 means 1000 particle with a diameter of 0.5 μm per cubic foot. This requires an air exchange of 80 times per hour for the total volume of 20.000 cubic meter.

2.2 Base-build infrastructure

The entire process technique is divided into the real process and the base-build and hook-up technology. The process technology is highly innovative and will

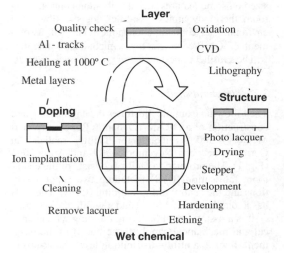

Figure 1. DRAM 300 mm wafer process.

be provided worldwide by a few specialized suppliers. The base-build is a standard technology and generally includes basic mechanical, electrical and process-related equipment such as boiler, chiller, cleanroom, chemical and HVAC systems. Figure 1 illustrates in principle the process steps in the DRAM chip production.

3 CONSTRUCTION TECHNOLOGY

3.1 Construction performance

Traditional manufacturing facilities are designed with priority on the optimal and economic consumption of materials based on the geometry and load function only. The highly competitive semiconductor market introduces new qualities for the construction process. It requires a comprehensive design with major respect to the total time of base-build construction. Due to the relatively low percentage of construction cost of approximately 6% on the total volume of investments, the design focuses on a simple, modular and flexible structural system and an optimized logistic flow. This demands intelligent segmental pre-cast system, standardized components and operation research models. The time-to-market criterion leads to a fundamental change in the approach for design and opens the field for new materials such as expensive fiber-reinforced-polymers (FRP) and smart systems.

Experiences of two 300 mm facilities designs recently constructed in Germany will be basis for this paper. The base-build construction for a wafer fabrication with a total volume of 1.1 Billion Euros was recently completed within 18 months. It will be emphasized on some features such as vibration control, clean room thermodynamics, fast-track logistic flows and environmental contamination policy. The risk assessment of GMP-contracts for semiconductor facilities will be a further important feature of fast-track projects.

3.2 Structural shell

The following example illustrates the engineering and construction of a DRAM (Dynamic Random Access Memory) 300 semiconductor facility realized in Germany between November 1999 and April 2001 (Fig. 1). The production facility consists of the cleanroom fabrication (FAB) including two support sections and the central utility building (CUB). The FAB has a total length of 154.80 and a width of 68.86 m.

It is a 4-story manufacturing building with chemical and mechanical supply (base-build) in the basement, floor 2, a utility distribution level (hook-up) in floor 3, the cleanroom level in floor 4 and the non-pressurized plenum in floor 5.

The described system is quite similar to most of the recent facilities under construction. For instance new designed wafer production facility has virtually identical dimensions in geometry.

The total investment for the entire semiconductor facility was 1.1 Billion US$ excluding the claim volume. The costs for civil construction and base-build were estimated of approximately 210 Million US$.

Figure 2 shows the construction sequence from erecting the column to the launching of waffle table elements and main steel girders.

In this case the excellent soil condition allowed a shallow foundation with the slab on grade. Controlling the crack width in order to meet the coating code required a high percentage of reinforcement in the base slab.

Figure 2. Semiconductor Greenfield site.

Frames, braced through two stair towers on each side, achieved the horizontal stability of the structure. In order to control the vertical deflection of the cleanroom ceiling, fixed frames with pre-cast columns of strength 45 MPa and an erected steel truss girder with a total span of 65 m were launched. A maximum height of 6.20 m was calculated in the centre of the main girder. The great span of 65 m was necessary to achieve a column-free cleanroom of about 7000 square meter.

The structural system of the inner structure is a conventional pre-cast system. The slab system in the cleanroom area over floor 3 consists of a two-way supported waffle table with a standard span of 7.20×7.20 m. It forms the base slab for the vibration-sensitive equipment. Shear walls were arranged in both directions to increase the horizontal stiffness for dynamic excitations. Maximum live loads up to 20 kN/m^2 were considered for the process equipment.

Modelling and analysis were applied with linear finite-element analysis for the shell structure and strut-and tie models for detailing. The design was performed according to German design standards.

The described structural system is quite similar to most of the recent facilities under construction. For instance a new designed wafer production facility as virtually identical dimensions in geometry.

4 GENERIC VIBRATION CRITERIA

4.1 Basic methodology

Most demanding issues in the design are the vibration-sensitive process tools. Designing and operating microelectronic manufacturing facilities are carried out on the basis of generic vibration criteria (Eibl 2003b). The photolithographic process with steppers

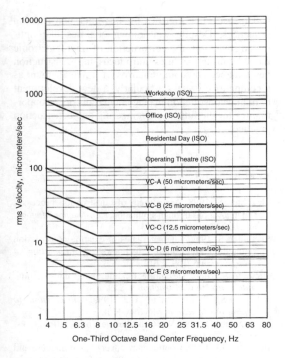

Figure 3.   Generic velocity spectrum.

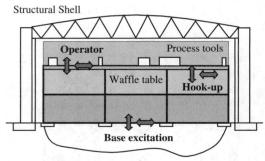

Figure 4.   Vibration excitation.

in the wafer production requires the extreme vibration specification of class VC-E for the waffle table structure. This limits the root-mean-square (rms) velocity on the waffle table level in the vertical and two horizontal directions to 3 μm/sec in the frequency range between 8 and 80 Hz as shown in Figure 3. The criterion is based on one-third octave band vibration velocity spectra due to vibrations dominated by broadband or random energy.

It has been found in various studies that while equipments and people may exhibit maximum sensitivity on constant velocity curves.

4.2   Structural dynamics

Three main induced excitations are crucial for the waffle table structure and subsequently for the production process. Particularly, the base, operator and process excitation affects the dynamic behavior on the waffle table level in floor 4 (Fig. 4).

The separation of inner and outer structure minimizes the environmental impacts such as turbulent winds and snow loads.

It is obvious that contractual guaranties for such extreme vibration criteria are major sources for construction risk.

5   CONSTRUCTION LOGISTICS

5.1   Basic methodology of fast-track

On the worldwide volatile chip market, the time-to-market is the crucial criterion for the semiconductor industry. This affects authoritative the entire value chain from engineering design to implementation of microelectronic manufacturing facilities. Key driver in this construction process are a modular shape grammar and an integrated fast-track approach.

The fast-track model splits up the design, procurement and construction phase into process clusters in order to reconnect direct dependent process parts of design and construction. The benefit is a significantly shortened overall schedule. However, this kind of fast-track approach consist major risk potential due to the increase of interfaces and complex dependencies between single tasks (Macomber 1989, Bommeli 1999, Nücke & Feinendegen 1998, Eibl 2003a). It requires more flexible multi-disciplinary resources.

Figure 5 illustrates a typical construction sequence to erect pre-cast columns, slabs and waffle table elements with several mobile cranes and one heavy load crane.

5.2   Just-in-time (JIT)

One key element of the fast-track construction is the Just-in-Time (JIT) logistic of the material suppliers. Therefore, the deployment of pre-cast structural members does not only enhance the construction sequence, it also allows a Just-in-Time production within the supply chain. The entire construction consists of a pre-cast elements completed by in-situ shear walls and steel girders.

With respect to the restricted construction site, the logistic played the important role in this fast-track project. The term logistic does not only mean the typical construction sequences but also the infrastructure works and the supply and launching of the process tools.

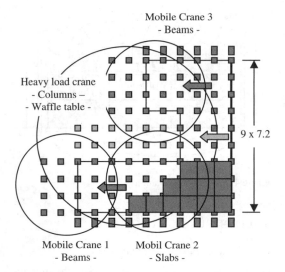

Mobile Crane 3
- Beams -

Heavy load crane
- Columns –
- Waffle table -

9 x 7.2

Mobile Crane 1   Mobil Crane 2
- Beams -   - Slabs -

Figure 5.   Pre-cast logistic sequence.

5.3 *Digital construction management*

A new approach to develop and control construction processes are the deployment of digital construction management tools (Slaughter 1998, Eibl 2002). An existing one is at Stanford University developed 4D model (Liston, Fischer & Winograd 2001). It links 3D CAD drawings with a construction schedule. This allows the real-time visualization and simulations of the entire construction process. The benefits are a better understanding of multi-functional interfaces, a minimization of design faults and an operation research-based optimization of construction sequences (Hillier & Lieberman 1995). It should be stressed that such tools do not only provide a one time optimized technical solution. Actually, the power of such systems is that they could be used to control in real-time often disturbed construction operations.

6 CONCLUSION

The present paper illustrates on crucial issues in the construction management of semiconductor facilities. It outlined the importance of modular pre-cast systems and Just-in-Time logistics for fast-track construction sequences. Despite well-known qualities like optimized structural, the construction of microelectronic manufacturing facilities introduces the construction performance and comprehensive risk management as a competitive issue. Particularly, a new development of digital construction management tools opens opportunities for the future in engineering and construction practice.

REFERENCES

Slaughter, S. 1998. Assessment of construction processes and innovations through simulation, *Construction Management and Economics*, 17.
Slaughter, S. 1997. Characteristics of existing construction automation and robotics technologies. *Automation in Construction* 6, 109–120.
Howe, A.S. 2000. Designing for automated construction. *Automation in Construction* 9, 259–276
Hillier, F.S. & Lieberman, G.J. 1995. *Introduction to Operations Research*. McGraw-Hill.
Macomber, J.D. 1989. You Can Manage Construction Risks. *Harvard Business Review*.
Bommeli, M. 1999. Contingency covers Force majeure and liquidated damages insurance, *Report Swiss Reinsurance Company*.
Nücke, H. & Feinendegen, S. 1998. Integrated Risk Management. *Report KPMG*.
Liston, K., Fisher M. & Winograd, T. 2001. Focused Sharing of Information for Multi-Disciplinary Decision Making by Project Teams. *IT Com* Vol. 6, pg. 69
Eibl, S.J. 2002. Digital Construction Management (DCM) – Strategic Information System for construction process control. *Internal report*.
Eibl, S.J. 2003. Risk Allocation in GMP Semiconductor Projects. *5th Asia Pacific Structural Engineering and Construction Conference APSEC*. Johor Bahru, Malaysia.
Eibl, S.J. 2003. Design Methodology for Vibration-Sensitive Cleanrooms. *The Second International Conference on Structural Engineering, Mechanics and Computation SEMC*. Cape Town, South Africa, submitted.
Eibl, S.J. 2003. Competitive Construction Management for Microelectronic Manufacturing Facilities. *Construction in the 21st Century, Sustainability and Innovation in Management and Technology*. Hong Kong, China, submitted, 2003.
Tidd, J., Bessant J. & Pavitt, K. 2001. *Managing Innovation*, John Wiley & Sons, New York.

System-based Vision for Strategic and Creative Design, Bontempi (ed.)
© 2003 Swets & Zeitlinger, Lisse, ISBN 90 5809 599 1

Construction productivity of multistory buildings in developing countries

E. Koehn & P. Shukla
Department of Civil Engineering, Lamar University, Beaumont, TX, USA

H.J. Tohme
Water Utilities Engineer, City of Beaumont Water Utilities Division, Beaumont, TX, USA

ABSTRACT: In developing countries such as India or Bangladesh, construction of different types of multistory buildings requires both skilled as well as unskilled labor during the various phases of a project. Here, labor saving mechanical equipment may be available and can possibly be utilized in metropolitan regions or cities. However, in all other parts of the country most of the construction work is labor intensive. In particular, the role of labor in the construction of multistory buildings will be studied in this presentation. The economic use of specialized machinery for excavation and the placement of concrete will be presented. An effort will be made to investigate the special skills and labor productivity of particular regions of the country. This directly impacts construction costs in various regions. It is shown that the prime reasons for the shortage of large construction equipment is its high capital expense combined with the low cost of local construction labor.

1 INTRODUCTION

The rapid increase of the urban population in developing countries such as India has forced the reevaluation of the importance of high-rise buildings. In organizing the various construction operations of multistory buildings, timely completion and quality must be considered. The quality of construction is dependent, in part, upon the construction techniques adopted to erect the building.

In most developing countries such as India, the construction industry is highly dependent upon the labor force. However, in metropolitan cities, where the population growth rate is high, the use of mechanical equipment may also play an important role in increasing construction productivity. Heavy machinery is scarcely available to small contractors, but CIDC (Construction Industry Development Council), an organization in operation since August 8, 1996, has attempted to overcome this problem by establishing the Construction Equipment Bank where modern equipment is available at reasonable rental prices (Deepak 2002). Many private equipment rental agencies have also joined the effort to improve the availability of new highly efficient equipment.

2 LABOR

The availability and expertise of laborers greatly impacts productivity and the quality of workmanship in the construction industry (Koehn 1990). In India, as in most developing countries, illiterate workers dominate the workforce. In fact, the construction industry presently employs roughly 31 million workers throughout the entire country (Deepak 2002). The general tendency of Indian construction laborers is to migrate from city to city or region to region in search of work, often bringing their family with them. Consequently, most workers have never settled in one place long enough to establish themselves in communities, making it difficult to unite and develop bonds within the workforce for protection of rights. While health and safety of workers are not major concerns of the employer, the Indian government has established a number of laws to improve the working conditions for laborers, such as the Minimum Wage Act, the Contract Labor Act, and the Prohibition and Regulation Act of 1986 that concentrated on the prohibition of child labor (Child 2000). Still, the laws have not been properly implemented or enforced because of a weak and/or corrupt administrative system.

Since India is a large country, geographical diversity has given rise to specialization within the construction workforce. Different regions of the country are known for having specialized workers for particular types of work. A study of the overall construction industy throughout the country reveals that laborers in the evacuation and earthwork field normally come from Andhra Pradesh, concrete workers from Karnataka, carpenters from Rajasthan, masons from Uttar Pradesh, and those who place reinforcing bars from Bihar. This is not intended to convey the idea that a particular kind of work is done only by laborers from a specified region. However, the productivity and quality of work are viewed as superior by craftsman from these areas (Koehn 1995).

Some contractors in the building industy tend to use the same laborers and craftsman for an entire construction project. Minimizing the number of subcontractors involved in the construction of a multistory building project is one of the concepts being used in developing countries to improve productivity, minimize the cost, and maintain a schedule. However, this approach can reduce the quality since the crafts are often not as specialized in the work they must accomplish. The negative results of such projects may be reflected in noticeable below average quality which often reduces the selling price.

3 MULTISTORY BUILDINGS

As previously mentioned, construction of multistory buildings can be a labor-intensive operation in developing countries such as India. However, equipment such as elevators, excavators, concrete mixers, and concrete vibrators are often used at sites located in large metropolitan areas. According to a recent census performed by the Indian government, March 2001, the urban population is roughly 27.8% of the total population. This data shows an increase of 2.1% in the proportion of urban population in the country during the 1991–2001 time span and more growth is expected in the coming years (Census 2002). Increasing urban population requires the construction of additional multistory buildings within cities to solve the housing problems in the country.

There are principally two different types of multistory buildings being constructed in India. They can be categorized according to the number of stories or heights of the facility such as:

- Low rise multistory buildings
- High rise multistory buildings.

3.1 Low rise multistory buildings

A low rise structure can be defined as a building having a maximum of four stories, constructed for residential purposes in semi-developed areas, requiring the utilization of laborers with average skills. There are two basic types of low rise multistory buildings based on the particular construction material used:

- Brick masonry load-bearing structures accompanied by reinforced concrete columns
- Reinforced concrete framed structures.

3.2 High rise multistory buildings

High rise buildings can be defined as having five or more stories, constructed in highly-populated areas to satisfy the need of the housing and office shortage, or a combination of both. This type of building requires higher skilled laborers. The work can be subdivided according to the techniques and material utilized as follows:

- Reinforced concrete framed structures
- Steel structures with reinforced concrete slabs.

4 CONSTRUCTION PRODUCTIVITY

Obviously, different buildings require various specialized crafts according to the type of construction utilized. From the beginning to the end, a multistory building passes through different phases of construction. All multistory buildings, however, require excavation and concrete laborers. At every phase, productivity, in terms of funds expended or quantity of work accomplished and time consumed, is evaluated. The use of equipment and labor for similar activities may also be compared. The following is a discussion of the productivity involved with the construction of various stages of a multistory building.

4.1 Clearing

Clearing a site for a multistory project is usually accomplished with the assistance of mechanical equipment. Normally, a front end loader is used, however, if the site is large and the area needs to be leveled or cleared, tractors or dumptrucks may be used as shown in Figures 1 and 2.

Generally, on large sites, laborers are employed for minor clean up work only. This may not be the case

Figure 1. Excavation Equipment.

for smaller projects. For site clearing of large sites, therefore, the comparison between the productivity of laborers and equipment is difficult to accomplish. One problem in India and other developing countries is that the concept of "hazardous waste" does not get a great deal of attention. Since it is normally not considered, there generally are no safety plans for "hazardous waste" if it is encountered during clearing operations. In any case, for the protection of workers, mechanical equipment should be utilized as much as possible for clean up operations.

4.2 Excavation

In India, today, almost all commercial buildings are constructed with underground parking facilities. Here, the use of equipment is essential in order to excavate the volume of soil required. The use of laborers is normally not feasible because of time constraints associated with manual work. However, in the case of residential multi-story buildings, underground parking is usually not required, and therefore tends to be eliminated. Also, the height and area of footings are normally small in comparison to the plan of the building. The columns may also be spaced in a manner such that equipment is difficult to utilize. Here, manual excavation may prove to be a less expensive and more convenient option as shown in Figure 3. Nevertheless, if a raft foundation is specified, the use of equipment is obviously more productive. Equipment may also be utilized if there is no constraint with the space in which to store the excavated earth.

The following calculation illustrates a comparison of excavation work done in ordinary soil using equipment or laborers (Dutta 1998). Assume roughly $30 \, m^3$ of soil is to be excavated for a foundation. This also includes disposal of the material. The project should take five excavation laborers and four disposal laborers one eight hour day to accomplish. In comparison, if the same quantity of work is accomplished by using

an excavator with a bucket size of one m^3, the duration will be approximately three hours. The cost of the equipment will be greater than that of the laborers, but productivity in respect of time consumed will be considerably different for the two methods.

4.3 Concrete

To achieve overall construction productivity on any multistory building project, the system utilized to place concrete must be carefully analyzed. In developing countries like India, most contractors, 98%, use conventional manual methods to place concrete as shown in Figures 4 & 5. The other 2% utilize ready-mixed concrete (Jain 2002).

Below is a comparison of placing concrete using laborers versus concrete pumps (Dutta 1998). Mixing, pouring and finishing roughly $3 \, m^3$ of concrete requires five laborers working one eight hour day. Alternately, a concrete pump can move roughly $20–25 \, m^3$ of ready mix concrete in less than thirty minutes, and it will take three laborers approximately four hours to finish it. Concrete pumps not only save time, but can also deliver roughly up to $40–50 \, m^3$ per hour with no aggregate segregation, and accurate water cement ratio.

Other factors to take into consideration when placing concrete include overcrowded work sites, limited access to higher levels of the building, and transportation of the concrete. Normally, at multistory building sites, concrete placement occurs in conjunction with and parallel to masonry work. As slabs on the upper levels are poured, masonry work begins on the lower

Figure 2.   Clearing and Leveling.

Figure 3.   Manual Excavation.

Figure 4.   Concrete Mixer.

Figure 6.   Formwork.

Figure 5.   Mechanical Vibrator.

level as soon as the formwork and shoring are removed. Unfortunately, often there is only one elevator to be used for all purposes at a site. Nevertheless, taking all items into consideration, the use of ready mix concrete and a pump vastly increases the productivity rate.

4.4   *Other activities*

Productivity of multistory building construction also involves other important operations such as placing rebars, formwork, falsework, scaffolding, etc. If these operations are not well coordinated, they can affect the overall project cost and duration. As reinforcement, formwork, and falsework are directly related to placing concrete, a delay in these activities ultimately affects the total project duration.

4.4.1   *Reinforcing bars*
Normally on building sites in developing countries such as India, re-bar work is done manually although such techniques may jeopardize the safety of workers. It is known that the manual cutting and bending of bars takes more time and is labor intensive compared to the use of machines. However, the unavailability and costliness of machines is a major problem in developing regions. Therefore, in order for re-bar work not to delay the project, it is recommended that it should be scheduled to start as early as possible.

4.4.2   *Formwork*
Formwork is one of the important phases of construction since it may account for roughly fifty percent of the total cost of placing reinforced concrete. Two materials, timber and steel are principally used to form columns as shown in Figure 6. Generally, steel or plywood are used to form the slab as shown in Figure 7, and timber shoring or falsework are used as the vertical supports. The drawback to timber is that a long preparation time normally is required since the height and length may have to be readjusted at each floor. Timber shoring is more difficult to adjust than steel members, especially, if it consists of unfinished material as shown in Figure 8. If steel shoring is utilized and proper maintenance is provided, it can be used numerous times. Construction of time-consuming formwork should be used for special purposes only. Since cost is a factor and steel is more expensive than timber forms and shores, contractors often prefer to use timber members. Nevertheless, due to unfinished

Figure 7. Placing Concrete.

Figure 8. Falsework.

Figure 9. Bamboo Scaffolding.

can be used for various heights with proper modifications. Overall, the use of steel scaffolding should increase the productivity of a project.

5 CONCLUSION

Construction productivity is becoming an increasingly vital factor for the construction industry in developing countries. As the population of urban areas increase, additional housing must be provided in a shorter period of time. In general, productivity can be increased by employing modern construction equipment and techniques. Yet, the unavailability of construction equipment in general, especially in remote areas, in addition to a large illiterate labor force are major obstacles to improving productivity. Specifically, in India the establishment of the Construction Equipment Bank and the Construction Workers' Training Institute (CWTI) under the National Academy of Construction (NAC), should enhance the development of construction techniques, increase productivity, and decrease accidents at the worksite. It is hoped that with time, realistic rules and regulations, and government support, more efficient and safer construction operations will be achieved in developing countries.

rough materials and improper techniques, lower quality and productivity is often attained (Koehn 1994).

4.4.3 Scaffolding

Scaffolding is also an important factor that indirectly affects construction productivity. It is normally required for installing the facade of a building. In India, temporary scaffolding is generally constructed of bamboo wood as shown in Figure 9. Unfortunately, this type of material may be dangerous and also takes considerable time to erect. Steel scaffolding can be erected faster, is safer than bamboo scaffolding, and

ACKNOWLEDGEMENT

The authors wish to recognize Ms. Linda Dousay for her assistance with the production activities involved with the preparation of the paper.

REFERENCES

Census of India 2002. Official web site of the Government of India, Http://www.censusindia.net/results/state.php/stad-A.

Child Labor 2000. http://www.indianembassy.org/policy/Child-Labor/childlabor-2000.htm.

Deepak, G. 2002. Construction industry development council. *Construction Journal of India*. (313).

Dutta, B.N. 1998. *Estimating and costing in civil engineering*, UBSPD. New Delhi.

Jain, A.K. 2002. Ready mix concrete – Growth prospects in India. *Construction Journal of India*. (1502).

Koehn, E. & Regmi, D.C. 1990. Quality in construction projects – International firms and developing countries. *Journal of Professional Issues in Engineering*, ASCE. (116)4, 388–396.

Koehn, E. et al. 1995. Safety in developing countries: Professional and bureaucratic problems. *Journal of Construction Engineering and Management*. ASCE. (121) 261–265.

Koehn, E. & Atuahene, F. 1994. Labor/political factors for international firms and developing regions. *Journal of Professional Issues in Engineering Education and Practice*. ASCE. 119(4), 698–713.

A life-cycle energy model of the UK steel construction sector

J. Ley
Corus Research Development and Technology, Port Talbot, UK

M. Sansom
The Steel Construction Institute, Ascot, UK

A.S.K. Kwan
Cardiff University, Cardiff, UK

ABSTRACT: This paper describes the steps used to couple results from a dynamic Material Flow Analysis (MFA) of the UK steel construction sector, with the results from a recent Life-Cycle Assessment (LCA) study of the UK steel construction sector (European Commission. 2002)

Information on the historical consumption of construction steel, typical lifetimes, statistical end-of-life distributions and re-use and recycling rates, have been used to develop a dynamic model of the yearly flows of steel within the construction sector.

The data from the dynamic MFA model are coupled with the LCA results to determine the total annual energy consumption of the UK steel construction sector.

Results show that 81% of the energy consumed by steel construction products in 1998 was by the production of finished steel for the sector.

1 INTRODUCTION

Steel is used in many markets in the UK including automotive, packaging and engineering steels. The construction sector represents the largest consumer of steel in the UK-25% of the total market in 1998 (UK Steel Association. 2001).

A paper has already been written (Ley et al. 2002a) which explains in detail the commercial and strategic benefits for the steel industry in the UK of predicting the scrap arising from a construction steel MFA. This paper builds on that work, by coupling dynamic MFA results with energy consumption data from a recent LCA study of the steel construction sector, producing a life-cycle energy model of the sector. The model can be used to identify industries within the construction sector that consume the greatest amounts of energy. This will assist policy makers and businesses in the sector, by helping to identify areas of the construction industry where priorities for environmental improvement are required.

Data for the steel construction MFA has been collected as total tonnage flows of steel through the UK economy. On their own, results from the MFA can be used to identify resource consumption and waste arising from the sector. Environmental impacts resulting from these flows such as CO_2 emissions or energy burdens are not determined in the MFA. Data are derived from the LCA of steel construction products project on CO_2 emissions and energy burdens at a functional unit level (e.g. per tonne). By coupling the results of these two studies a model is developed that quantifies the total energy burden of the UK steel construction sector.

2 A DYNAMIC MFA OF THE UK STEEL CONSTRUCTION SECTOR

A MFA is used to examine: the materials flowing into, and out of, a given system; the stock held within the system; and flow routes within this system. An MFA essentially comprises the following steps (Hendricks et al. 1997): 1. Definition of study goal(s); 2. System description; 3. Data acquisition; 4. Material balances (modelling and scenario building); and lastly, 5. Interpretation.

The material flows of construction steel in the UK are a complex system, in which materials and products are re-used or recycled a number of times (McLauren et al. 2000). This system exhibits dynamic characteristics, resulting from time lags in the system due to the long and varying lifetimes of construction steel products. To effectively model the flows of steel through the construction sector a dynamic model has been developed that uses historical consumption data as a basis. The system boundary used is shown in Figure 1.

The starting point for this study is the consumption of construction steel products in the UK (Fig. 2). Data have been collected on the historical consumption of steel products by the UK construction sector from 1956 to 1998 for six generic product categories. These data are integrated with statistics on the trade

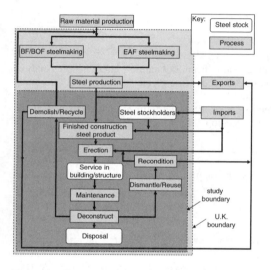

Figure 1. System model used to represent the UK steel construction sector.

of finished construction steel products to determine the consumption of construction steel products in the UK. Between 1900 and 1956 statistics on the consumption of construction steel have been estimated from total UK steel consumption statistics, by extrapolating average construction steel market share data from 1956 to 1998, to this data. Figure 2 shows the results of this analysis.

Once erected, steel construction products enter the use phase where they will remain until the end of their service lives. It is not possible to define a definite lifespan for any steel product. However, data exist in the UK for "insured lifespan" of steel construction products (Building Performance Group 2000) derived from a survey of UK building surveyors. Clearly these figures are only *average* lifespan figures due to varying user occupancies for buildings, and using a single figure as the lifespan for each steel product would result in a rather discontinuous model. A normal distribution has thus been used to provide a range of lifetimes (see Table 1), with a minimum and a maximum service life (*a* and *b* respectively in following formulae) assigned to each product. These values have been derived from literature and discussions with experts in steel construction.

The standard normal distribution, based around a mean value μ and a standard deviation σ (such that $\mu = (a + b)/2$ and *a* and *b* are $\pm 3\sigma$ from μ), has

Table 1. Steel construction lifetimes used for modelling.

Years	Sections, rebar, plate, hollow sections & light sections	Sheet
$\mu \pm 3\sigma$	60 ± 30	25 ± 10

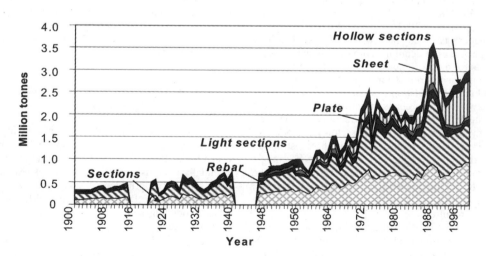

Figure 2. Historic consumption of construction steel in the UK. 1900–1998.

been adopted to provide the probability density function. The range from a to b thus covers 99.7% of all cases (Melo 1999). The probability P that a product is scrapped t years of service is given by Equation 1:

$$P_t = \int_t^{t+1} \frac{1}{\sigma\sqrt{2\pi}} \exp\left[-\frac{1}{2}\left(\frac{x-\mu x}{\sigma x}\right)^2\right] dx \qquad (1)$$

where $a < t < b$, and the probability corresponds to the area under the normal distribution curve, with the probability density function of the system represented by Equation 2:

$$f(x) = \frac{1}{\sigma x\sqrt{2\pi}} \exp\left[-\frac{1}{2}\left(\frac{x-\mu x}{\sigma x}\right)^2\right] \qquad (2)$$

The probability of a steel product reaching its end-of-life is thus determined, for each year between, a to b. These probabilities are then multiplied by the historic consumption tonnages for the relevant year to estimate the tonnage of steel reaching its end-of-life.

Table 2. Re-use and recycling rates of steel construction products.

%	Sections	Rebar	Cladding	Purlins and rails
Recycling	86	91	79	89
Re-use	13	1	15	10
Landfill	1	8	6	1

There are three end-of-life routes for construction steel; recycling, re-use or landfill (Fig. 1). No UK data exist on the tonnage of construction steel deconstructed each year for recycling, re-use and landfill. A survey was thus undertaken of trade association members of the National Federation of Demolition Contractors (NFDC, its 160 members are reportedly responsible for 90% of the UK deconstruction activities) to determine recycling, re-use and landfill rates. A response rate of 30% provided the results shown in Table 2.

The total tonnage of steel arising at the end-of-life can be multiplied by the end-of-life rates (determined from the NFDC survey) to give a estimate of the tonnage of steel being recycled, re-used and landfilled. Figure 3 shows the predicted arising of construction steel scrap for recycling from the modelling. Earlier papers (Ley et al. 2002a, b) describe the validation of the model.

3 STEEL CONSTRUCTION LCA DATA

The data used for coupling the LCA with the MFA came from a European Commission project (2002). This was a pan-European, three-year project undertaken by the Steel Construction Institutes of three countries, Sweden, Netherlands and the UK. Additional technical and financial support was provided for the project by, Corus.

The aim of the project was to gather "cradle to grave" LCI data for steel construction products manufactured in Western Europe. This must be taken as

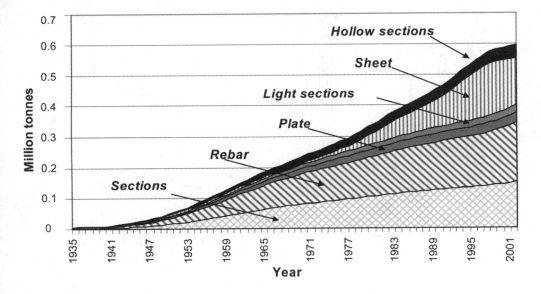

Figure 3. Estimated construction scrap steel arisings.

311

a limitation for the modelling used in this paper, in that the LCA data is not UK specific but a European average.

A total of sixteen steel construction products were studied, these products can be grouped to the six finished steel products studied for the construction MFA, hence allowing the coupling of the data from the two projects.

LCI data were collected at all five stages of the life-cycle phase of steel construction products: (1) production of intermediate (semi-finished) steel products, e.g. plate, sections etc; (2) production of finished construction steel products, typically either through fabrication or cold rolling; (3) construction of steel construction products; (4) in-use phase of steel products; and (5) end-of-life phase (the environmental impacts associated with demolition and deconstruction, scrap processing and landfilling of steel construction products).

For every phase in the life-cycle, data on environmental inputs and outputs have been collected, these inputs and outputs include: raw material extraction, emissions to air, water and land, and waste. For the purposes of this study, the environmental indicator that has been chosen is energy consumption. The reason for choosing energy consumption is that it is a reasonable indicator of the intensity of certain environmental impacts, showing correlation with SO_x, NO_x and CO_2 emissions (Amato 1996).

Allocation is an important methodological consideration for calculating whole-life LCI data for metal products. This is as a consequence of the ability of metals to be recycled and the high recycling rates of metals.

Several different methodologies exist for dealing with allocation, with no consistent method being recognised, as a result the LCI data used in this study is in the most unallocated form (European Commission 2002).

4 COUPLING OF LCA AND MFA

Figure 4 shows the results obtained by coupling the MFA and LCA data. It is clear that the greatest energy burden for steel products consumed by the UK construction sector, occurs during the production of semi-finished steel, for construction applications.

LCI data on the maintenance of steel construction products have been included in the modelling; these data have been incorporated into the energy consumption of the end-of-life phases, as it is assumed that all steel construction products being deconstructed will have been in-use, and maintained.

On behalf of the UK steel production industry, the UK steel association has entered into an umbrella agreement (DEFRA 2001) with the UK government

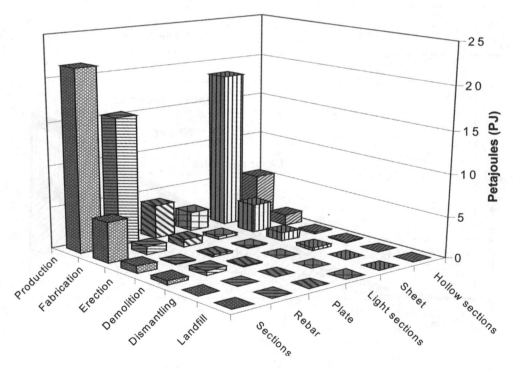

Figure 4.   Total energy consumption of the UK steel construction sector for 1998.

to reduce global warming gas emissions to contribute to meeting Kyoto targets. The correlation between gas emission and energy consumption has been determined; targets have been set for the steel industry's energy consumption. These figures can be used to validate the energy consumption figures predicted for the production of steel construction products from the dynamic life-cycle energy model.

For 2002, a target of 388.2 PJ of energy consumed by the UK steel industry was set (DEFRA. 2001), from the life-cycle model, the production of steel products for the UK construction sector was calculated to account for 67.2 PJ in 1998. Based on the 2002 target this accounts for 17% of the total energy consumed by the UK steel sector.

The Iron and Steel Statistics Bureau (ISSB) produce annual statistics on the consumption of finished steel by different markets in the UK. For 1998, the construction sector accounted for 25% of the total demand for steel. Accounting for the fact that the energy consumption for the steel sector is unknown for 1998, the energy consumption figures estimated from the modelling differ by 7% from the ISSB annual statistics, this is considered to be a reasonable difference, and suggests the model is producing accurate results.

The European Commission LCA report concluded that, steel production typically accounts for 75% of the whole life-cycle energy impacts (it was also found that production had the greatest environmental impact in terms of CO_2 emission and waste generation).

The life-cycle energy model builds on these results, by incorporating the total steel flows of the UK steel construction sector, the total energy consumption of the construction sector is determined. The modelling shows an average 81% (ranging from 76% to 90%) of energy consumed by the steel construction sector in 1998 accounted to the production of semi-finished steel for the sector.

5 CONCLUSIONS

The life-cycle energy model builds on two previous studies of the UK steel construction sector, an MFA and an LCA. By coupling these two studies, the total energy consumption of steel products; produced, fabricated, erected, maintained, demolished, dismantled and landfilled for the UK construction sector, in 1998, has been derived.

This work is an initial attempt of ongoing work at coupling an MFA and an LCA, the following limitations from the coupling of the methods have been determined:

- For validating the life-cycle energy model, energy consumption data is compared between 1998 and 2002; and,

- The validation data used for 2002 is not actual data but a target set.

Previous work has been undertaken (Ley et al. 2002b) that predicts a 78% increase in the tonnage of construction steel reaching its end-of-life in 2015, compared to current arisings. By using the UK steel industry's predictions on the consumption of construction steel, future work will be undertaken to investigate the effect of predicted increasing tonnages of scrap steel on the energy consumption of the steel construction sector in the UK.

Investigations will also be undertaken in coupling the MFA with other environmental indicators, such as VOC emissions and waste.

The model shows that steel used in construction activities, downstream of production, have relatively minor energy consumption impacts, with production accounting for 81% of the total energy consumption of the sector in 1998. The focus for improving the energy consumption of the sector should currently be directed at production.

ACKNOWLEDGMENTS

The authors gratefully acknowledge financial support and assistance from the Engineering and Physics Science Research Council, Corus and the Steel Construction Institute. The authors are also grateful to the following organisations in providing assistance, data or critical analysis: The Iron and Steel Statistics Bureau, Corus Construction & Industrial, National Federation of Demolition Contractors, HM Customs & Excise, and the Centre for Environmental Strategy, University of Surrey.

REFERENCES

Amato, A.1996. A comparative environmental appraisal of alternative framing systems for offices, PhD thesis, Oxford Brookes University.

Building Performance Group Ltd (BPG). 2000. Building fabric component life manual.

DEFRA. 2001. Umbrella climate change agreement for the steel sector.

European Comission. 2002. Life-cycle assessment (LCA) for steel constuction. Report EUR 20570 EN. *ECSC steel publications*. Brussles.

Hendriks, C., Obernosterer, R., Müller, D., Kytzia, S., Baccini, P. and Brunner, P.H. .2000.: Material flow analysis: a tool to support environmental policy decision making. Casestudies on the city of Vienna and the Swiss lowlands. *Local Environment*. 5(3). p 311–328

Ley, J., Sansom, M. and Kwan, A. 2002a. Material flow analysis of the UK steel construction sector. Conference proceedings from the *Steel in Sustainable Construction*. IISI world conference 2002. Luxembourg. 15–17 May 2002. p 259–266

Ley, J., Sansom, M. and Kwan, A. 2002b. Determining the U.K. stock of construction steel through material flow analysis modelling. Proceedings from the *4th AECEF International Symposium*, Porto, Portugal. 18–20 September 2002. T.31–39

McLaren, J., Parkinson, S. and Jackson, T. 2000. Modelling material cascades – frameworks for the environmental assessment of recycling systems. *Resources, Conservation and Recycling*. 31. 83–104

Melo, M.T. 1999. Statistical analysis of metal scrap generation: the case of aluminum in Germany. *Resources, Conservation and Recycling*. 26. 91–113

UK Steel Association. 2001. Key steel statistics. Pocket edition.

System-based Vision for Strategic and Creative Design, Bontempi (ed.)
© *2003 Swets & Zeitlinger, Lisse, ISBN 90 5809 599 1*

Robotics and the construction industry

N. Pires
Department of Mechanical Engineering, University of Coimbra, Portugal

T.D. Pereira
Department of Civil Engineering, University of Coimbra, Portugal

ABSTRACT: This article first explains why it is still difficult to use robots on construction sites. The authors argue that robotics can actually be utilized in the upstream industries, either in component manufacture or in constructive systems capable of being undertaken in a traditional factory setting. Two examples of this concept are presented. Further developments, extending this concept to a wider range of components and constructive systems, will have major implications for the constructive process that extends from the project design phase to the technologies employed on the building site.

1   INTRODUCTION

One of the chief characteristics of construction industry is enormous labour costs. There are considerable variations, depending on the type of project and works involved, but they may account for as much as 50% of the total.

If robotics aims to replace men with machines, then the construction industry is a vast field for the development of its applications.

2   ROBOTS ON SITE AND IN PRE-FABRICATION

When considering using robots for construction, the building site is normally the production site *par excellence*. We have to borne in mind that this working environment and the types of tasks to be carried out have the following characteristics:

Building sites have a considerable geographical dispersion, especially those owned by the largest companies;

The final products are not repetitive, since each project is unique;

A large number (hundreds) of different activities are carried out on building sites, with little repetition;

On sites, many tasks are being done at the same time, and they are interlinked in terms of the resources allocated to them;

Building sites are relatively dynamic places, with systematic changes of jobs and the surrounding environment;

Building sites are hostile in that they are replete with obstacles, uneven surfaces, ladders, spans over empty spaces, etc.;

They are unstructured to the extent that they are not set up to have known references for the movement of robots;

The tasks involved are complex in the cognitive sense, and they therefore require knowledge from experience and the use of certain sensory capacities;

Even tasks with repetitive operations would require the robot to systematically change position, usually by shifting orientation so that it could begin a new cycle.

All this implies that using robots in practice, on actual work sites, would depend on their being portable, being able to move around, to "sense" the environment, to process the data and information received and, based on all the information available, to perform a task. As building sites are unstructured localities, they present a considerable challenge to mobility and recognition of the workplace environment.

For the use of robots on actual building sites to be effective we would have to concentrate especially on the domains detailed below:

Locomotion: robots would have to be able to move about with a certain degree of "intelligence", which implies providing them with the means to go up ladders, cross spans, avoid obstacles; that is, the means of locomotion implies the existence of viable paths. This situation is quite different from real building sites, where surfaces are not smooth, but are littered with rubbish, materials stacked ready for use, obstacles, etc. They would have to provide the means for guidance, or organize pre-defined routes (likely to be repetitive), or structured environments with references identifiable by robots.

Vision: most of the capacities required imply the use of artificial vision, with recognition of the range of environments in which the robot operates.

Being prepared for hostile environments: robots should be ready to work outdoors, moving around in difficult conditions, unprotected and subject to the unexpected, such as falling from heights, falling materials, impacts, atmospheric agents, etc.

Handling unwieldy or heavy loads: robots could perform tasks involving the handling of heavy loads, such as beams or prefabricated panels (which can weigh several tons), and large elements.

Handling fragile materials: robots could handle breakable materials, like some ceramic products (tiles, bathroom fittings) or glass.

Current technology in the domain of robotics could overcome each of these difficulties. As we have discussed before (Pereira 2002), this would not, however, be economically viable, even if major changes were made to building sites. The use of robots in construction should only be undertaken away from the problems intrinsic to building site environments. The hypothesis that seems to offer the best chance of taking the greatest advantage of robots today lies in carrying out repetitive tasks, on a large scale and with a fixed job, in a factory situation.

To benefit from the potentials and virtualities of advances in robotics it would be necessary first to modify the conceptual understanding of the construction industry, more specifically, the construction process itself.

By having robots carrying out tasks in factory environments, where there are no problems in terms of moving around and identifying the place of work, we come up against implications and problems related mainly to pre-fabrication.

In terms of technology, designers would have to adapt their plans to use components provided by pre-fabrication, reducing, as far as possible, the amount of elements made on site. Preparation of the works prior to execution on site would thus become more important. In execution, with the prior manufacture of components to be incorporated, construction would increasingly become an assembly industry.

With respect to the economic implications of producing those elements (components or constructive systems) to be incorporated into buildings, construction would be more and more reliant on the upstream industry. The viability of these (upstream) firms would depend on sales volume. This in turn would be critically dependent on the popularity of their products and the capacity of the company to produce them at a cost that justified the change in technology. It should also be mentioned that, in many countries, jobs are overwhelmingly carried out by low-cost labour, and immigrant workers are frequently employed. In Portugal, for example, after decades of African workers, there is now an influx of emigrants from Eastern Europe. Ukrainians, Moldavians and Romanians are now commonly seen on our building sites.

Regardless of these implications, it should be stressed that some robotic systems have the potential for immediate use in the environment of pre-fabrication for the construction industry. Robot manipulators in particular have features and a level of technical development that are quite capable of meeting the demands of the tasks in question. In this domain, the advance of robotics technology could make it applicable in a good many construction processes.

Industrial robot manipulators are essentially machines with control over position and movement, to which work tools can be adapted. In addition, they have a high degree of precision and speed of execution. can accept several communication interfaces, have various input/output possibilities, force control, visual servoing (see Pires 2000). But they need to be integrated and adapted to the specific manufacturing requirements, in terms of both working tools and programming.

Next we shall look at two implementation cases that are in progress.

3 WELDING ROBOT

The first case we shall now examine it was designed to install robot manipulators in one of the country's leading metal construction firms. The robots' work is to solder metal structures.

The system comprises an industrial robot, a welding machine and a personal computer running Windows NT 4.0 or Windows 2000 (Fig. 1).

In this specific welding system we used a FANUC manipulator but there are other commercial available industrial robots.

Focusing our attention on the computer, we must stress that as it will be used for modelling, monitoring and controlling tasks, it must include Visual C++, Basic or Matlab programming tools.

It also use software for controlling, programming and monitoring the robot. It should be noted that the connection to the programming environments (Visual C++ and Basic), to mathematics environments (Matlab), and other tools for analysing and presenting results (Excel, etc.) capable of real-time intervention,

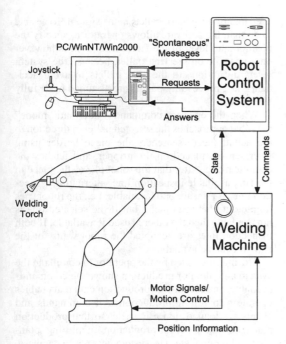

Figure 1.   The welding system.

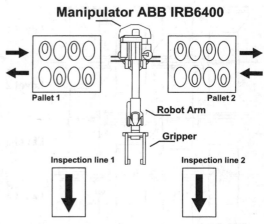

Figure 2.   Basic layout of the system.

mean that a powerful setup for R&D uses can be obtained, as is desired for robotized welding.

In order to achieve our objectives, the first goal is certainly to characterize and define the interface with the user (which implies understanding the production process) and defining the kind of information to be requested.

Later, with the working system it is possible to develop procedures for the technological process. In this peculiar case that will make it possible to simplify and characterize the preparation phase (setting up all the parameters and trajectories), and to identify a minimum (but sufficient) group of parameters for monitoring the way to achieve welding of constant quality, within pre-defined ranges.

For this purpose, it is intended to use robots together with an architecture database that contains all the variables of the welding process and the dimensions of the pieces to be welded, the weld points programmed for the beginning and end of the operation. This database will help to reduce the work times related to changing the product, adjusting and programming the robot.

For current manufacturing operation, it is intended that the operator should choose a product code and thickness from the database. All the variables will be listed in a dialogue box; the operator should determine three or four spot welds, and their parameters, if necessary.

Once adjustments have been made, the operator starts the programme cycle. The robot can then begin or end a welding procedure, it can be commanded to follow trajectories (wholly simulated) or to proceed with the welding, step-by-step.

For this, the user sends the full definition of the task, including welding spots and parameters (speed, tension and intensity), type of trajectory and precision, all of which information is stored in a file.

This information can be reused countless times, forming production routines that the operator can use whenever the components to be welded have the same characteristics.

4   DE-PALLETIZING ROBOT FOR THE NON-FLAT CERAMIC INDUSTRY

In the next example, presented above, a few features currently available and possible on manufacturing systems may be easily explored to extend the off site construction tasks, namely pre-fabrication and assembly. The example works with non-flat ceramic products, is tolerant with considerably high product placement errors, and presents an easy to use interface with operators.

The main objective here was to build a robotic system that could be used to feed the final inspection lines (Fig. 2). The system should be able to work with pallets composed by 4 levels of ceramic pieces, 8 pieces per level placed in a special order to keep pallet equilibrium, and with levels separated with pieces of hard paper. The rule used to arrange the pieces in the pallet is to place them alternatively one up–one down, starting from the ground level, then swap to one down–one up in the next level (Fig. 3) and keep the procedure in the proceeding levels. Levels are numerated from up

317

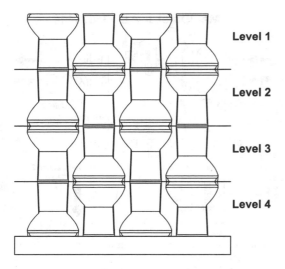

Figure 3.   Organization of the ceramic pieces on the pallet.

to bottom, i.e., level 1 is the top level and level 4 is the bottom level.

Actually pallets are assembled manually by operators at the end of the high temperature oven. This means that the robotic system must be tolerant with possible medium-large palletizing errors, coming from misplaced pieces both in position and orientation, and showing also significant variations from level to level.

Another important thing is that pallets are fed into the system by human operators using electro-mechanic pile drivers, which also introduces some variation in the pallet. Sometime in the future AGVs will be used to fulfill the task, reducing considerably the variations introduced and increasing efficiency of the system.

Other important requirements include:

a) Possibility to easily introduce new product models;
b) Possibility to parameterize the operation on each model, so that best performance per model is achieved;
c) Possibility to change model under production without stopping production;
d) Possibility to monitor production using a graphical interface;
e) Obtain medium cycle times of about 12 seconds per piece, which means a new piece in each inspecting line every 24 seconds.

The system is completely operated using a graphical panel running on the PC, built using ActiveX controls in Visual C++.

When the system is started, the operator needs only to specify what product model will be used in each pallet, and if first pallets are fully assembled. Sometimes, due to production flows, there are some non-fully assembled pallets on the shop floor, and there is the need to introduce those pallets in the system. To be able to do that, the software allows operator to specify the position and level of the first piece. That is however only possible on the first pallet, because the system resets definitions to the next pallets to avoid accidents, i.e., proceeding pallets are assumed to be fully assembled.

When the operator commands "automatic mode" the robot approaches the selected pallet in direction to the actual piece, searchers the piece border using laser sensors placed on the gripper, and fetches the ceramic piece. After that the robot places the piece in the first available inspection line, alternating inspection lines if they are both available, i.e., the robot tries to alternate between them, but if the selected one is not available then the other is used if available. If both inspection lines are occupied the robot waits for the first to became available.

The interface used by the operator to command the system and monitor production shows the commands available, and the on-line production data that enables operators to follow production. All commands and events are logged into a log file, so that production managers can use it for production monitoring, planning, debugging, etc. The system uses also a database, organized in function of the model number, where all the data related to each model is stored. That data includes type of the piece, dimensions, height where the gripper should grab the piece, average position of the first piece of the pallet, height of the pallet, etc. Accessing and updating the database is done in "manual mode", selected in the PC interface. There is a "teaching" option that enables operator to introduce new models and parameterize the database for that model. When that option is commanded, the robot pre-positions near the pallet and the operator can jog the robot using function keys to the desired position/orientation. Basically the de-palletizing operation is preformed step-by-step and the necessary parameters acquired in the process, inquiring the operator to correct and acknowledge when necessary. The operator is only asked to enter the "model number", and to teach the height and the width of the piece. All the rest is automatic. After finishing this routine the model is introduced into the database, and the system can then work with that model number.

Figure 4 shows the system in operation. It proved to be very easy to operate, and the interface with operators showed to be efficient and easy to use. Operators adapted quickly and like to use it.

One of the most important things about introducing robots into production systems, that share also a very high degree of human labour, is the interface between machines and humans. In some sense the interface should be easy to operate, but it should be designed in a way that there are no sudden moves, i.e., operation must start or resume slowly and take always paths well

Figure 4.   Picture of the system under working conditions.

known by the operator. Predictability is an important thing. Safety is another important thing, since humans tend to adapt quickly and relax safety procedures. Because of that, intrusion into the cell must always act on the emergencies of the system as quickly as possible (using class 5 safety equipments), and should be logged for proper action. We adopted to add a special procedure for after emergency re-start that is time consuming, and requires operator login to resume.

In that case, all emergencies are logged with the ID of the operator which prevents operators of being too much confident.

The average cycle time obtained is lower than 12 seconds, which complies with the requirement of one piece on each inspection line every 24 seconds.

Another important thing is the time to production, when a new model is introduced. Adding a model should be done easily by any operator, and should not take too long, so that normal production would not be affected.

With the actual system, a new model is introduced and ready to be handled by the system in less than 5 minutes, including verification tests used to check if programming was well done.

5   CONCLUSIONS

The possibility of incorporating in building a significant percentage of pre-fabricated elements, produced by robots, assumes the existence of an industry upstream in which manufacturing tasks are performed in a controlled environment, and not on site.

Cheap labour is an impediment to significant change in current construction processes, and to the large-scale introduction of robotics in this industry.

While research continues in this area, implementation will increase in fields where productivity gains outweigh the equipment and implementation costs.

Robot manipulators are now a good investment, given their possibilities and flexibility.

REFERENCES

Pires, N. 2000. Using Actual Industrial Robot Manipulators With Construction Tasks, *Proc. of the 17th IAARC Conference, Taipei, Taiwan.*

Pereira, T. et al. 2002. The Use of Robots in the Construction Industry, *Proc. of the XXX IAHS Conference, Coimbra, Portugal.*

System-based Vision for Strategic and Creative Design, Bontempi (ed.)
© *2003 Swets & Zeitlinger, Lisse, ISBN 90 5809 599 1*

A review of capital procurement in the UK National Health Service

D.G. Proverbs, M. Sutrisna
School of Engineering and the Built Environment, University of Wolverhampton, Wulfruna Street, West Midlands, UK

G. Riley
Sandwell Healthcare NHS Trust, Sandwell General Hospital, West Bromwich, West Midlands, UK

ABSTRACT: The National Health Service is one of the most complex organizations in Europe and is one of the largest clients of the UK construction industry. The estate on which healthcare services are produced is vast, with a current market value of £23 billion. Despite this level of investment, procurement in the NHS has come under criticism. On the backdrop of long-term major investment planned for the NHS, this paper presents a critical review of current procurement practices. Existing procedures are identified as being fragmented, with very little expertise shared across NHS Trusts, and having led to a large number of suppliers and a diluting of procurement expertise. Procurement is extremely time consuming and often demands that staff with skills in operational health care management are deflected from their main duty. Furthermore, because of the fragmentation and independence that exists across the numerous Trusts, each project requires a unique and time consuming design and opportunities for employing standard and or prefabricated solutions are not realised. National and local NHS guidelines only serve to compound this fragmentation and are unequivocal in their support of competitive tendering procedures.

1 INTRODUCTION

The National Health Service (NHS) is one of the most complex organizations in Europe, employing 1 in 20 of the working population of the United Kingdom. With an annual expenditure of £42.5 billion, the NHS is responsible for over 400 Healthcare Trusts whose principal aim is to provide local healthcare services to the public. This is achieved on over 1200 hospital sites and over 11,000 GP surgeries across the land (Priestly 2000).

The estate on which healthcare services are produced is vast, with a current market value of £23 billion. The building stock from which healthcare is delivered ranges from primary care practices, to large, multi-disciplinary and specialized hospital sites, having a replacement value of over £72 (NHS Estates 2000a).

Over 60% of the current NHS Estate is over 35 years old. Some of these existing buildings suffer greatly from decaying construction, poor energy efficiency, failing plant and machinery and so on. Twenty per cent of NHS annual expenditure is allocated to maintaining this estate.

The Government's plan for investment in the NHS, namely *A Plan for Investment, A plan for Reform* (Department of Health 2000), which sets out plans for

investment in NHS with sustained increases in funding was presented by the Secretary of State for Health to parliament in July 2000. Proposed major investment in NHS buildings included:

- 100 new hospitals over the next 10 years;
- 20 new general Diagnostic and Treatment Centres developed by 2004;
- Up to 3000 family doctors' premises substantially refurbished or replaced by 2004; and
- 500 new one-stop primary care centers by 2004.

These new and improved facilities are to be provided through a mixture of public capital, private finance and NHS Local Improvement Finance Trust (NHS Lift). Objectives of the NHS Plan include:

- An extended role for Private Finance Initiative representing £7 billion of new capital investment by 2010;
- 40% of total value of the NHS Estate will be less than 15 years old by 2010;
- By 2004 the NHS will have cleared at least a quarter of its £3.1 billion maintenance backlog accumulated through two decades of under investment.

On the backdrop of this planned sustained investment, this paper aims to critically review current capital procurement practices in the NHS with a view to identifying weaknesses and shortcomings. Procurement practices are first considered followed by an evaluation of current national and local NHS guidelines. Finally a summary of the review is provided and plans for the introduction of a new procurement system are briefly discussed.

2 NHS CAPITAL PROCUREMENT

Capital procurement is a very significant part of the Governments' drive to modernize the NHS. The NHS spends in excess of £2 billion a year on capital investment and has the largest capital procurement programme in Government with over 1800 major capital schemes. These developments range from the construction of large new hospitals, to smaller capital projects to modernize existing facilities in line with current standards. Similarly, the level of technical expertise required on these projects varies significantly.

2.1 Fragmented design and procurement organisations

Unlike other government departments and private sector organizations, the NHS has over 500 individual organizations that can procure buildings. These are commonly found within each NHS trust, which have their own capital design and production departments, with very little expertise shared across organizations. This fragmentation has led to a large number of suppliers and a diluting of procurement expertise, which is contrary to many of the principles of best procurement practice as identified in the Egan Report (Egan 1998).

The process of procurement is time-consuming, deflecting organizations from their other tasks and requiring those with skills in operational health care management to learn new skills and processes on a steep learning curve. Many NHS Trusts contract out much of the work involved to the private sector, and even then the private sector "charges the NHS for reinventing the wheel" (NHS Estates 2000b). Individuals who become engaged in major procurements generally move on to other related tasks, and much of their knowledge and experience is therefore lost.

2.2 Site-specific user requirements

Each NHS Trust have their own strategic direction, which influences their planned construction programme. Within this construction programme, each project will have a set of user requirements, which may differ from hospital to hospital due to factors such as:

- Type of development;
- Location of development;
- Size/number of functional units required for this development;
- Consultants specialty;
- Operational policy for the development;
- Business direction of the Trust;
- Strategic direction of the Trust;
- Estates strategy of the Trust;
- Equipment preferences of the users/Trust; and
- Staffing issues.

As well as site-specific user requirements, each NHS trust will have its own set of procedures for gaining appropriate advice from a range of professionals within the NHS, which must be adhered to within the construction process. These professionals include:

- Trust Health and Safety Committee;
- Trust Financial Advisor;
- Trust Performance Management Team; and
- Trust Infection Control Team.

It is clear that there can be no standard design solution for hospital developments due to the issues mentioned above. Although hospital designs are based on a series of standard briefing notes and technical memorandum (NHS Estates 1990–2002), the specific user requirements and site-specific procedures are key to producing a design solution which is practical, functional and operational.

Defining an adequate design brief for each development is therefore time consuming, as this will involve close liaison with staff (including senior nurses, consultants, management teams, etc.) as well as internal bodies (such as health and safety committees, infection control and so on) who will all contribute to the finished design. Although time consuming, this is one of the most important parts of the construction process as it ensures that the strategic, business and operational requirements of the Trust are met within the development.

2.2 Choice of contractor

Main building contractors are chosen from an approved list of contractors, which can be compiled by various agencies who will carry out the necessary financial checks prior to entering into any contractual arrangements.

At the tender stage of a project, the design team, in conjunction with the NHS Trust project team, will compile a list of contractors to be approached to tender for the construction works. These contractors are chosen according to the size of the individual development, their experience in working for other local NHS Trust's, and by gaining references for that contractor from other NHS Trust's for which they have carried out similar sized and type of developments. That is, each Trust is responsible for firstly identifying and then procuring suitable contractors. As such, most contractors are employed on a short-term competitive basis, which is known to be counter-productive and goes against much modern thinking. Benefits afforded by long term relationships based on trust and mutual agreement as reported in many recognized sources are therefore not realized.

3 CURRENT NHS EXECUTIVE NATIONAL PROCUREMENT GUIDANCE

Each NHS trust is provided with detailed guidance on how it should be operated by the governing body, the NHS Executive. This guidance includes procurement of construction works for the modernization of the NHS.

NHS capital investment is central to the continual development and modernization of the NHS in line with the NHS Plan (Department of Health 2000). To ensure that adequate guidance and control measures are in place, the NHS Executives, have issued a series of national guidance which NHS Trusts, with their individual construction organizations, are required to follow. The following sections critically appraises these guidelines.

3.1 Capital investment manual

A series of documents, under the main heading of "The Capital Investment Manual" (NHS Executive 1994) was published to provide detailed guidance on the capital appraisal process, as well as providing a framework for establishing management arrangements to ensure that the benefits of every capital investment are identified, evaluated and realized.

The NHS Executive guidance is presented in a series of documents covering a range of issues involved in the capital development process including project organization, private finance and commissioning. The document which covers the procurement stage of a development is called "Management of Construction Projects". This document describes the development process under 6 stages:

- Stage 1: Full business case leading to approval;
- Stage 2: Design;
- Stage 3: Tender and contract;
- Stage 4: Supply and construction;
- Stage 5: Technical commissioning and handover;
- Stage 6: Post completion.

Each stage follows from the proceeding one, providing clear guidance on the application of the procedures contained therein, and on good practice. The subject of procurement is covered in Stage 3 of the process where the document identifies that NHS Trusts should have "procurement procedures in place", and must "comply with these policies, whether they have capital works projects or not". It is therefore up to each individual NHS Trust to have their own specific rules and procedures on procurement and as such these are likely to vary from one Trust to another. This lack of a consistent approach only serves to complicate what is already a complex process and no doubt causes much confusion and poor resource utilization on behalf of tenderers.

The document also refers each NHS Trust to another guidance document, named "Concode" which specifically "provides guidance on the contracting aspects of health building projects, including the implementation of policy and EC directives" (NHS Executive 1995). This is said to "help trusts in the appointment of works contractors and consultants, and the use of various forms of contract".

3.2 Concode – contracts and commisssions for NHS estates

"Concode" provides NHS Trusts with guidance on different forms of contract and procurement available for construction (NHS Executive 1995). Volume 3 of these documents provides information on the different types of contract strategy available for projects, and also provides guidance on how each should be evaluated to allow the NHS Trust to choose the most appropriate contract strategy for a particular project.

The document provides an evaluation of six different forms of contract strategy (design and build; develop and construct; traditional with quantities; traditional with approximate quantities; management contract; construction management), identifying where each should be used depending on the particulars of the project and amount of risk the NHS Trust wishes to be exposed.

A major omission of the document is a failure to identify partnering as a recommended procurement strategy. This mirrors the guidance provided within the Capital Investment Manual (and in the local guidance – see later), which all advocate some form of competitive tendering, in whichever contract strategy is chosen.

4 CURRENT LOCAL NHS TRUST PROCUREMENT GUIDANCE

Each NHS Trust is required to draw up their own set of Standing Orders and Standing Financial Instructions, following guidance from the NHS Executive. All orders and instructions contained within the Standing Orders and Standing Financial Instructions are mandatory to all NHS Trust staff within that organization. For the purposes of this review, the documentation of one NHS Trust (Sandwell Healthcare NHS Trust) have been considered.

Procurement of construction works is dealt with in Section 9 (Purchasing and Contracting Procedures) and Section 10 (Building and Engineering and Matters) of the Trusts Standing Orders (Sandwell Healthcare NHS Trust 1998a, 1998b).

Clauses within the document require that:

(i) Compliance with Concode (clause 9.1.2);
(ii) Tenders must be based upon a competitive element, regardless of the purpose of tender (clauses 9.3.3, 9.3.5). Two exceptions to this requirement are provided allowing the NHS Trust to approve a tender without the use of a formal competitive procedure but neither of these permit partnering as an alternative solution;
(iii) For any one case, the minimum number of tenderers should be three (no upper limit is stated) (clause 9.4.4);
(iv) No type of negotiation takes place with a supplier of goods and services, unless formal approval is gained from the Director of Finance. Therefore contact with tendering contractors to discuss such issues as constructability is not permitted which prevents the possible benefits both the Latham (1994) and Egan (1998) reports were striving to achieve;
(v) Lowest tender shall be accepted unless the Chief Executive agrees that there are good and sufficient reasons to the contrary (clause 9.4.5);
(vi) Competitive tenders will be sought for all schemes in excess of £5000 (clause 10.1.1). This low threshold means that competitive tendering will therefore be required in nearly all cases.

In summary, competitive tendering is advocated as the main form of procurement to be used. The guidance refers to "*Concode*" to establish which form of competitive tender is appropriate to that particular project. Partnering is not mentioned as an approved form of procurement, and therefore cannot be used at present by NHS Trusts.

5   SUMMARY

A review of current systems of procurement within the NHS has been presented, including local and national guidance provided to NHS Trusts. This has demonstrated how each of the NHS Trusts have to work independently in procuring construction works and the problems this can create. An overview of the contractor selection procedures has been provided together with an indication of the nature of site-specific characteristics that influence each project. Current practices, structure and policy are considered remarkably rigid and enforce the use of competitive tendering practices. It is only with expressed authorisation of senior management that alternative procedures can be pursued.

Notwithstanding the weaknesses of current NHS procurement practices, proposed changes are now being considered and a new NHS capital procurement system, "*NHS Procure21*", is now being trialled. This new system proposes the appointment of Principle Supply Chain Partners (PSCP) and recognizes partnering as key aspect. Five PSCP's are to be appointed under long term framework agreements, to take single point responsibility for design and construction of healthcare projects. This, it is hoped, will bring about significant cost savings for the NHS. The authors hope to report on the piloting of the new system in the near future.

REFERENCES

Department of Health 2000. The NHS Plan, A Plan for Investment, A plan for Reform, Department of Health.

Egan, J. 1998. Rethinking Construction, Department of the Environment, Transport and the Regions.

Latham, M. 1994. Constructing the Team, Final Report of the Government/Industry Review of Procurement and Contractual Arrangements in the UK Construction Industry. HMSO, London.

NHS Estates 1990–2002. Health Building Notes, London, HMSO.

NHS Estates 2000a. Sold on Health: Modernising Procurement, Operation and Disposal of the NHS Estate. London, HMSO.

NHS Estates 2000b. NHS ProCure21: Building Better Health, Briefing for NHS Colleagues. London, HMSO.

NHS Executive 1994. Capital Investment Manual, London, HMSO.

NHS Executive 1995. CONCODE Contracts and commissions for the NHS estate–Policy, London, HMSO.

Priestly, K. 2000. NHS Procure21 – Building Better Health, NHS Estates.

Sandwell Healthcare NHS Trust 1998a. Standing Orders, Sandwell Healthcare NHS Trust.

Sandwell Healthcare NHS Trust 1998b. Standing Financial Instructions, Sandwell Healthcare NHS Trust.

Riley, G. 2002. A Study into the Introduction and Implementation of a New Capital Procurement System in the NHS. Undergraduate final year dissertation, University of Wolverhampton.

System-based Vision for Strategic and Creative Design, Bontempi (ed.)
© 2003 Swets & Zeitlinger, Lisse, ISBN 90 5809 599 1

Construction techniques for efficient and economical housing

R.K. Jain

Deptt. of Arch. & Plng., IIT Roorkee, India

ABSTRACT: Provision of inexpensive housing in urban areas of developing countries is gaining an alarming proportion. The answer to this vexed issue would be to develop cost effective and fast method of construction. Major issues effecting provision of housing are:-

(i)   Housing types and the efficient methods of construction.
(ii)   Shortage of high density housing in the vicinity of employment centers.
(iii)   Need for speedy & economic construction through improvisation in traditional methods of construction with newer and emerging techniques.
(iv)   Management of the labour component (which ranges between 15–20% of the total cost of the building).

This paper aims to analyze various existing techniques and methods of construction deployed in housing construction so as to established a suitable method of construction for mid rise walkups which would be relevant to the context of developing countries.

The study would be substantiated by case studies to compare the cost in-terms of land, labour and time, involved in three distinct construction techniques used in the construction of housing for lower/middle income group people in a metropolitan region.

1   INTRODUCTION

With over half of humanity now living in cities and towns, the challenge of the urban millennium is to improve the living environment and augment the housing supply. The rapid urbanization has resulted in a continuous increase in the number and size of urban centers both demographically and spatially, leading to the shortage of housing stock. As a result, the requirement for housing is gaining alarming proportion the world over and more so in developing countries and specially for lower and middle income groups.

India's urban population which was 285 M in 2001 is likely to be 366 M (+81 M from 2001) in 2011 and 459 M (+174 M from 2001) in 2021. India has formulated "National Housing and Rehabilitation Policy" in 1998 with the aim to provide *Housing* for all. Although there was a shortage of 6.64 M urban dwellings in 2001 only 71.01% households has pucca houses. The high cost of land has further aggravated this problem.

Government have launched certain schemes to encourage housing construction activities but these schemes still needs certain modifications/improvements etc. specially in terms of improved technologies and associated infrastructure services.

In India, housing construction is undertaken with traditional methods and material which are time consuming and at times the shortage of materials and poor management causes delay. This serve as a great impediment in increasing the productivity. Attempts have been made for quite some time to industrialize the building process while planning work operation leading to higher skills, greater speed and better quality of work at optimum cost.

Due to the pressure on land, the need of 4–5 storey residential walkups has been felt. It is generally observed that the housing shortage is possible to be overcome with adopting a density of 500 to 750 persons per Ha for small and medium towns. These densities could be achieved by 4 or 5 storey walkup apartments without lift.

Another aspect is the traditional methods of construction which are inadequate and where labour accounts for 20–25% of the cost. Although unskilled labour is cheap in the country the excess labour results in lower productivity where as the skilled labour is scarce and costly. We therefore have to evolve/establish a better constructional method for raising walk-ups to provide an effective solution to housing demands in cities and towns for lower and middle income groups.

Table 1. Design features.

Construction stages	In-situ wall & slab	Partial prefab component	Fully prefab component
1 Foundation	Footing	Footing	Footing
2 Walling external & Internal	In-situ, Load bearing walls 23 cm thick	In-situ, Load bearing walls 23 cm thick	RCC panels prefabricated on site with plaster finish 15 cm & 2 cm
3 Roofing & stair	In-situ work	Precast roofing (RCC planks & joists	RCC panels prefabricated on site
4 Doors/windows & ventilators	Prefabricated steel frames & flush door shutters	Prefabricated steel frames & flush door shutters	Prefabricated steel frames & flush door shutters
5 Finishes	In-situ work	In-situ work	In-situ work
6 Sanitation W.S. & Elect.	Site work	Site work	Site work

Table 2. Comparative merits and demerits.

In-situ wall & slab	Partial prefab component	Full prefab component
All manual	Partially manual	Buildings components are produced in bulk in factory or site using assembly line technique.
Too much time consuming	Speed more than traditional method	Maximum speed in construction
Wastage of material	Less wastage	No wastage
Lack of coordination between labour & professionals	More coordination	Max coordination
		Construction possible year round
Variation in the quality of component	Possible to achieve standardization in the components	Standardized component & better quality control
Less capital investment	More capital investment than traditional	Needs heavy capital investments

2 SCOPE

The paper attempts to compare and analyze the cost, labour and time involved in three selected construction methods, i.e. In-situ wall and slab, partial prefab component and fully prefab component, based on the capabilities of the local contractors and available pre cast facilities and to determine the most suitable method of construction in the prevailing economic situation for Middle income group and Low income group houses in a metropolitan region.

3 ANALYSIS OF SELECTED CONSTRUCTION TECHNIQUES

The method of construction is affected by availability of material and technical know how along with the limiting factors of cost and time.

We have selected the following methods for the construction of multifamily walkups.

(i) In-situ wall and slab construction
(ii) Partial prefab component construction
(iii) Fully prefab component construction (with traditional foundation)

For the purpose of analysis, a housing block of 16 dwelling units in 4 floors (4 D.U. per floor) is selected.

Table 3. Estimation of labour.

	No. of labour		
Type of labour	In-situ wall & slab	Partial prefab component	Fully prefab component
Mistri	244	244	268
Mason	1680	1680	480
Beldar	1363	1340	1636
Coolhe	2954	2889	3365
Bhisti	592	580	488
Carpenter	652	636	635
Black smith	542	510	814

The basic design and architectural form used by CBRI for apartments for low and middle income group was taken as a basis for all the designs. The main features of these designs are as given in Tables 1 and 2.

The quantities of material in each method of construction have been worked out and accordingly the labour involved has been estimated as given in Table 3.

The total time taken in different stage of building construction in each method has been computed. Figure 1 shows the comparative analysis of time taken by selected construction methods.

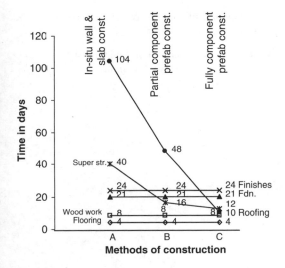

Figure 1.   Comparative time for construction stages.

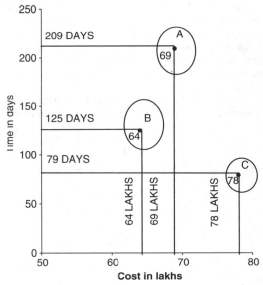

Figure 3.   Comparative cost and time factor.

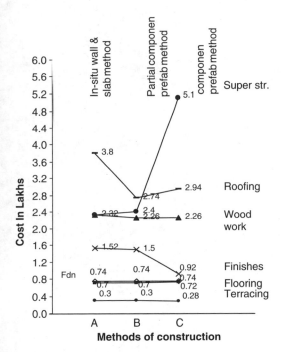

Figure 2.   Comparative cost for construction stages.

After this the cost has been worked out for each method of construction, excluding the cost of land, water supply, electrification, land development and roads etc. which are assumed to be constant for each case. These values are shown in Figures 2 and 3.

4   CONCLUSION & RECOMMENDATIONS

On comparing the cost and time for the three methods of construction following observations are derived.

Construction stage	Cost in million Rs/Man days		
	Traditional method	Partial prefab component	Fully pre fab component
Foundation (In-situ)	No saving	No saving	No saving
Super Stru.	7.2/40	7.6/16	13/12
Roofing/Stairs	10.8/104	8.2/48	8.8/10
Doors/Windows	7.0/8	6.8/8	6.8/8
Flooring	2.75/4	2.75/4	2.75/4
Terracing	0.9/8	0.9/8	0.78/8
Finishing	4.6/24	4.6/24	4.6/24

On the above comparison the partial prefab component method is recommended for erecting walls, pre cast lintels and sunshade etc. being 71.0% economical than fully component prefab method ($(13.0 - 7.6)/7.6 = 71.0\%$)), though the traditional method is 5.6% economical than partial prefab component method it involves 150% more time.

The saving in time for the above work in fully prefab component method is $(16 - 12)/12 = 33.4\%$ over partial prefab method, but it involves high skill and machinery and also has drawback such as leakage in rains, therefore, it is not preferred.

For roofing it is recommended to adopt fully pre-fab component method which is very fast and has a saving of 22.72% in cost (10.8 − 8.8/8.8).

Other components provide small saving in cost and time over each other, hence it could be decided by the Architect In charge as per the site conditions/ resources.

To augment the development of these methods to achieve economy & speed in construction through optimums use of material & time efforts should be made at National level to:

- Develop and organize building industry.
- Give incentives to building industry.
- Train skilled personals.

Automating quantity takeoff and decision support for in-place reinforced concrete structures

R. Drogemuller, S. Foo & C. McNamara
CSIRO, Melbourne, Australia

J. Oliver
Rider Hunt, Sydney, Australia

ABSTRACT: The availability of vendor neutral data exchange standards such as the Industry Foundation Classes (IFC) enables the semi-automation of many processes within the Architecture, Engineering & Construction industry. The aim of the project described in this paper was to see how well the IFCs support the takeoff of quantities and the preparation of estimates. The current focus is on in-place reinforced concrete since this provides many challenges. The current implementation is described as well as the lessons learned during its development.

1 INTRODUCTION

Taking off quantities and preparing estimates is a time consuming and error prone task. It is normally performed under considerable time pressure. Any IT tools that can simplify or speed up this process will have significant benefits to the users through increasing efficiency during the process and reducing problems during the subsequent contract due to improved accuracy.

The starting point of this project is the vision of the shared project database. The participants within a project share relevant information in a database and read or write the data they need as and when appropriate (Fig. 1). There are many issues that need to be resolved before this vision becomes a reality.

The underlying assumption is that the architect will prepare the initial layout of a building and hand this over to the engineering specialists to allow them to add the information from their area of expertise. We focus on the interaction between the architect, the structural engineer and the estimator. The structural engineer will gradually refine the design and add extra information, such as reinforcing bar layouts, etc which will be handed back to the architect and the estimator in an iterative manner. The estimator has a database of costs where each item has specific rules that define whether the unit rate for that item will be applied to a particular building element.

The scope of this work is the sharing of information across multiple computer applications under the control

of a single user. The Industry Foundation Classes (IFCs) are being used as the interface standard within this project. The IFCs are a vendor neutral specification for the exchange of information about building projects (IAI, 2000). Using the IFCs is attractive for developers of software that require information from architectural CAD systems. The IFCs free developers from dependence on a particular CAD vendor thereby increasing the available market for their products.

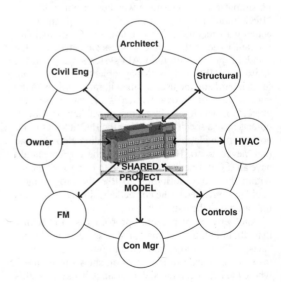

Figure 1. Concept of Shared Project Model.

The quantity takeoff and estimating process is error-prone and time critical. Providing support for these processes will provide considerable benefit to the users. Automatic quantity takeoff software has been developed for a number of areas but these usually involve the counting of discrete elements (i.e. number and types of doors) or measurement of linear elements such as pipe work. If automated quantity takeoff and estimating software is to have an impact on industry it must be able to handle "messy" areas such as reinforced concrete.

The technical starting point for this project was to take the standard item descriptions used by an Australian quantity surveying (cost engineering) company and to develop methods for extracting the correct information from a file exported from standard IFC compliant architectural CAD systems. The architectural CAD programs ArchiCAD, Architectural Desktop, Allplan and Microstation Triforma all produce IFC files (IAI, 2000). A common factor across these CAD systems is their support for object-oriented three dimensional modeling. This enables the user to define columns, beams, slabs, etc and to manipulate them in either two or three dimensions. The time required to create the plans, elevations, sections, etc from the three dimensional model is substantially reduced. More savings can be realized when the documents are modified since changes can be made to the central model and immediately replicated in the plans, sections, etc.

One issue that quickly arose when producing IFC files within the CAD systems was that "cheating" was not allowed. For example, a user *could* create a table using the "column", "beam" and "slab" tools and then assign the material "timber" to them. This would give the expected appearance when viewing the project, but when the information is exported to the IFC file there is no simple way to determine whether an object labeled "IfcColumn" (the IFC designation for columns) was actually a structural column or a table leg. Another significant issue is that objects that are created with the standard tools within the CAD systems are given the appropriate IFC names. Many objects inserted from the standard and the user-defined libraries are given the generic type of "proxy" which is the name used for objects for which there is no recognizable type. Not all objects have a specific type since the IFC definitions do not cover the entire spectrum of building elements and may never do so. However, where the objects should have an IFC defined type there had to be an attribute set within the proxy definition so that the proxy object could be converted to the correct definition when it was imported into the database.

Another area of potential problems is in checking that all building elements of the same type do not "clash". For example, poor attention by a CAD operator can easily lead to the situation shown in Figure 2 where the beam and the slab overlap. Checking for this situation in the general case is complicated by the

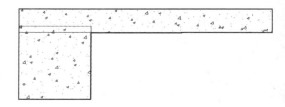

Figure 2. Illegal overlap of members.

requirement that some building elements, such as reinforcing, should be embedded in other elements. Obviously, care is required in resolving the clash detection problem.

A general principal underlying this work is to require the minimum change in existing industry work practices. Previous discussions have indicated that the more users have to change the way they work to use new software and processes the less the likelihood that the software will be successfully adopted.

The problems that have been addressed in this work are:

- Given the current lack of structural engineering software that supports the IFCs, how does the structural engineer add the required structural information to a product model exported from architectural CAD systems in a simple manner?
- How can the various building elements be mapped automatically to a cost database?
- How can the information be shared across the three different disciplines?
- How can the accuracy and adequacy of the information be checked?

2 DOCUMENTATION AND ESTIMATING CYCLE

The focus of this project lies in the brief but intensive period between completion of building documents and the completion of estimates of the project's cost. The completed three dimensional building model is taken as an input as is generated in the top four architectural CAD systems. This provides the source data for extraction of the quantities and development of an estimate.

A generic list of items from a bill of quantities provides the basis for taking off the quantities and matching the quantities with unit rates to build up a total estimate.

The estimator needs to be confident that the estimate is a true reflection of the project cost.

3 MODELLING REINFORCED CONCRETE

In-place reinforced concrete is an extremely flexible and durable material with many desirable properties.

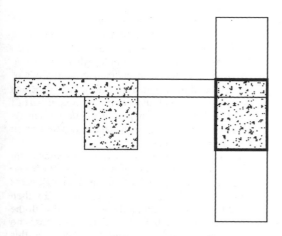

Figure 3.   Section through penetration.

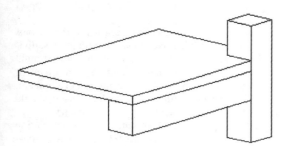

Figure 4.   Standard R-C configuration.

It is used extensively throughout the world because of its flexibility and other desirable properties. However, the flexibility of concrete means that automating the take-off of reinforced concrete quantities is difficult. A simple example illustrates this point.

Figure 3 shows a small detail of a typical reinforced concrete corner detail, with a column, two beams and a slab. This configuration presents no significant problems. However, Figure 4 shows the same configuration with a slot cut between the edge beam and the main floor slab. Structurally, this requires an additional beam to support the edge of the slab. The building elements were added in a typical sequence used by a CAD operator – draw the column, beams and slab, then cut the hole. The problem that arises here is that the perimeter beam is modeled as a beam on a slab, even though the "slab" is now the same width as the beam. According to the quantity takeoff rules used in Australia the perimeter member should be measured as an isolated beam as shown by the heavier outline (Fig. 5). Since a guiding principal is not to force unnecessary tasks on users methods of resolving this issue automatically are being developed.

The final major issue in extracting quantities is that the reinforcing steel configuration is seldom fully

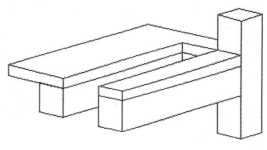

Figure 5.   Penetration near perimeter of Slab.

documented in CAD. Much of the transfer steel is referenced in the specification text rather than being explicitly drawn. In the future, specifications may be linked directly to a central building model, allowing direct querying of this information. Currently, a user entered weighting factor is provided that allows the user to estimate the extra percentage of weight of steel that will be required. While this is not an ideal solution, it matches current Australian industry practice.

This project commenced in June 2001 when there was no structural engineering software available that supported the IFCs. Consequently, simple spreadsheet-based software was developed to allow the addition of reinforcing layouts to the concrete elements. This is handled by attaching text strings specifying the reinforcement configuration to concrete elements. Even now only two of the major CAD systems support reinforcing bar configuration.

4   A SOFTWARE ARCHITECTURE FOR QUANTITY TAKEOFF AND ESTIMATING

When preparing a bill of quantities or an estimate using current computer based systems the user will sit at their computer with a stack of relevant paper documents alongside. As building elements are measured off the drawings with a scale rule the user marks the measured element with a highlighter to avoid double measurement. In order to replicate the existing environment, two main user interfaces are provided – the typical spreadsheet like user interface of an estimating system as well as a viewer that allows the user to explore the building model in three dimensions. An additional user interface has been developed to allow the addition of reinforcement data to building models produced by CAD systems that do not support the addition of reinforcing bars or mesh.

Underlying these user interfaces is a shared object-oriented database that supports the IFC data exchange standard. The IFC files generated by a CAD system are read into the database. The files for each project are stored in separate repositories so that multiple

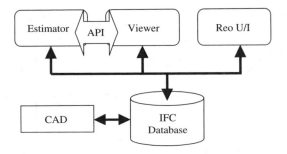

Figure 6. Software architecture.

projects can be accessed from the one database. The EDM database used in this project supports the importing of different versions of schema and mapping these versions to the schema used by the various programs. This provides a level of protection from releases of new versions of the IFC model.

5 EXTRACTING REINFORCED CONCRETE DATA

Within the approximately 20 sections that specifications (CIS, 2003) and bills of quantities are normally divided into in Australia, this project is concerned with three – concrete, reinforcement and formwork. While this does not appear to be a significant proportion of the trades the range of options available within these trades means that most of the possible issues arising from automating quantity takeoff need to be catered for in these trade sections. Since these three sections also form a cohesive whole the work is of practical interest to structural engineers, cost engineers/quantity surveyors, estimators and sub-contractors.

When extracting the data for structural concrete slabs, beams, columns, walls and proxy objects need to be checked to see if they are made from concrete. Proxy objects are created by the CAD systems when they are exporting library objects which the CAD system can not readily catergorise. The CAD systems being used to generate the input data have been extended to allow the user to add an explicit attribute that defines the appropriate "type" of an object for future processing. The CAD vendors are aware of this issue and are adapting their systems to provide this as a built-in facility (i.e Graphisoft's GDL (GDL Technology, 2002)).

The major issues that needed to be resolved for concrete were:

• Identification of composite objects
• Handling voids in elements

The resolution of these problems required some meta-level reasoning facilities within the system. The working methods used in the construction industry vary consideration. The meta-level reasoning allows customization of the aggregation of objects and of the minimum sizes of openings or voids that are included in the measurements. For example, when measuring the volume of concrete in either a ground floor or suspended reinforced concrete slab attached beams are included as though they were an integral part of the slab under Australian practice. This system is flexible enough to be able to handle differences in such measurement rules.

The identification of beams and thickenings that should be included as part of a slab is not a trivial exercise. The slabs are identified first and the beams and thickenings on the next level down are then checked to see if they should be aggregated with the slab for measurement purposes. Currently there is no simple system to allow the user(s) to check that this process has identified the correct relationships. In the near future the Viewer will be configured to support this kind of checking.

There are also some idiosyncrasies of the various CAD systems such as lack of support for stories, division of curved members into multiple short straight segments, etc. These have either been resolved or methods for resolving them are under development. This is consistent with the approach that users should not be asked to do anymore than is necessary.

Of the major CAD systems, only Microstation Triforma and Allplan support reinforcement layouts "out of the box". This has made obtaining or generating test files more difficult. As mentioned previously, the major issue with measuring reinforcement is that not all of the reinforcement is explicitly drawn. Ligatures and other small or repetitive elements are often referenced in notes or the specification. The modeling of reinforcement as three dimensional elements is difficult and tedious. If reinforcement is ever to be fully modeled in three dimensions then user-friendly and sophisticated documentation systems will be required. Checking that the reinforcement is placed appropriately is also difficult. Since reinforcing bars and mesh can pass through two or more members checking for containment, minimum cover and congestion is a major task.

None of the CAD systems support formwork design. Tipos (Cimware, 2003) is add-on software for AutoCAD that supports the design of formwork. Fortunately, under Australian measurement rules the measurement of formwork is relatively simple since the choice of the particular system is the responsibility of the contractor. This means that the critical information required is the height of the formwork above support locations (to allow for design of propping systems) the soffit (underside) area of concrete members, the vertical faces of members and any set downs, joints and other features. Identification of surfaces that will have special treatments is problematic.

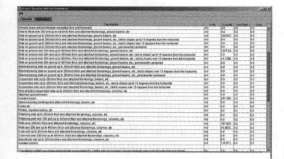

Figure 7. Estimator user interface.

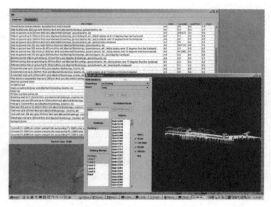

Figure 8. Interaction between Viewer and Estimator.

This could also be supported through extensions to the Viewer.

6 AUTOMATING THE QUANTITY TAKE-OFF PROCESS

There are two ways of using this system – by starting with the Estimator or the Viewer. The appropriate starting point depends on the focus of attention of the user at the time. Since both components interact with each other in a seamless manner the method of initiation is not important.

When a user is generating a bill of quantities or an estimate they will normally start with the Estimator. The Estimator has a typical user interface consisting of broken into rows containing textual descriptions of the particular item, the units of measurement, the measured quantity, the unit rate and the item cost. The costs per section are given at the bottom of the window as is the total for all of the measured sections. The method of operation is simple and flexible. A configuration file written in XML stores the natural language description of an item, a query which represents a formal description of the item as a database query, the units and the unit rate of the item. The separation of the description from the actual database query used means that this system can be used in any country.

When the user asks for an estimate to be generated the program reads in the configuration file and builds a decision tree that represents all of the queries against the items. This ensures that an element is only measured once. The queries at each leaf in the decision tree are fired against the database in a more detailed query first sequence. Eventually the entire decision tree is traversed and the relevant element identifiers have been stored against each node. The tree is then traversed again to run the query that extracts the required data for each element listed against that node. The values at each node are added to give the quantity and then multiplied by the unit rate to give the cost for this item.

Generating a bill of quantities or an estimate automatically is easy for the user, but how much faith can the user put in the result. Have the people preparing the building model and documents stuck to the required protocols? Are the queries against each item accurate? Have all of the building elements been measured against the appropriate items. Without the drawings alongside the computer neatly marked up with highlighter how does the estimator know that everything is ok?

The Viewer component provides a mechanism to allow the user to check that everything is as it should be. The user can select an item in the estimate, "right click" with the mouse and generate a list of the identifiers of the building elements that have been placed against this item. The user can then choose to view all of these elements within the current context within the Viewer. These will be highlighted when the Viewer comes to the front. If the user recognizes that an element is included under the wrong item it can be "dragged and dropped" onto the correct item.

The estimating component and the viewing component interact to allow answers to be given to questions such as:

- Which elements in the building are included in this item in the Bill of Quantities?
- Which item(s) in the Bill of Quantities contain this building element?
- Which building elements have been included in (this section of) the Bill of Quantities?
- Which building elements have not been included in (this section of) the Bill of Quantities?

The Viewer incorporates some ideas that allow user control of the information that is presented in the three dimensional view of the model (Fig. 8). Once a model is opened, the selection panel (on the left) displays the project hierarchy – a project may contain sites, sites can contain buildings, buildings contain stories. The user can choose the current focus of interest. Within this scope the user can also filter the view by discipline. Currently the only discipline supported is "structural". It is also possible to make elements transparent so that building elements behind or contained in this element are visible while retaining the visibility of the spatial relationships. Transparency is currently entirely under user control. Automating transparency switching to allow the software to show hidden elements is possible but is not planned in the near future.

The Viewer also supports some of the functions that allow the user to remedy some of the idiosyncrasies of the various CAD systems.

7 FUTURE WORK

Now that this system works for preparing estimates for detailed documentation the next step is to move further forward in the design process to support cost planning processes (Ferry, Brandon & Ferry).

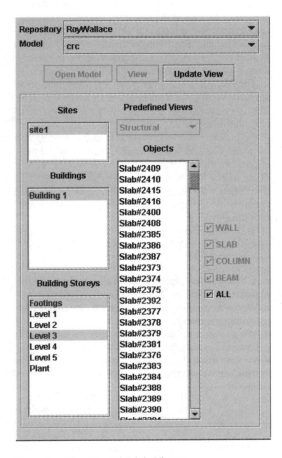

Figure 9. View Control Tab in Viewer.

The Viewer provides an integral part of this system by allowing direct manipulation of the building model to support functionality required by the quantity take-off/estimating process. It also allows the user to "browse" the model in conjunction with the Estimator. The Viewer has been developed so that it can be used as a stand-alone component or in partnership with other interfaces. By exposing various functions as externally accessible programming interfaces the Viewer can be used in parallel with other software.

The underlying quantity take-off algorithm is built on a decision tree which makes it feasible to track the changes that users make by hand and automatically identify the distinguishing characteristics between the shifted element and those still listed under the original item. This could be built into a "learning" system.

8 CONCLUSION

The information that needs to be shared across the various disciplines is stored in a common database. The information required by a particular discipline can then be retrieved from this database, manipulated and the new or revised information written back into the database for access by others.

The lack of structural software supporting the IFCs is expected to change in the near future with the completion of the structural engineering extensions to the IFC model in May 2003. This will add significant value to the processes described in this paper.

ACKNOWLEDGEMENT

This project is supported by the Cooperative Research Centre for Construction Innovation (CRC-CI, 2002) under contract 2001-007-C. Bovis Lend Lease, Ove Arups, Queensland Department of Public Works and Rider Hunt have all supplied information to this portion of the project and contributed their industry expertise. University of Sydney, Key Centre for Design Computing researchers are contributing to other aspects of this project and have been involved in discussions on portions of this work.

REFERENCES

Cimware, 2003, http://www.cimware.de/
CRC-CI, 2002, http://www.construction -innovation.info
Ferry, Brandon & Ferry, Cost Planning of Buildings
GDL Technology, 2002, http://www.gdltechnology.com/
IAI, 1999, http://cig.bre.co.uk/iai_international/ Technical_ Documents/documentation/R20/Online_Documents/ index.htm
IAI, 2000, http://cig.bre.co.uk/iai_international/copyright_ ifc2x.htm

System-based Vision for Strategic and Creative Design, Bontempi (ed.)
© 2003 Swets & Zeitlinger, Lisse, ISBN 90 5809 599 1

Analyses on the productivity of multi-skilled team in the reinforced concrete construction site of the residential buildings

K. Endo
Department of Architecture, Kogakuin University, Tokyo, Japan

H. Kanisawa
MONOTSUKURI Institute of Technologist, Saitama, Japan

Y. Kimura
Seisaku Sekkei Co., Ltd., Tokyo, Japan

ABSTRACT: Division of labor among various skilled workers has long played a vital role in achieving the building projects in the history of Japanese construction industry. Meanwhile, Japanese skilled workers have not clearly defined how the scopes of their own work should be. Under such a circumstance, the construction community has long kept arguing about possible introduction of a concept of multi-skilled workers along with such issues as the shortage of skilled workers and the intended rationalization of building construction practices. In 2000, the Ministry of Construction announced an innovation strategy for the specialty contractors, in which the multi-skilled worker concept was positioned as a future vision of construction labor and as a potential means of productivity improvement in the construction industry. However, the multi-skilled worker concept has not established itself as a continuous company activity. This paper firstly enumerates, identifies and examines various multi-skilled workers. The examination based on Industrial Engineering was carried out on two reinforced concrete work projects that multi-skilled workers executed on some high-rise residential buildings. Further, using a process control software (MS-Project & Primavera) with microcomputers to reproduce the processes and compare the result by simulation with certain work efficiency data of single-skilled workers. Through the above-mentioned research, the authors have come to believe that appropriate conditions for multi-skilled workers to function effectively have been arranged for implementation.

1 THE BACKGROUND OF RESEARCH

It has been proposed since the 1990s within the Japanese construction industry that use of "multi-skilled workers" is essential in construction work. This trend is due to (1) the deplorable shortage of skilled workers in the construction sector and (2) the industry has been unable to boost its productivity as has been expected from the recent technological advancement such as industrialized construction methods. One of the causes of this situation is the difficulty in realizing good coordination between the existing jobs (such as carpenters, scaffolding erectors, reinforcing steel bar workers) and the new categories of their work being created by new technology.

Multi-skilled workers are capable of performing fieldwork by combining more than one construction jobs. They should not only serve as an effective means of solving many problems being confronted by the Japanese construction industry but also can be positioned as one of the future visions of construction labour.

2 THE PURPOSE OF RESEARCH

While such expectations as mentioned above are being entertained, multi-skilled workers are not so widely being used in the actual scenes of construction yet. Also, there are few actual cases of construction firms establishing the use of multi-skilled workers on a continual basis. Thus, the specific purpose of this paper is to analyze the data which was obtained from a survey of an actual case of the reinforced concrete (RC) frame-building work of a high-rise apartment housing that has been performed by a multi-skilled workers' team so as to identify the following three points.

- Extract the production characteristics of the RC frame-building work that used the industrialized methods of construction.
- Extract the production characteristic of the multi-skilled workers themselves.
- Based on the result of above two points, conditions for effective functioning of multi-skilled workers by themselves.

Table 1 below summarizes the status of the two surveyed projects (Project A and Project U).

Table 1. Status of multi-skilled workers in the Japanese construction industry.

The objectives of using multi-skilled workers
1. To boost productivity
2. To expand the scope of business of subcontractors
3. To be capable of flexibly responding to fluctuating seasonal business demands
4. To become more adaptable to technology innovation and new construction methods

Types (levels) of multi-skilled workers
1. Trained in the skills of multiple jobs that are more or less independent with each other
2. Trained in the skills of multiple jobs that are closely related with each other
3. Trained only to be able to support peripheral skills before or after the main process

3 AN OUTLINE OF RESEARCH

3.1 *An outline of the projects as survey object*

Table 2 is a summary of the two surveyed projects. Both cases were performed by multi-skilled workers who used industrialized construction methods being aimed at rationalizing the business with a focus on the introduction of pre-cast concrete (PCa).

3.2 *Method of survey and contents of survey record*

One surveyor each took charge of 2 or 3 multi-skilled workers, to record their work performance per minute from the start of the day through the end. Building space covered by the survey was one full floor. The survey was scheduled as follows:

- Project A: 2001/8/8 ~ 2001/8/13, 2001/8/20
- Project U: 2001/9/4 ~ 2001/9/10

3.3 *Data recapitulation and normalization*

As shown in Table 3, the data gathered from the field sites was recapitulated to show the result of 4,567 work elements for Project A and 5,140 for Project U. The terms in the table are defined as follows:

- Scheduled working time: Total scheduled working hours not including lunch recess time
- Scheduled recess time: Habitually established work-recess time, AM around 10:00 & PM around 15:00
- Net scheduled working time: Scheduled working time minus scheduled recess time

Table 2. Summary of the two surveyed projects.

Item of project	Project A	Project U
Name of company in charge of frame-building	Company O	Company M
Main use of the project	Offices & multi-dwellings	Offices & multi-dwelling
Construction method used (abbrev.)	RC	RC (partially S)
Total construction period	2001.1 ~ 2002.4	2000.4 ~ 2002.7
Basement + floors + top structure	1 + 21	1 + 30 + 2
Max. height (m)	69 m	107 m
Floor subject to the survey	9F	18F
No. of cycle days	7 days	6 days
Type of structure	Rahmen (rigid frame)	Rahmen (rigid frame)
Pillar building method	Half PCa	Conventional
Beam building method	Half PCa	Half PCa
Floor: dwelling	Half PCa	Half PCa
Floor: balcony, etc.	Half PCa	PCa (partly Half PCa)
Concrete setting method	V & H separate	V & H together
	Pump + hopper	Pump + hopper
Tower crane	1 unit	1 unit
Remarks	Steel bars by other company	

- Other non-working time: Time to meet such needs as toilet, using water fountains, etc.
- Net actual working time: Net scheduled working time minus other non-working time.

4 ANALYSES OF THE CHARACTERISTICS OF PRODUCTIVITY

This section consists of two steps: (1) Analysis of the characteristics of the industrialized construction methods, and then (2) Analysis of the productivity of multi-skilled workers.

4.1 Specific characters of the industrialized construction methods

The elements of Construction Process Chart embrace various human actions such as set-up operations, minor and miscellaneous light work elements. In the conventional genre of construction methods, these work actions have been treated as an intangible or inherent portion of the main jobs or main construction activities as clearly stated in the construction contracts. Thus, such data has never been explicitly reflected in the actual process control. However, in the area of industrialized construction method it is possible to select from among versatile construction methods, where different collateral works depending on the selected methods come up. Most of them are what you cannot see unless you actually perform them on the field sites and therefore are making it difficult for the planners to estimate necessary man-hours, to establish level of productivity, and to decide which jobs should best be in charge

of the project. With these types of work named as "non-explicit work-groups," this paper extends discussions below in this section.

4.1.1 How should the "non-explicit type of work" be positioned

All the work-steps, as written on the work process charts, were segregated based on the data obtained in the survey. Then, as shown in Table 4, the extracted work-elements were sorted out in 28 different elements in three different groups. The groups are defined as follows:

Main work-group: The types of work that directly reflect the works written on the process charts, and are segregated by the work-elements that consist each main work.

Collateral work-group: The types of peripheral work-steps that can be found before or after the main work-steps and are not explicitly written on the process charts (such as bringing in members of frameworks, setting up materials (unpacking, tooling, etc.), cleaning).

Non-work group: Non-productive time elements as shown in the table.

Above analyses with the two projects under survey revealed that there are over three times as many work-elements as those explicitly countable in the process, as shown in Table 5.

Table 3. Working time data obtained in the survey (unit of survey time: minute).

	Project A	Project U
Total attendance (persons surveyed)	75	82
Total no. of recorded work-elements (data items)	4,567	5,140
Total of recorded time: A	655:27	649:08
Lunch recess time: B	85:41	105:33
Scheduled working time: A − B	569:46	543:35
Scheduled recess time: C	44:01	0:00
Net scheduled working time: A − (B + C)	525:45	543:35
Other non-working time: D	6:05	1:12
Net actual working time: A − (B − C + D)	519:40	542:23

Remarks: "Scheduled recess time": It is customary in the most part of Japanese working environment to set one recess period or (tea break), 15 to 20 minutes at about 10:00 AM and another about 3:00 PM every working day.

Table 4. Classification of construction work and segregation of work-elements.

Main work group	Marking, welding, bar arrangement, assembling, dismantling, erection, molding, mounting, demounting, concrete laying, slinging, hoisting, push-up, fabrication, deburring of form, adjustment
Collateral work group	Unloading, replacing, transporting, pile-up, temporary storage, preparation, cleaning, tidying up
Non-work group	Moving, shop meeting, idling, taking rest (lunch, scheduled recess, using toilet, etc.)

Table 5. Number of work elements (Process Chart vs. actual work.

	Project A	Project U
Work-elements as designated on the Process Chart	25	23
Work elements as actually extracted in the survey	115	72

337

4.1.2 How should the "collateral type of work" be positioned

Analyses of both main work-group and collateral work-group clarified that the ratio of collateral work against main work in Project A was about 30% and that in Project U a little over 23% (ref. Table 6).

4.1.3 How should the "conventional type of work" be positioned

Some of the industrialized construction methods abundantly using PCa, prefabricated reinforcing steel bar, etc. may involve some conventional methods that require manual work (such as jointing members of PCa materials). In this paper, this type of work is named "conventional work-steps."

Their time and ratio data are summarized in Table 7.

- Panel zone mold: Mould for column–beam–floor joints
- Joint mold: Mould for beam–beam PCa joints
- Build-up mold for openings: Mould for the openings of vertical plumbing of facilities and walls surrounding staircase spaces, etc.

Analyses as described above resulted in showing a high ratio of 17.2% for actual working time in Project A. Meanwhile in Project U, the corresponding ratio at 5.3% is less than one third at Project A, because Project U gave no data for conventional type or work even though both projects indicated similar time and ratio for panel-zone mould. This difference is due to the fact that there is no beam–beam joints in Project U

and also that its staircase spaces had been planned to require no build-up moulds. This fact should imply the importance of production design.

4.2 Production characteristics of multi-skilled workers

Production characteristics of multi-skilled workers are discussed from the following perspectives.

4.2.1 The operational rate of multi-skilled workers

There have been various approaches adopted in pursuing research over productivity and operational rates. In this paper, the values calculated on Table 8 are named "rates of operation" as one of the measures to identify the production characteristics, by which per-day ratios against the scheduled daily work were calculated. Table 9 shows a breakdown of non-work elements.

The analysis resulted in very high operational rates even considering a possibility of omitting second-level

Table 7. Ratio of conventional type work-elements (time unit: minute/percentage against actual working time).

	Project A			Project U		
	No. of work spots	Time	Ratio (%)	No. of work spots	Time	Ratio (%)
Panel zone molding	23	28:43	5.5	21	28:38	5 3
Joint molding	14	45:49	8.8			
Opening build-up molding		14:39	2.8			
Total	37	89:11	17.2	21	28:38	5.3

Table 6. Breakdown of collateral work group (time unit: minute).

	Project A		Project U	
	Main work group	Collateral work group	Main work group	Collateral work group
PCa	200:59	59:22	111:02	23:14
	77.2%	22.8%	82.7%	17.3%
Temporary set-up	49:33	8:26	19:08	0:00
	85.5%	14.5%	100.0%	0.0%
Mold	91:40	26:46	110:02	16:40
	77.4%	22.6%	86.8%	13.2%
Concrete	20:27	48:52	28:08	8:52
	29.5%	70.5%	76.0%	24.0%
Steel bars			144:10	31:14
			82.2%	17.8%
Steel frame			2:30	0:19
			88.8%	11.2%
Others	0:00	13:35	0:00	47:04
	0.0%	100.0%	0.0%	100.0%
Total	362:39	157:01	415:00	127:23
	69.8%	30.2%	76.5%	23.5%

Table 8. Operational ratio of multi-skilled workers.

	Project A	Project U
Scheduled working time (hours): A	569:46	543:35
Non-working time (hours): B	40:18	36:14
Operational ratio: (A − B)/A (%)	85.2%	93.3%

Table 9. Breakdown of non-working time.

	Project A	Project U
Moving	7:55 (19.6%)	10:12 (28.2%)
Briefing/shop meeting	8:32 (21.2%)	15:35 (43.0%)
Taking rest	6:05 (15.1%)	1:12 (3.3%)
Idling	17:46 (44.1%)	9:15 (25 5%)
Total	40:18 (100.0%)	36:14 (100.0%)

data as the research data was taken on the minute-level time-unit. In Project A, the ratio of the net working time (or scheduled working time minus non-working time) was 92.3% as shown in Figure 8.

4.2.2 Working characteristics of multi-skilled workers

Figures 1 and 2 reflect percentages of various types of work (such as PCa, steel bars, molds, concrete, temporary set-up, etc.) being performed by each of the multi-skilled workers who were respectively assigned in the project being surveyed. In the figures, signs such as "UR3" represent individual workers' codes, and information shown in the brackets is the name of the group where workers belong, Job No. 1, No. 2 and No. 3, years of job experience in that order.

"Name of the group" here indicates the unit of work and its control as respectively set up by Company O and Company M. It is indicated in the second alphabet of the worker code. In Project U, teams working on steel bars and moulds are formed as also taking care of temporary building work, too. "Trainee" in Project A represents "non-Japanese trainees."

[Job No. 1] indicates the type of work that the individual worker performed spending the largest portion of his or her scheduled time. It is divided into [Main] and [Collateral] jobs. The same pattern applies to [Job No. 2] and on.

It has been known from above observations that each individual worker spent approximately 80 ~ 90% of their time covering No. 1 through No. 3 jobs, and that the scope of work by multi-skilled workers embraces at most three types of work. Also, the workers' group classification does not necessarily match their No. 1 jobs (particularly remarkable in Project A), and therefore it became clear that traditional categories of their work and types of site operations to be fit into the industrialized methods of operation.

Different characteristics of specific types of multi-skilled workers can be found depending on the size of their No. 1 jobs, as defined below.

– Those workers whose No. 1 main jobs cover 60% or over perform very little of other types of work in the main category.
– Those workers whose No. 1 main jobs cover around 50% can be sub-grouped as (1) those who also perform some 20% of other types of work in the main category, or (2) those who least perform other types of work in the main category but mainly perform some collateral types of work.
– Those workers whose No. 1 main jobs cover around 40% perform another main job (taking up about 15 ~ 20%). Few workers perform three types of main jobs together.
– Those workers whose No. 1 main jobs cover around 30% perform other main jobs (on a similar level as No. 1) and the rate of their performing other types of main job seems to rise.
– While no clear correlation is observed between the volume of performed No. 1 jobs and the number of job experiences of individual workers, less experienced workers tend to perform more than one main jobs and their ratio of collateral job performance may go up accordingly.

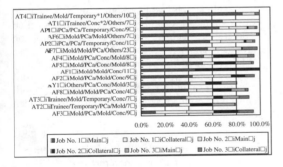

Figure 1. Breakdown of various types of work (Project A). *1: Temporary: temporary set-up, *2: Conc: concrete.

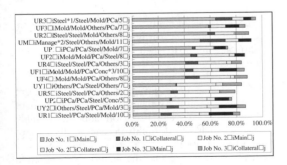

Figure 2. Breakdown of various types of work (Project U). *1: Steel: steel bar, *2: Manage: management, *3: Conc: concrete.

4.2.3 Characteristics of combination work

Survey data of combination work where plural workers in teams perform the same work together was analyzed. "Combination ratio," as shown in Tables 10–12 for each worker, reflects the ratio of his combination work against his own scheduled working time. Figures elsewhere in the matrix represent a percentage of his time spent in teaming up with one of other workers against his own scheduled working time. Tables 10 and 11 are the survey data dealing with all types of work being performed on Projects A and U respectively, and Table 12 with PCa work on Project U only.

The data on combination ratios apparently indicates that Project A ratios are high and Project U rather low.

This result suggests that the industrialized methods such as PCa method call for the necessity for

Table 10. Matrix of combination work (covering all works in Project A).

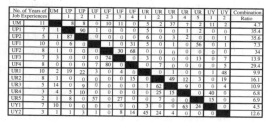

No. of Years of Job Experiences	AP1	AP2	AY1	AF1	AF2	AF3	AF4	AF5	AF6	AF7	AF8	AT1	AT2	AT3	Combination Ratio
AP1	9		67	5	0	1	4	1	2	8	0	2	0	5	6	53.8
AP2	1	58		13	0	11	4	0	2	0	0	1	0	6	5	62.6
AY1	3	13	39		0	0	1	1	0	0	0	0	0	18	26	21.9
AF1	9	0	0	0		100	0	0	0	0	0	0	0	0	0	0.5
AF2	9	1	29	0	0		0	10	3	17	12	24	0	1	1	25.2
AF3	8	13	16	2	0	0		2	0	0	7	60	0	0	0	16.4
AF4	8	1	1	0	0	6	1		83	0	7	1	0	0	0	41
AF5	7	3	3	0	0	2	0	90		0	0	1	0	0	0	37.1
AF6	23	35	2	0	0	34	0	0	0		1	7	0	7	7	29.3
AF7	4	0	0	0	0	21	8	20	0	1		8	0	5	32	33
AF8	7	5	3	0	0	26	43	2	2	4	5		0	9	0	29.2
AT1	7	0	0	0	0	0	0	0	0	0	0	0		0	100	71.9
AT2	11	6	8	8	0	1	0	0	0	2	2	4	0		48	65.1
AT3	7	6	6	10	0	0	0	0	0	1	8	0	19	39		54.5

Table 11. Matrix of combination work (covering all works in Project U).

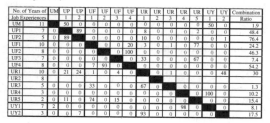

No. of Years of Job Experiences	UM	UP1	UP2	UF1	UF2	UF3	UF4	UR1	UR2	UR3	UR4	UR5	UY1	UY2	Combination Ratio
UM	11		8	8	0	10	11	0	5	2	37	7	2	11	2	4.7
UP1	7	1		90	1	0	0	0	5	0	1	2	0	0	0	35.4
UP2	5	1	87		0	0	0	0	6	0	3	2	0	0	1	35.6
UF1	10	0	6	0		1	0	31	5	0	1	0	56	0	1	7.3
UF2	8	1	0	0	0		30	68	0	0	0	0	0	0	0	3.4
UF3	7	3	0	0	0	74		0	3	0	0	13	0	7		13.9
UF4	8	0	0	0	7	80	0		0	7	0	0	0	0	5	29.4
UR1	10	2	19	22	3	0	4	0		0	1	0	0	1	48	9.9
UR2	8	1	0	0	0	0	15	0		49	12	3	0	19		16.1
UR3	5	14	0	9	0	0	0	0	1	62		9	0	0	4	10.9
UR4	3	4	5	10	0	0	0	0	25	15		0	40	0		6.8
UR5	2	1	8	0	57	0	27	0	0	7	0		0	15	0	6.9
UY1	7	10	0	0	0	0	0	0	3	0	0	63	24		0	4.5
UY2	3	1	1	3	1	0	8	14	45	24	4	0	0	0		12.6

Table 12. Matrix of combination work (covering PCa works in Project U).

No. of Years of Job Experiences	UM	UP1	UP2	UF1	UF2	UF3	UF4	UR1	UR2	UR3	UR4	UR5	UY1	UY2	Combination Ratio
UM	11		50	0	0	0	0	0	0	0	0	0	0	50	0	1.9
UP1	7	0		89	0	0	0	0	8	0	0	0	2	0	0	48.4
UP2	5	0	89		0	0	0	0	10	0	0	0	0	0	1	76.4
UF1	10	0	0	0		0	0	20	3	0	1	0	77	0	0	24.2
UF2	8	0	0	0	0		0	100	0	0	0	0	0	0	0	46.3
UF3	7	0	0	0	0	0		0	33	0	0	0	67	0	0	7.4
UF4	8	0	0	0	7	93	0		0	0	0	0	0	0	0	54.2
UR1	10	0	21	24	1	0	4	0		0	1	0	0	0	48	30
UR2	8															
UR3	5	0	0	0	33	0	0	0	67	0		0	0	0		1.3
UR4	3	0	0	0	0	0	0	0	0	0		0	100	0		10.2
UR5	2	0	11	0	74	0	15	0	0	0	0		0	0	0	15.4
UY1	7	2	0	0	0	0	0	0	0	0	0	98	0		0	8.1
UY2	3	0	0	7	0	0	0	0	93	0	0	0	0			17.5

combination work. The following specific factors seem to support such suggestion.

– As Project A uses PCa for building pillars, and has an outside company to supply steel bar workers, the ratio of Multi-skilled Workers working on industrialized construction methods such as PCa work tend to rise.

– Above situation can also be supported by (1) the relatively high combination ratios of the workers in PCa work-teams (members can be identified by the second letter of the worker codes bearing alphabet "P." and (2) the overall tendency of PCa work as shown in Table 12 is showing an overall tendency of higher combination ratios.

Other specific characteristics of combination work are as follows:

– Combination patterns among the workers are diverse, and their teammates may not necessarily the same individuals at all time.

– Particularly, less experienced workers tend to mate with more members.

– Conversely, combination by type of work to be performed, the teammates may be more fixed.

– Less experienced workers are being combined with well-seasoned workers.

– One characteristic as seen from the team angle is that combination ratios of steel bar work-teams are relatively low.

5 CONCLUSIVE COMMENTS

There are a few perspectives from which our survey observations are conclusively summarized.

5.1 Characteristics of industrialized construction methods versus production characteristics of multi-skilled workers

– Within the industrialized construction methods there are more than double as much "non-explicit type work" existent as the number of work-elements as explicitly recorded on the construction process charts.

– Particularly, many of collateral types of work are non-explicit, representing some 20~30% of total work volume. It is highly probable that multi-skilled workers are helping to raise the construction productivity.

– While productivity of multi-skilled workers may go down under the realm of "conventional work pattern," it should be possible to reduce their work depending on the way production design has been developed.

5.2 Specific characters of multi-skilled workers and their production characteristics

– The operational rates of multi-skilled workers are high, with least idling time and other non-productive time.

– The job styles of multi-skilled workers are diverse, and generally can hardly typify. Their styles may shift according to such factors as years of job experiences.

– As the industrialization of work methods such as PCa become more advanced, necessity for team operation grows. As there is no fixed pattern of multi-skilled workers' team formation, it is highly probable that their flexibility in changing the style of formation helps improving their own productivity.

– It is also possible that the team-based operation may contain a mechanism to supplement the work of less experienced workers and a function to develop on-the-job training activities.

5.3 Some observations to help establishing the conditions on which multi-skilled workers can be more effectively utilized

It is highly possible that the positive production characteristics of multi-skilled workers as being discussed in this paper (such as their working morale and flexibility in team formation) have been substantiated by some specific conditions as listed below.

- Sub-contractors (as specialty project facilitator) under the conditions of assuming the whole RC building construction work or its equivalent pattern. Thus, they are in an advantageous position to be given the right to manage and control their field construction activities.
- Above situation provides some incentives for them to be willing to improve work effectiveness all by themselves and to endeavor to shorten the construction schedule.
- Since the multi-skilled workers are directly employed under the same umbrella as all other concerned personnel, they can easily develop a highly collaborative working condition.
- The multi-skilled workers have been well trained at the school that is managed by their very employer.

Conclusively speaking, it seems to be necessary for us to consider that multi-skilled workers can no more be treated as a "substitute job group" among many conventional jobs, but should be accepted as a new type of production system equipped with those positive production characteristics as have been discussed so far.

For that purpose, the following specific conditions should be positively considered by all concerned parties.

- New patterns of construction contracts that formally consider the production work by multi-skilled workers
- New perspectives to realize better planning and managing the production work by multi-skilled workers
- New perspectives to find better positions for specialty subcontractors who directly hire multi-skilled workers and how to best evaluate their service
- New patterns of training and development to help multi-skilled workers better function at work.

REFERENCES

Architectural Institute of Japan, 1990. *Recommended Practice for Method Improvement on Construction Work.*
Rimura, Y. & Endo, K. 2001. *Feasibility study of Versatile Worker in building construction – Part 1. Arrangement of general idea for Versatile Worker*, in the Architectural Institute of Japan bulletin.

System-based Vision for Strategic and Creative Design, Bontempi (ed.)
© 2003 Swets & Zeitlinger, Lisse, ISBN 90 5809 599 1

Comparative study of UK and Italian refurbishment sites involving demolition activities and structural instability: risk factors and Health & Safety management strategies

B.M. Marino Duffy
Ove Arup and Partners, London, UK

C.O. Egbu
School of the Built and Natural Environment, Glasgow Caledonian University, UK

C.J. Anumba
Department of Civil and Building Engineering, Loughborough University, UK

A. Gottfried
Building Engineering and Territorial Systems (ISET) Department, Polytechnic of Milan, Italy

B. Neale
Health and Safety Executive, Bootle, UK

ABSTRACT: Recent statistics show that refurbishment works involve more risk than new construction sites. Risk factors are heightened on those sites involving demolition activities and temporary works. Evidence of these factors is given in this paper, which is based on a study funded by the UK Health and Safety Executive (HSE) and developed by the Loughborough University, the Polytechnic of Milan and Glasgow Caledonian University. This study has investigated the main Health and Safety (H & S) risk factors in refurbishment works and H & S management practices. This paper analyses and documents the results of a comparative exercise on H & S management practices between the refurbishment sectors in the UK and Italy. Some of the key risk factors identified, mainly associated with the lack of design and planning for demolition activities, include the knowledge of the site and structure, workforce supervision, selection of subcontractors, communication, safety information and training. The paper concludes that, despite some examples of good H & S management, some important areas need urgent attention such as H & S management practices for small-medium sites involving further opportunities for new empirical research in H & S management for refurbishment sites.

1 INTRODUCTION

The past 30 years have witnessed a significant increase in refurbishment works both in the UK and Italian construction industries. The refurbishment sector, in its many forms, accounts for more than 40% of the total UK construction output. Although no official statistics on the actual value of refurbishment output exist, this sector has increased in the past 30 years from the 22.46% to the 43% of total construction output.

In Italy more detailed statistics are available, the data shows the increase in refurbishment work in the past 10 years. According to the statistics provided by CRESME (Research Centre on the Construction market) and ISTAT (Italian Statistics Central Institute)

in 1995 refurbishment accounted for the 57.5% of total construction output, this percentage being composed of 30% of ordinary maintenance works.

In 1999, the refurbishment sector registered a 3% increase and the latest data available shows an 11% increase in the year 2000.

The increase in refurbishment activity, and the corresponding increase in accidents related to it, surprisingly was not accompanied by any relevant empirical research especially in the management of health and safety. Although neither the UK nor Italy differentiates between new construction and refurbishment accident data, statistics suggest that refurbishment, in its different interpretations, accounts for a substantial proportion of injuries and fatal accidents. Recent provisional accident statistics provided by the HSE show that 40.6% of construction fatalities occurred on refurbishment sites. The new British Standard on Demolition, BS6187: 2000 is supposed to lead to a more focused approach to demolition but the health and safety aspects of refurbishment works involving demolition still need to be addressed. Refurbishment works involving demolition and structural instability can be considered among the most dangerous activities to be undertaken on site and therefore require a rigorous health and safety management strategy. In this context the research work, which this paper is based on, focuses on sites where demolition and structural instability are involved. Therefore whenever it will be referred to refurbishment sites it will imply the presence of demolition and structural instability.

2 THE RESEARCH PROJECT

2.1 Aim and objectives

This paper reports the final results of a one-year research project aimed at the investigation of Health and Safety in refurbishment sites involving demolition and structural instability.

Giving the greater incidence of health and safety problems in refurbishment sites than new construction projects, a set of objectives was set up prior to the beginning of the research activities. The specific objectives that led the research process were identified as follows:

- To determine the main factors associated with the relatively high level of hazard and health and safety incidence on refurbishment involving demolition works.
- To investigate the health and safety management strategies in current usage, for refurbishment work involving demolition activities.
- To undertake comparative studies of the situation in the UK with that in Italy where there are many historic buildings and refurbishment works involving partial demolition are common.
- To produce a checklist of issues to consider in managing Health and Safety incidence on refurbishment projects involving demolition work, and also to identify areas where guidance should be provided.
- To make recommendations for further research in this area, as well as appropriate education and training provisions relevant to the major stakeholders associated with refurbishment activities involving demolition work.

2.2 Research methodology

The research work aimed to address the lack of targeted studies on health and safety in refurbishment works by identifying and analysing those key factors

influencing the health and safety management of refurbishment projects. In this context the research focused on refurbishment sites involving partial demolition due to the higher and more complex levels of risk involved than in total demolition works[1]. A combination of research strategies was used through the different stages of the research project:

- A review of UK and Italian refurbishment literature and accident statistics analysing, where possible, the incidence of demolition works.
- A review and elaboration of the incidence of demolition methods and techniques on refurbishment sites.
- A review of archive documentation from HSE, in particular accident investigation reports related to structural collapses.
- Selected interviews with health and safety officers and managers from contracting organisations, HSE representatives, structural engineers and site managers.
- Case studies based on a selection of large and small refurbishment projects in the UK and in Italy, involving demolition activities and temporary works.

Since the research led to the identification of key health and safety factors it was necessary to select suitable refurbishment sites to verify and document the assessment of such key factors in current practice. The number of investigated case studies cannot be statistically analysed, however, they provided significant insights into the refurbishment sector and the related health and safety issues. The typologies of the selected case studies, both in Italy and in the UK, covered different types of refurbishment sites. These include old residential houses, office buildings and industrial areas providing a comprehensive range of refurbishment health and safety issues for the development of all the findings and considerations of the research project.

3 HEALTH AND SAFETY FACTORS IN REFURBISHMENT PROJECTS INVOLVING DEMOLITION ACTIVITIES

The research project initially involved the review of selected scientific and technical literature related to demolition methods, techniques and equipment employed on refurbishment sites. The British Standard 6187 "Code of practice for demolition" proved to be a very useful reference for the identification and classification of demolition methods and techniques.

The study of demolition methods helped in the definition of the general risks involved in demolition operations. The review of technical literature and the

---

[1] Total demolition works are often carried out with mechanical equipment and remotely from the construction to be demolished.

analysis of HSE accident investigation reports showed that most of the health and safety risks in demolition activities are related to an unplanned or premature collapse of the structure leading to focus the research activity on "why do collapses happen?".

In order to investigate the predictable causes of structural collapses the demolition process was identified as an independent project with design, planning and execution phases. Such division of the demolition process facilitated the identification of key health and safety factors that are detailed as follows:

- Design phase:
  - Structural knowledge of the structure;
  - Structural knowledge of any adjacent construction;
  - Demolition equipment and methods selection;
- Planning phase:
  - Site knowledge;
  - Health and Safety risk assessment;
  - Development of safe sequences of demolition activities;
  - Limitation of the level of subcontracting;
  - Pre-qualification and selection of specialist contractors;
- Execution phase:
  - Workforce supervision;
  - Control of method statements implementation;
  - Communication of unplanned discoveries;
  - Safety information and training selection.

Once these factors were identified and analysed the research project developed into the investigation of health and safety management strategies applied to refurbishment projects.

4 HEALTH AND SAFETY ISSUES IN REFURBISHMENT PROJECTS INVOLVING DEMOLITION ACTIVITIES

The investigation of the selected case studies, the study of the HSE accident investigation reports and the interviews with health and safety professionals led to the identification of the following key issues to be implemented in health and safety management strategies for refurbishment projects:

- Demolition design and planning
- Selection and use of plant and equipment
- Workforce pre-qualification, selection and supervision
- Communication of project requirements and Health and safety information
- Health and safety education and training systems

The key health and safety issues identified can be summarised as follows:

- Demolition design and planning: demolition works need to be tackled as a part of a whole project with the proactive involvement of the Client with the selection of competent structural engineers, specialist contractor and subcontractors. The co-operation and exchange of information between all the parties involved in the project is vital to ensure high health and safety standards during site activities.
- Selection and use of plant and equipment: due to the relatively high risk of accidents related to their use, demolition tools and equipment have to be assessed and selected for specific use.
- Workforce, pre-qualification, selection and supervision: the findings from the research work strongly recommend that workers be assessed for their ability to understand procedures and safety instructions. Workers employed in demolition activities have to be specifically trained on each aspect of the work they are undertaking.
- Communication of health and safety information: the case studies showed that communication is a key factor in completing a project safely. Communication must also be organised at all the different levels and stages of a refurbishment project.
- Health and safety education and training systems: all the key functionaries involved in a refurbishment project are required to have adequate health and safety education. The case studies provided good examples of how construction organisations are implementing and evolving their internal health and safety training systems.

5 COMPARATIVE STUDY OF MANAGEMENT PRACTICES IN THE UK AND ITALIAN REFURBISHMENT SECTORS

The investigation and analysis of health and safety issues to be considered in the implementation of health and safety management strategies for refurbishment projects required a significant number of case studies on sites involving demolition activities and structural instability problems. The selected refurbishment sites were investigated through contact and interviews with professionals directly employed on those sites; these included structural engineers, general contractors and specialist demolition contractors. The study of the refurbishment sites was developed through site visits and the analysis of project documentation, method statements and health and safety plans. The case studies provided good examples for the implementation of health and safety management strategies and the findings were used for the identification of those health and safety issues to be considered in the management of refurbishment sites. The comparative study of Italian and UK refurbishment sites produced the following main findings:

1. The Italian interpretation of the EU directive 92/57 (interpreted in the UK with the CDM regulations)

requires the Client to appoint an Execution Phase Coordinator. He/she has to coordinate and supervise the application of all the health and safety procedures developed in the pre-tender health and safety plan. The appointment of this Coordinator provides a more efficient control of Client's health and safety requirements for refurbishment and demolition activities.

2. The implementation of method statements, still poorly diffused in the Italian construction industry, was recognised to improve the quality of communication and information of demolition sequences and of the related safety procedures.

3. The use of foreign nationals as building workers is widespread in the UK and Italy. Therefore communication problems and health and safety training are crucial issues for the construction industry in both countries.

4. Refurbishment sites in Italy have to deal with many logistic and archaeological issues that need to be co-ordinated with health and safety requirements. This is mainly due to the relatively high presence of refurbishment sites in historical centres. In this context the use of temporary structures (i.e. scaffolding, facade retention etc.) needs to be particularly addressed. Italian case studies provided examples of good sequencing of demolition and reconstruction activities that, when accurately planned, can significantly reduce the use of temporary structural support.

5. Special requirements by the English and Italian Heritage proved to have a considerable effect on the development of refurbishment projects. The case studies showed how the need to preserve some elements or parts of the building under refurbishment involves substantial changes in the development of demolition methods and planning and the related health and safety procedures.

6 FURTHER RESEARCH AND DEVELOPMENTS

The research project investigated the key health and safety factors and management strategies to be implemented for refurbishment projects involving demolition activities and structural instability.

Due to the peculiarity and complexity of the activities involved, health and safety aspects require to be properly addressed and planned. Indeed health and safety have a great influence in the design and management of refurbishment projects. It can also be recognised that these are the most influential factors for the selection of demolition methods to prevent structural collapses caused by structural instability.

Some of the main conclusions from the research project include the following:

1. Prior to undertaking any demolition activity on site that may interfere with the structural stability of the building, preliminary surveys and site investigations have to be carried out by structural engineers as well as specialist demolition contractors.

2. Refurbishment projects involving demolition activities, require the appointment of competent and qualified professionals who are going to implement health and safety in the development of any stage of the project, from design to execution phase.

3. Refurbishment projects are more likely to involve complex activities that require the acquisition of various information related to the existing structure as well as the integration of many health and safety aspects. Therefore, there is the need for a key figure in charge of the coordination of all structural information elaborated during the design phase, the supervision of the design of temporary works, and the planning of demolition activities. The research project has identified this figure as the Temporary Works Coordinator.

4. Clients need to be more involved in the health and safety management of the refurbishment projects that they procure. They have to appoint, in "reasonable time", qualified engineers and specialist contractors and subcontractors. In this context, Clients who are not frequently involved in the procurement of refurbishment projects should be given more advice and guidance about their responsibilities concerning health and safety legislation.

5. The field of application of CDM regulations should be extended to smaller-sized sites. In this context, many refurbishment sites would then have to apply these regulations with an increased involvement of Clients and designers.

6. Communication of project information and the Client's health and safety requirements has to be considered a priority issue for the development of effective health and safety management strategies.

7. Health and safety education of foreign language workers is a crucial issue. New communication systems such as drawing-based method statements or the use of pictures or video for health and safety training is strongly recommended.

Following the main conclusions developed from the research work and from case studies further areas of research were identified:

1. Client's role: to investigate the role of Clients in the refurbishment process developing comparisons between occasional and experienced Clients as well as providing recommendations that can be made available (i.e. through Planning Offices) for occasional Clients;

2. Communication: to investigate current communication methods and strategies as well as the use of IT tools in the development of health and safety

plans, method statements, health and safety audits on sites etc;

3. Education and training: to investigate current construction workers training schemes and identify those training subjects that should be improved for refurbishment/demolition works; recommendations for the development of professional training schemes for personnel employed on refurbishment sites should be developed as well;

4. Management: To investigate the current knowledge and usage of health and safety management tools (i.e. health and safety plans, method statements etc) by key functionaries involved in refurbishment work as well as making recommendations for the effective usage, update and management of health and safety documents on site as well as their communication to the workforce;

5. Decision support: to develop a practical decision support system that organisations and individuals involved in refurbishment works could use to make decision for a safer execution of site's activities as well as developing a new process model for refurbishment works, which ensures that safety considerations are taken into account from the earliest stages in the planning and design of refurbishment works.

Clearly, there is ample evidence from the foregoing that the results from this research project have been highly significant. The project team plans to build on these results by further publishing activity, presentations at industry forums, and seeking funding to undertake some of the further research areas outlined above.

REFERENCES

British Standard Institute, 2000. BS 6187 *Code of practice for demolition*, London: BSI.

Construction Industry Research and Information Association (CIRIA 1994) *A Guide to the Management of Building Refurbishment*. CIRIA Report No. 133. London: CIRIA.

Douglas, N. 1988. *Refurbishment, Rehabilitation and Renovation, Managing Construction Worldwide*, Vol. 3, Construction Management and organisation in perspective, London: SPON/CIOB/CIB, pp 67–81.

Egbu, C.O. 1994. *Management education and training for refurbishment work within the construction industry*. PhD Thesis, Vols. I and II, Department of Civil Engineering and Construction, University of Salford, UK.

Egbu, C.O., Marino, B., Anumba, C.J., Gottfried, A., Neale, B. 2002. *Managing Health and Safety in Refurbishment Projects involving Demolition and Structural Instability*, in J. Hinks, D. Shiem-Shin Then, S. Buchanan (eds), Applying and Extending the Global Knowledge Base, proceedings of the CIBW70 commission Facilities management and Maintenance Global Symposium 2002, The Netherlands: CIB.

European Directive 92/57/EEC. *Implementation of minimum safety and health requirements at temporary or mobile construction sites*.

Gottfried, A., Trani, M.L. 1999. *Safety and health design and management on the construction site: Guidelines for roles and application tools*, in A. Singh, J. Hinze, R. Coble (eds) "Implementation of Safety and Health on Construction sites", Rotterdam: Balkhema.

Health and Safety Executive (HSE 1988). *Blackspot Construction: A study of five years fatal accidents in the building and civil engineering industries*, London: HMSO.

Italian Decree of the President of the Republic n. 164/56, *Rules for the prevention of accidents on construction workplaces*.

Italian legislative decree n. 528/99, *Implementation of European directive 92/57 concerning minimum health and safety procedures on temporary and mobile sites*.

Marino, B.M. 2001. *Methods and tools for Quality and Safety management on refurbishment sites*, PhD Thesis, Building Engineering and Territorial Systems Department, Polytechnic of Milan.

System-based Vision for Strategic and Creative Design, Bontempi (ed.)
© 2003 Swets & Zeitlinger, Lisse, ISBN 90 5809 599 1

Integrated risk management for construction system providers

T.A. Busch
Institute for Construction Engineering and Management, Swiss Federal Institute of Technology, Zurich, Switzerland

ABSTRACT: The research approach "Construction System Provider" (CSP) has been developed at the Institute for Construction Engineering and Management. A CSP offers lifecycle oriented integrated services for building constructions, i.e. planning, turnkey construction and contracting. The transfer of cost, deadline, quality and functionality risks to the provider requires an Integrated Risk Management (IRM) which comprises project risks as well as general corporate risks. At the Swiss Federal Institute of Technology, Zurich, a research project was started to develop this process. The first phase "systematic risk management on project level", completed in December 2002, is focussing on the offer phase and includes the sub-processes risk identification, evaluation, classification, response and estimation of the costs of residual risks and controlling. The second phase covers the cross-project risk aggregation throughout the company and its consideration in financial accounting using a "risk pool". The required model is deduced by theoretical support and logical thought processes. Cross-project risk aggregation benefiting of Markowitz's portfolio theory leads to lower project risk premiums (with the same statistical certainty) compared to single project view. IRM contributes to a risk-oriented realization of planned earnings and thus to an increase of entrepreneurial success for the CSP.

1 INTRODUCTION

In response to growing national and international competitive pressure, the European building industry's customers are increasingly focussing on those core competencies, which are relevant to ensure their ability to compete. In consequence of the outsourcing of a wide range of services relating to the whole lifecycle of a building, Construction System Providers (CSP) are increasingly approached to offer integrated services for building constructions.

The research approach "Construction System Provider" has been developed at the Institute for Construction Engineering and Management of the Swiss Federal Institute of Technology, Zurich, Switzerland (Girmscheid 2000). The execution of integrated building services, i.e. planning, turnkey construction and facility management during building operation, is the core business of a CSP. They offer actively complete one-stop solutions in certain market segments. Totally tailored to customers' requirements lifecycle oriented solutions base on an optimized system concept integrating both functional and technical aspects. With the system concept the CSP brings to bear his core competencies and improves them steadily cross-project.

Cost, deadline, quality and functionality risks are shifting to the provider as demand grows on the part of customers for integrated services. To enable CSP to cope with this increased work, they must ensure in the resource based approach the efficient use of well-established methods of corporate management and develop integrated risk management as a new key competence that takes into account both general corporate risk factors and operative risk factors on project level (Girmscheid 2001).

To elaborate the required processes and methods the Institute for Construction Engineering and Management conducts a research project in tight cooperation with the Swiss General Contractors' Association (SGCA/VSGU). The research project divides into two phases. The first phase "systematic risk management on project level", completed in December 2002, is focussing on the offer phase and includes the sub-processes risk identification, evaluation, classification, response, estimation of the costs of residual risks and controlling.

Second phase, which is in process, covers the cross-project risk aggregation throughout the company, the formation of a risk pool and its consideration in financial accounting.

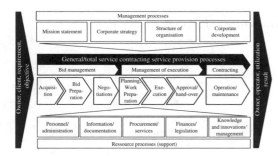

Figure 1. Service provision processes, management processes and support processes in building companies.

Figure 2. Risk components of a CSP.

2 CONCEPT

An integrated risk management process model for CSP, with particular emphasis on total and lifecycle oriented services is developed in tight cooperation with the Swiss General Contractors' Association (SGCA/ VSGU). The different process levels within the value chain of building companies are the following (Fig. 1):

– management processes
– service provision processes
– support processes.

It's intended to implement the integrated risk management processes into the companies' service provision processes which reflect the core business of a CSP.

2.1 Definition of the term "risk"

By risk one understands the possibility of a deviation from the business target system (strategic risk) or a goal deviation from precise project requirements (operative risk), whereby on the one hand potential positive deviations are called "opportunity" and on the other hand possible negative deviations are called "threat" (Chapman 1997). On corporate level these goals refer to the intended profit predetermined by the management; on project level the goals refer to specific project requirements in respect of costs, deadlines, quality and functionality.

It is not the objective of IRM to eliminate all possible threats of business acting. The Conscious accepting of risks and responding to them is immanent to entrepreneurship. Successful companies contrive it usually particularly well to take only such risks where the existing chances outweigh clearly in relation to the associated threats.

2.2 Risk components of a CSP

For structuring the total corporate risk of a CSP the following distinction into four main components is useful (Fig. 2).

2.2.1 Service provision risk
Project risks of a CSP consist mainly in service provision risks. They include risks which clearly relate to the service provision process and its corresponding resources. In opposite to risks based on demand for construction services, service provision risks include risks based on supply, which may lead in the unfavorable case to unforseen additional project costs.

2.2.2 Market risk
Primary origin of corporate risks is the market, because total future revenues can't be predicted precisely: the more inaccurate the prediction of future revenues, the bigger is the market risk. In branches which heavily depend on business cycles, i.e. the construction industry, market risk plays an important role.

2.2.3 Operating leverage
The extent of consequences which affects earnings through existence of market risk depends on the operating leverage. The operating leverage is defined as the fixed operating costs divided by total (fixed plus variable) operating costs. The most influencing factor is the rapidity of reducing costs in the company while revenues decrease. The higher the fraction of variable costs, i.e. costs depending on revenues, the more innocuous is a decrease of revenues.

2.2.4 Financial leverage
Varying profits influence the profitability of a company. Their impact depends on the capital lookup and the structure of financing. Companies with a low equity-to-assets-ratio are hit particularly hard by the effects of varying profits.

2.3 Aggregation of risks of a CSP

The entire corporate risk of a CSP consists of the risks emerging from the service provision process (the actual project business) and the risks of management and support processes.

The risk of the service provision process divides into:

– Project risks, which have been identified before disposal of the bid/contract signing. Therefore they were an element within the cost estimation/pricing.

- Project risks, which have been identified after disposal of the bid/contract signing. They were not a part of the estimating/pricing process.
- Project risks, which have not yet been identified.

The risks of the management and support processes correspond to the general corporate risk. It is influenced by the corporate strategy, organization, operating and financial leverage as well as personnel, management and IT.

For construction system providers in the construction industry a global corporate risk consideration is important due to several reasons:

- Only the global corporate risk consideration leads to an overview of total accepted risks.
- It allows drawing a conclusion about the amount of necessary reserves for contingencies.
- Due to the global corporate risk consideration forecasts of future risk accumulation in corporate business can be derived. It serves as a means of early warning of oncoming corporate threats.

In the context of the IRM three stages of risk aggregation can be differentiated hierarchically following the bottom-up principle:

- Risk aggregation on individual project level – singular approach: The singular approach considers individual projects and is used for risk management on the operative level. All risks identified and accepted by the CSP in the service provision process are quantified and aggregated to the total risk of the according project.
- Cross-project risk aggregation – superimposing approach: This approach consists of a cross-project aggregation of all projects and superimposes the total risks of the individual projects to the total operative risk of the CSP.
- Consideration of total corporate risk – integrated approach: The integrated approach consists of an all-over consideration of the company. In addition to the superimposing approach all general corporate risks are taken into account. Those include risks of the management processes (i.e. company development, strategy) and support processes (i.e. financing, personnel). The integrated approach results in a quantification of the total corporate risk of the CSP.

3 RISK AGGREGATION ON INDIVIDUAL PROJECT LEVEL – SINGULAR APPROACH

Each risk aggregation requires the results of the beforehand conducted risk management of the individual projects. Systematic risk management on project level is a process. The main goal of this process is to contribute to a successful settlement of the project and to achieving the planned profit. For this purpose

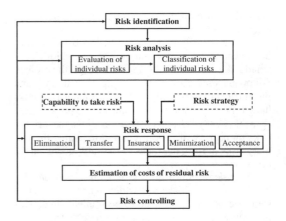

Figure 3. Risk management process.

tenders have to be selected in a risk-oriented way and in case of a positive decision to prepare the bid adequate risk costs have to be estimated. During the execution phase systematic risk management focuses on active risk response and the controlling of taken response measures.

The systematic risk management process comprises the consecutive partial processes illustrated in Figure 3:

- Risk identification
- Evaluation of individual risks
- Classification of individual risks
- Risk response
- Estimation of costs of residual risk
- Risk controlling.

Risk identification represents the "collection" of risks and is cause-related. Inadequate identification has a negative impact on the entire risk management process and, as such, on the completion of the project. Only those risks that have been identified by the company/project management can be minimized at a later date using appropriate response measures. Risk identification necessitates experience, know-how and creativity. The biggest benefit is achieved by combining intuitive methods like Pondering and Brainstorming with systematic procedures like filling out special checklists.

Evaluation and classification can be summarized under the generic heading of risk analysis. Risk evaluation aims to forecast the probability of occurrence and impact of each identified risk, i.e. the degree to which they could influence the project targets. Generally the probability of occurrence and the impact are estimated by considering likely risk scenarios. An important task is the detailed analysis of possible causes, the risk event itself and the possible effects. Afterwards values for both risk determinants can be derived from empirical data sets, expert guesses or estimations.

Risk classification represents the link between evaluation and response. By dint of their evaluation, identified risks are of varying significance for the project. Following Pareto's law of the "significant few" and insignificant many' only 20% of all identified risks have a significant impact on achieving the project goals (Curren 1988). The classification aims to sort the risks by priority of action required to enable the primary risks to form the focus of the subsequent partial processes.

The risk response process examines and decides how to tackle the risks, i.e. which active and reactive steps are planned and need to be implemented. This procedure is influenced to a considerable degree by the risk strategy implemented by the company resp. the willingness of the decision makers to take risks. A first step is to identify which alternative approaches are available, in order that a decision can then be made on which response is appropriate. Certain prerequisites/conditions need to be taken into consideration and observed. Generally elimination, transfer, insurance, minimization and acceptance are possibilities to respond to risk.

For the preparation of a bid estimating the costs of residual risk is necessary. This is done after the risk response process. As a modified risk situation could arise for the company once decisions have been made and measures taken, the company must conduct a renewed evaluation of the residual risks.

A powerful tool for cost estimation of residual risk is the Monte Carlo simulation. In opposite to deterministic modelling, in which for each input variable a single "best guess" is estimated, the Monte Carlo simulation generates a user-defined number of "what if" scenarios. The idea for this replication of an empirical data set was developed by Hertz (Hertz 1983). This method goes further by effectively accounting for every possible value that each variable could take and weights each possible scenario by the probability of its occurrence (Vose 1996). The simulation results in a density function of the costs of residual risk, which indicates the range of the costs and the mean value.

By using the according distribution function (Fig. 4) one is able to define a maximum value for costs of residual risk depending on a certain level of statistical security. Based on the statistical security of 70% which was selected as an example in Figure 4, the maximum value for the costs of residual risk is 0.9 million €. This means that in seven projects out of ten, the costs of residual risk will be below 0.9 million €. However in three projects out of 10 risks will cost more than 0.9 million €. Therefore it is important to perform the probabilistic risk analysis not only for one project but for the whole project portfolio of the company.

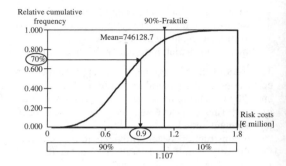

Figure 4. Distribution function of risk costs.

The final step is risk controlling which focuses on continuing to study the risk situation as presented in the previous partial processes throughout the remainder of the project. Moreover the selected response measures need to be examined to verify whether they were effective and efficient, and above all, to ensure that the desired effect has been achieved.

4 CROSS-PROJECT RISK AGGREGATION – SUPERIMPOSING APPROACH

The model of the cross-project risk aggregation is deduced using theoretical support and logical thought processes. The verification needs practicability and reliability testing which is done in cooperation with European construction system providers. Results will be available by the end of 2003.

4.1 Application of portfolio theory

The risk aggregation of all projects is consolidated in the "project portfolio". The portfolio theory of Markowitz describes the mechanism of risk diversification of all projects within the portfolio (Markowitz 1991).

The aim of portfolio analysis is to maintain the expected return and to minimize the risks of the portfolio. According to the theory, total risk of a project is made up of market risk and specific risk. Market risks which affect all individual projects cannot be eliminated or diversified. Specific risks which are associated only with a particular project can be avoided by deciding on another project with different specific risks. The effect of risk diversification accords to the specific risks of the various projects. Vital for diversification of the portfolio's overall risk are the correlation coefficients. If the correlation coefficient of two projects is less than +1, risk can be diversified. The Overall risk of the project portfolio will be reduced while the intended return remains constant because no two buildings are the same, that is, the correlation coefficient is less than $+1$.

Concerning new projects it's important to analyze as soon as possible (i.e. during the bidding phase) in which way these projects correlate with projects that are already part of the portfolio and therefore affect the overall risk. Single project analysis without forming a portfolio doesn't make use of the portfolio effect, which means that the according company has to take market risk and specific risk for each project. The cross-project analysis leads to lower risk premiums and therefore lower bid prices.

4.2 Formation of the risk pool

The costs of residual risk used within the project cost estimation are probabilistic values. In practice these estimated values are not exactly achieved. Cost overruns/shortfalls are the consequence. But estimated costs occur with a certain probability. The benefit by using probabilistic values only occurs over a "larger" basic population. Therefore companies have to accumulate an internal risk pool – i.e. an internal risk insurance – by depositing the risk premiums "earned" in projects to settle costs of risks occurred in other projects. This risk pool has to be integrated in a practical way into financial accounting. The risk pool is formed by accumulating all project specific risk premiums after contract signing. If the risk premium which is included in the specific project price is not exceeded by disbursements for occurred risks the rest ("earned risk premium") remains in the pool for future compensation payments to other projects. Consequence is a strict separation of estimated earnings and estimated risk. A continuous controlling of the existing internal risk coverage for projects which are under execution is enabled by the risk pool. After contract signing the risk premium of the corresponding project is deposited in the pool. A disbursement is only made upon request of the responsible project manager. Thereby the risk premium can't be used "accidentally" for different project expenditures and remains exclusively for risk coverage. After project completion it is verified if the amount of the previously estimated risk premium was sufficient for risk coverage. If this is not the case, causes have to be analyzed and guidelines for risk evaluation have to be adapted to assure adequate estimations in future.

Projects which have to be integrated into the risk pool differ in respect of their state of completion to a certain due date:

– Projects after contract signing, which are not yet under execution: For these projects the deposit is known, but no disbursements have been carried out so far. A distribution function of the residual risk costs, the risk premium, the corresponding statistical certainty and the range of those costs are known.

– Projects under construction: In the course of the project disbursements are carried out to settle costs of occurred risks. For these projects the remaining risk coverage is known at any time.

– Projects completed to the certain due date: For these projects it's important to reveal if the contractually agreed risk premium was sufficient. If there results a surplus, this remains within the pool.

An exemplified formation of the risk pool is shown in Figure 5. The account balance (financial capacity of the risk pool) is calculated by the sum of the balances of the three different project types.

4.3 Integrating total corporate risk into profit and loss account and balance sheet

According to world-wide financial accounting a basic rule has to be considered: A regulatory accounting principle is the recognition-of-loss principle which defines what kinds of risk and when they have to be integrated into financial accounting (Thommen 1999). It points out that profit and losses have to be treated differently:

– It's forbidden to account for earnings until they are not realized. That means, that the circumstances which create profit must have completely occurred (principle of realization).

– Losses have to be accounted for as soon as the causing risks have been recognized.

Following this rule, balance 1 ($+200,000$ in Fig. 5) has to be included into financial accounting as earnings because the according value is already realized. The deposits of projects, for which the contract was just signed but which are not yet under construction ($+1,800,000$), are not accounted. The biggest influence of the recognition-of-loss principle arises on projects which are currently under construction (balance 2).$\Delta_{\text{sum of negative balances}}$ is summed up only of the negative balances corresponding to the certain due date ($-50,000$ in Fig. 5). If it is likely that a contractually agreed risk premium is not exceeded in the project, the resulting positive balance (temporary) is not part of balance 2 because it is not yet realized. No more than after completion the positive project balance is accounted for in financial accounting. The balance$_{\text{financial accounting}}$ which is relevant for financial accounting is formed of the two components:

– Balance 1
– $\Delta_{\text{sum of negative balances}}$.

In the example balance$_{\text{financial accounting}}$ is equal to $+150,000$. The concept of the risk pool is just at the beginning of its research process. It will be permanently developed. The mechanisms between forecasting of risk costs, actually occurred risk costs and

353

Completed projects

Project P1	Project risk premium in the bid:1'000'000
	Expenditures for risk: 800'000
	Premium surplus: **200'000**

Project P2	Project risk premium in the bid: 800'000
	Expenditures for risk: 950'000
	Premium surplus: **-150'000**

Project P3	Project risk premium in the bid:2'100'000
	Expenditures for risk: 1'900'000
	Premium surplus: **200'000**

Project P4	Project risk premium in the bid:1'000'000
	Expenditures for risk: 1'200'000
	Premium surplus: **-200'000**

Project P5	Project risk premium in the bid:1'000'000
	Expenditures for risk: 850'000
	Premium surplus: **150'000**

Projects under construction

Project P6	Project risk premium in the bid: 1'000'000
	Expenditures for risk A: 100'000
	Expenditures for risk B: 200'000
	Expenditures for risk C: 50'000
	Expenditures for risk : 350'000
	Premium surplus actual: **750'000**
	Premium surplus target: **800'000**
	Δ **-50'000**

Project P7	Project risk premium in the bid: 1'200'000
	Expenditures for risk A: 200'000
	Expenditures for risk B: 50'000
	Expenditures for risk C: 50'000
	Expenditures for risk : 300'000
	Premium surplus actual: **900'000**
	Premium surplus target: **800'000**
	Δ **100'000**

Projects after contract signing

Project P8	Project risk premium in the bid: 1'100'000
	Expenditures for risk: ---
	Premium surplus: **1'100'000**

Project P9	Project risk premium in the bid: 700'000
	Expenditures for risk: ---
	Premium surplus: **700'000**

Balance 1:	+200'000

Balance 2 actual:	+1'650'000
Balance 2 target:	+1'600'000
Δ(only negative values are summed up):	**-50'000**
Balance actual$_{(riskpool)}$:	**+3'650'000**
Balance actual$_{(financial accounting)}$:	**+150'000**

Balance 3	+1'800'000

Figure 5.   Formation of the risk pool (exemplified)

adaptation need further research. Main goal is an iterative strategy for adjusting the described probabilistic concept.

4.4   Guidelines for a standardized risk management (companywide)

The application of a standardized companywide risk management requires a corridor by predefined guidelines which determine the procedure of the process. Thereby the results of risk management which are generated in the decentralized branches of the company become comparable and integrated improvements of the process can be put on. These guidelines describe for example:

– A standardized risk management adapted to different project sizes, types and complexities
– Measures to minimize psychological influences on risk evaluation
– Standardized processes, mile stones and points of decision
– Precise organizational competencies and responsibilities
– Verbalization of KO/OK criteria

– Standardized methods for estimating probabilities and impacts
– General plausibility checks for A- and B-risks.

5   CONSIDERATION OF TOTAL CORPORATE RISK – INTEGRATED APPROACH

In addition to the superimposing approach the integrated approach includes the general corporate of corporate strategy, organization, financial and operational leverage, personnel, management and IT. The problem of quantifying general corporate risks is not yet been solved. One of the goals of the oncoming project phase is the elaboration of different approaches which have to be tested by two case studies. The integrated approach gives an overview of the company's total risk situation and enables therefore conclusions at early stages concerning potential company threats and a risk-oriented rate of return.

6   CONCLUSION

For the client the assignment of a CSP using IRM results in a higher customer benefit because not yet identified project risks are subjected to the IRM of the CSP and uncovered with a range of their possible outcomes. IRM contributes to a risk-oriented realization of planned earnings and thus to the increase of entrepreneurial success of the CSP. By the application of IRM it is possible for the management to survey the situation of risk at any time. It provides banks as the lenders of capital with a transparent overview of the companies risk situation and it creates a competitive advantage for getting credit capital at better conditions. Under the point of view of a professional risk management a CSP will play an outstanding role in the construction industry compared to other competitors, because planned earnings are realized in a risk conscious way.

REFERENCES

Busch, T.A. 2003. *Risikomanagement in Generalunternehmungen.* Zürich: Eigenverlag des Instituts für Bauplanung und Baubetrieb IBB, ETH Zürich.

Chapman, C. & Ward, S. 1997. *Project Risk Management. Processes, Techniques and Insights*. Chichester: Wiley.

Curren, M. 1988. Range Estimating – Measuring Uncertainty and Reasoning with Risk. *Cost Engineering* 31, 3/1989: 18–26.

Girmscheid, G. 2000. Wettbewerbsvorteile durch kundenorientierte Lösungen – Das Konzept des Systemanbieters Bau (SysBau). *Bauingenieur* 75, 1/2000: 1–6.

Girmscheid, G. 2001. Ganzheitliches Risikomanagement in Bauunternehmen. *Bauingenieur* 76, 6/2001: 287–293.

Hertz, D.B. 1983. *Risk Analysis and its Applications,* Chichester: Wiley.

Markowitz, H.M. 1991. *Portfolio Selection*. Oxford: Blackwell.

Thommen, J.-P. 1999. *Betriebswirtschaftslehre*. Band 2, Zürich: Versus.

Vose, D. 1996. *Quantitative Risk Analysis – A Guide to Monte Carlo Simulation Modelling,* Chichester: Wiley.

Cost and risk management utilizing an integrated master plan

A.R. Minter, D.W. Ebersole, P.D. Howorth, M. Plank, K. Raum & I. Henderson
DynPort Vaccine Company, Frederick, Maryland, USA

ABSTRACT: Today's evolving market place requires that multifunctional teams be able to identify and control costs, schedules, and resources on large multinational projects where misaligned resources can cost hundreds of thousands of dollars per day. The authors examined possibilities on how to accelerate project schedules and reduce time-to-market projections by aggressively managing information using an Integrated Master Plan (IMP) tool. The paper will demonstrate why the IMP is an invaluable management tool both in terms of strategic planning and progress review. It will also explain the challenges and benefits of integrating this information together and how to develop sound business practices when using the IMP to identify, manage and mitigate cost and schedule risk.

1 INTRODUCTION

1.1 *DVCs mission and goals*

DynPort Vaccine Company LLC (DVC), a joint venture company between DynCorp and Porton International Inc., was awarded the Joint Vaccine Acquisition Program (JVAP) contract in November 1997 to develop and license biological defense vaccines to protect United States (U.S.) armed forces. These included vaccines for Smallpox, Tularemia, and Botulinum. In addition, DVC has contracted with the Department of Defense (DoD) and undertaken efforts to transition other vaccine candidates to full-scale development. These include Venezuelan Equine Encephalitis, Plague, and Next Generation Anthrax.

The working model for the contract is for DVC to serve as the Prime Systems Contractor, whose responsibility is to define technical specifications and requirements and identify qualified companies with the capabilities needed to develop and deliver the products. DVC has no production facilities of its own, so it subcontracts with qualified companies that possess the requisite experience, facilities and capabilities including:

- Defining processes for producing the product;
- Scaling-up these processes to manufacture required quantities;
- Developing the tests required to establish the product specifications;
- Determining the effectiveness of the product;
- Conducting clinical trials in humans to demonstrate safety;
- Submitting applications for licensure.

DVC oversees all of this effort through its Program Management Office of highly qualified staff of professionals with the requisite skills, experience, and responsibility for overseeing seven distinct manufacturing programs.

DVC must interact and engage in both government and private industry environments. Because these environments are uniquely different, the company has developed a fully integrated set of tools and processes that respond to these environments and provide rigor in the management of each program. In addition, DVC integrates a well-defined and robust risk management framework that enables each program to identify and focus on the areas that require attention and close management.

In summary, DVC's challenges include:

- Managing concurrent development on multiple programs;
- Emphasis on "due diligence" for DVC's direct control over subcontractor's processes;
- Evolving work scope requirements that dictate continual monitoring and application of recent changes across all programs;
- The Department of Defense (DoD) mandates significant planning and monitoring of progress; This requires the application of a DoD acquisition framework to all DVC programs as well as monthly reports on program status;
- Utilization of government funds and tight budgetary controls demand proactive management of each program.

2 RESPONDING TO THE CHALLENGE USING AN INTEGRATED MASTER PLAN APPROACH

2.1 *Overview*

DVC responded to these challenges by developing a comprehensive program management planning document, referred to as an Integrated Master Plan (IMP). The IMP outlines each program strategy along multiple dimensions and consists of five unique components, all interlinked and updated as needed. Each section, while unique in nature, serves a specific purpose. The sections that comprise the IMP include:

– Technical Approach Summary (TAS);
– Contract Work Breakdown Structure (CWBS);
– Schedule;
– Cost and Budget;
– Risk Management.

The intended purpose of the IMP is to provide technical, schedule, cost and risk information, identified by a unique CWBS identifier, to both internal and external stakeholders. It illustrates the long-range strategy required to develop the product by clearly delineating the scope of work within the project and controlling scope creep. The IMP serves as a strategic cost-modeling tool to ensure resources are properly aligned. It also holds a record of all identified risks in the program and is periodically updated to reflect progress and changes in program strategy including realized risks and funding adjustments. In short, it characterizes the contract between DVC and the U.S. Army, through the Joint Vaccine Acquisition Program (JVAP).

2.1.1 *Technical approach summary (TAS)*

The Technical Approach Summary (TAS) defines the technical strategies for advanced product development that will ultimately lead to licensure. It is a high-level description of the major steps required for licensure, including process development, manufacture, testing, process validation, and major regulatory submissions and milestones required during the development cycle. These steps can be matched specifically to the major elements of a program schedule and to the CWBS. The document is, therefore, not a detailed statement of work, but rather a statement of program, technical, and regulatory objectives against which subcontractors will provide statements of work for program execution. In this respect, the TAS provides the technical and regulatory basis of the cost estimate for the product licensure program. The document also captures product-specific performance targets as defined in the DoD Operational Requirements Document (ORD). These form part of an additional section within the document that details program-specific assumptions that underpin the technical and

regulatory sections. The TAS is maintained as a controlled document as part of the IMP through version control, and is updated as a result of changes to these assumptions, to regulatory requirements, or changes as a result of technical findings during product development. Therefore, the TAS also serves the essential purpose of maintaining product history.

2.1.2 *Contract work breakdown structure (CWBS)*

The CWBS is a product-oriented family tree composed of the processes, services, and other work tasks necessary to accomplish the project objectives as identified in the TAS. It organizes, displays, and defines the product activities to be developed. The CWBS acts as a framework for all activities in the program. Once items are catalogued, the CWBS aids in the management of activities by linking the technical approach, schedule, cost, and risk.

In addition, it provides a quick and easy reference point to drill down to lower levels, both within programs and to other products in the pipeline. Therefore, the CWBS forms the basis of task identification by assigning a unique number to a task that links all communications and deliverables. This reduces the likelihood of anything being overlooked. It also acts to identify all tasks that are crucial to the program and ensures that these activities are incorporated in the schedule, cost, and risk sections.

2.1.3 *Schedule*

The schedule consists of a dynamically linked set of tasks that not only shows the activities needed for development of the product, but also clearly identifies the linear relationship these activities have on other tasks downstream. To achieve this, the schedule is cross-referenced to the CWBS and TAS and is fully integrated with the cost section of the IMP.

Development of a schedule begins by examining and incorporating program development templates that already exist as part of lessons learned and best practices from other product pipelines. Once the backbone is in place, a more tailored approach is assembled using input from vendors and subcontractors. Common throughout any DVC schedule are milestones that have been agreed on between DVC and JVAP. These milestones serve as key performance indicators monitored by DoD officials on a regular basis.

DVC recognizes that an important aspect of the schedule design is its integration with the cost and risk sections of the IMP. Every month, as the schedule is updated with performance progress, the time phasing of cost and risk are also updated to coincide with the schedule. The schedule also allows DVC to more accurately predict schedule constraints and downstream impacts.

In addition, the establishment of dynamically linked tasks on the schedule also ensures that resources are acquired on a "just-in-time" basis. It is very costly to have under/over allocated resources not being maximized for performance. By linking different vendor schedules to the master schedule, DVC has solved this problem. When performance upstream causes the critical path to shift downstream, DVC is able to respond quickly by implementing risk mitigation plans. Since the schedule system is integrated with the cost system, impacts to the critical path and budget are assessed in real time – a most powerful tool.

2.1.4 Cost

The purpose of the cost section is to identify time-phased financial resources. By ensuring that the cost section is linked to the schedule, it is easier to mitigate situations where time and money may be an issue.

The main components of the cost section include the most likely budget estimates of timing and delivery of key products or results based on the CWBS, schedule, and basis of estimate. A beneficial aspect of the cost section is that each activity has links to the CWBS and schedule sections with a one-to-one match. Every activity within the cost section is time phased against the schedule. By having the exact dates integrated from the schedule to the cost section, DVC ensures the best timing and delivery of key resources.

The basis of the cost estimate is derived from subcontractor proposals, estimates, and industry practices. Therefore, the basis of estimate serves as a forecasting tool for DVC. Because the cost estimates are time-phased against the schedule, it is important to schedule first and estimate second. By following these guidelines, DVC is able to apply time-phased valuation of money and overhead rates in our cost projections to the customer.

Over time, DVC performs strategic budgeting exercises using the cost data. This allows us to respond to "what-if" drills from the customer. The data enables the team to generate monthly reports that give financial predictions based on trend analysis. These reports also enable the team to identify over-allocated resources that are misaligned in the wrong time periods, making the cost section of the IMP one of the most effective tools. This has proven to be very beneficial in making strategic financial decisions.

2.1.5 Risk

The purpose of DVC's risk section of the IMP is to eliminate or reduce management by crisis, through identification and mitigation of a risk event, and minimize the impact to the program's performance, schedule, and cost. This is achieved by ensuring that risk management is built into the overall approach and is designed to identify risks early so that appropriate action can be taken before the development pipeline is disrupted.

DVC recognizes that risk applies to every program and service within the company, and as such, all employees and associates play an important role in risk management. A Risk Management Team is responsible for ensuring that risks are identified, assessed, mitigated, and communicated. To assist the team in their efforts, DVC has developed a comprehensive risk manual built on industry best practices. The manual is integrated with JVAP's risk management framework, providing the customer with a seamless platform that reaches across all product pipelines and facilitates communication between DoD agencies and offices. This manual was designed using the following matrix and decision points:

- Risk Preparation;
- Risk Identification;
- Probability of Risk Occurrence;
- Risk Impact;
- Severity Index;
- Mitigation Strategy;
- Mitigation Selection;
- Contingency Planning;
- Risk Communications;
- Execution of Risk Plan;
- Reevaluation of Risk Plan and Analysis;
- Risk Repository.

The identification of risk events begins with extrapolating similar risks from other pipeline products using a comprehensive lessons-learned approach. Once similar risks have been identified and incorporated, the Risk Management Team proceeds line by line through the CWBS to identify inherent risks associated with each activity. The Risk Management Team assesses each risk event by applying rigid standards using the framework identified above. Following this exercise, a risk probability is calculated and a cost is determined.

With each identified risk event, a mitigation strategy is developed to ensure that proactive oversight is maintained at all levels of the program's development. Finally, once the exercise is completed, the risk budgets are incorporated into the program baseline depending on the risk severity index obtained. The risk budget, when added to the total program budget, gives a more realistic assessment of the program costs. This approach provides the product development team and senior management with a means of assessing the impact of changes in program strategies.

3 USING THE IMP DAY-TO-DAY

Good management practice dictates that work will be defined, planned, budgeted, and monitored. The IMP incorporates these good management practices by integrating technical effort, schedule and costs into a project plan. This plan is the basis for measuring performance against planned and actual work accomplished. Using this tool, product managers can better manage the work, communicate performance, and forecast estimates to complete.

Program schedules are based on the scope of the project plan. These schedules are updated on a monthly basis. Status information is provided to the product manager from internal and external sources (subcontractors) for this monthly update. This information is evaluated and validated prior to incorporating the reported performance into the schedule. The time-phased budget from the cost section is compared to the subcontractor's invoice to measure the value of the actual work accomplished. Variances from the plan provide the product manager with information useful in the management of the effort. Based on this information, corrective action plans can be developed, implemented, and monitored for more effective program management.

Adjustments to the IMP capture changes in each program. Shifts in project requirements and priorities, introduction of new technology, changes in regulations, adjustments in funding authorization and replacement of subcontractors are examples of the types of changes that a typical program deals with on a regular basis. Because change is a normal "condition" in development programs, adjustments to the IMP are always done in a controlled manner.

DVC uses a formal change control process to focus discussions about the impact of changes to the program and to adjust priorities. This approach helps to ensure that the IMP always contains the up-to-date "vision" of what the program is attempting to achieve. In addition, the document trail of controlled changes provides rich product history of why decisions were taken. This history is vital for long duration product development programs.

The IMP is the program's strategic plan against which all other activities and decisions can be assessed, and provides the team with a statement of the program's vision of how things are expected to proceed. Therefore, the IMP also acts as a mechanism to help unify teams working on the program and keeps them appropriately focused.

Product development is inherently associated with risks. With a defined plan, it is easier to communicate with team members when a risk has been realized and a different path is required to get to the next step. Program plan awareness by senior management and the customer creates the necessary foundation for understanding the issues when realized risks are escalated. In this instance, the IMP provides an invaluable tool in responding to "what-if" scenarios. Because these "what-if" drills occur frequently, the data contained in the IMP can be used to quickly provide the necessary information needed to assess the impacts on the program.

The integrated development, review and approval of the IMP results in agreement on the program's scope, budget and schedule. This provides management and the customer with the tools needed to report program status to outside stakeholders based on first-hand knowledge of the program requirements.

4 BENEFITS AND CHALLENGES IN USING THE IMP

The IMP serves as the basic contract with the customer. It provides the tools needed for the timely review of program performance and indicator of future trends. These data points are integrated with DVC's Defense Contracting Management Agency's certified Earned Value Management System (EVMS) and are fundamental in the development of monthly cost performance reports. As stated above, the schedule and cost sections are integrated, providing for the proper time phasing of resources on a "just-in-time" delivery basis. Because these sections are tied to one another, the management teams at DVC are given performance indicators well in advance to give ample time to identify and implement corrective action plans and risk mitigation.

The hallmark benefit of the IMP is that all aspects of the program are contained in one location and tool. This tool is accessible to all members of the team electronically. It is updated monthly, and because it is placed under formal change control, all members are ensured that they are viewing the latest version. Therefore, the IMP serves as an all-inclusive tool containing scope, schedule, cost and risk.

The challenges to using this tool include the monthly requirement of updating and providing the current status of all of the information. This requires due diligence from all members of the team to ensure that scope and performance impacts are incorporated and communicated to the customer. The initial resources required to implement the tool are expensive, but once the tools are set up, the maintenance becomes routine. Depending on the size of the program, the data points requiring data entry could be time consuming. Therefore, each team member has been assigned primary areas of responsibility for ensuring that updates are completed and verified on time.

However, in the end, the benefits far outweigh the challenges. Because DVC is committed to ensuring the success of the Program Management Office, the company is fully dedicated to providing the resources required to update and maintain the systems. In the past, DVC responded to "what-if" drills by assembling the entire team around a war room setting, and drawing out the strategy changes and their impacts to cost and technical scope. Now, by integrating all sections together, the drills are run with only a few key team members. Further, because the schedules are modular in nature, the "what-if" sessions begin with changes to the schedule modules. The cost, risk and technical changes naturally flow out from these schedule changes. This has reduced the amount of time required to respond to external challenges. When new innovations and strategies are discovered, the program's scope can be modified in as little as a few hours.

5 CONCLUSIONS

In this paper, DVC has shown how program changes and external influences dictate that our systems be integrated and responsive in providing accurate up-to-date reports. DVC must demonstrate to its external stakeholders that we are well positioned to respond to changing environments. DVC has responded in several ways. First, we provide rigor in our management approach by developing and utilizing fully integrated tools and processes that respond to changes. These integrated tools and processes are collectively known as the Integrated Master Plan and consists of a technical approach summary, contract work breakdown structure, schedule, cost, and risk sections. The technical approach summary defines the technical and regulatory strategies for advanced product development. The contract work breakdown structure is a product-oriented family tree composed of the processes, services, and all other tasks required to accomplish the objectives identified in the technical approach summary. The schedule clearly identifies the linear relationship between all activities and is integrated with the cost and risk sections to ensure that resources are acquired "just-in-time". Further, the cost system is a vital tool in DVC's management arsenal whereby all activities, costs and budgets are time-phased across the program's life span. As the schedule is updated every month, so too is the product's cost profile. Finally, the risk management plan integrates all sections together to determine what areas of product development require more rigorous management and oversight to mitigate impacts to the program's life-cycle schedule and cost.

DVC has also demonstrated that the day-to-day management of the IMP is vital in forecasting resource requirements, responding to customer "what-if" drills, justifying product requirements, assessing internal and external impacts to the schedule and cost, and performing strategic planning. We have shown how the integration of these tools allows us to maintain the project's strategy. By placing these documents under formal change control, DVC is able to quickly trace back the product history from planning through advanced development and licensure; thereby providing all team members with a history file and complex lessons learned that are applied to other DVC pipeline products.

However, with the integration of numerous tools that require constant updating, DVC has had to be sure that the processes are flexible enough to respond to real-time changes in strategy and external influences while still maintaining the integrity of the program. A system is only as good as its ability to accept input and generate accurate output in a dynamic environment. To that end, DVC's infrastructure and business approach is centered on dynamic processes that enable product teams to be innovative in responding to external challenges, thereby securing DVC's future in the biopharmaceutical arena.

5.1 *Disclaimer*

The views, opinions, assertions, and findings contained herein are those of the authors and should not be construed as official U.S. DoD or U.S. Department of Army positions, policies, or decisions, unless so designated by other documentation.

ACKNOWLEDGEMENTS

The Joint Vaccine Acquisition Program funded this program through the Department of Defense Contract # DAMD17-98-C-8024.

The working group wishes to thank the following for their contributions to this paper: Team JVAP, Randall Gaston, Terry Irgens, Michael Langford, Gretchen McLaughlin, Robert Shumate, Robin Sloan, Scott Stewart, and Becky Whitmore.

System-based Vision for Strategic and Creative Design, Bontempi (ed.)
© 2003 Swets & Zeitlinger, Lisse, ISBN 90 5809 599 1

Three missing elements of construction risk management: a conceptual exploration

C.-Yu Chang
Taiwan Construction Research Institute, Taiwan

M.-T. Wang
Century Development Corporation, Taiwan

ABSTRACT: This paper attempts to point out three areas that the mainstream construction risk management can improve. The first one is concerned with the exclusion of behavioural uncertainty stemming from opportunism as a source of risks. The second is related to the coupling effects of procurement system and project characteristics on behavioural uncertainty subject to external disturbances. The last one is to consider appropriate selection of procurement systems as a risk-mitigating strategy. By redressing the role of organizational factors in the identification of risks and the formulation of risk strategies, the mainstream construction risk approach can help users more fully take stock of impacts from different sources of risks and form appropriate risk strategies.

1 INTRODUCTION

In a knowledge economy, the only truth is that everything is changing and thus how to deal with uncertainty is definitely a tough task ahead. In a project-based industry, like construction, the importance of risk management will be growing. In fact, there has existed a voluminous amount of literature on this issue, from which a mainstream approach can be clearly identified, involving a process of risk identification, risk classification, risk analysis and risk response (Flanagan 1993). This process starts with the identification of risk sources, then classifies risk by identifying the consequence, type or impact of risk and analyze the probabilities and consequences associated with each individual risk sources and finally formulate strategies in response to expected risk exposures. Apparently, this logic is too obvious to defy. But, viewing from the lens of transaction cost economics, there are three critical elements missing in this framework. The first one is behavioural uncertainty stemming from opportunism and the second is the coupling effects of procurement system and project characteristics on behavioural uncertainty subject to external disturbances. Third, selection (or design) of project governance has been recognized as a risk strategy and attention paid to the effects of opportunistic behaviour (Floricel & Miller 2001, Turner & Simister 2001) However, in view that a complete picture is still vague and some fundamental problems, such as why opportunism matters, how to factor its effects into risk management framework need more exploration, this paper aims to give a more fuller exposition of their meanings and implications as a starting point of new research agenda of construction risk management.

2 RISK TRANSFER IN A CONSTRUCTION SYSTEM

2.1 *Construction system*

A construction system can be visualized in Figure 1 in which participants are subject to risk exposure depending on the size of the channels. When an external disturbance[1] (risks) acts upon this system, by way of risk management tools it can be transferred along the channels and absorbed by the buffers of agents (shown in red circles). A primary objective of risk management is to maximize the capacity of this system by finding the optimal design of the size of channels under the constraint of each buffer's capacity so as to prevent disruption of the system because of the failure of any party. Risk management strategies should be formulated by

---

[1] Under the condition that the quality of discussion is not sacrificed, in this paper, risk, uncertainty and disturbance are loosely used to indicate the same thing.

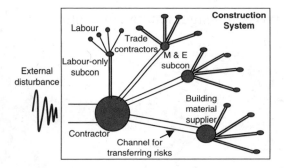

Figure 1. Risk transferring in the construction system.

Table 1. Three areas where this paper contributes to the mainstream construction risk management.

	Mainstream approach	What this paper adds
Source of risks	External risks	Internal risks (mainly arising from behavioural uncertainty)
Impact of risks	Direct impact of external disturbances	Rippling effects of external disturbances in a construction system
Risk strategies	Four categories of strategies: 1. risk avoidance 2. risk mitigation 3. risk transfer 4. risk allocation	Selection (Design) of project governance

allocating risks to those who are best able to manage them. In principle, the most appropriate bearers of risks depend on the nature of risks, so it is critical to the success of risk strategies to rightly identify the essential types of risks. Compared with the aforementioned approach placing the main focus on the analysis of external risks, this paper would like to stress that internal risks mainly arising from behavioural uncertainties should also be seriously considered in that the rippling effects that external risks might bring about would be too significant to be ignored. For this reason, the strategy of mitigating risks by selecting (designing) an appropriate procurement system is an important issue worth more attention. Three contributions made in this paper is summarized in Table 1.

2.2 Two sources of risks

In the literature, focus of construction risk analysis is placed on the external disturbances, evidenced by a fairly comprehensive list identified in Godfrey (1996), including political, environmental, planning, market,

economic, financial, natural, project, technical, human, criminal and safety. The job of risk management is to control these anticipated risks.

Another type of risks little discussed in the construction risk management literature is behavioural uncertainty. An opportunistic actor is assumed to have the proclivity to disclose the incomplete or distorted information so as to "mislead, distort, disguise, obfuscate, or otherwise confuse" his/her trading partners (Williamson 1985). When vulnerability happens, the weak party has to assume the risks of this opportunity being taken advantage by the advantageous party. The common scenario accompanied is a series of renegotiation and dispute resolution. The losses arising from this process can be labeled as type-II transaction costs, including legal fees (for hiring layer), opportunity cost of delay (if dispute cannot be resolved quickly), extra payment (if the vulnerable party gives in) and inferior quality (Chang & Ive 2000). The magnitude of losses from this risk depends on a triad relationship between project-related attributes, governance-related attributes and external disturbances. The analysis of this issue will be discussed in the following sections.

3 ANALYSIS OF CONSTRUCTION PROCESS

3.1 Dynamic process of construction

The construction procurement route in fact is a process of organising project participants. After the agreement is entered into, the estimated costs will be realised gradually. A complete description of the dynamic process of a construction transaction contains two parts: one is accounting based cost-benefit analysis and another is opportunity cost based cost-benefit analysis. To play a role in a project coalition, all participants need to spend "actual" resources in exchange for the expected profits, while at the same time they also lose the opportunity to switch the dedicated resources to the alternative use without costs. These two systems are complementary, one showing how much money has been spent and earned and another indicating how wisely you have exploited the economic value of the resources that you can control. In principle, opportunity costs play the role of choosing the right means to achieve the goal of enlarging accounting surplus. And the dynamic changing of opportunity costs and accounting costs will affect the interaction relation between trading parties in the course of transaction.

The vulnerability in the construction process can be analyzed from the perspective of economic rent. The condition under which the client is willing to initiate a project is the presence of non-negative economic rent at the outset, i.e.,

$$\text{Client's rent (CR)} = V - P \geq 0 \qquad (1)$$

where V is the value of the project to the client and P is the total payment to the agents involved for covering production costs incurred by them. We are concerned with the hold-up problem facing the client, were the project to be disrupted.

3.2 Hold-up problem in the construction process

3.2.1 Client's quasi-rent

We now turn to the hold-up problem that may happen after construction starts on site. The first scenario is that, were the project to be discontinued, the client as last resource is to alter the final purpose of the partly completed project. In this case, the client's quasi rent[2] (CQR) will be

$$CQR_{C1} = (V - V_C) - P_{Cu} \qquad (2)$$

where V_C is the return of the completed part of the project in its alternative best use and P_{cu} is the payment for the uncompleted part of construction work. Thus, Equation 2 stands for the cost-benefit appraisal of the remaining part of the project.

Correspondingly at this point, the original payment scheme can be divided into two parts: (1) payment made (P_{Cr}) and (2) payment to be made (P_{Cu}). These can be regarded as the client's evaluation of the project in terms of costs. For simplicity, we assume that the ex ante economic rent is zero due to competition in the market for which the project is built, i.e., the value of the project (V) can be expressed as

$$V = P_{Cr} + P_{Cu} \qquad (3)$$

Substituting Equation 3 into Equation 2, we can get

$$CQR_{C1} = P_{Cr} - V_C \qquad (4)$$

Normally, the value of a partly completed project is appreciably lower if the project is not completed to serve the planned function, i.e., $P_{Cr} \gg V_C$. As long as $CQR_{C1} > 0$, the client will stick to the original contract to carry on the project. Thus, $P_{Cr} - V_c$ is a source of the appropriable rent[3].

In the second scenario, the client may choose another option, that is, finding a replacement contractor to take over from the original contractor. In this case, the client's quasi rent CQR_{C2} is equal to the cost of switching to replacement contractor.

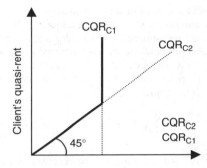

Figure 2. Client's quasi-rent at one point of time during construction process.

Thus, a measure for the lock-in effect on the client's side can be defined as

$$CQR = Min \{CQR_{C1}, CQR_{C2}\}$$

The graphical presentation of this function is shown in Figure 2. CQR_{C1} is descried as a vertical line, i.e., a constant because $P_{Cr} \gg V_C$ and, at a point of time, P_{Cr} is given. In contrast, CQR_{C2} will change as design/technology characteristics of the project, so it is a straight line going through the point of origin. When $CQR_{C1} \geqslant CQR_{C2}$, CQR is varying from 0 to CQR_{C1}; when $CQR_{C1} \leqslant CQR_{C2}$, CQR = CQR_{C1}. It means that the value of the partially-completed project in the alternative use is given, dependent on the final use of the project, but the cost of switching is endogenous, changing as design or technology adopted. This definition tries to capture the spirit of opportunity costs. More explicitly, the alternative option that the client has will always impinge upon his/her bargaining power in the current transaction, which will in turn affect the transaction hazards and the severity of the accompanying rent-seeking problems. We assume that the original function and scope of the project is chosen by way of sound feasibility study, implying that scrapping a project halfway will be much more costly than replacing the contractor. Thus, CQR_{C2} is the binding condition.

3.2.2 Contractor's quasi-rent

The contractor's hold-up problem involves fixed investment, which makes the analysis more complicated. For convenience of the following analysis, a simplified form[4] of the contractor's (expected) rent at the outset is expressed as,

$$BR_C = P_C - \sum_{t=1}^{T} (VC_t + I_t)$$

where P_C is the total payment for undertaking the construction work; VC_t indicates variable costs, such

---

[2] Quasi rent can be defined as a return in excess of the minimum needed to keep a resource in its current use.

[3] Appropriable rents can be redistributed, so their presence usually gives people an incentive to take advantage of other's vulnerability.

---

[4] We don't consider discounting factors in this formula.

as project overhead, or wages paid to supervisory personnel and payments to subcontractors; I_t refers to the lump-sum investment for machinery and equipment. The subscript t indicate the cost incurred at the period of t; T is the whole duration of the project.

At the post-contract stage, say t_1, the contractor's quasi-rent becomes

$$BQR_C = P_{Cu} - \sum_{t=t_1}^{T}(VC_t + S_t) \qquad (5)$$

where P_{Cu} is the payment to be received; S_t ex post opportunity cost of the lump-sum investment. Assume the ex ante profit is zero, so with reference to the expectation made at t_1,

$$P_{Cu} = \sum_{t=t_1}^{T}(VC_t + I_t) \qquad (6)$$

Substituting Equation 6 into Equation 5 gives

$$BQR_C = \sum_{t=t_1}^{T}(I_t - S_t) \qquad (7)$$

From Equation 7, we can realise contractor's quasi rent comes from the difference between ex ante and ex post opportunity cost of lump-sum investment. Take a numerical example for illustration. If we have the following information,

(1) a contractor spent £1,000,000 for purchasing a machine at the outset of a project;
(2) the prevailing interest rate is 8% per annum;
(3) the rental income of contractor's newly purchased machine is 3% of its purchasing price per annum;
(4) the total duration of the project is three years and t_1 is at the end of the first year.

Before the machine is purchased, the contractor can earn interest by depositing one million pound in the bank. However, after this investment is sunk, the alternative best use of this machine is assumed to be used for rent. For simplicity, we further assume that discounting is ignored and all income payment is made at the end of each year. Then at t_1, the contractor's quasi rent is equal to

$$BQR_C = 1,000,000 \times \sum_{t=2}^{3}(0.08 - 0.03) = 100,000$$

This means that, if at t_1, the maximum rent can be expropriated by the client is £100,000. Beyond this amount of money, the contractor would rather stop the project and rent the machine to other contractors. Nonetheless, generally speaking, most high-valued equipment and machinery in construction are removable and not specific to a particular project, so relative to the scale of the whole project, $I_c - S_c$ is not expected to be substantial.

3.3.3 Who is more vulnerable in the construction process?

From the above discussion, we come to realise that the client appears to be more vulnerable than the contractor at the post-contract stage since it is more costly for the client to find a replacement contract than for the contractor to switch the machinery or equipment to an alternative use.

One may be interested in the question as to whether the contractor's advantage on relatively slighter lock-in will be weakened by retention or postponement of payment. The answer is yes, but not much. There are three reasons. Firstly, the contractor can mitigate the negative effect of payment retention on cash flow by taking the strategy of "pay when paid" to subcontractors. Take an analogy of reservoir. This is just like controlling outflow in response to inflow so as to keep the reserve of the reservoir stable. If the contractor can easily transfer the pressure of keeping positive cash flow, the function of retention in disciplining the contractor will be weakened.

Secondly, to achieve the purpose of positive cash flow earlier, the contractor is liable to "frontload" the payment by setting the unit prices of cost items incurred at the early stage higher than it would be and evening out the unbalanced payment by lowering down the unit price of items incurred at the later stage. This strategy makes the contractor's payment ahead of cost, implying under this condition retention is not as effective as it appears to be.

Last, the strategy of payment retention is at best a preemptive instrument, and is not able totally to curb the potential opportunism from the contractor. Our reasoning is as follows. Payment retention is not the money that the client is entitled to determine whether to pay unilaterally. When disputes between both parties arise, the final resolution of disputes has to go through a pre-agreed-upon mechanism, such as third-party arbitration or the court. The key point is still whether the client can afford to the loss arising from going through this process. If no, the client's bargaining power coming from holding a part of payment due will lose a lot of its preemptive function.

4 COUPLING EFFECTS

As discussed above, the degree of vulnerability is a function of quasi rent, determined by the maximum between costs of switching and value losses from disruption. In principle, the higher is appropriable quasi rents, the more vulnerable is the party. Accordingly, it is necessary to explore the factors that may alter these

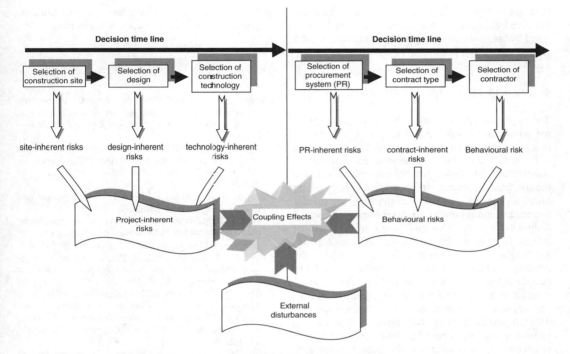

Figure 3. Coupling Effect between project-inherent risks and behavioral risks.

two costs items. This issue can be discussed from two aspects:

1. *Project-inherent risks*: In carrying out the project, the client has to make decisions on construction site, design of the project, and construction technology employed in the project. As a choice is made, there are risks following. For example, how remote the construction site, how special the design or how specific the technology employed will all have bearings on the costs of switching.

2. *Behavioral risks*: Another category of factors is associated with the way that the project participants are governed in the construction process. The alignment of project governance with project attributes can greatly reduce the proclivity of opportunism. Three choices are relevant here, including the selection of procurement system, contract type and contractor. Among them, selection of procurement system has the significance of first-order economizing[5] (Chang 2002).

As shown in Figure 3, the effects of external disturbances can trigger the happening of opportunistic behaviour. Its severity is determined both by

[5] A strategy can be said to be first-order economizing if its effect measured in cost term exceeds that other similar strategy can bring about.

project-related factors and governance-related factors. As a result, the impact of external disturbances should not only be treated on its own, but also consider their coupling effects. To make it more understandable, two examples are given here.

Consider a case where the price of a key building material, such as concrete, is roaring during construction (external disturbances). If this can be anticipated, the response may be to avoid this risk by changing design from concrete structure to steel structure. However, were this an unexpected event, the contractor for a concrete building project (project-inherent risks) under a lump sum contract (governance-related risks) must incur losses. Traditional wisdom may suggest that it is wise for the client to transfer the total risks to the contractor by this way. A possible coupling effect may arise from the contractor's attempt to recover losses by downgrading quality. This intention can be checked by intensifying site inspection, so it is not expected to be serious. But it is not always the case.

For a project that the client need to change order due to adverse ground conditions (external disturbances), no matter what type of contract is used, the client has to renegotiate the price of extra work with the contractor. To what extent overcharge may happen depends mainly on the choice of procurement system. Roughly speaking, it is easier to accommodate change order without serious hold-up problem in using management system

367

than design-build and traditional method. Hence, the negative impact of external disturbances can be mitigated by choosing an appropriate procurement system (Chang & Ive 2002)

5 CONCLUSION AND SUGGESTIONS

This paper attempts to highlight three critical but omitted points that should be considered in construction risk management. First, it is stressed that construction risks, in fact, have two sources-external disturbances and internal disturbances and the true risks inherent in the construction project can be revealed only by taking both into account. Second, risk strategies are usually formulated in response to the direct impact of external disturbances without consideration of its rippling effects. This paper set out a simple model for explaining that the client is in a more vulnerable position in the construction process that may induce the contractor to take advantage as chances arise. External disturbances, coupled with project-related factors, are the triggers to opportunistic behaviour, leading to transaction costs. Third, to reduce the negative impact of opportunistic behaviour, the alignment of procurement system with project attributes is an important strategy to mitigate transaction hazards. Only is this paper a first attempt to redress the importance of these three elements. More academic efforts should be made to enrich our grasp of the mechanism underlying external disturbances, project-related factors and project governance.

REFERENCES

Chang, C.Y. & Ive G.J. 2000. Two Ways Of Interpreting Construction Procurement In Terms of Transaction Costs,. *Bartlett Research Paper No. 13*, University College London.

Chang, C.Y. & Ive G. 2002. On The Economic Characteristics Of Construction Procurement Systems, *CIB Symposium "Procurement Systems and Technology Transfer"* in Trinidad & Tobago, January 2002.

Flanagan, R. & Norman, G. 1993. *Risk Management and Construction*, London: Blackwell.

Floricel S. & Miller R. 2001. Strategizing for anticipated risks and turbulence in large-scale engineering projects. *International Journal of Project Management* 19: 445–455.

Turner, J.R. & Simister S.J. 2001. Project contract management and a theory of organization. *International Journal of Project Management* 19: 457–464.

Godfrey, P.S. 1996. *Control of Risk – A guide to the Systematic Management of Risk from Construction*. London: CIRIA.

Williamson, O.E. 1985. *The Economic Institutions of Capitalism: Firms, Markets, Relational Contracting,* New York: The Free Press.

Chang, C.Y. 2002. *An Economic Interpretation of Construction Procurement Behaviour For Commercial and Industrial Buildings*, Ph.D. Dissertation, Bartlett School of Graduate Studies, University College London.

System-based Vision for Strategic and Creative Design, Bontempi (ed.)
© 2003 Swets & Zeitlinger, Lisse, ISBN 90 5809 599 1

Developing benchmarks for project schedule risk estimation

F.T. Edum-Fotwe
Department of Civil & Bldg Engrg, Loughborough University, Lough., Leicestershire, UK

Y. Nielsen
Department of Civil Engineering, METU, Istanbul, Turkey

ABSTRACT: The development of appropriate frameworks to facilitate the estimation of project durations on construction and engineering schemes could present considerable advantage to schedule risk estimation. The paper outlines a conceptual framework for developing and employing project schedule escalation profiles. It employs field data to establish the levels of escalation for different categories of projects, and explains how the escalation profiles can be employed to assist in estimating risk associated with project schedule of engineering schemes. The paper proposes that such profiles, appropriately customised, should form the basic building blocks for developing more accurate benchmarks to plan or monitor and control future projects.

1 INTRODUCTION

1.1 Background

Major engineering and infrastructure projects require risk evaluation along two fronts among many factors. These are project cost or budget and project schedule. While there are systems and protocols for appraising the cost aspect, there are in many cases no systematic methods for assessing the risks associated with schedule certainty, and where they exist often present a rather subjective approach.

Recent developments in comprehensive scope planning, better constructability initiatives and other productivity improvement schemes have shown that it is possible to minimise or eliminate project schedule overruns. This can be facilitated by the provision of better details to support the accurate estimates of project duration and is usually undertaken for most large-scale construction and engineering projects. The resource input for undertaking such detailed planning on large schemes forms a rather insignificant overhead contribution to the project costs. On small and medium sized schemes however, this planning and programming effort could form a significant proportion of the overall resource requirement for executing the project. The development of appropriate frameworks to facilitate the estimation of project durations can therefore be of considerable advantage to such small and medium schemes. Equally, it will help project organisations and policy makers gain a better appreciation of the

behaviour of schedule risk and the potential risks inherent in a ball path figure on what is adopted as the project duration.

The paper provides a background on why current research efforts need to be given to small and medium projects. It then addresses two major issues relating to construction and engineering projects that are classified in the range of small and medium schemes. First, it outlines a conceptual framework for developing and employing project duration escalation profiles. Secondly, it employs field data to establish the levels of escalation for different categories of projects, and explains how the escalation profiles can be employed to assist in estimating project duration for small and medium engineering schemes.

2 BENCHMARKING SCHEDULE RISK

2.1 Benchmarking explained

Many project-based organisations including the utilities as well as large public organisations such as government departments have embraced benchmarking as an important, systematic methodology for achieving their strategic objectives. Not only has benchmarking become a very popular management practice in private sector organisations, it is now being actively promoted and established in most public sector organisations, often driven by central governments.

Benchmarking is first and foremost a tool for improvement, achieved through comparison with other organisations that are recognised as superior in performance for a specific operation or function or internally set critieria. The philosophy behind benchmarking is that one should be able to recognise one's shortcomings and acknowledge that someone is achieving better performance, learn how this is being done and then implement it in one's own organisation. This attitude has to be inculcated in the organisation otherwise the full benefit of any benchmarking exercise is lost by the organisation.

In fiercely competitive sectors such as IT, benchmarking further accentuates the standard of competition and often leads to the purging of companies that do not or cannot maintain a competitive edge. This is equally the case for most construction organisations.

There are a wide range of activities that have emerged as being undertaken in the name of benchmarking and a variety of definitions existing. Similar findings emerged from a study conducted by Coopers & Lybrand regarding benchmarking activities in the UK. This includes the UK Government's definition, issued by the Department of Trade and Industry (DTI) as a *systematic approach to business improvement where best practice is sought and implemented to improve a process beyond the benchmark performance* (Partnership Sourcing). However, the following widely accepted definition put forward by Camp invokes its use as a driver of organisational performance and continuous learning.

Benchmarking is a positive, proactive process to change operations in a structured fashion to achieve superior performance.

The benefits of using benchmarking are that organisations are forced to investigate external industry practices that present superior performance and incorporate those practices into their own operations. This leads to profitable and high project performance to meet customer needs and present the project organisation with considerable competitive advantage. Benchmarking essentially involves *a process of improving performance by **continuously** identifying, understanding, and adapting outstanding practices and processes found inside and outside one's organisation*. It focuses on how to improve any given process or operation by exploiting *value improving practices* rather than merely measuring the best performance. Its essence therefore is *learning* and *adapting* outstanding practices and processes from any organisation, irrespective of geographical location, to improve performance and enhance competitiveness. Benchmarking effort often gathers the *tacit* knowledge and subtle activities within productive operations or services, including the know-how, judgments, and enablers that *explicit* knowledge and formal processes often misses.

3 THE BENCHMARKING PROCESS

The process of benchmarking for continuous improvement incorporates nine steps as illustrated in Figure 1.

Each of the principal steps are further elucidated below. The essence of such elucidation is to show the areas of the process that have relevance for the development and application of schedule escalation models in assessing risk associated with timely completion of tasks on projects.

3.1 *Select process to benchmark*

Once a decision has been made to employ benchmarking as an improvement mechanism, the immediate step is to identify the processes to focus on. This needs to tie in with the strategic objectives of the organisation or project. Any such benchmarking initiative should have a buy-in at the very top of the project organisation. It is useful at this stage also to form the benchmarking team or identify a designated person to be responsible for the whole exercise. Relevant training of the team or the designated person may be useful to the effective implementation of the benchmarking exercise.

3.2 *Determine scope of activities in process*

Establish the activities to be involved in the selected processes to determine which of them are critical to the efficiency of the process. Use of the Pareto principle should provide a rational basis for identifying these critical activities.

3.3 *Establish relevant metrics for activities*

Metrics give numerical or objective standards against which an organisation's own processes or project performance can be compared. These metrics are usually determined through a detailed and carefully analysed survey or interviews. Appropriate metrics for assessing the activities are then established. The adopted metrics need to link back into the company's strategic objectives in order to emphasise the relevance of any measurement effort. In other words, the adopted metrics should yield information relevant to the operations of the organisation or project. This stage forms the first critical step where schedule performance plays a key role and designated as A in Figure 1. Traditionally most metrics are defined as cost based values and contrasts with the schedule oriented values in this paper adopted to provide an indication of the level of risk associated with schedule certainty.

3.4 *Investigate practices*

Identify appropriate target organisations or projects to analyse and investigate their practices for the

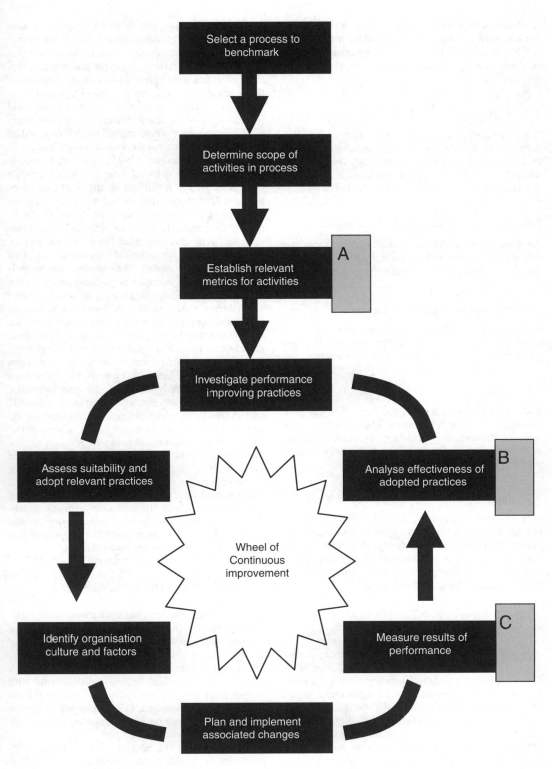

Figure 1.   Benchmarking process for attaining continuous improvement.

subtleties of their superior performance that relate to the selected activities. The baseline of the investigation will be the metrics. The scope of such investigation will be determined by the time and resources devoted to the exercise.

3.5 Assess suitability and adopt relevant practices

It is essential that the context of each superior performance is thoroughly assessed for its suitability to one's own organisation or project appreciated. This will help to establish why that practice results in superior performance within the particular organisation or project.

3.6 Identify organisation culture and factors

An appreciation of context, culture and the nuances that drives one's organisation or project will help to adapt the adopted practices for effective implementation.

3.7 Plan and implement associated changes

A careful plan detailing actions, milestones, and deliverables need to be drawn up for implementing the changes associated with adopting the new practices.

3.8 Measure results of performance

The metrics provide a basis for measuring the performance from the deliverables. The development of relevant frameworks provide a baseline for assessing such performance of the project with regard to schedule, designated as C in Figure 1.

3.9 Analyse effectiveness of adopted practices

It is essential that evaluation of the effectiveness of the adopted practices takes cognisance of change in competition to set new targets of performance for the practices. This step is also directly relevant to the development of frameworks for assessing schedule performance as designated in Figure 1 as B.

4 NATURE OF PROJECT SCHEDULE

Policy makers connected with the delivery of development projects and other constructed facilities often have to confront a situation whereby a quick decision is required as to the duration of a particular infrastructure scheme as part of the requirements for establishing a business case to justify the project. In very many cases such a decision must be made before other arrangements, such as financing and detailed planning, can be put in place. The analysis involved in establishing such a business case would usually be

quite comprehensive, and relies on the policy maker having a reasonably accurate knowledge of or information on the main features (eg. total schedule) associated with the proposed scheme. A simple tool that provides such information will greatly facilitate the decision of the policy maker at this initial stage of a project.

Several mathematical models for deriving and forecasting some of these features of a project are already in existence. These include models depicted by Seeley (1996), and other works including Flanagan & Tate (1997), Skitmore (1991), and Skitmore & Marsden (1999). The use of these and similar models have been greatly facilitated by the recent developments in IT. Although there have been advances in the deployment of IT systems to facilitate the establishment of the project duration, for example project planning software and estimating these developments, essentially aim at the technical expert who has to go through the full motions of the planning. For the policy maker, whose decision is required much earlier than the detailed design stage of the project, this presents a dilemma. Although the existing models are very useful and convenient for the policy maker, there are two major setbacks associated with them. First, these models have been developed primarily for large projects, and therefore present a scale problem when applied to small and medium projects. Secondly, most of the models simply turn out only cost estimates. These estimates are not associated with potential project durations, which are equally essential for the appraisal process of the development schemes. The relevance of duration contingency for projects derives from the fact that most development schemes need to establish a firm date by which time the investment would start to generate returns. Any extensions beyond that date often presents distortions in the income flows associated with the project investment. Establishing level of such duration contingency should enable policy makers to appreciate the level of risk associated with the projects they promote.

5 PROJECT SCHEDULE ESCALATION

Relatively, little attention has been given to the modelling of project characteristics and performance for medium and small schemes. Existing models that address project characteristics are based on records drawn mainly from large-scale projects, and for which data is readily accessible with occasional input with records from medium-sized projects. Cole (1991) and Popescu & Charoenngam (1995) provide examples that typify the large project orientation of schedule control in construction.

Early works in the control of project characteristics include developments by McCaffer (1975). This utilised regression techniques to establish a basis for predicting project costs from historical data. The main thrust of these early developments was to identify a generic pattern of the value and time relationships for the different stages of a project. Subsequent developments focused on further exploration of the relationship between the value and duration of projects. This includes work undertaken by Kumaraswamy & Chan (1995), Walker (1995), Kaka & Price (1991), Bromilow (1988) and Kenley & Wilson (1986). For example, using data from the Hong Kong construction industry, Kumaraswamy & Chan (1995) established that the estimation of project durations was often determined by a *rule of thumb* and *commercial and/or political considerations*. While this in itself is not necessarily wrong, it is important that such rules of thumb are derived from a rational basis. They further explored the relationship between the value and duration of the contracts that featured in their study and came up with mathematical models similar to those proposed earlier in other studies such as Kaka & Price (1991), Bromilow (1988). Bromilow's earlier work had led to the development of time-cost profiles for projects, which was typified by the sigmoid curve. Kaka & Price (1991) demonstrated that a strong relationship existed between the construction period and final project value and this could be related by:

$$T \propto C^B \qquad (1)$$

yielding

$$T = K \times C^B \qquad (1a)$$

where, T is the duration of construction period, C is the final project value, K is a constant describing the level of duration performance, and B is a constant describing how the duration performance is effected by the project size as measured by value. The model proposed by Kaka & Price (1991) gives values for B and K for public sector civil engineering works that were procured using fixed price contracts. Kumaraswamy & Chan (1995) also provide a good summary of the values for B and K for the proposed models that resulted from their studies. The strong correlation between cost and time attributes of construction projects was later confirmed in the work of Walker (1995).

More recently, Lee & Kyoo (1999) made use of a numerical approach to address the integration of the time and cost data sets for construction projects. They relied on the use of mathematical matrices, which are introduced to show the interrelationships between the time and cost data sets and to demonstrate their effect on each other. These interrelationships are exploited to solve the conflict that often arises from the differences between work breakdown structure and cost breakdown structure. This is achieved through several time and cost related matrix equations that are used for project planning or control. Feng et al. (1997) also employed a time-cost trade-off analysis to examine the relationships between project costs and duration. They utilised a genetic algorithm procedure for their analysis and argued that it enabled them to handle large volumes of data, the sort of which are associated with large projects.

These models provide a strong basis for employing one of the two variables of duration and cost as a predictor for the other. In the case of policy makers, project costs on small and medium schemes are determined by budgetary allocations, and this could be employed for one or more of several project options. As such the project budget provides the stable variable from which the duration of projects and associated levels of escalation that represent schedule contingency, can be estimated.

The next section of the paper provides a mathematical derivation of duration escalation for small and medium projects. The derived profile of escalation can be employed as part of the evaluation process and business case establishment required at the early stages of a project. This is based on the *non-linear* modelling of the project duration in a time cost plane.

To ensure that their model could be established with the linear regression approach, Kaka & Price (1991) as well as previous developers had to employ the log transformation to force the data into a linear relationship. Such transformation is a tacit acknowledged of the inadequacy of simple regression models to provide accurate representation of project cost-duration relationship. Kenley & Wilson (1986) for example had attributed lack of fit for transformed models to the *uniqueness* of each project and argued that this *uniqueness* resulted in a higher systematic error for any simple regression model developed with data from several projects. In particular, they concluded that forecasts of individual project cost and time profile are invalid when derived from a model that is established through simple regression of grouped data. Many relationships in construction operations and businesses often do not follow a straight line, and such transformation enables them to be modelled. The use of transformations however, has an effect on the predictive accuracy and efficient performance of the model that results from such developments. To overcome this potential inaccuracy inherent in transformed models Sohail & Edum-Fotwe (2000) utilised the non-linear regression approach for modelling the time cost relationships of small projects.

The general non-linear regression approach is a technique that fits a curve to a set of data. This is achieved with the use of a model equation that defines -*y*- as a function of -*x*- and one or more parameters. Details of how the general non-linear technique was employed to establish a time-cost plane for small and

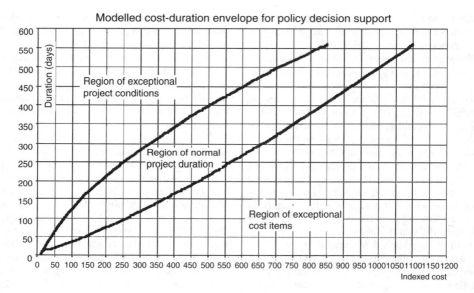

Figure 2. Time-cost plane for small infrastructure project.

medium projects can be obtained from Sohail & Edum-Fotwe (2000). Figure 2 presents a time-cost plane frame for small and medium infrastructure projects, and identifies three main regions for project schedule the boundaries of which are defined by the general exponential equation 2.

$$\text{Indexed project duration } = \text{EXP}[a+b/x+c\log x] \quad (2)$$

where: x is the indexed cost of the project.

The three regions provide the most likely scenarios of project schedule and cost performance for various types of schemes. An upper boundary demarcates the normal region from a region of exceptional project conditions with regard to schedule. The exceptional schedule conditions represent situations where a project experiences considerable schedule escalation without any commensurate cost escalation. An example of such a case is where a project is suspended due to either commercial or political demands, and later on re-activated.

A lower boundary equally separates the normal region from one of exceptional cost items. The region of exceptional cost reflects projects where a higher proportion of cost than expected is accounted for by capital items or major plant installations. The region of normal project duration provides a range within which projects of similar size are expected to lie with regard to duration if they are not characterised by any exceptional circumstances. Equally it provides an indication of the degree of escalation that can be associated with projects of different sizes within the region of normal project conditions. Sohail & Edum-Fotwe (2000) have outlined the mathematical models that

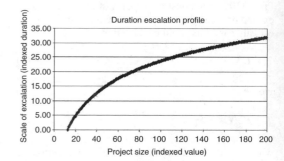

Figure 3. Escalation profile for small and medium infrastructure projects.

define the two boundaries. The general form of the expected escalation forms the thrust of this paper and has been derived by establishing the difference between the upper and lower boundaries of the normal region.

6 ESCALATION PROFILE OF PROJECTS

Figure 3 present the escalation profile associated with the region of normal project conditions. This was derived as follows:

$$\text{Schedule escalation} = \text{Upper} - \text{Lower boundary} \quad (3)$$

Based on the derivations of Sohail & Edum-Fotwe (2000) this yields:

$$\text{Indexed schedule escalation (ISE)} = y_{upper} - y_{lower} \quad (4)$$

Resulting in,

$$ISE = EXP[4.7-51.8/x-0.6\log x] \qquad (5)$$

7 DISCUSSION OF ESCALATION PROFILE

The analysis presented in this paper has demonstrated that by relying on the implicit assumption of a relationship between cost and duration of projects, it is possible to model the scale of schedule escalation of small projects. This has been derived for infrastructure projects based on modelling work undertaken by previous authors. Figure 3 has presented the profile of the escalation for indexed projects up to 200 in size (indexed value). For a definition of the indexed value of small and medium projects, readers are referred to Sohail & Edum-Fotwe (2000). Similar profiles can be generated for all the different sizes of small and medium projects represented in the model proposed by Sohail and Edum-Fotwe (2000). The general form of the escalation profile is reflected by the exponential Equation 5. The profile provided suggests the following behaviour of escalation for the different sizes of small and medium infrastructure projects.

- Between the sizes of 13 and 40 (indexed value) projects in the normal range experience the steepest growth in schedule escalation.
- Between the sizes of 40 and 500 (indexed value) small and medium projects experience a reducing marginal growth in schedule escalation.
- Beyond the size of 500 (indexed value), projects begin to experience reduced levels of escalation although the tailing off is at a very slow rate.
- Projects of indexed size below 10 (indexed value) cannot be captured by the profile.

The tailing off of schedule escalation for projects over size 500 (indexed value) could be accounted for by their relatively larger-size as projects of that size begin to reflect the characteristics of schemes that could qualify for medium to large-sized projects with exceptional circumstances.

The derived profile of schedule escalation presented in this study can provide a simple tool that can replace the current rule of thumb practice employed by policy makers for medium and small projects. This can be employed in establishing the expected level of schedule escalation for small and medium projects at the early stages when detailed design and analysis would not have been undertaken.

This will provide an indication of the degree of risk of schedule escalation for this category of projects. Small projects are of such a nature that their size does not economically permit the detailed evaluation and estimating effort that forms an insignificant part of a larger project. As a result consideration of alternative project options are often not undertaken. The use of the escalation profile, particularly in its graphical form should allow the simulation of several scenarios for a project by policy makers. The profile can also be employed as a control mechanism for projects by providing the duration limits beyond, which the project becomes untenable or would be considered as one with exceptional conditions.

8 BENCHMARKING SCHEDULE SCALATION

The schedule escalation profile can be of valuable assistance to small and medium AEC companies that usually undertake small and medium projects. Based on their historical project experience, a similar profile can be established and calibrated to the company's standards and requirements as a supplement to any business case and pre-design evaluation effort with obvious efficiency gains. The three regions in Figure 2 provide different contexts for any benchmarking exercise. The escalation profile in Figure 3 provide a baseline for comparisons, and this can be re-calibrated as improvement or changes in schedule performance data becomes available. Equally, a simplified profile that presents the escalation profile as percentiles can be generated for ease of use.

9 CONCLUSION

The paper has presented an overview of what is entailed in benchmarking as a background to developing metrics for schedule escalation. It employed the relationship between project cost and duration of small and medium projects was employed to establish the profile of the duration escalation that occurred on infrastructure projects. The analysis resulted in three categories of escalation that occurred for small and medium projects: increasing escalation, reducing marginal escalation, and reducing escalation. It also presented indications that there is an inverse relationship between project size and level of escalation. The derived escalation profile can be generated in graphical form or as a table that policy makers can use to establish the level of normal escalation to anticipate as part of the feasibility of small projects. The derived escalation profile presented in this paper was based on projects from the infrastructure sub-sector. Similar profiles can be generated with data from projects for any other sub-sector. In this way, it should be possible to employ the profiles as a benchmark for managing project escalation on small and medium schemes.

375

REFERENCES

Bromilow, F.J. 1988, The time and cost performance of building contracts 1976–1986, *The Building Economist*, **27**(September), pp. 4.

Cole, L.J.R. 1991, Construction scheduling: principles practices and six case studies. *Journal of Construction Engineering and Management*, ASCE, **117**(4), pp. 579–588.

Department of Commerce, 2001, *Housing and construction: new construction*, Stat-USA, 2001 Edition.

Feng, C.W., Liu, L. & Burns, S.A. 1997, Using genetic algorithms to solve construction time-cost trade-off problems *Journal of Computing in Civil Engineering*, **11**(3), pp. 184–189.

Flanagan, R. & Tate, B. 1997. *Cost control in building design: an interactive learning text*, (Oxford: Blackwell Science).

Kaka, A. & Price, A.D.F. 1991, Relationship between value and duration of construction projects. *Construction Management and Economics*, **9**, pp. 383–400.

Kenley, R. & Wilson, O.D. 1986, A construction project cash flow model – an idiographic approach. *Construction Management and Economics* **4**(3), pp. 213–232.

Kumaraswamy, M.M. & Chan, D.W.M. 1995, Determinants of construction duration. *Construction Management and Economics*, **13**, pp. 209–217.

Langford, D.A. & Rowland, V.R. 1995, *Managing overseas construction contracting*, (London: Thomas Telford).

Lee, H.S. & Kyoo, J.Y. 1999, Application of mathematical matrix to integrate project schedule and cost. *Journal of Construction Engineering and Management*, **125**(5), pp. 339–346.

McCaffer, R. 1975. Some examples of using regression analysis as an estimating tool. *The Quantity Surveyor*, **32**(5), pp. 81–86.

Popescu, C.M. & Charoenngam, C. 1995, *Project planning, scheduling and control in construction*. (New York: Wiley).

Seeley, I.H. 1996. *Building economics: appraisal and control of building design cost and efficiency*, Macmillan, Basingstoke.

Skitmore, M. & Marston, V. (eds) 1999, *Cost modelling*, Spon, London.

Skitmore, R.M. 1991, *Early stage construction price forecasting: a review of performance*, Occasional paper, Royal Institution of Chartered Surveyors, UK.

Sohail, M. & Edum-Fotwe, F.T. 2000. Cost-duration tool for policy decision on micro and small projects. *Journal of Financial Management in Property and Construction*, **5** (3), pp. 71–84.

Walker, D.H.T. 1995. An investigation in time construction time performance construction time performance. *Construction Management and Economics*, **13**, pp. 263–274.

System-based Vision for Strategic and Creative Design, Bontempi (ed.)
© 2003 Swets & Zeitlinger, Lisse, ISBN 90 5809 599 1

Practical cost management system for construction projects

K.A. Tenah
M.E. Rinker, Sr. School of Building Construction at Gainesville, FL, USA

ABSTRACT: The US construction industry suffered a steady decline in efficiency, productivity and quality from the mid-1960s to the early 1980s. American businesses and the entire nation paid a high price for the decline in efficiency, productivity and quality. The key factors that contributed to this decline include: low cost consciousness, lack of overall cost consideration, unfocused reports, inefficient information exchange, and passive attitude of learning from the past (CICE 1982). Improved cost control systems appear to be effective methods to bring the desired changes (Zhan 1996).

There has been an awareness and development of innovative forms of contracting during the last two decades. Among these innovative techniques and procedures are professional construction management (CM), design-build, build-operate transfer (BOT), total quality management (TQM), etc. Each of these has its unique strengths and conditions under which it can favorably operate to improve efficiency, productivity and quality. Even though new contracting practices and processes have been introduced in the past two decades, the traditional method of general contracting (GC) has retained its unshakable position and advantages where the design is substantially complete prior to beginning the construction phase.

This paper describes the current practical methods of cost control for contractors and parties involved in construction projects. It also provides guidelines on how to manage projects using an efficient cost control system which links the different phases (bidding, purchasing, construction and maintenance) into an integrated system. The paper emphasizes the interfaces of the mechanisms between the construction phases.

Efficient cost control practices are presented from the general contractors' point of view with emphasis at the project level. The basics of a cost control system are presented, followed by the internal and external relationships that must be addressed by project cost control. Cost control practices are examined during bidding, purchasing, construction and maintenance phases. An analysis is given on how to better manage direct labor, materials, equipment, overhead and subcontractors so that the general contractor can stay within budget and achieve the profit target. Change order control, including change order fundamentals, process and analysis, is also presented. The effect of the cost control system on the financial aspect of the company and the projects is also given. Finally, a project cost control model is presented.

1 FUNDAMENTALS OF EFFECTIVE COST CONTROL SYSTEM

1.1 *Definition of a cost control system*

A control system is basically a group of components that maintain a desired result by manipulating the value of variables in the system. An open-loop control system does not compare the actual result with the desired result to determine the appropriate control action. A closed-loop or feedback control system measures the difference between the actual value of the controlled variables and the desired value (set point). It then uses the difference to prescribe actions that will drive the actual value toward the desired value (Bateson 1989). The American Association of Cost Engineers (AACE) defines cost control as "the application of procedures

to follow progress in order to minimize cost with the objective of increasing profitability and assuring efficient operations." (AACE 1992 & 1993).

The dynamic nature of the construction industry dictates that there is a difference between the expectation and the actual result. In the eyes of the general contractor, materials, equipment, labor, overhead and subcontractors need to be constantly controlled during bidding, purchasing, construction and maintenance phases. Therefore, a close-loop multi variable cost control system is essential. Broadly speaking, project cost control for the general contractor starts at the very beginning of the bidding phase and continuously contributes its effort until the end of the construction or maintenance phase. Systematic cost control procedures attempt to limit costs to stay within budget, focus control efforts where they will be most effective, and achieve maximum control at minimum operating cost. In practice, most contractors do not consciously exercise cost control until well after mobilization, thereby losing the opportunity of potential cost savings. This is "cost control in a narrow sense".

1.2 Elements of a cost control system

There are three essential elements of cost control. The first is the establishment of goals or the optimum condition; the second is to measure performance variation against the optimum, and the third is to take corrective action in response to excessive variation.

A carefully prepared estimate is of utmost importance to the efficient cost control of projects. First, it steps up the baseline against performance is measured or computed. Estimate also provides all responsible parties with a clear picture of the project scope, description, quantities, costs and worker-hours. Secondly, from the inception to the completion of a project, almost every action taken is driven by the budget. For a general contractor, a budget lists all costs of equipment, materials, labor and indirect items, all broken down into sufficient detail to permit proper control.

An appropriate cost coding system is required so as to identify the various attributes of a project component and facilitate the use of the budget for the purpose of easier control. Coding consists of assigning a symbol or a group of symbols to each item to be controlled, so each coded item is distinguishable from all others. Usually, a coding system will distinguish between the different resource components, such as labor, labor burden, materials, equipment, subcontractors and others.

1.3 Measurement and trend identification

It is critical to know status at any stage and to be able to speculate the future trend of both cost and schedule. Realistic forecasting will locate potential problem areas and, with prompt corrective measures, costs can be kept under control. The first step is to measure the work-in-place status, then forecast the cost at completion so trend can be identified. Because of unique nature of each component, different measuring methods have been developed (Eldin 1989, Patrascu 1988) and these include: (a) cost ratio; (b) start finish; (c) incremental milestone; (d) units completed; (e) supervisor opinion; and (f) weighted or equivalent units.

Once an activity status is known, the earned value for this activity equals the activity budget times its percent complete. The overall percent completion for an entire project can be determined by earned work hours or dollars for all the project activities divided by the current project budget.

2 COST CONTROL VERSUS ACCOUNTING AND FINANCIAL MANAGEMENT

Costing in cost control is a process of recording all the expenditures which relate to specific items of work in such a way that the cost of that work can be readily identified. It classifies the cost incurred under appropriate headings and gives a considerable amount of information upon which management can take action. Sometimes it is referred to as management accounting.

Accounting, or financial accounting, on the other hand, is a book-keeping process involving number-gathering activities often related to generating a payroll and keeping track of accounts receivable and accounts payable. The information recorded is of a historical nature. Accounting deals with "real" money or the amounts actually disbursed or committed such as accounts receivable and accounts payable (Adrian 1979). Therefore, costing is a proactive process while accounting is an after-fact or reactive one. Accounting deals with asset accounts, liability accounts, equity accounts, income accounts, expense accounts and outside balance accounts (Jurkiewicz 1995).

Cost control deals with forecasted costs, actual costs, expenses, commitments, payments and others. The trial balance yields figures for the "current status" and the "current progress" of project costs, while in accounting, trial balance yields figures for "loss-and-profit statement" and "income statement".

Financial management is an inclusive term of which accounting is just a component. Financial management is usually focused at the company level. It includes a number of disciplines, all of which interact with others and share the same database, namely, construction accounting, financial analysis, financial forecasting, asset management, debt management, cash management and tax management. In short, cost control focuses on a more detailed level, while financial management focuses more on the whole company.

3 PROJECT COST CONTROL FOR THE GENERAL CONTRACTOR (GC)

Project cost control is, to a large extend, an after-fact function. Identifying trends to pinpoint potential problems of cost overrun helps the management team perform some proactive roles against future over-expenditure. In this sense, cost control possesses some proactive character. Once a measure is taken, the plan may be adjusted to reflect this change. All affected parties, including field personnel, subcontractors, suppliers and manufacturers, adopt the change accordingly and try to eliminate the negative variance. The outcome may prove positive. If not, another cycle of cost control commences.

The most efficient way to control project costs is to activate every involved staff in this effort. Costs can only be controlled by those who are doing the spending (Clark, et al., 1985). Under different contract types, the project organization will adjust the extent of control to different levels. With the decreasing order of control effort, there are lump-sum contracts, unit-cost contracts and cost plus fixed fee contracts.

The contractor's cost control, to be effective, must link all the different project phases (bidding, procurement, construction, and maintenance).

4 CHANGE ORDER CONTROL

The unique nature of construction projects, open air operations, stratified construction sequences, mobile work places and other unique characteristic makes modifications to the original scope, time, or cost of the work a normal part of the construction process. To formally announce such changes and to modify the contract between the owner and the contractor, a change order is issued to formalize the change in the work without resorting to a new contract. In general, change order requests are initiated by the owner and/or architect for additional work that is beyond the original scope of the contract documents. In some cases, the GC or subcontractors make change order requests based on differences of interpretation of the contract documents or due to differing field conditions.

It is the project manager's responsibility to develop a proposed change order based on information from the subcontractors or vendors and pricing all the work to be performed by the GC's own forces. A change order request that is initiated by either the owner or architect should be forwarded to all potentially affected subcontractors for their information and/or action.

Although change orders are inevitable in any large construction project, being proactive and taking preventive measures could largely decrease the frequency and probable adverse impact of changes rather than leaving it to chance.

The most common sources of change orders (Zahn 1996) include: (a) design error: lack of coordination among disciplines; contradiction; discrepancies; impossibility and inconsistencies; (b) ambiguous specifications, omissions in specifications; (c) owner's change of scope; (d) latent conditions: e.g., different site conditions; (e) delays due to unusual weather or man-made conditions not under the GC's control; (f) improvement in workmanship, time or cost due to value engineering, constructability etc.; (g) building code changes, etc.; and (h) other sources such as delays or interference by architect or owner (e.g., prolonged shop drawing approval).

5 PROJECT COST CONTROL MODEL

5.1 *Principles*

Even though the dynamics of each construction project and its operations calls for specific approach that is different from others, there are common guidelines that form the basis of efficient project cost control. The following ten principles depict this basis (Zahn 1996):

1. *Creating cost-consciousness among every member of the project management team.* With cost-consciousness, the project team would not only be cautious about it's own actions but also seek every chance to influence the subcontractors, vendors and its direct labor to make cost-effective decisions. Without it, the whole cost control cycle would lack smoothness. Instilling the cost-consciousness concept is largely in upper management's hands.
2. *Capturing data realistically in a timely fashion.* The construction operation depends on reliable and fast information exchange. How to record data, refine data and organize data in a meaningful format to provide the most probable picture of the project dictates the usefulness of the information and the effectiveness of the corrective measures. This principle is also critical for bidding and budget setup. Realistically capturing information on local markets (labor, union influence, subcontractor and vendor pool, material availability, etc.), project complexity, possible contingencies etc. would help develop a competitive and profitable bid as well as an executable budget.
3. *Setting up realistic budget.* It shows the general contractor's commitment to the owner. It establishes item by item targets to be measured against during project execution. Comparisons between as-built budgets and original budgets indicate the quality of the budget and should serve for the next budget preparation.
4. *Comparing to-be-committed to the budgeted before it is committed.* The first quantitative measure criteria against the budget is the ability to compare to-be-committed to budget prior to commitment. The comparison takes place when allocating resources (man-hours, people, etc.), during bidding, when subcontracting trades, when buying materials and equipment, when hiring direct labor, etc.
5. *Comparing actual cost to the budget.* This is the most often used comparison to measure project performance. The result is analyzed to initiate required corrective actions. Without capturing data accurately and timely which is Principle 3, the comparison in Principles 4 and 5 is meaningless.
6. *Recognizing the nature and the root cause of the variance instead of the accompanied symptoms when analyzing variances.* Distinguishing between the four types of causes (common cause,

special cause, structural cause and tampering) is critical because the appropriate managerial actions are quite different for each type.

7. *Allocating appropriate time and budget to each project task considering the overall benefit.* This is evidenced by (a) putting investment and effort in bidding and contract negotiation for smooth execution of later phases; (b) preparing a better budget to focus more effective comparisons; and (c) setting up and maintaining an accurate historical data bank for reference by management. Near-sighted focus on only local objectives instead of the overall project goal would lead to suboptimization or a short-term goal in one area being reached at the expense of other resources.

8. *Using the accumulated historical data to improve the cost control cycle.* Each project, once completed and well documented, generates invaluable historical data for better project management of the future projects. A small amount of time spent on organizing the data into a meaningful format is very worthwhile. Even during project execution, each cost control cycle forms the latest reference for the next cycle and this improvement should be continued cycle after cycle.

9. *Considering the overall cost effect as changes occur.* Not only direct costs and indirect costs need to be considered, but also the impact costs.

10. *Continuously improve the existing system even if it works well.* There is always a better way of conducting business. Every one in the project team, as well as in the company must participate in a disciplined way using the plan-do-check-act cycle.

5.2 *Proposed project cost control model (zahn 1996)*

The proposed model of practical cost control for construction projects is illustrated in Figure 1. The budget plan is developed to allocate resources appropriately into bidding, procurement, construction and maintenance phases in terms of general conditions, overhead, direct labor, materials, equipment and subcontracts (see Figure 1 where * is located). Notice that, in the bidding phase before the contract is signed between the owner and the general contractor, the budget to assign proper man-power, time to win the bid is decided by upper management.

Functional support from the central corporate department may be used. For example, use the corporate mechanical, plumbing and electrical (MPE) expert to assist in clarifying MPE quotes from bidders to keep the contractor competitive while minimizing the associated risks.

Once the budget plan is set up, execution of the plan commences. During execution, controlled variables that could affect the result such as management approaches, change orders, productivity, subcontracts coordination,

material handling, inclement weather, union activities, internal organization members interaction and external parties interaction, etc. are measured and analyzed.

These are cost measurements which evaluate the actual cost of work against the budget, schedule measurement which denotes actual progress as opposed to the planned project duration, and billing measurement which indicates the status of billing as either overbilling or underbilling. The results of the measurement are processed by comparison and analysis. If appropriate corrective action is not taken quickly when variance occurs, the contractor may soon face a big problem.

5.3 *The benefits and limitations of the cost control model*

The avoidable pitfalls for the proposed cost control model are: (a) the model is a closed-loop control system; and (b) it focuses on total cost management from an overall point of view.

The benefits of the model includes: (a) provision of the control objectives – overhead, general conditions, labor, materials and equipment – are constantly controlled, whether they are within the scope of the original contract or as modified by change orders; (b) coverage of each project phase – bidding, procurement, construction and maintenance – have different control objectives; (c) possesses proactive features by revolutionizing the definition of comparison and variances; and (d) serves as a guide to detailed cost control systems which may vary according to the company size, project features, and other constraints.

6 CONCLUSIONS

With today's ever increasing competition among construction companies, the efficiency of a project cost control system, to a large extent, governs the competitiveness of the firm, its market share, profitability and above all survival capability. Facing a steady decline in efficiency, productivity and quality from 1960s to early 1980s, the construction industry has made dramatic reforms to reverse this negative trend. Sophisticated project control software has been utilized on construction jobsites to facilitate timely data collection and prompt information exchange between the jobsite and the home office. The following are the conclusions this paper presents:

1. Organizations are restructuring around information by reducing the number of mid-level management jobs resulting direct and faster communication.
2. Bar coding has gained increasing usage in achieving more effective material management.
3. Management is more cost-conscious in its everyday decision-making than ever before.

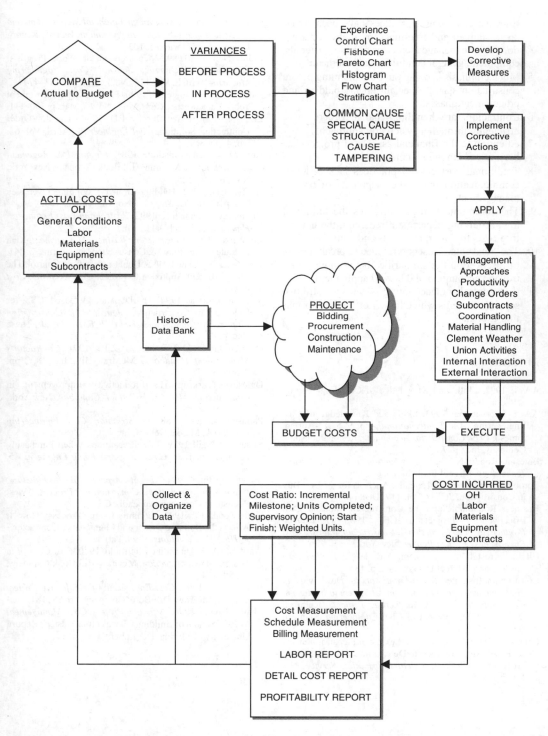

Figure 1.   Proposed project cost control model (There are numerous cycles of cost control that take place during project execution. Each cycle provides feedback for the following cycles whether they are adjacent or not).

4. Effective cost control practices have been developed, adopted and fine-tuned by many construction firms to manage their costs of labor, materials, equipment, general conditions and overhead.
5. Much emphasis is being put onto planning before construction starts, especially in the bidding and procurement phases.
6. Contractors are handling change orders more efficiently through a systematic approach.
7. Attention to the financial aspects of projects has been raised among all concerned.
8. Traditional cost control practices lack efficient communication with other segments of project management.
9. The communication gap involves the failure of the accounting department receiving the current true costs for labor, materials and equipment.
10. The "dual entry" cost control made a breakthrough of discovering the similarities between cost control and accounting and how to apply them.
11. Cost control and accounting systems are still two separate systems which hinder efficient information exchange.

REFERENCES

AACE 1992. Skills and Knowledge of Cost Engineering, *AACE*, p. 9–4.

AACE International 1993. Skills and Knowledge of Cost Engineering, *AACE International*, pp. 9–5, 11-Adrian, James J. 1979. *Construction Accounting*, Reston Publishing Company, Inc., p. 7.

Bateson, Robert N. 1989. *Introduction to Control System Technology*, Mreeill Publishing Company, p. 11.

Bernold, Leonhard E. 1991. Vendor Analysis for the Best Buy in Construction, *JCEM*, Vol. 117, Dec. pp. 645–658.

Business Roundtable and the Construction Industry Cost Effectiveness Project (CICE) 1982, *Measuring Productivity in Construction: a Construction Industry Cost Effectiveness Project Report*, New York.

Clark, Forrest D. & Lorenzoni, A.B. 1985. *Applied Cost Engineering*, Marcel Dekker, Inc., p. 136.

Construction Institute 1984. *A Framework for Designing and Analyzing Management and Control System to Implement the Productivity of Construction Project*, Technical Report 282, Department of Civil Engineering, Stanford University, June.

Cook, A.E. 1990. An Analysis of the Cost of Preparing Tenders for Fixed Price Contracts to Determine the Worth of Such Procedures, *CIOB, Technical Information Service*, No. 120, pp. 4–5.

Coulter, Carleton III. *Contractor Financial Management and Construction Productivity Improvement*, BCIAC Report, University of Florida, p. 103.

Eldin, Neil W. 1989. Measurement of Work Progress: Quantitative Technique, *Journal Cost Engineering Magazine*, AACE, Vol. 115, No.3, Sept. pp. 462–474.

Eldin, Neil W. & Egger, S. 1990. Productivity Improvement Tools: Camcorders, *JCEM*, Vol. 1 No. 16, Mar., p. 100–111.

Erickson, Leif T. & Murphy P.D. 1994. The Job-Order Contracting Solution, *Civil Engineering*, April, Vol. 64, No. 4, p. 68.

Fails Management Institute 1981. *Financial Management for Contractors*, McGraw-Hill Book Company, New York, NY, pp. 124–125.

Griffis, F.H. 1992. Bidding Strategy: Winning Over Key Competitors, *JCEM*, Vol. 1 No. 18, Mar., p. 164.

Humphreys, Kenneth K. 1992. *Project and Cost Engineers' Handbook*, Marcel Dekker, Inc. 1992, p. 292.

Jin, Weixin. 1988. *Constructor's Business Management*, Xian Institute of Metallurgy & Construction Engineering, p. 247.

Jurkiewicz, Wieslaw J. 1995. Dual Entry in Cost Control: The Most Efficient Approach to Project Cost Control", *Cost Engineering*, May.

Moselhi, Osama, 1994. DBID: Analogy-Based DSS for Bidding in Construction, *Journal of Construction Engineering and Management (JCEM)*, V. 120, No.4, Dec. p. 895.

O'Brien James J. & Robert G. Zilly, 1991. *Contractor's Management Handbook*, McMraw-Hill, Inc., NY. pp. 9–30, 13–25.

Oglesby, Clarkson H., Productivity Improvement in Construction, *McGraw-Hill Book Company*, New York, NY, 1989, p. 88.

Patrascu, Angel, 1988. *Construction Cost Engineering Handbook*, Marcel Dekker, Inc..

Stokes, McNeill 1989. Take Precautions When Purchasing Foreign Materials, *Consulting-Specifying Engineer*, V.5, May, p. 29.

Sweet, Justin, 1994. *Legal Aspects of Architecture, Engineering and the Construction Process*, West Publishing Company, Appendix C.

Underwood, J.T. 1993. Commissioning Process: How It Affects the Building Owner and Maintenance Contractor", *ASHRAE Transactions*, V. 99, Part 1.

Ward, Sol A. & Thorndike Litchfield, 1980. *Cost Control in Design and Construction*, McGraw-Hill Book Company, pp. 88, 164.

Ward, Sol A. 1992. *Cost Engineering for Effective Project Control*, McGraw-Hill Book Company, pp. 88, 181.

Zhan, Gaowu. 1996. *Efficient Project Cost Management System*, School of Building Construction Master's Report, University of Florida, December.

System-based Vision for Strategic and Creative Design, Bontempi (ed.)
© *2003 Swets & Zeitlinger, Lisse, ISBN 90 5809 599 1*

The cost caused by lack of interoperability in design

C.A. Jacoski
Regional Community University of Chapecó – UNOCHAPECÓ

R. Lamberts
Federal University of Santa Catarina – UFSC

ABSTRACT: The integration in design of civil construction and the transfer of information, is an indispensable theme for discussions of improvement processes in productive chain. The solution always in need of resources with the capacity to adapt the relationship among the participant agents of the process of elaboration of the design.

The discussion regarding the situation that gets to integrate the design stages necessarily goes by the solution of problems of the lack of interoperability among the computational tools. This paper analyses the cost caused by the lack of interoperability in 2D design. It presents a "study case" that took place in offices design in the South of Brazil.

1   INTRODUCTION

With the coming of the digital design and the performance in collaborate projects (Aouad 2000), the discussion emerges concerning the definition of an interoperability architecture, for distribution of the information among the several professionals involved in the design of civil construction. Because, although the computational tools contributes significantly in the process, still lack of solution about interruptions and productivity losses in the elaboration of design.

According to Brunnermeier & Martin (1999), interoperability is the ability to communicate data through different productive activities. It is essential for the productivity and competitiveness of a lot of industries due to the efficiency requested by the design and the production, with the coordination of different agents in the process.

Other productive chains also demonstrate concern in integrating of processes making use of digital data, looking for to eliminate the problems with the circulation of the information. A study regarding interoperability in the United States it was accomplished by NIST (National Institute of Standard and Technology) exclusively to the automobile industry. It was verified the loss of 1 billion dollars a year due to type of problem in digital design, mainly due to the time spent with correction and reconstruction of non-compatible files with other existent files (Brunnermeier & Martin 2002).

The types of architecture systems for integration in digital design, vary in function of the needs and forms of the participants performance, could appear in several forms, without the need of a specific pattern.

Rosenman & Wang (2001), affirm that many researchers figuring out the types of CAD systems generally uses larger focus in the aspect of the model of the product and adaptation of costs, while the architecture of the system doesn't receive the correct attention. Starting from the use of a more current collaboration in design becomes fundamental to discuss a new architecture for helpful systems of CAD. Some architecture of systems can be divided in:

Integrated way: The planners work in a same design, using a central mechanism of management. The users operate remotely from their house or either from work, the design that is being developed by many users;

Integrated distributed way: In this system the planners have a fixed atmosphere with a central one only working in safety and stability;

Discontinuous way: there is not a system with module of central control, but simply a group acting with management mechanisms, it demands the interoperability then more strongly for use of the different tools;

Way based on apprenticeship: This model base part of the apprenticeship, where the others subsequent, derived of this. It requests a great work of AI (Artificial Intelligence).

Autonomous way: This is based on the autonomy concept, where each model is implemented as a distributed group.

The communication relationships with the current tools getting the popularization easiness, being possible to correspond to the expectations of the horizontal communication, reaching the whole ones involved them in the process. The organizational structure becomes more flexible, facilitating the division of the process decision among other collaborators of the company, once everybody has access to the information.

In this sense, the data cannot have the use of restrictions due to the type tool that it is operated, nor the difficulty in the transfer of data among competitive systems, very auspiciously they are close to present these situations the design process, fitting to stand out that concentrate efforts for the elimination of these problems.

2 I.T. AND THE INFORMATION IN DESIGN

Several researches and professionals of the sector have sometimes discussed the use of I.T. in the construction. Already in 1994, Michael Latham (disclosed by *IAI-International Alliance for Interoperability*), evaluated the possibility that in the year 2000, money will be saved in design, of about 30% of the elaboration costs, due to the use of information technologies (http://www.iai-international.org).

Although the innovations of I.T. used in the Construction industry, is more and more present, some problems, many times of structural type, still continue to persist. The integration lack and the change of information among the elements along the constructive process, as well as lack of information system, it has been told in the literature as some of the impediments.

The productive chain of the civil construction, for characterizing as a broken into fragments industry, inexistent companies that can influence the market significantly, also presents serious difficulties with the information aggregation of the entire sector, due to dispersion of the data and the heterogeneity of participant agents. This problem is not just detected only in the productive chain, but it is a reflex that happens inside of each company. The flow of information among departments, among design, and sectors, in general, happens in a dispersed form and a lot of times without control.

A management design needs to be effective, have the definition of objectives and goals, and the transmission of these to the elements involved in the design in a simple, and clear way. Being created a permanent interaction among the several sectors of the company, through a better treatment of the information, the use

of same terminologies where "everybody speaks the same language", along the productive chain, being avoided ruptures in the transfer of tasks among the actors.

According to Caldas & Soibelman (2002), due to the limitations of the Construction Industry and the direction that it is taken in the integration sense and automation of the design processes, it justifies the need of the development of techniques for the management of the workflow of information, based on the automation of the methods for classification of the documents of design. Some benefits and applications in the sense of this methodology are presented:

- Organization of the information and access, through tools of searches;
- Identification of the materials acquired, as well as, a control system, automating the access through the specification of design;
- Analysis of data, identifying areas of problems and potential cause of productivity loss, increment of costs, and low quality;
- Generation of extracted knowledge of tasks, that could be applied in future activities and design.

According to Thorne (2000), the description and interoperability situation, depended strongly on the nature and of the type of data that will be communicated. For many engineering tools, the transfer of geometric data among systems applications is a routine accomplished automatically. That is possible, but rare (mainly in applications developed in the own company). To find transactions that request systems applications in both involved parts, there is an association, or application of specialist products that guarantee the success of the transfer.

The development of a model of objects for the construction industry, received from IAI biggest efforts. With the mission of define, publish, and promote specifications for classes of objects, this group offers a contribution for solution of interoperability problem. It was the creative organism of Industry Foundation Classes-IFC, that facilitates the sharing of design information through all its development and in technical applications.

According to Bazjanac & Crawley (1997), the use of the files IFC in simulation software, will facilitate:

- Interchange among the files directly and instantly;
- To distribute and to transfer information of common interest.
- Access without costs for the use of geometric data and others;
- Reduction in the cost of simulation design;
- Increment and better use of the simulation results and analysis.

3 DIVIDING THE USE OF I.T. EM THREE SITUATIONS

Resultant of the researches accomplished in the moment, and with some that are still in process, the formulation of a complex scenario, mainly with companies of design. Although there were difficulty divisions in the classification of these companies in relation to the effective use of I.T., it is evident that big part of the companies still not use, the effective resources facilitated by the computer tools and of the internet.

When dividing in sceneries the current performance of the companies, it can be distinguished in a selected group that could be segmented of the productive chain of design, the companies that are positioned in the vanguard of the innovation processes, and these are the companies that were researched in this project. It can be affirmed that many companies are going to be part of this scenario of innovative procedures (Innovative Scenario). Other, it is the future scenario, that can represent the consolidation of the use of the tools of I.T. already existent and that possesses wide possibilities to be explored, through investments of the companies and researches for consolidation of the results.

The world tendency exhibits digital design and documents are something consolidated. The change of the planner's performance (engineer or architect), it is something current.

The possibility of virtualization of processes in the construction industry necessarily requests the resolution of structural problems, as the standardization of specifications, common terminologies and the interoperability among the software.

Still about this, it can be presented as success factors for the total use of the resources of I.T. in the construction, the following items: Disposition to the innovation, common terminologies in the entire productive chain, specification of products and processes, code as auxiliary element to the electronic trade, tools necessarily interoperable, customization of the products, and others.

The associations of the productive chain and the processes integration through the information, have about essential point of support, the development of the use of I.T. in the construction industry. The integration of the information as a strategy can be configured as an essential mechanism for the decrease of mistakes, increase of the work in a team, efficiency gain and speed, with improvement of the quality and productivity.

The development of standard IFC can contribute considerably to the change and distribution of design information, reducing the interoperability problem, that associated to the language use of XML, realizing an integration of the database, so much internal in the company, as a whole productive chain.

The need of the agents of the national productive chain involvement is stood out, for a more effective participation in the inclusion of these innovations, because in another way, it can, in the future to come across with problems of adaptation of terminologies and syntaxes, used by these languages that are characterized as textual languages.

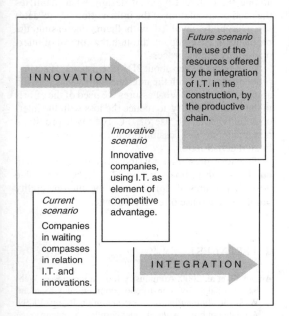

Figure 1. Scenarios related to the use of I.T. in the construction.

4 THE COSTS GENERATED BY THE INTEROPERABILITY LACK IN DESIGN OF 2D IN THE CIVIL CONSTRUCTION

The research was realized in design offices in the South of Brazil. It's demonstrated a significant loss for the section of design, even in 2D, due to interoperability lack, associated in interruption of design. This study revealed among other aspects, that several situations still exist, same if already considering some innovation aspects incorporated by this industry type.

The methodology used had to follow the designs, through a spreadsheet of control and identifications of situations. It also used the information accumulated by the company through the years.

The result points for a loss of around 20% of the total costs of design due to the factor of interoperability.

To facilitate the analysis, it was used only buildings of 12 floors. It was necessary to divide the types of designs, in order to identify the specific loss in each of

Table 1. Synthesis – Structural Design.

Design type	Type of costs with interoperability	Time* (hours)	Execution time of design (hours)	(%) loss
Structural design	Transfer	4	160	2,5
	Mitigation	9	160	5,625
	Interruption	9	160	5,625
	Others	4	160	2,5

TOTAL LOSSES IN THE DESIGN = 16,25%

*The time is given indeed in hours worked

Table 2. Synthesis – design electric.

Design type	Type of costs with interoperability	Time* (hours)	Execution time of design (hours)	(%) loss
Electric Design	Transfer	4	128	3,12
	Mitigation	8	128	6,25
	Interruption	8	128	6,25
	Others	4	128	3,12

TOTAL LOSSES IN THE DESIGN = 18,74%

* The time is given indeed in hours worked

Table 3. Synthesis – Design Hydraulic.

Design type	Type of costs with interoperability	Time* (hours)	Execution time of design (hours)	(%) loss
Design Hydraulic	Transfer	8	160	5
	Mitigation	8	160	5
	Interruption	12	160	7,5
	Others	10	160	6,25

TOTAL LOSSES IN THE DESIGN = 23,75%

* The time is given indeed in hours worked

Table 4. Synthesis – Architectural Design.

Design type	Type of costs with interoperability	Time* (hours)	Execution time of design (hours)	(%) loss
Architect Design	Transfer	10	200	5,0
	Mitigation	15	200	7,5
	Interruption	18	200	9,0
	Others	20	200	10,0

TOTAL LOSSES IN THE DESIGN = 31,50%

*The time is given indeed in hours worked

Table 5. General Synthesis.

Design type	Individual loss for design (%)	General (%)
Architectural	31,50	22,56
Hydraulic	23,75	22,56
Electric	18,74	22,56
Structural	16,25	22,56

them. Below are present the results of different types of design:

In table 5, is present a general result, with the total of losses identified in the "study case":

It was not the objective of this project, but it is possible to esteem the loss of the monetary cost with this type of problem. The calculation of losses can be esteemed in function of the financial movement generated by the sector, being distinguished the sub-sector designs.

5 CONCLUSION

It was detected through the research, a series of existent problems in the integration among the designs. From the identification accomplished in each one of the phases it was possible to accomplish the definition of the interference among the participant agents.

It was identified a high interdependence degree among the different types of design, what identifies the need of circulation of the information (up-to-date) for everybody involved with them, decreasing the problems in the company through the control of interoperability in this process.

Even being design about 2D, the existence of several problems related with the interoperability was verified among the designs. What assures the need of the efforts in the design industry, to reduce the loss with the interoperability. And the use of IFC files will propitiate new and innovative possibilities to the sector of designs in civil construction.

The loss presented for the offices of design in buildings with 12 floors, was in 22,56%, being possible through measures of elimination of the interoperability problems, decrease or even eliminate.

REFERENCES

Aouad, G. et al. 2000. An industry foundation classes Web-based collaborative construction computer environment: WISPER. *Automation in Construction*, n. 10, pp. 79–99. Available in http://www.elsevier.com/locate/autcon.

Betts, M. 1999. *Strategic Management of I.T in Construction*. London: Blackwell Science, 406 pg. ISBN 0-632-04026-2.

Brunnermeier, S.B. & Martin, S.A. 1999. Interoperability Cost Analysis of the US. Automotive Supply Chain. Final Report. *Research Triangle Institute/National Institute of Standard and Technology–NIST*, Mar. Available in: http://www.planetcad.com/COMP/Articles/NIST.pdf.

Brunnermeier, S.B. & Martin, S.A. 2002. Interoperability Cost in the US. automotive supply chain. *Supply Chain Management: An International Journal*, vol 7 (02), pp. 71–82. ISSN 1359-8546. Available in: http://www.emeraldinsight.com/index.htm

Bazjanac, V. & Crawley, D.B. 1997. The implementation of Industry Foundation Classes in simulation tools goes the building industry. *Building Simulation*. Available in: http://www.hvac.okstate.edu/pdfs/bs97/papers/P125.PDF

Caldas, C.H. & Soibelman L. 2002. Automated classification methods: Supporting implementation of pull techniques goes information flow management. In: IGLC, 10, Gramado–RS. *Proceedings… 2002*, 10. Available in: http://www.cpgec.ufrgs.br/norie/iglc10/papers/99-Caldas&Soibelman.pdf

Rosenman, M. & Wang, F. 2001. The component agent based open CAD system goes collaborative design. *Automation in Construction*, 10, pp. 383–397. Available in: http://www.elsevier.com/locate/autcon

Thorne, P. 2000. Product Dates Interoperability. *Planetcad*. Project N. M1975, 14 p. out. Available in: http://www.planetcad.com/COMP/Articles/Interoperability.pdf>

System-based Vision for Strategic and Creative Design, Bontempi (ed.)
© 2003 Swets & Zeitlinger, Lisse, ISBN 90 5809 599 1

The choice of the rib thickness in the mass-production of ribbed R/C floors

L. Fenu
Department of Structural Engineering, Cagliari, Italy

ABSTRACT: In the mass-production of ribbed R/C floors, the rib thickness is an important factor of the floor weight. In fact the thinner the rib, the ligther the floor, but especially if we design R/C floors without shear rein-forcements, we cannot make ribs too thin because it would be necessary to make too long heavier parts of floor made solid close to the ends. In this way the concrete removed below the neutral axis to make thinner ribs would be recovered in the heavier floor part. In this paper, for floors without shear reinforcements, we have studied how to choose the best rib thickness to make ligther R/C floors without too long heavier parts close to the ends.

1   INTRODUCTION

In this paper it is pointed out that by designing ribbed R/C floors without shear reinforcements with the par-tial-factor method, especially when the span-depth ratio is close to the limits imposed by the codes, if the ribs are too thin, a considerable part of the floor close to the ends has to be made solid to increase its resistance and thus, heavier than the ribbed part in the span. In fact, many authors, like for instance Mosley, Hulse & Bungey (1990), have pointed out that the length of this floor heavier part is usually governed by the shear resistance at the ultimate limit state.

Depending on the country, the current ribbed R/C floors are constructed by using different industrial-ized products, for instance Migliacci (1979) and Bacco & Ciancabilla (1994) illustrate many examples of some of the most popular ribbed R/C floors in Italy; therefore the rib thickness is pre-determined by the size of these industrialized mass-products and not by the designers of a building. For instance, for ribbed floors with hollow clay-blocks, it happens for the size of mass-products like partly prefabricated truss rib with clay slip-tile at the bottom as well as for the size of the hollow blocks, while also ribbed R/C floors with temporary or permanent shutterings have their rib thickness pre-determined by the size of a mass-product like the mould (Fig. 1).

Therefore the choice of the rib width is made by the manufacturing industry, and the only way to con-struct R/C floors without shear reinforcements and without stopping off the ribbed section too far from the floor ends, is to provide sufficiently thick ribs but

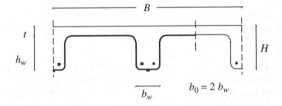

Figure 1.   Ribbed R/C floor without blocks interposed between the ribs and made by using a polypropilene mould.

without making the floor too heavy: this paper deals with this problem and illustrates a method that the manufacturers could use to choose the size of their mass-products that pre-determine the rib thickness in ribbed R/C floor construction.

2   RELATION BETWEEN THE RIB THICKNESS AND THE FLOOR HEAVIER PART LENGTH

In a single span R/C floor with partially fixed and/or simply-supported ends and with span l, consider a B width floor strip with flange depth t, ribs with an overall width b_0 and if present, blocks with an overall width $B - b_0$; the height of the ribs is h_w, the concrete cover is c and consequently, the effective depth is $d = (h_w + t) - c$ (Fig. 1). By using the partial-factor method, as usual the design concrete strengths are f_{cd} and f_{ctd}, as well as the design steel yield stress is

f_{yd}, while Q_k and G_k are the characteristic values of the imposed and permanent loads respectively, the latter sum of structural self-weight G_{1k} and of non-structural permanent loads G_{2k}.

Being ρ_{RC} and ρ_B the weights per unit volume of the reinforced concrete and of the blocks respectively, the permanent loads are a function of b_0, that is:

$$G_k(b_0) = \left[h_w (B - b_0) \rho_B + t B \rho_{RC} + h_w b_0 \rho_{RC} \right] + G_{2k}(b_0) \tag{1}$$

Obviously if there are no blocks interposed between the ribs, in this function we put $\rho_B = 0$.

By designing sufficiently-ductile sections at ultimate, and after having made the moment redistribution, the absolute design value of the bending moment at the ends is:

$$M_d(b_0) = \left| -\frac{1}{16} [\gamma_g G_k(b_0) + \gamma_q Q_k] l^2 \right| \tag{2}$$

so that, having calculated the top reinforcement A_s through M_d, we obtain the geometrical reinforcement ratio as a function of b_0, namely:

$$\rho_l(b_o) = \frac{A_s(b_o)}{b_o d} \tag{3}$$

The distance Δ_v between the support centreline and the point where the ribbed section stops off, is determined by the lack of shear resistance in the ribbed cross-section without shear reinforcement with respect to the design shear force $V_d(b_0,x)$ (Fig. 2), the latter being a function of b_0 through the structural self-weight $G_{1k}(b_0)$, and of the current abscissa x. According to the Eurocode 2 (1991), for members without shear reinforcements and not subject to axial compression, the shear resistance is

$$V_{rd}(b_0) = 0.25 \, f_{ctd} \, k \, [1.2 + 40 \, \rho_l(b_0)] b_0 \, d \tag{4}$$

and it depends on b_0 both directly, and through ρ_l, so that we can consider V_{rd} as a function of b_0.

In eqn.(4) ρ_l depends on the collapse mechanism, namely if the ends are fixed ρ_l is governed by the top reinforcement, while if they are supported ρ_l is governed by the bottom reinforcement. In the first case we obtain ρ_l from (3), while in the latter case, the bars taken into account for ρ_l are usually carried through to the support from mid-span and the values of ρ_l are in any case higher than those obtained from (3) with fixed ends. Therefore, when the ends are fixed, getting ρ_l from (3) and V_{rd} from (4), we have:

$$\Delta_v(b_0) = \frac{[\gamma_G G_k(b_0) + \gamma_Q Q_k] l/2 - V_{rd}(b_0)}{\gamma_G G_k(b_0) + \gamma_Q Q_k} \tag{5}$$

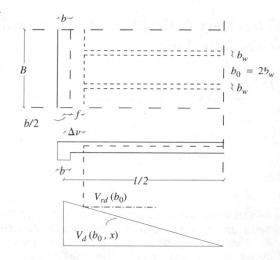

Figure 2. Lack of shear resistance close to the end of a ribbed R/C floor.

so that also Δ_v is a function of b_0; in the frequent case of floors supported by R/C girders with breadth b, the length of the floor heavier part is $f = \Delta_v - b/2$.

Besides, the length of the heavier part of floor may be, in general, determined by a lack of the moment of resistance with respect to the design moment. When the bending moment is negative, and the mechanical reinforcement ratio of the ribbed section $\omega_s = (A_s/b_0 d) f_{yd}/f_{cd}$ is a function of b_0 also through the cross-sectional area A_s of the top reinforcement, then the lever arm-effective depth ratio is

$$\zeta(b_0) = 1 - \frac{\omega_s(b_0)}{2 \cdot 0.85} \tag{6}$$

and the moment of resistance of the ribbed section

$$M_{rd}(b_0) = A_s(b_0) \, f_{yd} \, \zeta(b_0) \, d \tag{7}$$

is a function of b_0 through A_s and ζ.

By drawing the distance Δ_m between the support centreline and the section where the floor ribbed part is stopped off, from the lack of $M_{rd}(b_0)$ with respect to the bending moment $M_d(b_0,x)$, the latter being a function of both b_0 (through the structural self-weight $G_{1k}(b_0)$) and of the current abscissa x, we have:

$$\Delta_m(b_0) = \frac{l}{2} - \sqrt{\frac{l^2}{4} + 2 \, \frac{M_{rd}(b_0) - M_d(b_0)}{G_d(b_0)}} \tag{8}$$

Therefore $\Delta_v(b_0)$ must be constrained to be greater than $\Delta_m(b_0)$ to have in any case the moment of resistance

390

greater than the bending moment acting along a floor length Δ_v from the support.

3 CHOICE OF THE BEST RIB THICKNESS

The choice of the rib thickness in the construction of R/C floors by using mass-products may be made by minimizing the self-weight of the floor and its cost. Since the floor weight, as well as its cost is related to the volume of concrete topping, we consider the rib thickness that minimize the volume of concrete topping as the design objective to be found; therefore, by defining the objective function "concrete topping volume" but leaving aside the flange volume that does not change throughout the floor, for the floor symmetry (Figures 1 and 2), we have:

$$F_v(b_0) = \Delta_v(b_0) B\, h_w + \left(l/2 - \Delta_v(b_0) \right) b_0\, h_w \qquad (9)$$

so that F_v is a function of b_0.

Naturally F_v is subject to some constraints. For instance b_0 must be greater than a minimum limit value b_{min} governed by the size of the aggregates, the cover and spacing of the reinforcements, and the fire resistance.

Another constraint regards the length f of the heavier part at the floor ends as it must be limited: in fact it must be smaller than a maximum limit value not to modify excessively the stiffness of the end parts with respect to the ribbed ones. The codes usually do not limit the length of the floor solid part, but, in the current construction of R/C ribbed floors Santarella (1997) advises that a maximum limit value can be chosen to be twice the thickness of the floor or about a 10% of the span. Besides, in the case that the span-depth ratio is close to the maximum values usually admitted by the codes to limit deflections (for instance the Italian Code (1996) provides a limit of 25, while the Eurocode 2 limits the span-effective depth ratio, making it depend on the geometric characteristics of the floor and on the concrete stress level), both a limit based on a % of the span and a limit based on a multiple of the depth are strictly related. In the latter case, for instance, a reasonable maximum limit value of the length of the floor heavier part is $2H$ so that, if the floor is supported by an R/C beam with breadth b, Δ_v must be smaller than $b/2 + 2H$. In general we name Δ_{max} this maximum limit value.

Besides a reasonable minimum value of f is $H/2$, so that if the floor is supported by an R/C beam with breadth b, Δ_v must be greater than $b/2 + H/2$. In general we name Δ_{min} this minimum limit value.

Finally, since the length of the floor heavier part is found by the shear resistance lack, if $\Delta_v \geq \Delta_m$ the bending moment is in any case lower than the moment

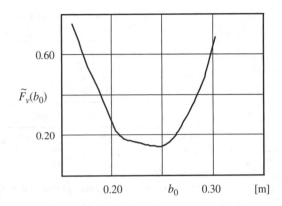

Figure 3. Pseudo-objective function obtained by using the Eurocode 2 for a one-way ribbed R/C slab with span of 6.00 m and loaded by 2000 N/m².

of resistance for all $x \leq \Delta_v$: consequently Δ_v is constrained to be longer than Δ_m.

Therefore we minimize the objective function $F_v(b_0)$ as a constrained function subject to:

$$g_1 = b_{min} - b_0 \leq 0 \;; \qquad g_2 = \Delta_{min} - \Delta_v(b_0) \leq 0 \;;$$

$$g_3 = \Delta_v(b_0) - \Delta_{max} \leq 0; \quad g_4 = \Delta_m(b_0) - \Delta_v(b_0) \leq 0 \qquad (10)$$

Then, by using the penalty function method (Comincioli, 1990), we define the following pseudo-objective function:

$$\tilde{F}_v(b_0) = \Delta_v(b_0) B\, h_w + \left[l/2 - \Delta_v(b_0) \right] b_0\, h_w + R \sum_{j=1}^{4} \delta_j(g_j)^2$$

$$(11)$$

with $R > 0$, $\delta_j = 0$ for $g_j \leq 0$ or $\delta_j = 1$ for $g_j > 0$.

Therefore we identificate the rib width b_0 that minimize $\tilde{F}_v(b_0)$, so that from function (5) we find also the value $\Delta_v \geq \Delta_m$ of the distance between the support centreline and the section where the ribs are stopped off: being Δ this found value, in the following examples, where the floors are supported by R/C girders with breadth b, we have $f = \Delta - b/2$.

In this specific instance, for $R = 10$ we emphasize very well the minimum of the function $\tilde{F}_v(b_0)$, yet it is sufficient $R = 1.5$ (Fig. 3).

The algorithm has been applied to an R/C floor with no blocks between the ribs, namely a one-way ribbed R/C slab with two ribs/m. The permanent load of the finishes G_{2k} is chosen to be 3800 N/m², that is a current value for the floors of the intermediate storeys in many apartment buildings, as well as in schools, hospitals and so on. We have examined a

Table 1. Optimum rib thickness of a ribbed R/C floor with no blocks. Reference codes: Eurocode 2 and Italian Code.

l = 6.00 m	2 ribs/m		B = 1.00 m			
H = 24 cm	h_w = 16.5 cm		t = 7.5 cm		b = 30 cm	

	Eurocode 2			Italian Code		
Q_k [N/m]	b_w [cm]	Δ [cm]	f [cm]	b_w [cm]	Δ [cm]	f [cm]
2000	12.7	27	12	16.5	27	12
3000	14.5	27	12	18.8	27	12
4000	16.3	27	12	19.2*	42	27

*The star indicates an unconstrained minimum.

span of 6.00 m, with a span-depth ratio of 25, that is a depth of 24 cm: this span-depth ratio is to be considered close to the limit value that avoids excessive deflections and, for instance, it is the limit prescribed by the Italian Code. Depending on floor thickness, the flange depth is chosen according to the current sizes of this type of floor. About the mechanical characteristics of the materials, we have assumed f_{ck} = 25 MPa and f_{yk} = 400 MPa. The results are reported in Table 1. The algorithm has been applied by using both the Eurocode 2 and the Italian Code.

The best rib obtained by using the Italian Code is wider than that obtained by using the Eurocode 2. The shear resistance calculated according to the Italian Code, with the contribution of the dowell action expressed by the coefficient $(1 + 50 \rho_l)$ instead of $(1.2 + 40 \rho_l)$ as Eurocode 2 requires, is in fact much more conservative than that calculated with the Eurocode 2. Therefore, the best rib thickness obtained by using the Italian Code is greater than that obtained by using the Eurocode 2.

The best rib thickness obtained by using the Eurocode 2 appears to be acceptable for an industrialized production of temporary or permanent shutterings to be used in the construction of this type of R/C floor. Table 1 shows that the solutions achieved by using the Eurocode 2 are always constrained by the minimum value admitted for the length of the heavier part of floor; besides, by using for instance a rib thickness of 14 cm, if we calculate the length of the floor heavier part by using eqn. (5), we find that it is smaller than its maximum limit value. By using the same algorithm with one-way ribbed R/C slabs with span of 7.50 m and floor thickness of 30 cm, with two ribs/m and flange thickness of 9 cm, we need a rib thicker than 14 cm only for imposed load of 4000 N/m², namely only in this case a rib thickness of at least 15 cm is required.

Therefore, for one-way ribbed R/C slabs, we have found that permanent or temporary formworks should allow to provide the required rib thickness of, for instance, 14 cm.

In the examples of Table 1 the constraint $g_4 \leq 0$, namely $\Delta_m \leq \Delta_v$, was never active, that is the rib thickness is influenced by the lack of shear resistance rather than the lack of moment of resistance close to the floor ends.

4 CONCLUSIONS

By designing ribbed R/C floors it is usually preferred to consider them as structures without shear reinforcements, but, if the ribs are too thin, the absence of shear reinforcements leads to have, close to the ends, a too long heavier part of floor made solid because of the reduced shear resistance at ultimate.

Actually ribbed R/C floors are very popular in many countries, but, to construct them without shear reinforcements, it is necessary that the ribs are sufficiently thick to avoid having too long heavier part of floor at its ends. On the other hand, if the ribs are too wide, the floor becomes too heavy and the advantages of the ribbed section vanish.

Consequently the problem is to make the floor lighter by removing the concrete below the neutral axis in the span, without making too heavier a considerable part of floor close to its ends.

This is a constrained nonlinear problem whose solution allows to find the best rib thickness. The constraints regard the minimum rib thickness, governed by cover, aggregate size and fire resistance, as well as the length of the floor heavier parts close to the ends, that can vary in a range between a minimum and a maximum limit, the latter to avoid too stiff solid ends with respect to the ribbed section in the span. Finally we have taken into account the further constraint that, in general, besides the lack of shear resistance, the length of the heavier part of floor can be determined by the lack of moment of resistance of the ribbed section. To achieve the solution, we have implemented an algorithm that finds the most convenient rib thickness by using nonlinear programming and by defining a penalty function that take into account the constraints.

Therefore, by optimizing the rib thickness with the proposed method, the manufacturing industry of pre-fabricated elements and mass-products for R/C floor construction, can choose the best rib thickness pre-determined by its mass-production that allows to achieve ribbed R/C floors without shear reinforcements in most cases.

REFERENCES

Bacco, V. & Ciancabilla, L. 1994. *Il manuale dei solai in laterizio*. Rome: Edizioni Laterconsult.

CEN – ENV 1992. 1991. *Eurocode 2*, part 1.

Comincioli, V. 1990. *Analisi numerica*. Milan: Mc Graw-Hill.

Migliacci, A. 1979. *Progetti di strutture* 1th part. Milan: Masson.

Ministero LL. PP. 1996. D.M. 09.01.96: *Norme Tecniche per il calcolo, l'esecuzione ed il collaudo delle strutture in cemento armato normale e precompresso e per le strutture metalliche*.

Mosley, W.H., Hulse, R.J. & Bungey, H. 1996. *Reinforced concrete design to Eurocode 2*. Houndmills, London: Mc Millan Press Ltd.

Santarella, L. 1997. *Prontuario del cemento armato*. Milan: Hoepli.

5. Human factor, social–economic constraints on the design process

System-based Vision for Strategic and Creative Design, Bontempi (ed.)
© 2003 Swets & Zeitlinger, Lisse, ISBN 90 5809 599 1

Reciprocal model of construction safety culture

W.F. Maloney
University of Kentucky

ABSTRACT: In the late 1980s, safety culture became a subject of considerable conceptual and research interest. It has been found to be a major influence on safety behavior and, consequently, safety performance. Safety culture has been viewed in organizational terms as monolithic, i.e., an organization has a single safety culture, which is stable over time. This may be true for relatively permanent organizations such as manufacturing firms. However, for construction project organizations, viewing safety culture as a monolithic, stable concept is questionable. Construction project organizations have a finite duration and consist of multiple organizations acting in concert for the duration of the project. It is more accurate to view the safety culture of a construction project in terms of a culture that emerges from the interaction of the cultures of the various organizations and groups participating in the project. This paper examines the emergent nature of a construction safety culture.

1 INTRODUCTION

Occupations in the construction industry continue to be among the most dangerous. In the United States between 1000 and 1200 construction workers were killed each year from 1997 to 2001, accounting for approximately 20% of the total number of work related fatalities while the industry accounted for only about 6% of the total jobs in the United States. Moreover, these fatalities occurred in spite of presumed major safety improvements in the industry during this time.

Given the safety performance of the construction industry, Dester & Blockley (1995) ask the question: "Is the accident rate in construction high simply because construction is inherently more dangerous than other industries?" They answer by asserting that there is a widespread perception that there are "inherent reasons" for the poor safety record in construction. These "inherent reasons" are derived from the characteristics of the industry (Davies & Tomasin 1990). They observe that the "inherent reasons" for poor safety performance in the industry should be viewed as hazards within the context of a positive safety culture. Given the characteristics of the industry, what constitutes a positive safety culture for the industry?

2 CULTURE

2.1 *Organizational culture*

The culture of an organization is a "set of tacit assumptions about how the world is and ought to be that a group of people share and that determines their perceptions, thoughts, feelings, and, to some degree, their overt behavior" (Schein 1996) and it consists of three elements:

1. the assumptions that are the essence of the culture;
2. the espoused values that often reflect what a group wishes ideally to be and the way it wants to present itself to the public; and
3. the day-to-day behavior that represents a complex compromise among the espoused values, the deeper assumptions, and the immediate requirements of the situation.

2.2 *Subcultures*

An organization does not have a single culture that is uniform across the organization. Instead, an organization's culture should be viewed as the aggregate of a series of subcultures (McDonald & Ryan 1992). Schein (1996) observed that these subcultures include the executive, engineer, and operator cultures, each of which possesses the cultural elements discussed above. The organization's culture emerges from the interaction of the sub-cultures. The potential influence of each of these sub-cultures on the culture of the organization can be understood by examining several of the assumptions held by members of each sub-culture (Schein 1996), which include:

- Executive Sub-culture
  - Financial survival is equivalent to perpetual war with one's competitors.
  - People are a necessary evil, not an intrinsic value.

— The well-oiled machine does not need people, only activities that are contracted for.

• Engineer Sub-culture
— Engineers are … pragmatic perfectionists who prefer "people-free" solutions.
— Engineers are proactively optimistic that they can and should master nature.

• Operator Sub-culture
— Because the action of any organization is ultimately the action of people, the success of the enterprise depends on knowledge, skill, learning ability, and commitment.
— No matter how carefully engineered the production process is or how carefully rules and procedures are specified, operators must have the capacity to learn and deal with surprises.
— Only the individuals performing a task possess the proper knowledge, skills, and orientations to make decisions as to how the work is to be performed and evaluated.

These assumptions have ramifications for the emergent culture. Executives see workers as a cost that needs to be controlled, engineers see people as a source of variability that needs to be eliminated, and operators, or the people performing the work, see themselves as the solution to problems.

Schein argues that a distinction must be made between cultures that arise *within* organizations from the unique experiences of its members from those that arise outside of the organization whereby the shared assumptions derive from a common educational background, the requirements of a given occupation, and the shared contact with others in the occupation.

He asserts that the executive and engineering cultures arise, to a major degree, from outside the organization because executives and engineers are members of occupational communities. For engineers, the shared assumptions are based on common education, work experience, and job requirements. For executives, the assumptions result from the executive's focus on maintaining the financial survival and growth of the organization and association with others facing the same challenges.

In contrast, Schein postulates that the operator culture arises from within an organization because the technology and work processes employed by the organization are specific to that organization. Workers for Company A performing a particular job rarely have the opportunity to interact with workers from Company B performing the same job utilizing the same technology and work processes. The opportunity for sharing is minimal and, thus, the operator culture is local.

Construction constitutes an exception to the belief that the operator culture is local. Unlike manufacturing (upon which Schein's conceptualization appears to be based) and many other industries, in which technology is constantly changing and varies between firms in the same industry, technology in construction is relatively stable and there is little variation in the technology employed by firms in the industry. Consequently, operatives can move from employer to employer with little or no learning curve to experience.

2.3 *Occupational communities*

Schein postulates that executives and engineers constitute occupational communities as defined by Van Maanen and Barley (1984): "a group of people who consider themselves to be engaged in the same sort of work; who identify (more or less positively) with their work; who share a set of values, norms, and perspectives that apply to, but extend beyond, work related matters; and whose social relationships meld the realms of work and leisure." Construction operatives likewise constitute an occupational community.

Occupational communities operate with the belief that only members of the community have the appropriate knowledge, skills, and orientations required to make decisions as to how the work is to be performed and evaluated. Thus, only members of the community should determine the content and evaluation of their work. This only becomes a problem if the employing organization attempts to impose a requirement that is contrary to the practice of the community.

3 CULTURE AND BEHAVIOR

Behavior, Schein's third cultural element, is the observable evidence of culture. Human behavior is an element in a triad consisting of the person, the environment or situation in which the person functions, and the behavior in which the person chooses to engage, as shown in Figure 1.

This triad has been described as one of reciprocal determinism (Bandura 1986) where reciprocal means mutual action between causal factors and determinism simply means the production of effects by certain factors. The reciprocal influences do not operate simultaneously nor are they necessarily of equal strength.

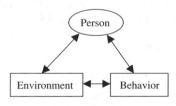

Figure 1. Behavior model.

There is a process of action and reaction or one of "perpetual dynamic interplay" (Cooper 2000). For example, a worker may engage in a behavior that causes damage to an eye. Management reacts by mandating that workers must wear safety glasses, which in turn causes workers to make the decision to wear eye protection.

Cooper has applied this model to safety and, in particular, safety culture. He defines culture as "the product of multiple goal-directed interactions between people, behavior, and the situation" and this product as "that observable degree of effort by which all organizational members direct their attention and actions toward improving safety on a daily basis" (Cooper 2000). Thus, the focus is on behavior.

Behavior can be categorized into compliance and participation. A worker performing a task in a manner that minimizes risk to him and others by using a prescribed procedure engages in a compliance behavior. Similarly, workers who remediate a safety hazard situation or attend safety training engage in a participation behavior.

Each of the elements exists in a state of reciprocal determinism. Cooper's concept of culture as a product and the nature of the product still apply. Given this, a basic question that must be addressed is how does a project manager create a culture that encourages a worker to perform a task safely, remedy a hazardous situation, report a serious hazard, or challenge a co-worker performing a task in a risky manner while at the same time encouraging project supervisors to value safety as well as production.

3.1 Behavioral choice

The environment within which an operative performs his work is a significant influence on the operative's behavior. To improve safety performance, it is imperative to understand that the individual worker makes the decision as to how to perform the task. He can choose to perform the task in a low-risk manner utilizing established procedures or he can choose to perform the task in a high-risk fashion. For example, a worker given the assignment of removing concrete using a jackhammer may choose to dress in athletic shoes and short pants and use no eye protection. Conversely, the worker may elect to wear steel-toed shoes, long pants, foot shields, and wear safety glasses with a face shield. In making this choice, the worker is influenced by his occupational community, his employing organization as well as his own predilections.

4 INFLUENCES ON BEHAVIOR CHOICE

As depicted in Figure 2, the worker's employing organization and his occupational community both influence him in his behavioral decision-making. Feedback from his behavior influences him in the future as well as influencing the occupational community and the employing organization. Improved safety performance requires an understanding of these influences.

4.1 Person

In making a behavioral choice, an individual is influenced by both latent and learned factors that are independent of the job. These include:

- Personality – is the worker a risk seeker or a risk averter? A risk averter will be much more cautious and choose low-risk behaviors than will a risk seeker.
- Intrinsic safety motivation – how strongly is the worker internally motivated? A worker motivated by a desire to be a stable provider for his family will make different decisions that a worker without this desire.
- Fit for duty – is the worker in an appropriate frame of mind for the work to be undertaken? A worker under the influence of alcohol or drugs will not have the proper mental faculties to make safe work decisions. Similarly, a worker who has been awake all night with a sick child will also not be able to focus on making safe decisions.
- Knowledge, skills, & abilities – does the worker have the wherewithal to make and carry out low-risk behavior decisions that result in safe performance? Abilities are those mental and physical ones with which the individual is born. Knowledge and skill are acquired through education, training, and experience. It is useful to distinguish between the knowledge and skill that the worker brings to the job and that provided by the employing organization through training.

4.2 Occupational community

In a comparative examination of the administration of work in manufacturing (bureaucratic organization) with

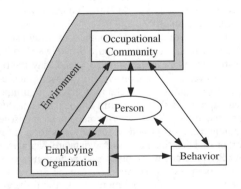

Figure 2. Modified behavior model.

that in construction (craft organization), Stinchcombe (1959) states "Mass production may be defined by the criterion that *both* the product and the work process are planned in advance *by persons not on the work crew.*" In the construction craft organization, the architect and/or engineer define the product while the craft workers who will perform the work plan the work process, including the following elements:

- The location at which a particular task will be done.
- The movement of tools, of materials, and of workers to this work place, and the most efficient arrangement of these workplace characteristics.
- Sometimes the particular movements to be performed in getting the task done [*This would include how to perform the task safely*].
- The schedules and time allotments for particular operations.
- Inspection criteria for particular operations (as opposed to inspection criteria for final products).

Stinchcombe further states, "In construction all these characteristics of the work process are governed by the worker in accordance with the empirical lore that make up craft principles. These principles are the content of the workers' socialization..."

Socialization into the construction worker occupational community may begin in childhood if members of the worker's family are construction workers. It continues through any or all of the following: secondary school, vocational education, military or apprentice training, and on-the-job training. The outcome of the socialization process is that the worker learns the way things are done in the craft. The cohesiveness of the occupational community is a function of the strength of the socialization process.

The strength of construction worker occupational communities is an empirical question. Stinchcombe's characterization of craftwork systems was published in 1959. Since then, there have been two forces significantly influencing the U.S. construction industry: (1) the erosion of market share and decline of the construction craft unions and (2) the industrialization of the construction process.

At the time of this work, members of the construction craft unions performed approximately 80% of the construction work in the United States. Today, the figure is closer to 20%. Consequently, fewer construction workers are entering the industry through union sector apprenticeship programs. Unions, as an institution, and their related labor-management sponsored training programs provide a formal basis for a strong worker socialization process. No data are available on the relative strengths of union and nonunion occupational communities. However, it can be argued that unionized communities are more cohesive and, thereby, exert a stronger influence on behavioral choice.

The industrialization of the construction process is a manifestation of the engineering subculture identified by Schein. Industrialization reflects efforts to minimize variability in the production process by reducing the work of craft workers in the field. Prefabrication and modularization are two of the techniques employed in the industrialization of construction. These processes result in the product and the work process being designed and planned by someone other than the individuals performing the work, i.e., the bureaucratic administration of work. The assembler has replaced the craft worker. Industrialization results in technology being firm specific as opposed to industry specific, which minimizes the role of workers in work process design.

4.2.1 *Occupational community culture*

The occupational community has its own culture. Climate is the manifestation of culture and consists of the rewards, policies, practices, and procedures used by an organization (Schneider 1975). Each community has its own culture and climate influencing its members. For example, in the United States, structural ironworkers have historically resisted any effort requiring them to tie-off when working on high steel. Community members reward or sanction members for conformance with or violation or accepted norms.

4.3 *Employing organization*

The employing organization influences the worker in his behavioral choice through the following factors:

- The task the worker is to perform: the technology and work process to be employed; where the task is to be performed; the specifications or expectations for the outputs or results of the work process; and the time within which the task is to be completed.
- The work setting (Reimer 1976) within which the task is to be performed, which includes: structural components such as the physical boundaries; inanimate objects within the boundaries, people as objects within the boundaries, and the weather; time and space; and a dynamic component representing the worker in the work setting responding to what is there and what is happening.
- The management systems in place for planning, organizing, staffing, directing, and controlling the work and the project.

Thus, the employing organization specifies what the worker is hired to do, where he is to do it, and the management system to be employed in doing it.

In addition, the employing organization creates the fit between the person and the job, which results in psychological factors potentially influencing the worker's decision-making. There is a significant body of research on the relationship between psychological factors and worker health (Karasek & Theorell 1990) and some work on the relationship between psychological factors and injury severity (Gillen et al. 2002). Karasek has developed the Job Content Questionnaire (JCQ) that contains six scales: decision latitude, psychological demands and mental workload, social support, physical demands, job insecurity, and exposure to physical hazards. As shown above, the situation or work environment in which a worker performs his or her tasks is a primary determinant of behavior; the psychological factors arising from that environment should have a significant impact of safety behavior. The JCQ is widely used in occupational health and should be used to identify the relationship between psychological factors and safety performance. Understanding this relationship would facilitate the development of strategies for job redesign and training that would reduce the aspects of the job that create job stress, which in turn should improve safety behavior.

4.3.1 Employing organization culture

A construction organization consists of a stable core of professional, technical, and administrative employees and a group of contingent craft employees hired on an as needed basis to perform the actual construction work. The stable core provides the basis for the organization's culture, which results from the interaction of the executive and engineer/technical subcultures within the organization.

The management system of the employing organization embodies the climate of the organization, i.e., the rewards, practices, policies, and procedures of the organization. For example, the management system may establish a requirement that a worker performing a specified task be given specialized training in safe performance of that task. Providing rewards for safe performance or sanctions for unsafe performance influences safety motivation.

4.4 Emergent culture

The safety culture of the construction project emerges from the interaction of the cultures of the various occupational communities and employing organizations participating in the project. It is a function of the relative strengths of the sub-cultures, with the stronger sub-culture providing more of the elements of the emergent culture. The safety climate arising from the emergent culture provides the framework within which project workers make behavioral choices.

5 CLIMATE

Several recent papers have examined the relationship between safety culture, safety climate, and safety performance (Glendon & Litherland 2000, and Neal,

Griffin, & Hart 2000). Although the existence of potential sub-cultures is recognized, this work assumes a single organization. A construction project has been described as a temporary, multiorganization. As such, there is a significant conceptualization problem. A stable organization may contain one or more stable sub-cultures. During its finite life, a construction project contains varying combinations of contracting organizations and workers, the confluence of which results in a cultural potpourri. As a consequence, a worker employed on the project at one point may function within one safety climate and a significantly different safety climate if employed at another point in the project.

5.1 Safety climate stability

A construction project is focused on the contractual completion date. Construction work is oriented toward the performance of a series of short-term operational milestones. As the project moves toward completion, the intensity of the work process, time pressure, and stress increase. The pressure for production increases, which raises the question as to the relative importance of production vs. safety.

As cited above, Cooper defines safety culture as "the product of multiple goal-directed interactions between people, jobs, and the organization" and the product as "that observable degree of effort by which all organizational members direct their attention and actions toward improving safety on a daily basis." Because of the pressure for timely completion of the project, the question of stability of the cultural product over the life of the project must be raised. Similarly, how stable is the safety climate if early in the project workers are rewarded for safe and high quality work and during the later stages of the project safety and quality are ignored and, instead, output is rewarded?

6 CONCLUSION

The varying subcultures on a project are relatively stable. However, their reciprocal interaction may result in a varying safety climate. The existence of construction workers as an occupational community, the safety climate resulting from the interaction of the various subcultures, and the stability of that climate require a great deal more research to improve construction safety performance.

REFERENCES

Bandura, A. 1986. Social Foundations of Thought and Action. Englewood Cliffs, New Jersey, Prentice Hall.

Cooper, M.D. 2000. Toward a model of safety culture. *Safety Science* 36: 111–136.

Davies, V.J. & Tomasin, K. 1990. *Construction Safety Handbook.* London: Thomas Telford.

Dester, W.S. & Blockley, D.I. 1995. "Safety – behavior and culture in construction." *Engineering, Construction and Architectural Management* 2(1): 17–26.

Gillen, M., Baltz, D. et al. 2002. Perceived safety climate, job demands, and coworker support among union and nonunion injured construction workers. *Journal of Safety Research* 33: 33–51.

Glendon, A.I., and Litherland, D.K. 2000. Safety climate factors, group differences, and safety behaviour in road construction. *Safety Science* 39: 157–188.

Karasek, R.A. & Theorell, T. Healthy Work. 1990. New York: Basic Books.

McDonald, M. & Ryan, F. 1992. Constraints on the development of safety culture. *The Irish Journal of Psychology*, Vol. 13, No. 2, pp. 273–281.

Neal, A., Griffin, M.A. et al. 2000. The impact of organizational climate on safety climate and individual behavior. *Safety Science* 2000: 99–109.

Riemer, J.W. 1975. *On Building Buildings: The social organization of a transitional work setting.* Ph.D. dissertation, University of New Hampshire.

Schein, E.H. 1996. Three cultures of management: the key to organizational learning. *Sloan Management Review* (Fall 1996): 9–20.

Schneider, B. 1975. Organizational climates: an essay. *Personnel Psychology* 28: 447–479

Stinchcombe, A. 1959. Bureaucratic and craft administration of production: a comparative study. *Administrative Science Quarterly* 4: 169–197.

Van Maanen, J. & Barley S.R. 1986. Occupational communities: culture and control in organizations. *Research in Organizational Bevhavior*, Volume 6. B.M. Staw and L.L. Cummings. Greenwich, CN. JAI Press Inc.: 287–365.

System-based Vision for Strategic and Creative Design, Bontempi (ed.)
© 2003 Swets & Zeitlinger, Lisse, ISBN 90 5809 599 1

Impossibility claims in construction projects

Y.M. Wong, T.W. Yiu , S.O. Cheung & C.H. Suen
Construction Dispute Resolution Research Unit (CDRRU), Department of Building and Construction,
City University of Hong Kong, Hong Kong

ABSTRACT: Claims are inevitable in construction contracts and previous studies have identified sources of claims, including complexity of project, unclear contract terms and traditional confrontational culture. Thus, handling claims is part of the daily routine for project managers and contract administrators. The main purpose for making a claim is either to seek compensation or to discharge liability. The remedies available depend on the type of claims and the conditions of contract. Over the last decade, conditions of contract have become increasingly "water-proof", thus leaving limited situations for which contractors can seek a contractual remedy. This paper deals with situations where a contractor can rescind a contract. In general, parties can rescind the contract if they have performed the obligations in the contract or by mutual agreement. In situation where it is physically impossible to perform the requirements of a contract, the parties may claim for "impossibility". In construction practice, to raise an impossibility claim, parties seek to discharge the contract so that they can be free from the contractual obligations to complete the job and/or obtain certain compensation for the actual loss incurred. Problems arise as parties may use this remedy as an excuse for non-performance. This paper presents a comprehensive review on impossibility claims, in particular on its relevance and current development in the construction industry. The legal reference of the doctrine of frustration in common law is also examined.

1 INTRODUCTION

Claims are inevitable in construction projects. In fact, the numbers of claim grow as the size and scale of a project increases (Frederick & Turner 1999, Sykes 1999). Generally speaking, from the contractors' point of view, making a claim is either to seek compensation or to discharge liability. Some of the more common claims include extension of time, late instruction, damages, etc. The remedies available mainly depend on a number of factors, including the type of damage, the financial situations at the time of claim, the conditions of contract, contracting parties' business relationships, etc. (Davenport 1995) Interestingly, there arises a situation where the contractor finds it is physically impossible to perform the contract requirements (Kululanga 2001). In this circumstance, impossibility claims allow the contractor to discharge the contract, that is, free from the contractual obligations (Chiu et al. 1991, Morgan 2000). However, it is quite difficult to define the term "impossibility", in addition, there are concerns over the use of impossibility as an excuse for non-performance (Mckendrick 1995). To answer these concerns, this paper is set to provide a comprehensive review on impossibility claims, particularly in the construction industry. Some of the key topics to

be discussed are as follows:

- the case laws, general practices and contractual provisions dealing with impossibility claims;
- the rights and obligations of contractual parties;
- a case study on impossibility claim.

2 IMPOSSIBILITY CLAIM

Impossibility claim can be submitted by a contractor when the construction work becomes impossible to carry on for a certain period of time or for an indefinite duration neither at the fault of the contractor nor the employer. In practice, impossibility claim can be submitted either at Common Law – Frustration or under contract terms, under the Clause "Physical Impossibility" (Fig. 1).

2.1 *Frustration claims*

In common law, frustration is one of the four ways of discharging a contract. Frustration is pleaded instead of physical impossibility claims when there is no express contractual provision. In fact, frustration is not restricted to physical impossibility of performance,

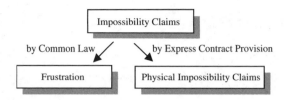

Figure 1. Impossibility claims.

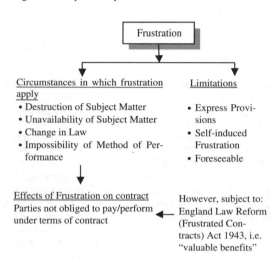

Figure 2. Functions and effects of frustration.

as in Krell v. Henry[1] (Ruff 1999). There are typical circumstances where the doctrine of frustration may be applied: (1) destruction of the subject matter, (2) unavailability of the subject matter, (3) change in law, and (4) impossibility of method of the performance. If the contract is proved to be frustrated, the effect of frustration is to automatically terminate all contractual obligations of both parties. Such effect becomes effective from the date of the frustrating event. In respect of the arrangement of payment, the England Law Reform (Frustrated Contracts) Act 1943 provided certain rules to be followed in case of frustration. However, the application of the doctrine of frustration is limited under three conditions: (1) Contractual Provision for the Event, (2) Foreseen and Foreseeable Events, and (3) Self-induced Frustration. Figure 2 summarizes the circumstances where frustration apply and its effects.

2.2 Express contract provision – physical impossibility claims

Claim based on "Physically impossible" can be found on a contractual term in the conditions of contract.

Table 1. List of examined overseas conditions of contract.

Country	Conditions of contract
United States	AIA
Australia	Australian Standard
Australia	C21
United Kingdom	ECC
Japan	ENAA
FAR	United States
FIDIC	England
GC/Works/1	England
ICE 6th Edition	England
JCT 80 and 81	United States
Singapore	Construction Industry Development Board (Singapore)

For example, in accordance with the General Conditions of Contract for Civil Engineering Works (1999 Edition) from the Government of Hong Kong, clause 15 states that "*Save in so far as it is legally or physically impossible the Contractor shall execute the Works in strict accordance with the Contract to the satisfaction of the Engineer and shall comply with and adhere strictly to the Engineer's instructions on any matter related to the Contract whether mentioned in the Contract or not.*"

Similar clause can also be found in other standard form of conditions of contract, such as ICE Conditions of Contract. The most well known cited authority for the meaning of physical impossibility is the case "Turriff Ltd v. The Welsh National Water Development Authority"[2] decided in 1973. In the Turriff case, physical impossibility could likely be defined as "commercial impossibility". The judgment in that case support that "from a practical commercial point of view", it was impossible for the contractor to fulfill his obligations so as to follow the employer's requirements on the design and specification of essential structural units "on an ordinary commercial competitive bases as the parties intended". To conclude, physical impossibility is related to "the precise limits of the specification and that could not be relieved by a deviation on the part of the contractor" (Eggleston 1993). To better understand the level of adoption of physical impossibility clauses. A literature review was conducted to study construction contracts in Hong Kong such as GCC for E&M, Design and Build, E&M Term, Civil Term, and Building Term. Furthermore, overseas Conditions of Contract are also included in this study. A list of examined conditions of contracts is shown in Table 1 below.

---

[1] [1903] 2 K.B. 740 (CA).

[2] [1994] CLYB 122, previously unreported.

3 OBSERVATIONS AND DISCUSSIONS

The following findings are noted:

- Most of the international contracts do not address expressly for the case of legal or physical impossibility. Only two international contracts, FIDIC and ICE 6th Edition, clearly indicate the right of discharge from further obligations to perform due to legal or physical impossibility.
- Although no express statement on the matter of impossibility, most of the other international contracts seem to have a common view that contractor will not be liable for failure of performance beyond contractor's control. Frustration (non-defined) or force majeure (non-defined) or specified force majeure events may lead to termination of contract or constitute an excuse of performance, as provided in the contracts of Australian Standard, ENAA, JCT 80 and JCT 81. Those causes may also lead to impossibility of performance without either fault of the contractual parties. In the contracts of AIA, Singapore, whether impossibility can be an excuse of performance depends on the applicable law, common law or local law.
- all of the Hong Kong Government forms provide similar wordings in clause 15 regarding the case of impossibility, except the general conditions of contract for Design and Build contracts.
- all the government forms contain a frustration clause, which provide the same payment arrangement in case of frustration as that mentioned in Special Risk clause.
- for the contracts of Airport Core Programme Civil Engineering Works Part I, in addition to "war", the causes of the frustration may be "any other supervening event which may occur independently of the will of the parties", but not the "inclement weather conditions of any kind adversely affecting the progress of the Works". In spite of more description and exclusion of "inclement weather" to frustration, there is still lack of specified events for frustration.
- for the Private Standard forms, HKIA forms (With/Without Quantity) have no express provision for the impossibility claims. Similar to some of the international contracts, HKIA forms state that suspension of works exceeding the specified period due to force majeure (non-defined but may be the cause which constitutes impossibility for further performance), may lead to termination of contract.

3.1 Interpretation of Clause 15 in government forms

Clause 15 has come from (and "negates") the English legal concept that a party may be bound to do the impossible under the contract[3]. This clause 15 is evolved from the clause 13(1) of the ICE Conditions of Contract. It was notified in Turriff case that the ICE Conditions of Contract in Clause 13 provided an exemption for non-performance on grounds of "physical impossibility"[4]. Therefore, the clause 15 of the government contracts provides that if strict compliance with the terms of the Contract is proved to be impossible, the contractor shall be excused from performance[5]. This clause also gives the Architect (or Engineer or Supervising Officer or Maintenance Surveyor or Surveyor) power to issue instructions for the Works[6]. "The operation of this clause is a question of mixed law (definition of physical impossibility) and fact (evidence showing that the definition of physical impossibility is satisfied)"[7].

Though the loss would lie where it falls under the rule of common law, it is presumed that the contractor is entitled to breach of contract damages if he is forced to strive for the impossibility and payment may be recovered on a quantum meruit basis for the work done before the discovery of the impossibility.

4 INCIDENCES OF PHYSICAL IMPOSSIBILITY CLAIMS

There are three leading cases closely related to Impossibility Claims. These are discussed in this section:

4.1 Turriff case[8]

Turriff, the Main Contractor was required by the Employer's novel design to construct a sewage scheme by making use of specified culvert units, which were manufactured by Sub-Contractor. Turriff found that it was impossible to lay and join the culvert units with a specified tolerance of $\pm 1/16$th of an inch. It was held that when the performance in accordance with specification and drawings became impossible, Turriff were not obliged to comply with them. Also, the Sub-Contractor, subject to the same benefits and limitations as the Contractor, was not required to do what was impossible when the Contractor was excused from doing it.

4.2 Yorkshire case[9]

The case concerned a contract for tunnel construction. At the stage of inviting tenders, the Employer required

---

3 Ibid[53].
4 Ibid[15].
5 Ibid[53]; Ibid[2].
6 Ibid[2].
7 Ibid[53].
8 Ibid[15].
9 (1985) 32 B.L.R. 114.

tenderers to supply programme for the works (but not a method statement) along with their tenders. However, an approved method statement, which is submitted by the Contractor and accepted by the Employer for the construction of the works upstream, had incorporated in the formal agreement signed. It was held that the method statement formed part of the contract and the Contractor was obliged to follow it. Thus, due to the impossibility within clause 13(1) of the ICE Conditions (5th Edn) (i.e. impossibility to perform in strict accordance with this method statement), the Contractor was entitled to a variation order necessary for completion of the works under clause 51 and entitled to a payment under clauses 51(2) and 52. In the judgment, Skinner J stated that "the plaintiff could have kept the programme and methods as the sole responsibility of the contractors under clause 14(1) and (3); the risks would then have been the respondents' throughout." That means if the Employer did not incorporate the method statement in the agreement but use another way to handle the submission of method statement by the Contractor, the risk of impossibility to follow the method statement should have shifted to the Contractor.

4.3 Holland case[10]

There were three parties involved in this case, Sub-Contractor, Main Contractor and Employer. The dispute matter was the backfilling of the trench to sea bed level, where insufficient backfilling materials obtained from the dredging areas as well as dumping ground. Both Sub-Contractor and Main Contractor claimed for additional cost for the additional backfilling materials, based on the clause 12 – "adverse conditions" and clause 13 – "impossibility" for the argument. They failed in the first place and then went to appeal. The Court of Appeal allowed the Sub-Contractor Appeal but just partly allowed the Main Contractor since there was an agreement between the Main Contractor and Employer that the Main Contractor's liability extended beyond obtaining backfill from previously excavated material and additional dredging of the dumping ground. According to the judgement, the sub-contract works were not "legally or physically impossible to complete" within the meaning of clause 13(1) of the ICI Conditions (same as ICE Conditions, 5th Edn, with certain modifications). Besides, "Adverse conditions" within clause 12 were not restricted to supervening events but also pre-existing conditions. It is noted that whenever Main Contractor or Sub-Contractor claim for impossibility under the contract, it may not be a case of impossibility in a matrix of fact and true construction of the contract.

---

[10] (1987) 37 B.L.R. 1 (CA).

5 CASE STUDY OF IMPOSSIBILITY CLAIMS IN HONG KONG

Further to the detailed explanation of three key cases of impossibility claims. A case study of impossibility claim in Hong Kong is described in this section. The study was conducted together with a local practitioner, who has intensive experience in construction contracts of Hong Kong.

5.1 The case

A contractor, C, entered into a Sewage Contract with Hong Kong Government under the Government of Hong Kong, General Conditions of Contract for Civil Engineering Works (1993 Edition). C was responsible for the excavation of tunnel from about 3 km long and 130 m below the datum. The project commenced in 1997 and proposed to be completed on 20th August 2000. However, C found it impossible to carry out the project in 1998 and thus raised an Impossibility Claim.

According to C, when using the tunnel boring machine and excavating the tunnel, the face of the tunnel collapsed. Verbal discussion with the Engineer and Government was made regarding the collapse of tunnel and the potential of impossibility claim and followed by a written notice. The collapse of tunnel identified that the ground was different from that was assumed. i.e. much softer than that was anticipated as contemplated by Engineer's prescribed method of excavation. At the time of tender, the Contractor had assumed that the Engineer's Design was correct and that the Engineer's assumptions were reasonable. Since the contract was based on the assumptions made by the Engineer, the Contractor's risk for the ground condition should only be to the extent within the boundary of the contract where those assumptions could be applied. Therefore, it was impossible to construct strictly in accordance with the contract. In the Contractor's point of view, variation was needed to continue the work.

Also, the extent of ground investigations was insufficient. Those investigations were carried out by the Engineer when designing the project. However, the engineer changed the tunnel alignment at the last

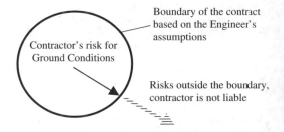

Figure 3. Liability of the contractor's risk.

moment during the design. Also, the contractor had no design responsibility for the permanent work and the Engineer chose to design some temporary work which supposed is the contractor's responsibility. Therefore, the Contractor has no responsibility for the cause of impossibility.

C relied on the wordings in clause 15 for the Impossibility Claim because the clause 15 touches the fundamental basis of the argument that relief should be given in case of impossibility to comply with the contract strictly with the Engineer's specification. Although clause 85 (frustration clause) may also be used, it is a subjective clause and legal support will be necessary to demonstrate the case. Clause 15 specifies the case for the impossibility of "strict accordance with the Contract" but the clause 85 does not. The doctrine of frustration at common law was also not preferable because the Contractor was looking for a mechanism under the contract provisions.

The following contract clauses were used in the submission:

Clause 15 – demonstrate in itself is impossibility;
Clause 13 – to identify extent of the risk of ground condition and limit the Contractor's risk for ground condition;
Clause 23 – refer to design responsibility in respect of permanent works and temporary works, so as to establish responsibility of the Contractor;
Clause 50 – delay caused by Employer's own Engineer.

In fact, there is no direct entitlement subject to the clause 15. But for the clause 60 – Variations, Engineer can issue variation necessary for the completion of the works to remove impossibility. Therefore, it may say that clause 15 indirectly leads to the claim entitlement.

5.2 Outcomes

To substantiate the claim, the following items are present to the Engineer and Employer by the Contractor:

1. Geological information such as side wall mapping
2. Government investigation reports
3. Specialist consultants' analysis on the ground, which has already excavated so as to determine the ground condition forehead.
4. A risk assessment report on the likely ground condition on the remains of the tunnel prepared by the consultant, who was employed by the contractor
5. The fact that the Independent Checking Engineer (ICE), whose concern is on the safety, was not happy to issue the Certificate for the method statement which incorporated Engineer's design. The ICE did not agree the methodology of the Engineer's design.
6. "What if Scenarios" proposed by the Contractor on the basis of the ground conditions.

7. Different methods of construction for excavation under another part of the works, which were proposed by the Contractor.
8. Other information prepared by the specialists in order to help the Engineer to assess the situation, including contract references like clause 61 for valuation of variation and clause 63 for assessment of loss and expense arising from the event.

Government admitted that it is necessary to issue variation so as to remove the impossibility. As the Contractor progress to the tunnel, the Contractor kept encountering problems and so the Engineer had to issue different variations to suit the actual conditions encountered. Settlement and agreement was made between the Contractor and Employer, without the necessity to bring the issue to the Mediation or Arbitration. It is suggested that there is a trend for the increase in number of impossibility claims because many contractors nowadays sometimes too quick to accept the risk of ground condition and his responsibility. When submitting the impossibility claim, people should be sensible to try the argument in the right circumstances.

6 CONCLUDING REMARKS

Impossibility claims can be invoked either under common law – frustration claim or by contract provision – physical impossibility claim. In respect of frustration claim, the doctrine of frustration can be applied under four circumstances: (1) destruction of subject matter, (2) unavailability of subject matter, (3) impossibility of method of performance, and (4) change in law. Once the frustration is established, the parties are automatically relieved from their contractual obligations at the date of frustrating event. Actually, it is not an easy task to establish a frustration claim, the operation of doctrine of frustration has its own limitations.

Regarding the study of local and overseas Conditions of Contract such as FIDIC, ICE, ECC and the Hong Kong Government Conditions of Contract, clear terms are provided for physical impossibility claims. However, the others have no express provision or mechanism to deal with the case of impossibility.

From the analyses and decided cases described in this paper, for the use of "impossibility" as an excuse for non-performance, it is necessary to prove that strict compliance with the contract requirements such as specifications and method statements is not possible. As the contractor is not obliged to perform with deviation of contract requirements, it shall be a valid impossibility claim if strict compliance with contract requirements is impossible.

The case study reported in this paper illustrates the concepts and application of a claim based on impossibility.

REFERENCES

Chiu, C. & Roebuck, D. 1991. Hong Kong Contracts. Hong Kong: Hong Kong University Press.

Davenport, P. 1995. Construction claims. Sydney: Federation Press.

Eggleston, Brian. 1993. The ICE conditions of contract: sixth edition: a user's guide. England: Blackwell Scientific Publications.

Frederick, D. & Turner, A. 1999. Building contract claims and disputes, 2nd ed. Harlow: Longman.

Kululanga, G. 2001. Construction contractors' claim process framework. *Journal of Construction Engineering and Management*, 127(4): 309–314.

McKendrick, E. 1995. Force majeure and frustration of contract. London: Lloyd's of London Press.

Morgan, C. 2000. When fulfilling the contract becomes impossible. Asia Engineer 2(2): 22–23.

Ruff, A. 1999. Nutcases contract law, 2ed. London: Sweet & Maxwell.

Sykes, J. 1999. Construction claims. London: Sweet & Maxwell.

System-based Vision for Strategic and Creative Design, Bontempi (ed.)
© 2003 Swets & Zeitlinger, Lisse, ISBN 90 5809 599 1

Engineering the World Trade Center disaster recovery

D.A. Cuoco
The Thornton-Tomasetti Group, Inc., New York, USA

ABSTRACT: The cleanup of the World Trade Center disaster site was one of the most complex and dangerous construction projects in history. It was also one of the safest. The immensely successful completion of this undertaking was the direct result of the unwavering cooperation and coordination of firefighters, police officers, rescue workers, government employees, construction contractors, and structural engineers.

1 INTRODUCTION

The tragic events of September 11, 2001 will be forever etched in history, and have had an immeasurable impact on the lives of the individuals and families that were directly affected.

In response to the airplane attacks and collapse of the World Trade Center towers on the morning of September 11, 2001, the New York City Mayor's Office of Emergency Management immediately dispatched emergency response teams, including hundreds of police officers and firefighters, to the World Trade Center site. Simultaneously, the New York City Department of Design and Construction (DDC) retained four major construction management firms to assist in the search and rescue operation, as well as the writer's firm which was charged with responsibility for all structural engineering operations at the site.

Two days after the attacks, approximately 40 engineering firms, comprising over 400 structural engineers, were mobilized by the Structural Engineers Association of New York (SEAoNY) and were retained as consultants to the writer's firm to monitor the demolition and stabilization work at the site.

From September 13, 2001 through mid-July 2002, work at the site proceeded continuously on a 24-hour basis, seven days a week.

2 THE ATTACKS

The first plane made impact with One World Trade Center (the north tower) at 8:46 a.m., striking the north face of the building between the 94th and 99th floors, and creating an opening that extended across approximately 60% of the width of the building.

Figure 1. View looking north, showing the south face of Two World Trade Center (right) and the south face of One World Trade Center (left).

The southeast corner of Two World Trade Center (the south tower) was struck by the second plane at 9:03 a.m., between the 78th and 84th floors, resulting in an opening that extended across approximately 50% of the width of the building (see Figure 1). Two World Trade Center was the first to collapse, 56 minutes after being struck, at 9:59 a.m. This was followed by the collapse of One World Trade Center at 10:29 a.m., one hour and 43 minutes after being struck.

3 EMERGENCY DAMAGE ASSESSMENT

The condition and stability of the remaining structures and portions of structures at the collapse site was

Figure 2. North face of Bankers Trust building, impacted by portions of the façade of Two World Trade Center.

uncertain, at best. Therefore, one of the first priorities was to immediately assess the condition of buildings adjacent to the collapsed towers (see Figure 2). This was critical to ensure that no other buildings, or parts of buildings, were about to collapse and endanger the hundreds of rescue workers that were searching for survivors.

On the afternoon of September 11th, senior representatives from the writer's firm conducted an initial walk-through of the area with city officials to survey the situation and begin planning for widespread building inspections and on-site engineering operations to assist rescue crews. By the morning of September 12th, more than 30 structural engineers from the writer's firm had been mobilized to conduct building inspections.

Portions of several buildings adjacent to the collapse site were determined to be in need of immediate temporary shoring in order to prevent further damage or collapse, and were cordoned off until the shoring could be installed. Broken windows with hanging glass were widespread throughout the area, and best efforts were made to cordon off the most precarious conditions until netting could be installed.

4 FOUR SECTORS

Realizing the scope of the project was too large for one construction manager to handle, the DDC divided the site into four sectors, and assigned one construction manager to each sector. Bovis Lend Lease was the construction manager assigned to the area where Two and Three World Trade Center had stood. The area containing One and Six World Trade Center was assigned to AMEC (formerly known as Morse Diesel). The eastern portion of the site included Four and Five World Trade Center and was assigned to Tully Construction. The area north of Vesey Street, which included Seven World Trade Center, was assigned to the joint venture of Turner Construction and Plaza Construction.

5 MONITORING OF DEMOLITION AND STABILIZATION OPERATIONS

The construction managers immediately mobilized demolition contractors to begin the cleanup operation. Four engineering inspection teams were formed, with one team assigned to each of the sectors to work with a specific construction manager, in order to monitor the demolition activities and identify any areas in need of stabilization. Starting on September 13th, this monitoring was performed on a 24-hour, seven-day-a-week basis by more than 400 engineers from approximately 40 regional structural engineering firms. These firms, engaged as consultants to the writer's firm on September 13th, were mobilized and initially coordinated by the Structural Engineers Association of New York (SEAoNY). This ensured that experts were always available to consult with construction workers and rescue crews on the safest ways to carry out their operations.

6 SUPPORT OF CONSTRUCTION EQUIPMENT

One of the most challenging structural engineering tasks was the design of grillages and reinforcement of existing support members to allow placement of cranes, grapplers, and other pieces of heavy equipment needed to remove debris. Large cranes with long reaches and capacities of up to 1,000 tons were needed to provide access to the search and rescue are as, which were designated by the New York City Fire Department. The cranes had to be placed at very specific locations to meet the Fire Department's needs, making the structural issues especially challenging. Construction managers provided details about the weight and size of each crane to the structural engineers, who then had to figure out how to support it. In some cases engineers made use of collapsed building structures for support, while in others new support structures had to be designed and quickly fabricated, often in a single night (see Figure 3).

Figure 3. Grillage for 300 ton crane located between Four and Five World Trade Center, fabricated in a single night.

Figure 4. Installation of tie-backs to stabilize slurry wall.

These design problems had to be solved at an accelerated pace, under intense time pressure, and without the benefit of advanced computer modelling techniques, but rather with hand calculations and sound engineering judgment.

Valuable assistance regarding capacities of existing structural members was provided by Leslie E. Robertson Associates, the Trade Center's original structural designer. Though at one point more than 30 cranes were simultaneously on the site, there was not a single case of a crane support problem during the entire rescue and recovery effort.

7 SURVEY MONITORING PROGRAM

As one of a number of safety measures taken for every one working at the Trade Center site, survey points were set up on certain structures and portions of structures that were severely damaged and at risk of becoming unstable. As demolition work continued, these survey points varied both in number and location. Survey crews from the DDC monitored the points every 30 minutes, 24 hours a day. This survey monitoring proved to be very useful in enhancing safety conditions. In one case, a large piece of the façade from Two World Trade Center that had become embedded in the ground near Four World Trade Center was found to be moving, and the piece was pulled down before it could collapse.

8 THE SLURRY WALL

One of the most serious concerns during the recovery effort was that significant damage might have been done to the massive slurry wall around the Trade

Center's perimeter, which holds back water from the Hudson River. When crews were able to gain access to areas near the slurry wall, they found that the wall was in fact stable, due to portions of basement slabs that had remained intact after the collapse and debris that had piled up against the wall. To clear the area within the slurry wall, this debris had to be removed, jeopardizing the wall's stability. Working with key Port Authority staff members, engineers undertook a major stabilization effort. For this part of the engineering operations, the writer's firm engaged Mueser Rutledge Consulting Engineers, whose specialists designed a procedure for the sequential installation of approximately 1,000 tie-backs to prevent movement of the wall. The tie-backs were drilled from inside the slurry wall downward through the soil and into bed rock, where they were grouted and prestressed, then locked against the wall to provide lateral stability (see Figure 4).

9 ADDITIONAL BUILDING INSPECTIONS

In order to allay the concerns of building owners and residents in the general area of Lower Manhattan surrounding the Trade Center site, all buildings were inspected in the area bounded by Chambers Street on the north, Rector Street on the south, William Street on the east, and the Hudson River on the west. This area, comprising more than 400 buildings, was divided into 16 zones. Working with the New York City Department of Buildings, the writer's firm engaged SEAoNY engineers to conduct inspections of all of these buildings in a two-day period within the first week after September 11th. Only eight buildings outside the World Trade Center site were found to have sustained significant damage, all of which was repairable.

411

10 MANAGEMENT CHALLENGES

One of the main engineering management challenges involved in the recovery effort was scheduling the members of the engineering teams to ensure that a sufficient staff was available 24 hours a day. Engineers from the writer's firm established and supervised briefings at shift changes to ensure continuity of engineering issues and decisions. Working in two daily shifts (8 a.m. to 8 p.m., and 8 p.m. to 8 a.m.), 12 engineers from the writer's firm were present at the field office and on the site to manage and supervise the ongoing structural issues at all times. An additional 16 engineers drawn from the SEAoNY firms provided assistance as well during the first five months of the recovery operations. Scheduling the engineering shifts required accommodating people's personal schedules as well as ensuring sufficient periods of rest between shifts each week. Full-time staffing by the writer's firm began on the morning of September 12, 2001, and continued through May 2002, when a smaller staff began to handle the on-site work through its completion in mid-July 2002.

11 THE RESULT

Over the course of 10 months, more than 1.6 millions tons of debris were removed from the site where the World Trade Center once stood. The recovery program was completed $1 billion under its original cost estimate and four months ahead of its originally estimated schedule. Most importantly, it was carried out safely, without a single major injury among the thousands of recovery workers at the Trade Center site, a reflection of the hard work and dedication of everyone involved.

12 CONCLUSION

Structural engineers have truly played a crucial role in enabling the intense search and rescue/recovery efforts at the World Trade Center to proceed without hindrance on a 24-hour basis, while maintaining safety in an environment fraught with the risk and danger posed by partially collapsed and severely damaged structures. It has been stated many times by DDC personnel as well as by firefighters and police officers, that structural engineers have saved lives. The success of these efforts is a direct result of the untiring commitment of many firms and hundreds of structural engineers.

ACKNOWLEDGMENT

Many engineering firms contributed the expertise of their staffs to the rescue and recovery work at the World Trade Center, which proved critical to the rapid and safe completion of these efforts. The firms included Arup, Buro Happold, Cantor Seinuk Group, Consoer Townsend Envirodyne Engineers, Dewhurst MacFarlane, DeSimone Consulting, DiSalvo Ericson Group, Edwards & Kelcey, Engineering Systems, Einhorn Yaffe Prescott, Fletcher Thompson, Gilsanz Murray Steficek, Goldstein Associates, Guy Nordenson Associates, Hoy Structural Services, The Office of James Ruderman, HLW International, Howard I. Shapiro and Associates, Koutsoubis, Alonso Associates, Leslie E. Robertson Associates, Lockwood Consulting, Lucius Pitkin, M.G. McLaren, Mueser Rutledge Consulting Engineers, Murray Engineering, Parsons Brinckerhoff, Robert Silman Associates, Rosenwasser/Grossman Consulting Engineers, Severud Associates, Simpson Gumpertz and Heger, Skidmore, Owings & Merrill, Superstructures, Turnasure, Tylk Gustafson Reckers Wilson Andrews, Vollmer Associates, Weidlinger Associates, Weiskopf & Pickworth and Wiss, Janney, Elstner Associates.

System-based Vision for Strategic and Creative Design, Bontempi (ed.)
© 2003 Swets & Zeitlinger, Lisse, ISBN 90 5809 599 1

Highest and best use of people

W.L. Kelly

Value Engineering Services Transworld (VEST), Walla Walla, Washington State, USA

ABSTRACT: Management must establish responsibilities and relationships to structure production from an organization. However, organization structure is distorted by characteristics of individuals. Were people predictable as robots managing them may be automated, but they are not. Effectiveness and efficiency need periodic checks and adjustments to counter human variables and faulty procedural and systemic elements.

This paper examines some human characteristics and quirks that distort planning plus a method to assess how well organization procedures and processes perform in their presence. An audit system must readily determine deviation from intended actions to expose areas requiring correction. Function Analysis, FAST diagramming and Linear Responsibility Charting combine to form a prime tool for such analysis.

1 ORGANIZATION COMPLEXITIES

1.1 *Organization charts and their weaknesses*

Organization Charts are wonderful myths. They intend to distribute authority, responsibility, tasks and relationships of units; however, they get sabotaged by human idiosyncrasies.

Organization charts expand into standards, rules, flowcharts, job descriptions and process details all bound into procedural manuals. Eventually excessive details and oversight suffocate productivity. These areas need periodic checks and adjustments to keep an organization healthy and competitive.

For example I lead a Value Engineering study on a process requiring 17 signatures of folks in separate offices to approve each change order request. With normal diversions it took weeks to obtain all signatures. Each signer sent comments demanding response and approval cycles continued until all reviewers were satisfied. Organization efficiency equaled that of a snail on a sight-seeing tour.

1.2 *People impacts*

Realistic organization charts evolve as people learn who produces; is trustworthy; knowledgeable, works well with others, is prompt and similar attributes. Shortcuts to those folks establish true lines of interaction and form a working organization chart.

Most people want to succeed; however, definition of success varies greatly. Some want a paycheck, some to just get by and others hunger for power.

Motivation only comes from one's self. Pleas and pressures to motivate usually produce theater. Five people per hundred will not work even under threat. Another 5 per hundred are self-driven to excel. Remaining effort varies from just above acceptable threshold to constantly producing their very best.

People who have time to waste like to spend it with those that don't. They feel joined to entrepreneurial people without sweating. They dampen productivity and foster resentment.

The German scientist, Ringelmann had workers pull against a meter (scale) in units of one, two, three and eight people. Measurements showed the average force generated ranged from 63 kg (139 lbs) for one, 53 kg (117 lbs) for three and 31 kg (68 lbs) for eight persons. The study suggests this conclusion:

- Individual effort contracts relative to the number of people assigned to complete a task. Mentally unemployed continually test lowest limits of effort other members will tolerate and let them remain in a unit or team.
- Highly motivated people attack problems in concentrated, intense manner. They tend to ignore, run over or ostracize slow moving members.

These and other human characteristics distort all plans whether structuring an organization, team or individual work assignments. Management should factor them into creating and relating staff.

1.3 *How to diagnose health of an organization*

How does one test organization effectiveness and efficiency, doing the right things and doing the right things right? First, clearly identify main problems that require solution.

They can be very large, reorganizing the entire company due to loss or gain of major contracts or acquisition of another company. They can be process like design, quality control, contract administration, production, estimating or eliminate bottlenecks. They may be positions, what tasks consume most of their time, have they assumed duties outside their responsibility, and with whom do they interface and in what capacity? Answers point to wrong priorities, excess or lack of supervision, empire building, etc.

To solve any of those or other problems requires complete factual knowledge of Who Does What.

Division and subdivision managers are responsible for specific areas of activity. People are responsible to perform work to complete activity tasks.

The following process brings order and simplicity for diagnosis and cures for organization health.

2 FUNCTION/LINEAR RESPONSIBILITY CHART PREPARATION STEPS

2.1 *Team leadership and responsibilities*

A Certified Value Specialist leads a 5-member core team having expertise in each area being studied. The team also needs a grasp of Value Engineering principles and techniques. That is why the leader is a CVS. Five is an ideal size for any team. Temporary members counsel the team when special expertise is required for unique problems.

The core team processes information, performs function analysis, prepares FAST diagrams and linear responsibility charts (see Figures 1 and 2). The team both interviews and guides additional interviewers to obtain data and complete linear responsibility charts. Finally, the core team summarizes conclusions and recommends solutions for problems addressed.

Results show essential activities, distribution of unit responsibilities and participation of individuals in completing various tasks.

2.2 *Information gathering and processing*

Start information gathering with mission, goals, objectives and existing organization charts. Charts do not accurately portray how work is done. People determine who produces and who doesn't; shortcuts around poor procedures; what procedures can and cannot be ignored, etc. However, existing charts will convert to functions needed for FAST diagramming.

Obtaining organization data requires input from people who can clearly define unit responsibilities, activities, relationships and authority. Expect lots of argument caused by perception versus fact, turf wars,

etc. This phase uncovers many inefficiencies as well as possible cures. Record all such observations.

Reliability of all data regarding responsibility and participation is highest when people are interviewed in small groups to temper responses. Interviewers must pursue conflicting views to arrive at truth.

For each activity determine who does the work and how individuals relate to others. Show types of relationship, such as, supervise, edit, approve, is informed, consult, etc., to reveal who does what. Do not accept "we" to identify individual responsibility. Do not attempt to include importance of positions.

2.3 *General approach to analysis*

Dedicate sufficient essential resources for thorough analysis and exclude no part of an organization from study. High level areas result in high level savings and efficiencies. They are tempting targets; however, the goal is to find and cure problem areas causing pain.

2.4 *Definitions for level of studies*

Organization divisions and subdivisions manage major and secondary level activities, respectively. Their executives show participation in satisfying level of activities for their units as well as themselves. Staff individuals perform work to satisfy tasks that derive from each activity.

Do not mix unit and executive responsibilities with worker's tasks on the same chart. Specify what is sought from analysis, what a chart should disclose. Keep it specific and simple.

2.5 *Three interrelated levels of charts are used*

Phase I: Highest level charts show responsibility for managing major activities. Major activities are placed on the "X" axis. Major divisions are atop columns on the "Y" axis and President, VP and CFO equivalents follow division titles.

Phase I shows if responsibility is rightly claimed, claimed by an unintended unit or executive, overlaps others, is not claimed at all or is shared with other units as a percentage of involvement.

Phase II: Mid-level charts identify subdivisions responsible for managing secondary level activities. Each major activity from Phase I is subdivided into supporting activities which are listed on the "X" axis in descending level of indenture. Organization subdivisions and their Manager, Assistants and top Supervisors are listed atop "Y" axis columns.

Phase II shows if responsibility is rightly claimed, claimed by an unintended unit or executive, overlaps others, is not claimed at all or is shared with other units as a percentage of involvement.

Phase III: Each supporting activity from Phase II is broken into individual tasks which are listed on the "X" axis in descending level of indenture. Job titles top "Y" axis columns.

Phase III shows individual contribution to each task and the form it takes. Charts display individual duties, types of participation and relationships. (See suggested performance standards in Section 3 for all Phases.)

2.6 Value Engineering definition of function and its role in linear responsibility charting

Information gathering is followed by converting items, activities and tasks into Value Engineering language, Functions.

In all three Phases each activity or task on the "X" axis shall be defined as functions.

Value Engineering defines function as a two word definition of the intended use of an item, activity or concept. Functions consist of an active verb that defines required action and a measurable noun that receives that action. The noun is measurable because value may be attached to it.

There is no one correct function, no generic description applicable to specific items. There are only valid functions that are consensus descriptions a team agrees best describe intended use. Functions become a universal language for all participants and rapidly promote understanding and dialogue.

Function analysis effort should convert items and activities into a group of 30 to 60 functions. That is sufficient to begin forming a FAST (Function Analysis System Technique) diagram.

2.7 FAST diagram preparation and use

A Function Analysis System Technique (FAST) diagram formats functions on a page to structure the study item. It verifies or corrects function definitions, rids or adds functions and relates them all.

A team selects the most important function from the group and places it at the left margin. Start left to right asking How is a function satisfied with answers in function terms. Develop 4 or 5 answers and check logic by asking right to left Why is this function performed with answers in function terms.

After answers in both directions are logical continue How–Why questions for another set of answers. If logic is wrong change descriptions, remove or insert functions or rearrange functions until logic tracks in both directions.

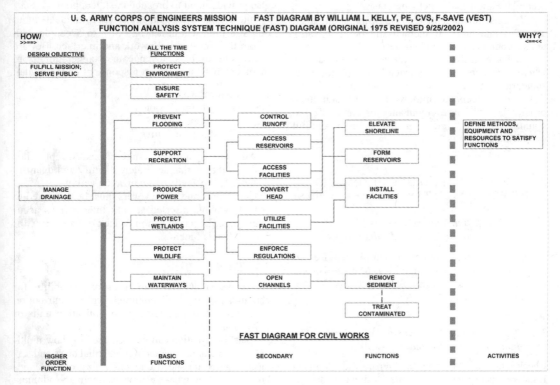

Figure 1.

The When question relates concurrent functions.

Main line functions are called the Critical Path of Functions. Each of those is asked, When (a function) occurs what effects does it cause, good or bad. Answers as functions go below it. Next ask, When (a function) occurs what functions occur at the same time but are not caused by it. They go above it.

Why questions direct thoughts and resulting functions to continuously higher viewpoints. How questions lead to ever smaller details. When functions expose consequences and parallel activity.

Higher Order Functions are prime objectives. Basic Functions are major components to achieve them. Secondary Functions satisfy Basic Functions. When How answers are detailed descriptions it is an activity and one has left function definitions. Scope lines go right of Higher Order and left of Activities.

Alternative solutions occur during FAST diagram preparation. Record every idea to consider in final analysis of organization structuring. See Page 5 for a typical FAST diagram.

2.8 Linear charting layout

"X" axis input describes essential organization activities to satisfy its mission. They range from major to secondary and finally, elemental tasks.

"Y" axis input identifies responsibility to satisfy activities and tasks. It includes major organization units, subunits and individual staff.

Display contribution by entering symbols at axes where it occurs. Prepare legends for performance standards and place at bottom of each chart.

Do not accept definitions as, "we administer programs", "we have cognizance of changes", "we maintain security", etc. Get direct, finite, truthful, quantifiable answers.

3 RESPONSIBILITY DESCRIPTIONS AND PERFORMANCE STANDARDS (EXAMPLES)

3.1 Typical activity descriptions as "X" axis functions for divisions and subdivisions

Establish Mission, Define Goals, Implement Recommendations, Coordinate Activities, Manage Budget, Balance Workload, Ensure Sales, Identify Market, Promote Safety, etc.

3.2 Typical task descriptions as "X" axis functions for individuals

Check Estimates, Write Specs, Prepare Bids, Maintain Database, Incorporate Comments, Design Foundations, Troubleshoot Software, File Data, etc.

3.2 Typical performance standards for units or individuals on the "Y" axis

Phase I for Major Activities:

TR	Total responsibility
SR (%)	Share responsibility (%)
PWPS	Perform work with present staff
PWMS (%)	Perform work with modified staff (% of change)

Only top executives take part in this phase, such as President, Vice-President, CEO, or equivalent, the "Buck Stops Here" group.

Phase II for Secondary Activities:

TR	Total responsibility
SR(%)	Share responsibility (%)
PWPS	Perform work with present staff
PWMS (%)	Perform work with modified staff (% of change)

Managers, assistants and major supervisors take part in this phase.

Phase III for individuals expressed as job titles.

Subdivisions qualified to satisfy a Secondary Activity also qualify their staffs to complete Phase III. However, if skills are scarce for critical functions, qualified individuals from other subdivisions should also provide input to broaden the talent pool.

Interviewers lead data gathering. Individuals input one at a time within a group of 3 to 5 people with whom they most closely work and interface. Beware indications of bias, revenge or exaggeration from members that could distort response of an individual.

PW	Perform work
GS	General supervision
DS	Direct supervision
CA	Coordinate activities

All above symbols are suggestions. Accept, tailor or develop ones that accurately identify and quantify data needed to analyze organization activity.

Core teams and interviewers must be dedicated to ensure symbols inserted at axes intersections accurately describe participation or lack of capability, for each "X" axis function.

3.4 Results

"X" rows show distribution of responsibility for activities or tasks. "Y" columns display contribution to listed activities or tasks by organization units or individuals.

Chart information can be processed to show multitudes of critical data including: Essential tasks and services required for specific functions or projects; duties broken down by type-executive, supervisory, administrative, or worker; duplication, overlap, underserved,

FIRST PHASE
1) MAJOR ORGANIZATION DIVISIONS ARE LISTED ON ("Y" AXIS) INCLUDE TOP EXECUTIVES FOR EACH
2) MAJOR ACTIVITIES ARE HIGHER ORDER AND BASIC FUNCTIONS FROM FAST DIAGRAM. SUPPLEMENT IF NEEDED AND LIST ALL ON ("X" AXIS)
3) INSERT SYMBOL AT AXES INTERSECTION THAT BEST SHOWS PERFORMANCE RESPONSIBILITY

	EXECUTIVE OFFICE	Commander (Example)	Deputy Commander (Example)	ENGINEERING DIVISION	OPERATIONS DIVISION	REAL ESTATE DIVISION	PROCUR. & SUPPLY DIV.	CONSTRUCTION DIVISION
FULFILL MISSION								
SERVE PUBLIC								
MANAGE DRAINAGE								
PREVENT FLOODING								
SUPPORT RECREATION								
PRODUCE POWER								
PROTECT WETLANDS								
PROTECT WILDLIFE								
MAINTAIN WATERWAYS								

SECOND PHASE
(1) ORGANIZATION SUB-DIVISIONS ARE LISTED ON ("Y" AXIS) INCLUDE TOP EXECUTIVES FOR EACH
(2) ACTIVITIES REQUIRED TO SATISFY FIRST PHASE FUNCTIONS ARE DEFINED AS FUNCTIONS AND LISTED ON ("X" AXIS)
(3) INSERT SYMBOL AT AXES INTERSECTION THAT BEST SHOWS PERFORMANCE RESPONSIBILITY

	ENGINEERING DIVISION	Planning Branch	Chief, Planning Branch	Assistant Chief, Plan. Br.	Design Branch	Found. & Materials. Branch	Service Branch
PREVENT FLOODING							
Control Runoff							
Elevate Shoreline							
Form Reservoirs							
Install Facilities							
Coordinate Activities							
Establish Goals/Objectives							
Set Budgets							
Conceive Projects							
Design Projects							
Specify Requirements							
Estimate Costs							
Monitor Expenditures							
Align Corridors (Road/Hwy/RR)							
Prepare Plans							
Manage Water							
Manage Power							
Protect Environment							
SUPPORT RECREATION							

THIRD PHASE
(1) INDIVIDUALS EXPRESSED AS JOB TITLES ARE LISTED ON "Y" AXIS
(2) ACTIVITIES (TASKS) TO SATISFY SECOND PHASE FUNCTIONS ARE DEFINED AS FUNCTIONS ON THE "X" AXIS
(3) INSERT SYMBOL AT AXES INTERSECTION THAT BEST SHOWS PERFORMANCE RESPONSIBILITY (PERFORMANCE STANDARDS FOR PHASE 3 VARY FROM PHASES 1 AND 2)

NOTE:
REVIEW SECTION 3 OF Highest and best use of people FOR EXAMPLE RESPONSIBILITY DESCRIPTIONS AND PERFORMANCE STANDARDS. SHOW PERFORMANCE STANDARDS AS FOOTNOTES FOR ACTUAL STUDIES.. ALL MATERIALS FROM FAST DIAGRAM TO LRC CHARTS ARE EXAMPLES ONLY.

	FOUND. & MATERIALS. BR.	SOILS SECTION	Chief, GS-13	Civil Engineer, GS-12	Civil Engineer, GS-11	Civil Engineer, GS-11	Civil Engr, Tech., GS-9	Technician, GS-7	Technician, GS-5
Quantify Conditions (Subsurface)									
Expose Subsurface									
Open Access									
Sample Materials									
Classify Materials									
Characterize Materials									
Consult Geologists									
Stabilize Slopes									
Support Loads									
Measure Movement									
Measure Force									
Quantify Seepage									
Plan Explorations									
Interpret Findings									

Figure 2.

needless, overworked and other faults are exposed. Duties of a specific unit or person are summarized.

3.5 Summation

When creating or modifying an organization do not dump existing elements into a stew and hope the result tastes good. Start with a clean sheet of paper, clear missions, goals and objectives. Convert those to functions and arrange them into a FAST diagram. Fill out adding only units and individuals with skills that satisfy functions. Keep the organization lean.

Practice makes perfect. The VELRC process structures diagnosis and cures for organizations. It brings simplicity, objectivity and discipline to the process.

System-based Vision for Strategic and Creative Design, Bontempi (ed.)
© *2003 Swets & Zeitlinger, Lisse, ISBN 90 5809 599 1*

Barriers to constructability in Saudi Arabian construction industry

S. Assaf, O. Jannadi & F. Al-Yousif
King Fahd University of Petroleum & Minerals, Dhahran, Saudi Arabia

ABSTRACT: This paper discusses the barriers to constructability in Saudi Arabian construction industry. A survey of 92 General Contractors, was conducted through a structured questionnaire to rate and discuss constructability barriers. The participants were asked to check all the activities that their organization may perform during the conceptual, design, and construction phases. The research inference was derived from the participants' opinions about constructability related issues such as: inserting construction knowledge into the design phase, frequency of some constructability barriers, type of projects require constructability practice, and difficulties due to using traditional method (design without construction knowledge input). Also, all participants were asked if constructability should be included as another specialty during design phase. The data collected was analyzed descriptively and results were tabulated. As a result of this research, a good level of constructability awareness among the General Contractors in the Saudi Arabian Eastern Province was recognized but there is still a lot to be done due to constructability barriers existence.

1 INTRODUCTION

Today's construction industry is characterized by the huge volumes of knowledge and the different specialized disciplinary inputs. This is a logical outcome to the natural tremendous growth that is needed to satisfy the humanity needs and improvement. Studying today's construction industry, one will be exposed to many disciplines such as: design/engineering, planning, procurement, operation/maintenance, project management, and field construction. Every discipline became a standalone science that has its regulations, standards, codes, methods, techniques, equipment, and talents. ... etc. This made it difficult to a single professional to gain the overall knowledge, and this is why the story of the so-called "master builder professional" that used to manage all the required talents started to diminish. This good thing, which is improvement and growth, created a problem that should be solved. Difficulties started to appear with the increasing gap between these different disciplines. At this stage CONSTRUCTABILITY came to the picture bridging the gap between construction disciplines.

Involving construction experts who have enough experience at the very beginning of a project maximizes benefits. "It has been shown that the integration of construction knowledge during the planning, design and procurement phases of a project bring extraordinary benefits into the delivery of the project. This is due to the fact that these are the phases in which one is able to influence the overall project the most." (Lores 1997). Lores is highlighting the importance of the participation of owners, consultants, suppliers, designers, and builders (immediate users of the designers product) in exchanging knowledge during the pre-construction stage to develop the best design solution. The main purpose of this paper is to identify the barriers to constructability practices in the Saudi Arabian Eastern Province construction industry.

2 RESEARCH METHODOLOGY

The questionnaire used in this research was developed by Lores (1997) some modification in order to suit the region and to be more effective (Al-Yousif 2001). The questionnaire was distributed to 92 General Contractors. The questionnaire included three parts:

2.1 *First part*

To obtain information about the organization and its characteristics, this is because it was expected that the organization characteristics might influence the answers to the rest of the questionnaire.

2.2 *Second part*

To obtain information about the organization's activities during the conceptual, design and construction phases of the project and the implementation of the constructability program.

2.3 *Third part*

To obtain the opinions on the following issues:

Inserting construction knowledge into pre-construction phase, rating a list of constructability barriers, type of projects with which constructability should be implemented, difficulties encountered using the traditional method (design without construction knowledge input), effectiveness of construction contractors participation during the design phase and constructability as a new specialty during the design phase.

Descriptive analysis was used to analyze the collected data. Yes/No frequencies were counted and proportions were calculated, then results were presented in tables and graphs for all questions in the survey.

3 DISCUSSION AND ANALYSIS

Out of the 92 Questionnaires sent, 37 (40%) responded. 6 of these did not fit under the General Contractors category and therefore they were excluded. The remaining 31 responded General Contractors were entered to the database.

As per the response, the majority of the participating organizations was of the Saudi nationality (about 87%) and had up to SR. 100 millions annual project volume. The majority of them worked in General Building Construction projects (77%) and Industrial projects (55%) under the Construction Management and Design-Build method of contract. Many of them performed work in both private and public sectors.

Regarding Constructability awareness, (84%) of the participants was familiar of the term. This indicates that constructability is very common in this part of Saudi Arabia among the General Contractors. An expected reason for this high percentage could possibly be the result of Saudi Aramco's existence in the province that stipulates the need for constructability for all General Contractors as a key requirement for qualification. (77%) of the General Contractors were commonly practicing constructability during the pre-construction phase of projects and only (3%) of them never practiced constructability during this phase. The General Contractors who thought that constructability should be implemented in all projects were (71%), while (26%) thought that it should be implemented in large projects and (16%) in complex projects (Table-1).

Using the traditional method of construction contracting, (90%) of the General Contractors were facing specification problems. Also, unrealistic schedules, physical interference and tolerance were common

Table 1. Respondents' opinions about constructability related issues.

Opinion of respondents	% frequency (n = 31)
Have you heard of the term constructability before?	
Yes	84%
No	16%
How often do you participate by inserting construction knowledge during the pre-construction phase of projects?	
Commonly	77%
Seldom	20%
Never	3%
Where do you think constructability should be implemented?	
All projects	71%
Large projects	26%
Complex projects	16%
Certain type of projects	10%
Small projects	3%
Using the traditional method (design without construction input), have you encountered any of the following difficulties?	
Specification problems	90%
Unrealistic schedule	77%
Problems with physical interference	70%
Tolerance problems	53%
Weather related problems that could be avoided during design phase	30%
Do you agree that the participation of construction contractors during the design of a project can help to produce better drawings, specification, and buildable project?	
Yes	90%
Sometimes	10%
No	0%
Do you think constructability should be included as another specialty during the design phase of the project such as: architectural, mechanical, and electrical ... etc?	
Yes	74%
No	13%
Sometimes	13%

difficulties encountered by some of the General Contractors. As agreed by the majority, the participation of the construction expertise during the design phase could produce better specification and drawings. (74%) of the General Contractors agreed that constructability should be included as another specialty (Table-1). This research classified constructability barriers that the General Contractors face as per their selected ratings: Always: equals to "Yes", sometimes:

Table 2. Rating the constructability barriers.

Barrier description	% frequency (n = 31)		
	Yes	Some times	No
Design without construction input is the traditional form of contracting	33	44	23
Owners do not care about constructability in the contracting strategy	29	52	19
Owners do not choose constructability in their projects	29	55	16
The concept is unknown by the owners	19	71	10
Reluctance of field personnel to offer pre-construction advise	13	64	23
The concept is unknown by the contractors	13	52	35
The concept is unknown by the designer	10	60	30
Designers' lack of construction experience, construction technologies	10	77	13
There are no proven benefits of constructability	3	30	67

Table 3. How general contractors implement the constructability concept.

Phase	Activities performed	% frequency (n = 31)
Conceptual phase	Preparation of schedule, estimates and budget	81
	Selection of major construction methods and materials	71
	Advise owners on the contracting strategy	58
	Suggest structural system	55
	Advise owners on establishment of project goals and objectives	52
	Execution of feasibility studies and advise in the selection of the site	39
	No participation	10
Design-procurement phase	Preparation of schedule, estimates and budget	77
	Analysis/revision of specifications to allow easy construction	68
	Advise design team about material and engineering equipment sources	65
	Insert into design the concern of accessibility of personnel, materials, and equipment	58
	Analysis of the design to enable efficient construction	52
	Promote designs that facilitate construction under adverse weather conditions	29
	No participation	10
Construction phase	Careful analysis of layout, access, and temporary facilities to improve productivity	97
	Planning field tasks sequence to improve productivity	90
	Capture and transfer of lessons-learned to future projects	81
	Use of pre-assembly or pre-fabrication for work execution	77
	Innovative use of construction equipment and tools	68
	Innovative use of materials	58
	No participation	3
Constructability program	Organization management support constructability	81
	Assignment of constructability coordinator in the organization level and in the project level	68
	Tracking of constructability is included in the contract document	58
	There is an organizational policy statement toward the implementation of constructability	55
	All of the above (organized formal constructability program)	6
	None of the above	5

means that the barrier exist but not in all cases, never: equals to "No".

The most significant barriers encountered were:
Design without construction inputs is the traditional form of contracting, owners do not care about constructability in the contracting strategy, owners do not choose constructability in their projects.

The least selected barrier was:
There are no proven benefits of constructability, *this means that General Contractors are very well aware*

of the benefits of constructability. Regarding the implementation of the constructability concept:

During the conceptual phase:
The most common activities by the General Contractors were the preparation of the schedule, estimates and budget, the selection of the major construction method, and advising the owner of the contracting strategy. Execution of feasibility studies and advice of the selection of the site were the least common activities to be performed by the General Contractors during the conceptual phase and the reason for this is that owners in most cases choose to make the feasibility study with other specialized consultants.

During the design procurement phase:
The most common activities by the General Contractors were preparation of the schedule, estimates and budget, analysis/revision of specification to allow easy construction and advising the design team about sources of materials and engineering equipment.

Above-mentioned activities during the conceptual and the design/procurement phases were very much expected from the General Contractors because they have the experience and the information to perform these services. Also, it is very common that a General Contractor reviews specification and drawings before starting the construction phase.

During the construction phase:
The most common activities by the General Contractors were careful analysis of the layout, access and temporary facilities to improve productivity, and capture and transfer lessons learned to future projects. This indicates that General Contractors are practicing constructability in the construction phase.

Regarding constructability programs, (81%) of the participants responded that their managements are supporting constructability, (68%) responded that they assigned a constructability coordinator in the organization level and in the project level, (58%) responded that constructability is included in the contract document, (55%) responded saying there is an organizational statement towards the implementation of constructability, and only (5%) of the respondents did not take any action to implement a constructability program. This proves that constructability programs are most commonly implemented by the General Contractors. An expected reason for this high percentage of constructability programs implementation in this region is, as stated earlier, the stipulation of Saudi Aramco for constructability in construction projects.

4   CONCLUSIONS

As a result of this research, it is recognized that constructability is known as a term, concept, application,

and to a lesser degree as a formal program. Constructability barriers exist in the Saudi Arabian construction industry.

- General Contractors in common were having the same opinion about the barriers to constructability, irrespective to their work volume, type of work, or type of contracts.
- The most significant barriers to constructability highlighted by the General Contractors were as follows:
  - Design without construction inputs in the traditional form of contracting
  - Owners do not care about constructability in the contracting strategy
  - Owners do not choose constructability in their projects
- The least selected barrier to constructability as per the survey among the General Contractors was as follows:
  - There are no proven benefits of constructability
- Other constructability barriers exist as proven by this study, but as believed by the General Contractors that they occur but not always. They are as follows:
  - Designers' lack of construction experience and knowledge of construction technology
  - Reluctance of field personnel to offer pre-construction advise.

ACKNOWLEDGEMENT

The authors appreciate the support of King Fahd University of Petroleum & Minerals during the course of the study

REFERENCES

Al-Yousif, Fawzi, 2001. *Assessment of Constructability Practices Among General Contractors*, M.S. Thesis King Fahd University of Petroleum & Minerals, Dhahran, Saudi Arabia.

ASCE Committee on Construction Management. Constructability and Constructability Programs: White Paper, *J. Construction Engineering and Management*, 199, 117(1): 67–89.

Construction Industry Institute, Constructability: a Primer, Publ. 3–1, University of Texas at Austin, Austin, TX., 1986.

Kartam, N.A., Making Effective use of Construction Lessons Learned in Projects Life Cycle. *J. Construction Engineering and Management*, Vol. 122, No. 1, March 1996: 14–21.

Kish, L. *Survey Sampling*. John Wiley and Sons Inc., New York, 1995.

Lores, G.V. 1997. *Assessment of Constructability Practices among General Contractors in the South East of the United States*. Thesis, University of Florida, Gainesville, FL.

O'Connor, J.T. & Miller, S.J. 1994. Barriers to Constructability Implementation. *Journal Performance of Constructed Facilities*, Vol. 8, No. 2.

O'Connor, J.T. & Miller, S.J. 1995. Overcoming Barriers to Successful Constructability Implementation Efforts, *J. Construction Engineering and Management*, Vol. 9, No. 2, May.

Paulson B. 1976. Designing to Reduce Construction Cost, *Journal of the Construction Division*, ASCE. Proceedings of the American Society of Civil Engineers, Vol.102, Dec: 587–594.

Russell, J.S. & Gugel, J.G. 1993. Comparison of Two Corporate Constructability Programs, *Journal of Construction of Engineering and Management*, Vol.119. No. 4, Dec.

Ethics of surveyors – a study of Hong Kong SAR

R.F. Fellows & A.M.M. Liu
Department of Real Estate and Construction, The University of Hong Kong, Hong Kong SAR, China

ABSTRACT: This paper investigates ethics amongst surveyors in Hong Kong – in particular, impacts of major situational variables on perceptions of ethics and ethical behaviour. Objectives of the study are to investigate: dominant ethical climate and culture types amongst organizations in Hong Kong which employ surveyors; any relationships between ethical climate and culture types; any effects of the existence of ethical codes. Hong Kong constitutes a unique environment of an overlay of UK-based behaviour and culture on a widespread base of Chinese culture. The empirical work was of survey design and comprised a questionnaire which was devised by adaptation of existing instruments. The data were analysed using principal component factor analysis, correlation and ANOVA. The results yielded a number of factors for each of ethical climate and ethical culture. The strength of factors present differed between organizations with a large number of respondents indicating uncertainty of the presence of ethical codes.

1 INTRODUCTION

The Oxford English Dictionary provides a variety of definitions of "ethics", all of which relate to morals (e.g. "the whole field of moral science."). Perhaps the definition which is most pertinent to this paper is, "The moral principles or system of a particular leader or school of thought; the moral principles by which any particular person is guided; the rules of conduct recognized in a particular profession or area of human life".

Rosenthal & Rosnow (1991: 231) note, " … ethics *refers* to the system of moral values by which the rights and wrongs of behavior … are judged" [word in italics added]. Not only should ethics refer to values but, in order to secure operation, reference must be made to principles and standards regarding behaviour.

Hinman (1997) distinguishes morals and ethics by regarding morals as first order beliefs, and practices about what is good and what is bad which guide behaviour and ethics as second order, reflective consideration of moral beliefs and practices.

Such issues of definition and perspective, both theoretical and operational, have generated four primary paradigms for ethical analysis (Leary 1991: 261–262). In deontology, a universal moral code is held to apply. In skepticism, (alternatively, relativism; subjectivism) ethical rules are arbitrary and relative to culture and to time; that view is extended in ethical egotism where ethics become a matter of the conscience of the individual such that the individual is the arbiter of ethics

(what is right and what is wrong). Thus, egotism concerns pursuit of self-interest and so, can be related to common business criteria (notably, profit maximisation). Teleology constitutes a utilitarian approach (utilitarianism; consequentialism) where ethics are dependent upon the (anticipated) consequences – that suggests a cost–benefit view, perhaps invoking the judgmental criterion of "the greatest good for the greatest number" which, itself, is likely to necessitate subjectively determined weightings. Objectivism asserts that there are definitions of what is right and what is wrong which are accepted generally (either universally or more locally).

Perspectives on ethics are, to some degree, at least, culturally dependent. Chinese perspectives on ethics are influenced by the notions of Confucius, who built on earlier Daoist concepts. Here, the emphasis is different from Western ethical/moral ideas of what **is** good (and bad) by focusing on **how to become** good. In one sense, *dao* may be used to signify the proper way of life. *De* is a concept similar to the Aristotlean concept of virtue but incorporates kindness and self-sacrifice and emphasizes how to achieve virtue. *Jen* concerns love, benevolence and humanism and is actioned as proper motivation; thus, *jen* has an inward focus to guide behaviour. The external-focus equivalent of *jen* is *i* and is a result of socialization. Hence, an example of *jen* is to love one's parents, an example of *i* is to pay respect to an older person. A well known result of the adoption of Confucian ethics is the hierarchy of respectful (harmonious) relationships: sovereign – subject, father – son, husband – wife, brothers, friends (the male emphasis is clearly evident!).

2 DILEMMAS

Ethical dilemmas arise for a number of major reasons. First, there is no universal theory (set) of ethics. Second, as theories of ethics differ, an individual often is obliged to select actions from mutually exclusive alternatives and has conflicting theoretical guidance. Third, although it is apparent that, at the primary (basic) level, a set of universal "goods" exist, at the secondary (culturally-shaped definitions and codes of conduct) and tertiary (specific codes of behaviour) levels, notable differences apply. Thus, dilemmas arise due to differences in ethical manifestations which are culturally dependent.

Consistency is a significant ethical consideration such that views and behaviour should be applied across people and time. This is, of course, problematic as situations and individuals are rarely identical to previous occurrences – so the questions become ones concerning degrees of difference – issues of judgement. A further complication arises as environments and human views evolve, including attempts to "rectify past errors". Consistency has a cultural dimension too which is manifest particularly in Trompenaars & Hampden-Turner's (1997) dimension of particularism – universalism.

Much of ethics is concerned with means – the behavioural considerations of what to do and how to do it. However, there are ends dimensions also. What is known, when and by whom as well as considerations of the anticipated consequences of alternative bahaviour merit examination. Especially where environmental inputs are involved – natural resources such as ground, seed, water, sunlight – the decision involves not only the labour power expended by the individual but issues of ownership (forms) of the non-labour resources.

In the context of professionals, where a profession may be regarded as a body of unique, expert knowledge, Bayles (1988) identifies professional ethics as a system of behavioural norms. Such norms relate to the employment of the particular knowledge and so, concern the relationship between experts and "lay" persons. Generally, then, the behavioural rules seek to ensure that (unfair) advantage is not taken by the expert over the lay person due to the knowledge differential – the application of "customer protection" through (professional) self-regulation. Commonly, the issue of disclosure of interests arises – the professional must disclose any own interests in the subject matter of the relationship to the client. Then, continuity of the relationship is on the basis of "informed consent" on the part of the client.

3 ETHICS AND CONTRACTS

Particularly in "Western" societies, the post industrial revolution period has witnessed enormous increase in the use of contracts to govern relationships – notably in business circumstances. What has occurred is the accentuation of legally encapsulated rights, duties and remedies, seemingly at the expense of relational duties and reciprocation (in the sense of "consideration" in contract law). The growth of "legalism" is based around the cultural dimension of individualism. However, other factors appear to be important too – notably, the total amount of a good (a "desirable") and the distribution of that good: enter the ethical notion of "greed"!

In the legal(istic) context of governance/regulation, the domain of ethical rules relates to means primarily – such as in codes of conduct of professional institutions. It may be argued that a system of common law (or religious law) has a strong ethical/relational base but that may not be reliable in terms of the current state of development. In UK, for instance, the doctrine of "equity" was developed to cope with inequalities in legal practises, the "statute of interpretation" was instigated to assist legal decision makers to follow the intent of legislation (especially when confronted with conflict in the statutes etc.).

Professional Codes of Practice/Conduct are contracts entered into by members of the organization – usually, a professional institution, which form the legally – enforcable requirement for the behaviour of members. Stewart (1995: 11) notes that such codes, "do not teach morality, ethics or values: they lay down rules for conduct and, unless they are used in a positive manner as a basis for teaching principles, they will in daily practice be no more than guidelines for action". Thus, the issue of enforcement is important. Enforcement concerns not only checks and detection of transgressors but imposition of consequences upon such transgressors. If detection is unlikely, consequences are inadequately negative (from transgressors' perspectives) or both, then transgression is far more probable in an opportunistic environment.

Principles have been developed by which appropriateness of behaviour is judged. One of the best-known of such principles is used in UK to determine the required *reasonableness* of behavior of a person in "everyday" situations – that refers to the behaviour expected of the "man on the top (deck) of the Clapham omnibus". However, in special circumstances, other tests are used to determine what behaviour is appropriate to fulfill the requirement of reasonableness. For professionals/experts (and those "holding themselves out" to have special skills), the behaviour required is that of an ordinary practitioner – *Bolam v Friern Barnet Hospital (1957)*; other situations give rise to higher levels of skill being required (to avoid liability for – professional – negligence).

4 PERSONAL SHIELDING

Leisinger (1995: 184) quotes Lay (1993: 9) in that, " … the morals we have do not regulate how institutions should treat people, only how people should treat people". In addition, ethical problems may occur incrementally – through individual steps of negligible ethical detriment but accumulating to an ethical problem. Thus, although it may be easy and tempting to dismiss a marginally unethical (or immoral) action as being insignificant, at least, in its own consequences, that is a dangerous perspective due not only to accumulation but also to its possible impact on the person's perspective on what is of ethical significance in the future – a possible progressive change or erosion of ethical standards.

Langlois & Schlegelmilch (1990) found that many large companies in Europe had documented codes of ethics. However, they also found that the codes addressed only parts of business ethics, usually concerning personnel and reliability matters and that, although national differences exist, large companies tend to employ standardized codes.

5 ORGANIZATIONAL ETHICS

Cohen (1993) defines ethical climate as employees' prevailing perceptions of organizational signals regarding norms in making decisions which have a moral component.

Treviño (1986) developed a model of organizational ethical culture including the organization's normative structure (norms of appropriate behaviour), referent to others' behaviour and expectations concerning obedience to legitimate authority – which encourage people to take responsibility for the consequences of their decisions and actions.

Hartman (1996), for example, notes that organizational culture may be employed by management as a tool to change behaviour, implement decisions etc. – often through the application of incentives, rewards and punishment systems. Others regard culture as a situational "given" within which managers and others must operate. (Irrespective, the question arises of the ethics of any attempt to change the behaviour of others.)

Normally, ethical codes occur as sets of written rules, procedures or/and components of mission statements. They are regarded as a formal basis for self-regulation by employees and/or members of a profession. De George (1995) contends that ethical codes are helpful in resoling specific issues faced by persons. Weller (1988) argues that ethical beliefs and behaviour can be improved by the existence and enforcement of corporate policies. Reeck (1982) notes that ethical codes provide guidance for professionals in their determining appropriate action – they aid consistency and stability in deciding about moral issues. However, Henry (1995)

cautions that ethical codes do not, themselves, solve moral dilemmas but do help to raise levels of awareness and so encourage ethical practise.

Thus, Etheridge (1996) raises the imperative for effectiveness of ethical codes of implementation via appropriate promulgation and training for the changing of attitudes and behaviour. In a study of ethics in businesses in Hong Kong, Etheridge (1996) found that the existence of ethical codes assisted managers in recognizing moral parameters.

6 MODEL

In developing a model, a systems approach was adopted. The goals, behaviour, performance, outcome (GBPO) cycle was employed as the basic cognitive logic for the model (Vroom 1964; Naylor Pritchard & Ilgen 1980; Liu & Walker 1998). The individual, local and cosmopolitan levels of ethical influence (Victor & Cullen, 1988) were employed. That perspective facilitates examination of impacts between levels (Waters 1978; Clinard 1983), important in organizational investigations, as well as considering internal–external orientation.

7 TESTING

7.1 Data collection

The population is 5124 members of the Hong Kong Institute of Surveyors (HKIS). The usable sample comprises five Government departments, seven surveying consultancies, four development companies and four contractors. Responses were obtained from 130 surveyors, 36 of whom are corporate members of HKIS.

The ethical climate questionnaire (ECQ) developed by Victor & Cullen (1987, 1988) formed the basic instrument for researching ethical climate. Investigation of ethical culture followed the work of Treviño, Butterfield & McCabe (1998). In both sections, questions from Liu (1999) were incorporated to reflect the GBPO model adopted. The resultant questionnaires were then edited to yield a concise instrument. Following a few demographic questions, 24 questions concerned ethical climate types, 7 concern ethical culture and 6 concern ethical codes. For those 37 questions, the 6-point Likert scale used semantic indicators from "completely false" to "completely true" to reflect a respondent's perception of the applicability of each statement in their organization.

7.2 Data analysis

The data were analysed using the Statistical Package for the Social Sciences (SPSS) 10.0; the methods of factor analysis, correlation analysis and one-way analysis of variance (ANOVA) were employed. A principal components factor analysis was carried out using the full data set to examine the variables regarding ethical climate and culture. Variables from the questionnaire which loaded on a factor at 0.4 or above were assigned to that factor. Factors with eigenvalues greater than 1 were retained. Varimax rotation was carried out to aid interpretation and Cronbach's alpha was calculated to test reliability. Correlation analysis, using Pearson's product moment, was performed on the factors to investigate any relationships between them. ANOVA was conducted to examine consistency of respondents' opinions across employer types, public/private sectors and with/without ethical codes; the 5% significance level was used.

8 RESULTS

From the factor analysis, the loadings of variables yielded eight factors relating to ethical climate:

1 – "caring for people in the organization"
2 – "organizational efficiency"
3 – "personal morality"
4 – "laws and professional codes"
5 – "friendly atmosphere"
6 – "protection of interests"
7 – "self centrism"
8 – "organizational rules and procedures".

Two factors were found in respect of organizational culture:

9 – "ethical management"
10 – "obedience to authority".

For ethical codes, the following two factors were found:

11 – "code implementation"
12 – "code effectiveness".

Mean scores for each attribute at employed for analysis and the results are shown in Tables 1 to 3.

As noted by Victor & Cullen (1987), it is common for a few ethical climate types to co-exist within a single organization.

For contractors, the dominant climate is "personal morality" whilst, for all other types of organization (and generally for the sample), the dominant climate is "laws and professional codes" (a fairly close second for contractors). That confirms the impact of professional codes of conduct and the legal system on the behaviour and standards of professional surveyors irrespective of their working context however, for those in contracting organizations, that business context and operation promotes a higher level of independence for the individual surveyors, reflected in the importance

Table 1. Factor Correlation Matrix – Total Sample.

	1	2	3	4	5	6	7	8	9	10
1				#	#	#			#	
2			@			#				
3		@			@			#		
4	#				#	@	#		#	
5	#		@				@		#	
6	#	#		@					@	
7				#	#				#	
8			#							#
9	#			#	#	@	#			
10							#			

Key (all tables): @ significant at 5%
significant at 1%
@ or # negative correlation

Table 2. Correlation Matrix – With Code Sub-sample.

	1	2	3	4	5	6	7	8	9	10	11	12
1				@	@			#				#
2			@		#							
3		@					#					
4					#		@		#		#	#
5	@			#			#		#		#	#
6	@	@										
7				@	#						#	#
8			#						#	#		
9	#			#	#						@	#
10							#					@
11				#	#		#	#	@			#
12	#			#	#		#		#	@	#	

Table 3. Correlation Matrix – Without Code Sub-sample.

	1	2	3	4	5	6	7	8	9	10
1			#	#	#		#		#	
2				@		#				
3	#									
4	#	@				@	@		#	
5	#								@	
6		#		@					#	@
7	@			@					#	
8										
9	#			#	@	#	#			
10						@				

of the personal morality climate. The least likely climate is "self centrism"; for developers, the least likely climate is "organizational rules and procedures" – perhaps due to the necessary dynamism of such organizations; that climate type is also joint least likely for contractors. That reflects the fairly low level of individualism (Hong Kong culture tends towards collectivism) and that surveying requires a high level of interaction and liason to be effective. The findings support the view of Meyer & Rowan (1977) that organizations develop structures and systems which reflect the norms of the society/profession.

Amongst contractors, the personal morality climate is significantly more common than amongst developers and the public sector. The importance of personal morality amongst contractors reflects that surveyors in contractors have a high level of discretion in their work – results are important rather than "public visibility" – but in public sector organizations it is important to follow detailed procedures and to be seen to be doing so. Amongst developers, due to the financial stakes, major decisions tend to be the province of top management and discretion of more junior personnel is limited.

Public sector organizations exhibit significantly greater emphasis on rules and procedures than do contractors. Given that the activities of surveyors in the public sector are quite difficult to monitor, the importance of rules and procedures increases.

For those organizations believed to have an ethical code, its implementation is significantly more common in the public sector than amongst developers. The significant difference in code effectiveness is for the public sector over contractors.

Comparing the ethical climate and culture factors amongst public and private sectors, the significant differences are:

1. Private sector is stronger on personal morality – the surveyors in the private sector have more decision freedom.
2. The public sector emphasizes organizational rules and procedures, laws and professional codes – due to requirements for "visibility"/public accountability.
3. The public sector enjoys a more friendly atmosphere – promoted through a less competitive context and (consequently) more personal support in job execution.

Comparing the ethical climate and culture factors amongst respondents who perceived their organization to have and not to have an ethical code, significant differences are that with code organizations emphasise:

1. Caring for people in the organization.
2. Laws and professional codes.
3. Friendly atmosphere.
4. Protection of interests.
5. Ethical management.

9 CONCLUSIONS

The factor analysis identified eight factors regarding ethical climate and four factors regarding ethical culture, two of which concern ethical codes. The study confirms that it is rather difficult to distinguish ethical climate and culture but such differentiation may be useful as categorizing variables between climate as the ideational level (values and beliefs) and culture as the phenomenal level (observable behaviour).

The climate types, "caring for people in the organization", "laws and professional codes", and "friendly atmosphere" are strongly associated with each other. Despite the finding of Kohlberg (1981) that "caring", and "rules and procedures" climates are not compatible, the instant result is explained by the laws and professional codes being exogenous to the organizations employing the respondents and so are part of the environment to foster ethical behaviour. As such, their emphasis is on caring for others which is the crux of the other two climates.

In agreement with Victor & Cullen (1987), the "personal morality" climate is found to be incompatible with the "organizational rules and procedures" climate – the former stresses the individual level of decision making whilst the latter concerns accountability and tends to reduce organizational flexibility.

Ethical culture factors tend to be associated quite closely with several climate factors. "Ethical management" is strongly related to "caring for people in the organization", "laws and professional codes", "friendly atmosphere" and "protection of interests"; that association can be regarded as human orientation. The negative relationship of "ethical management" and "self centrism" reinforces the observation. The "obedience to authority" factor is, however, relatively independent of the others.

The diversity of responses from people in the same organizations over the existence (and operation) of an ethical code indicates identification and communication problems. The strong relationship between "code implementation" and the climates of "laws and professional codes", "friendly atmosphere", and "ethical management" indicates that such climates aid the implementation of ethical codes. However, "self centrism" and "obedience to authority" climates impair the implementation and effectiveness of ethical codes.

The strong negative relationship between "personal morality" and "organizational rules and procedures" in organizations which do have an ethical code suggests that extensive formalisation and implementation of the code detracts from individuals morality through inflexibility and being a substitute for personal moral decision making.

Organizations have more than one ethical climate type – their presence concerns degree rather than absolute existence/absence. The dominant climate type perceived by surveyors in Hong Kong is "laws and professional codes"; "self centrism" is least likely. Public sector organizations emphasise rule oriented environments, including ethical codes. Private sector organizations have stronger climates of personal morality. That reflects the accountability requirement in the public sector and the flexibility and speed of response through empowerment of personnel to take decisions in the private sector.

Ethical codes are implemented more effectively in the public sector; their existence is less clear in the private sector where their existence, in some instances, may be for image purposes. Organizations which do have ethical codes place emphasis on human aspects of their activities. To be effective, awareness of the code and effective communication are essential.

REFERENCES

Henry, C. 1995. Introduction to professional ethics for health care professionals, In Henry, C., Jane, P. (Eds.), *Professional Ethics and Organizational Change in Education and Health*, London: Edward Arnold, 13.

Bayles, M.D. 1988. The professional – client relationship, In Callahan, J.C. (Ed.), *Ethical Issues in Professional Life*, Oxford: Oxford University Press, 113–119.

Bolam v Friern Barnet Hospital, 1957. 1 W.L.R. 582.

Clinard, M.B. 1983. *Corporate Ethics and Crime*, Beverley Hills: Sage.

Cohen, D. 1993. Creating and maintaining ethical work climates: Anomie in the workplace and implications for managing change, *Business Ethics Quarterly*, 3 (4), 343–358.

De George, R.T. 1995. *Business Ethics (4th edn.)*, Englewood Cliffs, N.J.: Prentice Hall.

Etheridge, J.M. 1996. *The Influence of Corporate Codes of Ethical Conduct on Ethical Standards in Hong Kong Companies*, Hong Kong: Business Research Centre, School of Business, Hong Kong Baptist University.

Hartman, E. 1996. *Organizational Ethics and the Good Life*, New York: Oxford University Press.

Hinman, L.M. 1997. *Ethics: A Pluralistic Approach to Moral Theory*, Orlando: Harcourt Brace Jovanovich.

Kohlberg, L. 1981. *Essays on Moral Development. Volume 1: The Philosophy of Moral Development*, San Francisco: Harper and Row.

Langlios, C.C., Schlegelmilch, B.B. 1990. Do corporate codes of ethics reflect national character? Evidence from Europe and the United States, *Journal of International Business Studies*, 4, 519–539.

Lay, R. 1993. Dis Macht der Moral, *Unternehmenserfolg durch ethisches Management [Success in Business through Ethical Management]*, Düsseldorf: Econ Taschenbuch Verlag.

Leary, M.R. 1991. *Introduction to behavioral research methods*, Belmont, Calif.: Wadworth.

Leisinger, K.M. 1995. Corporate Ethics and International Business: some basic issues, In Stewart, S., Donleavy, G. (Eds.), *Whose Business Values*, Hong Kong: Hong Kong University Press, 165–202.

Liu, A.M.M. 1999. Culture in the Hong Kong real estate profession: a trait approach, *Habitat International*, 23 (3), 413–425.

Liu, A.M.M., Walker, A. 1998. Evaluation of project outcomes, *Construction Management and Economics*, 16, 209–219.

Meyer, J.W., Rowan, B. 1977. Formal structure of organizations as myth and ceremony, *American Journal of Sociology*, 83, 340–363.

Naylor, J., Pritchard, R.D., Ilgen, D.R. 1980. *A Theory of Behavior in Organizations*, New York: Academic Press.

Oxford English Dictionary

Reeck, D. 1982. *Ethics for Professions: A Christian Perspective*, Minneapolis: Augsbury Publishing.

Rosenthal, R., Rosnow, R.L. 1991. *Essentials of Behavioral Research: methods and data anlaysis (2nd edn.)*, Boston, Mass.: McGraw-Hill.

Stewart, S. 1995. The ethics of values and the value of ethics: should we be studying business values in Hong Kong?, In Stewart, S., Donleavy, G. (Eds.), *Whose Business Values*, Hong Kong: Hong Kong University Press, 1–18.

Treviño, L.K. 1986. Ethical decision-making in organizations: a person-situation interactionist model, *Academy of Management Review*, 11, 601–617.

Treviño, L.K., Butterfield, K.D., McCabe, D.L. 1998. The ethical context in organizations: influences on employee attitudes and behaviors, *Business Ethics Quarterly*, 8 (3), 447–476.

Trompenaars, F., Hampden-Turner, C. 1997. *Riding the waves of culture: understanding cultural diversity in business (2nd edn.)*, London: Nicholas Brealey.

Victor, B., Cullen, J.B. 1987. A theory and measure of ethical climate in organizations, In Frederick, W. C. (Ed.), *Research in Corporate Social Performance and Policy*, Greenwich CT.: JAI Press, 51–57.

Victor, B., Cullen, J.B. 1988. The organizational bases of ethical work climate, *Administrative Science Quarterly*, 33, 101–125.

Vroom, V. 1964. *Work and Motivation*, New York: Ridley.

Waters, J.A. 1978. *Climate for Creativity*, Elmsford, NY.: Pergamon.

Weller, S. 1988. The effectiveness of corporate codes of ethics, *Journal of Business Ethics*, 7, 389–395.

System-based Vision for Strategic and Creative Design, Bontempi (ed.)
© 2003 Swets & Zeitlinger, Lisse, ISBN 90 5809 599 1

Organizational culture of the Chinese construction companies: towards a C-E Model

A.M.M. Liu & S.B. Zhang
Department of Real Estate and Construction, The University of Hong Kong, Hong Kong

ABSTRACT: The vast economic growth in China in the past decade has brought about a good opportunity for the development of China's construction industry. The Chinese construction companies have become very active in the construction industry. Though the economic growth in recent years has brought about opportunities for them to develop, they are also faced with many challenges and uncertainties resulting from the fast changing economic environment. They have been criticized for their poor performance and low effectiveness in terms of quality and profitability. Given that organizational culture plays a significant role in work performance and effectiveness, this paper presents a Culture-Effectiveness Framework for investigating the organizational culture and effectiveness of Chinese construction enterprises. The culture–effectiveness (C-E) relationship has been receiving increasing attention in organizational research. However, there remain significant questions over the existence and strength of such a relationship. This paper will develop a model for investigating the C-E relationship within Chinese contracting organizations. The research concerns examination of organizational cultures of the representative contractors. Finally this paper discusses briefly the methodology for the investigation of O-E relationship within the setting of the Chinese contractors.

1 INTRODUCTION

The past decade has witnessed China's high-speed economic growth that has brought about a good opportunity for the development of China's construction industry, signified by the pervasiveness of construction sites all over China. The value of the total investment in fixed assets in 1999 amounted to 2988 billion RMB Yuan while it was only 91 billion in 1980 (National Bureau of Statistics 2000). The Chinese contractors are often accused of poor performance and low effectiveness in terms of quality, and profitability (Yao 1998, Sha & Lin 2001). How to improve the effectiveness of the Chinese construction companies remains a focus of investigation.

2 ORGANIZATIONAL CULTURE AND EFFECTIVENESS: A REVIEW

In the past twenty years, it has been more and more recognized that organizations, ostensibly similar as they are in terms of structure, have been found to differ substantially in their performance and effectiveness.

There seems to exist something that permeates organizational life, which influences every corner of the organization. Hence, the study of organizational culture stemmed from such realization by organizational scholars as well as practitioners, with a belief that once the ambiguity and unpredictability of organizations are better understood, their performance and effectiveness could be greatly improved by adopting better organizational designs (Brown 1998). As Schein (1985) puts it, "The concept of organizational culture holds promise for illuminating this difficult area" (pp. 1–2). Hofstede (1986), when discussing the concept of "culture", notes that ideas arrive when their time has come. As a matter of fact, since the early 1980s, culture studies have acquired prominent status in the management field.

The purpose of studying culture is many fold; but the principal purpose is to find out how it affects the organizational performance, with a view to improving the performance effectiveness, which is arguably one of the most important organizational-level variables. Such culture-effectiveness link studies, according to some organizational scholars (Vesson 1993, Wilderom et al. 2000), can be roughly divided into the following stages.

(1) The Budding Stage

In the field of organizational studies, the culture–effectiveness link studies actually emerged along with the emergence of the school of human relations in the first half of last century, with the *Hawthorne studies* being the pioneer, indicating implicitly how group culture affects performance. Jaques (1951 & 1965) related the customary and traditional ways of thinking and doing things to the working behaviours of employees. Although he did not directly study the effects of the commonly shared "ways of thinking and doing things", his findings indicated that culture could be serious barrier to productivity if it was not congruent with the organizational structure and environment. Pfiffner & Sherwood (1960) suggested that there might be a relationship between the culture and the effectiveness of a firm, but they did not make any further investigation of the nature of such a hypothesized link. Silverzweig & Allen (1976) were the first to intentionally and explicitly look into the effect of culture on the performance of a company. Of their eight case studies, which involved various branch organizations that suffered losses and intended to raise their effectiveness, six organizations improved their performances substantially after changing their culture. Such findings led them to suggest that there was a close link between culture and performance of a company.

(2) The Promulgation Stage

The end of 1970s marked a clear change from the implicit attention to the culture-performance/effectiveness link, with the attempt to explain the shining success of the Japanese enterprises at that time. Ouchi was one of the outstanding scholars to arouse people's attention to the importance of employees' commitment and the unitary vision for the company's success, by arguing (Ouchi & Jaeger 1978, Ouchi & Johnson 1978) that emphasis on certain humanistic values contributed to the company's economic performance. These values include employee-concern and consensual decision-making, which generally characterized the Japanese enterprises. Based on their experiences with more than 30 Japanese and American companies, Pascale & Athos (1981) put forward a similar idea that the higher productivity of Japanese firms were attributable to their emphasis on human relations, by arguing that focus on skills, style and employee goals would lead to high performance. That the strong culture made the difference between successful firms and less successful ones was claimed by Peters & Waterman (1982), who argued that superior performance was only to be achieved if the firms moved to a more adaptive and humanistic approach from pure technical and rationalistic approach. In the same year, Deal & Kennedy (1982) also put out a similar view that a strong culture was not only able to respond well to the environment, but also to the changing circumstances, thus enhancing the performance of the firms. This period was characterized with a relatively popular but supposed belief that a link existed between culture and performance, without much substantial evidence.

(3) The Testing Stage

The doubts, skepticism and even contradictory findings (Carroll 1983, Hitt & Ireland 1987) concerning the culture-performance link led to a large scale of empirical studies from the end of 1980s to present, attempting to test such theoretically disputable link, as a further step in exploring and uncovering the cultural phenomenon of organizations. The major researchers include: Barley et al. (1988), Cooke & Rousseau (1988), Dennison (1990), Rousseau (1990), Calori & Sarnin (1991), Gordon & DiTamaso (1992), Kotter & Heskett (1992), Marcoulides & Heck (1993), Petty et al. (1995), Dennison & Mishra (1995), Wilderom & Van den Berg (1998), and Sawner (2000). The findings of these researches, though different to some degree, show such a culture-effectiveness link. Relying solely on the co relational techniques, most of the studies were not able to establish a firm direction of such relationship. Despite this fact, a significant correlation may indicate a causal relationship between organizational culture and effectiveness that should be further investigated (Wilderom et al. 2000).

While culture has been gaining in popularity in the general management studies, culture studies in the construction industry seems also to have been intensified. Maloney and Federle (1991 & 1993) introduced the Competing Values Framework as their paradigm for analyzing the cultural elements in American engineering and construction organizations. Gale (1992) looks at culture as a means to reduce conflicts in construction. Seymour & Rooke (1995) present their views of the culture of the construction industry and relevant research. Rowlinson & Root (1996) offer their views of the impact of culture on project performance. Hall & Jaggar (1997) note the importance of culture difference in international construction. Liu & Fellows (1999a & 1999b) highlight the culture issues in project procurement and also explore the impact of culture on project goals. With Hong Kong real estate profession as the research context, Liu (1999) made an exploration of the relationships between cultural dimensions, strength and the real estate professionals' perceived job satisfaction.

At the present stage, culture research is still trudging through the jungle, and findings seem to be not so consistent with one another, and even contradictory, due to the complex and broad nature of the constructs of the organizational culture and effectiveness and a lack of a integrative and comprehensive framework for the research.

3 DEVELOPING OC-OE LINKAGE FRAMEWORK

3.1 Introduction

Much of the research on organizational culture has emphasized the central importance of the values and beliefs that lie at the core of an organization's social system. However, one of the key challenges in research of organizational culture and effectiveness (C-E) link relates to the establishment of a theoretical basis for explaining the assumed links (Wilderom et al. 2000). In such C-E link studies, most of the ideas about the relationship between culture and effectiveness have attributed the success of organizations to some combinations of values, beliefs and practices. Such ideas implicitly suggest a general framework that organizational effectiveness is a function of organizational culture.

Although this framework shows the link between these two organizational variables- culture and effectiveness, it offers nothing more than a very superficial one, without indicating the mechanism on how organizational culture operates on the final organizational outcome, leaving such an "organic process" ignored as a "black box". In order to substantiate the assumed link, the organizational culture operating mechanism on behaviour has to be tackled in more detail.

For studying the organizational behaviour, one of such traditional theories is the **S-O-R** (Stimulus-Organism-response) sequence (Naylor et al. 1980) which has been applied by Liu (1994 & 1995) in her modelling of the construction procurement process, resulting in her version of **B-P-O** (behaviour-performance-outcome) Cycle with project goals in construction research (Liu & Walker 1998).

Given the idea that organizational culture is the "software of the mind" (Hofstede 1991) that is shared by organizational members, it influences the cognition and perception of its members, guide their behaviour, integrate its internal processes to ensure the capacity to continue to survive and adapt to the environment (Parsons 1951, Schein 1985, Cooke & Rousseau 1988, Denision 1990, Denision & Mishra 1995, Cameron & Quinn 1999),. Therefore, it is argued here that organizational culture can be also taken as the "stimulus" of the behaviour in the organization.

3.2 Applying Schema Theory to Organizational Behaviour

Based on a detailed review of the social cognition literature, Markus & Zajonc (1985) conclude that schema theory is the most useful and pervasive perspective on the mechanics of social cognition. Many definitions appear in the current literature. However, the definition offered by Marshall (1995) might be the most comprehensive: "A schema is a vehicle of memory, allowing organization of an individual's similar experiences in such a way that the individual can easily recognize additional experiences that are also similar, discriminating between these and ones that dissimilar; can assess a generic framework that contains the essential elements of all these similar experiences, including verbal and nonverbal components; can draw inferences, make estimates, create goals, and develop plans using the framework; and can utilize skills, procedures, or rules as needed when faced with a problem for which this particular framework is relevant (p. 39)." As implied from the above definition, schemas serve as mental maps which enable individuals to orient themselves within their experimental terrain and guide interpretation of the past and present, and also expectation for the future (Louis 1983, Harris 1996). Summary of the seven functions is the most comprehensive, listed as below (Taylor & Crocker 1981):

- Providing a structure against which experience is mapped;
- Directing information encoding and retrieval from memory;
- Affecting information processing efficiency and speed;
- Guiding filling gaps in the information available;
- Providing templates for problem solving;
- Facilitating the evaluation of experience;
- Facilitate anticipating of the future, goal setting, planning, and goal execution.

Schemas are of a dynamic nature. As schemas incorporate more and more new information, they become expanded and more and more elaborated (Lord & Foti 1986, Bartunek & Moch 1987, Fiske & Taylar 1991, Harris 1996).

The Schema theory suggests very important implications for expanding our understanding of the role of organizational culture in guiding sense-making in organizations. According to Rumelhart (1984), knowledge about any stimulus can be schematized, and therefore individuals can have at their disposal many schemas. Harris (1996) argues that organization-context-specific schemas are most relevant to understanding organizational culture, since social knowledge is generally contextually bound. Culture scholars usually stress the human motivation from the perspective of culture. However, to assume that individuals are endowed with a fixed set of needs and that a social institution is there to satisfy them commits a fallacy of abstract individualism and yet to assume that culture is unproblematically internalized is to "oversocialize" the individual and oversimplify the process by which a person actively appropriates socially shared meaning (Kashima 1997). Strauss (1992) argues, in a broader sense, that human motivation is "*the product*

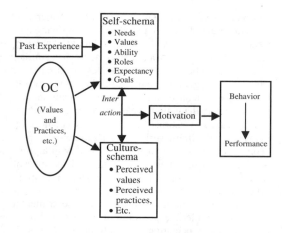

Figure 1. Organizational Culture, Schemas and Performance.

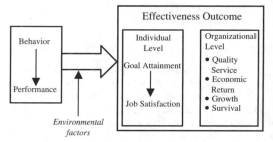

Figure 2. Performance and Effectiveness Outcome.

of interaction between events and things in the social world and interpretations of those events and things in peoples' psyches (p. 1)".

Following these points, and within an organizational setting, it is argued here that an organizational member is motivated both inherently (from "within self") and culturally (from intra-organizational cultural elements) and his behaviour in the organization is mainly governed by the interaction between the self-in-organization schema (hereinafter abbreviated "self schema") and the organizational culture schema (hereinafter abbreviated "culture schema") of that individual. To elaborate this argument, definition of each of these two concepts will be given, following which it is postulated that the interaction between self-schema and culture schema, when cued, is an information-processing and sense-making process that result in decision making for the choice of behaviour in the organization. See Figure 1.

Motivation theories suggest that people do what they do to satisfy their needs. Given all human conscious behaviours are motivated by their needs and goals (Newstorm & Davis 1993) among others, individuals tend to evaluate their performance against the level of attainment of such goals and level of satisfaction of their needs as their behavioural outcomes. Such evaluation by organizational members is a process of comparing the organizational rewards of their behaviours and performance against what was expected (goals) by them. Under the organizational settings, rewards are basically classified as two categories: extrinsic rewards and intrinsic rewards (Robbins 1996) that make employees attain their goals and satisfy their needs, as the outcome of their performance. However, the satisfaction of the employees does not solely depend on having their own goals met and their own needs satisfied. They are

also concerned about the fairness of the rewards according to the equity theory (Adams 1965, and Goodman 1974). So the level of satisfaction is also influenced by the outcome of their "horizontal" comparison with other organizational members, particularly their peers.

The above analysis focuses on individual or micro level of outcome effectiveness. However, performance of organizational members also leads to the organizational or macro level of outcome effectiveness, as the performance of the organization is, to a large extent, attributable to the aggregation of the individual performance moderated by the external environment. The organizational-level effectiveness in culture studies are multi-dimensional, usually centering on such dimensions as customer service quality, market share and economic return, external adaptation and ultimate survival. Figure 2 indicates the relationship between performance to effectiveness outcome.

3.3 Research Hypothesis

A number of hypotheses can be inferred from the above discussion of the research framework. However, with the research purpose focused on investigating the organizational culture and effectiveness relationship, the following hypothesis will be tested against the Chinese construction companies:

"The relationship between organizational culture and effectiveness is reciprocal. Organizational culture is both an asset and a liability, depending on its positive or negative impact on the organizational effectiveness."

4 PROPOSED METHODOLOGY

The research methodology comprises three stages: (1) The first stage is a pilot study, with the purpose to identify the suitable culture measuring instrument before using it for the major survey. The two instruments used in the pilot survey are OCI (Cooke & Szumal 1993) and OCAI (Cameron & Quinn 1999), which have been tested and proved to be most valid and reliable in measuring organizational culture in the western countries. Five construction companies were randomly selected from the *A Complete List of the Chinese Construction Enterprises* published by the Ministry of Construction of China. The pilot study is now completed and the results show that OCI is more suitable for measuring the organizational culture in a valid and reliable way. Details of the pilot study are not given in this paper. (2) With OCI as the culture measuring instrument and a self-developed organizational effectiveness survey instrument, a major survey will be conducted to capture the organizational culture profiles and the effectiveness of the Chinese construction companies. Cluster analysis techniques will be applied for analyzing the collected data to classify the sample companies into groups with same or similar culture profiles. Then the culture profiles will be used as a variable to explain the variance of the organizational effectiveness so that the effect of culture on organizational effectiveness can be tested. (3) As a step to test the effect of the effectiveness outcome on the organizational cultures, case studies will be also conducted. The methodology for Stage 3 is subject to further development.

5 CONCLUSION

This paper has reported a theoretical framework developed from our on-going research that concern the investigation of the culture and effectiveness of the Chinese construction companies. It also offers a hypothesis, inferred from the discussion of the research, with a final discussion of the methodology for testing the hypothesis by collecting empirical data from the Chinese construction industry. Currently, the research is still going on. Findings of the next stage research concerning the culture profiles of the Chinese construction companies and OC-OE relationship will be published hopefully in due course.

REFERENCES

Adams, J.S. 1965. "Inequity in Social Exchanges", in Berkowitz L. (ed.), *Advances in Experimental Social Psychology*, New York; Academic Press, 1965, 267–300.

Barley, S.R., Meyer, G.W. & Gash, D.C. 1988. "Cultures of Culture: Academics, Practitioners and the Pragmatics of Normative Control", *Administrative Science Quarterly*, 33, 24–60.

Bartunek, J.M. & Moch, M.K. 1987, "First-Order, Second-order, and Third-order Change and Organizational Development Interventions: A Cognitive Approach", *Journal of Applied Behavioural Science*, 23, 483–500.

Brown, A. 1998. *Organizational Culture*, Second Edition. London: Financial Times Pitman Publishing.

Calori, R. & Sarnin, R. 1991. Corporate Culture and Economic Performance: A French Study. *Organization Studies*, 12, 49–67.

Cameron, Kim S. & Quinn, Robert. E. 1999. *Diagnosing and Changing Organizational Culture-Based on the Competing Values Framework*. ADDISON-WESLEY.

Carroll, D.T. 1983. A Disappointing Search for Excellent. Harvard Business Review, 61(6), 78–88.

Cooke, R. A. & Rousseau, D. M. 1988, Behaviour Norms and Expectation, *Group & Organizational Studies*, Vol. 13, No. 3, 245–273.

D'Andrade, R.G. 1992. "Schemas and Motivation", in D'Andrade R. G. and Strauss, C. (Eds) *Human Motives and Cultural Models*, Cambridge: Cambridge University Press.

Deal, T.E. & Kennedy, A.A. 1982. *Corporate Cultures: the Rites and Rituals of Corporate Life*. Reading, MA: Addison-Wesley.

Denison, D.R. 1990. *Corporate Culture and Organizational Effectiveness*. John Wiley& Sons.

Denison, D.R. & Mishra, A.K. 1995. Toward a Theory of Organizational Culture and Effectiveness, *Organizational Science*, Vol. 6 No. 2, 204–223.

Fiske, S.T. & Taylor, S.E. 1991. *Social Cognition*, (2nd ed), Reading, MA: Addison-Wesley.

Gale, A.W. 1992. "The Construction Industry's Male Culture must feminize if conflict is to be reduced: The role of Education as A Gatekeeper to Male Construction Industry", In Fenn, P. and Gamerson, R. (eds) *Construction Conflict Management and Resolution*. London: E. & FN Spon.

Goodman, P.S. 1974. "An Examination of Referents Used in the Evaluation of Pay," *Organizational Behaviour and Human Performance*, 170–195.

Gordon, G.G. & Di Tomaso, N. 1992. Predicting Corporate Performance from Organizational Culture. *Journal of Management Studies*, 29, 783–798.

Hall, M.A. & Jaggar, D.M. 1997. "Should Construction Enterprises, Working Internationally, Take Account of Cultural Differences in Culture? In *Proceedings of the 13th ARCOM Conference*, Cambridge, 1997 pp. 1–10".

Harris, S.G. 1996. "Organizational Culture and Individual Sense-making", in Meindle J. R. Stubbart C. and Porac, J. F (Eds), *Cognition within and between Organizations*, Thousand Oaks: SAGE Publications.

Hitt, M.A. & Ireland, R.D. 1987. Peter and Waterman Revisited: the Unended Quest for Excellence. Academy of Management Executive, 1(2), 91–98.

Hofstede, G. 1986. The Usefulness of the Organization Culture Concept. Journal of Management Studies. Vol. 23, No. 3 (pp. 253–257).

Hofstede, G. 1991. *Cultures and Organizations: Software of the Mind*, London: Mcgraw-Hill.

Jaques, E. 1951. *The Changing Culture of a Factory*. London: the Tavistorck Publications.

Jaques, E. 1965. *The Changing Culture of a Factory*. London: the Tavistorck Publications.

Kashima, Y. 1997. "Culture, Narrative, and Human Motivation", In Munro, D and Schumaker, J.F. and Carr, S.C.(eds) *Motivation and Culture*, New York: Routledge.

Kotter, J.P. & Heskett, J.L. 1992. *Corporate Culture and Performance*. New York: Free Press.

Liu, A.M.M. & Fellows, R.F. 1999a. Culture Issues. In Rowlingson, S. and McDermott, P (eds.) *Procurement*

Systems: A guide to best practice in construction. London: E&N Spon.

Liu, A.M.M. 1999. Culture in the Hong Kong Real-Estate Profession: A Trait Approach, *HABITAT INTL*. Vol. 23, No. 3, pp. 413–425.

Liu, A.M.M. & Fellows, R.F. 1999b. The Impact of Culture on Project Goals. In Ogunlana (ed) *Profitable Partnering in Construction Procurement*, London: E&FN Spon.

Liu, A.M.M. & Walker, A. 1998. Evaluation of Project Outcomes. *Construction Management and Economics*, 16, 209–219.

Lord, R.G. & Foti, R.J. 1986. "Schema Theories, Information Processing, and Organization Behaviour," in Sims, H. P, and Gioia, D. A. (Eds), *The Thinking Organization: Dynamics of Organizational Social Cognition*, San Francisco: Jossey-Bass, 20–48.

Louis, M.R. 1983. "Organizations as Cultural-bearing Milieux", in Pondy, L. R., Frost P.J, Morgan G., and Dandrigdge T.C. (Eds.), *Organizational Symbolism*, Greenwich, CT: JAI, 39–54.

Maloney, William F. & Federle, Mark O. 1991. Organizational Culture and Management, *Journal of Management in Engineering Vol. 7*, No. 1.

Maloney, William F. & Federle, Mark O. 1993. Practical Models for Organizational Assessment, *Journal of Management in Engineering Vol. 9*, No. 1

Marcoulides, G.A. & Heck, R.H. 1993. Organizational Culture and Performance: Proposing and Testing a Model. *Organizational Science*, 4, 209–225.

Markus, H. & Zajonc, R.B. 1985. "The Cognitive Perspective in Social Psychology", in G. Lindzey and E. Aronson(Eds), *The Handbook of Social Psychology(3rd ed., v. 1)*, New York: Random House, 137–230.

Marshall, S.P. 1995. *Schemas in Problem Solving*, Cambridge: Cambridge University Press.

Naylor, J.C., Prichard, R.D. & Ilgen, D.R. 1980. *A Theory of Behaviour in Organizations*, New York: Academic Press.

National Bureau of Statistics, 2000. *China Statistical Yearbook*, Beijing: China Construction Industry Press.

Newstorm, J.W. & Davis, K. 1993. *Organizational Behaviour-Human Behaviour at Work*, New York: McGraw-Hill.

Ouchi, W.G. & Jaeger, A.M. 1978. Type Y Organization: Stability in the Midst of Mobility. *Academy of Management Review*, 3, 305–314.

Ouchi, W.G. & Johnson, J.B. 1978. Types of Organizational Control and Their Relationship to Emotional Well-being. *Administrative Science Quarterly*, 23, 293–317.

Parsons, T. 1951. *The Social System*, Glencoe, IL: Free Press.

Pascale, R. & Athos, A. 1981. *The Art of Japanese Management*. New York: Simon & Schuster.

Peters, T. & Wateman, R.H. 1982. *In Search of Excellence*. New York: Harper and Row.

Petty, M.M., Beadles, N.A., II, Lowery, C.M., Chapman, D.F. & Connell, D.W. 1995. Relationship between Organizational Culture and Organizational Performance. *Psychological Reports*, 76, 483–492.

Pfiffner, J.M., & Sherwood, F.P. 1960. *Administrative Organization*. Englewood Cliffs, NJ: Prentice hall.

Robbins, Stephen P. 1996. *Organizational Behaviour Seventh Edition* Prentice-Hall International, Inc.

Rousseau, D.M. 1990. Normative Belief in Fund-Raising Organizations: Linking Culture to Organizational Performance and Individual Response. *Group and Organizational Studies*, 15, 448–460.

Rowlinson, S. & Root, D. 1996. *The Impact of Culture on Project Management: A Final Report*, Unpublished working report.

Rumelhart, D.E. 1984. "Schemas and the Cognitive System," in Wyer R. S. and Srull T. K. (Eds), *Handbook of Social Cognitions* (Vol 1.), Hillsdale, NJ: Lawrence Erlbaum, 161–188.

Sawner, T.E. 2000. *An Empirical Investigation of the Relationship between Organizational Culture and Organizational Performance in a large Public Sector Organization*, Unpublished Doctoral Dissertation, The George Washington University.

Schein, E.E. 1985. *Organizational Culture and Leadership: A Dynamic View*. San Francisco: Jossey-Bass Inc., Publishers.

Seymour, D. & Rooke, J. 1995. "The Culture of the Industry and the Culture of Research", *Construction Management and Economics*, 13, pp. 511–523.

Sha, K. & Lin, S. 2001. "Reforming China's Construction State-Owned Enterprises", *Building Research and Information*, 29(4), 270–276.

Silverzweig, S. & Allen, R.F. 1976. Changing the Corporate Culture. *Sloan Management Review*, 17(3), 33–49.

Strauss, C. 1992. "Models and Motives", In D'Andrade R. G. & Strauss, C. (Eds) *Human Motives and Cultural Models*, Cambridge: Cambridge University Press.

Taylor, S.E. & Crocker, J. 1981. "Schematic Bases of Social Information Processing", in Higgins, E.T., Herman, C.P. and Zana, M.P. (Eds) *Social Cognition: The Ontario Symposium*, Vol. 1 Hillsdale, NJ: Erlbaum.

Vesson, Mats A. 1993. *Cultural Perspectives on Organizations*, Cambridge: Press Syndicate of the University of Cambridge.

Wilderom, C.P.M. & Van den Berg, P.T. 1998. A Test of the Leadership-Culture-Performance Model within a Large Dutch Financial Organization. In S. Havlovic.Ed. *Best Paper Proceedings, of the Annual Meeting of the Academy of Management*, San Diego, CA.

Wilderom, C.P.M., Glunk, U. & Maslowski, R. 2000. Organizational Culture as a predictor of Organizational Performance. In Ashkanasy N.M., Wilderon, C.P.M., and Peterson M.F. (eds.) *Handbook of Organizational Culture & Climate*, 2000, Thousand Oaks: Sage Publications, Inc.

Yao, B. 1998. *Construction Management*, Beijing: China Construction Industry Press.

Environment friendly design of residential buildings in hot-dry climate

R. Ahuja & V.M. Rao

Dept. of Arch. & Planning, I.I.T. Roorkee, India

ABSTRACT: Residential buildings especially in hot-dry climate need to be provided with natural cooling systems, if artificial systems of cooling can not be provided due to economic reasons. Parameters which influence natural cooling of such buildings can be classified as (i) surrounding environmental factors and (ii) parameters associated with the buildings. Present paper describes influence of above parameters in providing natural cooling of residential buildings in general and in hot-dry climate in particular. These effects are supported by case studies of few residential buildings.

1 INTRODUCTION

In most of the developing countries like India, more than 50% of the population, stay in rural area. Dwellings in rural areas do not have artificial systems of cooling or heating. Even more than 50% of the houses in urban area also do not enjoy these facilities. This is primarily due to poor economic conditions of the residents and secondly due to shortage of electric power to operate cooling and heating facilities. Most of the residential buildings in urban areas are provided with environment friendly designs to have the advantage of natural cooling during summer and heating during winter.

Surrounding environmental factors which influence cooling of such buildings include landform and its orientation, vegetation pattern, water bodies, street width and orientation, open spaces and built form etc. Parameters associated with the buildings include roof form and its material, thickness and type of walls, window openings – its design and positioning, shading devices, overhangs and louvers, skylight openings etc.

In the present study, detailed analysis has been carried out for understanding the influence of above parameters in providing thermal comfort to the residents in hot-dry climate. Six residential buildings in Gulbarga city of Karanataka State in India have been taken as case studies for observing passive cooling systems used in these buildings.

2 SURROUNDING ENVIRONMENTAL FACTORS

Where artificial systems of cooling is not affordable, residents in urban area of developing countries consider achieving natural cooling systems while planning and designing individual residential buildings or colony of such buildings as a whole. Surrounding environmental factors which influence cooling of such buildings include landform and its orientation, vegetation pattern, water bodies, street width and orientation, open spaces and built form etc.

2.1 Landform and its orientation

The land form or topography of a site and surroundings could either be flat, sloping or undulating. If the land is flat, similar conditions would prevail over the entire site. However, in case of undulating ground in hot-dry climates, constructing a building in a depression implies relatively lower air temperature. It is due to the fact that cool air being heavier than hot air, tends to settle down in depressions while hot air rises. Similarly while making a building on slopes, leeward side is preferable. Nevertheless, warm winds would be minimum on either slope.

Landform orientation has little meaning when the land is flat. However, the orientation of slopes would make a difference. In area of hot-dry climate, a north slope would be preferable as it would receive least direct radiation. It is true only if the slope is steep enough to shade the building.

2.2 Vegetation pattern

Vegetation and trees in particular effectively shade and reduce heat gain. They increase humidity level. They also cause pressure differences thereby increasing and decreasing air speed or directing air flow. They can, therefore, direct air into a building or deflect it away.

Plants, shrubs and trees absorb radiation in the process of photosynthesis. As a result they actually cool the environment. In hot dry climates where heat gain is to be minimized, trees can be used to cut off the east-west sun as well as hot breezes.

2.3 *Water bodies*

Water absorbs relatively large amount of radiation. They also allow evaporative cooling. As a result, during day time area around water bodies are generally cooler. At night, however, water bodies release relatively large amount of heat to the surroundings. In hot-dry climates, water bodies can be used both for evaporative cooling as well as minimizing heat gain. Taking into account wind pattern and vegetation, cool breeze can be made to enter into the house. Similarly a roof pond minimizes heat gain through the roof.

2.4 *Street width and orientation*

The amount of direct radiation received on the street (and to some extent the lower floors) is determined by the street width. The orientation affects the time of the day when the radiation is received. Modulating the street width and orientation can very effectively minimize or maximize heat gain. Street width to building height ratio also affects the daylight received.

In hot-dry climates, the prime need is to minimize heat gain. This could be achieved by cutting off the sun. Small street width to building height ratio ensures narrow streets and thereby shading. In particular, streets running north-south should be narrow. This would enable mutual shading from morning and evening sun. However, this aspect can be considered advantageously only when planning and designing new residential colonies.

2.5 *Open spaces and built form*

Open spaces have to be seen in conjunction with the built form. Together they can allow for free air movement and increased heat loss or gain. Open spaces in any complex are inevitable. The question is how should they be and how much should there be? After all, any built mass modifies the microclimate. An open area, especially a large one allows more of the natural climate of the place to prevail.

Open spaces gain heat during the day. If the ground is hard and building surfaces are dark in colour, then much of radiation is reflected and absorbed by the surrounding buildings. If however, the ground is soft and green, then less heat is reflected.

In hot-dry climates, compact planning with little or no open spaces would minimize both heat gain as well as heat loss. When the heat production of the buildings is low, compact planning minimizes heat

gain and is desirable. This is how traditional settlements often are.

3 PARAMETERS ASSOCIATED WITH THE BUILDINGS

3.1 *Building configuration*

In hot-dry climate regions, it is desirable to lower the rate of temperature rise of the interior during day time in summer. To achieve this, the building should preferably be compact. The surface area of its external envelope should be as small as possible, to minimize the heat flow into the building. The ratio of the building envelope's surface area to its volume or ratio of floor area to its volume determines the relative exposure of the building to solar radiation. The best layout is that of a patio or a courtyard surrounded by walls and thus partially isolated from the full impact of the outdoor air. This configuration is very common in hot-dry climate.

3.2 *Building orientation*

The main objective in deciding upon a given orientation in hot-dry climate regions is to minimize the impact of the sun on the building in summer. Pattern of solar radiation on different walls results in a clear preference for north-south orientation of the main facades, and especially of the windows. Such orientation enables easy and in expensive shading of the southern window in summer. The heating effect of solar radiation impinging on walls can further be minimized by choosing reflective colours of the walls.

3.3 *Other parameters*

Other parameters associated with buildings, proper planning of which can provide thermal comfort to occupants of such buildings in hot-dry climate, include roof form and its materials, thickness and type of walls, windows openings – its design and positioning, shading devices, overhangs and louvers, skylight windows etc. Due to paucity of space, influence of these parameters is not being discussed here.

4 CASE STUDIES

In order to see the practical use of above listed parameters in providing natural cooling in hot-dry climate regions, six residential buildings in Gulbarga city of Karanataka State in India have been considered. Description of each of these houses is given below. Before going into case study, a brief description of the traditional residential architecture of Gulbarga needs be given.

Figure 1. View of courtyard at first floor level of Mr. Ramchandra Patil's house.

Figure 2. Exterior view of Mr. Baswaraj Patil's house.

The most prominent characteristic of any traditional building in Gulbarga is thick external wall having small openings which reduce transfer of heat. The plan of the building is square or rectangular in shape with central courtyard. Rooms are arranged around the courtyard. All doors open towards the courtyard. Only main door is placed on the external wall. Roof is constructed with well compacted mud supported by wooden joists and planks. Material of construction is stone, mud and wood.

4.1 House of Mr. Ramachandra Patil

It is 80 years old two storied building. Plan of the building is simple, square and symmetrical about East-West axis. The building is functionally convenient. The main entrance is from the Southern side. The first entry leads to front yard. Then it goes to main building. The plan of the building is compact. All rooms are arranged around central courtyard. Doors of all the rooms are opened to the central courtyard (Fig. 1).

All external and internal walls are constructed with stone, mud and lime mortar. The external wall thickness is 2'–9' and the internal walls are 1'–6" thick. The external walls being thick, it reduces the heat inside during day time. Small openings are provided to get required ventilation and to stop solar radiation, glare and dust. Two stair cases lead to the upper floor on either side of entrance. Roof is flat in nature and constructed with compacted mud and lime mortar finish on the top. The court yard and roof top is used for sleeping at night in summer.

This house is provided with no artificial cooling system. Still occupants enjoy good thermal comfort.

4.2 House of Mr. Baswaraj Patil

It is believed that the building is around 200 years old (Fig. 2). It is a two storied building. The plan is simple but more functional. It is almost square in shape and symmetrical about North-South axis.

The main entrance is towards North. It is 6' wide and 10' in height. The main entrance leads to the verandah. There are four stair cases leading to upstairs, two in front and two in rear side. First floor is raised towards the south side. It creates shadow on the terrace in the afternoon. All the door openings leads to the central courtyard. The courtyard is measuring about 24'–24' in size. It admits the light inside the building. The building is having only one external entry. The backyard is used for general utility purpose.

External walls are 3' thick and internal walls 1'–6". Materials used for the construction of walls are stone, mud and lime mortar. The time-lag factor of external walls is more then 12 hours. So it absorbs the heat during day time and release at night. Thus it maintains daytime comfort, but at night hours some discomfort is felt during summer because of small ventilation. Roof is made with well compacted mud.

But throughout the year the building is comfortable without using artificial systems of cooling.

4.3 House of Mr. Parvath Gouda

It is a two storied building which is about 250 years old. The plan of the building is square in shape with attached back yard. The building is compactly planned with central courtyard measuring 33' × 23' (Fig. 3). The main entrance is from East side. Entrance gate is 6' wide and 10' in height. On all sides, external wall of 3' thick are made. Internal walls are 1'–6" thick. Small openings are provided on the external walls to get light and required ventilation. From the main entry there is separate entry for cattle shed. Only one external entry is provided in the building for security reasons.

For the construction of wall, the material used is stone masonry. On roof, a layer of well compacted mud is present which is in good condition till now. Rooms have been constructed on southern side of the first floor, and remaining portion is open terrace. The major light is admitted through central courtyard.

Figure 3. View of courtyard in Mr. Parvath Gouda's house.

The building functions according to seasonal change. In summer, one feels cool and comfort inside during daytime. Courtyard and roof top is used for sleeping as the rooms remain hot at night due to small ventilation. During winter, the heat stored in walls during daytime radiate at nights in the rooms and provides the comfort without using mechanical system. The backyard of the building is used for general utility as well as to maintain privacy.

4.4   House of Mrs. Ratna B. Kalamdani

The building is two storied located near the main road on Gulbarga-Bangalore highway. The building faces towards South. While designing the building Architect has considered all the climatic factors.

The plan of building is almost square in shape with few offsets only (Fig. 4). The main offset is provided near the main entrance in southwest direction where water pond is located (Fig. 5). From water pond the water channel is provided below the flooring. Few openings are provided on the water channel in the floor. The direction of wind is from South-West to North-East. When hot wind is funneled from South-West direction, the pressure is created in the main offset and hot air pass through the water channel. The water pond cools the air by evaporation and gets into the building through openings provided in the flooring.

The staircase is located in the centre of the building between hall and dinning room. The advantage of staircase is it gives double height to the roof. It gives free air circulation inside the building. Hot air passes through openings provided in the roof.

The material used for the construction of walls is brick. All the external walls are of one and half brick thick and all internal walls are one brick thick. Further whereas, internal walls are made solid, external walls are provided with openings in it by using rat-trap bond. The technique used for the construction of external wall is to minimize the heat transfer from outside to inside the building.

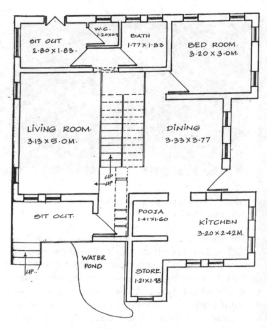

Figure 4. Ground floor plan of Mrs. R.B. Kalamdani's house.

Figure 5. View of water pond at Mrs. R.B. Kalamdani's house.

Architect has not used the plastering or any treatment to external surface of the wall. He exposed the brick with red oxide coat on it. It is because cement is a good conductor of heat.

Material used for the construction of roof is R.C.C slab. But the slab is made in slopping form. The inclination is given to the roof considering sun path diagram so that maximum reflection of solar radiation takes place. The holes are provided in the first floor slab to pass lighter air from ground floor to first floor and from first floor to dormer window which is provided in the roof slab. Thus circulation of air occurs in the building.

All the window and ventilator openings provided on external wall are of size 2′ × 5′. Whereas ventilator is made of fixed glass, window is provided with wooden shutter. The purpose of providing wooden shutter is due to the fact that timber is a good insulator of heat.

Architect has also planned a good landscape which is suitable for hot-dry climate. On west and south sides, trees of larger height have been planted. It creates shadows on the building as well as open spaces to keep it cool.

4.5 House of Mr. M.B. Patel

The building is two storied. The road is facing towards the south west of plot. Architect has considered the climatic factors in the design of building.

The building is planned in such a way that rooms are arranged around the central courtyard. The plan is fitted in to the site which makes 45° to the main road. The main concept of this system is to generate required movement of air in different spaces of building by minimum use of mechanical or electrical energy. Four vertical towers are used to extract hot air from the building. Above the courtyard, the technique used is such that cool air passes downward and circulates through all the rooms to achieve thermal comfort in the rooms.

All walls, internal and external, are constructed with brick masonry with one and half brick thickness. The roof is constructed with R.C.C slab with insulation materials covering laid by Madras hollow block and covered with terracotta tiles. The roof is made sloppy to create wind pressure and pass through fine openings provided above courtyard for evaporative cooling.

A ventilator duct is provided connecting to each room to remove hot air. On east and west sides, plastic barrels are placed very close to wall for rain water collection used for evaporative cooling.

There are no windows towards east and west sides of the wall to avoid direct sunlight. Architect minimized the window openings. They are of 2′ to 3′ wide and 4′–6″ in height. In windows the evaporative cooling system has been provided. The openings are provided in duct tower to extract hot air and convert it into down draft evaporative cooling system.

4.6 House of Mr. S.V. Bakshi

It is a single storey building with total built up area of 850 sq. ft. Building was completed in 1995. Plan of the building is rectangular in shape with one of the long walls being a common wall. Building is symmetrical about shorter axis. Main entrance of the house is from east side. All windows in the building are of same size i.e. 2′–6″ × 4′–6″.

Figure 6. Front view of Mr. S.V. Bakshi's house showing windows.

The central courtyard acts as a passage to flow hot air from the rooms. The courtyard can be operated according to the season to control the air flow. For the construction of walls, architect used rat-trap bond to reduce temperature by providing the cavities in the wall. No plastering has been done on either side. Material used for window is pre-cast blocks laid over one another (Fig. 6). Design of the blocks is such that it maintains privacy and permits flow of air through it.

Architect of the house tried to provide maximum comfort with the help of passive cooling technique with minimum energy and cost.

5 CONCLUSIONS

Following conclusions are drawn from the study presented herein with respect to environment friendly design of residential buildings in hot-dry climate.

(i) To minimize energy demand and provide better degree of natural conditioning, it is essential to give climatic considerations for designing of residential buildings.

(ii) For a building to function in co-ordination with the environment, there should be a relation between the interior and exterior environment, orientation, building form, materials etc.

(iii) Orientation of the overall built form should be in co-ordination with the orientation of the sun and prevailing wind direction.

(iv) Land-scaping is a passive energy saving technique. It controls wind, solar radiation and temperature extremes of climate.

(v) Rectangular form of the building should be elongated along east-west direction, i.e. the orientation of the building should be north-south.

(vi) When buffer spaces are provided between exterior and interior spaces, heat from outside dissipates before entering interiors. Non-habitable rooms such as toilets, stores and galleries can be provided as heat barriers in the worst orientations on the outer periphery of the building.

(vii) Heat removal can be affected by natural or induced ventilation, evaporation of water and the use of heat sinks.

(viii) Provision of a central courtyard is preferable which helps in achieving shaded spaces, natural light in most of the places and better circulation of air without providing much openings on the exteriors surfaces. However, provision of courtyard is effective only if it has a plan area and volume relationship proportional to built-up area and its volume.

(ix) Thick walls create thermal time-lag, thus creating comfortable conditions.

(x) As the position of a window goes higher, light penetration increases with lesser heat gain.

(xi) Size and location of ventilators be decided in such a way that it helps to take the hot air out and improves cross ventilation.

REFERENCES

Agarwal, K.N. 1967. Thermal data of building fabric and its application in building design, *Building Digest*, No. 52, June, CBRI, Roorkee, India.

Anderson, B. 1977. *Solar energy fundamentals in building design – total environment action*. McGraw-Hill Book Co.

Chand, I. & Krishak, N.L.V. 1986. Window design for natural ventilation in tropics. *Building Research Note*, No. 52, July, CBRI, Roorkee, India.

Cowan, H.J. 1980. *Predictive methods for the energy conserving design of buildings*. Applied Science, London

Gupta, V. 1992. Energy conservation – Indian myths and realities. *Architecture + Design*, Vol. 9, No. 3, May–June.

Hobbs, J.E. 1980. *Applied climatology – a study of atmospheric resources*. Butterworths, London.

Krishan, A. 2000. Climate responsive architecture – a design handbook for energy efficient buildings. Tata McGraw-Hill Pub. Co. Ltd., New Delhi.

Krishan, A. & Agnihotri, M.R. 1992. Bio-climatic architecture – a fundamental approach to design, *Architecture + Design*, Vol. 9, No. 3, May–June.

Rai, G.S. 1992. The listing of heritage. *Architecture + Design*, Vol. 9, No. 3, May–June.

Rai, S. 1991. Attuned : climate sensitive design and energy efficient buildings. Indian architects and builders, April.

Rao, K.R. & Prakash, C. 1972. Thermal performance rating and classification of walls in hot climate. *Building Digest*, No. 101, October, CBRI, Roorkee, India.

Sharma, M.R. 1969. Orientation of buildings. *Building Digest*, No. 74, December, CBRI, Roorkee, India.

Straaten, V.J.F. 1967. *Thermal performance of buildings*. Elsevier Pub. Co., Amsterdam.

Watson, D. 1979. *Energy conservation through building design – an architectural record book*. McGraw-Hill Book Co.

System-based Vision for Strategic and Creative Design, Bontempi (ed.)
© *2003 Swets & Zeitlinger, Lisse, ISBN 90 5809 599 1*

Claim analysis involving multiple compensable factors

A. Singh
University of Hawaii at Manoa, USA

ABSTRACT: Among the problems in claims analysis is that multiple factors impinge on specific causal conditions that result in compensable breach. The isolation and analysis of those multiple factors is a matter of concern, since claims must be calculated accurately for the sake of fairness to all parties involved in the dispute. This paper discusses a particular problem combination that covers efficiency losses for acceleration, quantity changes, delay, overtime, overmanning, overcrowding, weather change, and disruption. Final claim costs are calculated.

1 INTRODUCTION

Techniques have been presented for independent application of claims problems (Schwartzkopf 1995). However, claim situations are seldom straightforward owing to multiple factors acting together. The claim analysis has to therefore follow a sequence of approaches that incorporates all the underlying factors.

The problem involves a delay for notice to proceed that pushes work from the early autumn season to mid-winter, a change order that increases work quantity, an acceleration directive, work disruption due to hoist breakdown, and work interference due to overcrowding – in that order. To overcome these hurdles, the contractor must modify his work schedule for weather changes, use learning curve equations to adjust for work disruption, and incorporate losses through overcrowding owing to the work interference, and use overmanning and overtime, The details are presented below, starting with the problem definition.

2 THE PROBLEM

1056 sq.m. of masonry work for a high-rise building was scheduled over 22 workdays by a subcontractor using four masons and four assistants. Each floor required equal masonry work. Each mason's average productivity was estimated at 12 sq.m./day for the six floors of the building. Each mason is paid $25 an hour; the assistant – $12 per hour.

The masons work normally at a learning curve ratio of 95%, with each unit of work measured at 48 sq.m. of combined work output of the whole crew.

However, for each floor increase, the masons start the first unit of the next floor with a learning loss of 2% on the same exponential learning curve. The average man-hours used to perform 48 sq.m. of work is 32 man-hours – one days' work for the crew.

A number of things happen on this project. First of all, owing to delays in owner and contractor scheduling, the start of work is delayed from September, when temperature averages 82 degrees F at 50% H, to January, when the temperature is 45 degrees F at 40% H.

Next, the owner issues a change order and increases the height of the building by two stories. These two additional stories have masonry of 150 sq.m. and 125 sq.m. respectively, with the higher storey having 125 sq.m. Inspite of this substantial change order, the contractor insists that the masonry subcontract work be completed in only one extra week (5 additional workdays).

In the original schedule, the masonry subcontractor would not have experienced any overcrowding. In the modified scheme for the additional floors, however, the HVAC crew is expected to be active in the same workspace as the masons, resulting in 50% overcrowding.

This meant that the masonry subcontractor has to use overmanning and overtime to increase his work output. However, he is limited to only one hour of overtime per working day owing to security reasons.

Now, after completing the 3rd floor, the subcontractor is delayed by three days to move onto the 4th floor due to hoist mechanical problems, thereby disrupting work altogether. The maintenance of the hoist is the responsibility of the contractor. This disruption makes the masons lose an estimated 5% on the learning curve while transferring from the 3rd floor to the 4th. Nevertheless, the contractor decides to give no relief to the subcontractor and demands that work be completed as scheduled (Singh 1991).

3 RESOURCE ALLOCATION TASKS

In this problem, the subcontractor is faced with three tasks:

1. After the initial delay and change order, he has to redesign his work force to finish the entire eight stories in only one extra week
2. He has to redesign his work force after the third week of hoist downtime
3. He has to submit a claim for the effect of the changes, disruption, and acceleration directive.

4 SOLUTION METHODOLOGY

There are two distinct phases to a complete solution.

Phase 1

1. Use the data from the original plan for completing six floors at 32 man-hours per day, to calculate the value of the exponent, n, and the constant, A in the learning curve equation.
2. Find the total man-hours used per floor, and then calculate the straight time duration per floor.
3. Consider weather effects and overcrowding for the upper two stories
4. Make an estimate of overtime and overmanning to overcome time restraints.

Phase 2

5. The subcontractor needs to redesign his work allocation after he has completed the 3rd floor, since there was a disruption to the work due to hoist problems. Hence, all the above calculations of Phase I need to be repeated with the new time constraints in mind – but only for floors 4 to 8.

5 LEARNING CURVE EQUATION

5.1 *Calculate exponent, n, and constant, A*

Given that the learning ratio is 95%, $Y_2/Y_1 = A \cdot (2)^n/A \cdot (1)^n = 0.95$. Therefore, $n = -0.074$

Let A_1 be the constant for the 1st floor, and A_2 for the 2nd floor ... and so on until the 6th floor.

Each unit of work is measured in packages of 48 sq.m. Since floors 1 through 6 have 176 sq.m. of masonry, there will be 176/48 = 3.67 units of work for each of those floors. Let Y_{ij} represent the jth unit of work on the ith floor. Corresponding to these units of

work and nomenclature, we have the following Y terms and data points for each floor:

$$
\begin{aligned}
&\text{1st floor: } Y_{11}, Y_{12}, Y_{13}, Y_{13.67} \\
&\text{2nd floor: } Y_{21}, Y_{22}, Y_{23}, Y_{23.67} \\
&\text{3rd floor: } Y_{31}, Y_{32}, Y_{33}, Y_{33.67} \\
&\text{4th floor: } Y_{41}, Y_{42}, Y_{43}, Y_{43.67} \\
&\text{5th floor: } Y_{51}, Y_{52}, Y_{53}, Y_{53.67} \\
&\text{6th floor: } Y_{61}, Y_{62}, Y_{63}, Y_{63.67}
\end{aligned}
\tag{1}
$$

From which it follows that,

$$
\begin{aligned}
Y_{11} &= A_1 (1)^{-0.074} & Y_{12} &= A_1 (2)^{-0.074} \\
Y_{13} &= A_1 (3)^{-0.074} & Y_{13.67} &= A_1 (3.67)^{-0.074} \\
&\quad\ldots\ldots \\
Y_{61} &= A_6 (1)^{-0.074} & Y_{62} &= A_6 (2)^{-0.074} \\
Y_{63} &= A_6 (3)^{-0.074} & Y_{63.67} &= A_6 (3.67)^{-0.074}
\end{aligned}
\tag{2}
$$

From the basic learning curve equation, we also know that $Y_{11} = A_1$, $Y_{21} = A_2 \ldots Y_{71} = A_7$. We also know that for each new floor that starts, there is a 2% learning loss for the first unit of work on the next floor. This implies that there will be 2% extra man-hours used than the amount of man-hours used for the just-previous unit. Hence,

$$
\begin{aligned}
Y_{21} &= A_2 (1)^{-0.074} = A_2 = 1.02 * Y_{13.67} \\
&= 1.02 * A_1 (3.67)^{-0.074}
\end{aligned}
\tag{3}
$$

Thus,

$$
\begin{aligned}
A_3 &= 1.02 * A_2 (3.67)^{-0.074} = A_1 (1.02 * (3.67)^{-0.074})^2 \\
&\ldots, \text{and so on, till} \\
A_6 &= 1.02 * A_5 (3.67)^{-0.074} = A_1 (1.02 * (3.67)^{-0.074})^5
\end{aligned}
\tag{4}
$$

Given that $Y_{ave} = 32$ man-hours

$$
Y_{ave} = 32 = \left. \sum_{i}^{6} \sum_{j}^{3.67} Y_{i,j} \middle/ 6*3.67 \right.
\tag{5}
$$

and solving for A_1 by using eqn. 5, we have:

$$
Y_{ave} = \{ A_1 (B + B^2 + B^3 + B^4 + B^5 + B^6) \}/ \{22\}
\tag{6}
$$

where, $B = [(1)^{-0.074} + (2)^{-0.074} + (2)^{-0.074} + (3.67)^{-0.074}]$

The above equation yields a value of $A_1 = 37.25$ man-hours.

Therefore, the A constants for the other floors can be calculated from eqns. 3 to 5 to be

$$
\begin{aligned}
A_2 &= 34.51 & A_3 &= 31.97 & A_4 &= 29.62 \\
A_5 &= 27.44 & A_6 &= 25.42
\end{aligned}
$$

Table 1. Man-hours and duration based on original design.

Floor	Total Man-hours	Duration (days)
1st floor	140.80	4.40
2nd floor	130.44	4.08
3rd floor	120.85	3.78
4th floor	111.97	3.50
5th floor	103.73	3.24
6th floor	96.09	3.00
Total		21.99

5.2 *Man-hours and duration of work for each floor*

The total man-hours for each floor can be found by adding the Y_{ij} values for that floor. Thus,

$$[\text{TOTMHRS}_i] = \sum_{j=1}^{k} Y_{ij} \qquad (7)$$

where, $\text{TOTMHRS}i$ = Total Man Hours for the floor i; i = the floor being evaluated, 1 through 6; j = the number of units on floor i; and k = total number of units on that floor.

The values we get for all Y values is

$Y_{11} = 37.25; Y_{12} = 35.38; Y_{13} = 34.34; Y_{1,3.67} = 33.83$
$Y_{21} = 34.51; Y_{22} = 32.78; Y_{23} = 31.81; Y_{2,3.67} = 31.34$
$Y_{31} = 31.97; Y_{32} = 30.37; Y_{33} = 29.47; Y_{3,3.67} = 29.04$
$Y_{41} = 29.62; Y_{42} = 28.14; Y_{43} = 27.31; Y_{4,3.67} = 26.90$
$Y_{51} = 27.44; Y_{52} = 26.07; Y_{53} = 25.30; Y_{5,3.67} = 24.92$
$Y_{61} = 25.42; Y_{62} = 24.15; Y_{63} = 23.44; Y_{6,3.67} = 23.08$

The total man-hours per floor are easily obtained from the above. Dividing these total man-hours by 32, which is the man-hour input of mason teams per day, gives us the duration taken by masons for each floor. This information serves to confirm and check our calculations, thereby allowing us to plot the learning curve profiles for the six floors. The manhour and duration data is given in Table 1.

The total duration calculated, 21.99, is equal to the 22 days duration originally planned, ignoring rounding errors in the calculations. The man-hour profile, as originally planned for the first six floors, is plotted in Figure 1.

5.3 *Man-hours for the 7th and 8th Floors*

Floor 7 has only 150 sq.m of masonry corresponding to 3.125 units of work, while Floor 8 has only 125 sq.m of work corresponding to 2.604 units of work. Thus,

$$Y_{7,1} = A_7 (1)^{-0.074} \dots Y_{7,3.125} = A_7 (3.125)^{-0.074} \text{ and}$$
$$Y_{8,1} = A_8 (1)^{-0.074} \dots Y_{8,2.604} = A_8 (2.604)^{-0.074} \qquad (8)$$

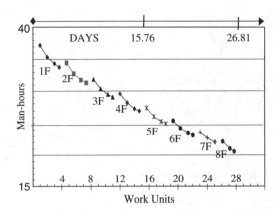

Figure 1. Initial duration results.

Table 2. Man-hours & duration for 7th and 8th floors (ST).

Floor	Total Man-hours	Duration (days)
7th floor	90.19	2.82
8th floor	63.63	1.99
Total		4.81

Now, $Y_{7,1} = A_7 (1)^{-0.074} = 1.02*Y_{6,3.67} = 1.02*A_6*(3.67)^{-0.074} = 23.55 \text{ MHrs}$, which implies that $A_7 = 23.55$. From these, it can be calculated that

$Y_{7,2} = 22.68; Y_{7,3} = 22.01; Y_{7,3.125} = 21.95$
$Y_{8,2} = 20.98; Y_{8,2.604} = 20.57$

The corresponding Total man-hours and Duration for 7th and 8th floors are given in Table 2.

The straight time duration for completing 7th and 8th floors is within the five extra workdays granted to the subcontractor. Thus, the subcontractor will be able to complete the project within 27 days in straight time, considering no adverse weather, and no overcrowding. However, we know that adverse weather and overcrowding exist, so the subcontractor needs to re-calculate his durations as per these adverse effects.

6 EFFECT OF WEATHER

Work was originally scheduled for September when the temperature was an average of 82 degrees F at 50% H. The work was then shifted to January when the temperature expected was 45 deg. F at 40% H. Since this is a masonry problem, we opt to use Grimm and Wagner's isopleths (Fig. 2). From Figure 2, we find the mason productivity in September is approximately 92% of

445

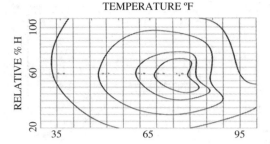

TEMPERATURE °F

Figure 2. Weather chart.

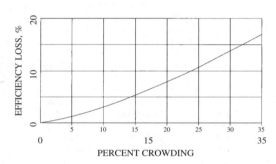

Figure 3. Chart for overcrowding.

ideal; in January, the mason productivity is 61%. Hence the relative effect of weather on efficiency is 61%/92% = 0.663 in January compared to what it would be in September.

7 OVERCROWDING ON 7TH AND 8TH FLOORS

The HVAC crew will be active in the last week of work on the 7th and 8th floors, resulting in 50% overcrowding. Using the chart in Figure 3 (U.S. Army, 1979) for overcrowding, we discover that the efficiency loss is 17%.

8 DURATION ADJUSTMENT FOR WEATHER CHANGE AND OVERCROWDING

The expected duration is calculated by dividing the straight time (S.T.) duration by the weather and overcrowding factors. Overcrowding is only for Floors 7 and 8. Taking from Tables 1, 2 and Section 7, the expected durations for floors 1 through 8 are therefore as follows:

Floor 1, 6.64 days; Floor 2, 6.15 days; Floor 3, 5.70 days; Floor 4, 5.28 days; Floor 5, 4.89 days; Floor 6,

Table 3. Durations and costs with overmanning only.

OM	25%	50%	75%	100%	125%	150%
Dur	35.14	30.91	27.10	26.08	23.18	20.37
$	52009	54898	56146	61760	61760	61760

Table 4. Calculation of costs for O.T. scenarios.

OM level, Crew size	S.T. Dur (Days)	O.T. Days 1 hr/ day	Total OT$	Total ST$	Total ST$ + OT$
25%, 5	32.50	32.00	8880	48100	56980
50%, 6	28.47	28.00	9324	50563	59887
75%, 7	25.02	25.00	9713	51841	61554
100%, 8	24.35	24.00	10656	57661	68317
125%, 9	21.49	21.00	10490	57249	67739
150%, 10	19.36	19.00	10545	57306	67851

4.52 days; Floor 7, 5.12 days; Floor 8, 3.42 days. These total to 41.73 days of work, which is not acceptable.

9 DURATION DESIGN BY OVERMANNING

We need to consider the duration improvements we can achieve by using overmanning (OM) and overtime (OT). Let us first consider the improvements through OM. Since OM can only be undertaken in steps of discrete number of workers, we can consider reasonable OM only for 25%, 50%, 75%, 100%, 125%, and 150% OM.

Using the chart for OM (refer US Army, 1979), which states that the maximum efficiency loss is restricted to 20% for 100% OM and more, we calculate that the modified project duration design and labor costs are as those in Table 3.

These durations fare much better than the 41.73 days calculated earlier. OM of 100% or more produces durations within 27 workdays. Now, let us see if OT can reduce the costs.

10 EVALUATION WITH OVERMANNING AND OVERTIME

To incorporate overtime, an iterative measure of calculation is used. Calculations for 75% OM are given in Singh (1991). The effects of OT are over and above those of weather change, overcrowding, and overmanning. Based on these calculations, the revised duration and cost design are provided in Table 4.

The results show that using 5–9's along with 75% OM results in feasible duration schedules (less than 27 work days). Clearly, going with 5–9's and 75% overmanning gives the lowest cost solution at $53,228.94.

11 CLAIM AT START OF WORK

Upon starting his work in January, the subcontractor's work schedule design cost is $61,554. Based on his original estimate for completion of six floors in 22 days, the labor cost was $37*5*8*22 = $32,560. Thus, the claim by the subcontractor made to the contractor upon the start of work is $61,554 − $32,560 = $28,894.

12 HOIST BREAKDOWN

Owing to the hoist breakdown and delay, the subcontractor has to further speed up his work, since the contractor gives him no relief. Not only that, his workers lose 5% on the learning curve. Now, the entire learning curve calculations must be repeated to establish new constants (exponent value is unchanged). All other sets of calculations must also be redone in the same manner as before. The work until the 3rd floor has been completed per schedule in 11.04 days.

13 RECALCULATING THE LEARNING CURVE

Let $Y_{4'}$, $Y_{5'}$, $Y_{6'}$, $Y_{7'}$, and $Y_{8'}$ represent the recalculated Man-hour values of the 4th, 5th, 6th, 7th, and 8th floors respectively.

With a learning loss of 5%, the 4th Floor now starts with

$$Y_{4'1} = A_{4'} \cdot (1)^{-0.074} = A_{4'} = 1.05 * Y_{3,3.67}$$
$$= 1.05 * A_3 (3.67)^{-0.074} = 30.49 \qquad (9)$$

The value of the other Y terms follows as given below for the redesigned curves. Floor 5 and subsequent floors start with only a 2% learning loss over previous floors, since the work is now continuous and there is no work disruption.

$Y_{4'1} = 30.49$; $Y_{4'2} = 28.97$; $Y_{4'3} = 28.11$; $Y_{4'3.67} = 27.69$
$Y_{5'1} = 28.24$; $Y_{5'2} = 26.83$; $Y_{5'3} = 26.04$; $Y_{5'3.67} = 25.65$
$Y_{6'1} = 26.16$; $Y_{6'2} = 24.85$; $Y_{6'3} = 24.12$; $Y_{6'3.67} = 23.76$
$Y_{7'1} = 24.23$; $Y_{7'2} = 23.02$; $Y_{7'3} = 22.33$; $Y_{7'3.125} = 22.27$
$Y_{8'1} = 22.72$; $Y_{8'2} = 21.58$; $Y_{8'2.604} = 21.17$

14 REDESIGNING THE SCHEDULE

The revised total man-hours and the redesigned durations are shown in Table 5, after considering weather and overcrowding (refer calculations in Section 8). To convert Total man-hours to work duration, we need to divide by 32 man-hours – the number of man-hours worked per day by four workers.

Table 5. Total initial man-hours and duration for Phase 2.

Floor	Total M-Hrs	Duration (Days)	Weather Factor	OC Factor	Expected Duration
4th	115.26	3.6	0.663	1	5.43
5th	106.76	3.34	0.663	1	5.04
6th	98.89	3.09	0.663	1	4.66
7th	92.35	2.89	0.663	0.83	5.25
8th	65.47	2.05	0.663	0.83	3.73
Total		14.97			24.11

Table 6. Calculation of costs for O.T. scenarios – Phase 2.

OM Level, Crew Size	ST Dur (Days)	O.T. Days 1 hr/day	Total OT$	Total ST$	Total ST$ + OT$
25%, 5	18.76	18.00	4995	27765	32760
50%, 6	16.50	16.00	5328	29304	34632
75%, 7	14.45	14.00	5439	29940	35379
100%, 8	14.00	14.00	6216	33152	39368
125%, 9	12.53	12.00	5994	33380	39374
150%, 10	11.16	11.00	6105	33034	39139

It is seen that the new expected duration for completing the remaining floor is 24.11 days without overtime and/or overmanning. 11.04 real days have already elapsed from the total allowable of 27 days. Moreover, three days were lost in hoist breakdown. This leaves 27 − 11.04 − 3 = 12.96 real days for completing the 4th to 8th floors. Obviously, overtime and overmanning are indicated to complete on schedule; a schedule shrinkage of approximately 100% is required.

Because workers have had a three-day break, their O.T. efficiency cannot be considered continuous from where they left off. Giving allowance for efficiency recuperation due to the break, we assume to start the 4th floor efficiency loss for OT as if the workers had recovered six days of OT losses after three days of break. Therefore, we restart our efficiency calculations using OT values from 2nd wk. onwards.

The revised calculations, on the same pattern as Tables 3, 4, and 5 are now performed. The final solutions are shown in Table 6. This time around, the optimal solution is with 125% overmanning. The project is thus completed in 11.04 + 3.00 + 12.53 = 26.58 days, which is acceptable.

15 FINAL UTILIZATION AND COST

The first three floors were constructed according to design, then there was a three-day disruption, after which a redesign was undertaken and the project completed according to the redesign. The final, as-built work durations and costs were as follows:

Floor 1 = 3.98 days;   Floor 2 = 3.67 days;
Floor 3 = 3.39 days;   Floor 4 = 2.81 days;
Floor 5 = 2.60 days;   Floor 6 = 2.39 days;
Floor 7 = 2.74 days;   Floor 8 = 2.00 days.

For Floors 1 to 3:
Use 5–9's with 75% overmanning, implying 7 masons and 7 assistants used. Time spent = 11.04 days; cost = $27,148

For Floors 4 to 8: From Table 7, cost = $39,374
Total Cost = $66,522
At this stage, the three days of lost mason-days during hoist breakdown should be added to the claim. That value is 3 days * 5 mason teams * $37 per team per hour * 8 hours per day = $3,552. Thus, the final claim is $66,522 less the original estimate of $32,560 plus $3,552 = $37,514

16   SUMMARY AND CONCLUSIONS

Three designs are necessary to arrive to the final solution of this problem, as follows:

1) The original estimated design.

2) Redesign owing to delay, change order, and acceleration directive.

3) Redesign owing to hoist breakdown.

In this particular case, it was seen that the subcontractor was entitled to a claim for $37,514.

This project involved work delay resulting in weather changes, quantity changes, acceleration directives, and work disruption. To calculate the proper resource allocation schedules, the subcontractor had to use charts relating to weather productivity, overtime, overmanning, overcrowding, and learning curve equations and tools. Thus, the small claims problem illustrated here is a complex scenario covering and integrating multiple factors encountered on construction sites.

REFERENCES

Grimm, C.T. & Wagner, N.K., 1974. Weather Effects on Mason Productivity, *ASCE J. of the Constrn. Division.*
Schwartzkopf, W. 1995. *Calculating Lost Labor Productivity in Construction Claims,* NY: John Wiley and Sons, Inc.
Singh, A. 2001. Claim Evaluation for Combined Effect of Multiple Claim Factors, *Cost Engineering,* 43(12), Dec.
US Army Corps of Engineers, 1979. *Modification Evaluation Impact Guide,* Washington DC: Dept. of Army.

System-based Vision for Strategic and Creative Design, Bontempi (ed.)
© 2003 Swets & Zeitlinger, Lisse, ISBN 90 5809 599 1

How soccer results effects concrete cracking

S.P.G. Moonen
Eindhoven University of Technology, Eindhoven, the Netherlands

ABSTRACT: This paper underlines the importance of a proper schematization. In practice the time spent for designing the structural scheme is only a fraction of the time required for making calculations. And yet designing a proper structural scheme is often underestimated. This view is exemplified by a study of the cause of cracks in prefabricated elements of the stand of a newly build soccer stadium. After initial check-up of calculations, materials and realization and after studying the live load during a match an incorrect structural scheme was discovered that accounted for the crack formation.

1 CRACKS IN NEWLY BUILD STAND

Shortly after the opening of a new soccer stadium several cracks were discovered in some prefabricated slabs of the stands. The city council, owner of the stadium, contacted an independent firm of consulting engineers to advise on the structural reliability of the stands. The consulting engineer researched several possibilities to find out what could have caused the observed cracks. At first all calculations of the structural engineer and detailed calculations of the manufacture were thoroughly studied. Secondly the concrete quality of the prefabricated elements was checked. By checking origial cube tests, by laboratory tests of concrete cubes, poured when producing the elements, as well as by laboratory tests of concrete cores bored from the soccer stadium it was found that the concrete used was of an excellent quality. Thirdly all working documents of builder and manufacturer were studied, also without results.

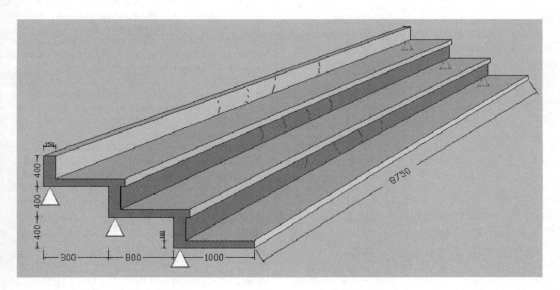

Figure 1. Prefabricated concrete element used as stand in a soccer stadium. The length of the element is 8.75 meter, the width was three times 0.8 meter to support three rows with seat in the stands. Shortly after opening cracks were observed in some elements. These cracks, sketched in this drawing, were found at the backside of the element.

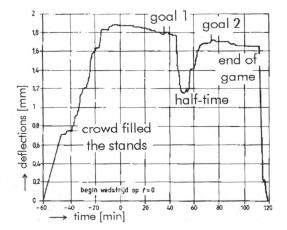

Figure 2. Time deflection graph of the absolute deflection at midspan of a stand with a span of 8.75 meter (Fig. 1). The final score of this soccer game was 2-1, in favor of the supports sitting on top of the measured stand. Both goals of the home team can be seen in the graph by a short increase of the deflection. The goal against at the end of the game did not disturb these supporters and can not be seen in the graph. It was a nerve-racking match so this response of cheering crowd is considered representative.

After having controlled all the documents the consulting engineer draw the conclusion that overload was most likely to account for the cracks. Because all calculations did follow all applicable codes, the engineer assumed that overload due to dynamic response of a cheering crowd caused the cracks.

2   EFFECT OF A CHEERING CROWD

At that stage the engineer approached the department of Structural Engineering of Eindhoven University of Technology asking how the dynamic load of the stand was to be measured. We decided to initially perform a test of measuring static deformations underneath the stand during a soccer match. On a Sunday morning a simple test set-up was build underneath the stand with observed cracks. This test set-up consisted of an independent frame to vertically attach electronic potential meters to measure deflections at midspan of the prefabricated element. This maximum measured deflection (precision 0.01 mm) was written to disk every two seconds. The result is shown in a time-deflection graph (Fig. 2). The horizontal axis is the elapsed time where 0 is arbitrary chosen as whistle signal of the referee to start the game. The vertical axis shows the absolute deflection. This graph clearly shows the deflection when the crowd filled the stands,

when part of the crowd left during half-time, et cetera. Also cheering of the crowd when the own team scored goals can be seen at the time-deflection graph.

All measured deflections were relatively small, less than 2 mm of a span of 8750 mm ($<0.0003l$). The effect of a cheering crowd was of such a small magnitude that dynamic load is interpreted a negligible factor. During the match we observed the public on top of the measured element. Because there was hardly no room for people to stand in between seats, the maximum static live load is the weight of 2 people per m^2. The prefabricated elements were calculated using a live load of 4 kN/m^2, accordingly underestimating the absolute load on the prefabricated elements could not account for the observed cracks. Neither could dynamic load by the crowd explain the observed cracks.

3   BACK TO SQUARE ONE

Since every considered hypothesis could not be justified, a renewed study of the soccer stadium was made. Finally a logical explanation was found in the structural schematization that was used in designing the prefabricated elements. One must consider the specific construction to find the proper scheme. The stands are made of prefabricated elements with a span of 8.75 meter (Fig. 1). Each element has 3 risers and 3 treads. Two concrete beams support the element (Fig. 3). Thus the structural scheme is a element with two line-supports.

But this structural scheme is not always valid, especially in a situation where the stadium is not filled to capacity. Consider for instance a situation where two following elements are fully loaded by a live load (consider the elements left of line B and in between lines A and B in Fig. 4) but the next element has no live load (elements right of line A in Fig. 4). This situation will for example occur when a part of the stand is not used to separate rival supporters. In this specific load case the two concrete beams supporting these three elements deform differently. The concrete beam underneath the two fully loaded elements will bend more than the concrete beam underneath a fully and a none-loaded element. As a consequence some elements in between line A and B in Fig. 4 (with a maximum live load) are no longer supported on the 6 risers shown in Fig. 1. Depending on the position of the slab regarding the supports of the concrete beam (Fig. 3) the difference in settlements on the left and right of an element will vary. For the elements in an unfavorable position the initially load will be transmitted to 3 out of 6 supports. In this scheme the element will twist due to the stiffness of the element so the other supports will be loaded one after another. Every time the element meets a support a new structural scheme arises.

Figure 3   Photo of the soccer stadium under construction. The supporting scheme of the prefabricated element to be used as stand is sketched.

Figure 4.   A specific load case occurs when two rival supporters are separated by an empty part of the stand. In this photo of a similar stand two lines (A and B) are drawn to indicate the position of the supporting beams underneath the prefabricated elements. The beam at line B is fully loaded while the beam at line A bears half the live load compared to beam B. Consequently the deflections of beam A and B will differ. Concrete elements in between line A and B are fully loaded, but are subjected to different settings at the supports.

We have made computer calculations using a 3D-final elements model to model consecutive support situations. Initially the result of dead load of beams and elements was calculated. By looking at the deflections of the concrete beams we found the most unfavorable element in between the concrete beams. This approach also showed which three supports of this element would initially touch the supporting concrete beam. Than we changed the scheme to an element with these three instead of six supports and recalculated the compound structure. This time we applied life load in very small steps. After every step the results was added to the already calculated response

of dead load. By iteration we found the load where the deflection of one of the three "floating supports" of an element matched the deflection of the concrete beam underneath. Than we changed the scheme accordingly and continued to apply small load partitions. In all cases the principle of super positioning is used to combine the outcome of calculations with different structural schemes. It was found that the most unfavorable element, initially put on three supports, changed to an element with four supports when 86% of the maximum life load, being $4.0\,kN/m^2$, was applied. The stiffness of elements was such that a realistic life load never loaded the fifth or sixth support. Because reinforcement in the prefabricated elements was not geared to torsion, several locations were found with tensile stresses exceeding the maximum tensile strength of concrete.

This approach showed that this could have well caused the observed cracks, because the calculated element and the calculated peaks in tensile stresses matched more or less the observed cracks. Also the location where the initial cracks were found matched the situation where a part of the stand was unused to separate supporters.

Another possibility to have this load case is when the stadium is not filled to capacity and spectators are gathered at midfield. We have closely inspected the stadium at the locations where this load case can occur and found some similar cracks in the prefabricated elements at these locations.

By discovering the cause of the observed cracks we could report to the owner of the stadium that the structural safety of these elements is established. Since these cracks are in an inside area the durability is also no problem. Left is an aesthetical question. But considering the cause of these cracks it is likely that cracks will return, so repairing the cracks will not last long.

4   CONCLUSION

Sometimes a fully loaded situation is not decisive for the structural design. A cantilever beam is a well-known example of a scheme that has to be calculated with different load cases to find the structural criteria. The simple structure that is the center of interest in this paper (Fig. 1) gives a concealed example of a structure where a partially loaded structural scheme is decisive.

But it is also possible that within one load case several different structural schemes have to be considered. The described case in this paper shows a specific load situation that should have been calculated by different consecutive structural schemes.

The final explanation for the cause of cracks in a newly build soccer station was a uneven distribution of load. Since soccer results effects the admission figures of a game, the location of a load situation causing cracks as described in this paper will move towards midfield by reducing spectator. That's how soccer results can effects concrete cracking.

REFERENCES

Ketelaars, J.J.B. & van Wier, J. 1995. Belasting en respons zittribunes experimenteel bepaald. Een onderzoek naar het gedrag van voetbalsupporters. (Experiments regarding load and response of stands with seats. A study of the behavior of soccer supporters) *In Cement 1995, nr. 12.*

Moonen, S.P.G. & Ketelaars, J.J.B. 1996. Slecht voetbal leidt tot scheuren, tribune elementen numeriek nader onderzocht (Bad soccer results introduces cracks in concrete, prefabricated elements for stands are studied numerical) *In Cement 1996, nr. 1.*

6. Structural optimization and
evolutionary procedures

Identification of Strut-and-Tie mechanisms in reinforced concrete structures using the cell method and genetic optimization techniques

D. Baron & S. Noè
Department of Civil Engineering, University of Trieste, Trieste, Italy

G.A. Rassati
Department of Civil and Environmental Engineering, University of Cincinnati, Cincinnati, USA

ABSTRACT: The design of reinforced concrete elements by means of Strut-and-Tie (S&T) modelling is based on the identification of discrete truss resistant mechanisms within the overall structure, preliminary to the strength, deformability and/or ductility verifications. For complex structural concrete elements this phase can be somewhat simplified, and, most of all, made less dependent on the intuition and on the past experience of the designer, by adopting appropriate automatic techniques. The technique presented in the paper performs the search for the ideal S&T mechanism by means of a combined use of an elastic solver and an optimization algorithm. Namely, the proposed technique is a combination of the discrete continuum analysis method called *Cell Method*, which is applied to the elastic analysis of the considered structure, and of genetic optimization techniques, which are used to search for the solution. After a brief presentation of the implemented identification algorithm, and after the description of the adopted numerical method, some example structures are analyzed, and their resisting mechanisms to the applied loads are highlighted and commented. It is concluded that the proposed method is suitable for the search and identification of S&T mechanisms within reinforced concrete structures and elements, provided that adequate computing resources are available.

1 INTRODUCTION

The traditional approach to the design of reinforced concrete slender elements focuses mostly on cross-sections of regions in which the Bernoulli hypothesis of linear strain distribution is assumed valid (B-regions). Usually separate checks are carried out for different actions, such as bending moment or shear force. Specific detailing rules finally allow the dimensioning of regions where the Bernoulli hypothesis cannot be considered valid, i.e. those regions corresponding to static and/or geometric discontinuities (D-regions) due to restraints, concentrated loads, or cross-sectional variations.

Recent design provisions (ACI 2002; CEB-FIP 1993; CEN 1991) devote increasing attention to design approaches based on discrete resistant models. Such models are constituted by pin-ended two-force members, subjected to uniaxial stress state (struts and ties), connected together in correspondence to regions subjected to multi-axial stress states (nodes).

These models have been originally adopted for the idealization of shear-resistance mechanisms in reinforced concrete (Mörsch 1912) and for the analysis of members with low span-to-depth ratio (i.e. deep beams, walls), in which the role of stress diffusion is paramount in defining their static behavior. Similar models can be adopted for the modelling of D-regions in slender elements. The adoption of the discrete modelling offers the advantage of highlighting the load path, thus clarifying the actual structural behavior. Similarly, it allows to clearly identify the local resistant mechanisms, thus providing useful insight data for detailing.

In the last two decades, the demand for more thorough design approaches for D-regions has been expressed, leading to wide-spread research on strut-and-tie (S&T) models for structural concrete (Marti 1985; Schlaich et al. 1987; Schlaich & Anagnostou 1990; Schlaich & Schäfer 1991; Collins & Mitchell 1980; Collins & Mitchell 1991).

The initial step of the design process by means of S&T analysis, preliminary to the strength, deformability and/or ductility verifications, is the identification of an ideal resisting scheme. The identification is not usually univocal, and therefore it relies on the interpretation of preliminary finite-element analyses and/or on the skill of the designer. Such approaches are practically viable only for simpler cases. For complex structural concrete elements this phase can be somewhat simplified, and, most of all, made less dependent on the intuition and on the past experience of the designer, by adopting appropriate automatic techniques instead of conventional methods.

A number of researchers in the last few years proposed and investigated different approaches to the automatic identification of S&T mechanisms in structural concrete (Orlando et al. 2000; Liang et al. 2002). Following in these tracks, the present work investigates the possibility of combining a evolutionary optimization approach with a new numerical method for structural analysis, in order to identify S&T mechanisms within and around D-regions in structural concrete.

A brief review of the identification procedure and criteria, and a number of examples of the application of the procedure to the solution of classic D-region problems are presented.

It will be concluded that the proposed approach is a viable solution for automatic identification of S&T mechanisms within D-regions, with the only setback of a non-negligible computation time.

2 IDENTIFICATION OF STRUT-AND-TIE MECHANISMS

The problem of the identification of S & T mechanisms in the domain representing the profile of a reinforced concrete element has been related to a problem of constrained maximum search.

Assuming that the stiffness of the material be proportional to its density, the solution sought corresponds to the particular mass distribution within the domain, which maximizes the structural stiffness (i.e. minimizes the elastic deformation energy), and satisfies the following constraints: a) conservation of the total mass of the system, b) compatibility with the predetermined range of the chosen design variables, and c) respect of load and displacement boundary conditions (Orlando et al. 2000).

The search for the optimal solution is based on the Genetic Algorithm technique.

For the solution of the elastic problem, the generic domain considered is discretized by means of a finite number of plane triangular elements, which will be in the following referred to as *cells*, with 3 nodes and 2 Degrees of Freedom (DOFs) per node.

The density values of each single cell have been chosen as design variables. The variable to be maximized for the search for the optimal solution is the average stiffness, defined as:

$$K_m = \frac{\sum_{i=1}^{n} \frac{F_i}{u_i}}{n} \qquad (1)$$

where F_i is the nodal force associated with the i-th DOF; u_i is the displacement associated with the i-th DOF; and n is the total number of applied forces F_i.

The constraints for the optimum search are defined as follows:

$$\rho = \frac{\sum_{iCel=1}^{NTotCel} A_{iCel} \cdot \rho_{iCel}}{A_{tot}} = 1 \qquad (2)$$

$$0 < \rho_{min} \leq \rho_{iCel} \leq \rho_{max} \qquad (3)$$

$$F = K \times U \qquad (4)$$

where ρ is the average density of the system; $iCel$ identifies the current cell; $NTotCel$ is the total number of cells in the discretization of the structure; A_{iCel} is the area of current cell; ρ_{iCel} is the density of current cell; A_{tot} is the total area of the domain; F is the vector containing the imposed loads; K is the stiffness matrix; and U is the nodal displacements vector.

The elastic modulus for the current cell is calculated using:

$$E_{iCel} = \rho_{iCel} \cdot \bar{E} \qquad (5)$$

where $\bar{E}$ is the reference Young's modulus for the chosen material.

The constraint expressed by Equation 2 corresponds to the imposition of mass conservation with respect to the reference structure. The density of the reference structure has been conventionally assumed to be unitary. Equation 3 defines the variation range of the design parameters (i.e. of the local density). Equation 4 is equivalent to imposing compatibility and equilibrium conditions.

For the example problems presented in the following, it has been assumed that the design variables could only be equal to the limits of the variation range (chosen as $\rho_{min} = 0.2$ and $\rho_{max} = 2.6$). The choice of such values requires the optimal solution to be characterized by a high-density-to-low-density cell number ratio approximately equal to 0.5. The adoption of two very different values for the density (and thus for the stiffness) of the cells of the domain facilitates the identification of the most effective regions of the structure in increasing the overall structural stiffness, i.e. the resisting mechanism.

The fitness function adopted within the optimization genetic algorithm (see Paragraph 4), is:

$$fitness = \frac{K_m}{K_{m,1}} p(\rho) \qquad (6)$$

where K_m is defined in Equation 1, $K_{m,1}$ is the average stiffness of the reference structure with unitary uniform density, and $p(\rho)$ is a penalty function, given by the Gaussian:

$$p(\rho) = \frac{1}{a}\left[\frac{1}{b\sqrt{2\pi}}\exp\left(-\frac{(\rho-1)^2}{2b^2}\right)\right] \qquad (7)$$

with a and b predetermined constants. In the presented examples the adopted value for a is 8.0 and for b is 0.05. By means of the function defined in Equation 7, the solutions, which do not respect the constraint expressed by Equation 2, are penalized.

3 THE CELL METHOD

The Cell Method (CM) (Tonti 2001) is a new numerical method for the solution of field problems, such as elasticity or fluid dynamics. It provides a means of obtaining a discrete formulation of the field equations without resorting to a preliminary differential formulation.

The CM has been adopted in order to carry out the elastic analyses within the algorithm for the search for the resistant mechanism.

The assumption has been made of a plane stress problem in a constant-thickness structure with isotropic material.

The mesh of triangular constant-thickness cells, by means of which the structure has been discretized, is defined as primal complex. The choice of the triangular shape for the cells is not mandatory for the CM, but has been adopted because it provides significant case of modelling, especially in the case of complicated structures with holes and/or irregular shapes. Following the practice of algebraic topology, a branch of topology that uses cell complexes, the vertices, edges, faces and cells are considered as "cells" of dimension zero, one, two, and three, respectively. In short they are denoted as 0-cells, 1-cells, 2-cells and 3-cells.

In addition to the primal cell complex, the CM requires the identification of a dual complex of cells, with 0-cells (nodes) internal to each 3-cell of the primal complex. The choice of position of the vertices (0-cells) of the dual complex within the 3-cells of the primal is as well arbitrary. In the presented examples, the centroidal subdivision has been adopted. The dual complex is thus obtained placing the dual 0-cells corresponding to the centroids of the primal 3-cells and connecting them via the centroids of the primal 2-cells (Fig. 1).

In the discretized field equations, the configuration variables of the problem (i.e. cinematical and geometrical variables like absolute and relative displacements and strains) are written with reference to the 0-cells (nodes) and to 1-cells (sides of the triangles) of the primal cell complex. The source variables (i.e. dynamical and statical variables like body and

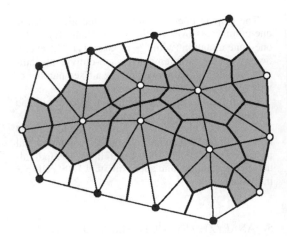

Figure 1.   Primal complex (triangles) and dual complex (polygons).

surface forces and stresses) are written with reference to the 2- and 3-cells (i.e. surfaces and volumes of the polygonal prisms) of the dual complex.

In the hypotheses of homogeneous and isotropic material, and uniform strain field within each single primal 3-cell, the fundamental equation of the system can be written by imposing the equilibrium of each dual 3-cell under the combined action of the external body-, surface- and point forces, and of the surface forces exchanged with the adjacent dual 3-cells through the shared faces (dual 2-cells). These forces are calculated based on the internal deformations in each primal 3-cell, function of the relative displacement of the primal vertices (0-cell) and of the constitutive law of the material.

Furthermore, it is noteworthy that, under the adopted hypotheses, the stiffness matrix obtained through the CM is coincident with the one calculated via classical Finite Elements Methods (FEM).

4   SOLUTION OF THE OPTIMIZATION PROBLEM BY MEANS OF GENETIC ALGORITHMS

The solution approach to the problem of structural optimization has been implemented using the genetic algorithms theory (Golberg 1989, Gen & Cheng 1997).

For a given problem, all the members of the population share the same mesh idealization. The chromosome, i.e. the algorithmic codification of the characteristics of a single individual, is made of a number of genes equal to the total number of the 3-cells of the primal complex. Each gene contains the information on the density of the relevant cell, coded as a real number in the given range.

The genetic operators implemented are a classic one-point cross-over (with 70% probability) and a one-gene mutation (with 5% probability). The evolutionary operator implemented is a 5-individuals tournament with elitarism, maintaining a fixed number of individuals per generation.

The fitness function is defined in Equation 6 and the penalty function in Equation 7.

The genetic algorithm working parameters, tuned down in order to maintain reasonable computational times, are respectively 3000 generations, 100 individuals per generation, and approximately 1200 cells per individual.

5 ANALYZED STRUCTURES AND RESULTS

In the following, some examples of identification of S&T mechanisms in structures with D-regions by means of the proposed approach are presented and discussed.

The dimension of the cells of the meshes is a compromise between the necessity of achieving a sufficient detail in the results and the amount of computing time required. In fact, refining the mesh for a more in-depth evaluation of the problem implies two negative consequences: a) an increase of the size of the matrices of the linear system of Equation 7, which must be solved for each individual of each generation; b) an increase of the length of the chromosome and, in consequence, the size of the population and/or the number of generations needed for convergence.

In the presented Figures, a darker shade of grey represents cells in which the prevailing principal stress is compressive (strut cells) and a lighter shade of grey represents tie cells. White cells can be considered to be almost ineffective due to their lower stiffness (density).

The results are also presented by means of a graphical representation of the principal stresses in each cell.

5.1 Wall with centered transverse load.

The first example refers to a simple case of D-region: a square wall simply supported at the bottom corners and with a vertical point load at the middle of the upper edge (Fig. 2). The S&T mechanism appears clearly already in Figure 3, where the resistant cells are shown in shades of grey. The presence of "voids" within the S&T elements is consistent with the objective of the search, i.e. to identify the solution with the maximum stiffness-to-density ratio. The use of the graphical representation of the principal stresses (Fig. 4) shows more evidently the elements of the resistant mechanism.

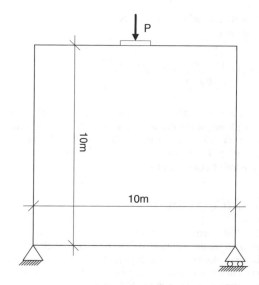

Figure 2. Wall with centered load on top side.

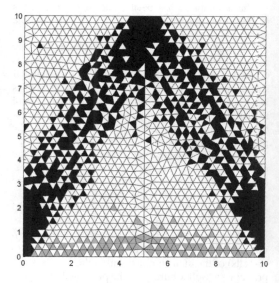

Figure 3. Active cells under prevalent compression (dark grey) and under prevalent tension (light grey).

5.2 Variable cross-section wall

In Figures 5–7 the case of a wall with variable cross-section, loaded on the bottom side is shown. In this case, the locations of all the struts and of the ties around the hole are very well recognizable. Conversely, the identification of the ties radially departing from the internal corners and related to the change of direction

458

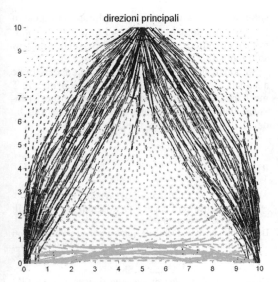

Figure 4. Maximum principal compressive (dark grey) and tensile (light grey) stresses.

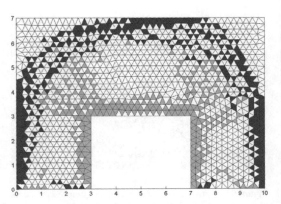

Figure 6. Active cells under prevalent compression (dark grey) and under prevalent tension (light grey).

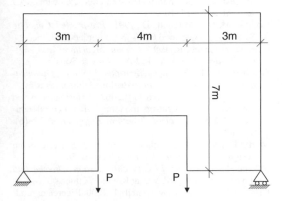

Figure 5. Wall with variable cross-section.

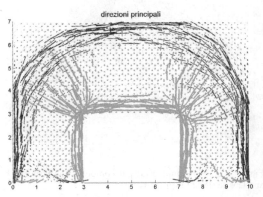

Figure 7. Maximum principal compressive (dark grey) and tensile (light grey) stresses.

of the struts, requires the designer's personal judgment. To this purpose, the graphical representation of the principal stresses is much helpful.

5.3 *Wall with opening and transverse load.*

The last of the presented examples (Figs 8–10) is a classic case (Schlaich & Schäfer 1991). The remarks made for the previous examples are still applicable. The results are comparable with those obtained by a number of researchers by means of different approaches (Baldassino 1998; Orlando et al. 2000).

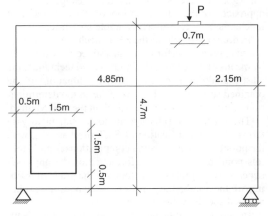

Figure 8. Wall with opening and transverse load.

459

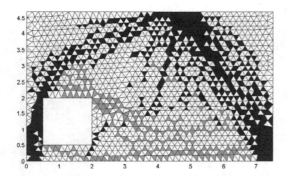

Figure 9. Active cells under prevalent compression (dark grey) and under prevalent tension (light grey).

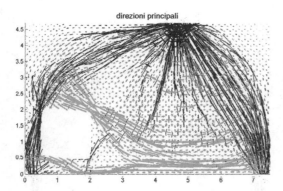

Figure 10. Maximum principal compressive (dark grey) and tensile (light grey) stresses.

6 CONCLUSIONS

The goal of the study was to investigate a new approach to the identification of S & T resistant mechanisms in reinforced concrete structures.

In order to search for the S&T mechanism, the proposed approach performs a constrained maximization by means of a Genetic Algorithm-based technique; the elastic analyses necessary to the evaluation of the obtained solutions, and in particular to the determination of their stress state, are based on the Cell Method.

The obtained results appear to be satisfactory in terms of the identification of S&T mechanisms, with the possible downside being computational time. From this point of view, the performance of the approach depends on a number of factors, i.e. the grade of refining of the mesh, the type of the genetic algorithm adopted and the value of its parameters.

In case of complicated structures the main advantage is just given by the evolutionary approach to the solution, which guarantees the exploration of most of the solutions domain, as opposed to traditional optimization methods which tend to focus on one narrow solution path.

In conclusion, the proposed method appears to be adequate for the automatic determination of S & T mechanisms in reinforced concrete structures, provided that suitable computational resources can be devoted to the solution of the problem.

REFERENCES

ACI. 2002. *ACI-318 Building Code requirements for structural concrete and commentary*. Farmington Hill, MI: American Concrete Institute.

Baldassino, N. 1998. Modellazione strut and tie di elementi strutturali in calcestruzzo armato. in P.G. Malerba (ed.), *Analisi limite e non lineare di strutture in calcestruzzo armato*: 317–352. Udine: CISM.

CEB-FIP. 1993. *Design of concrete structures. CEB-FIP-Model Code 1990*. London: Thomas Telford.

CEN. 1991. *Eurocode 2: Design of concrete structures – part1: general rules and rules for buildings*. ENV 1992-1-1. Bruxelles: Comité Européenne de Normation.

Collins, M.P. & Mitchell, D. 1980. Shear and torsion design of prestressed and non-prestressed concrete beams. *PCI Journal* 25(5): 32–100.

Collins, M.P. & Mitchell, D. 1991. *Prestressed Concrete Structures*. Englewood Cliffs, NJ: Prentice-Hall, Inc.

Gen, M. & Cheng, R. 1997. *Genetic algorithms and engineering design*. New York: John Wiley & Sons.

Goldberg, D.E. 1989. *Genetic Algorithms in Search, Optimization, and Machine Learning*. Boston: Addison-Wesley.

Liang, Q.Q., Uy, B. & Steven, G.P. 2002. Performance-based optimization for strut-tie modeling of structural concrete. *ASCE Journal of Structural Engineering* 128(6): 815–823.

Marti, P. 1985. Basic tools of reinforced concrete beam design. *ACI Structural Journal* 82(1): 46–56.

Mörsch, E. 1912. *Der Eisenbetonbau, seine Theorie und Anvendung*. Stuttgard, Verlag Konrad Wittner.

Orlando, M., Severi, M. & Spinelli, P. 2000. Ricerca di modelli strut-and-tie negli elementi in c.a. mediante un metodo di ottimizzazione strutturale topologica. In *Proc. 13th C.T.E. Congress, Pisa, 9–11 November 2000* (in italian).

Schlaich, J. & Anagnostou, G. 1990. Stress field for nodes of strut-and-tie models. *Journal of Structural Engineering* 116(1): 13–22.

Schlaich, J., Schäfer, K. & Jennewin, M. 1987. Toward a consistent design of structural concrete. *PCI Journal* 32(3): 74–150.

Schlaich, J. & Schäfer, K. 1991. Design and detailing of structural concrete using strut-and-ties models. *The Structural Engineer* 69(6): 113–125.

Tonti, E. 2001. A direct discrete formulation of field laws: the cell method. *Computer Modelling in Engineering and Science CMES* 2(2): 237–258.

System-based Vision for Strategic and Creative Design, Bontempi (ed.)
© 2003 Swets & Zeitlinger, Lisse, ISBN 90 5809 599 1

Strut-and-Tie model of deep beams with web openings using optimisation technique

H. Guan & J. Parsons
School of Engineering, Griffith University Gold Coast Campus, Queensland, Australia

ABSTRACT: Reinforced concrete deep beams, as often used in tall buildings and foundations, are of considerable interest in structural engineering field. Over the past two decades, numerous design models for deep beams have been suggested. However even the latest design codes still offer little insight into the design of deep beams in particular when complexities exist due to the introduction of the web openings. An well-accepted approach for the design of deep beams with openings is the strut-and-tie model, which is primarily used to represent the actual load transfer mechanism in a structural concrete member under ultimate load. In this study, the development of the strut-and-tie model is transformed to the topology optimisation problem of continuum structures, by the use of the Evolutionary Structural Optimisation technique. The optimal strut-and-tie model is generated by gradually removing inefficient material from an over-designed area, until the performance index of progressive topologies reaches the maximum. Both the stress and displacement constraints are taken into consideration in the optimisation process. The influence on the strut-and-tie model in relation to the loading conditions in deep beams is investigated in some detail. The differences in the strut-and-tie model due to the location of openings are also discussed.

1 INTRODUCTION

In the engineering research field, fast, accurate and reliable methods of design are increasingly sort after. As new technology and ideas are generated, better design methods may be established. In recent years structural optimisation has become an area emerging that has the possibility of modifying classical design.

Reinforced concrete deep beam is a type of non-flexural member, which is generally defined as a member that has a span to depth ratio of less than 5. Deep beams have had significant research focus in recent decades. From published experimental studies completed by Kong et al. (1970), Rogowsky et al. (1986), Tan et al. (1995, 1997a, b, c) and Foster & Gilbert (1998), to finite element computer models implemented by Fafitis & Won (1994) and Wang et al. (2001), to the strut-and-tie model by Tan et al. (2002a) and the theoretical techniques related mainly to shear capacity by Ashour (2000), the deep beam interest is substantial.

In various forms of construction, openings in the web area of deep beams are frequently provided for essential services and accessibility, for example door openings, windows, ventilation ducts and heating pipes (Ashour & Rishi 2000). However limited research work has found to be carried out in this area by

Almeida & Pinto (1999), Maxwell & Breen (2000), Ashour & Rishi (2000) and Tan et al. (2002b). The presence of openings induces areas of discontinuity in deep beams, which only enhances the complexity of the nonlinear stress distribution along the depth of the beams. This in turn further complicates the design of deep beams and even the latest design codes still offer little insight into the design. An well-accepted approach for the design of deep beams with openings is the strut-and-tie model, which is primarily used to represent the actual load transfer mechanism in a structural concrete member under ultimate load. However many of the ways used in deriving the strut-and-tie model can be laborious and complex, because the compression strut from the loaded area generally separates and tracks around the opening before joining together again before the supports. This is especially true when predicting the correct strut-and-tie model for members with complex configurations (various location and size of openings) and loading conditions. Hence it would be advantageous if a simple and effective method of generating the strut-and-tie model can be derived.

In this study, the development of the strut-and-tie model is transformed to the topology optimisation problem of continuum structures, by the use of the Evolutionary Structural Optimisation (ESO) technique. The optimal strut-and-tie model is generated by gradually removing inefficient material from an over-designed area, until the performance index of progressive topologies reaches the maximum. Both the stress and displacement constraints are taken into consideration in the optimisation process. The influence on the strut-and-tie model in relation to the loading conditions in deep beams is examined, through the investigation on six simply supported deep beams with web openings. The differences in the strut-and-tie model due to the location of openings are also discussed. In addition, the computer generated optimal strut-and-tie models are compared with the available experimental crack patterns.

2 EVOLUTIONARY STRUCTURAL OPTIMISATION TECHNIQUE

2.1 Optimisation with stress constraint

In this study the strut-and-tie model of deep beams with web openings is developed by means of the Evolutionary Structural Optimisation (ESO) technique (Xie & Steven 1997), with both von Mises stress and displacement constraints.

The ESO method is based on a simple concept that by slowly removing inefficient material from an over-designed area, the residual shape evolves in the direction of making the structure better. In the case of deep beams, when lowly stressed material is re-moved the residual shape should represent the strut-and-tie model.

In the finite element analysis of a deep beam, the von Mises stress of each element σ^e_{VM} and the maximum von Mises stress of the structure $\sigma_{VM,max}$ are evaluated. A deletion criterion is the product of the rejection ratio RR_i and $\sigma_{VM,max}$. This deletion criterion represents the stress at which all elements with a lower stress are deemed insignificant. As such, an element is removed if its σ^e_{VM} is less than the deletion criterion or:

$$\sigma^e_{VM} \leq RR_i \times \sigma_{VM,max} \qquad (1)$$

A small value of RR_i (0.1%) is used to ensure that only a small number of elements are removed each time, where i indicates the iteration number.

2.2 Optimisation with displacement constraint

Quite often in a structure the displacement has to be limited to a certain value. Such displacement constraint is considered by specifying a particular maximum displacement value in the optimisation procedure. When this displacement value is reached the optimisation procedure will be terminated. The displacement control is performed by using a displacement sensitivity number which is expressed as:

$$\alpha_{d,i} = \sum_{k=1}^{L} \sum_{j=1}^{M} \lambda_{jk} \cdot | u_{ij}^T \cdot K_i \cdot u_{ik} | \qquad (2)$$

where $\alpha_{d,i}$ = displacement sensitivity number; u_{ik} = displacement vector of the ith element due to load case P_k; u_{ij} = displacement vector of the ith element due to the virtual unit load F_j; K_i = stiffness matrix of the ith element; L = total number of load cases; M = total number of displacement constraints; $\lambda_{jk} = |u_{jk}|/u_{jk}^*$ = weighting parameter indicating the contribution of the jth displacement constraint under the kth load case; $|u_{jk}|$ = change in displacement; and u_{jk}^* = prescribed displacement value.

In the optimisation process, the sensitivity number $\alpha_{d,i}$ is calculated for each of the elements that satisfies the stress condition (Equation 1). To minimise the displacement change $|u_{jk}|$, a number of elements with the lowest $\alpha_{d,i}$ are removed (Guan et al. 2001).

The finite element analysis followed by systematic removal of lowly stressed elements forms an optimisation cycle where RR_i remains constant. Such cycle or iteration is continued until no more elements are deleted. To proceed to the next iteration, RR_i is increased by adding the evolution ratio ER, which is also taken as 0.1%. The repeated cycle of optimisation process continues until a desired topology is obtained.

2.3 Performance index

As the optimisation cycle progresses, the resulting topology improves with increase in iteration. To identify the final topology which can be translated to the optimal strut-and-tie model, a performance index PI_d in terms of the nodal displacement is used (Liang et al. 2000), or:

$$PI_d = \frac{u_o V_o}{u_i V_i} \qquad (3)$$

where u = nodal displacement at the point where the displacement limit is imposed; V = volume of the structure; and subscripts o and i = the original stage and the ith iteration, respectively.

During the optimisation process, PI_d measures the efficiencies of the progressive topologies. As the optimisation procedure continues, the number of iterations increases, and PI_d also increases, until a certain point where the efficiency or performance of the model deteriorates. The maximum value of PI_d corresponds to the most efficient topology, which would lead to the optimal strut-and-tie model.

3 OPTIMAL STRUT-AND-TIE MODELS

3.1 Deep beam models

The effect one or two point loads has on the strut-and-tie model of deep beams with web openings is investigated (Parsons 2002). The location of openings is also a parameter to be examined. A total of six deep beams are studied and they are categorised into three groups. Each group has two beams, one is subjected to a mid-span concentrated load and the other under two point loads. Group 1 examines the differences in the strut-and-tie model when a single opening is located near the bottom left corner of the beams. Group 2 deals with two openings at mid-depth of the beams. Group 3 is similar to Group 2 except that the two openings are located at the bottom of the beams. All six beams are simply supported. Details and configurations of the six beams are respectively presented in Table 1 and Figure 1.

3.2 *Comparisons and discussions*

All six beams are optimised and the results are compared in three groups. Included in the comparison are the configurations of the beams, the initial, intermediate and final topologies, the optimal strut-and-tie models, as well as available experimental crack patterns. Note that the final topology is determined when the performance index reaches the maximum value. Note also that in the strut-and-tie models, the solid lines represent the tension ties while the dash lines denote the compression struts.

As can be seen in Figure 2 (Group 1), when the opening is located away from the load path, the compression transfer takes the shortest path between the load and support points, as suggested by the right-hand compression struts in both DB1-1-B and DB1-2-B. When the opening falls in the compression transfer path, the strut-and-tie model revolutionizes. This is indicated in both beams where the path are re-routed around the opening, thus introducing tension ties around the opening. As logic would tend to suggest that the compression struts pass the opening on its

left- and right-hand sides, while the tension ties connect the compression zones above and below the openings.

When the opening is close to the bottom of the beam, a horizontal tension tie forms connecting the left and right compression struts below the opening. There tends to be an additional tension tie above the opening in beam when two point loads are present (see DB1-2-B).

Comparisons of deep beams in Group 2 are presented in Figure 3. When the openings are located in the mid-depth of the beam, only one horizontal tension tie is present at the bottom of the beam that unites both left and right compression transfer. In both DB2-1-M and DB2-2-M where openings are located in the compression transfer zones, the load transfer is re-routed around the openings, thus forming additional tension ties at the top and bottom of the openings.

For Group 3, again when the openings are close to the bottom of the beam, an additional horizontal tension tie forms, as in the case of DB2-2-B.

Another important factor to note about the loading condition is that when a single concentrated load is present, a triangle-based strut-and-tie model forms, as can be seen in DB1-1-B, DB2-1-M and DB2-1-B. In this case the left-hand side of the triangle is the left re-routed compression transfer, while the right-hand side is the right compression transfer, with the lower tension tie forming the bottom of the triangle. On the other hand, if two point loads are present a trapezoid-based strut-and-tie model forms, as evident in DB1-2-B, DB2-2-M and DB2-2-B. The left and right re-routed compression transfers and the bottom of the trapezoid are formed in the same manner as the triangle-based strut-and-tie model, however it is necessary to have an additional horizontal strut between the loaded points to form the top side of the trapezoid.

Table 1. Details of deep beams.

Beam designation*	DB1-1-B	DB1-2-B	DB2-1-M	DB2-2-M	DB2-1-B	DB2-2-B
Overall dimensions (mm × mm)	1060 × 450	1325 × 750	1950 × 1000	1425 × 750	1300 × 750	1325 × 750
Number of opening(s)	1	1	2	2	2	2
Size of Openings (mm × mm)	200 × 150	225 × 150	200 × 200	225 × 150	225 × 150	225 × 150
Location of openings from bottom (mm)	100	100	400	300	100	100
Number of point load(s)	1	2	1	2	1	2
Magnitude of load(s) (kN)	210	97.5 × 2	618	720 × 2	97.5	97.5 × 2
Young's Modulus (×10⁴ MPa)	4.2095	3.0699	3.1451	2.8600	3.0966	3.0966
Poisson's ratio	0.2	0.15	0.2	0.15	0.15	0.15
Thickness of beam (mm)	100	100	100	100	100	100

*Note: DB–deep beam; first number – number of opening(s); second number – number of point load(s); B – opening at bottom; M – opening at mid-depth.

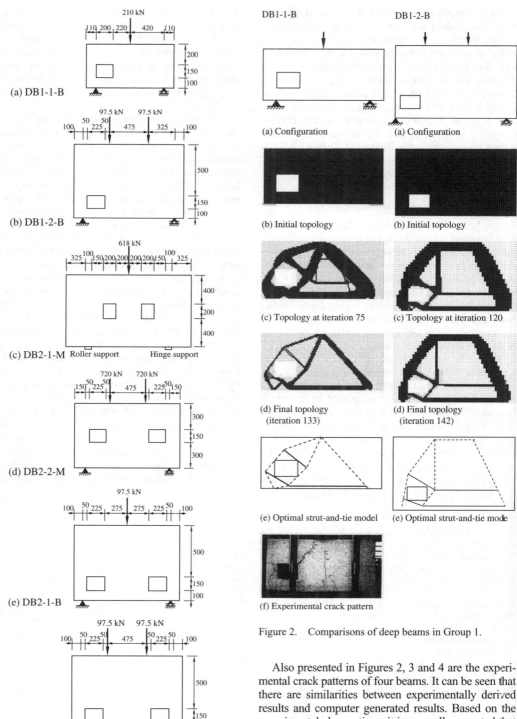

(a) DB1-1-B

(b) DB1-2-B

618 kN

(c) DB2-1-M   Roller support   Hinge support

720 kN   720 kN

(d) DB2-2-M

97.5 kN

(e) DB2-1-B

97.5 kN   97.5 kN

(f) DB2-2-B

Figure 1.   Configurations of deep beams.

DB1-1-B   DB1-2-B

(a) Configuration   (a) Configuration

(b) Initial topology   (b) Initial topology

(c) Topology at iteration 75   (c) Topology at iteration 120

(d) Final topology   (d) Final topology
(iteration 133)   (iteration 142)

(e) Optimal strut-and-tie model (e) Optimal strut-and-tie model

(f) Experimental crack pattern

Figure 2.   Comparisons of deep beams in Group 1.

Also presented in Figures 2, 3 and 4 are the experimental crack patterns of four beams. It can be seen that there are similarities between experimentally derived results and computer generated results. Based on the experimental observations, it is generally accepted that the first cracks appear at the top and bottom of the openings provided that the opening is in the compression transfer zone. As the load increases these cracks

464

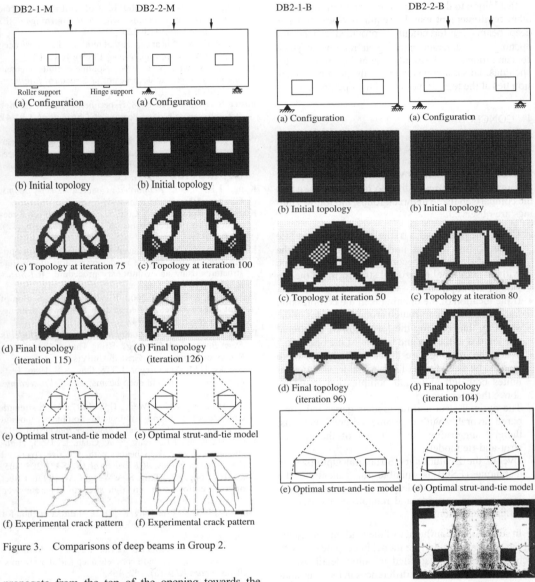

DB2-1-M

DB2-2-M

(a) Configuration

Roller support   Hinge support

(a) Configuration

(b) Initial topology

(b) Initial topology

(c) Topology at iteration 75

(c) Topology at iteration 100

(d) Final topology
(iteration 115)

(d) Final topology
(iteration 126)

(e) Optimal strut-and-tie model

(e) Optimal strut-and-tie model

(f) Experimental crack pattern

(f) Experimental crack pattern

Figure 3.   Comparisons of deep beams in Group 2.

DB2-1-B

DB2-2-B

(a) Configuration

(a) Configuration

(b) Initial topology

(b) Initial topology

(c) Topology at iteration 50

(c) Topology at iteration 80

(d) Final topology
(iteration 96)

(d) Final topology
(iteration 104)

(e) Optimal strut-and-tie model

(e) Optimal strut-and-tie model

(f) Experimental crack pattern

Figure 4.   Comparisons of deep beams in Group 3.

propagate from the top of the opening towards the loaded area and from the bottom of the opening towards the closest support. In addition to this diagonal or shear cracking, flexural cracking can occur at the bottom of the beams. However in relation to the distance that these flexural cracks extend, and the crack width at failure, they are generally considered to be minor issues, and the more predominate cracks that occur are shear related. Therefore it is safe to assume that the top and bottom of the opening are under high tensile stresses because that is where the first major cracks appear.

It should also be noted that the bottom of the beam also experiences reasonably high tensile forces. Therefore it is logical to place steel reinforcement in

these sections to counteract the low-tension capacity of concrete. Therefore as the strut-and-tie model is used to determine reinforcement layout it would be expected that tension ties would form in these places. As can be seen in all the beams under consideration, this is generally what happens. Thus it can be concluded that the computer generated strut-and-tie model does accurately predict where the steel reinforcement is to be placed.

465

In addition to these counter tension reinforcements, other reinforcement may be required. Some-times in deep beams reinforcement is provided around the opening to counteract cracking at regions of stress concentrations which would occur at the corners of the openings. This is again verified by the presence of tension ties at the top and bottom of the openings.

4 CONCLUSIONS

In this study, the influence on the strut-and-tie model in relation to the loading conditions in deep beams is examined, through the investigation on six simply supported deep beams with web openings. Based on the comparison made in three groups, the follow findings are observed:

- Under one point load, a triangle-based strut-and-tie model forms, whereas under two point loads, the strut-and-tie model becomes trapezoid in shape with an additional horizontal strut forming the top side of the trapizoid;
- If the location of the opening is in the compression transfer zone, it is re-routed around the sides of the opening, thus causing the formation of additional tension ties at the top and bottom of the opening;
- When the openings are lower in the beams there tends to be an addition of horizontal tension tie that unites both left and right compression transfers, above the openings;
- The optimal strut-and-tie models generated compared favorably with experimental crack patterns, thereby suggesting the accuracy of the optimal strut-and-tie models;
- Overall the Evolutionary Structural Optimization technique (ESO) is suitable for generating the strut-and-tie model in deep beams with web openings, as it is accurate and reliable in a variety of different situations.

In summary, the influence of the loading conditions on the optimal strut-and-tie model in deep beams with web openings is investigated in some detail. Along with this investigation, the differences in the strut-and-tie models due to the location of openings are also discussed. The study has provided some insights into various parameters that affect the load transfer mechanisms of deep beams with openings. The ESO method has proven to be accurate and efficient in generating the strut-and-tie model for a variety of deep beams with web openings.

REFERENCES

Almeida, A. & Pinto, N. 1999. High strength concrete deep beams with web openings. *ACI Special publications* l(186): 567–613.

Ashour, A.F. & Rishi, G. 2000. Tests of reinforced concrete continuous deep beams with web openings. *ACI Structural J* 97(3): 418–426.

Ashour, A.F. 2000. Shear capacity of reinforced concrete deep beams. *J Structural Engineering* 126(9): 1045–1052.

Fafitis, A. & Won, Y.H. 1994. Nonlinear finite element analysis of concrete deep beams. *J Structural Engineering* 120(4): 1202–1220.

Foster, S. & Gilbert, R. 1998. Experimental studies on high strength concrete deep beams. *ACI Structural J* 95(4): 382–390.

Guan, H., Chen, Y.J. & Loo, Y.C. 2001. Topology optimisation of bridge type structures with stress and displacement constraints. *International J Computational Engineering Science* 2(2): 199–221.

Kong, F.K. 1990. *Reinforced Concrete Deep Beams*. Glasgow: Blackie and Sons Ltd.

Kong, F.K., Robins, P.J. & Cole, D.F. 1970. Web reinforcement effects on deep beams. *ACI J, Proceedings* 67(12): 1010–1017.

Liang, Q.Q., Xie, Y.M. & Steven, G.P. 2000. Topology optimisation of strut and tie model in reinforced concrete structures using an evolutionary procedure. *ACI Structural J* 97(2): 322–330.

Maxwell, B. & Breen, J. 2000. Experimental evaluation of strut and tie model applied to deep beam with opening. *ACI Structural J* 97(1): 142–148.

Parsons, J. 2002. *Optimisation of the Strut and Tie Model in Deep Beams with Openings*. BEng Thesis. Gold Coast: School of Engineering, Griffith University.

Rogowsky, D.M., MacGregor, J.G. & Ong, S.Y. 1986. Tests of reinforced concrete deep beams. *ACI J, Proceedings* 83(8): 614–623.

Tan, K.H., Kong, F.K. & Weng, L.W. 1997a. High strength concrete deep beams subject to combined top-and bottom-loading. *The Structural Engineer* 75(11): 191–197.

Tan, K.H., Kong, F.K., Teng, S. & Guan, L. 1995. High-strength concrete deep beams with effective span and shear span variations. *ACI Structural J* 92(S37): 395–405.

Tan, K.H., Kong, F.K., Teng, S. & Weng, L.W. 1997b. Effect of web reinforcement on high strength concrete deep beams. *ACI Structural J* 94(5): 572–582.

Tan, K.H., Tang, C.Y. & Tong, K. 2002a. A direct method for deep beams with web reinforcement. *Magazine of Concrete Research*.

Tan, K.H., Teng, S., Kong, F.K. & Lu, H.Y. 1997c. Main tension steel in high strength concrete deep and short beams. *ACI Structural J* 94(6): 752–768.

Tan, K.H., Tong, K. & Tang, C.Y. 2002b. Consistent strut-and-tie modelling of deep beams with web openings. *Magazine of Concrete Research*.

Wang, F., Teng, S. & Fan, S.C. 2001. Softened damage model for finite element analysis of structural concrete deep beams. *ACI Structural J* 98(1): 27–34.

Xie, Y.M. & Steven, G.P. 1997. *Evolutionary Structural Optimisation*. London: Springer-Verlag.

System-based Vision for Strategic and Creative Design, Bontempi (ed.)
© 2003 Swets & Zeitlinger, Lisse, ISBN 90 5809 599 1

Analysis and optimization of a cable stayed bridge with external prestressing

G. Agostino
Civil Engineer Structural in Rome, Italy

ABSTRACT: In this occasion, a modelling structures with prefabricated collected ashlars through external prestressing, is applied to a cable stayed bridge to only span. Such modelling has for purpose the description of behaviour on service of structure as well as the research of optimal disposition of cables. All manages to an algorithm of calculation that has like object of optimization process the number minimization of cables to use (less cost) and of deformations sustained by the structure (durability major).

1   INTRODUCTION

In the last years the technique of external prestressing, as well as that with unbonded cables, that it represents of conceptual point of view a particular case of the first, it is getting a notable development, in a particular way at France and United States. This development is due to fact that this technique involves great advantages, either from economic point of view or to that structural. Such positive aspects are excited later on, if this technique is joined in prefabrication of decks through combined ashlars. At the same time, this structural technique is unfavourable from static point of view, because it presents a strength to inner break as regards to technique of traditional inner prestressing.

And so on it is formulated a simple modelling of structures with collected prefabricated ashlars through external prestressing or unbonded, that it looks for describe in an exhaustive way the behaviour in a phase of exercise. This modelling takes to an algorithm of calculation that has like purpose the research of optimal disposition of plan of cables all the time in conditions of exercise.

2   MODEL OF CALCULATION

The structure is schematized (Fig. 1) through a set plain elements beam (x) and of joints (y) that keep, among them, the structural continuity since we get in phase of exercise. Elements beam schematize the prefabricated ashlars.

This modelling of structure, that is the fundamental hypothesis of structural continuity among elements

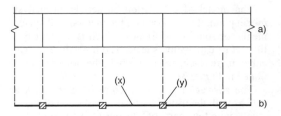

Figure 1.   a) Real structure, b) schematized structure.

beam, is justified from fact that the study is here faced only to the phase in exercise, they establish the absence of traction in joints, from which they obtain the absence of opening of joints and so the continuity above mentioned.

Although it regards the cables of prestressing, these are schematized like provided elements with only extensional rigidity and they are bounded only in the joints where are present the anchorage of same cables. They get in the model of calculation like nodal forces N (draught of cables) and $M = N \times e$ (moment is due to eccentricity of cables). The tract of structure established from ashlar generic, it will be therefore schematized as reported in Figure 2.

In the model of calculation, we leave out the effect arch that it establishes between the prestressing cables and the structure in R.C., once that the structure sustains some deformations, while they consider the variation of draught of cables between the initial and final conditions. The draught in generic cable, is considered constant along all the tract of cable that it goes from anchorage to other and it will result dependent on

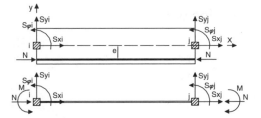

Figure 2.   Schematization generic ashlar.

displacements sustained from joints where have placed the devices of anchorage of the same cable.

Although it regards the materials, they have to face a linear analysis, is assumed that their behaviour is of linear elastic type.

The linear analysis is justified to results of experimental tests, existing in the literature, that they show a linear elastic behaviour of structure in phase of exercise before the opening of joints (in the case of beams to ashlar) or before of cracking (in the case of monolithic beams).

The model of calculation oneself is an analysis model plain, it is imposed on the method of displacements for solution of frames, which is implemented like set of calculation sheets. The procedures of calculation are re-engaged, briefly in the flowchart mentioned in Figure 3.

The answer of set of structure is re-engaged, as well as with the usual charts of stresses and displacements, with the charts of tensions to every joint.

Although it regards different dispositions of cables, these are obtained through an automatic procedure that explores in a casual way the different configurations. This happens fixing the value zero and one to inner of a table composed to a number of lines equal to ashlars that compose the beam and to a number of columns equal to a number of present cables, except one, the barycentric cable, that is always present because it is necessary to keep connected among them all ashlars of structure. Therefore to consider the element generic i-j at inner of table, if in it there is the value one this involves that in the ashlar i the cable j is present; the value zero means, instead, that in the ashlar i the cable j it is absent (Tab. 1)

Among infinite dispositions of cables that they'll result individual in a casual way, through a function of "search objective", only that satisfy all the imposed restraints are considered (principally, absence of tensions of traction and not overcoming of limit value of tension of compression in concrete).

Subsequently among this group of dispositions "possible" of cables, is chosen that optimal, that is that to which result minimum maximum values and minimum of deformed and the number of dispositions of anchorage of cables, that is the number of cables.

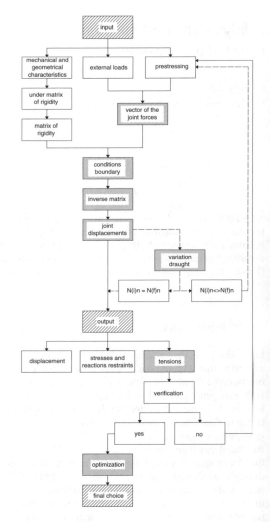

Figure 3.   Flowchart.

Table 1.   Disposition cables.

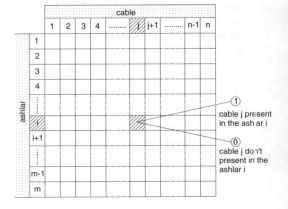

468

3 APPLICATION

The illustrated application in succession regards the plan of a stayed bridge with one span (length L = 121,5 m) and with only pole placed to external of deck (Fig. 4, 5, 6).

This work results that is established from the following structural elements:

– *Beam of deck* to prefabricated collected ashlars in dry with external prestressing of total length equal to 121,5 m, the ashlars are in total nine and have, every one, length of 13,5 m.

The section of generic prefabricated ashlar is a section caisson in reinforced concrete with slow framework that don't pass to an ashlar to other.

The complete section of all deck (Fig. 8) instead includes, as well as the section of ashlar, all additional works realized in following phases to position of ashlars.

– Pole in prestressing reinforced concrete, of height H = 50 m with inclination as regards to horizontal α = 55°, placed on the outside of deck in central position as regards to cross obstruction of the same. The section of pole is a rectangular section empty, in prestressing reinforced concrete, variable along the height: inner opening of dimensions equal to 2 m × 4 m; external obstruction with a short side equal to 5 m constant along the height and the long side variable between 15 m at the base

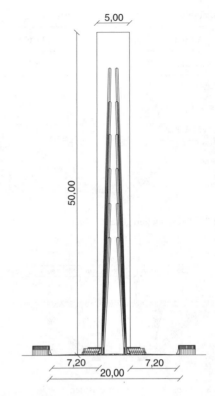

Figure 6.   Cross profile.

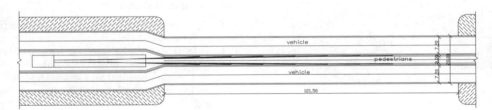

Figure 4.   Generic planimetry.

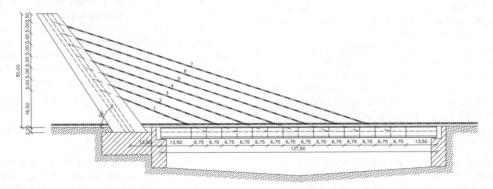

Figure 5.   Longitudinal profile.

Table 2.   Geometrical characteristics.

A (m^2)	y_{inf} (m)	y_{sup} (m)	I (m^4)
21,21	2,80	2,20	78,80

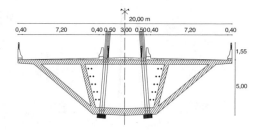

Figure 7.   Cross section generic ashlar.

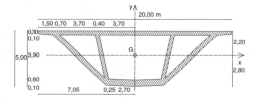

Figure 8.   Cross section generic ashlar.

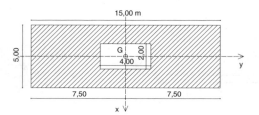

Figure 9.   Cross section of base of pole.

and 9 m to the top to the same pole. In Figure 9 and Figure 10 have reported the cross sections of pole in two specific points.

– Stays in steel, in number equal to 7, they anchored along the beam of deck in agreement of middle (at longitudinal sense) of every ashlar, excluded those of extremity (ashlar 1 and ashlar 9), and along the pole to a distance in vertical, one as regards to other, of 5 m, with the anchorage of stay n° 7 placed to 3,5 m from the top of pole. Every stay is composed from two cables with equal number of strands (Tab. 3).

The draught to assign stays has been defined so that to recover the fall of deck is due to its weight and to permanent loads (p$_1$, p$_2$). To a value of draughts we have arrived applying the "method of forces" to beam

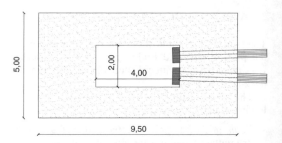

Figure 10.   Cross section pole in agreement of anchorage of stay n° 7.

Table 3.   Characteristic of stays.

n° stay	n° strands 0,6" to stay	n° strands 0,6" to cable	Draught (KN)	Inclination long. (°)	Inclination trasv. (°)	Length (m)
1	230	115	35114,98	21,78	85,67	56.87
2	126	63	19290,46	20,38	86,68	74.96
3	174	87	26611,79	19,56	87,3	92.93
4	164	82	25099,78	19,01	87,73	110.82
5	182	91	27882,47	18,63	88,04	128.67
6	140	70	21342,7	18,35	88,28	146.49
7	274	137	41882,92	18,12	88,47	164.3

constituent the deck. The mechanical and geometrical characteristics of strands are:

– $f_{p(0,1)k} = 1670$ N/mm^2, characteristic tension residual deformation 0,1%;
– $f_{pt} = 1870$ N/mm^2, characteristic tension of break;
– $E_p = 197200$ N/mm^2, elastic modulus;
– $A_p = 139$ mm^2, nominal area strand single;
– $\Phi_p = 15,2$ mm = 0,6", nominal diameter strand single.

In this occasion, they concentrate the attention on the plan and the verification of beam of deck, with the purpose to find those dispositions of cables to prestressing (rectilinear from joint to joint), so to avoid that it is verified the opening of joints in a phase of exercise. As result of that they consider only the analysis of the loads as regards, to the beam of deck from which we obtain the following values:

– ashlar 1–9: permanent p$_1$ = 622,19 KN/m; accidental q = 84 KN/m;
– ashlar 2-3-4-5-6-7-8: permanent p$_2$ = 623,62 KN/m; accidental q = 84 KN/m.

As well as, in agreement of schematized joints the anchorages of stays with the ashlars, are applied some concentrated equivalent forces to draught assigned to the same stays.

The beam of deck has been shematized (Fig. 11) as a set of elements beam that represent the prefabricated ashlars, and a set of joints that represent the bonds between the ashlars and points of anchorage of ashlars with same stays. The conditions of load to consider in following analysis are:

– C1: stays + permanent + prestressing;
– C2: stays + permanent + prestressing + accidental.

For constituent materials the beam are chosen mechanical characteristics as following:

– Concrete:
   $f_{ck} = 37,35\,N/mm^2$, characteristic strength cylinder;
   $R_{ck} = 45\,N/mm^2$, characteristic strength cubic;
   $E_c = 38237\,N/mm^2$, elastic modulus;
– Steel to prestressing:
   $f_{p(0,1)k} = 1670\,N/mm^2$, characteristic tension residual deformation 0,1%;

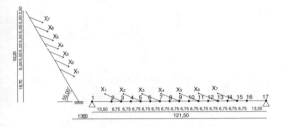

Figure 11. Calculation model.

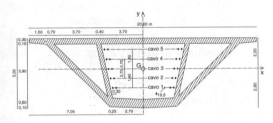

Figure 12. Position cables to prestressing.

Table 4. Possible dispositions of cables.

Dispos. n° cables	n° anchorage	Condition of load	max. height (mm)	height max./span	min. height (mm)	σ_{cmin} (N/mm²)	σ_{cmax} (N/mm²)
D1 36 72	1	0,00	0,00003	**3,36**	1,13	10,72
	2	−76,19	−0,00063	0,00	0,18	12,42
D2 36 72	1	−0,59	0,00001	1,94	1,79	11,61
	2	−78,66	−0,00065	0,00	0,20	13,22
D3 40 80	1	0,00	0,00004	**5,27**	1,79	12,17
	2	−73,84	−0,00061	0,00	0,20	12,85
D4 40 80	1	0,00	0,00003	4,12	1,13	12,44
	2	−75,61	−0,00062	0,00	0,23	13,65
D5 48 96	1	−0,93	−0,00001	**0,73**	1,79	11,95
	2	**−79,62**	−0,00065	0,00	0,13	13,65
D6 40 80	1	−0,53	0,00003	3,53	1,13	11,85
	2	−75,93	−0,00062	0,00	0,18	13,56
D7 40 80	1	0,00	0,00002	2,41	1,79	12,21
	2	−76,95	−0,00063	0,00	0,17	13,37

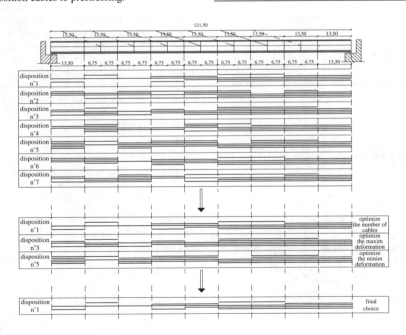

Figure 13. Process choice of disposition cables.

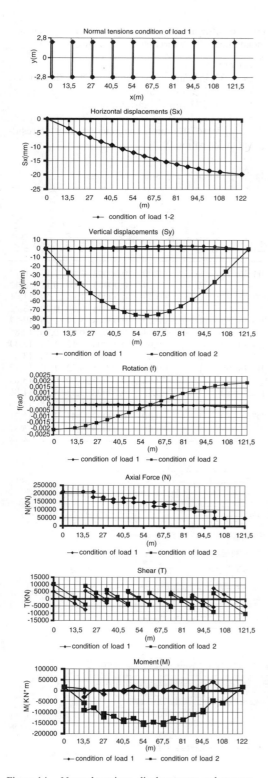

Figure 14. Normal tensions, displacements and stresses.

Table 5. Table of disposition cables.

Ashlar	Cable 1	Cable 2	Cable 3	Cable 4	Cable 5
C1	1	0	1	0	1
C2	0	0	1	0	1
C3	0	0	1	0	0
C4	1	0	1	1	0
C5	0	1	1	1	0
C6	1	1	1	0	1
C7	1	1	1	0	1
C8	1	1	1	1	0
C9	1	1	1	1	0

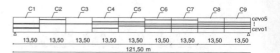

Figure 15. Optimal disposition of cables along structure.

$f_{pt} = 1870 \, \text{N/mm}^2$, characteristic tension of break;
$E_p = 197200 \, \text{N/mm}^2$, elastic modulus.

The restraints to respect in each part of structure and to every conditions of load are following:

$\sigma_{cmin} > 0$;
$\sigma_{cmax} < 0,6 \, f_{ck} = 22,41 \, \text{N/mm}^2$;
$\sigma_{pi} < 0,85 \, f_{p(0,1)k} = 1420 \, \text{N/mm}^2$;
$\sigma_{pf} < 0,6 \, f_{ptk} = 1122 \, \text{N/mm}^2$;

The cables to prestressing, of which is necessary to find the optimal disposition, are indicated like: cable1, cable2, cable3 (always present along the structure so that it keeps jointly all the ashlar), cable 4 and cable 5; each of them represent a resultant cable with eccentricity prearranged as regards to the barycentre G. Each of five resultant cables is established to four cables to 20 strands mm each one, they have placed symmetrically as regards to barycentre G so that it doesn't cause torsional effects (Fig. 12).
To every strands you have:

– $A_p = 139 \, \text{mm}^2$, nominal area;
– $\sigma_{pi} = 1316 \, \text{N/mm}^2$, tension of stretching;
– $\Delta\sigma_{r\infty} = 0,18\sigma_{pi} = 237 \, \text{N/mm}^2$, losses of relaxing;
– $\sigma_{pf} = \sigma_{pi} - \Delta\sigma_{r\infty} = 1079 \, \text{N/mm}^2$, tension of stretching in exercise (or final);

The draught in exercise, to every resultant cable, it is equal to $T = 4 \, (20\sigma_{pf} \times A_p) = 12000 \, \text{KN}$.
From code calculation result seven possible dispositions of cables that satisfy the limitations of cables that above mentioned; so dispositions are characterized from the sizes reported in Tab. 4.
In the same table, the number of cables is reported to number of total present cables in the structure, every one formatted from twenty strands and two final anchorages. The disposition selected of cables is

472

Table 6. Variation of draught DT for condition of load 2.

Ashlar	Cable 1		Cable 2		Cable 3		Cable 4		Cable 5	
	ΔT (KN)	ΔT (%)	ΔT (KN)	ΔT (%)	ΔT (KN)	ΔT (%)	ΔT (KN)	ΔT (%)	ΔT (KN)	ΔT (%)
C1	−540,4	−4,50	0,00	0,00	−354,4	2,95	0,00	0,00	0,00	0,00
C2	0,00	0,00	0,00	0,00	−354,4	−2,95	0,00	0,00	−597,1	−4,97
C3	0,00	0,00	0,00	0,00	−354,4	−2,95	0,00	0,00	0,00	0,00
C4	−314,0	−2,62	0,00	0,00	−354,4	−2,95	−454,9	−3,79	0,00	0,00
C5	0,00	0,00	−206,6	−1,72	−354,4	−2,95	−454,9	−3,79	0,00	0,00
C6	−145,9	−1,21	−206,6	−1,72	−354,4	−2,95	0,00	0,00	−407	−3,39
C7	−145,9	−1,21	−206,6	−1,72	−354,4	−2,95	0,00	0,00	−407	−3,39
C8	−145,9	−1,21	−206,6	−1,72	−354,4	−2,95	−175,5	−1,46	0,00	0,00
C9	−145,9	−1,21	−206,6	−1,72	−354,4	−2,95	−175,5	−1,46	0,00	0,00

that minimizes the maximum and minimum height as well as the number of cables. In this case, because, none of seven solutions minimize at the same time the three function object above mentioned, it is necessary to choice between:

- the D1 that minimize the number of cable;
- the D3 that minimize the maximum height;
- the D5 that minimize the minimum height.

To examine the three dispositions above mentioned, it is considered optimal the disposition n°1, because as well as to have the minor number of cables and so to be economically advantageous, it has an oscillation between the maximum height and minimum height (that is between the condition of load 1 and 2) very near to that minimum assumed of the disposition n°3. To disposition selected, summary in Table 5e, Figure 15, it is reported:

- the normal tensions in agreement of joints to the condition of load 1 (Fig. 14);

- the displacements and the characteristics of stress over the structure to every conditions of load (Fig. 14);
- the variation of draught DT to every cable is due to deformation of structure for condition of load 2 (Tab. 6).

REFERENCES

Virlogeux, M. 1983. La précontrainte extérieure. *Annales de l'ITBTP* n°420, dicembre 1983; Beton 219.

Virlogeux, M. 1991. La précontrainte et la construction des ponts à précontrainte extérieure au béton, in: La précontrainte extérieure. Le point de la question aujourd'hui (prima e seconda parte). *Annales de l'ITBTP*, n°498–499, novembre – dicembre 1991; Béton 283–284.

Bussi, F., Morano, S.G. 2000. Analisi fino a rottura di travi a conci prefabbricati e precompressione esterna, in *L'industria italiana del cemento*, Luglio–Agosto 2000.

System-based Vision for Strategic and Creative Design, Bontempi (ed.)
© *2003 Swets & Zeitlinger, Lisse, ISBN 90 5809 599 1*

Searching for innovative structural layouts by means of graph grammars and evolutionary optimization

A. Borkowski
Institute of Fundamental Technological Research, Warsaw, Poland

E. Grabska, P. Nikodem & B. Strug
Institute of Computer Science, Jagiellonian University, Krakow, Poland

1 INTRODUCTION

The aim of this research project is to develop new tools for the optimum design of skeletal structures. Contrary to presently available software that enables the user to optimize parameters of a structure having a priori given layout, the new system will generate layouts automatically or semi-automatically. The importance of layout optimization has been convincingly presented in the review paper by Rozvany et al. (1995).

Until now three main approaches were proposed for the layout optimization. One of them, made popular by the monograph written by Bendsoe (1995), is based upon the theory of homogenization. The second approach starts with random placement of cavities that are further subject to adaptation (Eschenauer & Schumacher 1994). This seems to lead to shorter calculation times as compared to the homogenization since the interior of cavities needs not to be processed. The third method follows the line of smooth optimization with the sensitivity analysis and the concept of topological derivative as its main part (Bojczuk & Mróz 1999). This derivative relates the cost of the structure with a certain change in its layout, e.g., with the introduction of a new node. After such derivative is obtained, the further procedure follows conventional gradient-based search.

In our opinion neither of the above-mentioned approaches takes into account the combinatory nature of the layout optimization problem. We believe that the natural way of thinking about the layout is to represent it in the form of a graph. Taking structural components as letters of an alphabet and casting their assembly rules into a grammar, we obtain a formal language describing certain class of structures. The present paper extends this methodology by combining the graph-based description with the genetic search.

2 OPTIMIZATION PROBLEMS IN MECHANICS

Prior to further considerations it is worth recalling the general formulations of optimum design in mechanics of continuum. Let deformable body of volume V be enclosed by a surface S (Fig. 1). The part S_t of this surface is subject to traction $\mathbf{t}$, the part S_u is fixed and the remaining part S_f is free.

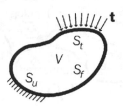

Figure 1. Deformable body.

Optimum design problems for such a body can be cast into 3 categories listed in Table 1. The optimization of support means that we are looking for such shape of the supporting part S_u of the body's surface that corresponds to the minimum total reaction force. The optimization of loading means that we are looking for such shape of the loaded part S_t of the body's surface that corresponds to the maximum total load. Both problems fall beyond the scope of the present paper. Let us consider, therefore, the optimum design of the deformable solid itself.

In this problem we consider S_t, S_u and t to be given. The goal of the optimization is to minimize the compliance of the body expressed in terms of the work done by the load t on the displacement u.

The main alternative is either to look for the optimal shape of the body or to optimize its internal structure (topology) (Fig. 2). Shape optimization is easier: we take the properties of body's material as given (e.g. homogeneous) and our goal is to find the best configuration of the free surface S_f.

The choice of topological optimization opens new alternatives. First, we may consider interior of the body to be a single-connected region filled with a material of variable density ρ. Assuming that the total amount of the material is fixed, we may look then for the best way of distributing that material within the body (compare Bletzinger et al. 1991).

Second, we may introduce cavities into V and we may optimize their shape, position and number under given properties of material surrounding them. This option is based upon the assumption of multiple connectivity

of V. There is, of course, whole spectrum of intermediate granularity of internal structure between the above mentioned two options (composites, periodic non-homogeneity, etc.).

Finally, we may give up the continuum model and fill V with a discrete structure, e.g. a collection of structural elements connected to each other in certain way. In the sequel we follow this approach for a simple reason: solutions of topological optimization problems tend to reveal discrete nature. We believe that it might be advantageous to begin with a discrete description of the problem instead of forcing the continuous model to reproduce the discrete optimal structure in an artificial way.

Let the considered object consist of m elements connected at n nodes. The optimum design of such object can be considered at three levels (Fig. 3):

– component level;
– geometry level;
– topology level.

At the topological level we must answer the following questions:

1. What is the best set of components (primitives) from which we are going to build the object?
2. How these components are to be connected?

Natural way to reason about topology is offered by mathematical linguistics: the first question regards the choice of *vocabulary*, the second one may be answered by choosing proper *grammar*. Since spatial relations between the components can be quite complicated, a string grammar would be insufficient. Therefore, we use graph grammars for the description of topology.

At the geometrical level we position components in space. If our object would be a truss, then the coordinates of nodes would be optimized at this level. Finally, at the component level we are looking for the best attributes of individual elements of the structure (e.g. the cross-sectional areas of bars or the parameters of their material).

These three levels build a hierarchical ontology leading from the higher abstraction (topology) towards the lower one (components). Strictly speaking, all

Table 1. Main alternatives in optimum design.

	Object of optimization		
	Body	Support	Loading
Given	S_t, S_u, t	S_t, t, ρ	S_u, ρ
To be found	S_f or ρ	S_u	S_t, t
Minimized	S_t	S_u	S_t

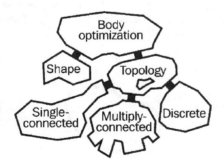

Figure 2. Structure of body optimization problem.

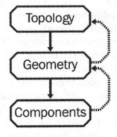

Figure 3. Multilevel optimization.

476

three levels are mutually coupled: the best topological solution is influenced by geometrical considerations that in turn depend to certain extent on components. However, a brute force attempt to solve the optimization problem in one step would be computationally too expensive. Therefore, in practice the coupling between levels is either completely or partially neglected. Solutions obtained this way should be regarded as suboptimal. It does not preclude their usefulness since anyway nobody expects the single-criterion optimization to produce the final design.

In order to overcome the above-mentioned complexity of the problem, we adopt the following multistep approach. First, we take components as being homogeneous and we choose a certain simple overall shape of the designed object. Under such assumptions, we perform the optimization of topology.

The second step is to find optimum geometry (shape) of the object that has the topology found in the previous step and the homogeneous components. During the third step we optimize the properties of components maintaining the topology and the geometry from the previous steps.

Usually the resulting solution is satisfactory. Otherwise, we can repeat the sequence of partial optimization until subsequent sub-optimal solutions show little difference.

3 GENERATING STRUCTURE BY GRAPH GRAMMAR

Conventional evolutionary techniques do not provide a flexible representation to handle nature of design, which is particularly important in conceptual and creative design. This paper presents our attempt of developing a new computational framework that supports design process in an evolutionary approach.

Our method is based upon the knowledge representation scheme proposed by the second author (Grabska 1994). This scheme is called the *composite knowledge representation*. First, the user defines internal structures of design solutions within the framework of graph transformations. A design solution structure is represented by a composition graph (CP-graph), i.e., a special directed graph with nodes representing components of the structure and edges describing relation between those components. To generate CP-graphs a finite mechanism of graph grammars is used. A family of CP-graphs can be generated by means of a graph grammar. Such a grammar describes all formally correct solutions, in our case – the layouts of the structure.

Graph grammars are systems of graph transformations in accord with formal rules called *productions*. Each production is composed of two graphs named left-hand side and right-hand side. The latter graph can replace the former if the former appear in the graph to be transformed. A CP-graph grammar allows one to generate potentially large numbers of layouts of design solutions. In order to restrict the number of generated solutions, one introduces a control diagram. This diagram defines the sequence in which grammar rules are to be applied.

Experience gained so far in this project has shown that plain graphs are less convenient for structural description than hierarchical graphs. The latter allow the designer to reason about the structure at different levels of abstraction. For instance, given a component layout, a designer might want a detailed view down to the level of sub-components together with relation between them. On the other hand, the de-signer, walking through some use case scenarios, will want a much-elided view of these same components. But, he is still working at the same layout, irrespective of a level of abstraction.

In our approach, nodes of hierarchical CP-graphs (hCP-graphs) can contain internal nodes. These nodes, called children, can in turn contain other internal nodes and can be connected to other nodes with the exception of its ancestor.

Figure 4 shows an example of a hCP-graph. Node $v7$ is a child of $v6$ and descendant of $v5$ so $v6$ is a direct ancestor of $v7$ and $v5$ is its ancestor and at the same time a direct ancestor of $v6$. More formally, a *hierarchical node* is a triple (i, B, C), where i is a node identifier, B is a set of bonds and C is a set of node's children. A bond is a pair (i, id), where i is an identifier of the node to which the bond belongs and id is the identifier of the bond itself. A node with no children is called a *simple node*. An edge e is a set $\{b, b'\}$, where b and b' are bonds belonging to nodes connected by the edge e. Node $v1$, shown in Fig. 4, is defined as $v1 = (1, 0, \{v2, v3\})$, and node $v4 = (4, \{(4, 1),(4, 2)\}, 0)$. In this example, the nodes $v2, v3, v4, v7$ and $v8$ are simple nodes, i.e., they do not contain internal nodes.

Let X be a set of hierarchical nodes with finite number of bonds and children. A hierarchical CP-graph

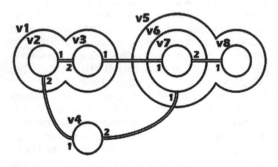

Figure 4.   Example of hierarchical graph.

G is defined as a pair (V, E), where V is a subset of X, and E is a set of edges, satisfying the following conditions:

1. node identifiers are unique (and hence bonds are also unique),
2. edges do not connect nodes related hierarchically,
3. at most one edge can be connected to a bond, a node may have at most one direct ancestor.

Nodes and edges in hierarchical graphs can be labeled and attributed. Labels are assigned to nodes and edges by means of node and edge labeling functions respectively, and attributes – by node and edge attributing functions. Attributes may represent geometrical properties (like size or position), but also other ones, for example the strength parameters of material. Graphs define only structures of designs in the first phase of composite knowledge representation. In the second representation phase, an interpretation of the structure is determined.

An *interpretation* of a given graph G is defined as a pair of functions (I_V, I_E), where I_V assigns geometrical objects to nodes and its fragments to bonds, while I_E establishes a correspondence between edges and sets of relations between objects (components of a design). Geometrical objects used depend on the domain of application.

When having layouts coded in the form of hCP-graph generated by an appropriate graph grammar, we restrict ourselves to a certain class of structures declared as correct or proper. The only way to overcome this restriction is to allow for a certain modification of these structures or/and grammars. The natural candidate for such a modification mechanism is the genetic search.

4 EVOLUTIONARY OPTIMIZATION

The Darwinian model of evolution in nature inspired the authors of evolutionary optimization. An exhaustive description of this methodology can be found in the monograph written by Michalewicz (1994). After it became known that the evolutionary search is well suited for non-differentiable and non-convex problems many researchers applied it for the optimum design of structures (see the review by De Jong et al. 1999). In particular, the topological optimization of trusses was considered by Grierson & Pack (1993), Hajela & Lee (1995), Koumousis & Georgiou (1994).

The main difficulty in applying evolutionary optimization for objects described by graphs lies in the non-applicability of the conventional crossover and mutation operators. These operators were originally defined for simple linear structures: the binary strings representing chromosomes. Graphs are much more complicated in their internal structure. This

circumstance is advantageous in terms of the expressive power of language based upon them. On the other hand, one has to introduce additional constraints in order to obtain meaningful offspring graphs after genetic operations were applied to their ancestors.

This difficulty with crossover operator can be overcome by introducing a similarity-like relation called *homology*. This relation is responsible for establishing sub-graphs of selected graphs that are homologous – or similar in some way – and thus can be exchanged in the crossover process.

The definition of this relation is based upon the assumption that both graphs selected for crossover represent designs having the same function and thus consisting of parts having similar or even identical functions (even if these parts have different internal structure, material or/and geometrical properties). In other words, both graphs are assumed to belong to the same class what is rather weak assumption in context of design.

The homology relation is defined on three levels that differ in terms of requirements put on graphs to be in the relation. The weakest of these relations is called *context free homology* and it only requires two sub-graphs to have either the same number of top-level nodes of identical labels (without considering the number and labels of their children-nodes or ancestors) or the same number of external edges (i.e. identical embedding of both sub-graphs). It is the least restrictive of the three relations as it allows for higher variety of new graphs to arise from a crossover but at the same time it is able to produce the least meaningful graphs or, in other words, the most "disturbed" ones.

On the opposite side, a *strongly context dependent homology* is defined. It requires that all top-level nodes of both sub-graphs have not only identical labels but also have identically labeled ancestors up to the top level of the hierarchy. The internal structure of a node and its attributes are not taken into account. Hence, the exchange of strongly homologous sub-graphs may produce quite new graphs.

When the context free relation is too weak, i.e., it results in too many graphs being unacceptable (rejected by fitness function) and the strong homology is too restrictive or results in that are very similar or even identical to its parents a *weakly context dependent homology* may be useful. It takes into consideration direct ancestors of a given node but not any ancestors of higher level in graph hierarchy.

Taking into account these levels of the homology relation, we are able to define the generalized crossover operation. The outcome of this operation is a pair of sibling graphs that inherit properties from their parents.

The generalization of mutation for graphs is simpler. We assume that random variation can affect attributes stored in nodes and labels attached to edges of the graph.

Other elements of genetic search, i.e., the number of individuals in a population, the mechanism of parents selection, the crossover and mutation probabilities were adjusted experimentally to the problem. The fitness function was based on the weight of the generated structure. The value assigned to each structure by the fitness functions played an important role in selecting parents for the crossover: it was subtracted from a constant and the resulting value gave the probability of a particular structure to be selected as a parent. The best members of the population were copied to the next one. Such elitism enabled us to preserve the best solutions during the evolution.

The proposed methodology is illustrated by the examples of optimum layouts for skeletal structures. The prototype software includes the graph editor, the graph grammar generator, the optimization module and the visualization tool.

5 NUMERICAL EXAMPLES

As a benchmark problem we take optimum design of a cantilever transmitting given force over a given distance to the rigid wall. Despite the fact that Michell (1904) solved this problem analytically almost hundred years ago, many researchers found the cantilever a good test for their concepts.

According to our methodology, the first stage of optimization should be performed under prescribed geometry and assuming uniform components. Let us begin with a rectangular shape of the cantilever shown in Figure 5a.

It is reasonable to assume that the considered truss consists of a finite number of repetitive panels. Figure 5b shows a collection of 3 panels that serves as an alphabet in our grammar. Note that this way we have introduced 3 levels of hierarchical topological description: the truss, the panel and the bar.

The goal of the first stage optimization is to establish a sequence of panels that minimizes the weight of the truss under given load and given ratio length to height.

Results of this stage are given in Figure 6. Starting with randomly generated population of 100 topologies (Fig. 6a shows one of them), the evolutionary algorithm ends up with 7 panels of type "X" (Fig. 6b). The fitness function is flat with respect to the number of panels. Therefore, some runs of the program produced 6 panels. On the other hand, uniform topology of the type "X" is clearly superior to any other combination of panels. It would be virtually impossible to obtain this conclusion by means of any other type of optimization.

The goal of the second stage is to find the best geometry for the prescribed topological scheme. Depending upon the choice of the degrees of freedom, this

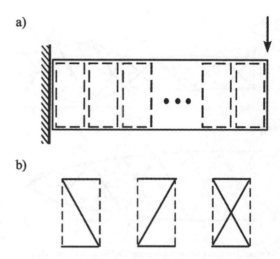

Figure 5. Modelling topology of cantilever: a) top levels of hierarchy; b) alphabet of panels.

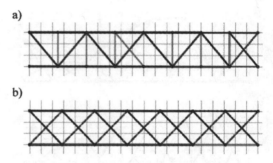

Figure 6. Topological optimization under given geometry: a) an exemplary member of the first population; b) the best solution.

problem may lead to several alternative solutions. One of them is shown in Figure 7. The truss was assumed to be symmetrical with respect to the horizontal axis. Thus, only the vertical distances from that line of 7 nodes building the chord were to be found.

Assuming the lower chord to remain straight, we obtain the solution depicted in Figure 8b. The slight discrepancy in the vertical positions of the right-hand nodes of the last panel comes from the circumstance that the loading was applied separately to each of them. In some runs these nodes merged into a single one.

It is worth noting that the search is very efficient due to the properly adjusted evolutionary algorithm. Despite the presence of very odd species in the initial population (compare Figs. 7a and 8a), the value of fitness function drops down significantly during the first few generations and then slowly converges towards the optimum (Fig. 9). In most cases 50-generations of

a)

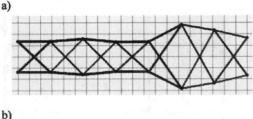

b)

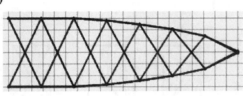

Figure 7. Symmetric truss generated by genetic search: a) an exemplary member of the first population; b) the best solution.

a)

b)

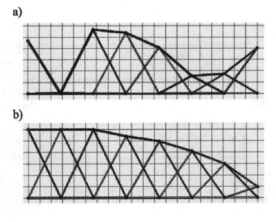

Figure 8. Truss with straight lower chord generated by genetic search: a) an exemplary member of the first population; b) the best solution.

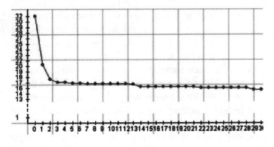

Figure 9. Evolution of fitness value.

50-individuals each was sufficient. The mean grade of the whole population converges even faster.

6 CONCLUSION

It seems that structural layout should be described in the most natural way, namely, be means of graphs. In order to describe a family of somewhat similar layouts one has to use a graph grammar. Modifying genetically such grammar, one obtains a broad collection of plausible layouts. This collection can be efficiently searched for the optimum layout. We hope that such procedure can lead the designer to unexpected innovative solutions bringing much gain in terms of the weight of the structure or in terms of other cost functions.

REFERENCES

Bendsoe, M. 1995. *Methods for the Optimization of Structural Topology, Shape and Material*. Berlin: Springer-Verlag.

Bletzinger, K.-U., Kimmich, S. & Ramm, E. 1991. Efficient modeling in shape optimal design. In B. W. E. Topping (ed.), *Computational Structures Technology*, Edinburgh: Herriot-Watt University: 1–15.

Bojczuk, D. & Mróz, Z. 1999. Optimal topology and configuration design of trusses with stress and buckling constraints, *Journal of Structural Optimization*, 17: 25–35.

De Jong, K., Arciszewski, T. & Vyas, H. 1999. An overview of evolutionary computation and its applications, In A. Borkowski (ed.), *Artificial Intelligence in Engineering*, Warsaw: WNT: 9–22.

Eschenauer, H. & Schumacher, A. 1994. Bubble method for topology and shape optimization of structures. *Journal of Structural Optimization*, 8: 42–51.

Grabska, E. 1994. Graphs and designing. In H. J. Schneider and H. Ehrig (eds), *Graph Transformations in Computer Science, Lecture Notes in Computer Science*, 776: 188–203.

Grierson, D.E. & Pack, W.H. 1993. Optimal sizing, geometrical and topological design using genetic algorithms. *Journal of Structural Optimization*, 6: 151–159.

Hajela, P. & Lee, J. 1995. Genetic algorithms in truss topological optimization. *Journal of Solids and Structures*, Vol. 32, No. 22: 3341–3357.

Koumousis, V.K. & Georgiou, P.G. 1994. Genetic algorithms in discrete optimization of steel truss roofs. *Journal of Computing in Civil Engineering*, Vol. 8, No. 3: 309–325.

Michalewicz, Z. 1994. *Genetic Algorithms + Data Structures = Evolution Programs*, New York: Springer-Verlag.

Michell, A. 1904. The limits of economy of material in frame structures, *Philosophical Magazine*, 8.

Rozvany, G., Bendsoe, M. & Kirsch, U. 1995. Layout optimization of structures, *Appl. Mech. Rev.*, 48: 41–119.

480

System-based Vision for Strategic and Creative Design, Bontempi (ed.)
© 2003 Swets & Zeitlinger, Lisse, ISBN 90 5809 599 1

An overall approach to structural design of steelworks using genetic algorithms

N. Bel Hadj Ali & J.C. Mangin
Savoie University, France

A.F. Cutting-Decelle
Evry University, France

ABSTRACT: The overall design of steel structures related to the definition of structural joints, connections and supports plays an important role in the analysis of steel structures and affects considerably its whole production cost. However, due to time and resource constraints, structural designers tend to limit the range of alternative configurations considered especially in early design. A genetic algorithm (GA) based optimisation method is presented for the overall design of steel structures. In the objective function, the whole production cost is minimised. The design constraints are formulated according to Eurocode 3. They are handled through the concept of penalty function. Three design variables are considered: cross-sectional size of members, type of beam-to-column connections and the type of supports. Optimisation results are shown to illustrate the proposed methodology and appropriate conclusions are drawn.

1 INTRODUCTION

In steel structure design, particularly at the conceptual stage, many uncertainties exist and affect the decision-making process with a major impact on the whole production cost of the final design. In early design, important decisions are taken and a very significant amount (70–80%) of the total project cost is committed (Rafiq 2000). It is therefore essential to ensure that decisions taken at this stage are the right ones; otherwise, as practice has shown, mistakes made at this stage can be very costly to correct later on in the design process.

Traditional optimisation of steel structures is based on producing efficient structures with minimum weight. However, although the weight of the joints is usually less than 5% of the total weight of the column/beam frames, their fabrication cost may be more than 30% of the total fabrication cost (Hamchaoui 1997). Consequently, studies have shown that minimum weight solutions may be up to 20% more expensive than solutions where the fabrication costs have also been taken into consideration to optimise the design (Steenhuis et al. 1998).

The structural response of a steel structure is closely related with the behaviour of its beam-to-column connections. In addition to the traditional approaches to

frame design in which connections are regarded as either "pinned" or "rigid", modern codes such as Eurocode 3 (EC3) recognise the concept of design that allows for "semi-rigid" and/or "partial strength" connections. This follows from an acceptance that the real behaviour of framework connections as observed in tests falls somewhere between these two extremes.

On the other hand, the design of the joints is usually performed independently of the frame analysis and of the design of the members. Consequently it must satisfy the stiffness requirements assumed in the frame analysis without any consideration of its impact on the structural design and the foundations design, which may lead to uneconomical solutions (Sellami 1995).

It is widely accepted, therefore, that improving the efficiency of structural design will require the integration of different activities of various disciplines involved in the design process. A GA based optimisation method is presented for the overall structural design, including the process of developing a well defined structural system, precise enough to serve as a basis for a more detailed structural analysis model. The methodology proposed here is based on a new concept for the economical design of steel structures where both the choice of members and the detailing of the joints are done with respect to the economy of the structure.

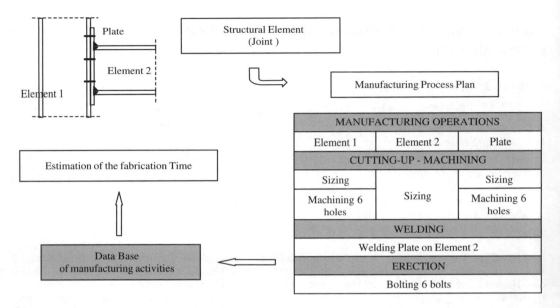

Figure 1. Procedure for fabrication time estimating.

2 OVERALL DESIGN OF STEEL STRUCTURES

The overall design of steel structures is formulated as a discrete optimisation problem in this section. For this problem, members and connections are designed. The constraints are explained, a cost function is defined based on minimising the production cost of the structure, and the design variables for the structure are identified.

2.1 Design constraints

At any stage of the design process, the structure must be analysed to determine stresses (e.g. buckling stresses, ...), strains and displacements. They are usually implicit functions of the design variables.

Expressed in terms of constraints, and formulated according to the EC3, we get:

$$\frac{N_{sd,i}}{N_{R,i}} + \frac{M_{sd,i}}{M_{R,i}} \leq \gamma_M \quad i = 1,...,n \tag{1}$$

where n = number of members; γ_M = security factor.

$$\frac{N_{sd,i}}{\chi_i \cdot N_{R,i}} + \frac{k_i \cdot M_{sd,i}}{M_{R,i}} \leq 1 \quad i = 1,...,nc \tag{2}$$

where nc = number of columns; χ_i = buckling coefficient; k_i = moment coefficient.

$$v_i \leq v_{\lim,i} \quad i = 1,...,nb \tag{3}$$

$$u_i \leq u_{\lim,i} \quad i = 1,...,nn \tag{4}$$

Equation 1 and Equation 2 define the local capacity and overall buckling checks for beams and columns. $N_{sd,i}$ and $M_{sd,i}$ in these equations are the ultimate axial force and the ultimate bending moment of member i. $N_{R,i}$ and $M_{R,i}$ are the axial force capacity and the moment capacity of the member i about the major axis. Equation 3 and Equation 4 define the serviceability limit state requirements for the structure design. They define the limitation of the vertical deflections of beams Equation 3 and the horizontal deflections of columns Equation 4.

2.2 Cost function

The overall cost of a steel structure is appraised using a cost aggregation form. In this study, the construction costs of a steel structure are split into the following categories:

1. Material cost
2. Fabrication cost
3. Erection cost
4. Foundation cost

2.2.1 Material cost

The material cost of a steel structure can be calculated in accordance with the mass of the steel parts of the structure (profiles, joints, supports, ...) and the unit price of steel (of different steel grades). Unit prices are provided by the suppliers of steel materials and components.

2.2.2 Fabrication cost

Fabrication cost is obtained by converting time needed to fabricate structural elements into a price by applying a cost per hour of workshop labour.

The fabrication time is evaluated by adding duration of elementary operations carried out to fabricate the structural element (cutting-up, machining, welding, bolting, etc.). The time considered in cost estimation takes into account the different phases within an operation, i.e. preparing, fabrication and handling.

Basic times of different manufacturing operations are evaluated according to the fabrication cost model of joints developed by Hamchaoui (1998). This model is based on a timing of the individual manufacturing activities met in a particular structural steel workshop, considered as being representative of a steelwork company.

In the estimating model and according to the joint type, an appropriate *process plan* can be selected, presented as a technical sheet prescribing all the individual manufacturing operations required on the joint parts.

2.2.3 Erection cost

The steel superstructure erection cost is estimated by applying an average cost per kg of steelwork.

2.2.4 Foundation cost

The foundation cost consists in the excavation cost, calculated considering the excavation volume, and the footings manufacturing cost which integrates:

shuttering as well as concrete manufacturing, reinforcement and pouring.

2.3 Optimisation variables

Three design variables are considered: the cross-sectional size of the structural members, the type of beam to column connections and the type of supports.

2.3.1 Structural members

Structural members are selected from available steel profiles. In this study, we use IPE and HEB profiles. Beams are selected from a set of 18 IPE profiles and columns are selected from a set of 19 HEB profiles.

2.3.2 Supports

For supports, two configurations are considered: simple base plate (considered as pinned supported), and stiffened base plate (considered as rigidly supported).

2.3.3 Connections

For beam to column connections, five configurations are considered:

1: Stiffened extended end plate connection;
2: Extended end plate connection;
3: Flush end plate connection;
4: Flange cleated connection;
5: Web cleated connection;

Figure 2 gives details of these connection types. The number of different connection types is deliberately limited to the most commonly used connections in Europe. This may encourage both designers and fabricators to use one of the preferred types, to increase standardisation and improve economy.

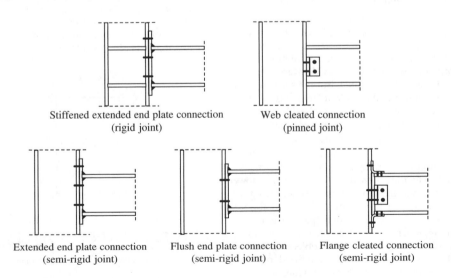

Stiffened extended end plate connection
(rigid joint)

Web cleated connection
(pinned joint)

Extended end plate connection
(semi-rigid joint)

Flush end plate connection
(semi-rigid joint)

Flange cleated connection
(semi-rigid joint)

Figure 2.   Type of connections considered.

483

The response of the structural joints in terms of flexural stiffness and resistance is determined according to the SPRINT model (Jaspart 1994). Through the SPRINT European project, simplified design procedures for structural joints were established in full agreement with the revised Annexe J of the Eurocode 3 "Joint in Building Frames". The SPRINT model is developed for standard combinations of connections of different profiles. For a given joint, design tables of the SPRINT model provide the designer with the values of the initial stiffness $S_{j,ini}$, the design moment M_{Rd} and the shear resistance V_{Rd} of the joint.

3 OVERALL OPTIMISATION OF STEEL STRUCTURES

The overall optimisation problem of steel structures is characterised by a finite number of variables of discrete type. Many methods have been developed and are used to optimise the design of structural systems. The majority of these methods use mathematical programming techniques and assume that the design variables are continuous. A few algorithms have been developed to handle the discrete nature of design variables such as Simulated Annealing and Branch and Bound algorithms. Genetic Algorithms are local search methods that belong to the class of stochastic search algorithms. Together with Simulated Annealing and evolution methods, they define search and optimisation methods. These methods are well suited to the definition of acceptable solutions in optimal structural design problems.

3.1 GA based optimisation of steel structure

Genetic Algorithms are search algorithms that use the principles of natural selection and genetics. They are robust algorithms capable of traversing large and complex search space to provide effective solutions to discrete optimum design problems. GAs were originally proposed by John HOLLAND. But the success of the method owes much to the work of Goldberg (1989).

Since GAs are directly applicable only to unconstrained optimisation, many researches have proposed solutions that can eliminate this limitation (Michalewicz 1995). Generally, most of the methods use the concept of penalty function, which penalises individuals violating constraints, and thus a lower chance is given to these individuals for surviving. By this way, the search for optimum is forced towards the feasible regions of the design space. The penalty function approach is implemented by integrating the penalty function into original objective function to yield a newly defined one (modified objective function), according to which the individuals are evaluated (Hasançebi & Erbatur 2000). In this study the transformation is based on the violation of normalised constraints so that unfeasible solutions are penalised in proportion of their degrees of constraints violation.

First, constraints (Equation 5) are transformed into normalised form (Equation 6):

$$f_i(I, X_c, X_s) \le b_i \tag{5}$$

$$g_i(I, X_c, X_s) = \frac{f_i}{b_i} - 1 \le 0 \tag{6}$$

where I, X_c and X_s are the vectors of the design variables.

A new objective function is defined where the violated constraints are penalised.

$$F = C\left(1 + K\sum_{i=1}^{m} P_i\right) \tag{7}$$

where C is the cost function of the initial problem, K is a constant to be selected depending on the problem, m is the total number of constraints and P is a penalty function computed as follows:

$$P_i = \begin{cases} g_i & \text{if } g_i > 0 \\ 0 & \text{if } g_i \le 0 \end{cases} \tag{8}$$

3.2 Coding of the structure

Design solutions are coded in the GA through n integer strings. The chromosome consists on three parts corresponding to the three design variables considered. The first part of the chromosome corresponds to the structural members, the second to the type of beam to column connections and the last one to the type of supports of the structure (Fig. 3).

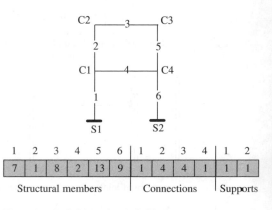

Figure 3.   Definition of an individual.

3.3 GA methodology

The algorithm first randomly generates a population of fixed size, which is one of its parameters. Each individual is evaluated with respect to the objective function and is then assigned a fitness value. The algorithm iteratively builds new generations of population which evolve through selection, crossover and mutation. To go from the current generation k to the generation $k + 1$, the following steps are repeated for all the members of the population:

- Selection: A roulette wheel selection favours high fitness individuals;
- Crossover: Couples of parents P_1 and P_2 are selected among the population according to their fitness. The crossover operator is applied on them with a probability P_c and couples of children are produced;
- Mutation: Individuals P are selected according to their fitness. The mutation operator is applied to them with a probability P_m and mutants P' are produced. The mutation operator alters one randomly chosen gene of an individual by changing its value;
- Evaluation: The fitness of the offspring is then evaluated before insertion in the new population.

Different termination criteria may be used to end the algorithm: number of generations (constant time), convergence of the population ...

4 NUMERICAL APPLICATION

In the new GA-based optimisation method we developed, we intend to optimise the overall design of a two-bay, two storey steel framework. The structure is loaded as shown in Figure 4. Optimisation variables are grouped into: three groups for members (M1, M2 and M3), two groups for connections (C1 and C2) and two groups for supports (S1 and S2).

To perform the structural analysis required for the frame, we used the *PEPmicro®* program developed by the CTICM (*French Industrial and Technical Centre for Steel Construction*). This program is devoted to the structural analysis of semi-rigid steel frames (Galea & Bureau 1998).

Several tests were carried out to fix the GA parameters (Bel Hadj Ali et al. 2002). For the example proposed here, optimisation results were quite satisfactory for a population size of *100* chromosomes running during *200* generations. Crossover probability was fixed to *0.8* and mutation to *0.05*.

The optimal design of the frame leading to a minimum production cost is presented in Table 1. This table also shows the optimum solution for the case when the connections are modelled only as pinned or perfectly rigid.

The comparison between the two results shows the importance of considering the cost of members, connections and foundations in the overall design of a steel structure. On the other hand, an actual semi-rigid behaviour of connections leads to a more accurate analysis of the structure and to an average overall cost saving of 16% (Fig. 5).

5 CONCLUSION

The GA-based optimisation method presented here proves to be satisfactory had exhibited a satisfactory in resolving the overall optimisation problem of steel structures. In addition, the method provides an effective means in performing overall design of steel structure. This is of a great importance especially in early design. In fact, concurrent generation and evaluation of many design alternative solutions in early design is considered as one of the main features of this method.

The GA-based optimisation method is being used in simulations on different types of structures.

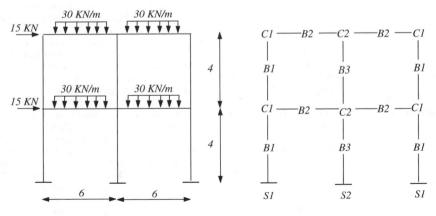

Figure 4. Optimised structure.

Table 1. Design solutions of the structure.

Variables	S1: Design solution with semi-rigid joints	S2: Design solution with classic joints
Memebrs: B1-B2-B3 Supports: S1-S2 Connections: C1-C2	HEB 160 – IPE 270 – HEB 100 Rigid – Pinned C1: Flange cleated connection; C2: Flange cleated connection;	HEB 160 – IPE 300 – HEB 100 Rigid – Pinned C1: Stiffened extended end plate connection (Rigid joint); L2: Stiffened extended end plate connection (Rigid joint);
Total Cost (Euros)	3498.0	4074.4
Connections cost/Total cost	16.5%	22.9%
Foundations cost/Total cost	14.1%	12.0%
Connections weight/Total weight	4.6%	6.2%
Total weight (KN)	17.93	19.79

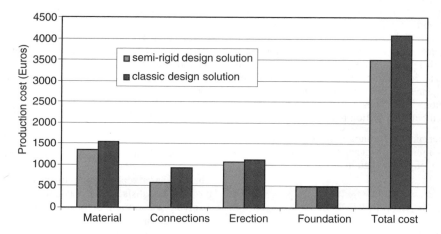

Figure 5. Cost savings in two cases of design optimisation.

Interesting results have been obtained and are being analysed in order to formulate decision support rules intended to improve the early design of steel structures.

REFERENCES

Bel Hadj, Ali, N., Mangin, J.C. & Cutting-Decelle, A.F. 2002. Optimisation of the steel structures design with genetic algorithms. *Proc. of the 3rd international conference in decision making in urban and civil engineering. London, 6–8 November 2002.*

Galea, Y. & Bureau, A. 1998. *PEPMicro – Analyse plastique au second ordre de structures planes à barres – Manuel d'utilisation*, CTICM, France.

Goldberg D.E. 1989. *Genetic Algorithms in Search, Optimization, and Learning.* Addisson Wesley.

Hamchaoui, M. 1997. *Conception économique des assemblages en Construction Métallique.* Thèse de doctorat, Université de Savoie, France.

Hamchaoui, M., Mangin, J.C. & Cutting-Decelle, A.F. 1998. Un modèle de calcul du coût des assemblages en vue d'une conception économique en Construction Métallique. *Revue de la Construction Métallique*, 4:5–20.

Hasançebi, O. & Erbatur, F. 2000. Constraint handling in genetic algorithm integrated structural optimization. *Acta mechanica.* 139: 15–31.

Jaspart, J.P. 1994. Steel moment connections according to Eurocode3, Simple design aids for rigid and semi-rigid joints. In: *COST C1 – Proc. of the second state of the art workshop*, Prague, 159–167.

Michalewicz, Z. 1995. A survey of constraint handling techniques in evolutionary computation methods. *Proc. of the 4th Annual conf. on evolutionary programming. Cambridge*, 135–155.

Rafiq, M.Y. 2000. A design support tool for optimum building concept generation using a structured genetic algorithm. *International Journal of Computer Integrated Design and Construction*, 2 (2): 92–102.

Steenhuis, M., Weynand, K. & Gresnigt, M. 1998. Strategies for economic design of unbraced steel frames. *Journal of Construction Steel Researches*, 46 (1): 88–89.

Sellami, M. Cutting-Decelle, A-F. & Mangin, J.C. 1995. Site influence and rules for steel structures optimal design. *Product and process modelling in the building industry; Proc. ECPPM. Dresden, Germany, 5–7 October 1994.* Rotterdam: Balkema.

Optimal arrangement of studded paving block system by multi-objective genetic algorithm

H. Furuta
Department of Informatics, Kansai University, Japan

T. Nishi
School of Informatics, Kansai University, Japan

ABSTRACT: In Japan, rapid aging has been in progress in recent years. Old people of 65 years and up will reach 25 percent of all the population in the coming 10 years. Super-aging society that has not been experienced so far in the world will appear. Then, it is necessary and desirable for aged people or handicapped people to participate in society and economic activities without obstacles. Under this situation, as the first step to achieve such a society the "traffic barrier-free law" was accomplished with the legal duty in May of 2000 in Japan. However, since this law provides only the minimum requirement and standard, it is more desirable to realize high quality life in future so that "universal design" should be pursued. Universal design means "the design of products and environments to be usable by all people to the greatest extent possible, without the need for adaptation or specialized design." In this study, an attempt is made to develop a method of providing the optimal arrangement of studded paving blocks installed for blind people as the first step toward the universal design. At the present circumstances of studded paving blocks, there are such problems as the complexity and difficulty in finding the way to go. Namely, it is not easy to recognize an appropriate route among many routes, because there are many branching points of guidance blocks due to a lot of gateways and ticket gates. Furthermore, rough studded paving blocks arise such problems as vibration and difficulty in going straight for wheelchair users. Applying the multi-objective genetic algorithm, it is possible to obtain the optimal arrangement of studded paving block systems. Several numerical examples are presented to demonstrate the efficiency and applicability of the system proposed here.

1 INTRODUCTION

In Japan, rapid aging has been in progress in recent years. Old people of 65 years and up will reach 25 percent of all the population in the coming 10 years. Super-aging society that has not been experienced so far in the world will appear. Then, it is necessary and desirable for aged people or handicapped people to participate in society and economic activities without obstacles. For that purpose, it is necessary to build the society that is safe and comfortable. Under this situation, in order to promote the convenience of transportation for aged people or handicapped people the "traffic barrier-free law" was accomplished with the legal duty in May of 2000 in Japan. However, since this law provides only the minimum requirement and standard, there are problems that should be solved in order that aged people or handicapped people can participate in society and economic activities without obstacles. It is more desirable to realize high quality

life in future so that "universal design" should be pursued. Universal design means "the design of products and environments to be usable by all people to the greatest extent possible, without the need for adaptation or specialized design."

In this study, an attempt is made to develop a method of providing the optimal arrangement of studded paving blocks installed for blind people as the first step toward the universal design.

Studded paving blocks were considered in 1960s for a walking support of blind people. Studded paving blocks are exactly guided to walking locations and walking courses when blind people are walking on road. Generally, studded paving blocks are installed on public facilities, such as station, hospital, and public office that require safety for anyone. Studded paving blocks do not need any special equipment to use, and are not necessary to change walking styles of blind people. Moreover, compared with electric devices, it is cheaper in cost.

However, at the present circumstances of studded paving blocks, there are such problems as the complexity and difficulty in finding the way to go. Namely, it is not easy to recognize an appropriate route among many routes, because there are many branching points of guidance blocks due to a lot of gateways and ticket gates. Furthermore, rough studded paving blocks bring such problems as vibration and difficulty in going straight for wheelchair users. Since studded paving blocks are installed only in consideration of blind people, it has been an obstacle for other pedestrians. In this study, it is attempted to provide an optimal arrangement of studded paving blocks for all pedestrians from a viewpoint of a universal design. Applying Multi-Objective Genetic Algorithm (MOGA), it is possible to obtain the optimal arrangement of studded paving block systems. Several numerical examples are presented to demonstrate the efficiency and applicability of the system proposed here.

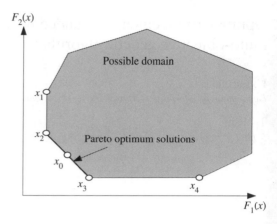

Figure 1.　Possible domain and Pareto optimum solutions.

2　MULTI-OBJECTIVE GENETIC ALGORITHM

2.1　Multi-objective optimization

2.1.1　Multi-objective optimization problems
Generally, multi-objective optimization problem is defined in terms of p objective functions $f_k(x)(k = 1, \ldots, p)$ are minimized or maximized in the range of $x \in F$. The essence of this problem is that an objective function cannot be minimized (or maximized) without increasing other objective functions because of the trade-off relations among the objective functions. "Pareto optimum solution" is utilized so that every objective function can be balanced. The definition of the Pareto optimum solution is described in the following.

Pareto optimum solution: When x^1, $x^2 \in F$ satisfy $f_k(x^1) \le f_k(x^2)(\forall k = 1, \ldots, p)$ and $f_k(x^1) < f_k(x^2)(\exists k = 1, \ldots, p)$, x^1 is dominant to x^2. When $x \in F$ being dominant to x^0 does not exist, x^0 is the Pareto optimum solution.

Figure 1 shows the Pareto optimum solutions in case of two objective functions ($p = 2$). The thick line of figure shows the Pareto optimum solutions.

2.2　Multi-objective optimization by genetic algorithm

2.2.1　Genetic algorithm
Genetic Algorithm (GA) is based on the natural selection theory of Darwin. It is an optimal search algorithm that models the process of living thing evolution, in which gene manipulations such as crossover, selection, and mutation are used repeatedly and generation progresses. An individual is a solution candidate of the optimization problem. Each individual has the fitness

to the environment. The environment corresponds to the problem space and the fitness corresponds to the evolution value of objective functions. The composition and arrangement of the genes of an individual are called Gene Type (GTYPE) of an individual. The character based on gene information in environment is called Phenomenon Type (PTYPE) of an individual. Each individual has GTYPE and PTYPE. GA operations are applied to GTYPE.

GA operations produce new children from parents by crossover and search the possible individuals other than the neighbor of the solution by mutation.

GA operations do not use special knowledge and information. This general characteristic is considered as one of reasons why GA has been successfully applied in various fields.

The evaluation of objective function is done on PTYPE (namely the solution) that is decoded from GTYPE. The rules of mapping from the objective space to GA space are called as "coding rules." Needless to say, the coding rules include the designs of crossover and mutation and so on. It is, of course, important to design the coding rules appropriately to solve practical problems effectively.

2.2.2　Generating Pareto optimum set by GA
When applying GA to a multi-objective optimization problem, it is important to evaluate and select the Pareto optimum solution appropriately.

Schaffer, Goldberg, and Tamaki have proposed the methods of generating the Pareto optimum set. In this system, the method proposed by Tamaki is used.

Tamaki improved Schaffer's method by combining the two methods shown below.

Parallel selection: A method of dividing the population of individuals into several partial individual groups corresponding to each objective function.

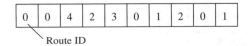

Figure 3. Structure of chromosomes for arrangement of studded paving blocks.

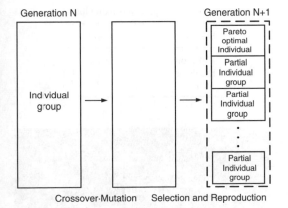

Figure 2. Parallel selection and Pareto preservation strategy.

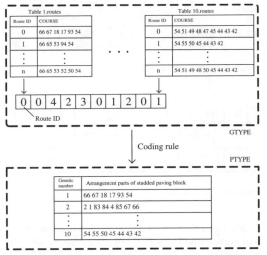

Figure 4. PTYPE and GTYPE.

Pareto preservation strategy: All the Pareto optimum solutions (individuals) in the population shall be added to the next generation in principle. This corresponds to the elite preservation strategy over the single-objective problem.

After performing crossover and mutation operations, all the Pareto optimum solutions are left in an individual group to the next generation by the Pareto preservation strategy. However, when there are more numbers of the Pareto optimum individuals than the size of an individual group, parallel selection is performed in those Pareto optimum individual groups. Moreover, when there are fewer Pareto optimum individuals than the individual group size, all the selected Pareto optimum individuals are left to the next generation, and parallel selection is performed in the remaining individual groups (Fig. 2).

By combining parallel selection and Pareto preservation strategy, the problem can be solved to obtain the Pareto optimum solution that is a compromise solution to the next generation. Moreover, the value of each objective function can be improved by parallel selection.

3 APPLICATION TO ARRANGEMENT OF STUDDED PAVING BLOCKS

3.1 Coding rules

In this study, chromosome is constructed to optimize the arrangement of studded paving blocks. Figure 3 shows this structure.

First, destination points are determined. The gene length GL is decided by the number of n points.

$$GL = \frac{n \times n - 1}{2} \tag{1}$$

The route from each origin to the destination is determined using the path planning system which applies the multi-objective genetic algorithm. This system can present plural routes to blind people by taking into account such three objective functions as walking time, waking load and easiness to recognize. Then, an appropriate root for blind people can be acquired among several routes obtained from the Pareto optimum solutions.

The chromosome is constructed from "route ID" which gives a number to each route. The genes of the chromosome are determined randomly from each ID number. A good route for blind people is considered to be also good for other pedestrians if walking time is not taken into account.

The arrangement part of studded paving blocks is determined with reference to each route ID. Figure 4 shows an example of conversion between PTYPE and GTYPE.

As a crossover, uniform crossover is used to perform global searching. Uniform crossover replaces genes partially between two individuals of parents, and generates two children. First, the mask arrangement with the same gene length is prepared, as shown in Figure 5. The mask arrangement is made to generate 0 and 1 at random.

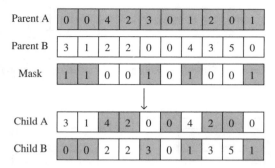

Parent A | 0 | 0 | 4 | 2 | 3 | 0 | 1 | 2 | 0 | 1

Parent B | 3 | 1 | 2 | 2 | 0 | 0 | 4 | 3 | 5 | 0

Mask | 1 | 1 | 0 | 0 | 1 | 0 | 1 | 0 | 0 | 1

↓

Child A | 3 | 1 | 4 | 2 | 0 | 0 | 4 | 2 | 0 | 0

Child B | 0 | 0 | 2 | 2 | 3 | 0 | 1 | 3 | 5 | 1

Figure 5.   Uniform crossover.

0 | 0 | 4 | 2 | 3 | 0 | 1 | 2 | 0 | 1

← Route ID: 0~3   ← Route ID: 0~5

0 | 1 | 4 | 2 | 3 | 2 | 1 | 2 | 0 | 1

Figure 6.   Mutation.

Mutation changes genes with other alternate genes that correspond to route ID of each gene by arbitrary probability (mutation rate) to each individual (Fig. 6).

3.2   Design of objective function

In this study, in order to define problems of arrangement of studded paving blocks, three objective functions are set up.

As mentioned previously, rough studded paving blocks arise such problems as vibration and difficulty in going straight for wheelchair users. This implies that a good route for blind people may not be good for wheelchair users. Then, it is possible to satisfy the requirement for both blind people and wheelchair users by decreasing crossing parts of the route. The crossing part (C_i) is decreased by taking the same route as the route for wheelchair users.

$$F1 = \sum_i C_i \qquad (2)$$

When the total distance of studded paving blocks becomes longer, the arrangement part increases, consequently, turning point increases. Therefore, the width of arrangement tends to spread as a whole. Therefore, the distance (D_i) of arrangement part (i) is minimized.

$$F2 = \sum_i D_i \qquad (3)$$

Finally, the degree of waking load (B_i) of arrangement part (i) is minimized so that studded paving

Table 1.   Degree of walking load.

State	B_i
Flat-ground	$D_i \times 1.2$
Escalator	$D_i \times 1.2$
Stairs	$D_i \times 3.0$

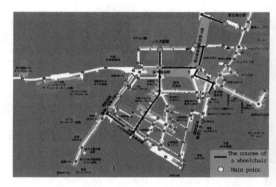

Figure 7.   Underground of Umeda in Osaka.

blocks do not induce many walking loads for blind people. The degree of load of each arrangement part changes with the state of passengers. Therefore, the degree of load is given according to the state of passengers (Table 1).

$$F3 = \sum_i B_i \qquad (4)$$

3.3   Application of MOGA

An example of local city is presented to demonstrate the applicability and efficiency of the proposed method. In this study, the city is the underground of Umeda, Osaka prefecture in Japan. The destinations are nine wickets of the station. The routes for wheelchair users are limited by stairs and bumps. In this system, each route for wheelchair users with the minimum distance is searched by Daijkstra's search algorithm (Fig. 7).

Table 2 shows all the destinations with corresponding gene number.

3.4   Results

This system is executed using the actual map of underground of Umeda in Osaka. Then, MOGA parameters shown in Table 3 are used.

The execution results of system are presented in Table 4. The arrangement part is shown in Figures 8–12. The Number in Table 4 corresponds to the results shown in Figures 8–12, respectively.

Table 2. Each destination.

Genetic number	Origin point	Arrival point
1	2	66
2	2	14
3	2	17
4	2	54
5	2	53
6	2	47
7	2	42
8	2	38
9	66	14
10	66	17
11	66	54
12	66	53
13	66	47
14	66	42
15	66	38
16	14	17
17	14	54
18	14	53
19	14	47
20	14	42
21	14	38
22	17	54
23	17	53
24	17	47
25	17	42
26	17	38
27	54	53
28	54	47
29	54	42
30	54	38
31	53	47
32	53	42
33	53	38
34	47	42
35	47	38
36	42	38

Table 3. MOGA parameters.

Population	Crossover	Mutation	Generation
200	0.8	0.05	200

Table 4. Results by MOGA.

Number	Crossing point	Distance	Degree of walking load
1	8	1599	2044.8
2	9	1416	1825.2
3	10	1276	1657.2
4	11	1153	1509.6
5	12	1121	1471.2

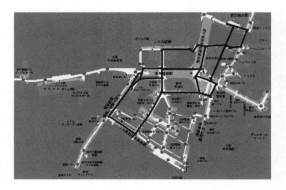

Figure 8. Result of Number 1.

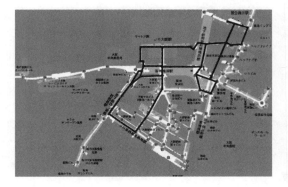

Figure 9. Result of Number 2.

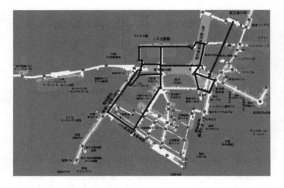

Figure 10. Result of Number 3.

Various arrangement patterns were obtained by this system, which have different characteristics. From Table 4, it is seen that No. 1 route has the minimum number of crossing points, other routes are shorter in distance and smaller in degree of waking load. From Figure 8, it is observed that the route for blind people contains the main flow line, and there are few crossing points in the route for wheelchair users.

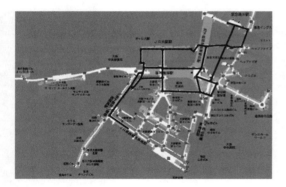

Figure 11. Result of Number 4.

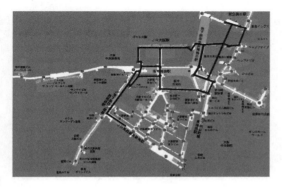

Figure 12. Result of Number 5.

However, when distance becomes longer, the number of crossing points increases and the walking load for blind people increases. From Figures 9–12, it turns out that several different arrangements of studded paving blocks are obtained, in which their distance and degree of walking load become smaller. Consequently, although the walking load and crossing points for wheelchair users increases, the walking load is decreasing for blind people. It is able to obtain the meaningful solution whose evaluation is inferior a little by including not only Pareto optimum solution but weak Pareto solution.

Arrangement of these studded paving blocks is able to mitigate problems, such as "the clarification of connectivity of main station wickets" and "the inclusion of main flow line" for blind people. Furthermore, studded paving blocks can be used as a sign connecting main wickets for other pedestrians. And such problems as vibration and difficulty in going straight for the wheelchair users is solved by having decreased

the number of crossing points. It is considered that the arrangement that adapts to the universal design is able to attain from these things.

In actual, arrangement of studded paving blocks is determined by taking into account of the opinion of not only blind people but also other pedestrians and administration. Better universal design can be achieved by showing plural solutions that satisfy each requirement of all people.

4 CONCLUSIONS

In this study, applying the multi-objective genetic algorithm, it is possible to obtain the optimal arrangement of studded paving block systems in which plural various arrangements that can mitigate the problems. Furthermore, this system is actually applied and verified for the underground of Umeda in Osaka to demonstrate the efficiency and applicability of the system. Consequently, by taking into consideration of blind people, wheelchair users and other pedestrians, problems of both blind people and wheelchair users can be solved, and plural arrangements which can use studded paving blocks as a sign are able to propose to other pedestrians. Furthermore, when considering universal design, the proposed method can clarify that there is a relation of trade-off between blind people and wheelchair users. Then, it is important how to compromise the relation of trade-off for among healthy people, handicapped people and aged people.

As a future subject, it is necessary to account for the main facilities other than station wickets considered in this study. However, when studded paving blocks are arranged as a whole, as the number of destination points increase, the number of crossing points increases and routes will be more limited because of more constraints and requirements. Then, it is necessary to examine the evaluation method more carefully.

REFERENCES

Kawauti, Y. 2001. The question to Universal design, Barrier-free, Gakugei Shuppan-Sha, April. (in Japanese)
Tuda, M. 1999. When a visually impaired person walks along a town, Toshi Bunka-Sha, July. (in Japanese)
Kubo, K., Furuta, H., Aihara, K. & Kamei, M. 1998. Application to the underground center optimum path planning of genetic algorithm, The collection of Japan Society of Civil Engineers annual academic lecture meeting lecture outlines Part 1 VOL. 53rd, common session P140–141.

Optimal design of space structures with stability constraints

A. Csébfalvi

University of Pécs, Pécs, Hungary

ABSTRACT: This paper provides a new tabu search algorithm for discrete minimal weight design of space structures with local and global stability constraints. In case of optimal design of shallow space structures the process of weight minimization can lead to design which exhibits dangerous stability loss, global and local buckling characteristics as well. Because of the highly nonlinear phenomena, it is essential to use appropriate and safe models that detect these effects as accurately as possible. In this paper, a non-linear path-following method is applied for the analysis of global non-linear stability problems. The geometrically non-linear truss structure is formulated as a large displacement model, using a total Lagrange representation. The design variables are the cross-sectional areas selected from a given set of cross-sections. To illustrate the essence of the algorithm computational results for two well-known shallow truss problems will be presented.

1 INTRODUCTION

One of the most important practical considerations in the structural optimization of trusses is the discrete optimization problem where the structural members are selected from an available catalogue. There are several exact and heuristic methods proposed solving optimization problems with continuous and discrete design variables. John & Ramakrishnan (1988) used a sequential linear programming procedure with branch and bound algorithm for large problems. In a comparison study Ringertz (1988) tested small size convex problems using branch and bound method. Arora et al. (1994) pointed out that the efficiencies of the branch and bound method is strongly depending on the number of variables. An effective higher-order approximation was presented (Salajegheh & Salajegheh 2002) for discrete optimization problem. Two optimization techniques were studied for mixed optimization problems (Kleiber et al. 1999, Stocki et al. 2001), where an equivalent-continuous optimization problem and alternatively a controlled enumeration method have been presented. The main advantage of the second method is that free from the convergence problems observed with the first algorithm for large number of design variables. The main disadvantage of the pure enumeration method can be seen in paper published by Pyrz (1990), that without any pruning rule it is applicable only for trivial cases.

To avoid the above difficulties, a new implicit enumeration method was presented by Csébfalvi & Csébfalvi (1999), where the discrete optimal design method was formulated as an exterior-point tree-search problem. A new implicit enumeration method was applied (Csébfalvi 2000) and a new simulated annealing algorithm was presented (Csébfalvi 2002) for shallow space trusses with stability constraints. The simulated annealing algorithm has proven to be a good technique (Leite & Topping 1999) for solving combinatorial optimization problems in particular for large flexible space structures.

2 DESCRIPTION OF THE PROBLEM

2.1 The optimal sizing problem

The geometrically nonlinear space truss structure is formulated as a large displacement model, where the total potential energy function can be described in the following way:

$$V(u_i, a_q, \lambda) = U(u_i, (a_i)) - \lambda p_i u_i \tag{1}$$

$$i = 1, 2, ..., n \qquad q = 1, 2, ..., e \tag{2}$$

where λ is the load intensity parameter, p_i is the applied external load vector, u_i is the nodal displacement vector, a_q is the vector of the member cross-sectional areas, and n is the number of nodes, e is the number of elements. The function $U(u_i(a_q))$ is the non-linear strain energy function supposed only linear elastic material.

The discrete optimization problem is discussed in terms of the nodal displacements and the cross section area of the truss members. The design variables a_q are selected from a discrete set of the predetermined $a_q \in A = \{A_1, A_2, \ldots, A_Q\}$ cross-sectional areas, such that minimize the total weight of the structure:

$$w(a_q) \to min! \tag{3}$$

subject to

$$V_{,i} = 0 \tag{4}$$

$$\lambda(a_q) = 1 \tag{5}$$

$$i = 1,2,\ldots,n \qquad q = 1,2,\ldots,e \tag{6}$$

where $V_{,i} = 0$ is the equilibrium criterion, $\lambda(a_q)$ the maximal locally and globally stable and stress feasible load intensity. We note that the path-following procedure of instability investigation is terminated when the unit load intensity is reached without any constraint violation.

2.2 The stability investigation

The proposed instability investigation (Csébfalvi 1998) is based on the perturbation technique of the stability theory and on the non-linear modification of the classical linear homotopy method. With the help of the higher-order predictor-corrector algorithm, we are able to compute an arbitrary load deflection path and detect the different type of stability points. Within the predictor step, we compute the solution of an implicit ODE problem and the corrector phase is the solution of a nonlinear equation system. The first-order derivatives are obtained from the equation system by nullspace computation of the augmented Hessian matrix. The higher order derivatives are obtained from the inhomogeneous equations using the Moor-Penrose pseudo-inverse.

The basic function of the stability investigation is the total potential energy function. The equilibrium equation system is obtained from total potential energy function. Starting from the zero point of the equilibrium path assuming that the Hessian is positive definite, the solution is obtained in terms of arch-length parameter of the equilibrium path t.

The stability criteria are given by the eigenvalue computation of the Hessian matrix $V_{,ij}$. In every step of the path-following process we get information about the displacement, stresses, local, and global stability of the structure. This higher order predictor-corrector method provides an accurate computation of the singular points. It is capable to compute not only points

but also segments of the equilibrium path. The curve segment approximation is the base of investigation of the singular points. Since we are concerned with finding feasible designs we must define a certain appropriate measure of performance. In the proposed path-following approach the applied measure of design unfeasibility $\lambda(a_q)$ is defined as the solution of the following system:

$$\lambda(a_q,t) \to max! \tag{7}$$

$$0 \le \lambda(a_q,t) \le 1 \tag{8}$$

$$\eta_i(a_q,t) > 0 \tag{9}$$

$$\underline{s} \le s_q(a_q,t) \le s_q^* \tag{10}$$

$$i = 1,2,\ldots,n \qquad q = 1,2,\ldots,e \tag{11}$$

where t is the arch-length parameter of the equilibrium path, η_i is the vector of eigenvalues of Hessian matrix $V_{,ij}$, and $\underline{s}$, s_q^* are the lower and upper bounds of the stress constraints.

The path-following process is terminated at the first constraint violation. In order to illustrate the essence of the path-following method the results of the 24-member dome structure (see in Fig. 2) optimization problem are shown in Figure 1. It is easy to realize

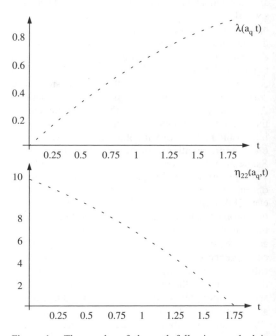

Figure 1. The results of the path-following method in terms of t parameter related to step 13 of Table 3.

494

that the structure loses its global stability at the load parameter intensity $\lambda = 0.91$.

The detected singular point is a single bifurcation point (exactly one eigenvalue will be zero, and the load derivative is positive).

3 OPTIMIZATION PROCEDURE

3.1 *The tabu search algorithm*

Tabu search (TS) is a computational process, which attempts to solve hard combinatorial optimization problems through controlled randomization. Other words, TS is a metaheuristic designed to finding near optimal solutions of combinatorial optimization problems. Basically it consists of several elements called the move, neighborhood, initial solution, searching strategy, intensification, diversification, stopping rules. For obtaining near optimum solutions of such problems, a better minimum of an objective function should be searched among a huge number of local minimum, since it is almost impossible to find an exact optimum. The "intensification" means decreasing of the objective function value to find a better solution closer to the local minimum. The "diversification", which means a jump from a searching region to other regions to avoid getting trapped in a single local minimum. In the case of the tabu search, the diversification is introduced as follows: if there are no improving moves, the move that least degrades the objective function is chosen. In order to avoid returning to the local optimum just visited, the reverse moves are forbidden. This is realized by storing those moves in a data structure called the tabu list. This contains s elements, which define forbidden moves, where s is the tabu list size. Once a move was stored in the tabu list, it would become available s iterations later.

The steps of the algorithm:

```
MaxStep = 1000
MaxNeighbourhoodSearch = 10
MaxTabuListSize = 50
Call ProblemDefinition
Step = 0: Node = 0
Call RandomInitialStructure:
BestWeight = Null:BestNode = Null
Call PathFollowingMethod
Weight(Node) = WeightOfStructure
LoadFactor(Node) = LoadIntensityFactor
For i = 1 To Groups: Areas(i, Node) = Area(i): Next i
If FeasibleStructure Then BestWeightUpdate
BestNode = Node

1:For Step = 1 To MaxStep
ActNode = BestNode:LastNode = Node
For n = 1 To MaxNeighbourhoodSearch
If RandomNeighbourStructure Then
```

```
Node = Node + 1
Call PathFollowingMethod
Weight(Node) = WeightOfStructure
LoadFactor(Node) = LoadIntensityFactor
For i = 1 To Groups: Areas(i, Node) = Area(i): Next i
Else
Exit Sub
End If
Next n
BestNodeUpdate
2:Next Step
```

3.2 *Numerical example*

Two of the frequently used test examples are considered. The geometry of the 24-member and the 30-member truss dome are shown in Figures 1 and 2. The results obtained using tabu search method have illustrated the usefulness of the method for medium-size structural design problems.

Table 1. The nodal points of the 24-member dome.

Nodes	X [m]	Y [m]	Z [m]
1	0	0	0
3	25	0	2
4	12.5	21.65	2
10	43.3	25	8.216
11	0	50	8.216

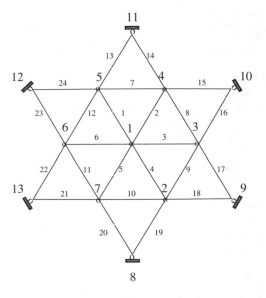

Figure 2. The geometry of the 24-member dome structure.

Table 2. The nodal points of the 30-member dome.

Nodes	X [m]	Y [m]	Z [m]
1	0	0	65.041
3	300	0	48.923
4	150	259.80	48.923
11	600	0	0
12	450	259.80	16.404
13	300	519.615	0
124	0	519.615	16.404

Table 3. The results of the 24-member dome.

S	N	Cross-sections	λ	Weight	F
0	0	{12.57,12.57,12.57}	0.721	234.946	S
1	1	{12.57,12.57,15.90}	0.875	269.671	S
1	2	{12.57,12.57,19.63}	0.889	308.567	S
1	3	{12.57,12.57,23.76}	0.900	351.634	S
1	4	{15.90,12.57,23.76}	0.899	365.414	S
1	5	{15.90,12.57,19.63}	0.888	322.347	S
2	1	{15.90,12.57,15.90}	0.873	283.451	S
2	2	{19.63,12.57,15.90}	0.872	298.886	S
2	3	{19.63,15.90,15.90}	1.000	312.622	F
2	4	{19.63,15.90,12.57}	0.727	277.897	S
2	5	{19.63,12.57,15.90}	0.718	264.161	S
3	1	{15.90,12.57,12.57}	0.719	248.726	S
3	2	{15.90,15.90,12.57}	0.728	262.462	S
3	3	{12.57,15.90,12.57}	0.730	248.682	S
3	4	{12.57,19.63,12.57}	0.736	264.068	S
3	5	{15.90,19.63,12.57}	0.734	277.848	S
4	1	{19.63,19.63,12.57}	0.732	293.283	S
4	2	{23.76,19.63,12.57}	0.731	310.373	S
4	3	{23.76,19.63,15.90}	1.000	345.098	F
4	4	{19.63,19.63,15.90}	1.000	328.008	F
4	5	{19.63,23.76,15.90}	1.000	345.044	F
5	1	{19.63,23.76,12.57}	0.736	310.319	S
5	2	{15.90,23.76,12.57}	0.737	294.884	S
5	3	{12.57,23.76,12.57}	0.739	281.104	S
5	4	{12.57,28.27,12.57}	0.740	299.707	S
5	5	{12.57,28.27,15.90}	1.000	334.432	F
6	1	{12.57,23.76,15.90}	1.000	315.829	F
6	2	{12.57,19.63,15.90}	1.000	298.793	F
6	**3**	**{12.57,15.90,15.90}**	**1.000**	**283.407**	**F***
6	4	{15.90,15.90,15.90}	1.000	297.187	F
6	5	{15.90,15.90,19.63}	1.000	336.083	F
7	1	{15.90,15.90,23.76}	1.000	379.150	F
7	2	{12.57,15.90,23.76}	1.000	365.370	F
7	3	{12.57,19.63,23.76}	1.000	380.756	F
7	4	{12.57,19.63,19.63}	1.000	337.689	F
7	5	{12.57,15.90,19.63}	1.000	322.303	F

* The optimal solution.

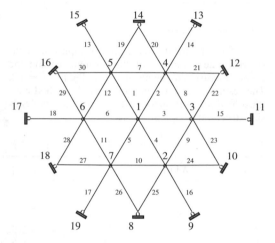

Figure 3. The geometry of the 30-member dome structure.

The elasticity modulus is $E = 7 \times 10^{10}$ N/m^2. The stress constraints are for tension and compression 25×10 N/m^2. The density is 27500 N/m^3. According to the requirement of the symmetrical structure, in both cases the members were partitioned into linking groups.

3.2.1 The 24-member dome structure
The cross-sectional areas of the truss-members with circular sections are selected from an available catalogue:

$A_i \in \{12,57; \ 15,90; \ 19,63; \ 23,76; \ 28,27; \ 33,18; \ 38,48; \ 44,18\} \times 10^{-4}$ m^2

The applied loads of the 24-member dome structure are $P_1 = 6$ kN at the nodal point 1, and $P_{2-7} = 12$ kN at the nodal points 2–7, that causes a bifurcation instability phenomena. Group 1 includes bars 1–6, group 2 includes bars 7–12, and group 3 includes 13–24. The results of the optimization process are shown in Table 3, where S denotes the actual step and N denotes the actual node of the process.

3.2.2 The 30-member dome structure
The cross-sectional areas of the truss-members with circular sections are selected from the catalogue:

$A_i \in \{12,57; \ 15,90; \ 19,63; \ 23,76; \ 28,27; \ 33,18; \ 38,48; \ 44,18; \ 50,27; \ 56,75; \ 63,62; \ 70,88; \ 78,54\} \times 10^{-4}$ m^2,

which is larger than the catalogue used for the 24-member truss dome.

The applied load of the 30-member dome structure is $P_1 = 15$ kN which acts at the nodal point 1. Therefore, the structure exhibits a snap-through, or limit point instability loss. The results of the optimal design of 30-member dome structure are demonstrated in Table 4. Group 1 includes bars 1–6, group 2 includes bars 7–12, group 3 includes 13–18, and group 4 includes 19–30 bars.

3.2.3 Results of the numerical examples
The results of the 24-member and 30 member shallow space trusses are presented in Tables 3 and 4 where the first column contains the steps, and the second is the

Table 4. The results of the 30-member dome.

S	N	Cross-sections	λ	Weight	F
0	0	{12.57,12.57,12.57,12.57}	0.453	3127.48	S
1	1	{12.57,12.57,12.57,15.90}	0.453	3459.08	S
1	2	{12.57,12.57,12.57,19.63}	0.453	3830.51	S
1	3	{12.57,12.57,12.57,23.76}	0.453	4241.78	S
1	4	{12.57,15.90,12.57,23.76}	0.459	4406.62	S
1	5	{12.57,15.90,12.57,19.63}	0.459	3995.35	S
2	6	{12.57,15.90,12.57,15.90}	0.459	3623.92	S
2	7	{12.57,15.90,15.90,15.90}	0.459	3790.93	S
2	8	{15.90,15.90,15.90,15.90}	0.574	3956.00	S
2	9	{15.90,15.90,19.63,15.90}	0.574	4143.08	S
2	10	{15.90,15.90,19.63,12.57}	0.574	3811.47	S
3	11	{15.90,15.90,15.90,12.57}	0.574	3624.40	S
3	12	{15.90,12.57,15.90,12.57}	0.535	3459.57	S
3	13	{15.90,12.57,19.63,12.57}	0.538	3646.64	S
3	14	{15.90,12.57,23.76,12.57}	0.541	3853.78	S
3	15	{12.57,12.57,23.76,12.57}	0.453	3688.70	S
22	110	{33.18,33.18,44.18,15.90}	1.000	7086.31	F
23	111	{33.18,28.27,44.18,15.90}	1.000	6843.26	F
23	112	{28.27,28.27,44.18,15.90}	0.983	6599.86	S
23	113	{28.27,23.76,44.18,15.90}	0.966	6376.62	S
23	114	{28.27,23.76,38.48,15.90}	0.966	6090.74	S
23	115	{33.18,23.76,38.48,15.90}	1.000	6843.26	F
24	**116**	**{33.18,23.76,33.18,15.90}**	**1.000**	**6068.32**	**F***

* The optimal solution.

nodes. In the following the cross-sectional areas are described, and the structural stability indicator. In the fifth column are the actual weight, and in the sixth the feasibility is signed related to the stress and stability constraints.

4 CONCLUSION

In this paper, a simulated annealing algorithm is proposed involving path-following method (Csébfalvi 1998) that provides an accurate computation of each type of the critical points. The results showed that the tabu search algorithm provides a computationally efficient heuristic algorithm find near optimal solutions.

REFERENCES

Arora, J.S., Huang, M.W. & Hsich, C.C. 1994. Methods for optimization of nonlinear problems with discrete variables: a review, *Structural Optimization* 8, 69–85.

Csébfalvi, A. 1998. A non-linear path-following method for computing the equilibrium curve of structures, *Annals of Operation Research* 81, 15–23.

Csébfalvi, A. & Csébfalvi, G. 1999. A new-discrete optimization procedure for geometrically non-linear space trusses, in: *Short Paper Proceedings of Third World Congress of Structural and Multidisciplinary Optimization* (WCSMO-3), Buffalo, New York, May 17–21, 1999, Vol. 1, 332–334.

Csébfalvi, A. 2000. Discrete optimization of shallow trusses with stability constraints, in: Camotim, D., Dubina, D. & Rondal, J. *Proceedings of Third International Conference on Coupled Instabilities in Metal Structures* (CIMS 2000), September 21–23, 2000, Lisbon, Portugal, 635–642.

Csébfalvi, A. 2002. A simulated annealing algorithm for discrete minimal weight design of shallow space trusses with stability constraints, *WCCM-V Fifth World Congress on Computational Mechanics,* July 7–12, 2002, Vienna, Austria, Eds.: Mang, H.A., Rammerstorfer, F.G. & Eberhardsteiner, J. On-line publication ISBN 3-950 1554-0-6. http://wccm.tuwien.ac.at/proceedings/download.html

Kleiber, M., Siemaszko, A. & Stocki, R. 1999. Interactive stability-oriented reliability-based design optimization, *Computer Methods Applied Mechanics in and Engineering* 168, 243–253.

Leite, J.P.B. & Topping, B.H.V. 1999. Parallel simulated annealing for structural optimization, *Computer & Structures* 73, 545–564.

Pyrz, M. 1990. Discrete optimization of geometrically non-linear truss structures under stability constraints, *Structural Optimization* 2, 125–131.

John, K.V. & Ramakrishnan, C.V. 1988. Optimum design of trusses from available section – use of sequential linear programming with branch and bound algorithm, *Engineering Optimization* 13, 119–145.

Ringertz, U.T. 1988. On methods for discrete structural optimization, *Engineering Optimization* 13, 47–64.

Salajegheh, E. & Salajegheh, J. 2002. Optimum design of structures with discrete variables using higher order approximation, *Computer Methods in Applied Mechanics and Engineering* 191, 1395–1419.

A design procedure for multi-component structures

Q. Li
School of Aerospace, Mechanical and Mechatronic Engineering, Faculty of Engineering, The University of Sydney, NSW, Australia

G.P. Steven
School of Engineering, University of Durham, Durham, United Kingdom

Y.M. Xie
School of Civil and Chemical Engineering, Royal Melbourne Institute of Technology, Melbourne, Australia

ABSTRACT: This paper aims at developing a design procedure for multi-component structural systems. The proposed approach consists of a simple cycle of a finite element analysis and a rule-driven element removal. With the procedure, the locations of interconnections and the topology of components can be optimized simultaneously as a whole. To make the interconnection elements carry as close to uniform a load as possible and/or to make the efficiency of components' material usage as even as possible, the fully stressed criterion is applied. To determine the presence and absence of the interconnection elements and component material, the efficiency of element usage is estimated in terms of elemental relative stress levels. This avoids the use of gradient-based optimization algorithms and allows designers to seek an optimization of multi-component system in their familiar design platforms. To demonstrate the capabilities of the proposed procedure, a number of design examples are presented in this paper.

1 INTRODUCTION

Most engineering structures consist of more than one part, component or structural element for the consideration of construction, transportation and maintenance. Pin joint trusses, concrete frame, steel bridge are some practical examples in structural engineering fields. It is more often than not that the structure engineers have to confront a range of design problems relating to both connection and component topologies. It has been acknowledged that a good connection design is best coupled with a good component design and *visa versa* (Chickermane & Gea 1997). For this reason, there is a demand to develop a systematic methodology to simultaneously optimize the connection and component so that the entire structural system is of the best possible performance.

In spite of its importance in practice, the design of multi-component structural systems has not been extensively investigated yet. One approach to the conceptual design of multi-component system is to model the whole design domain into a single component structure. As the first step, the interconnection details are not considered into the finite element analysis.

After an optimum is achieved, the individual shapes and connection patterns are then extracted from the topological result of the design domain. Obviously, such a sequential method can directly benefit from the existing well-established methodologies of single component optimizations (Bendsøe 1995; Rozvany et al. 1995 and Xie & Steven 1997). But the *post-processing* may provide incorrect interpretation in the structure layout due to the omission of all the interconnection details. Moreover, it is difficult to control the numbers and dimensions of the connections and components.

To properly describe multi-component system designs, Jiang & Chirehdast (1997) proposed a theoretical framework of connection optimization. With their method, the best location of connection elements is sought using mathematical programming. To solve the coupled problem of connection and component design, Chickermane & Gea (1997) considered the multi-component system as a whole, in which the optimization of interconnections and components are achieved simultaneously. This avoids the problem of the conditioned or local optimum due to the separation of these two design processes. In their solutions, the stiffness criterion is adopted. Later, a constraint on the maximum fastener load is integrated into the optimization to avoid excessive connection loads (Chickermane & Gea 1999). One common methodology in the above work is to model interconnections using linear spring elements, whereby different connection types are represented by different spring stiffness. The *densities* of the spring elements are treated as continuous design variables, which is closely similar to the Homogenization technology (Bendsøe 1995).

To have the interconnections carry as close to uniform a load as possible, Li et al. (1997 and 2001a) and Steven et al. (1999) developed a stress based approach to the connection optimization for multi-component system. The fundamental idea is to model the connection between components by using non-adjacent discrete brick elements for every possible candidate fastener location. The von Mises stress levels of interconnection elements are employed as an indicator to determine whether its presence is required.

The success in the connection optimization has motivated the authors to develop a systematic methodology for coupled design problems of both connection location and component topology. The Evolutionary Structural Optimization (ESO) method (Xie & Steven 1993, 1994 and 1997) will be adopted in this paper. A number of examples are presented herein to demonstrate the capabilities and efficacy of the proposed method.

2 RELATIVE EFFICIENCIES OF INTERCONNECTION AND COMPONENT MATERIAL

2.1 Connection elements

In the proposed procedure, brick elements are employed to model candidate interconnections. To reflect the situation of connection, such brick elements are isolated from each other as shown in Figure 1. The distance Δ between two connection elements is usually set up greater than or equal to the minimum manufacturing and assembly dimension Δ_{min}. For example, in bolted connections, the distance Δ_{min} may need to consider nut size and operational space for a spanner. To

comply with this requirement, an appropriate FE mesh would be needed to describe the connection region well.

The use of brick element seems to make the FE modelling of connection region and entire structure closer to practical situations since any type of fasteners would have a certain size in their cross section. With the different material properties of elements, different connection types can be represented in this proposed evolutionary technique.

In a multi-component system, it is frequently found that failure occurs either at the connection itself or around the attachment points in the connected components (Chickermane & Gea 1999). This may be caused by an inappropriate allocation of interconnections, e.g. some locations may require more connections than others under a certain load. A reliable sign of connection failure is excessive stress or strain. On the contrary, a low stress or strain level may reflect an inefficient use of the connections. Ideally, the stress levels in all connections of a multi-component system are near the same safe level. To represent the relative stress levels of the connection elements, a dimensionless factor is formulated by comparing the von Mises stress σ_i^C (Rosko 1995 and Young et al. 1999) of candidate interconnection i with the highest one $\sigma_{max_t}^C$ (or allowable stress $\sigma_{allow_t}^C$ of material of connection elements, but for convenience, the following formulation gives only the maximum) as

$$\alpha_i = \sigma_i^C / \sigma_{max}^C, \tag{1}$$

where subscript i denotes the number of the connection element, sub-subscript t means element i located in the tth connection region and superscript C means connection elements. From the viewpoint of structural strength, the factor reflects a relative efficiency of the interconnection usage.

At a more complex but more realistic situation, where the multi-component system is operated under a circumstance of multiple load cases, as governed by the finite element equation

$$Ku_k = p_k \quad (k = 1,2,\cdots,LCN). \tag{2}$$

The relative efficiency under all the load cases can be estimated by a weighted average scheme as

$$\alpha_i = \left(\sum_{k=1}^{LCN} w(p_k) \frac{\sigma_i^C(p_k)}{\sigma_{max_t}^C(p_k)} \right) \Big/ \sum_{k=1}^{LCN} w(p_k), \tag{3}$$

or by an extreme value scheme as

$$\alpha_i = \max_{k=1}^{LCN} \sigma_i^C(p_k) \Big/ \max_{i=1}^{M_t} \left\{ \max_{k=1}^{LCN} \sigma_i^C(p_k) \right\}, \tag{4}$$

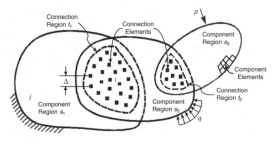

Figure 1. Modelling for multi-component system.

where LCN denotes the total number of load cases, $p_k (k = 1, 2, \ldots, LCN)$ the vector of the kth load case, $\sigma^C_i (p_k)$ the von Mises stress of the ith connection element under the kth load case, $w(p_k)$ gives the weighting factor for the kth load case, $\overset{LCN}{\underset{k=1}{max}}\, \sigma^C_i$ calculates the highest stress level of the ith connection under all load cases and $\overset{M_t}{\underset{i=1}{max}} \left\{ \overset{L}{\underset{k=1}{max}}\, \sigma^C_i(p_k) \right\}$ calculates the highest stress level at all load cases L over all interconnections M_i in the tth connection region. For convenience, the former is termed as the overall efficiency and the latter is named as the extreme efficiency. The efficiency factors provide a criterion to justify which connection elements should remain and which ones should be eliminated.

The formulation in Equations 1–4 may treat various connection regions differently, which implies that the goal of equal efficiency or iso-strength joints can be sought in individual connection regions. This provides a means of dealing with different connection types and sizes. On other hand, if the connection type and size among all connection regions are the same, the global maximum stress of all regions

$$\sigma^C_{max} = \overset{T}{\underset{t=1}{max}} \left\{ \sigma^C_{max_t} \right\} \tag{5}$$

is usually adopted as the reference stress ($\sigma^C_{max_t}$), where T denotes the total number of candidate connection regions. In this sense, an iso-strength design could be achieved over all connection regions.

2.2 Component material

It has been acknowledged that topology optimization of components is one of the most rewarding parts for the purpose of material saving. As mentioned before, this has been one of the main focuses of the previous investigations (refer to Bendsøe 1995; Rozvany et al. 1995, Hinton & Sienz 1995 and Xie & Steven 1993, 1994 and 1997). Different from previous studies, this paper carries out component design at the same time as connection design. The aim is to develop a coupling design procedure for multi-component structural systems.

Similarly to the formulation Equations 1–4 in the connection regions, the relative efficiency of component material usage can be respectively defined as

$$\alpha_j = \sigma^P_j / \sigma^P_{max_s}, \tag{6}$$

for a single load case, and an overall efficiency

$$\alpha_j = \left(\sum_{k=1}^{LCN} w(p_k) \frac{\sigma^P_j(p_k)}{\sigma^P_{max_t}(p_k)} \right) \Big/ \sum_{k=1}^{LCN} w(p_k) \tag{7}$$

or an extreme efficiency

$$\alpha_j = \overset{LCN}{\underset{k=1}{max}}\, \sigma^P_j(p_k) \Big/ \overset{N_s}{\underset{j=1}{max}} \left\{ \overset{LCN}{\underset{k=1}{max}}\, \sigma^P_j(p_k) \right\}, \tag{8}$$

for multiple load cases, where superscript P stands for component or part, subscript j denotes the element number of the component, sub-subscript s represents the sth component, N_s the total number of elements of component s and $\sigma^P_{max_s}$ the maximum stress over the sth component.

Likewise, if the material property and elemental sizes of all components are the same, the global maximum stress of all components

$$\sigma^P_{max} = \overset{S}{\underset{s=1}{max}} \left\{ \sigma^P_{max_s} \right\} \tag{9}$$

is usually taken as the reference stress ($\sigma^P_{max_s}$), where S denotes the total number of candidate components. This provides an indicator that could achieve an equal efficiency or iso-strength design over all candidate components.

3 EVOLUTIONARY OPTIMIZATION PROCEDURE

In the ESO method, to improve the efficiency of structure, those less efficiently utilized elements are gradually removed from a *conservative* design. As a result, the relative efficiencies (or stress levels) of remaining interconnections become more uniform than before. The ESO algorithm introduces a simple rejection mechanism. If the efficiency α_i of an element is lower than a threshold level or a so-called rejection ratio (RR) (Xie & Steven 1993), it will be removed from the design.

To tackle coupling design problems of both interconnections and components, the evolution criterion needs to be considered as a whole. From the definition of relative efficiencies as Equations 1 and 6, one can find that these factors reflect strength levels of interconnection elements and component materials respectively. To seek an iso-strength design over entire multi-component system, a unified threshold efficiency (or strength factor) is set for both design processes. That is to say that if the relative efficiencies of either connection elements or component elements satisfy

$$\begin{cases} \alpha_i \leq RR_{SS}\,(i = 1,2,\cdots,M_t;\ t = 1,2,\cdots,T) \\ \alpha_j \leq RR_{SS}\,(j = 1,2,\cdots,N_s;\ s = 1,2,\cdots,S) \end{cases}, \tag{10}$$

these connection or component elements will be removed from the system. Obviously, this forms a unified iso-strength criterion, in which the efficiencies of remaining interconnection and component elements approach an ideally equal level.

For clarification, a detailed optimization procedure can be organized as follows for the design of the entire multi-component system,

Step 1: Discretize the multi-component system using an appropriate dense FE mesh, assign the property type of connection and/or component elements to a number greater than 1, define ESO parameter ER, RR_0 and set $SS = 0$;

Step 2: Perform a FEA to determine the relative efficiency factor of all candidate connection and component elements as Equations 1–9;

Step 3: For all candidate elements, if their relative efficiency satisfies Equation 10, then remove them from the system;

Step 4: If a *Steady State* (i.e. no more elements can be removed based on the current threshold level) is reached, increase RR_{SS} by ER, $(RR_{SS+1} = RR_{SS} + ER)$ and set $SS = SS + 1$, repeat Step 3; Otherwise, repeat Steps 2 to 3 until an optimum is achieved.

The optimization procedure can be terminated at a point where either some form of optimum is attained in terms of a structural performance index (Querin 1997 and Liang et al. 1999) or a specified number of interconnections and volume ratio.

The ESO procedure presented herein only allows elements to be removed from an oversized multi-component system. It is worth pointing out that the work by Querin (1997), Yang et al. (1999) and Young et al. (1999) allows systems to gradually *grow* from a undersized structure into an optimum by both adding elements where the stresses are highest (over-utilized) and taking elements away where stresses are lowest (under-utilized). It is shown that the bi-directional ESO (BESO) approach can produce almost identical solutions to those by the ESO. For simplicity, only the ESO approach to multiple component systems is presented in this paper.

4 DESIGN EXAMPLES

To demonstrate the capabilities of the proposed procedure, Three examples are presented herein. Eight-node brick elements are used to discretize all components in these examples. To suppress checkerboarding patterns appearing in the component design processes a first order smoothing scheme is adopted (Li et al. 2001). In these evolutionary optimization processes below, an initial rejection ratio of $RR_0 = 0$ and an evolution rate of $ER = 1\%$ are adopted.

In all the design cases, two or three thick plates are jointed in an overlapping manner by such connection

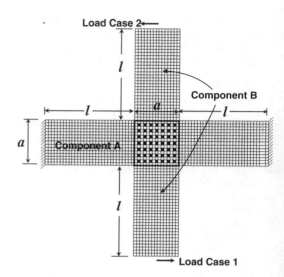

Figure 2. Initial finite element model of plates with the cross overlapped connection.

elements as spot weld, rivet, pin or threaded joints. The interconnection elements are modelled by 8-node bricks with 30% thickness and half the Young's modulus of the plates. Assume that the distance of 10 mm between two adjacent connection elements and between connections and edges is greater than the minimum requested space of manufacturing and assembly.

4.1 Cross connected structure

Cross-joints are one of the most representative junction types in structural engineering, in which one plate is perpendicularly attached to another at the middle position. As shown in Figure 2, the entire structure is fully supported at both ends of the horizontal plate and two load cases are applied at the ends of the vertical plate. The dimensions a and l are equal to 150 mm and 300 mm respectively.

During the evolving process, it is found that at some iterations, there are both connection elements and component elements removed at one cycle. But at other iterations, only connection elements or only component elements are taken away from the system. Figures 3 and 4 give the optimal topologies of the components for the overall efficiency (Equation 7) and extreme efficiency criteria (Equation 8) respectively. It is interesting to note that, whether the overall efficiency scheme or extreme efficiency scheme is used, the last four survived connection elements always locate at the outmost corner positions of the connection region in this design case. This appears to be in appropriate agreement with the conventional design. From this point, it also shows that such a traditional design is of the most uniform stress distribution.

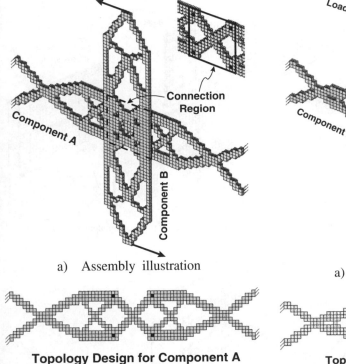

a)   Assembly illustration

Topology Design for Component A

Topology Design for Component B

b)   Component layouts

Figure 3.   Connection system design with the overall efficiency criteria ($V/V_0 = 40\%$).

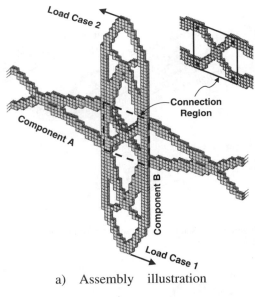

a)   Assembly   illustration

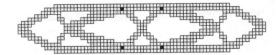

Topology Design for Component A

Topology Design for Component B

b)   Component   layouts

Figure 4.   Connection system design with extreme efficiency criteria ($V/V_0 = 40\%$).

However, the overall efficiency scheme and extreme efficiency scheme produce the different topologies of the components by comparing Figures 3b with 4b. It seems that the overall scheme gives more complex topologies than the extreme scheme, in particular near the overlapped connection region.

4.2   Design of T-joint structure

As the second example of multi-component system optimization, a T joint system is taken into account as shown in Figure 5. In this case, the layouts of the horizontal supporting plate and vertical loading plate are optimized in parallel with the interconnection design process. As more and more relative inefficient component elements and connection elements are removed from the structure, the stress levels in the remaining

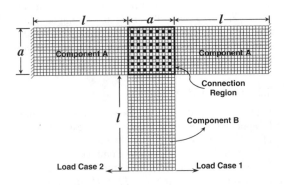

Figure 5.   FE modelling of T joint.

503

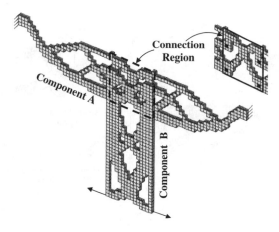

Figure 6. Assembly illustration of concurrently optimized T joint.

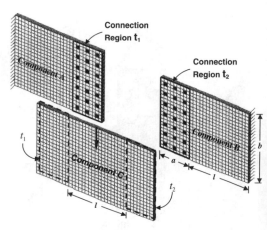

Figure 8. Fe model of three component system.

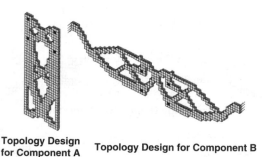

Topology Design for Component A **Topology Design for Component B**

Figure 7. Design of the component layouts ($V/V_0 = 40\%$).

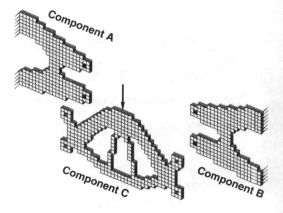

Figure 9. Optimization of connection location and component topologies ($V/V_0 = 40\%$).

structure become more and more uniform. It is found that the location of the last four survived interconnections in this design case, as Figure 7, is somewhat different from that in the case of connection-only design (Li et al. 2001a).

From the entire design process, it can be seen that the layout designs of the components are of remarkable affect on the localization of the connection elements, and *vice verse*. This reflects a strong coupling relation between these two design paths. For this reason, the design processes of these two types of elements should not be separated.

4.3 Design of three-component system

In this example, the structural system consists of three components as shown in Figure 8. The design domains of components A and B are taken as $(a + l) \times b = (90 + 180) \times 210\,\text{mm}^2$, central Component C as $(2a + l) \times b = (2 \times 90 + 180) \times 210\,\text{mm}^2$ and the connection regions (t_1, t_2) as $a \times b = 90 \times 210\,\text{mm}^2$. As illustrated in Figure 8, 3×7 potential fasteners are initially

distributed over the two symmetric connection regions and a point load is applied at the upper center of Component C.

Figure 9 gives the optimal designs of component topologies and fastener locations. It is interesting to note that the central region of Component C evolves towards a Michel type of structure as more and more inefficient material is removed. This is in accord with the typical single component design. As for the connection designs, two fasteners are required for each region and that are symmetrically located at the outmost two columns within these two connection regions. In this example, the structure with a total span of $3 \times l = 540\,\text{mm}$ is divided into three pieces, with the maximum of $2a + l = 360\,\text{mm}$ (Component C). This significantly reduces the dimensions of manufacturing, transportation and maintenance of the structure.

5 CONCLUDING REMARKS

This paper extends the evolutionary structural optimization method to the design of multi-component systems. To have the connection elements and component material carry as close to a uniform load as possible, elemental stress levels are employed to estimate the relative efficiency of connection or material usage in the study. With this concept, the absence and presence of an interconnection or a component element is determined in terms of its relative efficiency. In the optimization process, less efficient connection or component elements are gradually removed from the structural system by following the evolutionary procedure. This significantly simplifies the optimization process and makes the algorithm easy to be implemented into various design platforms.

To deal with the coupling problems of interconnection design and component design, a joint evolution criterion is presented. With the criterion, only one rejection ratio (or threshold) is used to concurrently drive two design processes for interconnection and component material. This forms a unified strength criterion for both categories of elements, where the deviation between the highest and the lowest one of the optimized structural system could be controlled to an ideal level.

To deal with multiple load cases, the overall efficiency scheme and the extreme efficiency scheme are adopted in the paper. The former explores the average extent of use in various load cases, while the latter reflects the highest stress or lowest strength in different load cases. These two schemes may lead to different connection patterns or component topologies. The choices of the schemes depend on the design requirements. Under some circumstances, designer should compare and analyze both solutions to determine the most suitable one.

The definition of the connection can be as broad as possible herein, which can include various fasteners such as pins, rivets, bolts, spot-welds, adhesive bonds that depend on the area of application. Although 8-node brick elements are employed to model the interconnection characteristics of the structural system, it is easy to be replaced by other element types when necessary. This work develops a very promising application area and a useful methodology for structure engineers.

ACKNOWLEDGMENT

This study is supported by Australian Research Council through projects F00105542 and DP0211041.

REFERENCES

Bendsøe, M.P. 1995. *Optimization of Structural Topology, Shape, and Material.* Springer-Verlag: Berlin.

Chickermane, H. & Gea, H.C. 1997. Design of multi-component structural systems for optimal layout topology and joint locations. *Engineering with Computers* 13: 235–243.

Chickermane, H., Gea, H.C., Yang, R.J. & Chung, C.H. 1997. Optimal fastener pattern design considering bearing loads. *Structural Optimization* 17:140–146.

Hinton, E. & Sienz, J. 1995. Fully stressed topological design of structures using an evolutionary procedure. *Engineering Computations* 12:229–244.

Jiang, T. & Chirehdast, M. 1997. A system approach to structural topology optimization: designing optimal connections. *ASME Transactions: Journal of Mechanical Design* 119:40–47.

Li, Q., Steven, G.P. & Xie, Y.M. 1997. Connection topology design using the evolutionary structural optimization method. *Research Report FEARC-97008*, Finite Element Analysis Research Centre, University of Sydney.

Li, Q., Steven, G.P. & Xie, Y.M. 2001a. Evolutionary structural optimization for connection topology design of multi-component systems. *Engineering Computations* 18 (3–4): 460–479.

Li, Q., Steven, G.P. & Xie, Y.M. 2001b. A simple checkerboard suppression algorithm for evolutionary structural optimization. *Structural Optimization* 22(3):230–239.

Liang, Q., Xie, Y.M. & Steven, G.P. 1999. Optimal selection of topologies for the minimum-weight design of continuum structures with stress constraints. *Proceedings of IMechE, Part C: Journal of Mechanical Engineering Science, Vol.* 213 (8): 755–762.

Querin, O.M. 1997. *Evolutionary Structural Optimization: Stress Based Formulation and Implementation.* PhD Thesis. Department of Aeronautical Engineering, The University of Sydney, Australia.

Rosko, P. 1995. Three-dimensional topology design of structures using crystal models. *Computers & Structures* 55:1077–1083.

Rozvany, G.I.N., Bendsøe, M.P. and Kirsch, U. 1995. Layout optimization of structures. *Applied Mechanics Review* 48:41–118.

Steven G.P., Li Q. & Xie Y.M. 1999. Connection Topology optimization by evolutionary methods, *Proceedings of NAFEMS World Congress '99*, Vol. 2:901–911.

Xie, Y.M. & Steven, G.P. 1993. A simple evolutionary procedure for structural optimization. *Computers & Structures* 49:885–896.

Xie, Y.M. & Steven, G.P. 1994. Optimal design of multiple load case structures using an evolutionary procedure. *Engineering Computations* 11: 295–302.

Xie, Y.M. & Steven, G.P. 1997. *Evolutionary Structural Optimization*, Springer-Verlag, Berlin.

Yang, X.Y., Xie, Y.M., Steven, G.P. & Querin, O.M. 1999. Bidirectional evolutionary method for stiffness optimization. *AIAA Journal* 37:1483–1488.

Young, V., Querin, O.M., Steven, G.P. & Xie, Y.M. 1999. 3D and multiple load case bi-directional evolutionary structural optimization (BESO). *Structural Optimization* 18:183–192.

System-based Vision for Strategic and Creative Design, Bontempi (ed.)
© 2003 Swets & Zeitlinger, Lisse, ISBN 90 5809 599 1

Discrete Lagrangian method for optimal design of truss structures

D.S. Junag, Y.T. Wu & W.T. Chang
Department of Civil Engineering, National Central University, Chung-Li, Taiwan, Republic of China

ABSTRACT: This paper studies the discrete sizing optimization of truss structures employing the discrete Lagrangian method (DLM). Theory of the DLM is briefly review first. A revised searching algorithm is proposed for weight minimization of truss structures subject to stress, buckling stress, and displacement constraints. Parameters that influence convergent speed and solution quality of the method are investigated and discussed. The feasibility of the DLM is validated by three design examples. The results from comparative studies of the DLM against other discrete optimization algorithms for the representative structural design problems are reported to show the solution quality of the DLM. It is shown that the DLM often finds good quality solutions by using appropriate weighting for the objective function and the changing speed for the Lagrange multipliers.

1 INTRODUCTION

It has long been recognized that engineers must consider integer or discrete values of design variables in structural design. For example, in steel structural design, the members have to select sections from a list of commercially available sections in many cases.

Many optimization algorithms have been developed to deal with discrete problems. These include branch and bound (B&B), simulated annealing (SA), genetic algorithms (GAs), penalty function methods, and so on. Some of them can be found in several good review papers on discrete structural optimization (Arora et al. 1994, Thanedar & Vanderplaats 1995). However, each method has its drawbacks, which include limited reliability, low efficiency, and being readily trapped at local optimum. For instance, GAs, which are recently the most known, can deal with discrete constrained optimization problems directly, because no function gradients and problem convexities are required when the method is adopted. However, they are also the most time consuming (Hunag & Arora 1997). Usually, an unspecified population number is needed to obtain a good quality solution. The strategies for handling constraint functions are also application-dependent (Coello 2002).

In this paper, a discrete Lagrangian-based searching algorithm (DLM) is employed for solving truss optimization of weight minimization problems. The DLM, as proposed by Wah & Shang (1997) for solving satisfiability problems, belongs to the class of neighborhood searching algorithms. In this method, a searching procedure using the concept of discrete saddle point was applied to prove mathematically that all saddle points found were also the constrained local minima. The method has been successfully applied to solve some nonlinear discrete constrained problems in computer science, such as satisfiability and QMF filter bank design problems (Wah & Shang 1997, Wah et al. 1997, Wu 1998).

This paper devotes to the application of the DLM to the minimum weight design of truss structures subject to stress and displacement constraints, where all member sizes are discrete. The results obtained using the DLM are compared with those acquired from other discrete optimization algorithms, such as GAs, the B&B method, and so on, to determine the correctness and efficiency of the DLM. Discussions of the factors that influence the convergent speed and solution quality of this method are presented through parametric studies.

2 CONCEPT OF THE DLM

The mathematical expressions for a general discrete nonlinear constrained optimization problem can be stated as: find a set of design variables $X = (x_1, x_2, ..., x_m)$ which minimize

$$f(X) \tag{1a}$$

$$\text{subject to} \quad g_j(X) \leqq 0, \quad \text{for } j = 1,2,...,n \tag{1b}$$

$$(x_i)_L \leqq x_i \leqq (x_i)_U, \text{ for } i = 1, 2, \dots, m \qquad (1c)$$

$$x_i \in D_i \qquad (1d)$$

in which n is the number of behavior constraints, $g_j(X)$; m is the number of design variables; $(x_i)_L$ and $(x_i)_U$ are the lower and upper bounds for the design variable x_i, respectively; and D_i is the available set of discrete variables for x_i.

Referring to Wah & Shang (1997), a discrete Lagrangian function can be defined as

$$L_d(X, \lambda) = f(X) + \sum_{j=1}^{n} \lambda_j \max(0, g_j(X)) \qquad (2)$$

in which λ_j is the Lagrange multiplier with respect to the inequality constraint function, $g_j(X)$.

We should also note that, in continuous problems, the inequality constraint, $g_j(X)$, is handled by adding a slack variable, s_j^2, to make it an equality constraint. In discrete problem, however, the value of the function $g_j(X) + s_j^2$ may be either positive or negative for any X. In this case, a constrained local minimum may not be a discrete saddle point, as defined later. In order to derive an efficient searching algorithm for discrete problems using the concept of discrete saddle point, the maximum transfer function, $\max(0, g_j(X))$, has been proposed (Wah & Shang 1997).

Similar to the Lagrangian methods for a continuous problem, a discrete saddle point (X^*, λ^*) of $L_d(X, \lambda)$ is defined as one that satisfies the following (Wah & Shang 1997):

$$L_d(X^*, \lambda) \leq L_d(X^*, \lambda^*) \leq L_d(X, \lambda^*) \qquad (3)$$

for all $X \in N(X^*)$ and all possible λ, where $N(X^*)$ is the neighborhood of point X^* as defined by the user that is reachable in finite steps.

The concept of discrete saddle point is very important in the theory of DLM since it is used both to derive the first order necessary and sufficient conditions for discrete problems, and also to develop an efficient algorithm for finding constrained local minima.

In Equation 3, the first relation $L_d(X^*, \lambda) \leq L_d(X^*, \lambda^*)$ is satisfied only when $\max(0, g_j(X^*)) = 0$ for all constraints. The second relation $L_d(X^*, \lambda^*) = L_d(X, \lambda^*)$ is also valid for all $X \in N(X^*)$ if $\Delta_X L_d(X^*, \lambda^*) = 0$. Therefore, one can conclude that a discrete saddle point must be a constrained local minimal point for non-negative constraints.

The discrete gradient of the Lagrangian function, $L_d(X, \lambda)$, at a point X for a fixed set of Lagrange multipliers was defined as (Wah & Shang 1997)

$$\Delta_X L_d(X, \lambda) = Y - X \qquad (4)$$

in which Y is a design point with the minimum value of discrete Lagrangian function including the point X and all neighboring points N(X). Obviously, if the point X is a minimum point, then the condition $\Delta_X L_d(X, \lambda) = 0$ must be satisfied.

In discrete design space, the set of all discrete saddle points of the discrete problems are the solutions of the following two sets of equations:

$$\Delta_X L_d(X, \lambda) = 0 \qquad (5)$$

$$\nabla_\lambda L_d(X, \lambda) = 0 \qquad (6)$$

Equations 5 and 6 are also the first order necessary conditions for the existence of the discrete saddle points in discrete space. For simplicity, the derivations and proofs of the first order conditions are not shown in this article, although readers may refer to Wu (1998) for details.

Since a maximum transfer function is used in the formulation of the discrete Lagrangian function, any point that satisfies Equations 5 and 6 is also a constrained local minimal point in discrete space.

3 SEARCHING ALGORITHM

To find a discrete saddle point, which is equivalent to the search for a constrained local minimal point in discrete design space, the following two equations have been proposed (Wu 1998):

$$X^{(k+1)} = X^{(k)} + \Delta_X L_d(X^{(k)}, \lambda^{(k)}) \qquad (7)$$

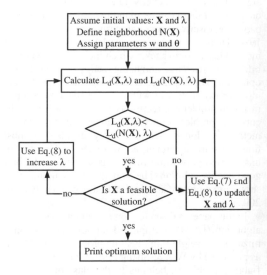

Figure 1. Design procedures of the DLM.

$$\lambda_j^{(k+1)} = \lambda_j^{(k)} + \theta \frac{g_j(X^{(k)})}{\max_{j=1}^n g_j(X^{(k)})}, \qquad (8)$$

$$\text{for } g_j(X^{(k)}) > 0$$

in which θ is a positive real number controlling the changing speed of the Lagrange multipliers, and k is the number of iterations. In Equation 8, a normalized form of the maximum transfer function is used to make the adjustment of θ easier.

According to Equation 7, the search will move along the direction of the maximum potential drop of the discrete Lagrangian function. At the same time, the Lagrange multipliers are increased by using Equation 8 to penalize the unsatisfied constraints until a discrete saddle point is reached.

In Lagrangian methods, the convergence speed and solution quality are significantly influenced by the relative magnitudes of the Lagrange multipliers with respect to the objective value. To ease the tuning of the balance between the Lagrange multipliers and the objective value, a dynamic weighting strategy was previously proposed by rewriting the Lagrangian function in the following form (Wu 1998):

$$L_d(X,\lambda) = wf(X) + \sum_{j=1}^n \lambda_j \max(0, g_j(X)) \qquad (9)$$

in which w is the weighting parameter for the objective function.

The dynamic weighting strategy proposed by Wu (1998) is attractive for amending a search that may diverge or converge slowly, and to ensure a good quality solution can be found. However, more computation is needed in order to trace the performance of the search when this strategy is used. For simplicity, a static weighting procedure (Juang & Wu 2003) is adopted in this paper. The searching procedures are shown in Figure 1.

4 NEIGHBORHOOD

In general, the choice of neighborhood, N(X), of a design point, X, is problem-dependent. One may choose N(X) to include the discrete points that are close to X or to include points that are far away. Mathematically, it can be written as

$$N(X) = \bigcup_{i=1}^m \bigcup_{j=1}^k (x_1,...,x_{i-1},x_i \pm \Delta(x_i)_j, x_{i+1},...,x_m) \qquad (10)$$

in which $x_i + (\Delta x_i)_j$ and $x_i - (\Delta x_i)_j$ are the j-th discrete samples above and below x_i, respectively. The parameter k defines the upper bound of the number of neighboring samples for the current design variable,

x_i. Note that the values of $+(\Delta x_i)_j$ and $-(\Delta x_i)_j$ can be different.

Experimentally, defining the neighboring points as the discrete points nearest to the current design point, X, is the most conservative way to locate a good quality solution. For simplicity, k was set to one for all examples presented in this paper.

We should also note that, according to the design procedures shown in Figure 1 and the N(X) defined in Equation 10, there is only one variable that can be changed in each search. Although it is possible to change more than one variable in each search, the improvement in the efficiency of the search is limited; in contrast, it may deteriorate the solution quality of the DLM (Juang & Wu, 2003).

5 EXAMPLES AND OBSERVATIONS

Below, three test problems are used to demonstrate the validity and efficiency of the DLM in the discrete sizing optimization of truss structures. In all three problems, the weight of the truss is minimized.

5.1 Non-convex 10-bar truss

Figure 2 shows the well-known 10-bar truss problem. Table 1 lists all information required for design.

To test the searching capability and robustness of the algorithm, five sets of initial design variables, as given in Table 2, were used in this example. The initial values for the Lagrange multipliers were all zeros. Both the changing speed for the Lagrange multipliers, θ, and the weighting parameter for objective function, w, were set to one.

The design histories of the 10-bar truss using the five sets of initial design variables are given in Figure 3, indicating is shown that the optimum solutions are all identical, regardless of the initial design points. The optimum solutions are compared

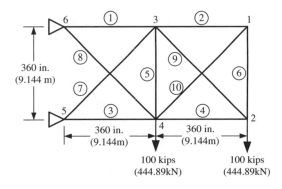

Figure 2.   10-bar truss.

in Table 3, which shows that the present results are lower than those previously reported.

Many values of w and θ have been previously tested for this example (Juang & Wu 2003), and the results for the initial design variables of Set 3 are shown in Figure 4, 5. These clearly show that smaller values for w or larger values for θ can speed up the convergence but the solution quality may get worse.

Table 1.   Design data for the 10-bar truss.

Material properties	Modulus of elasticity: $E = 10^4$ ksi (68.95 GPa) Weight density: $\rho = 0.10$ lb/in^3 (0.0272 N/cm^3)
Displacement constraints	$\delta_{all} = \pm 2$ in. (± 5.08 cm) along each degree of freedom
Stress constraints	$\sigma_{all} = \pm 25$ ksi (± 17.236 kN/cm^2) for all members
Available sections, in^2 (1 in^2 = 6.45 cm^2)	{1.62, 1.80, 1.99, 2.13, 2.38, 2.62, 2.63, 2.88, 2.93, 3.09, 3.13, 3.38, 3.47, 3.55, 3.63, 3.84, 3.87, 3.88, 4.18, 4.22, 4.49, 4.59, 4.80, 4.97, 5.12, 5.74, 7.22, 7.97, 11.50, 13.50, 13.90, 14.20, 15.50, 16.00, 16.90, 18.80, 19.90, 22.00, 22.90, 26.50, 30.00, 33.50}

Table 2.   Initial design variables for the 10-bar truss.

Set	Initial Design Variables (1 in^2 = 6.452 cm^2)
1	{1.62 in^2 for all members}
2	{4.49 in^2 for all members}
3	{33.50 in^2 for all members}
4	{Optimal solution solved by Cai and Thiereut (1992)}
5*	{1.62, 1.80, 4.97, 1.62, 22.00, 15.50, 7.22, 5.12, 1.80, 2.38}(in^2)

* Initial design variables were generated randomly.

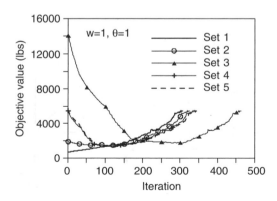

Figure 3.   Design histories of the 10-bar truss.

In general, the optimal set for w and θ is problem-dependent. However, according to the authors' experience, a wide-range of values for the two parameters can be selected to obtain a good quality solution. Normally, one can set θ to a fixed value first, say 1.0, and then adjust w to find a good quality solution.

An interesting phenomenon can also be observed from Figure 3 that, excepting Set 1, the searching trajectories of Sets 2 to 5 moved down into infeasible region first and then moved up to the optimal point. Clearly, the required iteration number for the initial design point of Set 1, which is the lower bound in the design space, is the lowest. The special phenomenon was caused by the fact that the penalties on the violated constraints were too small because the initial values for the Lagrange multipliers were set to zeros. Consequently, the objective value dominates the moving directions in the initial stages of the search. To amend the drawback, one can use a smaller value for w or a larger value for θ as those shown in Figure 4, 5.

5.2   25-bar space truss

The second example is a 25-bar space truss shown in Figure 6. The design data for the 25-bar truss are given in Table 4.

Table 3.   Comparisons of optimum solutions for the 10-bar truss.

	Cai & Thiereut (1993)	Rajeev & Krishnamoorthy (1992)	Ponterosso, & Fox (1999)	DLM
Weight lb (N)	5491.71 (24428.35)	5613.84 (24971.61)	5528.087 (24590.18)	5490.74 (24424.03)

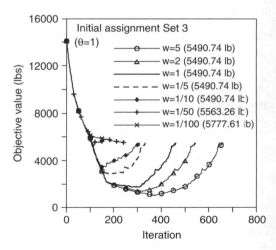

Figure 4.   Influences of w on convergent speed and solution quality for the 10-bar truss.

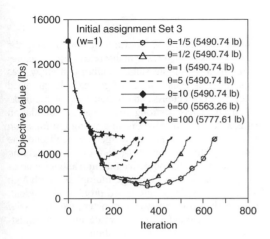

Figure 5. Influences of θ on convergent speed and solution quality for the 10-bar truss.

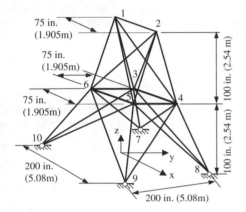

Figure 6. 25-bar truss.

Table 4. Design data for the 25-bar truss.

Material properties	Modulus of elasticity E = 10^4 ksi (68.95 GPa), Weight density ρ = 0.10 lb/in^3 (0.0272 N/cm^3)
Displacement constraints	δ_{all} = ±0.35 in. (0.889 cm) along each degree of freedom
Stress constraints	σ_{all} = ±40 ksi (275.8 MPa) for all members

Loading data (1 kips = 4.45 kN)	Node	P_x (kips)	P_y (kips)	P_z (kips)
	1	1	−10	−10
	2	0	−10	−10
	3	0.5	0	0
	4	0.6	0	0

Available sections (1 in^2 = 6.45 cm^2)	{0.1, 0.2, 0.3, 0.4, 0.5, 0.6, 0.7, 0.8, 0.9, 1.0, 1.1, 1.2, 1.3, 1.4, 1.5, 1.6, 1.7, 1.8, 1.9, 2.0, 2.1, 2.2, 2.3, 2.4, 2.5, 2.6, 2.8, 3.0, 3.2, 3.4, in^2}

Design variable linking is employed to obtain a symmetric structure with respect to both the y-z and x-z planes, and totally eight design variables are used to size the 25 members of the truss as shown in Table 5.

The parameters w and θ were all set to 1.0, and the initial design variables were set to $A_i = 1.0\,in^2$ for all members. The optimum solutions are compared as given in Table 6. The present results are also lower than those previously reported. The optimum weight of 485.30 lbs given in the Table can also be acquired using other initial assignments (Juang & Wu 2003). Note that the best solution using the DLM, which is also given in Table 6, can be obtained by tuning w to 1/9.5.

5.3 132-bar grid dome truss

The 132-bar grid dome truss, as shown in Figure 7, was previously studied by Salajegheh and Vanderplaats (1993) using the branch and bound methods. The truss is supported at all exterior joints, and is assumed symmetric about a vertical plane through joints 1, 40, and 52 and about a vertical plane through joints 1, 46 and 58. Thus, the problem has 36 independent design variables that are the areas of the members.

There are four independent load cases as given in Table 7 are imposed in the structure. The allowable displacements is set 0.645 cm along each degree of freedom, and the allowable stresses for all members are set to ±169.10 MPa. Other design data are given as follows: modulus of elasticity E = 67640 MPa, and

Table 5. Design variable linking of the 25-bar truss.

Design variable no.	End nodes of members
1	(1,2)
2	(1,4),(1,5),(2,3),(2,6)
3	(1,3),(1,6),(2,4),(2,5)
4	(3,6),(4,5)
5	(3,4),(5,6)
6	(3,10),(4,9),(5,8),(6,7)
7	(3,8),(4,7),(5,10),(6,9)
8	(3,7),(4,8),(5,9),(6,10)

Table 6. Comparisons of optimum solutions for the 25-bar truss.

Methods	Weight, lb (N)
Cai & Thiereut (1993)	487.41 (2168.11)
Rajeev & Krishnamoorthy (1992)	546.01 (2428.77)
Duan (1986)	562.93 (2504.04)
Ponterosso & Fox (1999)	490.87 (2183.50)
DLM w = 1, θ = 1	485.30 (2158.72)
w = 1/9.5, θ = 1	484.33 (2154.41)

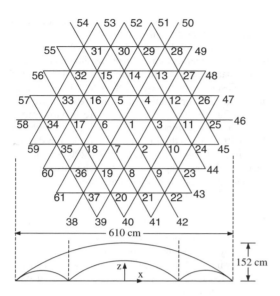

Figure 7. 132-bar grid dome truss.

Table 7. Loading data for the 132-bar truss.

Loading condition	Node	P_z (kN)
1	1	−4.363
2	1~4, 7~13, 19~28, 37	−4.363
3	All nodes	−4.363
4	1, 4~7, 13~19, 28~37	−4.363

Table 8. Comparison of optimum solutions for the 132-bar truss.

	Salajegheh & Vanderplaats (1993)		
	B & B round up	B & B discrete solution	DLM
Weight (kg)	94.71	87.20	83.65

material density $\rho = 0.0272 \, N/cm^3$. The cross-sectional areas of the available sections are given below.

$$\{1.0, 2.0, 3.0, 4.0, 5.0, 6.0, 7.0, 8.0, 9.0, cm^2\}$$

When applying the DLM to solve this problem, the initial design variables were set to $A_i = 1.0 \, cm^2$ for all members. The parameters w and θ were both set to 1.0. The optimum solutions are compared in Table 8, which shows that the DLM results in lower weight than those previously reported again.

6 CONCLUSIONS

In this paper, the DLM algorithm for minimizing the weight of truss structures with discrete design variables is presented. A simple static weighting strategy was adopted in this work. Three design examples are used to study the correctness and efficiency of the method.

The DLM has a strong mathematical foundation that can be used to solve discrete sizing optimization of truss structures. The convergence speed and the solution quality of the DLM rely on the weighting parameter, w, for the objective function and the changing speed, θ, for the Lagrange multipliers. Although the best values for w and θ are problem-dependent, proper values for the two parameters can be easily acquired by setting θ to a fixed value, and then adjusting w to obtain a good quality solution.

Comparative studies of three truss structures used in previous studies demonstrate that the DLM with static weighting can find good quality solution if appropriate values of w and θ are used. Analytic results also validates that the method is more robust than other search methods.

ACKNOWLEDGEMENTS

This work was supported by the National Science Council of the Republic of China under Grant No. NSC-91-2211-E-008-037.

REFERENCES

Arora, J.S., Huang, M.W. & Hsieh, C.C. 1994. Methods for optimization of nonlinear problems with discrete variables: A review, *Struct. Optim.*, 8:69–85.

Cai, J.B. & Thiereut, G. 1993. Discrete optimization of structures using an improved penalty function method, *Engng. Optim.*, 21:293–306.

Coello, C.A.C. 2002. Theoretical and numerical constraint-handling techniques used with evolutionary algorithms: A survey of the state of the art, *Comput. Meth. Appl. Mech. Engng.*, 191(12):1245–1287.

Duan, M.Z. 1986. An improved Templeman's algorithm for the optimum design of trusses with discrete member sizes, *Engng. Optim.*, 9:303–312.

Huang, M.W. & Arora, J.S. 1997. Optimal design with discrete variables: some numerical experiments, *Int'l J. for Numer. Methods in Engng.*, 40(1):165–188.

Juang, D.S. & Wu, Y.T. 2003. *Applications of discrete Lagrangian method to optimum structural design* (in Chinese), Technical Report No.NCUCE-2003-001, Dept. of Civil Engineering, National Central University, Chung-Li, Taiwan.

Lin, C.Y. & Hajela, P. 1992. Genetic algorithms in optimization problems with discrete and integer design variables, *Engng. Optim.*, 19(4):309–327.

Ponterosso, P. & Fox, D.S.J. 1999. Heuristically seeded genetic algorithms applied to truss optimisation, *Engineering with Computers*, 15:345–355.

Rajeev, S. & Krishnamoorthy, C.S. 1992: Discrete optimization of structures using genetic algorithms, *J. Struct. Engrg.*, ASCE, 118(5):1233–1250.

Salajegheh, E. & Vanderplaats G.N. 1993. Efficient optimum design of structures with discrete design variables, *Space Struct.*, 8:199–208.

Thanedar, P.B. & Vanderplaats, G.N. 1995. Survey of discrete variable optimization for structural design, *J. Struct. Engrg.*, ASCE, 121(2):301–306.

Wah, B.W. & Shang, Y. 1997. A discrete Lagrangian-based global search method for solving satisfiability problems, In D.Z. Du, J. Gu & P. Pardalos (eds) *Proc. DIMACS Workshop on Satisfiability Problems: Theory and Applications*, AMS, pp. 365–392.

Wah, B.W., Shang, Y. & Wu, Z. 1997. Discrete Lagrangian method for optimizing the design of multiplierless QMF filter banks, In *Proc. Int. Conf. on Application Specific Array Processors*, IEEE, pp. 529–538.

Wu, Z. 1998. *The Discrete Lagrangian theory and its application to solve nonlinear discrete constrained optimization problems*, Master Thesis, Dept. of Computer Science, U. of Illinois at Urbana-Champaign.

System-based Vision for Strategic and Creative Design, Bontempi (ed.)
© 2003 Swets & Zeitlinger, Lisse, ISBN 90 5809 599 1

The optimal topology of composite beams: analysis, design and experiment

B. Wethyavivorn
Associate Professor of Civil Engineering, Kasetsart University, Bangkok, Thailand

K. Atchacosit
Structural Engineer, Parsons Brinckerhoff Asia Ltd., Bangkok, Thailand

ABSTRACT: The process of development of the optimal topology of steel–wood composite beam including analysis, design, and experiment beams is presented in this paper. Finite element technique was used to perform stress analysis together with special algorithm developed to generate the optimal topology of the design area. The technique of closure of element or material deactivation was employed. This final design was then reanalyzed to investigate the stress level and evaluate the stability and failure conditions. Three full-scale composite beams with the span of 4 meters were built and tested and the load carrying behavior including failure mechanism was investigated.

It was found that the optimal topology technique worked well for this steel–wood composite beam design. The optimal topology design was obtained at the 99th evolutions and result in a cut down of more than 30% of steel by weight. The load deflection relationships from the experiment agreed well with one obtained from the analytical nonlinear material analysis.

1 BACKGROUND AND CONCEPT

Application of the electronic computing machine i.e. "computer" has been an integral part of structural system analysis for almost half of the century. This integral part has become inevitable in the last two decades as structures become more complex. Not until recently the computer were merely a tool for structural analysis, performing all entirely the tedious mathematical operations formulated from an numerical effort to overcome the specific comforting engineering situations which was mostly the analysis of stress of a structure with a predefined shape. Recent advancement of numerical technique such as the finite element method and greater speed of electronic computation has resulting an emerging technique where the analysis and design of a structural could be integrated in an interactive manner resulting in the shape or topology of the structural that could optimally carry the load. The optimal shape or topology could also accommodate other constraints such as architectural and production constraints. The optimal topology with boundary constraints has been a subject of interest of various researchers (Fernandes et al. 1999 and Liang et al. 2000). Although there has been applications of this type of technique in various industries such as machinery and aerospace industries, an application in construction industries has, however, been limited.

For this investigation, the confronting engineering situation was to develop a composite beam made of small size timber that can optimally carry loads. The problem has arises under continuous research attempts to develop bending member which could replace the large size timber from nature forest (Wethyavivorn et al. 2002, Wethyavivorn et al. 2003).

With the following specific objectives

1. to develop optimal design of this type of composite using available engineering and mathematical package tools.
2. to verify the obtained optimal design by the full-scale experiment.
3. to investigate the actual behavior including failure mechanism of this type of wood-steel composite.

2 RESEARCH DESIGN

In order to fully comprehend the behavior of this type of wood–steel composite beam both theoretical and experimental programs were developed. Apart from theoretical and experimental programs as the normal prerequisite of any solid conclusion. The process of

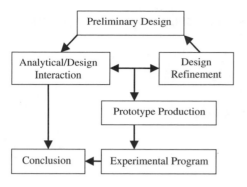

Schematic diagram 1.   Research design.

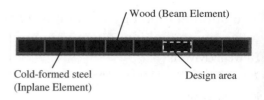

Figure 1.   Preliminary design.

Table 1.   Material properties for composite beam model.

Material	Property	Value
Wood	Modulus of elasticity	136,300 ksc
Cold-formed steel	Modulus of elasticity Shear modulus Poisson's ratio	1,840,000 ksc 710,000 ksc 0.3
Deactivated area (off element)	Modulus of elasticity	1/1000 ksc

obtaining the optimal topology also have to include the preliminary design and the design refinement processes both of which have integrated the architectural and production constraints the relationship of all the components of this research design was shown in the Schematic diagram 1. While detail of each component was elaborated in the following section. It should be emphasized at this stage that the analysis and design was integrated and it was possible that the optimal design target could not be achieved as a result of an over design in the preliminary stage this could lead to an preliminary design alternation.

3   STRUCTURAL MODELLING AND ANALYTICAL /DESIGN SCHEME

3.1   Structure modelling

Once the preliminary design, which was a result of harmonized considerations of architectural, engineering and production was obtained, finite element technique was employed to model such structure. Two dimensional rectangular plate-stress elements were used for top and bottom member the steel plate in both design and non-design areas. Beam elements were used for top and bottom wood members and the vertical wood members were modelled as pinned end struts to reflect the actual construction. The finite element model including it mesh as show in Figure 1 and it properties can be found in Table 1.

3.2   Analytical/design scheme

There are four stages of analysis which the structure has gone through after preliminary was obtained.

3.2.1   Material deactivation

Once the preliminary design and hence the design and non-design area were selected. The structure underwent a series of finite element analyses where lower stress elements were closed down or deactivated. The criteria of Von Mises stress target was used. For this particular problem, the target stress of the cold-formed steel plate was 900 ksc, with and the stress in wood was limited to 80 ksc.

In each cycle of analysis maximum Von Mises stress was calculated and material deactivation occurred to any element having average Von Mises stress less than 1% of the maximum. This percentage of maximum stress can be increased if the deactivation process did not proceed.

3.2.2   Design and analysis refinement

The engineering-based design generated by the material deactivation might not have an architectural appeal nor suitable for production. It was then necessary to make a design refinement which was a homogenization of engineering-based design, architectural appeal and production suitability. This refined design then reanalyzed to ensure that no stress violation occurred.

3.2.3   Stability evaluation

As the final design consisted truss-like panels with some slender areas in compression, stability failure was anticipated. Since only this local stability failure was investigated the non-design areas were presumable solid.

The elastic-buckling analysis was performed to determine the critical loads. The minimum critical load was compared to the design load to ensure safety. Critical loads were also valuable for the experimental program preparation.

3.2.4 *Non-linear material simulation*

Having passed the stress and stability criterion, the serviceability and material failure were then addressed. Under normal service load, it is required that the beam deflection should not be more than L/360. For this such complicated composite structure, it is almost inevitable to use finite element technique for such investigation, Moreover, to investigate its behavior up to material failure stage, it was also necessary to employ non-linear material finite element modelling technique. For this investigation, the cold-formed steel plate properties were obtained from previous experimental investigation (Wethyavivorn et al. 1999) where they were evaluate Elasto-plastic behavior with the yield point of 1500 ksc was assumed and wood was assumed to behave linearly up to failure at 800 ksc. The load-deflection curve of the composite beam was simulated at 1000 kg total load increment. This load-deflection simulation yield not only in deflection at service load and failure load, it also assisted in visualizing beam behavior and was very useful in experimental program preparation.

4 EXPERIMENTAL PROGRAM

Experimental program was designed to verify the theoretical load-carrying capacity and its anticipated behavior pattern. These included the load and deflection at service stage, local buckling modes and their failure loads, linear/nonlinear patterns, level of strains/yielded areas and maximum load at failure including failure behavior.

Three full scale prototypes of wood–steel composite were constructed from the final design blue print. Each beam span 4.0 meters and were made of cold-formed steel plate and hardwood with bolted joint construction as shown in Figure 2.

A special panel-wise loading frame was made to represent actual loading condition. As the frame was not perfectly rigid, it stiffener was also the integrated to the structural system analysis. Each composite was also instrumented with appropriate electronic strain gages for wood and steel. All strain gages were connected to an 8-channel data logger for data storage and retrieval. A dial gage were also installed at beam center to measure its maximum deflection at each load increment. Load was applied at 1000 kg inclement by the standard hydraulic jack and proving ring system. The experiment set up describe above has been shown in Figure 2.

5 RESULTS

5.1 *Optimal topology*

Applying the concept of material deactivation where under/stressed elements were collectively neutralized in the process of these analytical evolution until the Maximum Von Misses target stress of 900 ksc was archived, resulted in generations of beam that converged genetically to the optimal engineering-based design. This optimal design including its intermediate generations i.e. the 29th, the 59th are shown in Figure 3. The design was then subjected to final architectural/production refinement which also been shown in Figure 3.

Figures 4a–d show the genetic development of the maximum Von Mises stresses, the maximum shear stress, the percentage of steel weight reduction and the maximum deflection respectively.

Figure 2.   Specimen and experiment setup.

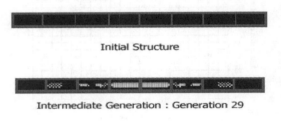

Initial Structure

Intermediate Generation : Generation 29

Intermediate Generation : Generation 59

Final Engineering-based : Generation 99

Final Architectural/production refinement

Figure 3.   Material deactivation.

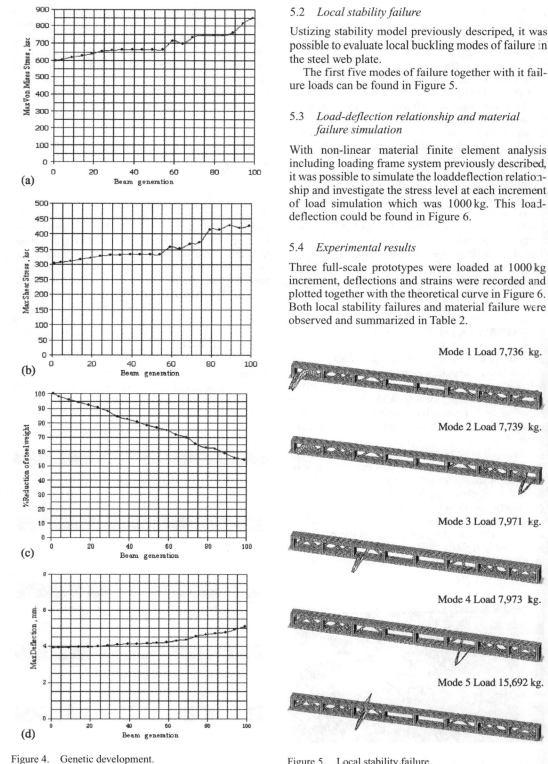

(a)

(b)

(c)

(d)

Figure 4. Genetic development.

5.2 Local stability failure

Ustizing stability model previously descriped, it was possible to evaluate local buckling modes of failure in the steel web plate.

The first five modes of failure together with it failure loads can be found in Figure 5.

5.3 Load-deflection relationship and material failure simulation

With non-linear material finite element analysis including loading frame system previously described, it was possible to simulate the loaddeflection relationship and investigate the stress level at each increment of load simulation which was 1000 kg. This load-deflection could be found in Figure 6.

5.4 Experimental results

Three full-scale prototypes were loaded at 1000 kg increment, deflections and strains were recorded and plotted together with the theoretical curve in Figure 6. Both local stability failures and material failure were observed and summarized in Table 2.

Mode 1 Load 7,736 kg.

Mode 2 Load 7,739 kg.

Mode 3 Load 7,971 kg.

Mode 4 Load 7,973 kg.

Mode 5 Load 15,692 kg.

Figure 5. Local stability failure.

518

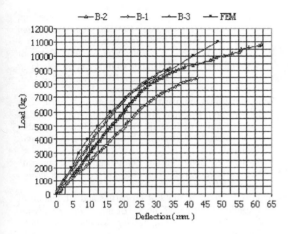

Figure 6.   Load deflection curve.

Table 2.   Failure load.

Prototype	Load (kg)	Observed failures
B-1	4600	Local buckling in the near-middle panel
	7500	Local bucking in the near-support panel
	8500	Split-fracture at the center bolt near of wood connection
B-2	4900	Local buckling in the near-middle panel
	7000	Local buckling in the near-support panel
	10800	Split-fracture at the center bolt near of wood connection
B-3	5000	Local buckling in the near-middle panel
	8500	Split-fracture at the center bolt near of wood connection
	9200	Split-fracture of wood at 50 cm from the center

Figure 7a, b show the local buckling failures of the near-middle, material failures at the connections is shown in figure 7c, d.

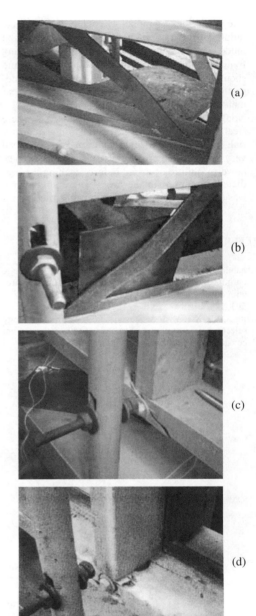

(a)

(b)

(c)

(d)

Figure 7.   Local buckling failures.

6   SUMMARY

The development and investigation of optimal topology for this class of composite has lead to the following perception.

1. The method of material deactivation, where the low-stress zone was collectively neutralized, worked well for this design situation. Only a simple algorithm had to be augmented to the general finite element package. Engineers should therefore be encourage to practice this design technique to get a more economic design and to also fully use the computation tool and capability.

2. For this investigation the material deactivation method has driven the maximum stress to 98% of the target which result in more than 30% reduction of steel plate weight.

3. The linear bucking model was able to predict local failure of this type of composite beam. The first mode was however overestimated since the loading frame was not integrated in this initial analysis and should be reinvestigated. This loading frame integration was however included in the nonlinear material analysis.
4. Nonlinear material finite element analysis where steel plate was presumable an elasto-plastic material. Yield load deflection pattern which agreed very well with experimental result. The prototypes, however, failure occurred before reaching the predicted maximum in the areas where solid wood was drilled in the bolt connection construction.

REFERENCES

Fernandes, P., Guedes, J.M. & Rodrigues, H. 1999. Topology optimization of three-dimensional linearelastic structures with constraint on perimeter, *Computer & Structure* 73: 593–594.

Liang, Q.Q., Xie, Y.M. & Steven. 2000. Optimal topology selection of Continuum Structures with displacement constraints, *Computer & Structures* 77: 635–644.

Wethyavivorn, B. & Rujirayangong, T. 1999. Proceeding, *The Engineering Technology Exhibition and Symposium 1999.November 1–2, 1999*. Bangkok, Thailand.

Wethyavivorn, B., Inpon, I. & Kulsuwan, M. 2002. Behavior of the Glue-laminated Bamboo Composite, *International Conference on Non Conventional Material NOCMAT/3, March 12–13 , 2002*. Hanoi, Vietnam.

Wethyavivorn, B., Sujjavanich, S., Junjorn, C., Surit, S. & Layangkoon, B. 2003. Study of Engineering Properties and Utilization of Juvenile Timber and Juvenile Timber Composite, *Final Report, National Research Council*. Thailand.

Atchacosit, K. 2002. Layout Optimization of Composite Beam, *Master Thesis, Department of Civil Engineering* . Kasetsart University, Thailand.

Junjorn, C. 2002. A study of Properties and Utilization of Juvenile Built-up Timber Beam, *Master Thesis, Department of Civil Engineering*. Kasetsart University, Thailand.

Wethyavivorn, B., Surit, S., Layangkoon, B. & Atchacosit, K. Optimal topology of structures with boundary constraints, *Proceeding of the Forth Regional Symposium on Infrastructure Development in Civil Engineering (RSID4), April 2003*. Bangkok, Thailand. (Full paper accepted for publication).

Design optimization of tall steel buildings

L. Catallo & L. Sgambi
University of Rome "La Sapienza", Rome, Italy

S. Tranquilli
Structural Engineer, Rome, Italy

ABSTRACT: In this paper a micro-level optimization is applied to tall steel buildings. In order to achieve the optimum structure the Fully Stress Design technique is used to get the full section response. With this technique is possible to find the correct position of the horizontal stiffening that minimizing the structural weight. The restrictions on horizontal displacements must be taken into account during all the analyses.

1 INTRODUCTION

This paper deals with a micro-level optimization of tall steel buildings; in order to achieve the optimum structure, the Fully Stress Design technique is used to get the full section response. This technique has been applied to tall buildings, finding the correct position of the horizontal stiffening that minimize the structural weight, with respect of the limitation about horizontal displacements. The buildings with several a numbers of storeys have been analysed for validation of the results.

2 DESIGN OPTIMIZATION

2.1 *Optimization problem*

If optimization can be considered as the search for the "perfect design", the different optimization techniques are the diverse paths able to reach the optimum point. Certainly this point cannot be reached, because it is impossible to get an optimum design under all points of view; however it is the idea that control the optimization methods. A simplified scheme of the optimization process is shown in Figure 1.

In all the optimum design procedures the modelization process is very important. In this process the real problem must be transformed into a mathematical problem, where the design parameters are present such as the variable vector. The model joints mechanicals, geometric and load variables with one or more objective functions and/or restraint functions.

The topic in the optimization process is the definition of the values of the variables, present in the variable

list (x), which minimize or maximize the object functions $F(x)$, under respect of the restraint conditions ($g(x)$ and $h(x)$ in Equation 1).

$$\begin{cases} \min F(x) \\ g_j(x) \leq 0 \quad j = 1 \dots m \\ h_j(x) = 0 \quad j = 1 \dots k \end{cases} \quad (1)$$

The Fully Stress Design method (FSD) has been used in order to solve the optimization problem. This classic method is based on a optimality criterion.

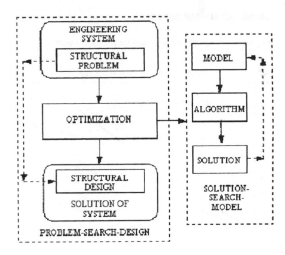

Figure 1. Optimization process.

The optimization problem (Equation 1) is indirectly resolved by the FSD optimality criterion.

2.2 Fully Stressed Design

FSD is a micro-level optimization method and its more important characteristic is the control of the stress state in some design section. If the beams have double T cross-section, it is possible to make a correlation between the geometric characteristics of a general section and the same characteristics of the reference section. These functions depend from the "omotetia" parameter a ($a = h_{general\ section}/h_{reference\ section}$), shown in Figure 2.

The correlation functions between the cross-sectional area (second moment of area) and the "omotetia" parameter is shown in Figure 3 (or in Figure 4 for the second moment of area). In this work IPE and HE-B beams have been investigated.

If the cross-section is subject to moments and axial forces, the top stress (S_{top}) and the bottom stress (S_{bot})

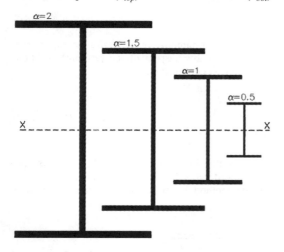

Figure 2. Example of different beam sections considered.

in the section are valuable by Equations 2 and 3 respectively:

$$\sigma_{top}(\alpha) = \frac{N}{A(\alpha)} - \frac{M}{W(\alpha)} \qquad (2)$$

$$\sigma_{bot}(\alpha) = \frac{N}{A(\alpha)} + \frac{M}{W(\alpha)} \qquad (3)$$

Both these functions depend on parameter a.

The σ_{top} and σ_{bot} values must be limited between the values:

$$\sigma^- \leq \sigma_{top}(\alpha) \leq \sigma^+ \qquad (4)$$

$$\sigma^- \leq \sigma_{bot}(\alpha) \leq \sigma^+ \qquad (5)$$

Introducing Equations 4 and 5 in Equations 2 and 3 one obtains a four equations system providing at least one real solution:

$$\begin{cases} N \cdot W(\alpha) - M \cdot A(\alpha) - \sigma^- \cdot A(\alpha) \cdot W(\alpha) = 0 & \to \alpha_1 \\ N \cdot W(\alpha) - M \cdot A(\alpha) - \sigma^+ \cdot A(\alpha) \cdot W(\alpha) = 0 & \to \alpha_2 \\ N \cdot W(\alpha) + M \cdot A(\alpha) - \sigma^- \cdot A(\alpha) \cdot W(\alpha) = 0 & \to \alpha_3 \\ N \cdot W(\alpha) + M \cdot A(\alpha) - \sigma^+ \cdot A(\alpha) \cdot W(\alpha) = 0 & \to \alpha_4 \end{cases} \qquad (6)$$

The design value is:

$$\alpha_{design} = \max(\alpha_i) \qquad (7)$$

Using this procedure, one is able to achieve a dimensioning of the structure where the resistant capacity is better used.

The design is based on the resistant criteria, but the limit values s^- and s^+ can be varied in order to take into account other structural criteria. In this case other criteria are indirectly satisfied by the FSD procedure.

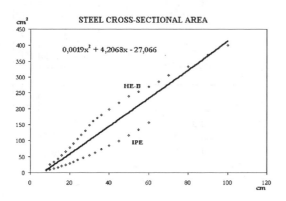

Figure 3. Relationship of steel cross-sectional area.

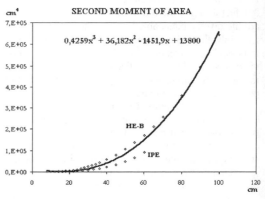

Figure 4. Relationship of second moment of area.

3 APPLICATIONS

In this chapter the FSD is applied in the design of tall building design procedure. The purpose of this study is to find out the correct position of the horizontal stiffening. The position and the design of these elements are very important in order to reduce horizontal displacements.

The total weight of the steel structure has been assumed as the objective function and the loads have been valued by the Italian Normative.

A planar frame with a number of storeys variable from 10 to 40, subject to vertical and horizontal loads, has been investigated.

Two cases have been studied:

– One horizontal stiffening is present;
– Two horizontal stiffening are present.

For each case the problem studied is the definition of the correct position of the horizontal stiffening.

3.1 *Search about optimal position of one horizontal stiffening*

As above-mentioned planar frames with 10, 20, 30 or 40 storeys have been considered. For each case the correct position of the horizontal stiffening has been valued by the FSD. The 10 storeys frame with the horizontal stiffening in the 7th storey is shown in the Figure 5, before (Fig. 5a) and after (Fig. 5b) the FSD optimization technique.

For the 10 storey frame, ten cases has been studied: in each case the horizontal stiffening position is changed. The FSD procedure is applied in each case, in order to

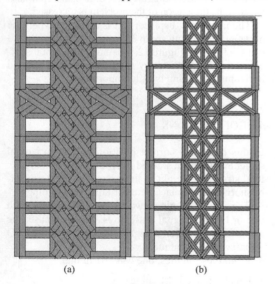

(a)   (b)

Figure 5.   Plane frame with ten-storeys: a) before optimization; b) after optimization.

get always an optimization structure. Figure 6 shows the outcome of the FSD procedure in terms of the total structural weight. As we can see from this figure, the optimum position for the horizontal stiffening is the 8th storey (80% of the total height of the frame). Figure 7 reportes the maximum lateral displacement when the horizontal stiffening position changes.

One can define a stiffening efficiency such as reduction of the maximum horizontal displacement compared to initial case of absence of the stiffening (as shown in Figure 8). In order to get the minimum horizontal

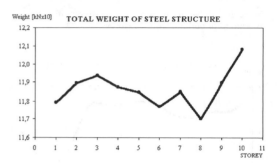

Figure 6.   Relationship weight *vs* position of horizontal stiffening, for building with 10 storeys.

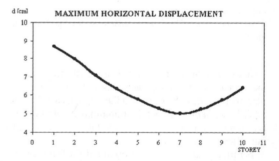

Figure 7.   Relationship maximum horizontal displacement *vs* position of horizontal stiffening, for building with 10 storeys.

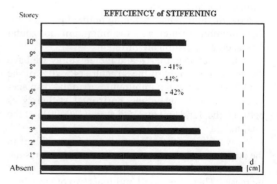

Figure 8.   Efficiency of storey's stiffening.

523

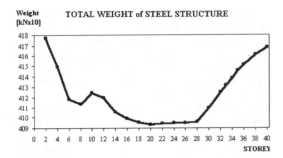

Weight
[kNx10]

Figure 9. Relationship weight *vs* position of horizontal stiffening, for building with 40 storeys.

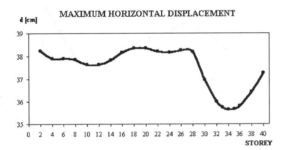

Figure 10. Relationship maximum horizontal displacement *vs* position of horizontal stiffening, for building with 40 storeys.

displacement, the best position is in the 7th storey where the horizontal stiffening decreases the horizontal displacement at the 44% respect at the original case. On the other hand, in order to get the minimum weight the best position is the 8 storey. However, in this case the stiffening efficiency decrease at 41%.

Similar graphs have been obtained for frames with 20, 30 and 40 storeys. In the last case results are reported in Figure 9 (weight versus number of storeys) and in Figure 10 (horizontal displacement versus number of storeys).

Now the horizontal stiffening optimal position for the minimum weight and the minimum horizontal displacement position are different.

In fact, between the 18 and the 28 storey we have the minimum weight of the structure (45–70% of the total height) while the minimum horizontal displacement is achieve when the horizontal stiffening is between the 32nd and the 36th storey (80–90% of total height).

As we can see from Figure 8 and Figure 11, if in the structure only one horizontal stiffening is present, its efficiency decreases when the number of storeys increases. Therefore in tall buildings two or more horizontal stiffenings are need.

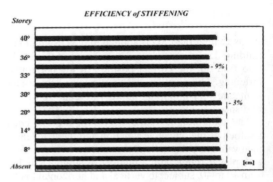

Figure 11. Efficiency of storey's stiffening.

3.2 Search about the optimal position of two horizontal stiffenings

In this paragraph the tall building with two horizontal stiffening is studied.

A plane frame of 40 storeys, with base of 27 m, a central vertical stiffening and three spans respectively of 5.5, 5e, 6 m, is investigated.

The objective function has been considered the total volume of the steel structure, and the optimal point represent the minimum weight design.

The building has 40 storeys, therefore $40 \times 40 = 1600$ cases with different horizontal stiffening position have been considered. The first result in term of the total weight versus horizontal stiffening position is reported in Figure 12.

Figure 13 shows the maximum horizontal displacement. In this case, figures are three dimensional surfaces because the dimension of the problem is increased.

The minimum displacement is achieved when the horizontal stiffening are in 30th and 36th storey. As we can see from the Figure 12, when one horizontal stiffening is in the 36th storey, the position of the second horizontal stiffening is little important.

4 CONCLUSIONS

In this paper the correct position of the horizontal stiffening has been studied in order to minimizing the total structural weight in the respect of the permissible horizontal displacement for tall steel buildings.

The work considere two cases, respectively with one or two horizontal stiffenings. For each case, the steel frame has been designed according to the FSD optimization technique.

From these studies, one can affirm that:

- One horizontal stiffenings:
  - The optimal position is between the 65% and the 85% of the total height of the structure.

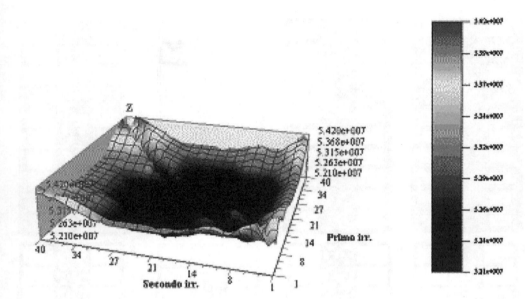

Figure 12. Surface of steel volume.

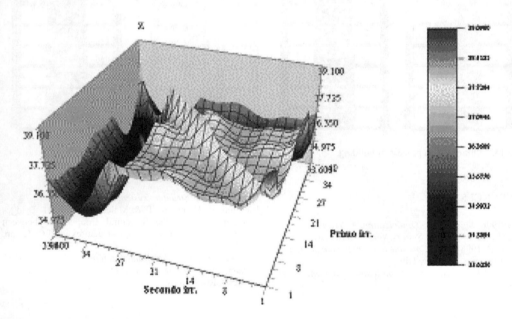

Figure 13. Surface of building's displacements.

- The weight of structure increases quickly with the increase of the height of the building, because more stiffening is need in order to limit the horizontal displacements.
- When the building is high only one horizontal stiffening is insufficient.
- Two horizontal stiffenings:

- In order to minimizing the total steel structural weight the optimum positions for the two horizontal stiffening are the 30th and 36th storey.
- when one horizontal stiffening is in the 36th storey, the position of the second horizontal stiffening is little important.

525

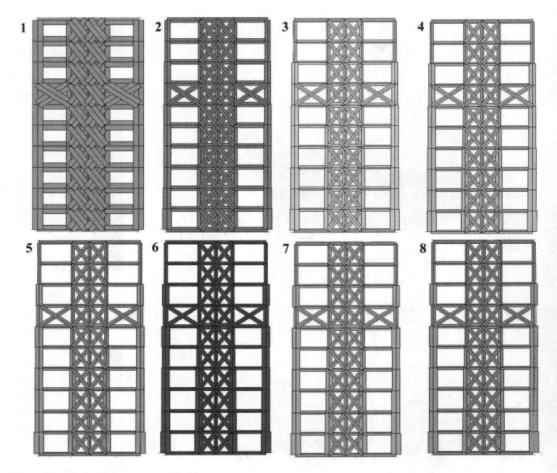

Figure 14.   Optimization process of building.

REFERENCES

Rao, S. 1996. *Engineering Optimization*. A Wiley.
Engel, H. 1997. *Structure System*. Verlag Gerd Hatje.
Taranath, B. 1998. *Steel, Concrete and Composite Design of Tall Buildings*. McGraw Hill.
Arora, J.S. 1989. *Introduction to optimum design*. McGraw-Hill.

Engel, H. 1997. *Structure systems*. Matje Verlag.
Biondini, F., Bontempi, F. & Malerba, P.G. 2001. Bridges Emerging from the Structural Cooperation between Straight and Curved Superstructures. ISEC01, pp. 877–882.
Tranquilli, S. 2002. *The optimization process in the preliminary design of tall steel buildings* (in Italian). Graduate thesis. Rome. Italy.

System-based Vision for Strategic and Creative Design, Bontempi (ed.)
© 2003 Swets & Zeitlinger, Lisse, ISBN 90 5809 599 1

Shape optimal design of skeletal structures

B. Harl, M. Kegl, D. Dinevski & M.M. Oblak
Faculty of Mechanical Engineering, Maribor, Slovenia

ABSTRACT: The paper describes an approach to shape optimal design of statically loaded skeletal structures. The proposed approach relies on the assumption that the shape of the finite element mesh is parametrized using the design element technique. Consequently the shape of the structure follows automatically the shape changes of a body, defined as an assemblage of rational Bézier bodies – the design elements. The conventional truss element as well as a high-accuracy beam element (both kinematically nonlinear) are employed as the finite elements. The optimization problem is defined in a form of a general nonlinear problem of mathematical programming. Since the shape parameters are continuous variables, a gradient based optimization procedure is proposed. The theory is illustrated by a numerical example.

1 INTRODUCTION

In the last decade the development of modern technologies and computer aided manufacturing emphasized the significance of shape optimal design. An attractive foundation for general shape design procedures is offered by modern numerical methods such as the finite element (FE) method and modern optimization algorithms.

With these key elements at hand we can address even sophisticated design problems such as determining optimal shape of a structure. Presently it seems that there are two main in-roads to this field.

The first approach is based on evolutionary concepts which gained significant attention in the last decade (see e.g. Bendsøe & Kikuchi 1988, Reynolds et al. 1999, Rozvany et al. 1992). By evolutionary methods, shape and topology optimization is performed simultaneously. In a most simplistic view, these methods remove or add material (finite elements) depending on the stress or compliance level in individual parts of the structure. Thus, these methods do not perform optimization in the strict mathematical sense (solving a problem of mathematical programming) but they exhibit remarkable and attractive properties. They are easy to implement and to use and they yield good results.

Unfortunately, those methods can not be implemented easily (or at all) for example for frequency constrained problems (see e.g. Dinevski et al. 2002), for skeletal structures and so on. For such problems the second approach based on geometrical parametrization of the finite element mesh (see e.g. Braibant & Fleury 1984, Shyy et al. 1988, Maute & Ramm 1995, Kegl & Antes 1998) seems to be a much better choice. By this approach the FE mesh geometry is parametrized so that its shape can be changed smoothly by varying a relative small number of parameters.

An attractive shape parametrization concept is offered by combining the *design element technique* (Imam 1982) and suitable design elements, for example, *Bézier bodies* (Kegl 2000). By this approach the geometrical body defined by the hull of the structure is divided into simpler geometrical objects called the design elements (DE). These can be parameterized in a rather simple way and the finite elements are then defined in the domain of the design element (Fig. 1) rather than directly in the real 3D space. In that way we get some kind of a "convective" finite element mesh, following automatically the geometry changes of the structure.

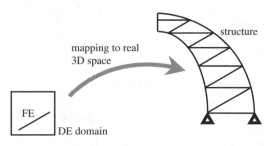

Figure 1. A FE is mapped from the DE domain to real 3D space.

By this approach finite elements virtually of any kind can be employed. The only reason for concern is the fact that during the optimization process the shape of the structure changes, which can lead to distortion of the finite elements and consequently to inaccuracies in the analysis. This however, is of less importance when skeletal structures are considered. When reshaping a skeletal structure namely, only the directions and the lengths of the elements (bars, beams, etc.) are changed. Thus, for skeletal structures the choice of the element is not of such importance as for continuous structures. In spite of that, it is a good idea to select an adequately accurate bar or beam element which accounts for kinematic nonlinearities. In that way possible structural stability problems are adequately captured and can be handled appropriately – either as an add-on to the optimization process or in some other way.

Fortunately there is a wide palette of fine beam finite elements available (see e.g. Ibrahimbegović 1995, Jelenić & Saje 1995). In this paper we employed a kinematically nonlinear bar element and the highly accurate beam element described in Kegl & Antes (1998).

The outline of this paper is as follows. Section 2 describes the foundations of the employed shape parameterization concept. In Section 3 the design problem is formulated. Section 4 describes the solution procedure and Section 5 presents a numerical example.

2 SHAPE PARAMETERIZATION OF A SKELETAL STRUCTURE

Let us consider a skeletal structure S and let the hull of the structure be the surface of the geometrical body B (Fig. 2).

Depending on the complexity of the shape of S, B can be regarded as assembled of any number of design elements D_i. For several reasons described in more detail in Kegl (2000), we take the design element D_i to be a Bézier body.

A Bézier body D can be regarded as the image of a unit cube U mapped into the real 3D space (Fig. 3). The position and shape of D is fully determined by the position of its *control points* q_{ijk}. A change of the position of q_{ijk} changes the position and shape of D. To be more precise: the position vector $\mathbf{r}$ of a generic point of D can be expressed in terms of q_{ijk} as follows

$$\mathbf{r} = \sum_{i=1}^{I}\sum_{j=1}^{J}\sum_{k=1}^{K} B_i^I(s_1)B_j^J(s_2)B_k^K(s_3)\mathbf{q}_{ijk} \qquad (1)$$

where $B_i^I(s_i)$ is the i-th univariate Bernstein polynomial (Farin 1993) of the order $I - 1$, expressed in terms of $s_i \in [0,1]$. One can say that the above relationship maps a point $\mathbf{s} = [s_1\ s_2\ s_3]^T$ from U into the point $\mathbf{r}$ in the real 3D space. Thus, $\mathbf{r} = \mathbf{r}(\mathbf{s})$.

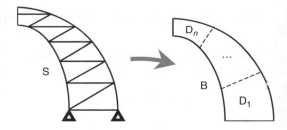

Figure 2. The hull of the structure defines the body B that is divided into design elements D_i.

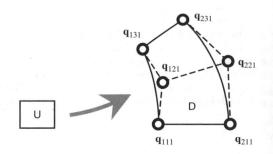

Figure 3. Shape and position of D is determined by the control points q_{ijk}.

Let us now assume that the positions of the control points q_{ijk} are known and that we want to add a bar or beam element to the FE model of the structure. The position of the FE is determined by the positions of its end nodes, here denoted as $\mathbf{r}_\alpha$ and $\mathbf{r}_\beta$. But instead of defining $\mathbf{r}_\alpha$ and $\mathbf{r}_\beta$. directly in the real 3D space, we define their pre-images $\mathbf{s}_\alpha$ and $\mathbf{s}_\beta$ in U. Now, the actual position of the nodes is calculated as

$$\mathbf{r}_\alpha = \mathbf{r}_\alpha(\mathbf{s}_\alpha), \quad \mathbf{r}_\beta = \mathbf{r}_\beta(\mathbf{s}_\beta) \qquad (2)$$

by employing Equation 1.

By defining all nodes of the FE mesh in U rather than in the real 3D space we actually get a structure which shape can be changed in a very elegant fashion by simply moving the control points q_{ijk}.

In realistic shape design problems, the majority of the control points is not allowed to move or they can move only in some prescribed directions. In order to achieve this, we simply introduce a set of artificial parameters assembled in the vector **b** and call these parameters the *design variables*. Depending on the design problem at hand, some components of the control points q_{ijk} are taken to depend on b while the others can be taken as constants. Anyhow, in generally we establish some relationship

$$\mathbf{q}_{ijk} = \mathbf{q}_{ijk}(\mathbf{b}) \qquad (3)$$

Let us now denote by the symbol $\mathbf{r}_\alpha$ the position vector of a generic node of the FE mesh of the structure. By combining Equations 1 and 3, we can write

$$\mathbf{r}_\alpha = \mathbf{r}_\alpha(\mathbf{s}_\alpha, \mathbf{b}) \tag{4}$$

In that way the shape of the whole structure is determined by a relative small number of parameters – the design variables assembled in the vector $\mathbf{b}$. By varying the values of the design variables $\mathbf{b}$, the shape of the whole structure is varied. The attractive properties of Bézier curves assure that the modified shape of the structure will remain realistic in the engineering sense. Additionally, certain geometric constraints, like continuous tangents across design element boundaries, can be taken into account with relative ease and without extending the optimization problem with additional constraints.

3 DESIGN PROBLEM FORMULATION

Let us consider a skeletal structure and let the geometry of the structure be described by suitable design elements. Let the control points $\mathbf{q}_{ijk}$ of the design elements be known and let us assume that we have already established their dependency on N design variables $\mathbf{b} \in \mathbf{R}^N$. The material, support and loading data is assumed to be known.

Thus we effectively have a finite element modeled structure which shape can be smoothly altered by varying the design variables. The shape optimal design problem may in this case be formulated in a form of a nonlinear problem of mathematical programming

$$\min h_0,$$
$$h_i \leq 0, \quad i = 1, \ldots, M \tag{5}$$

where M is the number of imposed constraints. The objective function value $h_0 = h_0(\mathbf{b},\mathbf{u})$ is often (but not necessarily) defined as the volume of the structure while the constrained quantities $h_i = h_i(\mathbf{b},\mathbf{u})$ usually concern nodal displacements and rotations, element strains and stresses, design variable limits, technological limitations and so on. The symbol $\mathbf{u}$ denotes the vector of structural response variables – usually nodal displacements in case of a statically loaded structure.

In problem (5) the design variables have to be considered as independent variables and the response variables as the dependent one. In other words, we actually have $\mathbf{u} = \mathbf{u}(\mathbf{b})$. This dependency is established implicitly by the structural equilibrium equation

$$\mathbf{F} - \mathbf{R} = 0 \tag{6}$$

where $\mathbf{F} = \mathbf{F}(\mathbf{b},\mathbf{u})$ and $\mathbf{R} = \mathbf{R}(\mathbf{b},\mathbf{u})$ are the vectors of internal and external forces, respectively. Internal forces obviously depend explicitly on $\mathbf{b}$ and $\mathbf{u}$. On the other side, external forces are often constant. However, they become dependent on $\mathbf{b}$ if, for example, the weight of the structure is taken into account. And if we additionally employ elastic supports, external forces will depend also on $\mathbf{u}$ (see e.g. Oblak et al. 1998).

The design problem to be solved can now be summarized as follows: find such values of the design variables $\mathbf{b}$ that the objective function will be minimized and the imposed constraints in Equation 5 will be fulfilled. The response variables $\mathbf{u}$ depend on $\mathbf{b}$ by the response Equation 6.

4 SOLUTION PROCEDURE

The problem (5) is a standard problem of mathematical programming and can be solved virtually by any method for nonlinear optimization. But since the design variables are continuous, a gradient-based algorithm (like e.g. the recursive quadratic programming method or approximation methods) is probably the most effective choice.

If we want to solve problem (5) by employing a gradient-based optimization algorithm, the solution procedure is iterative and can be outlined as follows:

1. Set $k = 0$; choose some initial $\mathbf{b}^{(0)}$.
2. Calculate h_i, $i = 0, \ldots, M$ at $\mathbf{b}^{(k)}$ (response analysis).
3. Calculate $dh_i/d\mathbf{b}$, $i = 0, \ldots, M$ at $\mathbf{b}^{(k)}$ (sensitivity analysis).
4. Submit the calculated values to the optimizer in order to get some improvement $\Delta\mathbf{b}^{(k)}$ and calculate the improved design $\mathbf{b}^{(k+1)} = \mathbf{b}^{(k)} + \Delta\mathbf{b}^{(k)}$.
5. Set $k = k + 1$ and check some appropriate convergence criteria – if fulfilled exit, otherwise go to Step 2.

The functions h_i, $i = 0, \ldots, M$ are expressed in terms of $\mathbf{b}$ and $\mathbf{u}$. Thus, in order to perform the response analysis, we have to calculate $\mathbf{u}^{(k)}$ at a given $\mathbf{b}^{(k)}$. This is done by solving the response Equation 6.

The derivatives $dh_i/d\mathbf{b}$, $i = 0, \ldots, M$ are expressed in terms of $\mathbf{b}$, $\mathbf{u}$ and $d\mathbf{u}/d\mathbf{b}$. For the sensitivity analysis at $\mathbf{b}^{(k)}$ we therefore need $\mathbf{u}^{(k)}$ and $(d\mathbf{u}/d\mathbf{b})^{(k)}$. The response $\mathbf{u}^{(k)}$ is already known from the response analysis, while $(d\mathbf{u}/d\mathbf{b})^{(k)}$ has to be calculated from the sensitivity equation. This equation can be derived by differentiating the response equation with respect to $\mathbf{b}$. By doing this and rearranging the terms, we get

$$\left(\frac{\partial \mathbf{F}}{\partial \mathbf{u}} - \frac{\partial \mathbf{R}}{\partial \mathbf{u}}\right)\frac{d\mathbf{u}}{d\mathbf{b}} = \frac{\partial \mathbf{R}}{\partial \mathbf{b}} - \frac{\partial \mathbf{F}}{\partial \mathbf{b}} \tag{7}$$

It should be noted that while the response equation may be nonlinear (kinematic or material nonlinearities) with respect to **u**, the sensitivity equation is always linear with respect to d**u**/d**b**. Even more, the term in parentheses on the left is the tangential stiffness matrix of the structure. This matrix is known (and already decomposed) from the response analysis. Thus, the sensitivity equation can be quite easily solved with a relative small computational effort. The only things we need are the partial design derivatives of internal and external forces – the terms on the right of Equation 7.

The calculation of $\partial\mathbf{R}/\partial\mathbf{b}$ depends on the problem at hand so that no general guidelines can be offered. For the calculation of $\partial\mathbf{F}/\partial\mathbf{b}$, however, we have to keep in mind that internal forces **F** depend on the nodal positions of the FE mesh.

Let us again denote by the symbol $\mathbf{r}_\alpha$ the position vector of a generic node of the FE mesh. In order to calculate $\partial\mathbf{F}/\partial\mathbf{b}$, we need the derivatives d$\mathbf{r}_\alpha$/d**b**. These quantities are easily derived from Equation 1 as follows

$$\frac{d\mathbf{r}_\alpha}{d\mathbf{b}} = \sum_{i=1}^{I}\sum_{j=1}^{J}\sum_{k=1}^{K} B_i^I(s_1) B_j^J(s_2) B_k^K(s_3) \frac{d\mathbf{q}_{ijk}}{d\mathbf{b}}\bigg|_{\mathbf{s}=\mathbf{s}_\alpha} \qquad (8)$$

Besides of its nodal positions, for a beam finite element we also need the geometrical properties as well as the orientation of its cross-section. The cross-sectional properties can be made design dependent as in conventional design procedures. For the orientation of the cross-section, however, we have several possibilities. One option is to provide the orientation by an additional node. In that case we will also need the derivative d$\mathbf{r}_\alpha$/d**b** of that node. Another option is to provide the orientation by some direction vector **e** which (in general) also has to be design dependent. In such a situation it is advantageous to have some convenient direction vector at hand. Such vectors are, for example, the tangent vectors of the parametric lines of the design element. These vectors as well as their design derivatives can be easily derived from Equation 1. In Kegl (2000) these expressions are offered in an explicit form.

5 NUMERICAL EXAMPLE

Let us now consider a 3D bridge structure shown in Figure 4. The arch and the span are modeled by beams while the "cables" (connecting the arch with the span) are modeled by truss elements. The Young's modulus of the employed material is E = 210000 MPa. The arch is rigidly supported at its both ends.

The initial dimensions of the structure and the supports are shown on Figure 5.

The structure is loaded by three different loads acting simultaneously:

1. its own weight (arch and cables),
2. the weight and external vertical loads of the span (200000 N/m of the span)

3. a transverse load in the z direction simulating the wind (200N/node of the arch).

A hollow square cross-sectional profile is used for all of the beam elements. The truss elements have a circular cross-section (Fig. 6).

The cross-sections of beam elements of the arch as well as cross-sections of the truss elements are considered to be design dependent (design variables b_0 through b_{16}). Three different □-profiles are employed (Fig. 4). The explicit design dependencies of all profiles are given in Table 1.

The shape of the arch is also considered to be design dependent. One design element with $5 \times 2 \times 2 = 20$ control points is employed (Fig. 7).

The positions of the control points depend explicitly on design variables as given in Table 2 (the positions of other control points can be obtained by symmetry). The X coordinates of all control points are constant.

So far we have introduced 16 design variables. These variables determine the shape of the structure

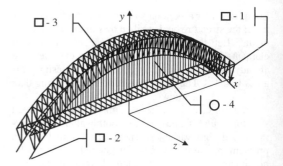

Figure 4. The 3D bridge structure.

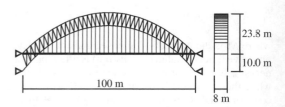

Figure 5. Initial design of the bridge.

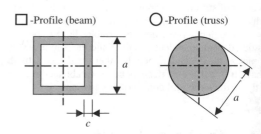

Figure 6. Cross sections of the beam and truss elements.

as well as the cross-sectional properties of most beam and truss elements. It should be noted that the structural symmetry requirements are taken into account automatically by symmetric definition of the control points coordinates in terms of the design variables.

Now it is time to formulate the design problem as follows: find such values of the design variables that the volume of the structure will be minimal and at the same time the constraints will be fulfilled. The constraints imposed are related to the

1. transverse displacement of the arch (max 1 cm)
2. vertical displacement of the span (max 2 cm)
3. tension stress in truss elements (max 120 MPa)
4. normal or shear stress in beam elements (max 25 MPa).

Table 1. The design dependencies of cross-sections.

Profile	Dimensions [mm]
□-1 (transverse-beams – vertical)	$a = 100 + 50b_{10}, c = 5 + 2.5b_{11}$
□-2 (beams along the arch)	$a = 300 + 150b_{12}, c = 40 + 35b_{13}$
□-3 (transverse-beams – horizontal)	$a = 100 + 50b_{15}, c = 5 + 2.5b_{16}$
○-4 (truss elements)	$a = 20 + 15b_{14}$

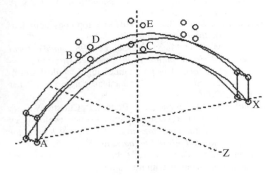

Figure 7. Initial shape of the design element and the positions of the control points.

Table 2. Design dependent coordinates of the control points.

	Y [mm]	Z [mm]
A	$-100b_5$	const.
B	$30000 + 1000b_8$	$4000 + 1000b_3$
C	$30000 + 1000b_9$	$4000 + 1000b_4$
D	$35000 + 1000b_6$	$4000 + 1000b_3$
E	$40000 + 1000b_7$	$4000 + 1000b_1$

The optimization problem was solved by an approximation method described in Kegl & Oblak (1997) and Kegl et al. (2002). The solution procedure was stable and the result was quite satisfactory (Table 3).

The initial and the final values of the design variables are given in Table 4.

The shape of the bridge changed significantly. The final shapes of the design element and the bridge is shown in Figures 8–10.

Table 3. Comparison of initial and optimal design.

	Initial	Optimal
Volume [m³]	52.47	34.04
Max constraint violation [%]	43.5	<0.01

Table 4. The limits, the initial and the final values of design variables.

i	b_{min}	b_{max}	$b_{initial}$	$b_{optimal}$
1	−5	5	0	−3.667
2	−5	5	0	−3.878
3	−2	5	0	−2
4	−5	5	0	−5
5	−10	5	0	−1.040
6	−10	5	0	−10
7	−10	5	0	5
8	−10	5	0	−0.132
9	−10	5	0	4.823
10	−1	1	0	−1
11	−1	1	0	−1
12	−1	1	0	−0.237
13	−1	1	0	−0.900
14	−1	1	0	−0.951
15	−1	1	0	−1
16	−1	1	0	1

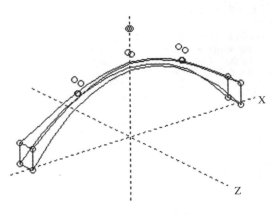

Figure 8. Final shape of the design element.

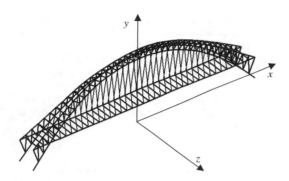

Figure 9.   Optimal design of the bridge.

20.6 m

9.9 m

Figure 10.   Optimal design and some dimensions of the bridge.

6   CONCLUSION

The design element technique and the Bézier body, acting as the design element, offer an attractive option for shape optimal design of skeletal structures. Geometrical constraints like symmetry requirement can be taken into account automatically by prescribing proper dependencies between the control points and the design variables. Behavioral constraints of any type (e.g. eigenfrequency) can easily be included into the design problem. General purpose gradient based optimizers may be employed to solve the problem efficiently.

REFERENCES

Bendsøe, M.P. & Kikuchi, N. 1988. Generating optimal topologies in structural design using a homogenisation method. *Computer methods in Applied Mechanics and Engineering* 71: 197–224.

Braibant, V. & Fleury, C. 1984. Shape optimal design using B-splines. *Computer Methods in Applied Mechanics and Engineering* 44: 247–267.

Dinevski, D., Oblak, M.M. & Kegl, M. 2002. Shaping optimal design of elastic planar frames with frequency constraints. *AIAA Journal* 40: 2113–2119.

Farin, G. 1993. *Curves and Surfaces for Computer Aided Geometric Design* (2nd edn). Academic Press: New York.

Ibrahimbegović, A. 1995. On finite element implementation of geometrically nonlinear Reissner's beam theory: three-dimensional curved beam elements. *Comput. methods appl. mech. eng.* 122: 11–26.

Imam, M.H. 1982. Three-dimensional shape optimization. *International Journal for Numerical Methods in Engineering* 18: 661–673.

Jelenić, G. & Saje, M. 1995. A kinematically exact space finite strain beam model – finite element formulation by generalized virtual work principle. *Comput. methods appl. mech. eng.* 120: 131–161.

Kegl, M. & Oblak, M.M. 1997. Optimization of mechanical systems: on non-linear first-order approximation with an additive convex term. *Communications in Numerical Methods in Engineering.* 13: 13–20.

Kegl, M. & Antes, H. 1998. Shape optimal design of elastic space frames with non-linear response. *International Journal for Numerical Methods in Engineering* 43: 93–110.

Kegl, M. 2000. Shape optimal design of structures: an efficient shape representation concept. *International Journal for Numerical Methods in Engineering* 49: 1571–1588.

Kegl, M., Butinar, B.J. & Kegl, B. 2002. An efficient gradient-based optimization algorithm for mechanical systems. *Communications in Numerical Methods in Engineering.* 18: 363–371.

Maute, K. & Ramm, E. 1995. Adaptive topology optimization. *Structural optimization* 10: 100–112.

Oblak, M.M., Kegl, M., & Dinevski, D. 1998. *Shape optimal design of elastic planar frames with elastic and skew-sliding supports.* Design Engineering Technical Conf., American Society of Mechanical Engineers. Paper DETC97/DAC-3733.

Reynolds, D., McConnachie, J., Bettess, P., Christie, W.C & Bull, J.W. 1999. Reverse adaptivity – A new evolutionary tool for structural optimization. *International Journal for Numerical Methods in Engineering* 45: 529–552.

Rozvany, G.I.N., Zhou, M. & Birker, T. 1992. Generalized shape optimization without homogenization. *Structural optimization* 4: 250–252.

Shyy, Y.K., Fleury, C. & Izadpanah, K. 1988. Shape optimal design using high-order elements. *Computer Methods in Applied Mechanics and Engineering* 71: 99–116.

System-based Vision for Strategic and Creative Design, Bontempi (ed.)
© *2003 Swets & Zeitlinger, Lisse, ISBN 90 5809 599 1*

Multidimensional design and systemic vision in structural engineering

F. Biondini
Department of Structural Engineering, Technical University of Milan, Italy

A. Marchiondelli
Consulting Engineer, Milan, Italy

ABSTRACT: The progressively growing human sensibility towards the quality of engineering structures is changing the conception of the design process, which must search for solutions not only technically realisable, inexpensive and safe, but also complying with more general satisfaction criteria, like human comfort, aesthetics and ecological needs. In this paper, the complexity of a *multidimensional design* is handled by introducing a set of *quality indices*, which represent the multiple targets of design, and by a *systemic vision* of the structural model, which can be viewed either as a whole having its own emerging properties, or as composed by elementary parts with their own specific characteristics. Moreover, in order to overcome the limits of mathematical optimisation methods in solving design problems of high complexity and dimensionality, the optimal structural morphology is searched for through a two-levels heuristic approach based on biologically inspired evolutionary procedures. The application to the optimal design of a cable-stayed bridge is finally presented.

1 INTRODUCTION

In the 20th century, besides scientific and technological progresses of great importance, we have got the continuous development of a growing human sensibility towards the quality of engineering works. In fact, all fields of production have favoured the establishment of a quality design aimed to conceive objects not only technically realisable, inexpensive and safe, but also complying with more general satisfaction criteria, like human comfort, aesthetics, ecological needs, and so on.

In the context of structural engineering, this new trend has found its most effective synthesis in the term *Conceptual Design*, which try to combine together two different needs (Malerba 2002): (1) The conception of design solutions that are efficient from the structural point of view and able to achieve the required service life by preserving themselves from the inevitable damage sources; (2) The adaptation of the structural forms to the functional, aesthetic and ecological demands, so that the construction can suitably receive the humans and become a part of the environment in a discreet and respectful way.

This paper presents a tentative to handle the complexity inherent to a *multidimensional design*. To this aim, the concept of sustainable design is firstly recalled and the minimal targets that should be considered in designing a sustainable building are identified. These multiple targets are then quantitatively translated in a set of *quality indices* which allow a synthetic judgement about the goodness of a design solution and a direct comparison among different design alternatives. In particular, the definition of such indices takes advantage from a *systemic vision* of the structural model, which can be viewed either as a whole having its own emerging properties, or, at the same time, as composed by subsystems with their own specific characteristics. Moreover, in order to overcome the limits of classical mathematical-based optimisation methods in solving design problems of high complexity and dimensionality, the optimal structural morphology is searched for through a two-level heuristic approach based on biologically inspired evolutionary procedures which operate on the basis of some analogies with the growing and evolutionary processes of natural systems. The proposed approach is finally applied to the optimal design of the structural morphology of a cable-stayed bridge.

2 MULTIDIMENSIONAL DESIGN

2.1 *Analytical vs synthetic design*

The awareness of the many factors influencing the quality of an object requires a radical change in the usual conception of the design process in the context of civil engineering too. In fact, in the past the designer, supported by his experience, intuition and cultural background, usually proceeded by discarding the solutions judged to be unfeasible and by choosing a structural scheme coherent with the basic technical and architectural requirements. The actual performance of such tentative scheme emerged from a series of analyses, which the designer exploited to make the adjustments eventually required to identify a definitive design.

This way of proceeding – that we may call *analytical design*, since it looks to a specific solution in the universe of design alternatives – does not give any guarantee that the adopted solution is actually the best possible. In fact, in this analytical process the designer usually refers to well-known schemes and to the results of analyses aimed to assess their performance, forgetting the actual role of the calculus in design, born as an aid to the general understanding of the problem and not as an alternative to the capability of making design choices and discovering new design solutions. For these reasons, the analytical design tends to produce repetitive structural schemes and, consequently, to limit the artistic sensibility of the designer which, on the contrary, is by nature daring and innovative.

Lately the designer has rediscovered his actual need: to achieve a synthesis, or to find, among all the possible configurations, the structure which better satisfies the desired requirements. In this relatively new design process – that we may call *synthetic design*, since it tends to explore the whole universe of design alternatives – the best solution is implicitly chosen through the preliminary definition of its target performances (Vincenti 1990). In this crucial phase, the designer must have a full vision of all the aspects influencing the quality of the final solution, not only from a structural point of view, but also with reference to other performances usually considered of secondary importance in the past, like the durability of the construction, the correct insertion in its context, the environmental impact, the aesthetic value, etc.

This approach clearly makes the design problem very complex and then less suitable to be formalised within the classical optimisation theory (Simon 1981). In fact, the typical mono-objective formulations looking for the most economical solution must leave place to more coherent multi-objectives formulations accounting for the actual complex nature of the problem. Moreover, the widening of the quality concept of constructions imposes a multidisciplinary design strategy, where the synergetic cooperation among several different fields (technical, economical, social, ecological, etc.) is required to effectively solve a *multidimensional design* problem.

2.2 The challenge of the sustainable design

The challenge of the designer of the future can be resumed in the management of the complexity inherent to the existing relationships among human society, natural environment and artificial built-up environment (Fig. 1). In fact, to safeguard the ecosystem of the planet and the human life quality, the new way of design must account for the global impact of any construction, during all its life cycle, on both the environment and society, not only with reference to the present generation, but with reference to the future one too.

These needs have been synthesised in the term *sustainability*, which in the years has assumed a wider and wider meaning aimed to sensitise a change of mentality and the adoption of a life style respectful of all the resources of the planet. Based on this concepts, the principle of sustainability invites to conceive a building not as something closed where to take shelter from the external agents, but to relate it to the surrounding environment and to make the construction contemporarily agreeable to humans and respectful of the loading capacity of the ecosystem.

A first step towards this new conception of design should clearly account for the mentioned multidimensionality of the problem. In particular, a minimal set of targets that should be considered as driving criteria in designing a sustainable building can be synthesised as follows:

– *Structural Efficiency*. The structure of a building must have sufficient strength and stability characteristics, with an overall stress distribution which allows a good exploitation of both the material properties and the structural volume.
– *Functionality*. A building must be able to comply in a satisfactory, ergonomic and comfortable way

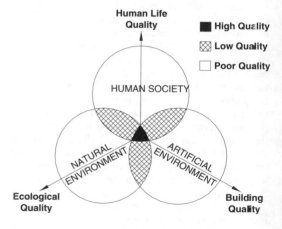

Figure 1. Design quality and relationships among human society, natural environment and artificial built-up environment.

with the functions for which it has been designed. Since this capacity is needed over the whole service life, the building should be also characterised by sufficient flexibility and versatility to allow changes of destination.

- *Aesthetics*. This property synthesises the exterior pleasantness of a structure, its architectonic originality and artistic value. Furthermore, aesthetics represents the most immediate way to express the social value of a construction and to acquaint the community with it. For these reasons, it is essential to pay great attention to factors as geometrical order and regularity, structural simplicity and clearness, lightness and harmony of the proportions, either of the structure as a whole, or of its elementary parts, especially in relation to the characteristics of the surrounding environment (Leonhardt 1980).
- *Economy*. The cost of a building includes not only the cost of construction, but also the cost of management and maintenance during the whole service life, as well as the cost of final dismission at the end of this period. Another important aspect deals with the social cost of a building. In fact, the production and use of materials and services determines, on both environment and society, effects having a well defined economic impact (alterations of the ecosystems, pollution, injuries to the human health, loss of value of material goods, non-enjoyability of immaterial goods, etc.), with long term repercussions on the future generations too.
- *Durability*. A building must assure all the performance mentioned above during its whole service life. To this aim, it is necessary to provide a continuous monitoring of the building in order to plan proper

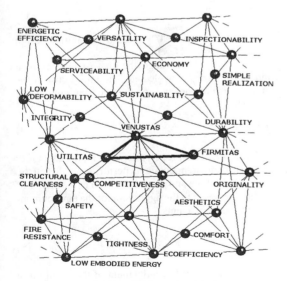

Figure 2. Targets of a multidimensional design.

maintenance processes and eventual restorations of its initial characteristics, inevitably altered because of the many potential sources of damage, coming for example from exceptional loading (fires, earthquakes, hurricanes, landslides) or from the ordinary interaction with aggressive environments (carbonation, corrosion, freezing and unfreezing cycles).

The first three targets mentioned above can be assimilated to the fundamental aspects already pointed out by Vitruvio as the essential characteristics of a construction: *firmitas*, *utilitas*, and *venustas*. In view of a multidimensional approach, we can imagine many of these targets, thought to be equally important, as located at the vertexes of a multidimensional solid completing the so-called *vitruvian triad* (Fig. 2).

3 SYSTEMIC VISION AND DESIGN QUALITY

3.1 *Holistic and sectorial levels*

It can be observed that every *structural system* is an unitary whole composed by a plurality of elementary parts, having their own specificity, that have to be organised in an appropriate way to create an organic and durable system with its own emerging properties (Fig. 3). The systemic unity so defined is contemporarily structured and structuring, since its status derives from the status of the subsystems and, at the same time, influences it.

Based on this *systemic vision*, the design process can be set at two different levels. At the first one, that we call *holistic level*, a structure is conceived like a unity and the global quality of its emerging properties can be evaluated. At the second level, that we call *sectorial level*, the subsystems forming the whole are considered separately and the local design requirements, as well as the compatibility between the different parts of the system, can be verified. Clearly, the two levels are highly interacting since every decision about the whole unit influences the choices regarding the substructures and, on the other hand, each single subsystem may present local demands which require some modifications of the global properties. It is important to outline that this synergetic interaction leads to *feedback* phenomena with global effects different from those that can be obtained from the analysis of the subsystems taken separately (von Bertalanffy 1969).

3.2 *Quality indices and measure of design goodness*

In order to make possible a hierarchical classification of the explored design alternatives, a direct measure of all the emerging properties of the structural system is needed. To this aim, a tentative set of *quality indices* related to the main multiple targets of a sustainable

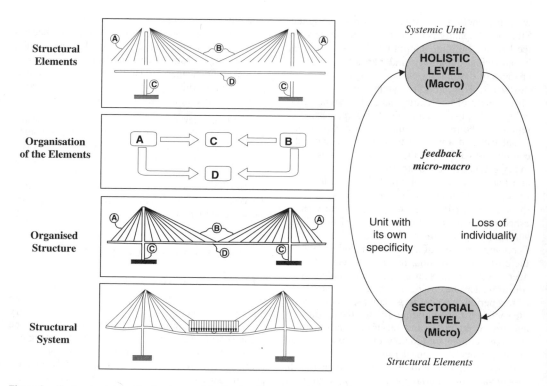

Structural Elements	
Organisation of the Elements	
Organised Structure	
Structural System	

Systemic Unit

HOLISTIC LEVEL (Macro)

feedback micro-macro

Unit with its own specificity

Loss of individuality

SECTORIAL LEVEL (Micro)

Structural Elements

Figure 3.   Systemic vision of a structure and feedback micro–macro between local and global emerging properties.

design, such as structural efficiency, serviceability, durability, economy and aesthetics, are introduced (Biondini *et al.* 2002). They allow a synthetic judgement about the goodness of a design solution and a direct comparison among different design alternatives. In particular, the unitary value of these indices corresponds to the best solution, while a zero value denotes the worst alternative.

Structural Efficiency. This aspect depends on the stress distribution σ over the structure and it can be related to a good exploitation of the material properties (*mechanical efficiency*):

$$a_{ME}(t) = \sum_{k=1}^{m} \frac{\int_{V_k} |\sigma| \, dV}{\sigma_{adm,k} V_k(t)} = \sum_{k=1}^{m} \frac{V_{R,k}(t)}{V_k(t)} \qquad (1)$$

and of the structural volume (*volumetric efficiency*):

$$a_{VE}(t) = \sum_{k=1}^{m} \frac{\int_{V_k} |\sigma| \, dV}{\sigma_{k,max} V_k(t)} = \sum_{k=1}^{m} \frac{V_{k,max}(t)}{V_k(t)} \qquad (2)$$

where V_k, $\sigma_{adm,k}$ and $\sigma_{max,k}$ are the material volume, the admissible stress and the maximum stress, respectively, of each subsystem $k = 1, \ldots, m$, while the time parameter t denotes a particular design solution.

Serviceability. This requirement depends on the deformability of the structure and can be related to the maximum displacement s_{max} over the structure:

$$a_S(t) = e^{-a_S \frac{s_{max}(t)}{s_{0,max}}} \qquad (3)$$

where the subscript "0" refers to an initial design solution taken as reference.

Economy. At this stage the cost of management and maintenance is neglected. The initial cost of the structure mainly depends on the material volume V:

$$a_E(t) = e^{-a_E \frac{V(t)}{V_0}} \qquad (4)$$

Durability. This property depends on the capability of the structure to maintain its performance during the structural lifetime and it can be related to the area A of material exposed to the aggression of the environmental and chemical agents:

$$a_D(t) = e^{-a_D \frac{A(t)}{A_0}} \qquad (5)$$

Aesthetic value. The judgement of the beauty of a structure is clearly a matter of opinion and depends of a number of subjective factors. To simplify the complexity of the problem, only the *geometrical aspect* is here considered and the attention is focussed on properties like regularity, order, proportion and orientation of the structure. For framed structures composed by straight truss and beam elements, such properties can be measured as follows:

(a) Regularity and Order

$$a_{REG}(t)=e^{-\alpha_R\left(\frac{\Delta\bar{l}(t)}{\Delta\bar{l}_0}\right)} \qquad a_{ORD}(t)=e^{-\alpha_0\frac{\Delta\bar{\theta}(t)}{\Delta\bar{\theta}_0}} \qquad (6)$$

(b) Proportion and Orientation

$$a_{PROP}(t)=e^{-\alpha_P\left(\frac{\Delta\hat{l}(t)}{\Delta\hat{l}_0}\right)} \qquad a_{ORIENT}(t)=e^{-\alpha_0\frac{\Delta\hat{\theta}(t)}{\Delta\hat{\theta}_0}} \qquad (7)$$

with:

$$\bar{l}(t)=\frac{1}{m}\sum_{k=1}^{m}l_k \qquad \bar{\theta}(t)=\frac{1}{m}\sum_{k=1}^{m}\theta_k \qquad (8)$$

$$\Delta\bar{l}(t)=\sqrt{\frac{1}{m}\sum_{k=1}^{m}\left(l_k-\bar{l}\right)^2} \qquad \Delta\bar{\theta}(t)=\sqrt{\frac{1}{m}\sum_{k=1}^{m}\left(\theta_k-\bar{\theta}\right)^2} \qquad (9)$$

$$\Delta\hat{l}(t)=\sqrt{\frac{1}{m}\sum_{k=1}^{m}\left(l_k-\hat{l}\right)^2} \qquad \Delta\hat{\theta}(t)=\sqrt{\frac{1}{m}\sum_{k=1}^{m}\left(\theta_k-\hat{\theta}\right)^2} \qquad (10)$$

where l_k and θ_k are the length and the inclination of an element with respect to a reference direction, respectively, and $\hat{l}$ and $\hat{\theta}$ are assigned optimal values.

The numerical constants α which appear in all the previous exponential terms are heuristically deduced. Proper values of such constants should be chosen in the range between 2.0 and 3.0.

4 BIOMIMETICS AND HEURISTIC DESIGN

4.1 *Heuristic vs mathematical optimisation methods*

From a theoretical point of view, a multidimensional design problem can be formulated as a multi-objectives problem and can be treated with classical optimisation methods. Of course, in structural engineering mathematical optimisation appears to be a powerful explorative tool for a rational search strategy, especially in solving well defined mono-objective problems. However, due to the high complexity and dimensionality of the actual design problem, mathematical methods often are not effective in finding the harmonisation which resolves the contrast existing among the multiple design objectives. This goal can be reasonably achieved only by means of extreme simplifications of the design model, sometimes so large that the nature of the original problem itself is fully violated.

A possible way to overcome this drawback is the development of proper heuristic methods proven to be effective by the experience. These methods don't search for the optimal solution, but simply proceed by looking for some improvements of the solutions already known. For this reason, they are usually less efficient of the classical mathematical techniques in exploiting the actual "mathematical optimum", but the obtained design solutions can be considered *almost optimal*, and then good enough from the engineering point of view. In addition, due to their wide generality, heuristic methods allow to easily handle multidimensional design problems characterised by high levels of complexity. Consequently, heuristic *almost optimal* solutions of well-posed design problems are usually much better of the "mathematical optimums" provided by simpler and ill-posed models.

4.2 *Biologically inspired evolutionary procedures*

One of the most promising heuristic method which has been recently applied to the identification of optimal structural morphology deals with evolutionary procedures which operate on the basis of some analogies with the growing and evolutionary processes of natural systems. Such procedures belong to the field of *biomimetics* and are based on the simple concept that by slowly removing and/or reshaping regions of inefficient material, belonging to a given over-designed domain, the structure modifies its shape and topology evolving toward an optimal configuration (Baseggio *et al.* 2000).

Based on these methods, in the following the optimal structural morphology is found through a two-level evolutionary approach (Biondini *et al.* 2000, 2002). The *external* morphology, i.e. the geometrical dimensions and the topology of the structural type, is optimised at the first level (*macro-level*) by simulating the *Biological Growth* (BG) of natural structures like bones and trees. The *internal* morphology, regarding the geometry and the shape of the cross-sections, is instead selected at the second level (*micro-level*) by means of a classical *Fully Stressed Design* (FSD) combined with a process of *Evolutionary Structural Optimisation* (ESO) which removes elements at low stress level.

To this aim, the structure is conceived like a *systemic unity* composed of different parts, called *zones*. Each *zone*, considered singly, has its own specificity (*sectorial level*), while it looses its individuality within the unity (*holistic level*). This duality, already pointed out at the conceptual level (Fig. 3), is taken on again at the methodological level by means of a *macro–micro* approach mainly based on BG and ESO evolutionary procedures. BG procedure, in fact, having the aim to optimise the shape of the structure, acts at the *macro level*, while ESO strategy collaborates with FSD to search for the optimal internal morphology at the *micro level*. However, on the basis of the desired effect, it is possible to keep active only one of the two above mentioned levels and to optimise only particular details or zones of the structure.

In general, the synergetic interaction between macro and micro optimisation leads to better results than those obtained when the procedures work separately. Moreover, it is worth nothing that in the presented approach the internal morphology is modified by means of discrete design variables (commercial sections), while the external one is optimised in a continuous way (node locations). The effectiveness and versatility of the evolutionary strategies are pointed out also by this aspect.

The basic steps of the overall procedure should be repeated until optimal configurations appear. In particular, the best structural solutions emerging from the evolutionary process are identified on the basis of the quality indices previously introduced.

4.3 Macro-optimisation of the external morphology

At the macro level the structure is viewed like a systemic unity whose behaviour is obtained by the structural relationships existing among its zones. The aim of the macro-optimisation is the search for the optimal external morphology, that is, in the first place, the identification of the resistant scheme and, in the second place, the correct sizing of the global system and the search for its optimal shape and topology.

The BG procedure allows the structure to evolve by adapting itself to the applied loads according to the *axiom of uniform stress*, which states that, in the optimal configuration, the stress distribution tends to be fairly regular over the structure (Mattheck & Burkhardt 1990, Mattheck 1998). The structural shape and topology,

therefore, are gradually modified by adding material in the zones with high stress concentrations and removing it from under-loaded zones (*Swelling Step*). In this paper, the axiom of uniform stress is generalised by stating that, in the optimal configuration, the structure is characterised by uniform performance everywhere (*axiom of uniform performance*).

The main steps of the BG procedure can be briefly resumed as follows (Fig. 4):

(A) *Basic Step:* A finite element analysis is performed to obtain the stress distribution, as well as the other parameters which define the structural performance measured by the quality indices previously introduced.

(B) *Swelling Step.* In the original BG procedure, the evolutionary forces which drive the swelling of the structure are based only on the stress state. In the present formulation, the Driving Forces $DF = DF(t)$ of each zone are instead computed with reference to the quality indices a_i as follows:

$$DF(t) = A\sum_i w_i \beta_i(t)[a_i(t) - a_i^{ref}(t)] \qquad (11)$$

where A is a suitable constant, w_i is the *weight* of the i-th component of the driving force, $\beta_i = \pm 1$ is an *evolutionary index* that defines the direction of such component, and a_i^{ref} is the target value of the quality index a_i, usually assumed with the current mean value over the structure. The DF causes a constant swelling strain distribution Δe_{SW} in each zone. Based on such strain distribution, the load vector Δf_{SW} equivalent to *swelling* is derived and the corresponding incremental displacement vector Δu_{SW} is evaluated:

$$\Delta f_{SW} = \int_V \mathbf{B}^T \mathbf{D}\Delta e_{SW} dV \quad \Rightarrow \quad \Delta u_{SW} = \mathbf{K}^{-1}\Delta f_{SW} \qquad (12)$$

being **B** the compatibility matrix of the finite element, **D** the constitutive matrix of the material and **K** the stiffness matrix of the structure. It is worth noting

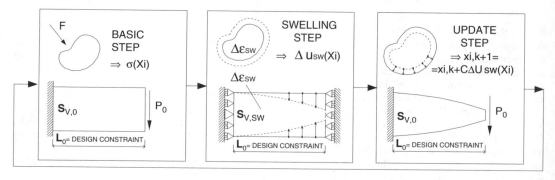

Figure 4. Fundamental steps of BG procedure.

that additional geometrical design constraints can be directly accounted for by replacing the actual boundary conditions of the *swelling model* so that swelling displacements which violate the constraints are not allowed. This concept is shown in Fig. 4, where the cantilever beam is forced to maintain its initial length during the evolution.

(C) *Update Step.* The location $\mathbf{x}_{i,k}$ of each node i of the finite element model at the current generation t is updated according to the swelling incremental displacements $\Delta\mathbf{u}_{SW}$ as follows:

$$\mathbf{x}_{i,t+1} = \mathbf{x}_{i,t} + C\Delta\mathbf{u}_{SW} \tag{13}$$

being C a suitable extrapolation factor which implicitly contains the constant A. Such factor may be either considered as time-independent, or varied during the evolution. In any case, its value should be chosen to assure noticeable shape variations and progressively decreasing driving forces.

4.4 *Micro-optimisation of the internal morphology*

At the micro level the attention is focussed on the single structural element and the micro-optimisation aims to determine the optimal internal morphology, that is the best sizing, geometry and shape of the cross-sections. As mentioned above, this is obtained by means of an effective collaboration between a FSD criterion, which exploits the material of each structural element in an optimal way, and the ESO procedure, which removes inefficient elements. This synergetic action leads to a powerful search strategy here called *Evolutionary Fully Stressed Optimisation* (EFSO).

In particular, since in the optimal structure each element is subjected to its allowable stresses under at least one load condition (Gallagher & Zienkiewicz 1973), FSD chooses, among many available commercial profiles, the cross-section of each element so that the material is stressed at its allowable levels. Clearly, in this process the allowable stresses of the materials must be properly modified to account for both local and global instability effects. In any case, when an element has a low mechanical efficiency, FSD changes its geometrical properties choosing an always smaller section. When the smallest available section is no longer able to fully exploit the material, the ESO procedure checks the efficiency of the element and eventually removes it by degrading its constitutive properties, typically the Young modulus (Xie & Steven 1993). In this study, the efficiency of the element is evaluated on the basis of its *mechanical efficiency*: if the value of the corresponding index is less than a given lower limit, the element must be removed. In the basic formulation the minimum portion of removable material is then identified with a single finite element. However, a more general formulation can be achieved if the control of efficiency is performed on a *minimum elimination unit* formed by a *group* of elements.

4.5 *Evolutionary design of a cable-stayed bridge*

The presented evolutionary procedure is applied to the optimal design of the cable-stayed bridge shown in Fig. 5. The loading condition is given by the self-weight of deck and pylon, evaluated with a weight density $\gamma = 25\,\text{kN/m}^3$, the prestressing of the stays $\sigma_{p0} = 1000\,\text{MPa}$, and a uniform load $q = 100\,\text{kN/m}$

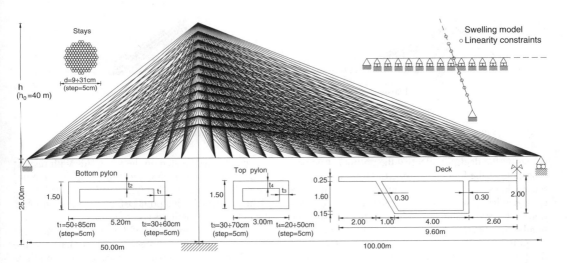

Figure 5. Cable-stayed bridge. Main dimensions of the initial design model and design variables.

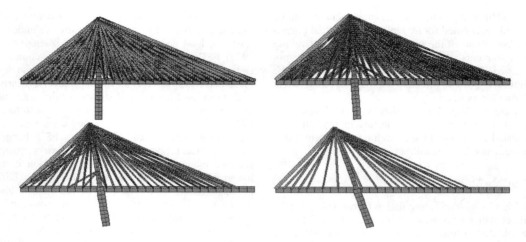

Figure 6.   Some steps of the evolutionary process driven by the index of mechanical efficiency.

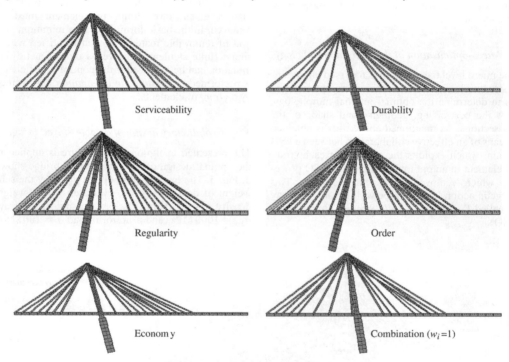

Serviceability

Durability

Regularity

Order

Economy

Combination (w_i=1)

Figure 7.   Some optimal configurations obtained by using different driving indices.

acting on the deck. To identify the optimal structural morphology, the following properties must be defined: the thickness of both the bottom and top pylon box cross-sections; the diameter of the stays; the inclination of the pylon and the height of its top part; the number of the stays and the location of their anchoring points along both the deck and pylon. The initial design domain is subdivided in 29 zones: the deck (1); the bottom and top parts of the pylon (2); the

groups of stays located on the same side with respect to the pylon and having the same anchoring point along the pylon itself (26). The swelling model allows to move the anchoring points of the stays and enforces the pylon to maintain its straight profile.

Fig. 6 shows some steps of the evolutionary process driven by the index of mechanical efficiency, while Fig. 7 makes a comparison between the solutions obtained by using the other quality indices previously

Table 1. Minimum and maximum values of the design variables for the optimal solutions.

Driving criterion (quality index)	t_1 [cm]	t_2 [cm]	t_3 [cm]	t_4 [cm]	d [cm]	h [m]
Mechanical efficiency	75–80	50–60	65–70	40–45	13–21	35.63
Serviceability	80–80	60–60	70–75	50–55	17–25	48.62
Durability	80–85	60–65	65–70	40–45	19–27	36.32
Regularity	75–75	50–55	70–75	50–55	13–29	49.36
Order	75–75	50–55	70–75	50–55	9–31	47.08
Economy	75–80	55–60	65–70	40–45	13–27	32.48
Weighted combination ($w_i = 1$)	80–80	60–60	65–70	40–45	15–25	39.06

defined. The main results of these search processes are all resumed in Tab. 1.

5 CONCLUSIONS

The main developments proposed in this paper can be resumed in the following points:

- *Multidimensional design*. The complexity inherent to the design process is taken into consideration by searching for feasible engineering solutions complying with several targets (*structural efficiency, serviceability, economy, durability, aesthetics*).
- *Quality indices*. The multiple targets are quantitatively translated in a set of indices which allow a measure of the goodness of a design solution and a direct comparison among different design alternatives (*hierarchical classification*).
- *Systemic vision*. In the design model, the structure is viewed either as a whole having its own emerging properties, or as composed by elementary parts with their own specific characteristics (*feedback*).
- *Heuristic methods*. The search process is based on design analogies which easily handle multidimensional and complex design problems, leading to heuristic *almost optimal* solutions usually much better of the "mathematical optimums" provided by simpler and ill-posed models (*biomimetics*).

The effectiveness of the proposed approach has been finally shown through the application to the optimal design of a cable stayed bridge. The analysis of the results shows how the evolutionary control of proper quality indices can effectively drive the *multidimensional design* process towards structural morphologies having desired performance.

REFERENCES

Baseggio, A., Biondini, F., Bontempi, F., Gambini, M., Malerba, P.G., Structural Morphology Optimization by Evolutionary Procedures. *Proc. of Structural Morphology Conf.*, 264–271, Delft, The Netherlands, August 17–19, 2000.

Biondini, F., Bontempi, F., Malerba, P.G., The Search for Structural Schemes by Optimality Criteria and Soft Computing Techniques. *Proc. of Structural Morphology Conf.*, 179–187, Delft, The Netherlands, August 17–19, 2000.

Biondini, F., Boiocchi, S., Malerba, P.G., Marchiondelli, A., Biologically Inspired Evolutionary Procedures for Conceptual Design of the Structural Morphology. *Proc. of 2nd Int. Conf. on Advances in Structural Eng. and Mechanics (ASEM'02)*, Pusan, Korea, 21–23 August, 2002.

Gallagher, R.H., Zienkiewicz, O.C. (Eds), *Optimum Structural Design*. John Wiley & Sons, 1973.

Leonhardt, F., Aesthetics in Structural Engineering. *Proc. of 11th IABSE Congress*, Vienna, August 31–September 5, 1980.

Malerba, P.G., Tools for Conceptual Design of Structures. *Proc. of 2nd Int. Conf. on Advances in Structural Eng. and Mechanics (ASEM'02)*, Pusan, Korea, 21–23 August, 2002.

Mattheck, C., Burkhardt, S., A New Method of Structural Shape Optimization based on Biological Growth. *Int. J. of Fatigue*, **12**(3), 185–190, 1990.

Mattheck, C., *Design in Nature. Learning from Trees*. Springer-Verlag, 1998.

Simon, H., *The Sciences of the Artificial*. MIT Press, 1981.

Vincenti, W.G., *What Engineers Know and How They Know It*. The John Hopkins University Press, 1990.

von Bertalanffy, L., *General System Theory*. George Braziller, New York, 1969.

Xie, Y.M., Steven, G.P., A Simple Evolutionary Procedure for Structural Optimization. *Computers & Structures*, **49**(5), 885–896, 1993.

System-based Vision for Strategic and Creative Design, Bontempi (ed.)
© 2003 Swets & Zeitlinger, Lisse, ISBN 90 5809 599 1

On the design of optimised R/C sections in bending

L. Fenu

Department of Structural Engineering, Cagliari, Italy

ABSTRACT: Reinforced concrete sections are usually designed at the ultimate limit state, subject to the serviceability requirements. Therefore we analyse how to minimize the depth of an R/C section in bending with both tensile and compressive steel, for instance at mid-span of a supported R/C beam. Since R/C beam design usually requires to minimize their depth, we minimize the depth of the mid-span section depending on the neutral axis-effective depth ratio and on the compressive-tensile steel ratio, and we show how to model the design process as a nonlinear programming problem constrained by the serviceability requirements.

1 INTRODUCTION

In this paper we analyse the design of R/C sections in bending at the ultimate limit state with the partial-factor method: we analyse how the design process can be modelled by using constrained nonlinear programming to have, in this way, a global point of view of all the steps of the design process.

According to CEB-FIP Model Code 1990 (1993), serviceability requirements regard for instance excessive levels of stress in concrete and steel, excessive crack widths, as well as excessive deformations and vibrations.

Since in many cases structures are not subject to valuable vibrations, and, for simple R/C members, if we opportunely limit the span-depth ratio, deflections are limited as well, we suppose that the design is not constrained by vibrations and deflections.

Besides, especially in a not aggressive environment, some codes, like for instance Eurocode 2 (1991), have pointed out that the crack width control can be satisfactorily substituted by the steel stress level control depending on the bar diameter.

Since all the codes limit the stress levels of both steel and concrete at serviceability, then we can model the design process with the partial-factor method by using constrained nonlinear programming in the frequent case where the only serviceability requirement is to limit steel and concrete stresses.

2 THE OBJECTIVE OF THE DESIGN

Consider an R/C section at mid-span of a supported R/C beam with span l, uniformly loaded by permanent loads G and imposed loads Q, and with constant rectangular cross-section along the beam.

Since usually the objective of the design is to have cross-sections with their depth as small as possible, pre-assigned the breadth b and the cover c and c' of the top and bottom reinforcements respectively, being the design unknowns the effective depth d and the cross-sectional area A_s the steel in tension, the objective of the design is to minimize the effective depth d. The designer choose the neutral axis-effective depth ratio $\xi = x/d$ depending on the desired R/C section ductility; for instance, in this paper ξ can vary in the interval $[0.26, 0.40]$.

Being f_{yd} and f_{cd} the design values of the steel yield stress and of the concrete compression strength respectively, by considering the internal forces of the section and having put $\beta_0 = 0.8$, in this interval the concrete compression force is $R_c = 8.5 f_{cd} \beta_0 xd$, while the steel tensile force is $R_s = A_s f_{yd}$; the compressive force of the steel in compression may be expressed as $R'_s = A'_s \cdot \chi'(\xi) f_{yd}$ where, changing ξ in the above interval, $\chi'(\xi)$ changes taking into account the variation of the steel compressive strain, so that we have:

$$\chi'(\xi) = \frac{|\varepsilon_{cu}|}{|\varepsilon_{yd}|} \frac{\xi - \delta'}{\xi} \quad \text{with } \chi' \leq 1 \tag{1}$$

and where $\delta' = c'/d$.

For the equilibrium equation of the section in the direction of the beam axis, the mechanical reinforcement ratio $\omega_s = A_s/(bd) \cdot f_{yd}/f_{cd}$ is a function of ξ:

$$\omega_s = \frac{0.85\,\beta_0\,\xi}{1 - \alpha\,\chi'(\xi)} \tag{2}$$

while for the moment equilibrium we have:

$$\mu = \chi'(\xi)\,\alpha\,\omega_s\left(\frac{\beta_0}{2}\xi - \delta'\right) + \omega_s\left(1 - \frac{\beta_0}{2}\xi\right) \qquad (3)$$

where $\alpha = \omega_s'/\omega_s$ is the reinforcement ratio between the compressive and the tensile steel and, in the following, it is assumed to vary in the interval [0, 0.60], while ω_s' is the mechanical reinforcement ratio of the compressive steel and $\mu = M_u/(bd^2 f_{cd})$ is the dimensionless ultimate moment. Therefore we have $\omega_s = \omega_s(\xi, \alpha)$ and $\mu = \mu(\xi, \alpha)$.

Being M_d the design moment at mid-span, by designing the section at ultimate for all ξ and α of the intervals [0.26, 0.40] and [0, 0.60] respectively, we get:

$$d(\xi, \alpha) = \sqrt{\frac{M_d}{b\,f_{cd}\,\mu(\xi, \alpha)}} \qquad (4)$$

that is also the effective depth d is a function of ξ and α. Therefore $d = d(\xi, \alpha)$ is the objective function of the design that has to be minimized; assigned the actions and the materials, the effective depth is above all affected by ξ and α, so that it is worth investigating how to achieve the minimum effective depth by making vary ξ and α. Since in eqn.(1) $\chi'(\xi)$ depends also on d through, δ', then for (4) χ' depends not only on ξ but also on α, and we have:

$$\mu(\xi, \alpha) = \omega_s(\xi, \alpha)\left[\chi'(\xi, \alpha)\,\alpha\left(\frac{\beta_0}{2}\xi - \delta'(\xi, \alpha)\right)\right.$$
$$\left. + \left(1 - \frac{\beta_0}{2}\xi\right)\right]$$
$$(5)$$

where, depending on d, also δ' is assumed to be a function of ξ and α.

Consequently in eqn. (4) we have d also in the right side through $\mu = \mu(\xi, \alpha)$, namely, in its turn, through $\delta' = \delta'(\xi, \alpha)$. Hence function $d = d(\xi, \alpha)$ is an implicit function, but we can approximate it with an explicit function to easier minimize d.

To achieve this aim we can get d by firstly assigning to δ' a reasonable temptative value $\delta'^{(0)}$ and evaluating then function (1), namely:

$$\chi'(\xi)^{(0)} = \frac{|\varepsilon_{cu}|}{|\varepsilon_{yd}|}\frac{\xi - \delta'^{(0)}}{\xi} \quad \text{with } \chi' \le 1 \qquad (6)$$

By substituting in eqn. (4) we get $d(\xi, \alpha)^{(1)}$ and, at a successive step, substituting $d^{(1)}$ in (6) we get:

$$\chi'(\xi, \alpha)^{(1)} = \frac{|\varepsilon_{cu}|}{|\varepsilon_{yd}|}\frac{\xi - \dfrac{c'}{d(\xi, \alpha)^{(1)}}}{\xi} \quad \text{with } \chi' \le 1 \qquad (7)$$

so that at the (2)nd step we can get also $d(\xi, \alpha)^{(2)}$.

At the (n)th step we obtain the approximated explicit function $d(\xi, \alpha)^{(n)}$: in general for $n = 3$ we have a good approximation. Therefore from now on we consider $d(\xi, \alpha) = d(\xi, \alpha)^{(n)}$ to easier optimize the effective depth.

Finally, from function $d(\xi, \alpha)$, we obtain the overall depth,

$$H(\xi, \alpha) = d(\xi, \alpha) + c \qquad (8)$$

and the tensile steel cross-sectional area,

$$A_s(\xi, \alpha) = \omega_s(\xi, \alpha)\,b\,d(\xi, \alpha)\frac{f_{cd}}{f_{yd}} \qquad (9)$$

Since the required effective depth $d(\xi, \alpha)$ varies continuously in its interval of definition, by a practice point of view we can assume that the provided effective depth is very close to the required one and that it changes with very small steps, for instance of one centimetre.

On the contrary the required steel cross-sectional area A_s changes continuously too, but, since in the market we can find only steel bars of assigned diameter, the provided steel area does not change continuously but by successive steps. Therefore we couple $A_s(\xi, \alpha)$ with a function $A_{sd}(\xi, \alpha)$ of the provided steel. In the following examples we consider a beam with $b = 30$ cm and we use a tensile reinforcement with four bars with the same diameter, while for the compression reinforcement we use two bars. Therefore, depending on the diameter and on the space limits, table 1 shows the cross-sectional area of the tensile steel and, assigned a cover of 4 cm, the space between the bars; an analogous table can be cast for the compressive bars in compression.

Table 1. Space limits and stress limits for the tensile reinforcement according to Eurocode 2.

ϕ [mm]	Tensile reinforcement	A_{sd} [mm^2]	Space [mm]	Space limits [mm]	Stress limits [MPa]
12	4ϕ12	452	58	100	320
14	4ϕ14	616	55	125	300
16	4ϕ16	804	52	150	280
18	4ϕ18	1018	50	175	260
20	4ϕ20	1256	47	200	240

Therefore, while changing ξ and α the required steel cross-sectional areas $A_s (\xi, \alpha)$ and $A'_s (\xi, \alpha)$ change continuously, changing the diameters both the provided steel cross-sectional area $A_{sd} (\xi, \alpha)$ and $A'_{sd} (\xi, \alpha)$ are a function of ξ and α with break-points and they are defined on the ground of table 1, making them higher as less as possible than $A_s (\xi, \alpha)$ and $A'_s (\xi, \alpha)$ respectively. Consequently $A_{sd} (\xi, \alpha)$ and $A'_{sd} (\xi, \alpha)$ approximate $A_s (\xi, \alpha)$ and $A'_s (\xi, \alpha)$ as much as possible.

3 SERVICEABILITY REQUIREMENTS

By choosing ξ and α in their interval of definition, the minimum effective depth is obtained from function $d(\xi, \alpha)$, but, depending on crack control and on stress limitations, not all the values of $d(\xi, \alpha)$ are achievable.

Consider an R/C cross-section in stadium II where x_f is the depth of the neutral axis and J_f, considering uneffective the concrete below x_f, is the moment of inertia of the cross-section.

Depending on d, A_{sd} and A'_{sd}, x_f is a function of ξ and α as well as J_f that depends on d, A_{sd} and A'_{sd} both directly and, through x_f, indirectly.

Therefore the stress of the tensile steel is:

$$\sigma_s(\xi, \alpha) = n \, \frac{M_k \left[d(\xi, \alpha) - x_f (\xi, \alpha) \right]}{J_f (\xi, \alpha)} \qquad (9a)$$

where M_k is the characteristic value of the mid-span moment for the required serviceability combination of G_k and Q_k, while the modular ratio n is chosen to be 15. The stress of the compression steel is obtained by linearity and usually it does not constrains the design, while the concrete stress at the upper edge is:

$$\sigma_c(\xi, \alpha) = \frac{M_k \ x_f(\xi, \alpha)}{J_f (\xi, \alpha)} \qquad (10)$$

Eurocode 2 limits concrete stresses to avoid excessive creep effects under the quasi-permanent load combination and logitudinal cracks under the rare load combination; besides steel tensile stresses must not exceed $0.80 f_{yk}$ under the rare load combination to avoid plastic steel deformations and large, permanently open, cracks.

Besides, according to Eurocode 2, since, depending on the bar diameter and space, steel tensile stresses are related with crack width, then, in the most common cases, we can avoid the serviceability verification of crack width by opportunely limiting steel tensile stress under the quasi-permanent load combination. Table 1 illustrates the limitation of steel tensile stresses of Eurocode 2 under quasi-permanent loads in a non aggressive environment; some authors, like Toniolo (1995), propose to extend this method to aggressive environments too.

Therefore, in accordance with table 2, we define a function that, depending on the bar diameter, describes the steel tensile stress limitation. In fact, as each bar diameter is obviously related with the bar cross-sectional area, then we can relate each diameter with the provided cross-sectional area $A_{sd} (\xi, \alpha)$, obtained by using four bars with the same diameter. Therefore, in the tensile reinforcement with cross-sectional area $A_{sd} (\xi, \alpha)$, tensile stresses must not exceed the stress limitations of table 1 for that specific diameter, that is each couple of ξ and α of the dominion of definition of function $A_{sd} (\xi, \alpha)$ is related in an univocal way with the steel limit tensile stress required for the diameter of $A_{sd} (\xi, \alpha)$ by the Eurocode 2. Hence, we implement function $\bar{\sigma}_s = \bar{\sigma}_s (\xi, \alpha)$ that defines the steel stress limitations of the indirect method of crack control for each A_{sd} obtained by all the values of ξ and α in the dominion of definition. Obviously, owing to the discontinuous size of the allowable bar diameters, function $\bar{\sigma}_s$, as well as functions A_{sd}, and A'_{sd}, is not free from break points.

4 NONLINEAR PROGRAMMING MODEL OF THE CONSTRAINED DESIGN

Since the objective of the design is to minimize the effective depth calculated at ultimate, $d(\xi, \alpha)$ can be assumed as the objective function of a nonlinear programming problem subject to some constraints defined by the serviceability requirements; therefore we must define the functions that take into account the design constraints to find the values of ξ and α that minimize d. In a previous work Fenu (2002) studied this problem but with only an indipendent variable.

Consider the serviceability requirement of limiting the crack width; by using the indirect crack control, we calculate the steel tensing stress $\sigma_{s1} (\xi, \alpha)$ in the quasi-permanent load combination, and, by using table 1, we obtain function $\bar{\sigma}_s (\xi, \alpha)$ to define the constraint,

$$g_1(\xi, \alpha) = \sigma_{s1}(\xi, \alpha) - \bar{\sigma}_s(\xi, \alpha) \leq 0 \qquad (11)$$

Besides, in the rare load combination, steel tensile stress limitations have to be taken into account, namely:

$$g_2(\xi, \alpha) = \sigma_{s2}(\xi, \alpha) - 0.8 \, f_{yk} \leq 0 \qquad (12)$$

Stress limitations of the concrete are taken into account analogously. In the quasi-permanent load combination the constraint is:

$$g_3(\xi, \alpha) = \sigma_{c3}(\xi, \alpha) - 0.60 \, f_{ck} \leq 0 \qquad (13)$$

while, in the rare load combination we have:

$$g_4(\xi, \alpha) = \sigma_{c4}(\xi, \alpha) - 0.45 \, f_{ck} \leq 0 \qquad (14)$$

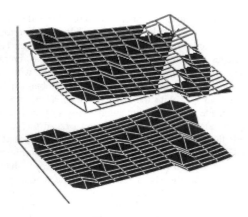

Figure 1. Functions $\bar{\sigma}_s\,(\xi,\alpha)$, $\sigma_{s1}\,(\xi,\alpha)$ and $g_{s1}\,(\xi,\alpha)$.

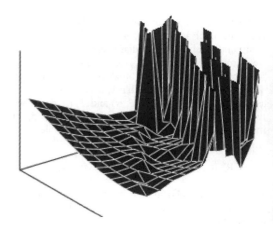

Figure 2. Pseudo-objective function.

Therefore the nonlinear programming problem of designing an R/C section at ultimate subject to the serviceability requirements is to minimize $d(\xi,\alpha)$ subject to $g_i\,(\xi,\alpha) \leqslant 0$, $i = 1 \ldots 4$.

To solve this problem we define an external penalty function (Comincioli, 1990):

$$P(\xi,\alpha) = \sum_{i=1}^{n} \delta_i\,g_i(\xi,\alpha) \quad i = 1 \ldots 4 \tag{15}$$

where $\delta_i = 0$ for and for $g_i\,(\xi,\alpha) \leqslant 0$ and $\delta_i = g_i\,(\xi,\alpha)$ for $g_i\,(\xi,\alpha) > 0$.

The pseudo-objective function is therefore:

$$\Phi(\xi,\alpha) = d(\xi,\alpha) + r_p \sum_{i=1}^{n} \delta_i\,g_i\,(\xi,\alpha) \tag{16}$$

where r_p is a positive real number chosen to be, in the following example, $1 \cdot 10^{-14}$.

In the following example, by using the Eurocode 2, we consider an R/C beam with $l = 5.2\,\mathrm{m}$, $b = 30\,\mathrm{cm}$, $c = c' = 4\,\mathrm{cm}$, concrete with $f_{ck} = 20\,\mathrm{MPa}$, steel with $f_{yk} = 400\,\mathrm{MPa}$, and loaded with permanent loads and imposed loads $G_k = 20000\,\mathrm{N/m}$ and imposed loads $Q_k = 10000\,\mathrm{N/m}$. For instance fig.1 shows the behaviour of functions $\sigma_{s1}\,(\xi,\alpha)$, and $\bar{\sigma}_s\,(\xi,\alpha)$, as well as of function $g_1\,(\xi,\alpha)$, and we see that for some values of ξ and α this constraint is active. In general some constraints can be never active for all values of the dominion of definition, and in this specific example the constraint $g_3\,(\xi,\alpha)$ is never active. Fig.2 shows the behaviour of the pseudo-objective function $\Phi\,(\xi,\alpha)$ and by searching for its constrained minimum, we find that, by using Eurocode 2 and assigned the materials and the beam breadth, the lightest R/C beam with constant cross-section governed by the section in mid-span has $d = 0.355\,\mathrm{m}$ for $\xi = 0.32$ and $\alpha = 0.5$.

5 CONCLUSIONS

The design of R/C sections with the partial factor method is in general made at ultimate by leaving to a successive moment the verification that serviceability requirements are met. Unfortunately, many times the serviceability requirements need that the section must be designed again, so that the traditional design is generated by trial and errors with many unnecessary calculations.

To better understand the design process, in this paper we have modelled it by using nonlinear programming so that the objective of the design, the minimization of the beam depth, has been modelled by defining the effective depth as a function of the neutral axis-effective depyh ratio and of the ratio between the steel in compression and that in tension: in fact these two ratio affect significantly the beam depth. To take into account the serviceability requirements we have defined the constraints of this nonlinear programming problem so that, by defining a penalty function, we have defined a pseudo-objective function to be minimized. In this way we have found the minimum depth of the section that, by using the traditional R/C sections design, we would find in a trial and error process after many attempts.

REFERENCES

CEN – ENV 1992. 1991. Eurocode 2, part 1.
CEB-FIP Model Code 1990. 1993. *Bulletin d'Information N°213/214*. London: Telford.
Comincioli, V. 1990. *Analisi numerica*, Milan: Mc Graw-Hill.
Fenu, L. 2002. Sul progetto delle sezioni in cemento armato allo stato limite ultimo vincolato alla limitazione del livello delle tensioni in esercizio. *Proc. of the 14° CTE Congress, Mantova, 7–9 November 2002*: 421–427.
Toniolo, G. 1995. *Cemento armato – Calcolo agli stati limite, Vol. 2A*. Milan: Masson.

7. Shaping structures and form finding architectures

System-based Vision for Strategic and Creative Design, Bontempi (ed.)
© 2003 Swets & Zeitlinger, Lisse, ISBN 90 5809 599 1

The design of structural systems for geometrically irregular buildings

M. Veltkamp & M. Eekhout
Delft University of Technology, Faculty of Architecture, Delft, Netherlands

ABSTRACT: Contemporary architecture shows an increasing number of undulating, irregularly double curved overall forms, also denominated as blob-architecture. Structural designers of these free form shapes are confronted with numerous differences relative to those in conventional buildings. This paper aims at a description of the context relevant to structural engineering, indicating the domains that are involved in the process from imagination to realisation of a free form building design. The paper concludes with the presentation of an interactive precedent-based database, which clarifies and exemplifies the architects', structural engineers' or manufacturers' points of view.

1 INTRODUCTION INTO CONTEMPORARY FREE FORM (BLOB) ARCHITECTURAL DESIGNS

"Undulating, irregularly double-curved and apparently lacking any rational relationship with basic principles of structural engineering"; these are the characteristics of contemporary "free-form", "liquid design" or "blob"-architecture. Although charged with the image of modernity, free form shapes have since long-time appeared in architecture – in a so far unravelled rhythm. Hence, a free-form shape is not an indication of innovation as such. Technical innovation is laid down in the addition of new techniques of materialization. Emergent three-dimensional drawing and modelling techniques – both virtual and physical – enable designers and engineers to economically handle the increasing geometrical complexity resulting from curved shapes and the increasing requirements in performance and quality.

Industry, familiar with standardised and mostly large rectilinear and planar elements, did not link up yet with the recent digital revolution that took place in design and production in the last decade. Lack of experience in projects of such complexity, as well as absence of a budget for integral innovation made builders revert to established craftsmen's techniques instead of high level industrialisation and prefabrication to materialize unconventional building shapes. Not surprisingly, clients were often confronted with a considerable exceeding of budget.

Situated in an architectural environment where conceptual designs are diminishingly based on technical (e.g. structural) or materialistic input, the transition from imagination to realisation is at stake, and all participating domains will have to evaluate their position.

The paper is subdivided into two parts. In the first part, the position of structural engineering as part of building technology is put in context with the domains of architectural imagination and practical production. Next, the implications of free-form building designs on structures are discussed. For this, basic constituents and their interrelationships are distinguished. The paper concludes with the introduction of an interactive database. This web-based application integrates data specific on architectural, mechanical and production-related aspects of free form structures, with their interrelationships.

2 REALISING "BLOB"-DESIGNS

2.1 *Distinction of three contributing domains*

Throughout the entire process of transition from an initiative to the realisation, input from three different domains can be recognised. In later paragraphs, reference will be made to the description of the basic fields, and schemes will illustrate the alterations that have been signalled in current practice.

The first domain is architectural design, where desire is recognised and translated into imagination. In a later stage, a synthesis of this imagination is laid down in a (conceptual) design. The level of scale and the position on the sliding scale between conceptual ideas and practical outcome may vary.

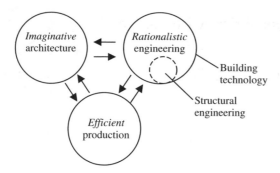

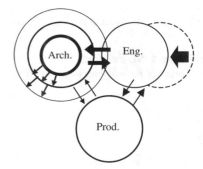

Figure 1. Domains contributing in a realisation process and the position of structural engineering within them.

Figure 2. Alternations on the standard configuration of domains as represented in Figure 1. In this example, the range of influence of the domain of architecture is expanding and has an emphasized core. Engineering has shifted towards architectural design, and the relationship of the latter with the domain of production is minimal. Arch. = architecture, Eng. = engineering, Prod. = production.

Second domain is that of technology in its widest meaning. Technology is applied to output or results from other domains, in this case the architectural design. Limiting the scope to the realisation process of buildings, the domain is denominated as building technology and is populated with different specialist-engineers. Their task is typically that of introducing a rationalisation of the process, in its transition from an architectural design to a technical design. This contribution of technology can have two appearances: either a contribution in content, or the provision of supportive technologies, that as tool for process-support can also find its way in the other domains (e.g. collaboration and data-exchange that make use of ICT).

The third domain is that of the transition from virtual plan to physical object. Constraints dominating this domain of production and realisation are highly practical and tangible.

2.2 Structural engineering as part of building technology

The justification of sufficient strength, stiffness and stability in a structural design is the engineer's contribution within building technology. Although situated amidst other engineering contributions, relationships reach beyond their proper domain, and directly affect architectural as well as production related features. In the next section an elaborate analysis of these relationships will be provided, which particularly apply to the structural design of free form building designs.

The distinction of the three individual domains risks to be read as a serial walkthrough, which is not necessarily the case, as will be shown later. Variations occur in their consecutive order, their relative importance, the mutual dependency, the degree to which they are interwoven and their representation in terms of parties or people (Fig. 2). In either case, the contribution of the three different domains has become indispensable due to the ongoing increase of complexity and for budgetary and legal constraints.

Variations in the relative position of building technology directly influence the position of structural engineering. In the next paragraph the position of technology is considered on a high level of abstraction. Afterwards, the focus will shift towards the constituents within structural engineering.

2.3 Varieties in arrangement of the domains, with respect to structural design

Figure 3a shows a schematic view of an approach from technical design towards architectural design. When the technique primarily consists of structural design, it is frequently denominated "archineering". The Spanish architect and civil engineer Santiago Calatrava and the Belgian engineer-architect Philippe Samyn are examples of persons adhering to this approach. In their work, mechanical and structural principles steer the architectural form finding, whereas architectonic principles (e.g. composition, scale and directionality) simultaneously influence the starting points of structural decision-making. Thus, the relationship is recursive, and the result is multiple: both an architectural and a structural design.

Since structural starting points are identifiable on the global level of the design and is lacking a relationship with the aspects of production, this category will not be discussed any further.

Different from the previous configuration is the approach in which production-aspects and structural design are in relative proximity (Fig. 3b). The approach was originally based on the application of structural systems in prefabricated producer's systems, making use of an assortment of basic members. Typical examples are the space-frames consisting of nodes and linear tubular element that were built frequently in the 1980s. Typical for that time was the close relationship that also

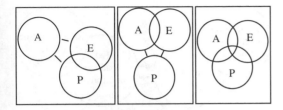

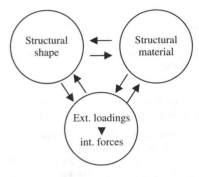

Figure 3. (a) Architectural design in alliance with structural design. (b) Production-aspects in alliance with structural design. (c) The three domains in close relationship. A = architecture, E = engineering, P = production.

Figure 4. Structural action determined by the interaction between structural shape, structural material and external loadings and internal forces.

existed with architectural design, where the abundant application of space-frames resulted in the High-Tech Movement (Fig. 3c).

The efforts made by several producers is exemplary for the close involvement of the domain of production. They developed their own application of the space-frame structural system, and offered it as a standard product to the market. The initial exploration resulted in unique applications on the global level, making use of identical members. When these explorations appeared to be exhausted, minor manipulations on the system were made, thus extending the field of application towards geometrically irregular building designs.

Also significant in their close relationship between the three domains, is the movement of concrete shell-builders that emerged in the 1950s. Even though all domains were present, here it was the advantageous structural action, resulting in low costs of material that was directing this movement.

3 STRUCTURAL ENGINEERING OF AN ARCHITECTURAL "BLOB"-DESIGN

By manipulating its constituents, the structural designer controls the structural performance of a structural design (Fig. 4). This performance is determined by the relationship between the constituents of a structure: a loading that is received needs to be transferred to a support making use of a structural material in a certain geometrical arrangement, where the shape itself has also an influence on the load. In the structural design of a geometrically free form building, the constituent "force" is basically the same as in conventional structural design, whereas "geometry" and "material" introduce specific issues.

Major modifications do occur in the relationships between the basic constituents, and will be commented separately. The relationships are present on all levels of scale, during all phases of the process and throughout all levels of abstraction. Ideally, structural designers are able to control all these internal relationships thanks to

profound understanding of the structural action and extensive knowledge on the availability of structural components. Thus, full insight is available in the internal relationships and the consequences of modifications. In addition, external relationships occur with other fields of technology, as well as with architectural design and production-related aspects. In the case of severe requirements from the other domains, relationships have proven to become multiple, and risk becoming too numerous to be controlled. This has been signalled in numerous building projects with an increased geometrical complexity, both in history and at present.

3.1 Implications on the basic constituents of structural design in "blob"-buildings

3.1.1 Geometry
The description of the (by definition irregular) unmaterialised geometry is by itself a cause of error. Double curved, non-parallel lines complicate quick verifications of the consistency of the geometry. Loss of data when transferring virtual models from modelling applications to drawing programs, or between two not fully compatible drawing applications are common practice and thus cause additional workload. Packages comprising functionalities in both modelling and drawing, as well as in the analysis of statics and in the preparation of shop drawings exist (for instance CATIA, originating from aerospace industry, but entered in the domain of building industry via Frank O.Gehry's design of the Bilbao Guggenheim museum), but both the purchase and the training of users are extremely costly. In addition, building budgets are seldom taking investments into account that apply to a single project.

3.1.2 Material
Although realistically conservative in its use of structural materials, metals, wood and stone-like materials

may not be the only possible materials. Composites of combinations in structural applications of existing and new fiber-based materials may possess potentials specifically attractive for application in free-form building designs.

3.2 Implications on the internal relationships of structural design in "blob"-buildings

Whereas basic constituents of structural design are relatively little more complicated, the complexity of their interrelationships radically intensifies the working field of the structural engineer amidst the other domains, as Figure 5 illustrates.

3.2.1 Relationship between structural shape – external loadings/internal force

Structures in blob-designs represent the same awkwardness as their shape. Starting from the reception of a load, interaction of shape and (external) load causes effects, the complications of which cannot be fully overseen. This is the case in the determination of the distribution of wind loads on irregularly double curved surfaces. Free form objects have not been classified, nor have the qualitative and quantitative relationships with windflows around them been established. As a solution, conservative assumptions are being made. Thus, potential gains in terms of reduced amount of material resulting from a diminished wind load are left aside.

Load transfer within the structure takes place according to the inner geometrical arrangement of the actual structure. Due to the irregular arrangement of the structural elements, its structural action is multiple and not easily identifiable or classifiable into a category of a singular static principle according to the sectional forces occurring. Consequently, design strategies become multiple, and the necessity of a deep understanding of the structural behaviour primordial (Wagner & Bögle, 2002).

3.2.2 Relationship between structural material – structural shape

An ideal mechanical action at times can be far beyond practical reality. Practical constraints involve the availability of structural materials, workmanship and numerically directed robots in the case of automated production processes to manipulate the elements and assemble the components. Structural optimisation as form finding method is possible via finite element analysis, but the optimisation method so far uniquely considers and optimises the relationship between material and shape (Williams, 2000). Production technologies necessary for the actual realisation are not taken into account in the optimisation process, but would imply a valuable contribution to the viability of free form building designs.

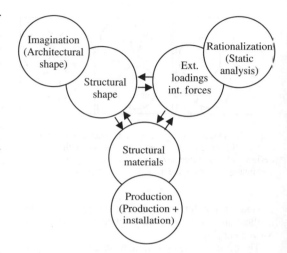

Figure 5. Relationships between the major domains in realising buildings and the constituents of structures.

3.2.3 Relationship between structural material – external loadings/internal force

Due to structural shapes resulting from strongly external parameters, conservative assumptions on external loads and eventually an increased weight of a cladding, structures applied in free form buildings may have an unfavourable ratio between load bearing capacity and dead weight. In the construction phase, proper connections between structural elements as well as with cladding elements applied in a later stage are thus confronted with relatively large variances in deflections.

4 STRATEGIES FOR THE FUTURE OF REALISING BLOB-DESIGNS

4.1 Integrated approach with structural engineering

As has been shown, the already multiple task of the structural designer has become even more complicated with the introduction of geometrical arbitrariness in the overall shape. The times when structural form finding was uniquely left to the structural engineer are over. Even though variations do exist in the relationship between structural shape and architectural shape, they have become multiple and more constrained. Thus, within structural engineering the importance of the phase of structural design is increasing, since is has become crucial in the viability of the entire project.

Within structural design, the focus should no longer be on optimisation of a single relationship, or the implementation of a single structural scheme (for instance those presented by Heino Engel, 1997). Combinations of structural schemes possess opportunities for the multitude of requirements in structural design. Engineers themselves play a crucial role in the success of the integrated approach, and should therefore communicate the merits of contemporary structural engineering with architects and manufacturers.

Already desirable in the structural design of conventional buildings, design on macro-meso-microlevels (respectively the structure of the entire building, a secondary component, a single structural element) of scale should alternate quickly and be carried out simultaneously with the architectural and manufacturing constraints in mind during all phases of the realisation process.

As a first aid in the phase of conceptual design, an application has been developed that assists the architect, structural engineer and manufacturer in overseeing the consequences of their input on other domains, and vice versa. This application – the Blob Inventory Project – is described in the next section.

4.2 *Implications on the production of structural elements: towards mass-customization*

As a result of the increasing geometrical complexity and irregularity in architectural designs, application of standardised parts is at stake. Benefits that have been achieved through standardisation still apply, but may shift to a different level of scale, or extended with a custom-made addition.

On macro-level as well as on micro-level of scale, parametrical geometrical descriptions are applied to keep control on the geometry. Realised buildings in which parametrical descriptions were applied prove that geometrical parameters – and thus regularity – can result in free form buildings on the global level (see the next paragraph as an example).

Although geometrical parameters originate from the geometrical description, they can be related to production technologies. Geometrical manipulations could thus be related to a numerically controlled practical manipulation. For instance in the case of a steel structure: CNC-cutting is the answer of production technology to results from the definition of a shape (two- or three-dimensional), whereas bendingequipment can be associated with a constant (or variable) radius (in one or two directions) of a linear or planar element.

As already stated before, practical limitations occur when such geometrical data needs to be transferred, and expanding functionalities in drawingsoftware packages are not compatible with those used by the manufacturers.

4.3 *Example of a rationalized design method with respect to production technology: application of quadrangular glass panels*

Aiming at a transparent and design of a transparent double curved surface, the application of translational surfaces provides an economically viable alternative.

The method was applied to a surface, functioning as a roofing in the Berlin Zoo. Here, the global shape of two merged bulbs was set up according to a freely drawn single curved polygonal (the generatrice) which was moved along another line (the directrice, in this case the top-limitation of the section). Both generatrice and directrice were required to be polygonal, where each straight section would in a later stage become the side of a glass panel. Via this method, the surface could be clad with planar quadrangular elements, making savings on the complexity of detailing (e.g. the summarised length of connections between glass panels, the complexity of nodes) and increasing the transparency (Schober, 2002).

5 IMPLEMENTATION OF THE INTEGRAL APPROACH IN THE BLOB INVENTORY PROJECT

5.1 *Introduction to the Blob Inventory Project (BIP)*

The observation has been made that architectural design, engineering and production are in relative loose connection, developing relatively independent towards a non-distinct direction. As a reply to this, a tool that will give insight in the mutual relationships is currently under development at Delft University of Technology, Netherlands.

The coverage of the data within the application is limited to the load bearing structure within realised examples of free form building designs. The insertion of precedents from other fields of industry (e.g. shipbuilding- and airplane-industry) is considered for later versions because of their geometrical analogies.

The actual tool is a web-based database that contains data on the design and production of structures in realised free form building designs. To allow interpretation and analysis of data, insertion of factual information is separated from interpretative information.

With its application in both research and practice, the BIP has a dual aim. The application in the research projects of the participating researchers involves the establishment of an overview of relationships. These relationships will serve as hypotheses in later design-case studies. Secondly, the application acts as a decision support system during conceptual structural design. Proposed to be used by architects, engineers and manufacturers, it provides direct feedback via precedents and general information on consequences of decisions taken on each of the three domains involved.

5.2 *Data-structure*

Since the aim of the BIP is to make users aware of the consequences of decisions on related fields as

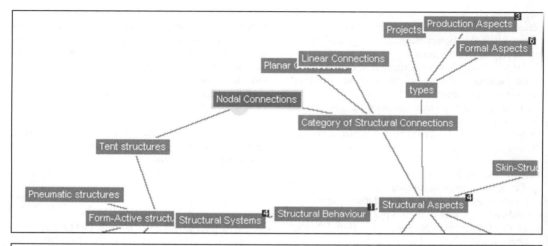

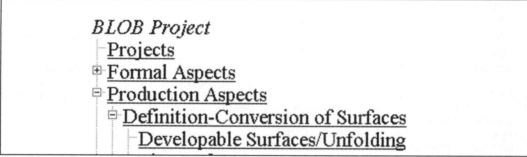

Figure 6. (a)(top) Relational representation of the features. (b)(bottom) Hierarchical representation of the features.

described before, they are identifiable individually in a predefined hierarchy of features related to any of the three main aspects: architectural design, structural engineering and production technology. In addition to this, explanatory relationships between sub-features can be established and commented according to precedent-studies.

5.3 *Functionalities of the application*

The application consists of a database and a user interface. The BIP makes use of data-documents in which specific information on a certain feature is described. These data-documents are grouped per project, but are also accessible via the feature the document is describing. The user interface both gives a hierarchical representation of the features and subfeatures, and a relational view where also relationships are represented. In both cases clicking on the features leads to general information on that feature. At the same time a list of related document is displayed, ordered per project and making use of a thumbnail and a summary for quick browsing. Clicking on this preview opens the actual document.

5.4 *Future use and developments*

The BIP is still under development and in use for internal research-goals only. In the nearby future, the database will be integrated in the educational curriculum of the Faculty of Architecture, supportive to the intent of research driven education. Future extensions of the functionalities aim at the implementation of an extensive search-option, also enabling multi-criteria analysis.

6 CONCLUSION

Being part of the technical domain, structural engineering is by its nature involved closely in both conceptual and practical considerations. Mutual influences have become multiple and crucial in the realisation process of designs for blob-buildings. Also the relationships within the domain of structural engineering are affected. Optimisation processes within structural design were previously focussing on singular relationships, but should incorporate all major interdependencies.

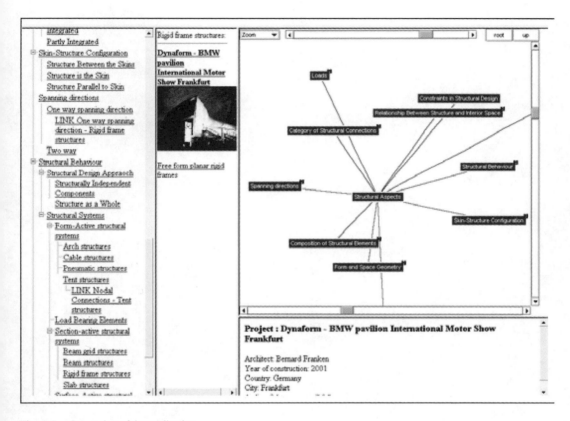

Figure 7.   Screenshot of the application.

The ability to control the complex relationships resulting from internal and external constraints has become crucial in the realisation process. An interactive database in which experiences from precedent-projects are gathered, offers the practical application of the required closer relationship between the domains of the architect, the structural engineer and the manufacturer. Assistance in the conceptual design by visualisation of interdependencies and feedback on consequences of design-decisions, will contribute to the viability of future projects.

ACKNOWLEDGEMENTS

The Blob Inventory Project is a collaborative project of the following researchers, all from Delft University of Technology, Netherlands: T. Kocatürk, M. Veltkamp and B. Tuncer. The participating researchers owe gratitude to J. Beintema for his contribution to the programming work.

REFERENCES

Engel, H. 1997. *Tragsysteme 2. auflage*, Ostfildern-Ruit, Verlag Gerd Hatje.
Schober, H. 2002. Geometrie-Prinzipien für wirtschaftliche und effiziente Schalentragwerke, *Bautechnik* 79: 16–24.
Wagner, R. & Bögle, A. 2002. Double-Curved Space Structures – Function and Construction, *International Journal of Space Structures* 17(2&3): 117–127.
Williams, C. 2000. The Definition of curved Geometry for widespan Structures. In M. Barnes & M. Dickson (eds), *Widespan Roof Structures*. London: Thomas Telford.

System-based Vision for Strategic and Creative Design, Bontempi (ed.)
© 2003 Swets & Zeitlinger, Lisse, ISBN 90 5809 599 1

Integrating architectural and structural form-finding processes for free-form digital architectures

T. Kocaturk, C. van Weeren & M.W. Kamerling
Delft University of Technology, Faculty of Architecture, Delft, The Netherlands

ABSTRACT: The new digital design approaches that encourages surface manipulations has led to the creation of inventive formal and spatial languages for architecture which brought to the front question of how to work out the spatial and architectonic results of such free, non-Euclidean forms, known as "Blobs". In order to work out the tectonic and spatial implications of such non-Cartesian, free-form buildings – the Blobs – it is important to develop new concepts in working methods of all parties involved in the building design and practice. This paper mainly describes the mutual influences of formal consequences of digital design approaches in architecture, emergent digital manufacturing technologies and structural form development processes for blob surfaces while offering alternatives for their integration. Particular emphasis is the relationship between two primary building systems; the superstructure and the exterior/interior skins.

1 INTRODUCTION

Once again, we are witnessing the reconstruction of the established relationship between architectural design and its means of production by taking advantage of the innovations offered by present-day science and technology. The dominant formal vocabulary of digital free-form architectures is their complex, double-curved surfaces which have special properties from a spatial, structural and aesthetic point of view. In order to exploit this potential, the design surface must be developed into rational cladding components combined with an appropriate supporting structure. Although there are built examples of complex free-form buildings (also known as *Blobs*) in which the main structural system is almost totally independent of the surface geometry, the real challenge in the current architectural and structural engineering practice is to develop the suitable structure for the architectural statement where the structural form becomes an elemental component of the architectural surface itself.

Advances in both architectural and engineering design practice, and the emerging digital manufacturing technologies have mutual influences in the development of the formal vocabulary of Blobs and the production of their components. In current practice, however, there is no established principle or theory concerning the design and production of free-form buildings that can be a useful source providing feedback to the designer especially in the conceptual design phase. In a CAAD environment, complex geometric forms exist entirely as surfaces without structural considerations. Parameters for gravity, material properties and manufacturing techniques can not yet be tested in design visualization software (Klinger 2001). Moreover, 3D data exchange between CAAD/CAM/CAE applications has not yet become a standard process. Therefore, to fully make use of new digital options in working with free forms, and of translating free-form structures into reality, architects and engineers must integrate their form generation and conceptual design processes with direct reference to advanced manufacturing technologies.

Although CAD/CAM has already become a standard process in automotive, shipbuilding and product design and production, yet, the potential of the digital fabrication technologies has not been truly embedded in building industry. This paper mainly describes the mutual influences of the formal consequences of digital design approaches in architecture (CAAD) and structural form development processes (CAE) under the influence of digital manufacturing (CAM) processes while offering alternatives for possible integration models. Particular emphasis will be the relationship between two primary building systems; the superstructure and the interior/exterior skins. Thus, the paper will mainly identify and analyze the current form generation approaches in CAAD environments (form-descriptions, design methods and techniques) for complex free-form surfaces to the degree they affect and inform the generation of the structural form and classify them according to their skin-structure configurations. The study will finally analyze a case study example in Netherlands, from the parameter based design through the materialization process of a blob structure, and explore the three distinct perspectives from the project architect, the structural engineer and the metal fabricator. The case study displays the current state-of-art and existing bottlenecks between the CAAD/CAE environments as well as offering alternatives for the enhancement and possible integration of these environments with reference to CAM technologies.

2 EMERGING RELATIONSHIPS BETWEEN STRUCTURAL ENGINEERING, ARCHITECTURAL DESIGN AND DIGITAL PRODUCTION PROCESSES

2.1 Role of structural engineers in the digital workflow

Digitally driven design and production processes also changed the clear division between the roles of architects and civil engineers which began to merge with the aim of developing suitable structures for free-form buildings. While architecture could realize variety in design through the variable combination of a limited number of structural forms and systems in the industrial age, the redefinition of design and production conditions opened up a vast potential for differentiation (Ruby 2001). Today, almost each Blob is unique and traditional structural solutions and structural form-generation methods face tremendous challenges and limitations. Consequently, structural engineers should develop new working methods for the development of 3D structural solutions to respond formal requirements of the new architecture with direct reference to emerging manufacturing technologies.

From a structural point of view, free-form means geometric and structural complexity, which is why "finite element" and "spatial vector framework" programs are employed even in the preliminary design phase. However, one of the main problems today is that there are not yet direct interfaces between engineering software and CAD software to interchange the form descriptions instantly from one software to another and manual inputs are no longer an option for the geometries of free-form bodies. This data transfer between both parties are essential especially at the early design phases when major decisions concerning the material properties and construction possibilities should be taken into consideration while choosing one of the free-form derivatives.

Over the last decade, optimization technology has evolved to be an established discipline within many industries. This has been facilitated by software developments, both to algorithm performance and tighter integration within the design environment and hardware developments. The field of structural optimization contains many different technologies, which are applicable to particular stages of the design process or a particular physical response of the system (e.g. linear elastic or highly nonlinear) (Jones 2001). Any optimization problem, irrespective of the optimization technology used, requires only three design functions to be defined. These consist of the design objective (e.g. minimize mass), which is achieved by the variation of design variables (e.g. structural shape) subjected to design constraints (e.g. displacements, stresses). The application of any topology optimization in the structural free-form development process can only benefit from early input of a multi-disciplinary team consisting of designers and manufacturing engineers. Accordingly, the design variables offered by the emergent manufacturing technologies for various materials will eventually affect the design objectives and constraints respectively.

2.2 Embedding emerging CAM processes in structural form-finding

The creative process of a structural engineer in form-finding process is generally confined in what is technically possible within the existing production processes. However, the newly developing manufacturing processes opened up an enormous opportunity that can inform the structural form-finding conceptions and development

While it is increasingly common in other industries to use additive technologies to make investment castings, "it is the emerging potential of additive processes that directly manufacture metal components from CAD models that could revolutionize the manufacturing of custom, projects specific structural metal components" in building practice (Rotheroe 2001). Today, both 3D printing and selective laser sintering (SLS) create steel skeletal structures that are sixty percent dense. Alternatively, laser and metal powder based processes produce metal by deposing molten metal on a layer-by-layer basis. Consequently, resultant material strengths equal or more often exceed those generated by established rolling and extrusion techniques. In aerospace industry, new methods are being developed to directly manufacture large free-form metal components which have enormous potentials to be imported to support the production of structural components in building practice. Consequently, these technologies will have a direct impact on the generation process of the structural forms in relation to their fabrication possibilities (Rotheroe 2001).

In contrast to traditional steel construction, which mainly consists of T-sections, angles, and I-beams, the new fabrication processes and installation devises "alternative systems which substitute for traditional beam and column and effectively accommodate for different load and support conditions" (Tehrani 2000). These findings will define totally new concepts and rules, new form-force relationships for the form-finding methods of structural engineers.

2.3 Configurations of surface and structure in current free-form design

The integration of the design and form development processes should link the form generation methods and form descriptions in the digital environment for both architectural and structural purposes. In current practice, Kloft observes a generation dependent overlap of working methods in designing free-form buildings and he argues that these approaches affect and inform the working method of structural engineer in a number of ways (Kloft 2001).

One approach is the definition of two independent surfaces as exterior and interior skins. The resulting cavity between these two surfaces is used for building services and for the load bearing structure. This assigns a rather modest status to the load bearing structure, since it is hidden behind these two surfaces. Although the skins undercover the structure, there is ample opportunity for optimization measures the scope of which is determined by the dimensions of the cavity and by the interaction with the materials for the inner and outer skin (Fig. 1).

One other approach is the generation of form through parameter-driven design processes where it is only the external skin that is defined (Fig. 2). In such processes, the actual form is achieved by capturing the

formal transformation process at a specific point and freezing the form. The consequences of this approach for structural form-finding are two-fold. Firstly, "structure becomes formally an elemental component, because it constitutes either the internal spatial enclosure beneath the skin or the skin itself becomes the structure, that is, external layer and internal layer are identical and only defined by the material thickness" (Kloft 2001). Secondly, since the master form is fixed, optimizations to the structure cannot be implemented by means of changing the form.

2.4 The influence of different structural approaches on the architectonics of blobs

The following analysis displays how the evolution of a form can be influenced by three different structural approaches in the conceptual design phase. These approaches effect, inform and transform the spatial and tectonic appearance of the architectural form and influence the production technology in a number of ways. It is essential for the designers to be aware of the formal, structural and production related consequences of their initial choices during the form development process by integrating these aspects into their conceptual design phase.

These approaches can be extended further and the formal consequences might be outlined for various design cases. Moreover, it is also important to note that these approaches are not always intentional and may arise due to practical reasons, economic/time constraints, lack of available materials and/or production techniques which can vary for each project and play a more dominant role in the final design.

In the first approach, the form of the structural elements derives from the variations of the wire frame divisions of the digital form and follow the contours of the master 3D geometry (Fig. 3). The master geometry is translated into rib-like structures of bones and skins and transferred into a new drawing file for engineering and manufacturing applications. The ribs are constructed as main structural frames which follow the local coordinates of the form in three directions.

The resulting morphology is non directional, homogeneous where tectonic expression is more on the skin. The inconsistencies in the structure mostly occur at the acute corners where there are rapid changes in the form.

Figure 1.   Frank Gehry's double skin approach in Guggenheim Museum in Bilbao.

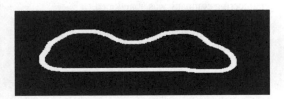

Figure 2.   Kas Oosterhuis' parametric design approach in "Space Station Module" (Oosterhuis 1999).

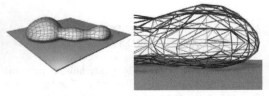

Figure 3.   Structural approach I (Joosen 2003).

Figure 4. Structural approach II (Joosen 2003).

Figure 5. Structural approach III (Joosen 2003).

Individual elements in the structure may be composed of either linear or curvilinear elements.

In the second approach, the structural framework creates a wire-mesh composed of either linear or curvilinear elements (Fig. 4). It is not the exact digital geometry which masters the frame composition, on the contrary, the digital form is divided into irregular surfaces which are defined and framed by the structural elements. The master geometry and the structural form are reconciled for the creation of the final surface form. The resulting morphology is homogeneous, non-directional and since the form is defined by both the structural elements and the surface in between, the resulting tectonic expression consists of a combination of both.

In the third approach, the structural frames are obtained either by cutting the 3D form in vertical and horizontal slices where each cross-section defines the contour of the frames or the frames follow any two main coordinates of the master geometry. Structural elements are generally arrayed in two main directions at certain intervals. The resulting morphology is directional, composed of arch-like frames and the tectonic impression is the structure itself, the form of which derives from the actual form of the skin. The actual curvilinear shape of the acute corners can only be provided by using secondary frames in a different configuration (Fig. 5). The structural form may be optimized as long as the frames follow the geometry of the master form.

3 CASE STUDY: FLORIADE PAVILION –
THE WEB OF NOORD-HOLLAND

The pavilion was designed by Oosterhuis.nl, an architectural firm established in Rotterdam. The building is designed in the form of a space-craft that landed in Floriade in Haarlemmeer. The building is composed of

Figure 6. North-Holland Pavillion by Oosterhuis.nl.

an outer and inner skin which interacts with the users. All electronic media are immersed in the interior skin. The users activate light, sound, images and the behavior of the body where the building body responds the users in return. The conversation is about the various real-time characteristics of the Noord-Holland in relation to the Floriade flower exhibition. The blob form of the building was sculptured in Maya in a parameter driven design process (Fig. 6).

The main structural idea originated in respond to a common problem in the materialization of blob surfaces: the acute corners. Thus, in order to avoid the discontinuity of the structure at corners and at the points of sudden curvature change, the main challenge was to design a structural system which could be continuous at every point and which could be adapted to any surface with complex geometry.

The initial structural solution, with direct consultation of the engineering firm (steel contractor at the same time), was decided as tubular steel frames with spherical steel nodes. The engineer was asked to create an extremely irregular 3D geometrical order with steel frames that would follow the digital master geometry. The generation of such an irregular lattice out of steel elements was quite an easy process with the available engineering software. This process would be followed by geometrical description of each irregular area in between the frames by NURBS that would be used as the main digital data to be transferred to CAM software for the production of the aluminum claddings with double curvature. At this point, the structural engineer was hesitant for the generation of this digital data concerning the risks involved in the production of the cladding with precise curvature for each unique surface area. Unfortunately, the engineering cost was over-exceeding the project budget so that the first solution of the first engineering company was abandoned.

The second structural solution was to develop a steel frame composed of planar elements creating triangular areas in between. The frames would follow the contour of the master geometry. The innovation in this scheme was the orientation of the steel elements. The form of each frame followed the curvature of the master form, the cross-section of which would be normal to that curvature at every point. This idea was mainly developed as a solution to cope with the acute corners

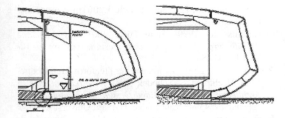

Figure 7. Cross-sections of the North-Holland Pavillion.

but was further developed to master the entire structural configuration (Fig. 7).

With a steel frame or space-frame system providing the 2D curvilinearity on the surface is quite a problem. To solve this, the steel elements would be folded to keep up with the curvilinear geometry where necessary. This could also contribute to the integrity of the structure. At this point the main corporation was made between the architect and the steel manufacturer. Unfortunately, the second structural consultancy firm put less effort in the decision process than expected. Another problem was the incompatibility of the software used by the architect and the engineer so that the architect had to prepare additional data for the engineers to make the necessary calculations

The only feedback from the engineers was the minimum thickness of the planar steel frames and the cross-sectional length of frames at the nodes. At this point it was the architect to prepare all the digital information to be sent to the CAM process for the water jet-cutting of the steel frames and the cladding. Before this, a mock up model was created to confirm the exact place of each frame element. The architectural 3D data was sent to CNC milling machine as .iges files for the solid prototyping of the foam model. After necessary modifications, the model was 3D scanned and the 3D data was updated accordingly. The 3D model was specified in Rhino.

In contrast to the engineering consultants, the architect and the steel manufacturer had a notable collaboration concerning both the decision process, 3D–2D data flow, and the final production process. The manufacturer was very experienced in the field and, thus, substituted the engineering work-load in many aspects including the design of the joints and bolts.

The data for CAM process were prepared as .dxf extension files in AutoCAD for the water jet-cut of the steel elements. The frame structure was assembled in the factory after all the elements being produced to check the accuracy of the geometry and the tolerances at the joints and bolt holes. Then it was de-assembled to be transported to the construction site in pieces. The aluminum claddings after being CNC-cut according to the geometry of each triangle were later cold-formed to fit the surface geometry and they were all mounted on site.

Since the corners of the claddings were bent to fit the geometry, unexpected distortions and displacements occurred at the middle part of these surfaces which caused unexpected changes in the geometry of the overall form. The respond of the surface to various forming processes is very determinant in deciding upon the final form to prevent unexpected behavior of the material. At this point, embedding material and surface properties into CAD software could be very useful to provide immediate feedback during design visualization and development.

4 CONCLUSION AND DISCUSSIONS

In order to solve existing bottlenecks in the realization of complex surfaces with suitable supporting structures, it is necessary to develop new working methods between architects, structural engineers and manufacturing parties. This includes direct coordination between these parties at certain stages of the design as well as enhancement of the digital media for both architectural and structural form-finding processes.

At present, the formal variety and architectonic multiplicity of the new digital architecture is still an exception other than a rule and formal experimentation cannot by itself create a new architecture unless its full performance is discovered. Consequently, the next step should comprise following directions in search for discovering the potentials of the Blobs:

– Parameters for gravity, material properties, and fabrication alternatives could be embedded into architectural design visualization software providing immediate feedback during form development.
– Types of curve and surface primitives could be created to work effectively in architecture. Architecturally useful vocabularies of three-dimensional curved elements can be developed as equivalents of grids, axes, and other traditional ordering devices. Shape grammars and languages of curved-surface, non-repeating architectural form can be specified.
– Structural form optimization software and their design variables and material libraries can be enriched with reference to the emergent manufacturing technologies and design parameters of CAD software.
– Structural engineers too can develop structural proto-typologies which are flexible to adapt various architectural contexts. Free-form prototypes of curved structural forms can be generated for further use and applications.

REFERENCES

Jones, R. D. 2001. An Overview of Optimization Technology: Delivering the Competitive Advantage [Online].

United Kingdom: Nafems Publications. Available from URL: http://www.nafems.org/publictions/downloads/Optimization.pdf

Joosen, G. 2003. Images from the graduation project at the Department of Architecture, Eindhoven University of Technology. Available from URL: http://www.gais.nl/ nyc.

Klinger, K. R. 2001. Making Digital Architecture: Historical, Formal, and Structural Implications of Computer Controlled Fabrication and Expressive Form [Online]. Paper presented in ECAADE Conference in Helsinki. Available from URL: http://www.hut.fi/events/ecaade/E2001presentations/10_02 _klinger.pdf

Kloft, H. 2001. Structural Engineering in the Digital Workflow. In P. C. Schmal (*ed.*), *Digital Real – Blobmeister: First Built Projects*: 198–205. Berlin: Birkhauser.

Kolarevic, B. 2001. Designing and Manufacturing Architecture in the Digital Age [Online]. Paper presented in ECAADE Conference in Helsinki. Available from URL:

http://www.hut.fi/events/ecaade/E2001presentations/05_03_kolarevic.pdf

Oosterhuis, K. 1999. Trans_Ports 2001. *Hypersurface Architecture II, Architectural Design*, vol 69 9–10/ Profile 141: 84–89.

Rotheroe, K. C. 2001. Manufacturing Freeform Architecture. In G. Bechthold, S. Schodek (eds), *New Technologies in Architecture, Computer-Aided Design and Manufacturing Techniques*: 43–47. Cambridge, Harvard University Press.

Ruby, A. 2001. Architecture in the Age of Digital Productability, In P. C. Schmal (*ed.*), *Digital Real – Blobmeister: First Built Projects*: 206–211. Berlin: Birkhauser.

Tehrani, N. 2000. Fabrications: The Tectonic Garden, Fabricating Coincidences. In G. Bechthold, , S. Schodek (eds), *New Technologies in Architecture, Computer-Aided Design and Manufacturing Techniques*: 65–67. Cambridge, Harvard University Press.

Zellner, P. 1999. *Hybrid Space: New Forms in Digital Architecture*. New York: Rizzoli.

An interdisciplinary approach to the design of free-form buildings

M.W. Kamerling & T. Kocaturk
Delft University of Technology, Faculty of Architecture, Delft, The Netherlands

ABSTRACT: The subject of this paper is the design of structures of Free-Form buildings within a multi-disciplinary team. For structures of Free-Form buildings the process of design is analysed. For this process three phases are distinguished. A typology of structural systems for Free-Form buildings is described. Recommendations for the structural design are given.

1 INTRODUCTION

Nowadays many architects all over the world are interested in Free-Form buildings, with a non Euclidean shape. These buildings are also known as Blobs (binary large objects). Thanks to the evolving computer technology architects can design and visualise complex 3D-forms with advanced digital software. For structural engineers and contractors these buildings are a nightmare as well as a challenge. Free-Form buildings are not based on the Euclidean forms, the curved surfaces are difficult to construct, the design is complicated and the cost of engineering excessive. Usually a multi-disciplinary team is needed to develop an adequate design. The members of the team must be skilled professionals, used to collaborate and able to design within a multi-disciplinary team.

In this paper a systematic design approach is described which can contribute to the collaboration within a multi-disciplinary team, reduce the cost of engineering and increase the quality of the structural design.

2 DESIGN

Designing is creating an object meeting the needs of users and the owner. The design of a structure is defined by the constraints determined by the demands and the aesthetic requirements. For Free-Form buildings the shape, created by the architect, has a great deal of influence on the structural design.

Generally a process of design knows three phases: the analysis, synthesis and evaluation (Fogue 1975). For the structural design of Free-Form buildings these three phases will be described.

2.1 *Analysis*

First the demands, conditions and constraints are analysed. The information of influence in the structural design process for Free-Form buildings can be divided in the following categories:
Architectural design approach;
Morphology;
Internal organisation;
Surface configuration;
Construction and production.

2.1.1 *Architectural design approach*
The methodology of the architect can have influence on the morphological flexibility needed to optimise the structural designing. Till now architects sculpture Free-Form with a scale model, for example architect F.O. Gehry used a model of clay to shape the Guggenheimer Museum in Bilbao, Spain. Nowadays architects as G. Lynn, P. Cook, K. Oosterhuis and L. Spuybroek use CAAD programs too. Blobs are often shaped with a parameter-driven method of design. Using this method the designer choose parameters and alter the geometry of a computer model till the shape fit the demands and the aesthetic requirements. For the structural engineer it is important to know the possibilities to change the shape slightly to optimise the structure. Knowing the design approach will be helpful to find the constraints.

2.1.2 *Morphology*
The form of the building will have consequences for the loads on the structure and on the structural system to redirect the forces. The shape of Free-Form buildings are irregular, the architectonic morphology will be defined by the enveloping surface. The volume can be shaped as a single volume or can be composed of several volumes. The surfaces of Free-Form buildings can

be anticlastic, single-clastic, synclastic or flat. With the CAAD software the surfaces are described with a mesh filled with patches. The grid of the mesh is mostly triangular, quadrilateral or orthogonal or a derivation of these patterns. The lines of the grid can be straight or curved. The shape of the patches can be generated automatically too. The shapes of these patches are based on mathematical equations, so these patches are shaped as flat, parabolic, spherical, conical or parabolic faces. Sometimes the architect does not object to construct the curved surface with flat elements. To facet the surface curved quadrilateral faces have to be split into triangular flat faces, so the patches of the surface are positioned on a triangular grid.

2.1.3 Internal organisation

A building is not a solid sculpture, it contains an internal space, divided often by walls and floors in partitions. The exterior can be either integrated with the interior or totally independent of the interior. The plan and the internal organisation of the spaces in the building will have consequences for the spans of the structure. The analysis concerning the spans is essential for the structural design.

For multi-storey buildings it is often possible to support the surface with the structure of the floors. For single storey buildings with a partitioned interior it is often possible to support the structure of the surface with columns or walls placed in the partitions of the internal spaces.

2.1.4 Surface configuration

For the envelope of conventional buildings we can almost always distinguish the roofs and facades, but for Free-Form buildings roofs and facades cannot always be distinguished. For these buildings the separation of exterior and interior is called the enveloping surface. The surface has to separate interior and exterior, visually and physically. The surface can be one single envelope or composed of two independent skins. The structure of a Blob with a separated internal and external skin can be positioned in the cavity between the skins. Within the depth of the cavity the shape of the structural elements can be optimised.

The demands concerning the aesthetics of the structural elements will increase in case the structure is in sight and not hidden behind the internal and external

surface. Especially for transparent Blobs the structural elements have to fulfil to the aesthetic demands.

The separation of interior and exterior has to resist heat, cold, rain, wind, sun and snow to keep a comfortable climate. Besides these aspects it also has to resist the loads acting on the surface. The building elements of the surface are structural integrated in case the surface is a part of the structural system and the structure collapses if a part of the surface is removed. The elements are not structural integrated if the surface elements don't contribute to the capacity of the main load bearing system and can be removed without any structural consequences for the main structure system.

2.1.5 Construction and production

The construction of a blob depends on the site and the available techniques. In the past building technique was a craft, but in the twentieth century building technique changed into a process of composing industrial mass-produced elements (Wachsmann 1959). Nowadays building technique is changing again. The age of digital production has already started. Repetition is essential for mass-produced elements. With CAAD-CAM technology elements can be produced one-by-one without repetition. For example the concrete Free-Form walls, designed by F. Gehry for the Zollhof complex in Dusseldorf, were made with individual polystyrene foam moulds milled on a CATIA-controlled CNC-cutter. Often a local contractor constructs the building, products are bought within a limited radius and the local available production and construction technique is decisive for the construction and design of the Blob.

2.2 Synthesis

With the received information the structural engineer has to develop concepts of the structural design. A structural design consists a structural system and a pattern on which the elements of the system are positioned. For Free-Form buildings several structural patterns and systems can be distinguished.

2.2.1 Structural pattern

Regular buildings are usually described with Cartesian co-ordinates and orthogonal grids to position the elements of the structure, partitions and envelope.

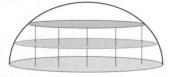

Figure 1. Interior of Free-Form building partitioned by floors. The internal skeletal structure of floors and columns can be used to support the surface.

Figure 2. Free-Form building with separated internal and external surface. The structure of the surface can be positioned in the cavity between the internal and external skin.

The surface of the blob is often visualised with a mesh and patches. The grid of these meshes, constructed to show the surface of the blob, is not always useful as grid to position the elements of the structure. The data exchange between architect, structural engineer and producer can be reduced if the grid is designed matching the pattern of structure.

Grids can be radial, orthogonal, skewed, parallel or triangular. For regular buildings the grid is composed of lines drawn on the plans. The structural elements of a conventional building are positioned in vertical faces perpendicular to the plan. The frames positioned in these imaginary faces can be modelled quite easily with 2D schemes. These grids can be applied for Free-Form structures too. Due to the simplicity, many Blobs are designed with plane frames and arches positioned on a grid constructed on the plan.

Grids can be constructed directly on the surface too. Systems are developed for spatial frames applied in domes to create a regular grid with repetition. For spherical domes the following grids can be distinguished (Engel 1997):

- Sphere rings with diagonal trussing;
- Spherical segments with parallel trussing;
- Spherical segments with hexagonal trussing;
- Geodetic grid patterns.

Geodetic grids were quite popular during the sixties and seventies of the twentieth century and are still applied. For example the domes of the Eden project St. Austell, GB, designed by N. Grimshaw, are composed of polygons positioned on a geodetic grid. Geodetic grid patterns are constructed by projecting the edges of a triangulated polyhedron on the surface. An advantage of a geodetic grid is the repetition of identical faces. For Free-Form buildings this advantage will be only valuable in case the Blob is composed of regular surfaces. For Blobs composed of irregular volumes the grid of the surface can be constructed by triangulating a modified polyhedron, which is changed by stretching, flattening or truncating. For these Blobs the faces on the surface will be similar but not identical (Labeur 2001).

2.2.3 *Structural systems*

In order to design concepts for the structure of Blobs it is recommended to study structures of Free-Form buildings constructed in the past. To compare structures several authors have described typologies of structures and structure systems. Nevertheless all systems have restrictions. To describe the structure systems applicable for Blobs a combination of typologies has to be used. Firstly the one- and two-way systems are distinguished. Structures are designed to channel the loads acting on the building to the foundation. Structure systems redirect the loads to the supports mainly in one direction or two directions, these systems

are called the one-way and two-way systems (Shodeck 2001). In the typology made by H. Engel the categories are distinguished by the redirection of the forces acting on the structural elements.

H. Engel distinguishes the form-active, vector-active, section-active and surface-active structure systems.

- Form-active structure systems redirect forces through form-design, for example cables and arches;
- Vector-active structure systems redirect forces through vector partition, for example trusses;
- Section-active structures redirect forces through mobilisation of sectional forces, for example beams;
- Surface-active structures redirect forces through surface resistance, for example shells (Engel 1999).

To classify the structures for Free-Form buildings we first have to distinguish the Blobs with an internal skeletal structure supporting the surface and the structure systems visually and morphologically integrated with the surface.

Internal skeletal structures are often applied for multi-storey Free-Form buildings, see figure 1. An internal frame of columns, beams and floors supports the structure of the surface. These internal frames are often positioned on an orthogonal grid and are similar to the structure of a conventional building. The structure of the surface consists secondary structural elements to support the cladding.

Structural systems morphologically integrated with the surface are independent of the internal space. Structural systems will be positioned on a pattern. For Free-Form buildings the following configurations can be distinguished:

- Surface-structures;
- Frames positioned on a radial pattern;
- Frames positioned parallel

The elements of surface structures are a part of the division of interior and exterior. Conform the typology of H. Engel we can distinguish the surface-active structure systems and the vector-active structure systems.

Blobs with a surface-active structure system are monolithic, constructed on site or composed of prefabricated concrete elements. For example the Sydney Opera House was composed of concrete shells constructed of prefabricated elements.

Figure 3. Frames of a Blob with a circular plan positioned on a radial pattern.

Vector-active structure systems will be more adequate for blobs with a transparent surface. These systems consist a spatial frame composed of bars, positioned on a surface grid as mentioned previously.

Frames on a radial pattern are often applied for blobs with a more or less circular plan. Frames positioned parallel are often applied for buildings with an elongated plan. A form-active structural system can be applied for Blobs with a curved surface. A section-active structural system will be applied for Blobs with a flat or slightly curved surface.

A surface-structure will be constructed as a two-way system. Structures, positioned on radial or parallel patterns, are almost always schemed as one-way systems. In general one-way systems can be often modelled with 2D schemes. For these systems the analyses of forces and deformations are often not very complicated.

2.3 *Evaluation*

The members of the design team have to evaluate the alternatives to find an optimal structure. Some of the alternatives will be rejected, other alternatives will be improved till the best possible design is developed. In the initial phase the provisional designs will be evaluated on criteria as estimated costs, aesthetics, usability, production and construction.

The costs of construction for Free-Form buildings are high. Lack of repetition, complicated topology, the variety of elements and complicated connections will increase the cost of construction and production. For most surface elements the cost of double curved elements are higher than the cost of flat elements. Sometimes it is possible to save money by composing a curved surface of flat triangular faces. Due to the irregular shape most faces of the surface of a Free-Form building are different in shape. Composing the surface of regular faces will increase the number of identical elements and reduce the costs of elements produced conventional without CAAD-CAM technology. For example the Garden of Eden is composed of truncated spheres, which are different of shape but nevertheless composed of identical elements (Kruit 2002).

In the sixties the traditional building technique was surpassed by the mass production. To reduce the cost buildings had to be composed of standardised and prefabricated elements. Nowadays techniques are changing. The cost of an element designed and produced by CAAD-CAM technology is fixed and does not decrease with the number of elements. Nowadays only some manufacturers of building elements apply these techniques but in the future CAAD-CAM technology will be widely adapted and applied.

3 DATABASE

Similar to this project a web-based database project has been initiated at the Delft University of Technology. This project aims to establish a theory that will account for how initial formal, structural and manufacturing related decisions, mutually influence, affect and inform the evolution of new configurational possibilities between the structure and the skin(s) in the design of Free-Form buildings. Based on the analysis of design and production processes as well as built examples of Free-Forms, the database serves as a catalogue of possibilities related to form and facilitate assessment of the impact of the early choices on the Free-Form building design and development. The project addresses to both architectural and structural professionals as well as to students of architecture (Kocaturk, Veltkamp, Tuncer, 2003).

4 METHOD OF DESIGN

The subject is so wide that a method of design to create always an optimal structure for all kind of Free-Form buildings cannot be given. Nevertheless the following strategy can be used to design the structure for single-volume buildings.

For Blobs with a highly curved surface, and the freedom to change the form with respect to the structural needs, it is a challenge to integrate the structure with the enveloping surface and to apply a spatial frame or a

Figure 5. The Webb of North Holland, Haarlemmermeer, the Netherlands. The structure of this exposition Hall consists steel arches, positioned on a radial pattern.

Figure 4. Frames of a Blob with an elongated plan positioned parallel.

monolithic structure. These surface structures will be only successful in case the form is the result of the collaboration of architect and structural engineer and the surface can be shaped with respect to the forces and construction.

For buildings with a double skin the structure can be optimised within the depth of the cavity between the external and internal skin.

For single-volume buildings a linear structure is a good choice if a surface structure cannot be applied. These structures can be designed quite simple. A pattern of faces, orthogonal on the plan, is constructed, radial or parallel and structural frames are positioned in the constructed faces.

5 CONCLUSIONS

Free-Form objects are difficult to design due to the irregular shape. The designer of the structure has to be a skilled professional. The skills needed to design a Blob do not only concern the structural analysis. Thanks to the advanced software available nowadays the structural analyses are not so difficult anymore. To construct Free-Form buildings the professionals have to collaborate and communicate. The structural engineer has to be able to explain the advantages of structural configurations. To increase the quality of the design of

a building, with a complicated geometry, the planners of the design team have to integrate the design with respect to the construction and manufacturing.

The cost of construction of blobs are excessive, still these buildings will be designed, provided engineers are able to construct possible but improbable designs and owners want extraordinary and unique designs.

REFERENCES

Engel, H. 1999. *Structure systems*, Verlag Gerd Hadje, 2e edition, ISBN 3-7757-0706-9.
Foque, R. Ontwerpsystemen. 1975. een inleiding tot de ontwerptheorie, Het Spectrum, ISBN 90 2745831 6.
Kocaturk, T, Veltkamp, M, Tunger, B. 2003. Decoding digital Free-Form complex surfaces. Conceptual integration of CAAD/CAM/CAE processes in Building practice, International Conference of Computer Aided Architectural Design Futures, 28–30 April 2003, Tainan, Taiwan.
Kruit, C.C. 2002. Blob: Vormtrend of nieuwe manier van werken, Bouwen met staal 169 december.
Labeur, M., B.Sc, Hermans, M., M.sc, 2001. The web of North Holland, Diana World nr.1.
Shodeck, D.L. 2001. Structures, fourth edition, Prentice Hall; ISBN 0-13-027821-1.
Spangenberg, ir. W. 2002. Vorm en constructie integraal; ontwerpen, Cement nr 3.
Wachsmann, C. 1959. Wendepunkt im Bauen, Otto Krauskopf verlag, Munich.

Form finding research: development between empirical and numerical methods

D. Abruzzese & A. Tursi
Università di Roma "Tor Vergata", Italy

ABSTRACT: The object of form-finding research techniques is to obtain the most efficient shape for static tasks. In civil engineering work, it is applied mainly to bridges and large roofs, the most important structural themes. This research had a strong development in the middle of last century, for the work of both architects and engineers. At the beginning, projects were inspired by natural shapes, like bones, shells and spider nets. The research about tensile structures, like those of Frei Otto, increased the knowledge of the design of shape for various load conditions. Many techniques, like soap films and numerical models, were derived from mathematical research on minimal structures. In Italy, Sergio Musmeci studied the form-finding technique as applied to compressed shell, using method developed for tensile structures: the only difference is the sign of the stresses. But the best spatial shape to transmit them must be the same. He used, at the beginning, empirical models. Later in the '70s, the improved computer power, allowed for the use of numerical methods.

1 HISTORICAL BACKGROUND

In the middle of last century some architects and structural engineers, who were architecturally inclined, began to write a new chapter in the history of structures. The opportunity of saving material, offered by the form-finding technique, gave impetus to this research. This research had the objective of finding the most efficient shape for any structural problem. In the beginning *form-finding* was considered a research field for both architects and engineers, because structure and shape are closely related.

The problem of form is studied, both, from a geometrical and naturalistic point of view. In fact researchers dedicated much time to the observation and analysis of natural structures, including those of bones, shells and spider nets. These were considered structures optimised by the process of evolution. This observation stimulated the design of some new artificial structures.

Among the main researchers in this field we recall pioneers such as Eduardo Torroja, Pier Luigi Nervi, and Felix Candela. Later came Heinz Isler and Frei Otto.

In Italy one of the latest form-finder has been Sergio Musmeci, who collected the results of Otto's research, about tensile structures using models of soap films. Musmeci performed a theoretical investigation in structural optimisation, too general to be usable in specific solutions. (Musmeci 1968).

Between 1960 and 1970, he started to design bridges working mainly on physical models. He adopted some simple model like soap film on wire structure, considering that membrane under tensile stress will work in the same way like compressed shell.

In the '60s, programmable computers were not yet in use. A few simple finite element models were considered and solved, even by hands, to verify the stress state of the structures, which were empirically designed, such as roofs and bridges.

Often, the risks associated with such large structures, which were difficult to calculate, required extensive tests on large scale steel or concrete physical models, to validate the efficiency of the design. Only in the '70s it became possible to use efficient mathematical tools on affordable computers, to investigate more accurately form-finding, thus saving costs of model making through the use of simple algorithms.

This paper presents original computational aspect of the design of some Musmeci's daring structures. Also, in this paper some interesting comparisons are presented between the earliest approach to form-finding from the Italian engineer Musmeci, and modern evaluation tools widely adopted by structural engineers. This research stems from the analysis of elegantly shaped structures, emblematic for this research area.

2 THE ROLE OF TENSILE STRUCTURE IN FORM FINDING RESEARCHES

One of the main field of development and application of form finding techniques is the architecture of tensile-structures. Wires and membranes do not have a rigid shape, and their forms are conditioned by load conditions. So it is necessary to know loads exactly, then to develop techniques to define the shape. In the '50s many large roof's structures were accomplished by steel wire-net, like the Saddle of Kongresshalle in Berlin and Raleigh Arena in USA (1951–'54). In 1964 Jawert designed, for Ice Palace in Stoccolm, a wire-beam system, which was very light and stable (Matildi et al. 1971).

But the best results in tensile structures were obtained by German architect Frei Otto. His research, which started in the later '50s, led to structures – both wire nets and membranes – free from defined and rigid edges. So, the edge's profile, in Otto's projects, are conditioned by inner tensions. His first important structure is the German Pavillon at Montreal's Expo' in 1967. This was followed by the gigantic roof for Olympic complex of "Monaco '72" (Otto 1984).

The geometry of tensioned membranes corresponds to the configuration of minimum energy, i.e. the minimal surface, a famous mathematical problem. As many mathematicians of the XIX century, Otto used, at the beginning, empirical models, like soap films. Only later, as for the Monaco's roof, he adopted numerical techniques, thanks to the improved power of computers.

2.1 Minimal surface

The problem of the surface of minimum area for given boundary conditions was recognized for the first time by famous Italian mathematician G.L. Lagrange, in

1760 (Lagrange 1776). He discovered the geometrical condition that minimal surfaces must satisfy, in every point, is that the curvature of two normal sections, respectively perpendicular, must have equal values but opposite sign. So every point is a saddle, whose sections curve upward in one direction and downward in a direction perpendicular to the other. Maybe the aesthetic charm of this family of surfaces is rooted in this geometrical equilibrium.

Belgian physicist J.A.F. Plateau, in later 19th century, postulated a question known as the *Plateau problem*: "Is there a surface of least area, for every arbitrary complicated boundary?"

Due to the inadequate mathematical tools of that time, he solved empirically the problem by soap films, obtaining the surface dipping in a soap-water solution a steel wire shaped in form of the boundary curve. This method easily solved the problem of obtaining the minimal energy (and also area) shape for a given boundary. Schwarz in 1865 and Rieman gave proofs of existence of a minimal surface for certain less complicated contours.

Two independent solutions to the problem were given in '30s: by the American mathematician J. Douglas in 1931 (Douglasand 1931) and by Hungarian T. Radò in 1933 (Radò 1933).

In recent years, greater computer power, allowed for analytical experimentation, that permitted form-finding for the geometry of very complicated surfaces.

Complementary to the numerical methods, and equally important, are the use of visualization, by computer graphic, to obtain the spatial perception of the surfaces (Polthier 2002).

3 DEVELOPMENT OF FORM FINDING METHODS: THE EXPERIENCE OF MUSMECI

3.1 The teaching of Pier Luigi Nervi

One of the most famous Italian engineers, in structural field, is Pier Luigi Nervi. He built many large roofs and domes worldwide. His early experiences were the concrete geodesic hangars in '30s, and after 2nd world war he applied that experience for sport and expò palaces, like Turin Hall in 1948 and the two Olympic domes for "Rome '60". He had great intuition for statics. But mathematical tools, in those years, were inadequate to design exact shape of complex monolithic structures (Nervi 1965).

Nervi solved the problem by helping himself with simplified graphic models in two dimension and verifying the project by large scale models (Piga 1996). His structures are not strictly thin shells, given the presence of stiffening ribs. Also, he never applied strictly form-finding techniques. But Nervi was always

Figure 1. Steel wire net of Monaco's tensile roof (from Otto 1984).

Figure 2. The dome of Nervi's Sport Palace in Rome, 1957 (from Nervi 1965).

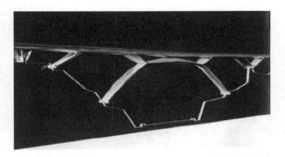

Figure 4. Model of Astico's bridge (from Archivio Musmeci).

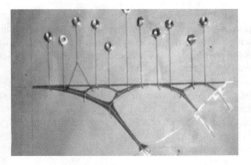

Figure 3. Inverted image of the antifunicular model (from Archivio Musmeci).

Figure 5. Model of Tor di Quinto's bridge (from Archivio Musmeci).

aiming to the reduction of the quantity of material, and consequently, the weight of the structure and its cost. His research produced elegant and light structures, expressing perfect execution, great care of the details, as well as great balance.

3.2 First form finding experiences: antifunicular bridges

In 1950, at Nervi's office, Musmeci designed his first bridge. Differently from Nervi, he researched a scientific approach to develop efficient shapes.

The most interesting thing in the design method, based upon an antifunicular model, is to guarantee only compressive stresses, and a highly efficient use of structural material.

In 1956 he designed, for a competition, a bridge of 200 m for Astico's valley, in north-east of Italy (Musmeci 1957).

He used the same antifunicular method. The arches, this time, are not monolithic but composed of hinged struts. The struts have a three-dimensional shape, with a flat section at the ends which becomes curved in the middle, in order to stiffen the elements against instability due to compression. The resulting profile gives the illusion of a circular arch, even if the axes of struts are rectilinear.

3.3 Birth of equal-compressed membrane: Rome Tor di Quinto's bridge

The Tor di Quinto's bridge in Rome, designed for a competition in 1959, is an important step in Musmeci's research.

First of all, he decided to obtain the most efficient shape for the six identical supports in reinforced concrete. To simplify the problem, he reduces the unknown shape from a volume to a surface of constant thickness. The form-finding problem is thus reduced to the well known mathematical problem of the minimum surface.

Like Frei Otto and in the same period, Musmeci used tensioned soap films to obtain a compressed structure, like the concrete shells of the supports for the bridge. This research produced two compressive stresses in orthogonal directions, in every point of the surface, with an efficient shape, of spatially compressed arches. Consequently, it can obtain a more rigid structure and a reduction of material.

The soap film model were made of rigid steel wire edges and flexible thin wires. Thus the edge's profile was not distinguishable with regard to the unknown shape of membrane.

A second step in the design, after the soap film model, was the rubber foil model. This was larger and more stable and gave an accurate definition of the form.

4 AN APPLICATION OF MUSMECI'S RESEARCH: THE BRIDGE IN POTENZA

4.1 Project's statement

In 1967 Musmeci began to design a bridge, using a uniformly compressed shell, to be built in Potenza, in south of Italy (Musmeci 1977).

He developed the idea of unique shell element for the entire length of the deck, attempting to eliminate supports elements of his previous project. The valley in Potenza is not much deep, and continuous shell can stretch down until it touches the ground.

4.2 Minimal surface: from objective to a device

The first form-finding step, as usual, was a soap film model. But this time the minimal surfaces became a reality. The proportions of the bridge, with a very narrow deck relative to the length, gives a minimal surface which is too flat in the transverse direction.

It is important to realize that Musmeci's purpose was not only structural efficiency but also to communicate, by new shapes, the image of engineering in step with science. So he gave up uniformity of stresses in all directions, in favour of a more fluid and dynamic form.

For this reason, the soap model gives proportions three times larger in the transverse sections. His task remains limited to show general aspect of researched surface.

He based the method on the concept that for similar radii of curvature there correspond similar concavity (second derivative). This method is valid only for small curvatures, and gives only an approximate idea of the needed general shape, but it should confirm research by physical models

4.3 Rubber foil model

The next step was a scaled rubber foil model, much larger and more accurate than the soap model.

In contrast to other projects and to the first soap model shape, contact between deck and shell was transformed from full length lines to points, spaced at equal distances. Uniform distances of support points should generate equal effort – roughly equal to the deck segment's weight.

In rubber model, equal loads were assured by wires and pulleys.

A regular grid was first designed on rubber foil for two reasons: a) for a relief of the form and b) to know the inner stresses on the elastic surface.

By knowing the deformation behaviour of the material under stress, and surveying the distance of grid's nodes in the model, it was possible to calculate the stresses.

Measurements showed that transverse efforts were not constant along the bay, but changed by about a 50% around a mean value.

It is the consequence of regular distance of contact points between shell and deck, because every point have the same vertical load, to sustain the weight of the same portion of deck. Because this points are in different type of section that have different curvatures.

This concept came a long way from the original idea of equal compression in the shell, like the previous transgression from equal stresses in transversal and longitudinal directions. In the real compressed bridge, horizontal stresses have been applied by precompressions, which are also different in the two normal directions.

Edge instability was a well known problem for compressed shells, and from the Zeiss domes experiences, in the twenties, the solution was to increase stiffness by introducing stiff elements along them. To simulate this aspect of concrete shell, in the rubber model, edges have been reinforced by gluing rubber strings.

4.4 From pencil to keyboard: finite element model solved by hand and with computer

To complete the form-finding work, before final design, a simple finite element model was solved by hand. The absence of a computer, still too expensive, required to a simplification the model. One that

Figure 6. Rubber foil model (from Musmeci 1977).

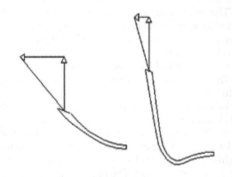

Figure 7. Different horizontal efforts in different sections for same vertical loads.

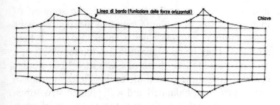

Figure 8. Plan view of FEM's net (from Musmeci 1977).

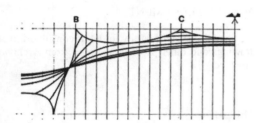

Figure 9. The shape obtained with finite-element model implemented by hand (from Musmeci 1977).

considers the membrane like a large-meshed wire net was used.

Knowing the horizontal tension in each of 21 different transversal directions at half bay (that is symmetrical), and the three-dimensional coordinates of upper and lower restraint, the z-coordinate of each node are calculated by applying the convergent algorithm (performed by hand).

This way it has been possible to verify the equilibrium in each node along the edges. For inner nodes, the algorithm finds a mean of nearby grid's points. To reduce the enormous number of operations by hand calculation, Musmeci didn't start from a flat membrane, as customary in computer models, but from node's z-coordinates near to equilibrium shape, given by the rubber's relief. The same was done for horizontal coordinates of the net boundary.

Later, during construction, Musmeci could use a computer to apply another finite element form-finding algorithm. The speed of automatic calculation could improve the number of cycles for a higher precision. In particular, the automatic model explored the shape only in the most delicate zones, near the piers, where transversal curvature, in a short space, moves from positive to negative extremes (Maurizio Leggeri 2002).

4.5 Form finding today: a comparison with modern numerical algorithm

The steps of this complex early form finding process have been verified and compared with the results obtained with an appropriate algorithm.

The complexity of the algorithm grew from the steps from the minimal surface in rigid boundary, through the

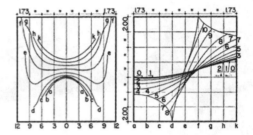

Figure 10. The shape of the most curved zone obtained with simplified computer model (from Musmeci, 1977).

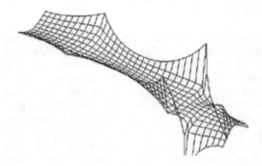

Figure 11. The shape obtained with author's algorithm.

introduction of free edges, then by changing of transversal efforts with respect to longitudinal ones. The latter step was first done in a uniform way for the entire profile, later it was made different in every section.

Here is presented the final result of this process, that has been useful to authors for appreciating the difficulties and variables in the modelling process. The power of the analytic approach with today's computers, that save time and money and increase the precision of results, is also appreciated.

The shape obtained with this software has been compared with the Musmeci's designs. In the diagram below the differences in height between the software result's and Musmeci's project in longitudinal section are indicated, for the middle points in each of 21 different sections of the 70 m span vault. The error range of our software's results, in a 14 m height vault, is 6 mm – the radius of the circles. In the key zone – left side – the differences are less than 2 cm (<0,2%).

4.6 The inner stresses: physical model and FEM

After conclusion of form-finding process, the next steps was the executive design, in which the concrete thickness and steel distribution were indicated. But form-finding gave only the shape of the tensioned membrane, modelled by a unique load condition corresponding, in a compressed concrete shell, to the dead load. It was necessary to verify the structure also under

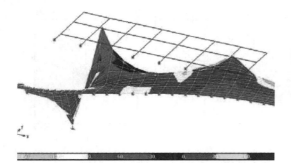

Figure 12. Finite element model of concrete compressed shell under dead load.

other conditions, like instability and discontinuities near the edges, as well as asymmetrical loads, such as wind and vehicles moving along the deck. The complexity of the shape, for the of mathematical tools of that time, led to empirical verifications, like those made by Nervi many years before. The first was a photoelastic model in 1/100 scale, followed by a large concrete model in 1/10 scale – 15 m length –, realized at ISMES institute in Bergamo, the same that made many models for Nervi's structures. The main result of this work was the necessity to thicken the edges, but the stresses, in the inner zones, came close to expectations. In particular, the model confirmed the hypothesis of constant longitudinal stresses, because measurements gave values of compression of $65-70 \, kg/cm^2$.

The analysis of a finite element model built to compare the results and to see the distribution of stresses in the entire shell confirms that never appear tensile stresses, but only compression's ones. The stresses increase in edges zones, like ISMES tests indicated, up to $120 \, kg/cm^2$. But, in inner zone the compression's values, in longitudinal direction, amount to, for a large part of the shell, between $60-90 \, kg/cm^2$.

5 CONCLUSIONS

The experiences in form-finding, in particular Musmeci's project, show the importance of complementary use of different approaches to solve the complex problem of the optimal spatial shape. It is clear that the power of computers permits the solution of many questions in a unique, rapid an inexpensive way. But, empirical models have been used often to help architects find the configuration, i.e. the topology, of a roof or a bridge like those of Frei Otto. New studies can still give some contribute to this field, in order to obtain efficient, balanced and well shaped structures, even appreciated from the architectural point of view.

ACKNOWLEDGEMENT

We thank Musmeci's family for let us consult original drawings and other precious material from Archivio Musmeci.

REFERENCES

Lagrange, G.L. 1776. *Essai d'une nouvelle méthode pour determiner les maxima et les minima des formules integrals indefinites.*

Douglas, J. 1931. *Solution of the Problem of Plateau,* 263–321, *Trans. Am. Math. Society,* n.33.

Radò, T. 1933. On the Problem of Plateau, *Ergeben. d. Math. u. ihrer Grenzgebiete.* Germany, Berlin: Springer-Verlag.

Frei Otto, 1956. Les toitures suspendues et les voilurs, *L'Architecture d'aujourd'hui,* n.3.

Musmeci, S. 1957. Il Ponte sull'Astico a Vicenza, *L'Architettura – cronaca e storia,* n.6.

Musmeci, S. 1959. Appalto concorso per il nuovo Ponte a Tor di Quinto, Roma, *Notiziario di tecnica moderna applicata all'ingegneria,* n.2–3.

Nervi, P.L. 1965. *Costruire correttamente,* Milano: Hoepli, 2nd ed.

Musmeci, S. 1968. Il minimo strutturale, *L'ingegnere,* n.5.

Osserman, R. 1970. A Proof of the Regularity of the Classical Solution to Plateau's Problem, *Ann. Math. 91.*

Musmeci, S. 1972. Il calcolo elettronico e la creazione di nuove forme strutturali, AAVV, *Architettura & computer.*

Musmeci, S. 1977. Ponte sul Basento a Potenza, *L'industria italiana del cemento,* 77–98, n.2.

Benvenuto, E. 1981. *La scienza delle costruzioni e il suo sviluppo storico,* Firenze, Italy. Sansoni.

Otto, F. 1984. *Natürliche konstruktionen,* Italian ed.: il Saggiatore.

Piga, C. 1996. *Storia dei modelli,* Seriate, Italy: ISMES.

Leggeri, M. 2002. *Private communication,* Potenza.

System-based Vision for Strategic and Creative Design, Bontempi (ed.)
© 2003 Swets & Zeitlinger, Lisse, ISBN 90 5809 599 1

On the shaping of cable-membranes by using "simulated annealing"

L. Fenu
Department of Structural Engineering, Cagliari, Italy

S. Manca
Structural Engineer, Cagliari, Italy

ABSTRACT: The search for the suitable shape of cable-membranes is an important design problem as, if the axial forces are unknown the shape is unknown too and viceversa so that, for instance, the shape wished by an architect could never be achieved if it does not match with reasonable values of tensile forces. Design methods for cable-membranes must therefore approximate as much as possible an assigned shape without violating the design constraints. Simulated annealing appears to be a good design method as, assigning only some elevations as boundary conditions and starting on from the architectural requirements, can achieve easily both a statical and architectural suitable shape of the cable-membranes.

1 INTRODUCTION

Since the cable-membrane shape cannot be assigned, for some decade after the second world war, before the computer aided design had its great development, their shaping was a structural problem. In the 1960s cable-membrane design was still difficult and in spite of numerous studies, F. Ot-to had to make costly phisical models to design his Munich Olympic stadium. In the 70's many studies were developed and, immediately afterwards, successfully used to design cable-membranes. Their design was studied by Spinelli (1977), Majowiecki & Tironi (1976), Spagnulo (1979), Cannarozzi (1981).

These studies lead to an effective design model that is still used and that, starting from an architectural design of the cable-membrane, approximates it with the closest statically suitable one. Since the problem is highly nonlinear and the solution has to be found among many combinations of the design variables, the problem is very complicated and in the past neither the computer powerful nor the non-linear algorithms were right to solve it: thus it was studied and successfully solved by linearization. Nowadays the highly increased computer powerful has lead to new algorithms that allow to solve this problem without any linearization.

2 CABLE-MEMBRANE EQUILIBRIUM

Consider in the horizontal plane x, y a rectangular network of orthogonal lines with both internal and edge nodes. Let's suppose that a reference system (O, x, y) has its origin at a corner of the rectangle. By choosing the edge nodes along the perimeter of this rectangular network, we can define different figures with different cable-membrane perimeters: for instance rectangular, rhomboidal, hexagonal and so on. The nodes on the perimeter have anyway assigned an elevation, while the elevation of the internal nodes is in general unknown, but, for some of them, depending on the design requirements, can be assigned opportunely too. The distances between the nodes are constant along the two orthogonal directions, namely Δx along the x direction and Δy along the y direction. Being N_{xi} the tensile forces of the cables parallel to the x direction and N_{yj} those of the cables parallel to the y direction, the tensile internal forces of each cable are obviously considered constant along it, but can vary for different cables, namely for $i = 1, ..., n_x$ and $j = 1, ..., n_y$ (Fig. 1).

In general each node is linked by the cables with four other nodes. These four nodes could be all internal too, or some of them could be peripheral, namely on the supported edge. Each internal node is subject to the internal forces of the two orthogonal cables and, if not supported and with assigned elevation, to the external actions acting on the node.

Being H_{xi} and H_{yj} the horizontal projection of N_{xi} and N_{yj} respectively, from the two equilibrium equations in the x and y directions of an internal node i linked with the nodes j, k, l, m, we have:

$$H_{x\,i-m} = H_{x\,i-l} \qquad H_{y\,i-j} = H_{y\,i-k} \qquad (1)$$

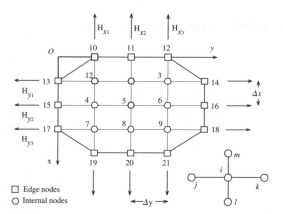

Figure 1. Scheme of internal and edge nodes of a cable membrane.

□ Edge nodes
○ Internal nodes

while, P_i being the node external load, for the equilibrium equation in the vertical direction:

$$\frac{H_{y\,i-j}}{\Delta x}(z_j - z_i) + \frac{H_{y\,i-k}}{\Delta x}(\hat{z}_k - z_i) + \frac{H_{x\,i-l}}{\Delta y}(z_l - z_i) +$$

$$+ \frac{H_{x\,i-m}}{\Delta y}(z_m - z_i) - P_i = 0 \qquad (2)$$

where we indicate with a circumflex accent the nodes with assigned elevation, so that, for instance, $\hat{z}_k$ is the assigned value of the elevation of node $\hat{k}$, while all the elevations without the circumflex accent are unknown. For instance in Fig. 1 if $i = 6$, we have $m = 3$, $l = 9$, $j = 5$, and $\hat{k} = 16$.

Consider firstly the case where no internal node have an assigned elevation.

Therefore from eqn. (2) we draw the system:

$$[J]\{z_i\} = [B]\{\hat{z}_k\} + \{P_i\} \qquad (3)$$

that is

$$[J]\{z_i\} = \{b\} \qquad (4)$$

where, N being the number of nodes whose elevation is unknown (namely in this case all the internal ones), and M the number of nodes with assigned elevation, $[J]$ and $[B]$ are $N \times N$ and $N \times M$ matrices respectively: for instance, in the cable-membrane of Fig. 1 without internal nodes with assigned elevation, $N = n_x \cdot n_y$ and $M = 2(n_x + n_y)$.

Since the nodes of vectors z_i and $\hat{z}_k$ are identified by one index, but they are located in the two-dimensional space of the rectangular network, then to easily find them it is necessary to substitute the single

index i with an appropriate double index, or to prepare an incidence matrix to map the i-th node in the network: we have chosen the latter way, and we have followed it to identify the node position in the similar way the finite element are identified through the incidence matrix in the FEM.

In the incidence matrix each row is related to an internal node with unknown elevation, and each element of the row identifies the four nodes close to this row node; in any row we find all the nodes related to a particular row node with an assigned order.

Consequently, besides a number of rows equal to the number N of internal nodes with unknown elevation, the incidence matrix has four columns, namely:

$$[I]_{N \times 4} = \begin{bmatrix} d & e & a & b \\ \cdot & \cdot & \cdot & \cdot \\ m & l & j & k \\ \cdot & \cdot & \cdot & \cdot \\ t & u & r & s \end{bmatrix} \qquad (5)$$

and it allows to assemble $[J]$ and $[B]$.

For instance the first row shows that node 1 is related to $\hat{d} = 10$, $e = 4$, $\hat{a} = 13$, and $b = 2$, while node $N = 9$ is related to $t = 6$, $\hat{u} = 21$, $r = 3$, $\hat{s} = 13$.

Since each i-th equation of system (2) is obtained by the equilibrium equation in the vertical direction of the i-th node, then $[J]$ has in its principal diagonal the coefficients of the elevation z_i of the i-th node, namely, being $H_{xi \to l} = H_{xi \to m} = H_{xi}$ and $H_{yi \to j} = H_{yi \to k} = H_{yi}$, the diagonal elements are:

$$-2\frac{H_{x\,i}}{\Delta x} - 2\frac{H_{y\,i}}{\Delta y} \qquad (6)$$

Besides, as the row depends on the equilibrium of an internal node close to other four nodes, in each row there are also the elements

$$\frac{H_{x\,i}}{\Delta x}, \quad \frac{H_{y\,i}}{\Delta y} \qquad (7)$$

and, in general, if all the four nodes close to the i-th node are internal and without an assigned elevation, each of them appears twice in the same row, namely the first is the coefficient of z_l and z_m, the latter of z_j and z_k. Otherwise, if the i-th node is related with peripheral nodes, the product of the assigned elevation with its coefficient will belong to the vector $\{b\}$.

Therefore in matrix $[J]$ each first index of each not null element is related with the i-th node whose equilibrium is governed by the i-th equation, while the second index is governed by the close nodes numbered according to the incidence matrix (4).

Successively, consider a matrix $[A]$ whose size is $N \times (N + M)$ and that is assembled by joining its two minors $[J]$ and $[B]$. In $[A]$ all the elements with two same indices are the same of the principal diagonal of $[J]$, while all the not null elements with the second index different from the first one and lower than N are the other not null elements of $[J]$.

Consider the case where all the internal nodes have their elevation unknown: if, besides the coefficient of the principal diagonal, the i-th row of $[J]$ has four coefficients, then the i-th row of $[A]$ has all the other elements null; otherwise, if $[J]$ has in this row less than four coefficients besides those of the principal diagonal, then the remainders regard edge nodes with assigned elevation close to the i-th node. In this case an extended incidence matrix $(N + M) \times 4$ allocates coefficients (7) in matrix $[A]$, and their second index in $[A]$ is higher than N. Having assembled in this way matrix $[A]$, by disjoining it to draw matrices $[J]$ and $[B]$, we find $[J]$ that has all the elements that coincide with those of $[A]$ and with both the same indices not greater than N, while to draw $[B]$ we have to leave the first index to the remaining elements of $[A]$ and to substitute the second index with a new one obtained by subtracting N to the index that identifies it in $[A]$.

Moreover, we can better the design process if we are able to easily assign the elevation of internal nodes too. Therefore, being their elevation known, we have so many fewer unknowns and equations as the number of internal nodes with assigned elevation. In fact if the generic elements of the p-th row of $[J]$ and $\{b\}$ are a_{pq} and b_p respectively, system (4) may be rewritten as:

$$
\begin{bmatrix}
a_{11} & a_{12} & \cdots & a_{1q} & \cdots & a_{1n} \\
a_{21} & a_{22} & \cdots & a_{2q} & \cdots & a_{2n} \\
\cdots & \cdots & \cdots & \cdots & \cdots & \cdots \\
a_{p1} & a_{p2} & \cdots & a_{pq} & \cdots & a_{pn} \\
\cdots & \cdots & \cdots & \cdots & \cdots & \cdots \\
a_{n1} & a_{n2} & \cdots & a_{nq} & \cdots & a_{nn}
\end{bmatrix}
\begin{bmatrix}
z_1 \\ z_2 \\ \cdots \\ z_p \\ \cdots \\ z_n
\end{bmatrix}
=
\begin{bmatrix}
b_1 \\ b_2 \\ \cdots \\ b_p \\ \cdots \\ b_n
\end{bmatrix}
\tag{8}
$$

Consider that a design requirement is $\hat{z}_p = z_p$, namely the internal node p has its elevation pre-assigned. Obviously the equation related to row p must meet with this condition, namely we have:

$$
0 \cdot z_1 + 0 \cdot z_2 + \ldots + 1 \cdot z_p + \ldots + 0 \cdot z_n = \hat{z}_p \tag{9}
$$

with, of course:

$$
a_{p1} = a_{p2} = \ldots a_{pn} = 0, \qquad a_{pq} = 1, \qquad b_p = \hat{z}_p \tag{10}
$$

Therefore system (4) loses an unknown as well as an equation, but it is convenient to leave it in its canonical form (8) and, according to (10), only substitute all the

coefficients with 0 except a_{pq} that is chosen to be 1, so that z_p is imposed to be $\hat{z}_p$ and condition (9) will affect all the equations of system (8).

3 CABLE-MEMBRANE DESIGN

Consider the cable-membrane design made by an architect that, for instance, has chosen all the node elevations for aesthetic reasons. Therefore, we have a matrix with the node coordinates and a function, the architect's design, that requires all the desired elevations z_{0i} of this nodes and that, for some of them like all the edge nodes and some internal ones, assigns the elevation values $\hat{z}_k$. Of course the precribed $\hat{z}_k$ cannot be changed, but the others usually do not match with the equilibrium conditions of the previous paragraph. Besides, the tensile forces of each cable must be limited, namely, with reference to the allowable cables, could have to be smaller than a maximum value and, to keep the cable in tension, higher than a minimum value: therefore, instead of the forces, we can limit their horizontal projection, and define an interval of definition of H_{xi} and H_{yj}, namely

$$
\bar{H}_{x\,min} \leq H_{x\,i} \leq \bar{H}_{x\,max} \qquad \bar{H}_{y\,min} \leq H_{y\,i} \leq \bar{H}_{y\,max} \tag{11}
$$

Therefore the problem is to approximate as much as possible the desired elevations z_{0i} with the unknown values z_i that satisfies system (4); this aim can be achieved by defining the following function

$$
f(H_{x\,i}, H_{y\,i}) = \max |z_i - z_{0\,i}| \tag{12}
$$

that has to be minimized subject to some design requirements.

For instance the design could be accepted only if the found values of are close enough to the desired ones, namely we cannot violate the constraint

$$
|z_i - z_{0\,i}| \leq \Delta \bar{z} \tag{13}
$$

otherwise the design should be made again.

Finally there could be some restraints of the interval of definition of H_{xi} and H_{yj}, for instance due to the availability of some cables: these unfeasible designs are well avoided by "annealing".

The problem defined above is nonlinear and it is described by Majowiecki (1996) that solve it by linearization.

In this paper we identified the cable-membrane with the closest shape to the desired one by using an algorithm of "simulated annealing" (Haftka & Gurdal, 1992).

Simulated annealing is an algorithm that simulates the annealing process: in general the annealing process is used to reach a more stable solidification of a liquid

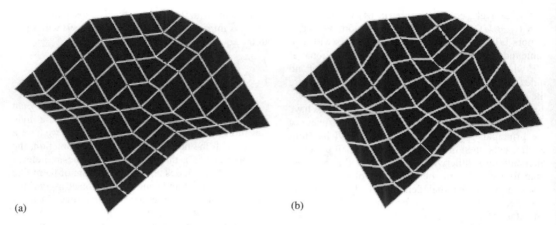

(a)   (b)

Figure 2.   (a) Starting surface to design a cable-membrane. (b) Cable-membrane design.

at a lower temperature after reheating. Therefore we find the closest cable-membrane to the desired one by simulating this phisical phenomenon. In fact simulating annealing is an euristic method: besides, since it can reject with an assigned probability some solutions that appears to be the best ones, it is a probabilistic search algorithm.

In general, by searching for the cable-membrane shape that is the closest to the architect's design, namely by shaping the cable-membrane to make it meet both the equilibrium equations and, as much as possible, the architect's design, we can fail to find an acceptable solution if, with a certain probability, we cannot reset the algorithm: in fact, problems with many design variables and with many constraints can reach solutions that are not the best ones.

Starting from a feasible solution, the algorithm rejects all the unfeasible values of the variables taking into account the constraints. Therefore the algorithm must be able not only to reject solutions that can be bettered, but also to choose the most favourable direction to achieve the best solution.

We have reached this aim by simulating annealing with a probability that we have chosen to vary between 0.8 and 0.1. By carrying on the iterations, namely by reaching lower energy levels, we must not only reduce the annealing probability, but also point the best solution in an efficient way. In fact, since the cable-membrane design usually deals with many variables, it needs an algorithm both efficient and robust: if we set opportunely all its parameters, simulating annealing has these two qualities. A good efficiency depends on the amount of the variable space that we investigate at each step, on how we reduce this space when we are going to reach the solution and on the memory of the previous search directions; only successful directions were stored.

Besides robust and efficient, simulating annealing is useful to face with any type of boundary conditions.

Being a zero-th order algorithm, therefore no derivatives are required neither in the calculations nor in the boundary conditions. Therefore, the boundary conditions require only elevation values and, by using equations (8) and (9), it is very easy to deal with boundary conditions of internal nodes too.

This easy way of inserting internal boundary conditions makes the design very powerful, as it allows the designer to assign a specific elevation to some nodes, leaving the remainders to find theirs through membrane equations. In Fig. 2 we show the design of a cable-membrane starting from eight plane surfaces with assigned median sharp edge elevations.

4   CONCLUSIONS

The design of cable-membranes cannot assign their shape, as shape and membrane behaviour are strictly related: therefore their design can be made by assigning a desired shape and by approximating it with a shape that allows the membrane to meet its equilibrium equations. This is a non-linear problem that in the past has been solved by linearization. Nowadays, by using powerful computers, it is possible to solve it by using adequate algorithms. In this case we have used an euristic algorithm, the simulated annealing.

It finds the solution by simulating the behaviour of a liquid that solidifies at different energy states and that achieves a more stable solid state by annealing, namely by solidifying after being reheated.

Being a zero-th order method, simulated annealing does not require any derivative and it is very easy to define the boundary conditions as only assigned elevations are required: therefore, besides boundary conditions of edge nodes, also those of internal nodes can be assigned very easily. Consequently, on the one hand it is very versatile and can be used to design many different cable-membranes with many different assigned node elevations and, on the other hand, it allows to solve complicated nonlinear design problems with many variables and constraints.

REFERENCES

Cannarozzi, M. 1981. Un procedimento di ricerca di forma per reti di funi. *Costruzioni metalliche,* 1, 181–194.

Haftka, R.T. & Gurdal, Z. 1992. *Elements of structural optimization.* Dordrecht: Kluwer Academic Publishers.

Majowiecki, M. & Tironi, G. 1979. Strutture spaziali leggere. Progettazione interattiva mediante l'impiego di elaboratore elettronico. *Acciaio*, 10, 421–427.

Majowiecki, M. 1996. *Tensostrutture: progetto e verifica.* Mila-no: CREA.

Spagnuolo, R. 1979. Il disegno delle reti di funi: la ricerca della forma, 2, *Acciaio,* 89–92.

Spinelli, P. 1977. Tensostrutture: indagine teorica ed applicazioni. Forma iniziale e orditi bidirezionali. *Costruzioni metalliche*, 4, 197–202.

8. Issues in computational mechanics of structures

Nonuniform torsion of bars of variable thickness

E.J. Sapountzakis & V.G. Mokos
Department of Civil Engineering, National Technical University, Zografou Campus, Athens, Greece

ABSTRACT: In this paper a boundary element method is developed for the nonuniform torsion of simply or multiply connected bars of arbitrary variable cross section. The bar is subjected to an arbitrarily concentrated or distributed twisting moment, while its edges are restrained by the most general linear torsional boundary conditions. Both the variable warping and torsion constants together with the torsional shear stresses and the warping normal and shear stresses are computed. Numerical results are presented to illustrate the method and demonstrate its efficiency and wherever possible its accuracy.

1   INTRODUCTION

One of the problems often encountered in engineering practice is the analysis of members of structures of variable cross section subjected to twisting moments. Box shaped bridges or concrete slab and beam structures of variable height are most common examples. The extensive use of the aforementioned structural elements necessitates a rigorous analysis.

When a member of variable cross section is subjected to general twisting loading, due to this variation and due to the arbitrary torsional boundary conditions applied either at the edges or at any other interior point is leaded to nonuniform torsion and its angle of twist per unit length is not constant along its axis.

Several researchers have dealt with beams of variable cross section ignoring the warping effects resulting from the corresponding restraints at the ends of the member. If the aforementioned structures are analyzed or designed for torsion considering only the effect of Saint-Venant torsion, the analysis may underestimate the torsion in the members and the design may be unconservative. On the contrary, relatively little work has been done on the problem of nonuniform torsion of bars of variable cross section. This work employs the finite element method upon polynomial approximation of the torsional and warping rigidities using shape functions to derive the stiffness coefficients. This application of shape functions results inaccuracies in stress analysis of beams of variable cross section, as static and kinematic values at nodes and in the element region are computed only approximately and the element may not satisfy local and global equilibrium conditions. Also, in this work the approximation of the aforementioned rigidities in each section is accomplished

using the thin-walled beam theory introducing additional inaccuracies.

In this paper a boundary element method is developed for the nonuniform torsion of simply or multiply connected bars of arbitrary variable cross section. The bar is subjected to an arbitrarily concentrated or distributed twisting moment, while its edges are restrained by the most general linear torsional boundary conditions. The developed method is an improvement of that presented by Sapountzakis & Mokos (2002), since it takes into account the variable torsional and warping rigidities along the member length. Three boundary value problems with respect to the variable along the beam angle of twist and to the primary and secondary warping functions are formulated and solved employing a pure BEM approach, that is only boundary discretization is used. Both the variable warping and torsion constants together with the torsional shear stresses and the warping normal and shear stresses are computed. Numerical results are presented to illustrate the method and demonstrate its efficiency and wherever possible its accuracy.

2   STATEMENT OF THE PROBLEM

Consider a prismatic bar of length L with an arbitrarily shaped variable along its axis cross section, occupying the two dimensional multiply connected region Ω of the $\bar{x}, \bar{y}$ plane bounded by the $K + 1$ piecewise smooth curves Γ_i ($i = 0,1,\ldots,K$) i.e. they may have a finite number of corners, as shown in Figure 1. The material of the bar is assumed homogeneous, isotropic and linearly elastic with E and G its modulus of elasticity and shear modulus, respectively.

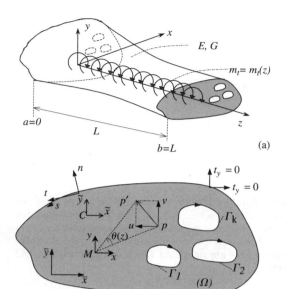

(a)

$\Gamma = \cup_{j=1}^{K+l} \Gamma_j$

(b)

Figure 1. Prismatic bar subjected to twisting loading (a) with variable cross section of arbitrary shape (b).

When the bar is subjected to the arbitrarily concentrated or distributed twisting moment $m_t = m_t(z)$, the displacement components in the x, y and z directions are given in terms of the angle of twist $\theta(z)$ as (Sapountzakis & Mokos 2002)

$$u = -y\theta(z)$$

(1a)

$$v = x\theta(z)$$

(1b)

$$w = \frac{d\theta}{dz}\varphi_M^P(x,y)$$

(1c)

while we define the primary and secondary parts of the shear stresses and the warping normal stress as

$$\tau_{zx}^P = G\frac{d\theta}{dz}\left(\frac{\partial \varphi_M^P}{\partial x} - y\right) \quad \tau_{zy}^P = G\frac{d\theta}{dz}\left(\frac{\partial \varphi_M^P}{\partial y} - x\right)$$

(2a,b)

$$\tau_{zx}^S = G\frac{\partial \varphi_M^S}{\partial x} \qquad \tau_{zy}^S = G\frac{\partial \varphi_M^S}{\partial y}$$

(3a,b)

$$\sigma_z = E\frac{d^2\theta}{dz^2}\varphi_M^P(x,y)$$

(4)

where $\varphi_M^P(x,y)$ is the primary warping function in the domain Ω with respect to the shear center M of the

cross section of the bar (Fig. 1) and $\varphi_M^S(x,y,z)$ is a fictitious function called as basic secondary warping function.

Defining the resultant of the primary shear stress distribution as primary twisting moment M_t^P and the resultant of the secondary shear stress distribution due to warping as secondary twisting moment M_t^S these moments can be written as

$$M_t^P = GI_t\frac{d\theta}{dz}$$

(5a)

$$M_t^S = -E\frac{d}{dz}\left(C_M\frac{d^2\theta}{dz^2}\right)$$

(5b)

where

$$C_M = \int_\Omega \varphi_M^{P^2}\,d\Omega$$

(6a)

$$I_t = \int_\Omega \left(x^2 + y^2 + x\frac{\partial \varphi_M^P}{\partial y} - y\frac{\partial \varphi_M^P}{\partial x}\right)d\Omega$$

(6b)

are the warping and torsion constants of the domain Ω, while the resulting total twisting moment of the cross section is given as

$$M_t = M_t^P + M_t^S$$

(7)

Substituting equations (5a,b) into equation (7) we obtain the expression of the total twisting moment for the beam with variable cross section as

$$M_t = GI_t\frac{d\theta}{dz} - E\frac{dC_M}{dz}\frac{d^2\theta}{dz^2} - EC_M\frac{d^3\theta}{dz^3}$$

(8)

The equation of equilibrium of the bar subjected to the arbitrarily distributed twisting moment $m_t = m_t(z)$ obtained by summing all the twisting moments acting on an element of the bar and taking into account the variable cross section of the bar can be written as

$$EC_M\frac{d^4\theta}{dz^4} + 2E\frac{dC_M}{dz}\frac{d^3\theta}{dz^3} + \left(E\frac{d^2C_M}{dz^2} - GI_t\right)\frac{d^2\theta}{dz^2}$$
$$- G\frac{dI_t}{dz}\frac{d\theta}{dz} = m_t$$

inside the beam   (9)

subjected to the following most general linear torsional boundary conditions for the beam problem including also the elastic support

$$\alpha_1\theta + \alpha_2 M_t = \alpha_3$$

(10a)

584

$$\beta_1 \frac{d\theta}{dz} + \beta_2 M_b = \beta_3 \text{ at the beam ends } z = 0, l \quad (10b)$$

where $d\theta/dz$ denotes the rate of change of the angle of twist θ and it can be regarded as the torsional curvature, while M_b is the warping moment due to the torsional curvature at the boundary of the beam given as

$$M_b = -EC_M \frac{d^2\theta}{dz^2} \quad (11)$$

Requiring both the primary and the secondary due to warping parts of the third equation of equilibrium and the corresponding parts of the traction vector on the free surface of the bar to vanish, we obtain the following Neumann problems for the primary warping function

$$\nabla^2 \varphi_M^P = 0 \qquad \text{in } \Omega \quad (12)$$

$$\frac{\partial \varphi_M^P}{\partial n} = yn_x - xn_y \qquad \text{on } \Gamma \quad (13)$$

and for the basic secondary warping function φ_M^S

$$\nabla^2 \varphi_M^S = -\frac{E}{G}\frac{d^3\theta}{dz^3}\varphi_M^P \qquad \text{in } \Omega \quad (14)$$

$$\frac{\partial \varphi_M^S}{\partial n} = 0 \qquad \text{on } \Gamma \quad (15)$$

where $\nabla^2 = \partial^2/\partial x^2 + \partial^2/\partial y^2$ is the Laplace operator and $\partial/\partial n$ denotes the directional derivative normal to the boundary Γ.

It is worthnoting that in the case the origin O of the coordinates is a point of the $\bar{x}, \bar{y}$ plane other than the shear center, the warping function with respect to this point φ_O^P is first established from the Neumann problem (12), (13) substituting φ_M^P by φ_O^P. Using the evaluated warping function φ_O^P, φ_M^P is then established using the transformation given by the following equation (Sapountzakis 2000)

$$\varphi_M^P(x,y) = \varphi_O^P(\bar{x},\bar{y}) - \bar{x}\bar{y}_M + \bar{y}\bar{x}_M + c^P \quad (16)$$

where, $x = \bar{x} - \bar{x}_M$, $y = \bar{y} - \bar{y}_M$, $\bar{x}_M, \bar{y}_M$ are the coordinates of the shear center M with respect to Oxy system of coordinates (Fig. 1) and c^P an integration constant. Moreover, the evaluated warping function φ_M^S from the solution of the Neumann problem (14), (15) contains an integration constant c^S (parallel displacement of the cross section along the beam axis), which can be obtained from

$$c^S = -\sum_{j=0}^{K} \frac{\int_{\Omega_j} \varphi_M^S d\Omega_j}{\int_{\Omega_j} d\Omega_j} \quad (17)$$

and the main secondary warping function $\bar{\varphi}_M^S$ is given as

$$\bar{\varphi}_M^S = \varphi_M^S + c^S \quad (18)$$

3 NUMERICAL SOLUTION

The numerical evaluation of the angle of twist θ is accomplished using a BEM approach similar to that presented in Sapountzakis & Katsikadelis (2000), while for the evaluation of the primary φ_M^P and secondary φ_M^S warping functions the BEM is employed as this is presented in Sapountzakis & Mokos (2002).

4 NUMERICAL EXAMPLES

On the basis of the analytical and numerical procedures presented in the previous sections, a computer program has been written and representative examples have been studied to demonstrate the efficiency, wherever possible the accuracy and the range of applications of the developed method.

4.1 Example 1

A clamped beam of length $L = 70.0\,m$, of a box shaped cross section with variable height ($E = 3.0 \times 10^7\,kN/m^2$, $v = 0.20$) eccentrically loaded as shown in Figure 2 has been studied. In Figure 3 the

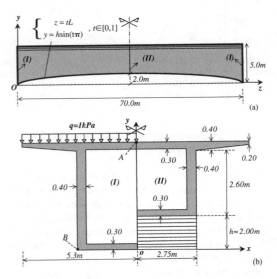

Figure 2. Longitudinal section (a) and transverse semisections at support and at midspan (b) of the box shaped beam of example 1.

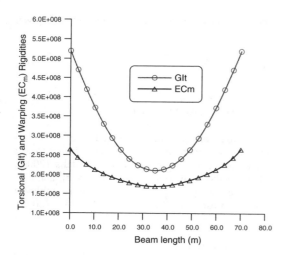

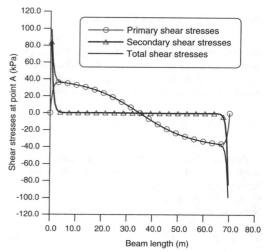

Figure 3. Variation of the cross section torsional GI_t and warping EC_M rigidities along the beam of example 1 (max $GI_t = 5.197\mathrm{E}+8\,kNm^2$, min $GI_t = 2.102\mathrm{E}+8\,kNm^2$, max $EC_M = 2.647\mathrm{E}+8\,kNm^4$, min $EC_M = 1.691\mathrm{E}+8\,kNm^4$).

Figure 5. Primary τ_A^P, secondary τ_A^S and total τ_A shear stresses along the beam at point A of the box shaped cross section of example 1 (max $\tau_A^P = 35.9804\,kPa$, max $\tau_A^S = 98.7663\,kPa$, max $\tau_A = 98.7663\,kPa$).

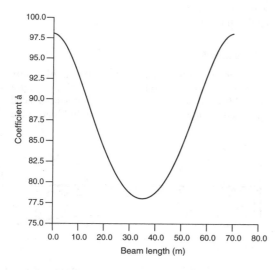

Figure 4. Variation of the coefficient ε along the beam of example 1 (min $\varepsilon = 78.0368$, max $\varepsilon = 98.0823$).

variation of the torsional GI_t and warping EC_M rigidities of the cross section along the beam together with their maximum and minimum values are presented. In Figure 4 the variation of the coefficient $\varepsilon = L\sqrt{GI_t/CM}$ describing the nonuniform character of the torsion problem leads to the conclusion that the reduction of the beam height results in strong nonuniform behaviour in torsional loading. Moreover, in Figure 5 the primary τ_A^P, secondary τ_A^S and total τ_A shear stresses at point A of the cross section along the beam are presented. From this figure, it follows that

the maximum secondary shear stress due to restrained warping $(\tau_{max}^S = 98.7663\,kPa)$ is greater than the maximum primary shear stress $(\tau_{max}^P = 35.9804\,kPa)$ and should not be neglected.

Finally, in Figure 6 the distribution along the beam of the normal stress due to warping $\sigma_z^{warp}(\sigma_{z,max}^{warp} = 22.884\,kPa)$ at point B of the variable cross section (Fig. 2) is presented as compared with the normal stress due to bending $\sigma_z^{bend}(\sigma_{z,max}^{bend.} = 237.208\,kPa)$ at the same point. The magnitude of the normal stresses due to restrained warping presented in this figure leads to the conclusion that this stress could possibly be ignored.

4.2 Example 2

A cantilever slab and beam structure of length $L = 20.0\,m$, with variable height of the stiffening beam ($E = 3.0 \times 10^7\,kN/m^2$, $v = 0.20$) eccentrically loaded as shown in Figure 7 has been studied. In Figure 8 the variation of the torsional GI_t and warping EC_M rigidities of the cross section along the beam together with their maximum and minimum values are presented. Moreover, in Figure 9 the primary τ_A^P, secondary τ_A^S and total τ_A shear stresses at point A of the cross section along the beam are presented. From this figure, it follows that the maximum secondary shear stress due to restrained warping $(\tau_{max}^S = 104.730\,kPa)$ is of the order of the maximum primary shear stress $(\tau_{max}^P = 288.764\,kPa)$ and should not be neglected.

Finally, in Figure 10 the distribution along the structure of the normal stress due to warping

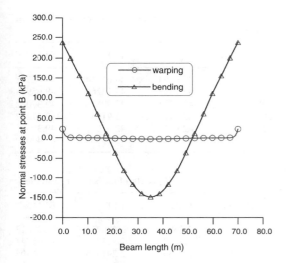

Figure 6. Normal stresses due to warping and due to bending at point B of the variable box shaped cross section of example 1.

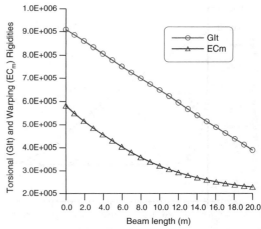

Figure 8. Variation of the cross section torsional GI_t and warping EC_M rigidities along the structure of example 2 (max $GI_t = 909086\,kNm^2$, min $GI_t = 388693\,kNm^2$, max $EC_M = 583217\,kNm^4$, min $EC_M = 228155\,kNm^4$).

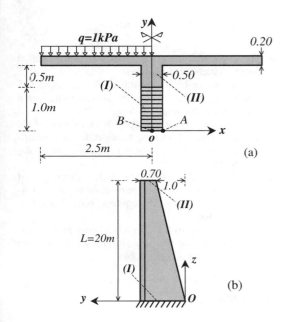

Figure 7. Transverse (a) and longitudinal (b) sections of the slab and beam structure of example 2.

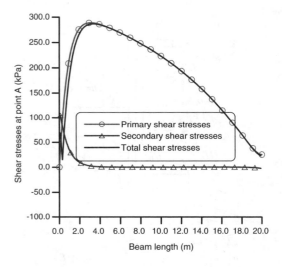

Figure 9. Primary τ_A^P, secondary τ_A^S and total τ_A shear stresses along the structure at point A of the cross section of example 2 (max $\tau_A^P = 288.764\,kPa$, max $\tau_A^S = 104.730\,kPa$, max $\tau_A = 288.764\,kPa$).

σ_z^{warp} ($\sigma_{z,max}^{warp} = 808.588\,kPa$) at point B of the variable cross section (Fig. 7) is presented as compared with the normal stress due to bending σ_z^{bend} ($\sigma_{z,max}^{bend} = 1347.070\,kPa$) at the same point. From this figure it is easily concluded that the contribution of the normal stresses due to restrained warping near the clamped edges of the beam should be encountered in its analysis.

4.3 Example 3

To examine the accuracy of the proposed method a cantilever beam of length $L = 40.0\,cm$, of a channel section varying in depth and width linearly, while its thickness remains constant (Fig. 11) clamped at the stronger end and twisted by a torque $M = 300\,kgm$ at the free end ($E = 2.1 \times 10^6\,kg/cm^2$, $G = 8.05 \times 10^5\,kg/cm^2$) has been studied. In Tables 1 and 2 the angle

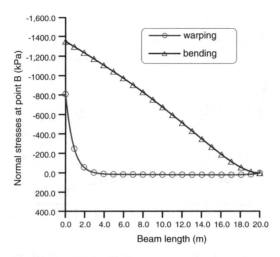

Figure 10. Normal stresses along the structure of Example 2, due to warping and due to bending at point B of its cross section.

Table 1. Angle of twist $\theta(L) \times 10^5$ of the beam of Example 3.

No. elements	FEM	TTT	BEM
3	45.6104	46.07014	53.46735
6	43.7473	43.12266	49.65918
10	43.4333	42.90516	49.37072
20	42.9479	42.91053	49.37232
40	42.9063	42.93026	49.39605
50	42.9014	42.93363	49.40019

Table 2. Derivative $\theta'(L) \times 10^5$ of the beam of Example 3.

No. elements	FEM	TTT	BEM
3	2.3604	2.488773	2.929523
6	2.3287	2.313715	2.705741
10	2.3166	2.291335	2.676505
20	2.2839	2.286150	2.669536
40	2.2820	2.285735	2.668915
50	2.2821	2.285736	2.668907

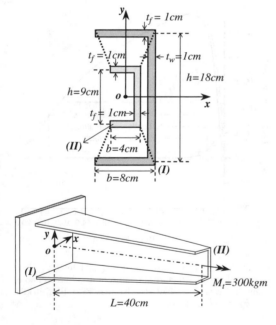

Figure 11. Cantilever beam of Example 3.

of twist θ and its derivative θ' at the free end, respectively, for various numbers of beam elements are given using the proposed method and calculating the torsional and warping rigidities either numerically as analyzed before (BEM) or employing the thin-tube theory (TTT), as compared with those obtained from a FEM solution (Eisenberger 1995).

5 CONCLUDING REMARKS

a. The presented numerical technique is well suited for computer-aided analysis.
b. The variation of the beam height, as expected, results in increment of the nonuniform beam behaviour in torsional loading.
c. The normal and warping shear stresses' magnitude due to restrained warping necessitates the consideration of these additional stresses near the restrained edges.
d. The developed method retains the advantages of a BEM solution over a pure domain discretization method since it requires only boundary discretization.
e. The inaccuracy of the thin-tube theory in calculating torsional and warping rigidities even for thin walled sections is remarkable.

REFERENCES

Eisenberger, M. (1995). Nonuniform Torsional Analysis of Variable and Open Cross-Section Bars, *Thin-Walled Structures*, 21, 93–105.

Sapountzakis, E.J. (2000). Solution of Nonuniform Torsion of Bars by an Integral Equation Method, *International Journal Computers and Structures*, 77, 659–667.

Sapountzakis, E.J. & Katsikadelis, J.T. (2000). Analysis of Plates Reinforced with Beams, *Computational Mechanics*, 26, 66–74.

Sapountzakis, E.J. & Mokos, V.G. (2003). Warping Shear Stresses in Nonuniform Torsion by BEM, *Computational Mechanics*, 30(2), 131–142.

System-based Vision for Strategic and Creative Design, Bontempi (ed.)
© 2003 Swets & Zeitlinger, Lisse, ISBN 90 5809 599 1

From load path method to classical models of structural analysis

F. Palmisano
Studio Vitone & Associati, Bari, Italy

A. Vitone & C. Vitone
Dept. of Civil and Environmental Engineering, Bari Polytechnic, Bari, Italy

ABSTRACT: Since most ancient times, building art used models to create and to work out the idea of the design. Only after Galilei this practice was adopted by Science as well and then models became also instruments to simulate and to analyse structural behaviour. The *STM* (Strut and Tie Model) inspired by truss – which goes back to the origin of r.c. structures in the late 19th century (Hennebique, Ritter and Morsch) – was recently brought up again by Stuttgart School. In the meantime interest grew in methods which would generate the *STM*, such as Load Path Method (*LPM*: Schlaich & Schafer 1996). The *LPM* (Palmisano 2001, Vitone, A. & V. 2001) has the peculiar capacity to make immediately understand the link between form and structure (Palmisano et al. 2002); this can be useful to recognise physical significance of other models, such as the de Saint-Venant beam.

1 LOAD PATH METHOD: THE ORIGINS

The Strut and Tie Model (*STM*), conceived by the French builder François Hennebique as simple representation of the involved static analysis of a r.c. element subject to shear and bending, has been later developed by Ritter and Morsch.

In the twentieth century several studies have been done about STM and the results became the basis of some prescriptions in Danish Code DS411 and in CEB-FIP Model Code 1990.

The Stuttgart School (CEB 1982, Schlaich et al. 1987) has recently proposed a global approach to the design of structures through *STM*. The accuracy of the results mainly depends on the way the model fits the actual structural configuration (Marano et al. 2001). However it is necessary a special care to design model geometry.

In this scene, the searching of instruments that reproduce less empirically the choice of model design, such as LPM (Load Path Method: Schlaich & Schafer 1996), becomes necessary.

2 LOAD PATH METHOD: BASIC PRINCIPLES

The most suitable orthonormal Cartesian system of architectural forces to physical environment in which they flow, is the one capable to bring back them only to vertical loads and horizontal thrusts. According to

this, structure can be read as the trace of loads path (De Tommasi et al. 2003).

The form of the structure is the result of their mutual integration and mainly of the influence of profiles traced by thrusts path, forced to deviate their natural horizontal flows to the soil, in order to go in search of equilibrium. Forces represent loads that, in the way from their application points (S) to the restraints (E), in every deviation node, have to apply thrusts (H) to the rest of the structure and to receive deviation forces equal and opposite to thrusts in order to respect equilibrium (Fig. 1).

The design of this load flowing through the structure can be approximated by polygonal lines with thrusts in every deviation node. Structure will be crossed by compression fluxes (dashed lines), when loads travel in the same direction of their path, and by fluxes in tension (continuous lines) along which loads go in the direction opposite to their path. According to classical theory, the basic principles that lead Load Path Method are equilibrium and congruence. Thrusts in deviation nodes are necessary in order to respect equilibrium and every path is possible if it is equilibrated.

Between infinite paths in equilibrium, loads have to choose the one in which their vectors invest the minimum quantity of strain energy, that is the only one equilibrated and congruent. At this purpose loads get energy from their own potential energy that decreases. Along a generic path (polygonal in this model), the calculus of the invested strain energy (D) is simplified in

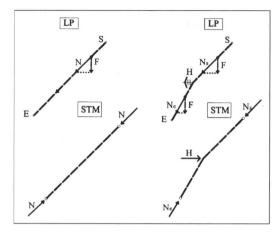

Figure 1. LP and STM.

the summation of the terms relative to every side of the traverse:

$$D = \frac{1}{2}\sum N_i l_i \varepsilon_i \qquad (1)$$

where "i" is the generic side of the load path; N_i is the intensity of the vector that brings load on that side of the load path; l_i is the length of the generic side and ε_i is the relative strain that is medium constant on l_i.

3 FROM LOAD PATHS BIAXIAL FLUXES TO PRINCIPAL STRESS LINES IN A CONTINUUM

A generic and uniform load paths flux (V1 and V2), made by paths in tension orthogonal to those in compression (Fig. 2o) is equivalent to the superimposition of three different uniform "elementary" fluxes; each flux is characterised by a physical significance of immediate perception: the *horizontal translation*, the *paths deviator*, the *loads distributor*, respectively represented in Figures 2a, b, c.

It's possible to observe that in each of these elementary fluxes loads travelling along the two orthogonal paths are equal.

The simple horizontal translation (*translator*) represents an indefinite flux of loads directed to the respective arriving station in the case that – for the complete and general paths identity – the solution with the minimum value of strain energy is the one with a uniform distribution of stresses: in every path, loads are equal (V/2), the inclinations ($\theta = 45°$) are equal and the mutual distances between paths are equal too.

It's possible to observe that paths crossing the vertical section have to be interpreted as LP of vertical loads

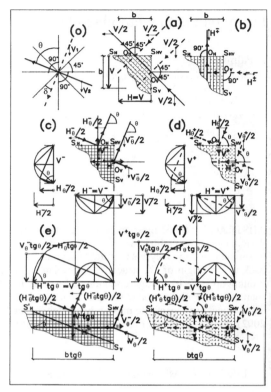

Figure 2. Horizontal translation, paths deviator and loads distributor.

V/2; on the other side, the ones that cross the horizontal section have to be interpreted as paths of the corresponding (and of the same intensity) horizontal thrusts. The transition from the discrete to the continuum body occurs without any variation: the two paths crash (going into the continuum body: Fig. 2a) and in this case loads have no reason for deviating or for moving, even only partly, from one path to the other. As a matter of fact, because of their mutual contact in the node, loads, even if they have the real possibility of choosing alternative paths, don't leave a path that, because of the supposed ideal conditions of homogeneity, requires the minimum investment of strain energy.

Deviator (Fig. 2b) is composed by a orthogonal paths (inclination $\theta = 90°$) flux of horizontal and vertical thrusts having the same intensity but opposite sense. In the simple horizontal translation it's possible to identify the case of vertical loads crossing the vertical section (along 45° inclined paths in tension or in compression) and, at the same time, of horizontal thrusts crossing (in the same way) the horizontal section. No horizontal thrust is transmitted to vertical section and no vertical thrust is transmitted to horizontal section. On the other side, in the case of *deviator*, quite the opposite happens. The two sections (vertical and horizontal) are crossed only by thrusts perpendicular to the sections and not by loads parallel to the sections.

Loads distributor represents the case of a flux in which both vertical loads and horizontal thrusts don't cross, respectively, the vertical and horizontal section, exactly as in the case of the *deviator* (and unlike the case of the *translator*), but they transmit to these sections orthogonal thrusts (Figs. 2c, d, e, f); both of these thrusts are either of compression or of tension.

The distributor flux is composed by orthogonal couples of paths which are 45° inclined, equidistant and crossed by equal loads. Unlike the case of horizontal translation, either them both are "going down" (compression) or them both are "going up" (tension). In the continuum, this model corresponds to an hydrostatic normal stress state. Paths inclination (nevertheless, these paths are always orthogonal in pairs) can be $\theta \times 45°$. In this case, at a parity of hydrostatic stress, the loads intensity has to change (Fig. 2).

Let's now observe what happens when the above mentioned elementary fluxes crash, at the same time, in the continuum.

The *deviator* effect on the *simple horizontal translation* is a rotation of the two 45° inclined axes, without having a modification of the travelling loads intensity (V/2): in this way it's possible to say that loads, "colliding" with the *deviator*, deviate but each of them fully remains on its own path (Fig. 3).

The *loads distributor* effect on a biaxial flux (that has endured a deviation δ from the 45° inclination: Fig. 4) of orthogonal couples of paths traced by the same loads is – just unlike the previous case – the transfer of a part of the travelling load from a path to the other one, without having any further deviation from their paths original inclination (θ).

From the superimposition of the three elementary fluxes the principal stress lines (in tension and in compression) rise in the continuum. In the areas where the hypothesis of perfect homogeneity is not valid, load paths must deviate to direct themselves to the arriving station following paths that need the minimum strain energy. But it's not only necessary the inclination suitability for the strain energy saving. In fact loads will also try to redistribute themselves between the two orthogonal paths, splitting themselves in parts no more equal but proportionate to the effectiveness of each of them.

The case of the de Saint Venant beam, analysed in the following paragraph, represents particularly significant scenery of the proposed model.

4 FROM LPM TO DE SAINT VENANT

The beam represented in Figures 5 and 6 is crossed by a total load V that goes from the section S-S to the

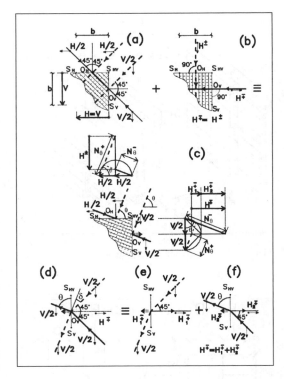

Figure 3.   Deviator effect on simple horizontal translation.

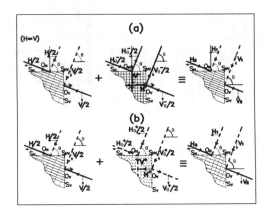

Figure 4.   Loads distributor effect on a biaxial flux of orthogonal couples of paths.

section E-E. Replacing V with an equivalent system of elementary equal loads $V^{(1)}$, we want to draw the path that each of these loads has to follow in order to get to the final station with the minimum (among the possible, that means equilibrated, paths) investment in strain energy.

591

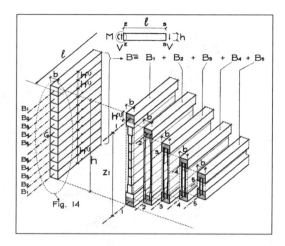

Figure 5. B subdivision into 5 beams.

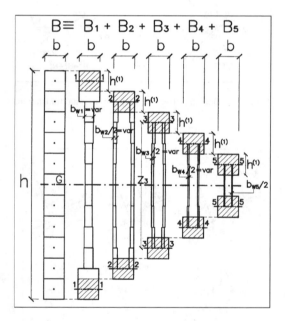

Figure 6. Front view of Figure 5.

In this way the LP(V) becomes a complex system, composed by as many paths (of elementary loads and of consequent thrusts) as the $V^{(1)}$ are. When the different LP($V^{(1)}$) are *superimposed*, loads don't change their paths. In fact the new (alternative) paths that will be possibly followed by loads, because of the superimposition, will need – according to the hypothesis made – a large investment in strain energy. In this way it's possible to bring back the analysis of a beam

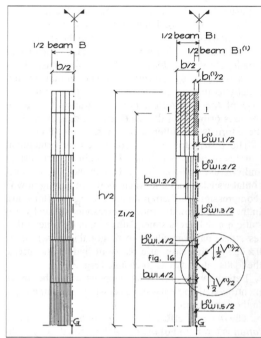

Figure 7. B_1 subdivision.

crossed by the whole load V to that of one or more portions of this beam; each portion is *detached* from the original body and it is crossed by the same load $V^{(1)}$ and only by this load. Following this method we can explore the structural behaviour with a detailing level that it's possible to expand at pleasure simply increasing number of elementary loads in which V is subdivided, and, consequently, reducing the dimension of the corresponding element in which the elementary load develops its path.

Interest towards the transformation of a complex organism analysis into that equivalent, very simple on single structural systems grows. In fact, single structural systems are made by members only subjected to normal stress, by – as we're going to see later on – orthogonal couples of diagonal 45° inclined members and by couples of longitudinal extreme booms (Fig. 13); this means that the analysis of a complex organism is transformed into the LP($V^{(1)}$) research.

Figures 5, 6, 7, 8, 9 show how to decompose load paths fluxes starting from a *physical* disintegration of the original structural body (B) into many, different in height, parts B_i (5 parts in the proposed example: B_1, B_2, B_3, B_4, B_5). Each of them has two longitudinal booms obtained by cutting B into horizontal *slices*, which are assumed, in the example, having the same height $h^{(1)}$.

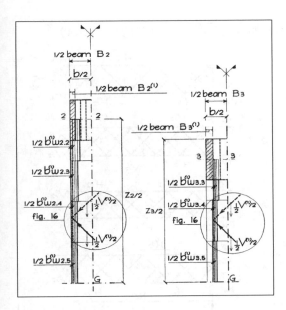

Figure 8. B_2 and B_3 subdivision.

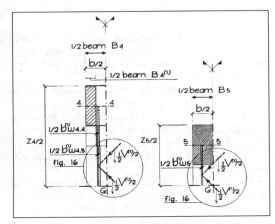

Figure 9. B_4 and B_5 subdivision.

In this way beam web is used to obtain many horizontal paths which are just useful to avoid the thrusts concentration only at the top and at the bottom of B.

On the other side, web is used to be crossed by vertical loads oblique paths as well as to canalise the above-mentioned thrusts. These vertical loads are included in as many 45° inclined strips.

Cuts in vertical layers, made to obtain the web of B_i from the B web, are represented in Figure 6.

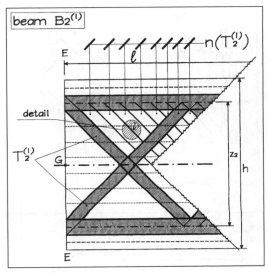

Figure 10. $B_2^{(1)}$ oblique slices.

In Figures 7, 8, 9 the B_i further subdivisions in many elementary parts $(B_i^{(1)})$ are represented. The number $[n(B_i^{(1)})]$ of these elementary parts is directly proportionate to the arm z_i. They have, at each level, the same web width $(b_{wj}^{(1)})$. This width has to change passing from one level to the other one, and, in particular, it has to decrease going down to B centre line, to leave place to the web of the least tall parts of the beam.

In the example showed in 7, 8, 9:

$n(B_1^{(1)}) = 5$; $n(B_2^{(1)}) = 4$; $n(B_3^{(1)}) = 3$; $n(B_4^{(1)}) = 2$;
$n(B_5^{(1)}) = 1$;
$b_{w1}^{(1)} > b_{w2}^{(1)} > b_{w3}^{(1)} > b_{w4}^{(1)} > b_{w5}^{(1)}$;
$b_{w1}^{(1)} = b_{w1\cdot1}^{(1)} = (1/5)\ b$;
$b_{w2}^{(1)} = b_{w1\cdot2}^{(1)} = b_{w2\cdot2}^{(1)} = (1/9)\ b$;
$b_{w3}^{(1)} = b_{w1\cdot3}^{(1)} = b_{w2\cdot3}^{(1)} = b_{w3\cdot3}^{(1)} = (1/12)\ b$;
$b_{w4}^{(1)} = b_{w1\cdot4}^{(1)} = b_{w2\cdot4}^{(1)} = b_{w3\cdot4}^{(1)} = b_{w4\cdot4}^{(1)} = (1/14)\ b$;
$b_{w5}^{(1)} = b_{w1\cdot5}^{(1)} = b_{w2\cdot5}^{(1)} = b_{w3\cdot5}^{(1)} = b_{w4\cdot5}^{(1)} = b_{w5\cdot5}^{(1)} = (1/15)\ b$.

To recognise structural elements carrying elementary loads $V^{(1)}$, all equal, it's necessary to make a further physical disintegration of the elementary beams $B_i^{(1)}$. In order to do this, we have to cut B into oblique (45° inclined) slices in the two directions. Having a look to Figures 10 and 11 (in which the case of $B_2^{(1)}$ is represented) it's immediately possible to understand that – if oblique slices are assumed so tall that they correspond to horizontal longitudinal booms ($h_w^{(1)} = \sqrt{2}\ h^{(1)}/2$) – we can obtain, by every elementary part of the beam, a number of trusses – having two booms and a web composed by diagonal member in pairs $(T_i^{(1)})$ – which is proportionate to z_i.

593

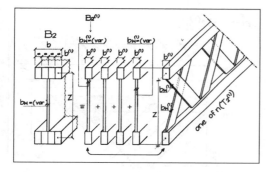

Figure 11. B_2 trusses.

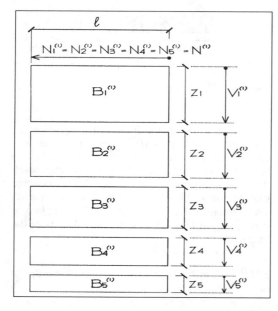

Figure 12.   Travelling load in every elementary part $B_i^{(1)}$.

In the example:

$n(T_1^{(1)}) = 10; \ n(T_2^{(1)}) = 8; \ n(T_3^{(1)}) = 6;$
$n(T_4^{(1)}) = 4; \ n(T_5^{(1)}) = 2.$

It's useful to underline that the $T^{(1)}$ of every elementary part of the beam can be considered all equal, because of the way in which they have been cut, on condition that:

(a) each of them should be given an equal part of the boom $((1/4)b_4^{(1)}$, in the example of Fig. 11: see also Fig. 8);
(b) B length (l) should be much bigger than the arm z.

This last condition is necessary to make negligible differences caused by the fact that between $T^{(1)}$ there is an offset of $h^{(1)}$ (Fig. 13).

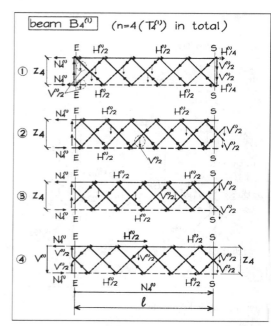

Figure 13.   Travelling load in $B_4^{(1)}$.

Elementary loads paths are inside the diagonal member of every $T^{(1)}$; these elementary loads paths are all the same and subdivided in equal parts between the two identical web paths $V^{(1)}/2$.

As a consequence, the whole travelling load in every elementary part of the beam ($V_i^{(1)}$) is proportionate to its arm z_i (Fig. 12) and the whole travelling load in every part of the beam (V_i) is proportionate to z_i^2 (see B_4 case in Fig. 13).

In the example (Fig. 14) it's possible to count 220 paths of $V^{(1)}/2$.

The detail of the i-node of Figure 15 is represented in Figure 16. We can observe that only the elementary loads of the $T^{(1)}$ constituting B_4 deviate: this deviation is necessary to make this elementary loads remain inside the above-mentioned beam and it produces horizontal thrusts that start off towards the extremity E, *moving back* along a path in tension.

Considering what mentioned in par. 3, we can transform the system of paths crossing the node into the equivalent biaxial flux of orthogonal paths, in tension and in compression. This flux is deviated from the 45° inclination and it's characterised by the fact that the descending load has an intensity different from the ascending one. These are the principal stress lines represented in Figure 17.

It's useful to understand that, in nodes above the longitudinal central line of the beam (in the proposed example), the deviation is a counterclockwise rotation

594

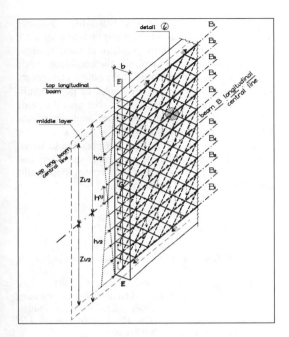

Figure 14. Travelling load in every part of the beam (axonometric view).

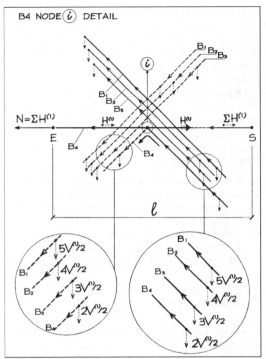

Figure 16. B₄ node "i" detail.

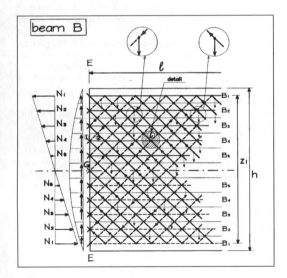

Figure 15. Travelling load in every part of the beam (lateral view).

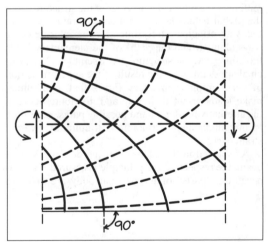

Figure 17. Principal stress lines.

of the two orthogonal axis, while the ascending load becomes bigger than the descending one. Both events are caused by needing of saving strain energy: the nearer load gets to the free longitudinal boundary, the more load tries to avoid it.

Horizontal thrusts fluxes going back to E contribute (also because of the *distributor*) to create the *deviator* which "flattens" paths in tension and, at the same time, makes more vertical the ones in compression in the approaching to the upper boundary (Fig. 4a).

Transfer of a part of the load from the descending path to the ascending one (which is better oriented toward the arriving station as a consequence of the suffered deviation) is a *load distributor* effect in that node (par. 3). At the same time, it guarantees, with horizontal thrusts, the deviator forming.

Opposite conditions occur in the node which is symmetrically under the longitudinal central line of the beam. Load tends to leave, more than ever, simple horizontal translation paths (par. 3) while they are getting nearer to the lower free boundary. For this purpose it uses two *devices*:

(a) it uses thrusts (that have sign opposite from the ones of the upper half part of the beam) to orient descending paths more than ever towards the E station (LP(45°) couple deviation);
(b) it uses load distributor to transfer part of the ascending load to the descending paths, which are more effective because of the experienced deviation.

5 CONCLUSIONS

Load path method is an instrument to analyse structural continuum. This method, such as finite elements methods, can give results of which precision depends only on the operator choice. On the other side, the used model seems to have the peculiar capacity to make understand – using its form geometrical outlines – the physical behaviour of the structure, from the global behaviour to the most accurate details. In this way principal stress lines can be interpreted as ways along which the paths of the elementary loads travelling into the structure are assembled. The principal stress lines are the result of the superimposition of very simple elementary fluxes that, combining, make loads orient their way and distribute between the alternative different and possible paths, according to the fundamental Principle of minimum invested strain energy.

As showed in the example of the de Saint Venant beam, the respect of this principle is assured if appropriate cut "parts" of the original body are given to equal elementary loads. In other words these parts are the ones chosen to make the corresponding simple LP reassembling in harmony without making loads – coming again in touch to rebuild the continuum body – changing the path that was of the single elementary systems, when they were separated. In these conditions the analysis of the last ones will give the same information of the most complex analysis of the whole structural organism.

In this way, in architecture, it's possible to transform the research of the correlation between form and structure into the research of the vertical loads paths and of the horizontal thrusts paths.

REFERENCES

CEB 1982. Detailing of concrete structures. *CEB Bulletin d'information n.150.*

De Tommasi, G., Monaco, P. & Vitone, C. 2003. A first approach to load path method on the masonry structures behaviour. In C. A. Brebbia (ed.), *Structural Studies, Repairs and Maintenance of Heritage Architecture VIII (in press).* Sothampton: Wit Press.

Marano, G.C., Palmisano, F. & Vitone, A. 2002. Utilizzo dello Strut and Tie model per la progettazione dei particolari costruttivi delle strutture in c.a.. In P. Spinelli (ed.), *Tecniche di progettazione strut and tie di elementi in cemento armato; Proc. Workshop, Firenze, 16 March 2001.* Firenze: Centro Stampa 2P.

Palmisano, F. 2001. L'organismo portante in c.a. ed i particolari esecutivi di un edificio residenziale. In M. Mezzina (ed.), *Costruire con il cemento armato.* Torino: Utet.

Palmisano, F., Vitone, A. & Vitone, C. 2002. Form & Structure. The Rome Auditorium: load path method (LPM). *D'Architettura* 18: 168–173.

Schlaich, J. & Schafer, K. 1996. Designing and detailing using Strut-and-tie Models. In K. Shafer (ed.) *Strut-and-Tie Models for the Design of Structural; Proc. Workshop, Tainan, 1996.* Tainan: National Cheng Kung University.

Schlaich, J., Schafer, K. & Jennewein, M. 1987. Toward a Consistent Design of Structural Concrete. *PCI Journal* 32 (3): 74–150.

Vitone, A. & Vitone, V. 2001. Il cantiere: progettare e costruire. Lo stadio San Nicola di Bari. In M. Mezzina (ed.), *Costruire con il cemento armato.* Torino: Utet.

System-based Vision for Strategic and Creative Design, Bontempi (ed.)
© *2003 Swets & Zeitlinger, Lisse, ISBN 90 5809 599 1*

Algebraic method for sensitivity analysis of eigensystems with repeated eigenvalues

K.M. Choi, S.W. Cho & I.W. Lee
Korea Advanced Institute of Science & Technology, Taejon, Korea

J.H. Lee
Kyungil University, Kyungsan, Korea

ABSTRACT: A simplified method for the computation of first-, second- and higher order derivatives of eigenvalues and eigenvectors associated with repeated eigenvalues is presented. Adjacent eigenvectors and orthonormal conditions are used to compose an algebraic equation. The algebraic equation developed can be used to compute derivatives of both eigenvalues and eigenvectors simultaneously. Since the coefficient matrix in the proposed algebraic equation is non-singular, symmetric and based on N-space, it is numerically stable and very efficient compared to previous methods. To verify the efficiency of the proposed method, the finite element model of the cantilever beam and a mechanical system in the case of a non-proportionally damped system are considered.

1   INTRODUCTION

Methods for computing eigenvalue and eigenvector derivatives have been studied by many researchers in the past 30 years. The importance of obtaining sensitivities for eigenvalue problems stems from the fact that partial derivatives with respect to system parameters are extremely important for effecting efficient design modifications for given situations, for gaining insight into the reasons for discrepancies between structural analyses and dynamic tests by varying its design parameters, and for indicating system model changes that will improve correlations between analyses and tests.

The sensitivity of eigenvalue problem with repeated eigenvalues has been a focus of recent interest. The most common circumstances under which repeated eigenvalues or nearly equal eigenvalues occur in typical structural or mechanical systems are instances where system symmetry exists, such as structures with two or more planes of reflective or cyclic symmetric or in the limiting case of axisymmetric bodies or certain reasons. In this case, since the eigenspace spanned by eigenvectors corresponding to repeated eigenvalues is degenerate, any linear combination of eigenvectors can be a eigenvector. For the eigenvector derivative to be found, the adjacent eigenvectors which lie "adjacent" to the m (multiplicity of repeated eigenvalue) distinct eigenvectors appearing when a design parameter varies

must be calculated first. To do so, the approximate eigenvectors could be varied continuously by varying the design parameter.

For the real symmetric case, a generalization of Nelson's method was obtained by Ojalvo and amended by Mills-Curren and Dailey. These methods are lengthy and complicated for finding eigenvector derivatives and clumsy for programming, because they basically follow Nelson's algorithm. Lee et al. (1999) developed an analytical method that give exact solutions while it maintains N-space, but it finds eigenvalue derivative from classical method as before.

In this paper, an efficient algebraic method for the eigenpair sensitivities of damped systems with repeated eigenvalues is presented. Contrary to previous methods, the proposed method finds the eigenvalue and eigenvector sensitivities simultaneously from one equation. The proposed method doesn't use a state space equation ($2N$-space), instead of it, the method maintains N-space because a singularity problem is solved by using only one side condition. The algebraic equation of the proposed method may be efficiently solved by the LDL^T decomposition method. If the derivatives of the stiffness, mass and damping matrices can be analytically found, the proposed method can find the exact eigenpair derivatives. And it only requires the corresponding eigenpair information differently from modal methods.

The second section of this paper presents the proposed sensitivity analysis method of damped systems with repeated eigenvalues. In the next section, the numerical stability of the proposed method is presented, and finally numerical examples.

2 EIGENPAIR SENSITIVITY IN DAMPED SYSTEMS

When an eigenvalue has multiplicity m and a design parameter is perturbed, the corresponding eigenvectors may split into as many as m distinct eigenvectors. For derivatives of the eigenvectors to be responsible, the eigenvectors must be laid adjacent to the m distinct eigenvectors that appear when a design parameter varies. Otherwise, the eigenvectors would jump discontinuously with a varying design parameter. Here the derivatives of these adjacent eigenvectors are sought.

The eigenvalue problem of a damped system can be expressed as

$$(\lambda^2 M + \lambda C + K)\phi = 0 \tag{1}$$

where M, C and K are the matrices of mass, damping and stiffness, respectively, and these are ($n \times n$) symmetric matrices. M is positive definite and K is positive definite or semi-positive definite. The first step in finding derivatives of eigenvectors of repeated eigenvalues is to find corresponding adjacent eigenvectors. Suppose that all eigenpairs are known and multiplicity of the eigenvalue λ_m is m. Define the following eigenvalue problem where Φ_m is the matrix of eigenvectors corresponding to the repeated eigenvalues, hence, its order ($n \times m$)

$$M\Phi_m \Lambda_m^2 + C\Phi_m \Lambda_m + K\Phi_m = 0 \tag{2}$$

where

$$\Lambda_m = \lambda_m I_m \text{ and } \Phi_m = [\phi_{i+1}\ \phi_{i+2}\ \cdots\ \phi_{i+m}] \tag{3}$$

I_m is the identity matrix of order m and λ_m is the eigenvalue of multiplicity m for the eigenspace spanned by the columns of Φ_m. The orthonormal condition for the ($i + 1$)th eigenvector is as follows:

$$\phi_{i+1}^T (2\lambda_{i+1}M + C)\phi_{i+1} = 1 \tag{4}$$

Since the multiplicity is m, the orthonormal condition for the matrix Φ_m is as follows:

$$\Phi_m^T (2\lambda_m M + C)\Phi_m = I_m \tag{5}$$

Adjacent eigenvectors can be expressed in terms of Φ_m by an orthogonal transformation such as

$$X = \Phi_m T \tag{6}$$

where T is an orthonormal transformation matrix and its order m;

$$T^T T = I_m \tag{7}$$

The columns of X are the adjacent eigenvectors for which a derivative can be defined. It is natural that the adjacent eigenvectors also satisfy the orthonormal condition:

$$X^T (2\lambda_m M + C)X = T^T \Phi_m^T (2\lambda_m M + C)\Phi_m T$$
$$= T^T T = I_m \tag{8}$$

The next procedure is to find T and then to find X and $\Lambda_{m,\alpha}$. If design parameter α varies, $\Lambda_{m,\alpha}$ is expressed as

$$\Lambda_{m,\alpha} = diag(\lambda_{i+1,\alpha}, \lambda_{i+2,\alpha}, \cdots, \lambda_{i+m,\alpha}) \tag{9}$$

where $(\circ)_{\alpha}$ represents the derivative of $(\circ)$ with respect design parameter α.

Consider another eigenvalue problem to find X and $\Lambda_{m,\alpha}$.

$$MX\Lambda_m^2 + CX\Lambda_m + KX = 0 \tag{10}$$

where the order of adjacent eigenvector matrix X is ($n \times m$) and the order of eigenvalue matrix Λ_m is ($m \times m$). Differentiating above eigenvalue problem with respect to the design parameter α, and rearranging yields

$$(\lambda_m^2 M + \lambda_m C + K)X_{,\alpha} + (2\lambda_m M + C)X\Lambda_{m,\alpha}$$
$$= -\left(\lambda_m^2 M_{,\alpha} + \lambda_m C_{,\alpha} + K_{,\alpha}\right)X \tag{11}$$

Pre-multiplying at each side of Equation 11 by Φ_m^T and substituting $X = \Phi_m T$ into it gives a new eigenvalue problem such as

$$DT = ET\Lambda_{m,\alpha} \tag{12}$$

where

$$D = \Phi_m^T (\lambda_m^2 M_{,\alpha} + \lambda_m C_{,\alpha} + K_{,\alpha})\Phi_m$$
$$E = -\Phi_m^T (2\lambda_m M + C)\Phi_m = -I_m \tag{13}$$

The orthogonal transformation matrix T can be obtained by solving Equation 12, and then the adjacent eigenvectors by relation $X = \Phi_m T$.

The proposed method starts with the equations of the derivative of the eigenvalue problem composed of the system matrices and the adjacent eigenvectors, Equation 11, and the orthonormal condition, Equation 8. Differentiating Equation 8 with respect to the design parameter gives

$$X^T(2\lambda_m M + C)X_{,\alpha} + X^T MX\Lambda_{m,\alpha}$$
$$= -0.5X^T(2\lambda_m M_{,\alpha} + C_{,\alpha})X \tag{14}$$

Since the unknown or interested values are $X_{,\alpha}$ and $\Lambda_{m,\alpha}$, Equation 11 and Equation 14 can be combined into a single matrix form as follows:

$$\begin{bmatrix} \lambda_m^2 M + \lambda_m C + K & (2\lambda_m M + C)X \\ X^T(2\lambda_m M + C) & X^T MX \end{bmatrix} \begin{Bmatrix} X_{,\alpha} \\ \Lambda_{m,\alpha} \end{Bmatrix}$$
$$= \begin{Bmatrix} -(\lambda_m^2 M_{,\alpha} + \lambda_m C_{,\alpha} + K_{,\alpha})X \\ -0.5X^T(2\lambda_m M_{,\alpha} + C_{,\alpha})X \end{Bmatrix} \tag{15}$$

where the order of coefficient matrix on the left side of Equation 15 is $(n + m) \times (n + m)$ and the matrix of the right side of equation is $(n + m) \times m$. The derivatives $X_{,\alpha}$ and $\Lambda_{m,\alpha}$ can be found by solving Equation 15.

Contrary to previous method, the sensitivities of the eigenvalue and eigenvector can be obtained simultaneously from one augmented equation. It maintains N-space without use of state space equation and finds the eigenpair derivatives simultaneously. The proposed method requires only corresponding eigenpair information differently from modal methods, and gives exact solution and guarantees numerical stability. Numerical stability is proved in the next section.

3 NUMERICAL STABILITY OF THE PROPOSED METHOD

Numerical stability is guaranteed by proving non-singularity of the coefficient matrix A^* in Equation 15. To prove that the coefficient matrix A^* is non-singular, introduce the determinant property such as

$$\det(Y^T A^* Y) = \det(Y^T)\det(A^*)\det(Y) \tag{16}$$

If $\det(Y^T A^* Y) \varkappa 0$ is proved with an arbitrary non-singular matrix Y, $\det(A^*) \varkappa 0$ is proved.

In this paper, the arbitrary non-singular matrix Y is assumed as

$$Y = \begin{bmatrix} \Psi & 0 \\ 0 & I_m \end{bmatrix} \tag{17}$$

where I_m is an identity matrix of order m and Ψ is a set of arbitrary independent vectors containing the adjacent eigenvectors of repeated eigenvalue λ_m of the systems, as follows

$$\Psi = [\phi_1 \ \phi_2 \ \cdots \ \phi_{n-m} \ x_1 \ x_2 \ \cdots \ x_m]$$
$$\text{when } X = [x_1 \ x_2 \ \cdots \ x_m] \tag{18}$$

where ϕ's are arbitrary independent vectors chosen to be independent to the adjacent eigenvector x's.

Since all the columns of the matrix Y are independent vectors, matrix Y is non-singular and it is invertible. Pre- and post-multiplying Y^T and Y to A^* yields

$$Y^T A^* Y$$
$$= \begin{bmatrix} \Psi & 0 \\ 0 & I_m \end{bmatrix}^T \begin{bmatrix} \lambda_m^2 M + \lambda_m C + K & (2\lambda_m M + C)X \\ X^T(2\lambda_m M + C) & X^T MX \end{bmatrix} \begin{bmatrix} \Psi & 0 \\ 0 & I_m \end{bmatrix}$$
$$= \begin{bmatrix} \Psi^T(\lambda_m^2 M + \lambda_m C + K)\Psi & \Psi^T(2\lambda_m M + C)X \\ X(2\lambda_m M + C)\Psi & X^T MX \end{bmatrix} \tag{19}$$

It is obvious that the last m columns and rows of the matrix $\Psi^T(\lambda_m^2 M + \lambda_m C + K)\Psi$ all have zero elements, which are provided by the eigenvalue problem $(\lambda_m^2 M + \lambda_m C + K)X = 0$, as follows

$$\Psi^T(\lambda_m^2 M + \lambda_m C + K)\Psi = \begin{bmatrix} \tilde{A} & 0 \\ 0 & 0 \end{bmatrix} \tag{20}$$

where $\tilde{A}$ is a non-zero $(n - m) \times (n - m)$ submatrix. The submatrix $\tilde{A}$ is a non-singular matrix having order of $(n - m)$ and rank of $(n - m)$, since it is given by eliminating the columns and rows having all zero elements from $\Psi^T(\lambda_m^2 M + \lambda_m C + K)\Psi$ of order n and rank $(n - m)$. That is, $\det(A) \varkappa 0$.

By the normalization condition,

$$\Psi^T(2\lambda_m M + C)X = \begin{bmatrix} \tilde{B} \\ I_m \end{bmatrix}$$
$$X^T(2\lambda_m M + C)\Psi = \begin{bmatrix} \tilde{B} \\ I_m \end{bmatrix}^T \tag{21}$$

where $\tilde{B}$ is generally a non-zero rectangular matrix. Substituting Equation 20 and 21, into Equation 19 yields

$$Y^T A^* Y = \begin{bmatrix} \tilde{A} & 0 & \tilde{B} \\ 0 & 0 & I_m \\ \tilde{B}^T & I_m & X^T MX \end{bmatrix} \tag{22}$$

To find the determinant of the matrix, apply the determinant property of partitioned matrices such as

$$\det\left(\begin{bmatrix} A & B \\ C & D \end{bmatrix} \right) = \det A \times \det(D - CA^{-1}B) \tag{23}$$

Hence the determinant of Equation 22 can be rewritten as

$$\det(Y^T A^* Y)$$
$$= \det(\tilde{A}) \times \det\left(\begin{bmatrix} 0 & I_m \\ I_m & X^T MX \end{bmatrix} - \begin{bmatrix} 0 \\ \tilde{B}^T \end{bmatrix} [\tilde{A}]^{-1} [0 \ \tilde{B}] \right)$$
$$= -\det(\tilde{A}) \neq 0 \tag{24}$$

The determinant of A^* thus is not equal to zero. In other words, the matrix A^* is non-singular. The proof is completed mathematically for the numerical stability of the proposed algorithm in the case of repeated eigenvalues.

4 NUMERICAL EXAMPLES

To verify the effectiveness of the proposed method, two examples are presented. The first example is the finite element model of a cantilever beam as the proportionally damped system. The second example is a 5-DOF mechanical system as the non-proportionally damped system.

4.1 Cantilever beam (proportionally damped system)

As an illustrative example in case of the proportionally damped system with repeated eigenvalues, the cantilever beam with square section is considered. It is FEM model composed of 20 elements and 21 nodes. Each node has four degrees of freedom (y-translation, z-translation, y-rotation and z-rotation). The structure has 80 degrees of freedom. Rayleigh damping($C = \alpha K + \beta M$) is considered. The design parameter is the beam width w.

Some results are shown in Table 1, 2, 3. The lowest 12 eigenvalues and their derivatives of the cantilever beam are listed in the second and third columns of Table 1. One can see that the derivatives of the repeated eigenvalues are different in that one is close to zero while the other is not. Since the design parameter is the width of the beam w, when w is varied, the repeated eigenvalues are split into distinct ones as the cross-section of the beam is no longer square after changing the width. To illustrate the sensitivity analysis results, the actual and approximate values of the changed system of $\Delta w/w = 0.01$ are represented in the second and third columns of Table 2. The second and third columns of Table 3 are the errors of the approximations. The errors are reasonably small and one can say that the proposed method gives good results for the case of repeated eigenvalues and for a proportionally damped system.

4.2 5-DOF non-proportionally damped system

As an illustrative example in case of the non-proportionally damped system with repeated eigenvalues, the 5-DOF mass, spring and damper system shown in Figure 2 is considered. The design parameter is the spring k_5. Assume that only vibrations in the vertical plane are possible.

Some results are shown in Table 4, 5, 6. The derivatives of the repeated eigenvalues are different since

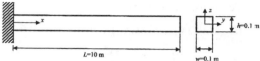

System data
Number of nodes: 21
Number of elements: 20
Number of DOF: 80

Material properties
Young's modulus: $E = 2.10 \times 10^{11}$
Mass density: $\rho = 7.85 \times 10^3 \, \text{kg/m}^3$
$\alpha = \beta = 0.0001$
Design parameter: width of beam

Figure 1. Cantilever beam with width w as the design parameter.

Table 1. The lowest 12 eigenvalues of the initial cantilever beam and results of the sensitivity analysis.

Mode number	Eigenvalues	Eigenvalue first derivatives
1, 2	$-1.4279\text{e-}03$ $\pm 5.2496\text{e}+00\text{i}$	$-2.8057\text{e-}10$ $\mp 3.5347\text{e-}10\text{i}$
3, 4	$-1.4279\text{e-}03$ $\pm 5.2496\text{e}+00\text{i}$	$-2.2756\text{e-}02$ $\pm 5.2494\text{e}+01\text{i}$
5, 6	$-5.4154\text{e-}02$ $\pm 3.2895\text{e}+01\text{i}$	$-6.6265\text{e-}10$ $\pm 2.3445\text{e-}10\text{i}$
7, 8	$-5.4154\text{e-}02$ $\pm 3.2895\text{e}+01\text{i}$	$-1.0818\text{e}+00$ $\pm 3.2886\text{e}+02\text{i}$
9, 10	$-4.2409\text{e-}01$ $\pm 9.2090\text{e}+01\text{i}$	$6.9247\text{e-}10$ $\mp 6.9600\text{e-}10\text{i}$
11, 12	$-4.2409\text{e-}01$ $\pm 9.2090\text{e}+01\text{i}$	$-8.4753\text{e}+00$ $\pm 9.2029\text{e}+02\text{i}$

Table 2. The lowest 12 eigenvalues and approximated eigenvalues of the changed cantilever beam.

Mode number	Eigenvalues	Approximated eigenvalues
1, 2	$-1.4279\text{e-}03$ $\pm 5.2496\text{e}+00\text{i}$	$-1.4279\text{e-}03$ $\pm 5.2496\text{e}+00\text{i}$
3, 4	$-1.4556\text{e-}03$ $\pm 5.3021\text{e}+00\text{i}$	$-1.4555\text{e-}03$ $\pm 5.3021\text{e}+00\text{i}$
5, 6	$-5.4154\text{e-}02$ $\pm 3.2895\text{e}+01\text{i}$	$-5.4154\text{e-}02$ $\pm 3.2895\text{e}+01\text{i}$
7, 8	$-5.5241\text{e-}02$ $\pm 3.3224\text{e}+01\text{i}$	$-5.5236\text{e-}02$ $\pm 3.3224\text{e}+01\text{i}$
9, 10	$-4.2409\text{e-}01$ $\pm 9.2090\text{e}+01\text{i}$	$-4.2409\text{e-}01$ $\pm 9.2090\text{e}+01\text{i}$
11, 12	$-4.3261\text{e-}01$ $\pm 9.3010\text{e}+01\text{i}$	$-4.3256\text{e-}01$ $\pm 9.3010\text{e}+01\text{i}$

the design parameter is the spring k_5; when k_5 is varied, the repeated eigenvalues are split into distinct ones since the structural symmetry is broken. The actual and approximate values of the changed system

Table 3. Errors of approximations.

Mode number	Eigenvalue	Eigenvector
1, 2	2.2283e-11	3.7376e-05
3, 4	2.6622e-08	1.0000e-04
5, 6	3.6899e-12	3.7376e-05
7, 8	1.6763e-07	1.0001e-04
9, 10	9.1432e-12	3.7376e-05
11, 12	4.6508e-07	1.0002e-04

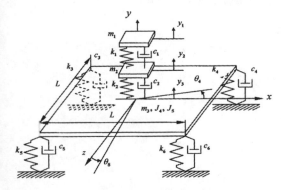

Figure 2. 5-DOF non-proportionally damped systems.
$m_1 = 200 \, kg$, $m_2 = 500 \, kg$, $m_3 = 1000 \, kg$, $k_1 = 10000 \, N/m$,
$k_2 = 20000 \, N/m$, $k_3 = k_4 = k_5 = k_6 = 1000 \, N/m$, $c_1 = 4 \, Ns/m$, $c_2 = 6 \, Ns/m$, $c_3 = c_4 = c_5 = c_6 = 40 \, Ns/m$.

Table 4. Eigenvalues of the initial 5-DOF system and results of the sensitivity analysis.

Mode number	Eigenvalues	Eigenvalue first derivatives
1, 2	−4.3262e-02	9.6943e-07
	±1.5023e + 00i	±1.7995e-04i
3, 4	−2.4000e-01	0.0000e + 00
	±3.4558e + 00i	±0.0000e + 00i
5, 6	−2.4000e-01	0.0000e + 00
	±3.4558e + 00i	±8.6811e-04i
7, 8	−3.5202e-02	−7.8926e-07
	±6.1354e + 00i	±2.9526e-05i
9, 10	−2.4535e-02	−1.8017e-07
	±9.7000e + 00i	±5.0001e-06i

of $\Delta k_5/k_5 = 0.01$ are represented in the second and third columns of Table 5. The second and third columns of Table 6 are the errors of the approximations. The errors are reasonably small and one can also say that the proposed method gives good results for the case of repeated eigenvalues and for a non-proportionally damped system.

Table 5. Eigenvalues and approximated eigenvalues of the changed 5-DOF system.

Mode number	Eigenvalues	Approximated eigenvalues
1, 2	−4.3243e-02	−4.3253e-02
	±1.5040e + 00i	±1.5041e + 00i
3, 4	−2.4000e-01	−2.4000e-01
	±3.4558e + 00i	±3.4558e + 00i
5, 6	−2.4000e-01	−2.4000e-01
	±3.4645e + 00i	±3.4645e + 00i
7, 8	−3.5210e-02	−3.5210e-02
	±6.1357e + 00i	±6.1357e + 00i
9, 10	−2.4537e-02	−2.4537e-02
	±9.7000e + 00i	±9.7000e + 00i

Table 6. Errors of approximations.

Mode number	Eigenvalue	Eigenvector
1, 2	8.1631e-07	2.9463e-05
3, 4	0.0000e-00	0.0000e-00
5, 6	2.1632e-06	5.2014e-06
7, 8	1.1763E-07	2.5394e-06
9, 10	4.3893e-09	1.6332e-07

The proposed method is verified through examples. The proposed method can be applied very well to the proportionally and non-proportionally damped systems and to the eigenvalue problem with repeated eigenvalues.

5 CONCLUSIONS

This paper proposes a simple algorithm for the calculation of eigenpair derivatives of the damped system with repeated eigenvalues. The proposed method finds exact eigenpair derivatives of the system by solving the linear algebraic equation without any numerical instability. In addition, derivatives of eigenvalues and eigenvectors can be obtained simultaneously from one augmented equation. This approach avoids the use of state space equation and considers the damping problem explicitly by introducing a side condition of differentiation of normalization condition. Thus computation for the equation with N-order can be maintained and the computer storage and analysis time required of the proposed method are smaller than those of previous methods. The proposed method can be inserted easily into a commercial FEM code since it finds the exact solution and treats a symmetric matrix.

REFERENCES

Ojalvo, I.U. 1988. Efficient computation of modal sensitivities for systems with repeated frequencies. *AIAA Journal* 26(3): 361–366.

Mills-Curran, W.C. 1988. Calculation of derivatives for structures with repeated eigenvalues. *AIAA Journal* 26(7): 867–871.

Dailey, R.L. 1989. Eigenvector derivatives with repeated eigenvalues. *AIAA Journal* 27(4): 486–491.

Lee, I.W. & Jung, G.H. 1997. An efficient algebraic method for computation of natural frequency and mode shape sensitivities: part I, distinct natural frequencies. *Computers and Structures* 62(3): 429–435.

Lee, I.W. & Jung, G.H. 1997. An efficient algebraic method for computation of natural frequency and mode shape sensitivities: part II, multiple natural frequencies. *Computers and Structures* 62(3): 437–443.

Lee, I.W. & Kim, D.O. 1999. Natural frequency and mode shape sensitivities of damped systems: part I, distinct natural frequencies. *Journal of Sound and Vibration* 223(3): 399–412.

Lee, I.W. & Kim, D.O. 1999. Natural frequency and mode shape sensitivities of damped systems: part II, multiple natural frequencies. *Journal of Sound and Vibration* 223(3): 413–424.

Jankovic, M.S. 1994. Exact *n*th derivatives of eigenvalues and eigenvectors. *Journal of Guidance, Control, and Dynamics* 17(1): 136–144.

System-based Vision for Strategic and Creative Design, Bontempi (ed.)
© *2003 Swets & Zeitlinger, Lisse, ISBN 90 5809 599 1*

Expression of rotational motion on flexible body

K. Miura & T. Nishimura
Department of Mechanical Engineering College of Science and Technology, Nihon University, Japan

T. Yamada
Honda R&D Co., Ltd. Tochigi R&D Center

ABSTRACT: It is available to grasp the angular displacement of a human body for instruction on a sport performance. Provided the instantaneous angular velocity is known, the angular displacement may be obtained by the integration of it. However, although the angular velocity and the rotational axis of a rigid body can be easily derived, how should the angular velocity of a flexible body be defined? The main purpose of this paper is to define the angular velocity and the rotational axis of a whole flexible body system. A family of compact generalized formulations of rotational motion for a flexible body or multibody is derived by adopting an instantaneous rotational axis of the whole body. Here, the current angular momentum of the whole flexible system is equated with the sum of the individual angular momentum on each element over the system. As an example, simulation of a motion analysis of human body on a sport, especially throwing motion analysis of a shot put, is carried out in order to verify the derived equations in the paper.

1 INTRODUCTION

Many mechanical systems such as robots, vehicles, aircraft, space structures and machine mechanisms which consist of interconnected components, so called a multibody system, are able to perform variable and large transformational and rotational displacements. The motion of subsystem (component) also is kinematically restricted because of different types of connecting joints. As a matter of the fact, the motion analysis of multibody system is very tremendously complex. Then, development of the method for analyzing a multibody system, which consists of rigid and deformable components interconnected each other, is required for an application of dynamics, structure dynamics, control theory, etc. Several formulations of dynamics are available for constructing motion equations for interconnected systems of multiple bodies. The dynamic equations that govern the motion of multiple body systems are highly nonlinear in most case, then one have to resolve the problem by the numerical calculation of the derived dynamic equations. In the actual methods for the dynamic analysis of multibody system, the expression of angle variables are required in order to define the orientation of the multiple body. Some of the most commonly used parameters for expressing the angle variables are Euler angles, Euler parameters, navigation angles and the direction cosines. On the actual analyzing procedure, the equations of motion are usually

resolved recursively so as to satisfy the actual restriction. For example, in a link structure, the velocity and acceleration of individual link are recursively transmitted from the base link to the top, and the joint torques can thus be obtained recursively from the top to base. After iterating those calculations, the motion of the whole link system tends to be cleared. These procedures on a dynamic analysis of multibody system are mainly developed for robotics, control of manipulator arms, and control of space structures; however these approaches are not suitable for grasping a broad view of motion for a flexible body, because the rotation of the whole system is difficult to define especially.

The authors have intended to establish an expression of motion of flexible body system which consists of interconnected rigid and deformable components. In a recent analyses of multiple body system, it is occasionally treated the problem on which the body element deforms elastically during the motion. However, on a certain kind of a flexible system, a plastic deformation or plastic hinge is induced by the inertia force or inertia moment of itself, and consequently, the initial configuration of the system can not be held during the motion. In such a problem, the position of the joint, that is the plastic hinge, cannot be specified preliminarily. This problem differs from the motion of ordinal multibody system.

It is occasionally required to grasp the outline motion of a human body on a sport in order to modify the performing posture. In this case, it is necessary to observe the motion in perspective. However it is hard to define the angular rotational motion of the whole body, while the translational motion is easily resolved, by observing the motion of a largely deforming body. The analysis of such a system is a very interesting problem, and when a flexible body system is moving and largely deforming, the problem is how to express the rotational motion of the whole system. Therefore the instantaneous rotation axis of the whole system should be derived, and then, the rotation of the whole system is resolved by the integration of the instantaneous rotation.

In this paper, in order to investigate a motion analysis of a flexible body system, a family of compact formulation of rotation for a multibody system which consists of rigid components is introduced. After all, the suggested formulation will be extended in future for a motion analysis of a flexible body system, which consists of variable type elements which have no joints like a cable or a membrane.

Furthermore, the expression of rotation on multibody system, suggested here, may be available for a motion analysis of a human body on a sport, and analysis of translation motion of an automobile, which is brought by a crash accident.

2 APPROACH

2.1 *Rigid rotation of a mass system*

A flexible body system, which consists of concentrated masses mutually interconnected by mass less link element, is discussed in this section.

The position vector of the i-th mass with respect to the centroid of the whole system is denoted by $\mathbf{r}_i$, and m_i is the mass of the i-th mass. The following equation is easily derived.

$$\sum_{i=1}^{n} m_i \mathbf{r}_i = 0 \qquad (1)$$

The velocity of the i-th mass is denoted by $d\mathbf{r}_i/dt$, and then, the angular momentum about the centroid is given by $\mathbf{r}_i \times (d\mathbf{r}_i/dt) m_i$. Therefore the total angular momentum about the centroid of the whole system is obtained by the sum of each angular momentum and shown by the following equation.

$$\mathbf{H}_G = \sum_{i=1}^{n} \mathbf{r}_i \times m_i \dot{\mathbf{r}}_i = \sum_{i=1}^{n} m_i \begin{Bmatrix} y_i \dot{z}_i - z_i \dot{y}_i \\ z_i \dot{x}_i - x_i \dot{z}_i \\ x_i \dot{y}_i - y_i \dot{x}_i \end{Bmatrix}_i$$

$$= \sum_{i=1}^{n} m_i \begin{bmatrix} 0 & -z_i & y_i \\ z_i & 0 & -x_i \\ -y_i & x_i & 0 \end{bmatrix} \begin{Bmatrix} \dot{x}_i \\ \dot{y}_i \\ \dot{z}_i \end{Bmatrix} \qquad (2)$$

where $\mathbf{H}_G$ is the angular momentum of the system. The above equation can be rewritten briefly as,

$$\mathbf{H}_G = \sum_{i=1}^{n} \mathbf{r}_i \times m_i \dot{\mathbf{r}}_i = \sum_{i=1}^{n} m_i \tilde{\mathbf{r}}_i \dot{\mathbf{r}}_i \qquad (3)$$

On the other hand, supposing that the whole system currently rotates with the angular velocity $d\Theta/dt$ (that is, equivalent angular velocity of system) around the centroid, and with using the relation of $d\mathbf{r}_i/dt = (d\Theta/dt) \times \mathbf{r}_i$, the angular momentum of the whole system is given by

$$\mathbf{H}_G = \sum_{i=1}^{n} \mathbf{r}_i \times m_i (\dot{\Theta} \times \mathbf{r}_i)$$

$$= \sum_{i=1}^{n} m_i \{ (\mathbf{r}_i \cdot \mathbf{r}_i) \dot{\Theta} - (\mathbf{r}_i \cdot \dot{\Theta}) \mathbf{r}_i \}$$

$$= \left\{ \sum_{i=1}^{n} m_i \begin{bmatrix} y_i^2 + z_i^2 & -x_i y_i & -z_i x_i \\ -x_i y_i & z_i^2 + x_i^2 & -y_i z_i \\ -z_i x_i & -y_i z_i & x_i^2 + y_i^2 \end{bmatrix} \right\} \dot{\Theta} \qquad (4)$$

The current inertia moment I_G of the whole mass system rotating about the centroid is given by

$$I_G = \sum_{i=1}^{n} m_i \begin{bmatrix} y_i^2 + z_i^2 & -x_i y_i & -z_i x_i \\ -x_i y_i & z_i^2 + x_i^2 & -y_i z_i \\ -z_i x_i & -y_i z_i & x_i^2 + y_i^2 \end{bmatrix} \qquad (5)$$

Consequently, the angular velocity of the system can be resolved by the following equation

$$\dot{\Theta}_G = I_G^{-1} \sum_{i=1}^{n} m_i \begin{bmatrix} 0 & -z_i & y_i \\ z_i & 0 & -x_i \\ -y_i & x_i & 0 \end{bmatrix} \begin{Bmatrix} \dot{x}_i \\ \dot{y}_i \\ \dot{z}_i \end{Bmatrix} \qquad (6)$$

2.2 *Rigid rotation of a flexible body system*

In this section, the angular motion of flexible body system including rigid bodies is studied.

Let introduce the local coordinate system Σ, which is embedded in the rigid body so as to coincide with the principal axes of the inertia tensor. It should be noted that Σ varies with the motion. Then, the inertia tensor with respect to the centroid of the i-th rigid body is expressed in the fixed coordinate system as follows,

$$I_{iG} = \Sigma_i \begin{bmatrix} I_X & 0 & 0 \\ 0 & I_Y & 0 \\ 0 & 0 & I_Z \end{bmatrix} \Sigma_i^{T} \qquad (7)$$

If the position of the centroid of the i-th rigid body is known as $(x, y, z)_i$, using the well-known procedure,

604

the inertia tensor around the centroid of the system is expressed by

$$I_i = I_{iG} + \begin{bmatrix} y_i^2 + z_i^2 & -x_i y_i & -z_i x_i \\ -x_i y_i & z_i^2 + x_i^2 & -y_i z_i \\ -z_i x_i & -y_i z_i & x_i^2 + y_i^2 \end{bmatrix} m_i \qquad (8)$$

Where m_i is the mass of the i-th rigid body. The inertia tensor of the whole system about the centroid can be obtained by the sum of each inertia tensor.

$$I_G = \sum_{i=1}^{n} \left\{ I_{iG} + \begin{bmatrix} y_i^2 + z_i^2 & -x_i y_i & -z_i x_i \\ -x_i y_i & z_i^2 + x_i^2 & -y_i z_i \\ -z_i x_i & -y_i z_i & x_i^2 + y_i^2 \end{bmatrix} m_i \right\} \qquad (9)$$

Supposing that the j-th rigid body rotates with respect to the centroid of the body element with the angular velocity vector $d\theta/dt$ which is measured on the local element coordinate, the angular momentum on the local coordinate is given by

$$\mathbf{H}_i^* = \begin{bmatrix} I_X & 0 & 0 \\ 0 & I_Y & 0 \\ 0 & 0 & I_Z \end{bmatrix} \dot{\theta} \qquad (10)$$

Then, the angular momentum, $\mathbf{H}_j$ is shown on the fixed coordinate as follows,

$$\mathbf{H}_i = \Sigma_i \mathbf{H}_i^* = \Sigma_i \begin{bmatrix} I_X & 0 & 0 \\ 0 & I_Y & 0 \\ 0 & 0 & I_Z \end{bmatrix} \Sigma_i^T \Sigma_i \, \dot{\theta} \qquad (11)$$

Moreover, as the j-th rigid body element has a relative translational motion to the centroid of the whole system, the angular momentum caused by the relative motion to the centroid of the element must be added to Equation 11.

$$\mathbf{H}_{iG} = m_j \begin{bmatrix} 0 & -z_i & y_i \\ z_i & 0 & -x_i \\ -y_i & x_i & 0 \end{bmatrix} \begin{Bmatrix} \dot{x}_i \\ \dot{y}_i \\ \dot{z}_i \end{Bmatrix} + \mathbf{H}_i \qquad (12)$$

The sum of each angular momentum gives the total angular momentum of the whole system, as follows

$$\mathbf{H}_G = \sum_{i=1}^{n} \mathbf{H}_{iG} \qquad (13)$$

The angular momentum introduced by the above equation, can be equated with the total angular momentum of the system, which supposedly rotates

with the equivalent angular velocity, under the current configuration. Hence the following equation is derived.

$$\mathbf{H}_G = I_G \dot{\mathbf{\Theta}}_G \qquad (14)$$

Where, I_G is the inertia tensor of the whole flexible body.

Finally, the equivalent angular velocity can be obtained by the following equation.

$$\dot{\mathbf{\Theta}}_G = I_G^{-1} \mathbf{H}_G \qquad (15)$$

By differentiating Equation 14, one can obtain the moment required for the rotational motion $\mathbf{M}_G$ of the whole system.

$$\begin{aligned} \mathbf{M}_G &= \dot{\mathbf{H}}_G \\ &= I_G \ddot{\mathbf{\Theta}}_G + \dot{I}_G \dot{\mathbf{\Theta}}_G \end{aligned} \qquad (16)$$

From Equation 16, the well-known Euler's equation can be introduced, as follows.

$$\mathbf{M}_G = I_G \ddot{\mathbf{\Theta}}_G + \dot{\mathbf{\Theta}}_G \times \left(I_G \dot{\mathbf{\Theta}}_G \right) \qquad (17)$$

The certain unknown external force or moment, which induces the observed motion, can be estimated by Equation 17.

2.3 Flexible body system contains deformable elements

In this section, the angular motion of flexible body system which contains deformable body elements is discussed.

Using expression of rotation as mentioned in previous paragraph, the angular motion of flexible body system can be revealed, if position of each body element is measured. However, the centroid of deformable body moves whenever the element deformation occurs. Since, it is very difficult to measure the centroid of deformable body element. If the mass distribution is variable, measurement of the centroid is exceedingly complicated furthermore.

As an example, a deformable body element, which is very long in comparison to its width and have a uniform circular section, such as a flexible rod, flexible beam, or cable element, are investigated. Here, the bending and torsional deformation within the element is considered. It is assumed that a plane section normal to its longitudinal axis remains plane after deformation, and axial tension is disregarded. In this case, the problem what to measure the position of centroid of body element arises as mentioned before.

To measure the deformation of thin rod element, the marking circumference lines are graduated in

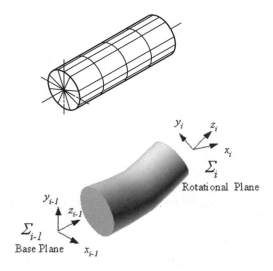

Figure 1. Marking of a deformable rod element.

equal increment on the body along longitudinal direction (see Fig. 1). In order to express the bending with sole curvature, the length of the component is properly taken as L, which depends on its diameter and stiffness. Moreover, the marking longitudinal lines are graduated equally round the circumference. Then, intersections of circumference and longitudinal lines are the target points to measure. If the positions of three points on the circumference of the rod element are measured, the position of center point and normal direction on the measuring cross section is obtained from a geometrical consideration. For the purpose of getting the three-dimensional position data, it is necessary to observe the rod element from two directions. Considering a dead angle, in order to obtain the three position data on the measurering cross section, eight or more points are required along the circumference line. One end plane of component is the base plane, and another plane is rotational plane. Searching the relation of transformation between the body-coordinates on the base plane and the rotational plane, the deformation is defined. By measuring the position and the direction on both end planes of the component, the curvature of deformed rod component is determined geometrically. And, the profile of the deformed rod component is approximated by an arc with the obtained curvature. As a necessary consequence, the position of the centroid and the inertia tensor of the rod component are able to determine by the arc profile. Finally, the position of the centroid and the inertia tensor of whole rod element are obtained. From the measurement of deformation and the measurement of motion, the angular motion of flexible body system containing deformable elements becomes clear, using the method of the foregoing paragraph.

For General deformable elements which have a few constraints on the deformation, it is difficult to determine the deformed profile; its analysis requires a special technique.

3 SIMULATION

The formulae mentioned in the previous section can be applied for various motion analyses, for example, a motion analysis of a human body on a sport. The human body is supposed to be a multibody system. The mechanical multibody system is required to behave exactly according to the order of an operator or director. Therefore the mechanical system can be designed so as to satisfy user's aims under the knowledge of motion analysis. However, since a human body cannot be designed by a mankind, the main purpose of motion analysis is to clear what is the ideal motion or what motion is safe free from sport injuries with an aid of the actual observation. Hence, on analyzing a human body motion, the experimental data obtained by an observation of the actual motion are usually used. Owing to the above mentioned matter, the conventional analytical method is not suitable for analyzing a human body motion. The trainer is eager to grasp the outline motion of the player, because it is more important to inform the player about the translational and rotational motion of the centroid of him in order to instruct his performance.

3.1 Summary of experiment

Throwing motion on a shot put is investigated here. The throwing motion of a subject, shot-putter, is recorded by two high-speed video cameras which are positioned as in Figure 2. The weight and dimension of subjects are shown in Table 1. The shot-putter's body is replaced by the link elements system, which is composed with 15 elements as shown in Figure 3.

However, since it is hard to know the mass distribution and the centroid and inertia moment of each body element, those element properties are estimated by citing (Hai-Peng 1984). The video image [250 pictures per second] data are converted into the position data of element joint on each image.

The two-dimensional position data on each picture are transformed into the three-dimensional position data by DLT method. The smoothing operation for the scattering position data is carried out by the properly truncated Fourier series.

3.2 Analysis of shot put motion

The recent shot put motion is classified into two styles, one is a glide shot and another is a rotation shot. The former is the usual one, and the latter is

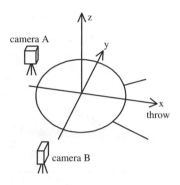

Figure 2.   Global coordinate and location of cameras.

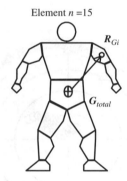

Figure 3.   Human Body.

Table 1.   Weight and dimension of subjects.

	Weight [Kg]	Height [m]	Ball [Kg]
Subject A (Glide)	103	1.81	7.26
Subject B (Rotation)	99	1.83	6.50

characterized by that the shot put motion completes through one and half revolution of the player's body around the z-axis. In this study, these two typical shot put motions are examined experimentally concerning to the rotation of the body.

The centroid of whole body is obtained by position data by usual procedure. If the axes of local coordinate embedded in the body element coincide with the principal axes of inertia moment, the angular momentum of the element about the centroid of element is given by Equation 13. Hence, the angular momentum of element about the centroid of the whole body is given by Equation 12. Then, the sum of the angular momentum of each element composing the body about the centroid gives the total angular momentum about the centroid of the body as Equation 13.

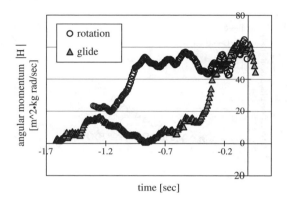

Figure 4.   Angular momentum.

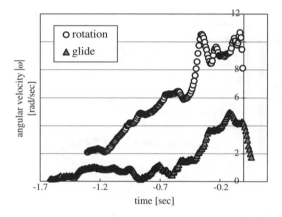

Figure 5.   Magnitude of angular velocity.

The total angular momentum of the whole system is shown in the Figure 4, where the difference between the glide shot and rotation shot is apparent. In the figure the time on the abscissa is described so that the instant of releasing a ball becomes the origin.

The total inertia tensor of the whole system about the centroid, Equation 9, can be obtained by the sum of each inertia tensor, Equation 8, and the angular velocity of whole system, that is equivalent angular velocity about the centroid can be obtained by pre-multiplying the inverse of the current total inertia tensor to the total angular momentum (referring Equation 14).

Figure 5 shows the magnitude of angular velocity of the whole system, and two kinds of shot put motion are compared in the figure. The different character of throwing motion is also comprehensible from the figure.

By integrating the angular velocity, the components of angular displacement are obtained as shown

607

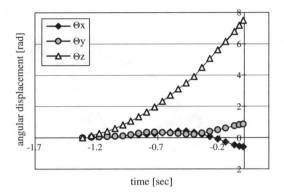

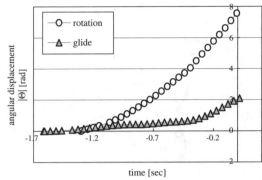

Figure 6.   Angular displacement of rotation shot.

Figure 8.   Magnitude of angular displacement.

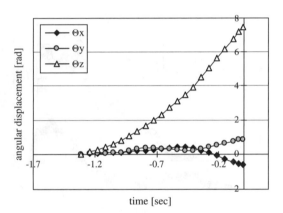

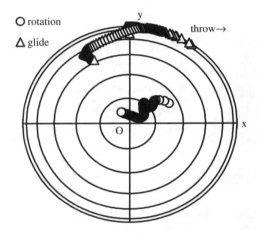

Figure 7.   Angular displacement of glide shot.

Figure 9.   Instantaneous rotational axis.

in Figure 6 and 7. Generally, shot putter's body makes a half revolution during the throwing motion on the glide shot, while on rotation shot put, it is usually mentioned that the player shot a ball under the rotation of one and a half revolution around the z-axis. This fact is almost confirmed from Figure 6. But the final angular displacement around the z-axis indicates about 7.5 radians in the figure. The actual turn of the studied subject seems to be slightly small. Although the rotational motion on the glide shot put is a bit, large angular displacement around z-axis is observed on the rotation shot put.

The magnitude of angular displacement on the glide shot put and rotation shot put are compared in Figure 8. The variation of angular displacement can be easily grasped from the figure.

Figure 9 shows the change of the unit vector whose direction indicates the instantaneous rotational axis of the whole body during throwing process. In the figure, the unit vector is projected to the x–y plane. It can be

seen that the rotational motion around z-axis is predominant on the rotation shot put, while the rotation around y-axis is mainly recognized on the glide shot put. The trajectory of rotational axis explains well the difference of the typical two motions in Figure 9.

4   DISCUSSION

If the position of joints, the degrees of freedom, the force and the moment, which is produced by an actuator, are preliminarily known, the conventional method can be applied for motion analysis. The conventional method, that is Euler angle or navigation angle, is available to express the posture of the system. However, the flexible body discussed here is caused to drive by actuators, ability of which is uncertain or unexpected. Moreover, a flexible cable or membrane structure and a flexible body, which is

608

brought plastic deformation by its own motion, have not a definite joint. The conventional method is not available for the motion analysis of such a system.

For example, provided that the instantaneous momentum and angular momentum of the flexible system are known by the actual observation, the reaction force and moment can be derived directly. An expression of the rotation of flexible body that is derived here would be extended to for a motion analysis of more flexible elements, such as cable systems, membrane structures.

For the motion analysis of the flexible body system contains deformable elements which are long in comparison to its width and have a uniform circular section, flexible rod, flexible beam, and cable element, the useful idea of observational method is introduced.

By applying the suggested formulations, the motion analysis of a shot put is carried out. The derived equations may be developed for the motion analysis of the flexible body such as a cable element, a membrane structure, and a flexible structure inducing plastic deformation caused by its motion in future.

5 CONCLUSIONS

A family of compact generalized formulations of rotational motion for a flexible body or multibody is derived by adopting an instantaneous rotational axis of the whole body. Here, the current angular momentum of the whole flexible system is equated with the sum of the individual angular momentum on each element over the system in order to resolve the instantaneous angular velocity vector.

REFERENCES

Hai-Peng, T. et al. 1994. Estimation of inertia properties of the body segments in Chinese athletes: Difference of the Chinese athletes and Japanese athletes, Japan *J. Phys. Educ.*, 38: pp. 487–499.

Hai-Peng, T. 1995. A Method To Determine The Angular Momentum of a Human Body, Japan, *J. Phys. Educ., 40:* pp. 161–169.

Ahmed, A.S. 1989. Dynamics of Multibody Systems, *Wiley-Interscience.*

System-based Vision for Strategic and Creative Design, Bontempi (ed.)
© *2003 Swets & Zeitlinger, Lisse, ISBN 90 5809 599 1*

Modified modal methods for calculating eigenpair sensitivity of asymmetric systems

Y.J. Moon & I.W. Lee
Korea Advanced Institute of Science & Technology, Daejon, Korea

J.H. Lee
Kyungil University, KyungsanSi, Kyungpook, Korea

ABSTRACT: It is well known that many real systems have asymmetric mass, damping and stiffness matrices. In this case, the method for calculating eigenpair sensitivity is different from that of symmetric system. To determine the derivatives of the eigenpairs in asymmetric damped case, a modal method was recently developed by Adhikari. When a dynamic system has many degrees of freedom, only a few lower modes are available, and because the higher modes should be truncated to use the modal method, the errors may become significant. In this paper a procedure for determining the sensitivities of the eigenpairs of asymmetric damped system using a few lowest set of modes is proposed. Numerical examples show that proposed method achieves better calculating efficiency and highly accurate results when a few modes are used.

1 INTRODUCTION

Natural frequency and mode shape of system are essential to understand dynamic behavior of structure. But design parameters can be varied with damage, deterioration, corrosion etc. and this causes variation in natural frequency and mode shape. The variation of eigenpair brings about variation of dynamic behavior of systems and this affects the stability of structure directly. Therefore eigen-sensitivity analysis has played a central part in structural stability analysis and has emerged as an important area of research. And eigenpair sensitivity is used in many areas, the optimization of structure subject to natural frequency, system identification, finite modelling updating, structural control etc.

For symmetric systems, modal methods (Murthy & Haftka 1988, Lim & Junkins 1987) and its modified ones (Wang 1985, Liu et al. 1987) approximate the eigenvector derivatives by a linear combination of the eigenvector. The modal methods employ a modal superposition idea. Therefore, the accuracy is dependent on the number of modes used in calculation. To guarantee the accuracy, the classical modal method needs higher eigenvector. Recently, Zeng presented modified modal methods such as multiple modal acceleration and shifted-poles method for the complex eigenvectors in symmetric viscous damping systems, which achieved highly accurate results when only a few modes are used.

However, in many problems in dynamics the inertia, stiffness and damping properties of the system cannot be represented by symmetric matrices. These kind of problems typically arise in the dynamics of actively controlled structures and in many general non-conservative dynamic systems, for example – moving vehicles on roads, missile following trajectories, ship motion in sea water or the study of aircraft flutter. The asymmetric of damping and stiffness terms are often addressed in the context of gyroscopic and follower forces.

To calculate the eigenpair derivatives in this case, Adhikari and M.I. Friswell proposed a modal method by modifying the modal method for symmetric damped systems.

In this paper, by combining the modal method by Adhikari and M.I. Friswell and modal acceleration and shifted-pole method by Zeng, modified modal methods for asymmetric damped system are presented. So highly accurate modal method for calculating the derivatives for asymmetric damped systems has been developed. And fewer eigenvectors required for the predetermined accuracy. As a result, the method is more efficient in computation than Adhikari's modal method.

Numerical examples show that proposed method achieves better calculating efficiency and highly accurate results when a few modes are used.

2 PREVIOUS STUDY

The general equation of motion for an N-degree of freedom system with damping is,

$$M\ddot{u}(t) + C\dot{u}(t) + Ku(t) = 0 \qquad (1)$$

where M, C and K are mass, damping and stiffness matrices, respectively. The traditional restrictions of symmetry and positive definiteness are not imposed on M, C and K, however, it is assumed that M^{-1} exists.

Equation 1 can be rewritten in the following state-space form,

$$A\dot{x}(t) + Bx(t) = 0 \qquad (2)$$

where

$$A = \begin{bmatrix} C & M \\ M & 0 \end{bmatrix}, \quad B = \begin{bmatrix} K & 0 \\ 0 & -M \end{bmatrix}, \quad x(t) = \begin{Bmatrix} u(t) \\ \dot{u}(t) \end{Bmatrix}$$

From the Equation 2, we obtain following two equations because of the asymmetricity of the system,

$$(sA + B)z = 0 \qquad (3)$$

$$y^T(sA + B) = \qquad (4)$$

where s is the eigenvalue, z is the right eigenvector and y is the left eigenvector which is related to the right and left eigenvector of the second order system. For distinct eigenvalues, two normalizing conditions by Adhikari are as follows,

$$y_j^T A z_j = 2s_j \qquad (5)$$

$$\{u_j\}_{n_j} = \{v_j\}_{n_j} \qquad (6)$$

where $\{*_j\}_{nj}$ denotes the j-th element of a vector n_j is chosen so that the corresponding elements of the eigenvectors are as large as possible. Thus,

$$\left| \{u_j\}_{n_j} \right| \left\| \{v_j\}_{n_j} \right\| = \max_n \left| \{u_j\}_n \right\| \{v_j\}_n \right| \qquad (7)$$

Differentiate Equation 3 with design parameter α. Using this equation, the derivative of eigenvalues can be obtained as:

$$s_{j,\alpha} = -\frac{y_j^T(s_j A_{,\alpha} + B_{,\alpha})z_j}{y_j^T A z_j}$$

$$= -\frac{y_j^T(s_j A_{,\alpha} + B_{,\alpha})z_j}{2s_j} \qquad (8)$$

To derive the eigenvector derivatives, we can expand $z_{j,\alpha}$ and $y_{j,\alpha}$ as complex linear combinations of z_i and y_i, for all $i = 1, \ldots, 2N$.

$$z_{j,\alpha} = \sum_{i=1}^{2N} a_{ji} z_i \qquad (9)$$

$$y_{j,\alpha} = \sum_{i=1}^{2N} b_{ji} y_i \qquad (10)$$

Differentiate Equations 3 and 4 and substituting the Equations 9 and 10 into that equations, we can obtain the coefficient a_{jk} and b_{jk}.

$$a_{jk} = -\frac{y_k^T[s_{j,\alpha}A + s_j A_{,\alpha} + B_{,\alpha}]z_j}{2s_k(s_j - s_k)} \quad \forall k = 1, \ldots 2N; k \neq j \quad (11)$$

$$b_{jk} = -\frac{y_j^T[s_{j,\alpha}A + s_j A_{,\alpha} + B_{,\alpha}]z_k}{2s_k(s_j - s_k)} \quad \forall k = 1, \ldots 2N; k \neq j \quad (12)$$

The expressions for a_{jk} and b_{jk} derived above are not valid when k is equal to j. To obtain a_{jj} and b_{jj}, we begin by differentiating Equation 5. And substituting the Equations 9 and 10 into that equation, gives:

$$a_{jj} + b_{jj} = -\frac{y_j^T A_{,\alpha} z_j}{y_j^T A z_j} \qquad (13)$$

The second equation is derived by using Equation 6. If the n_j-th elements of the left and right eigenvectors remain equal, then so do the corresponding elements of the derivatives. Thus,

$$b_{jj} - a_{jj} = \frac{1}{\{y_j\}_{n_j}} \sum_{k=1, k \neq j}^{2N} \left[a_{jk}\{z_k\}_{n_j} - b_{jk}\{y_k\}_{n_j} \right] \qquad (14)$$

So the derivatives of the eigenvectors are,

$$z_{j,\alpha} = \left\{ \sum_{k=1, k\neq j}^{N} \left[\frac{z_k y_k^T}{2s_k(s_j - s_k)} + \frac{(z_k y_k^T)^*}{2s_k^*(s_j - s_k^*)} \right] + \frac{(z_j y_j^T)^*}{2s_j^*(s_j - s_j^*)} \right\} f_j + a_{jj} z_j \qquad (15)$$

$$y_{j,\alpha} = \left\{ \sum_{k=1, k\neq j}^{N} \left[\frac{y_k z_k^T}{2s_k(s_j - s_k)} + \frac{(y_k z_k^T)^*}{2s_k^*(s_j - s_k^*)} \right] + \frac{(y_j z_j^T)^*}{2s_j^*(s_j - s_j^*)} \right\} g_j + b_{jj} y_j \qquad (16)$$

where

$$f_j = -(s_{j,\alpha}A + sA_{,\alpha} + B_{,\alpha})z_j, \qquad (17)$$

$$g_j = -(s_{j,\alpha}A + sA_{,\alpha} + B_{,\alpha})^T y_j \qquad (18)$$

612

3 MODIFIED MODAL METHODS

3.1 Modal acceleration method (MA method)

The convergence of Equations 15 and 16 is poor. To accurately calculate the eigenvector derivative, the higher modes are required. In a practical situation, there are only some lower modes available, and modal truncation errors will be significant. In response calculations, the modal acceleration approach is used to speed up the convergence and reduce the truncation errors.

At first, we consider the derivatives of right eigenvectors. Separate the response $z_{,\alpha}$ into a pseudostatic response z_{s0} and a dynamic correction response z_{d0},

$$z_{,\alpha} = z_{s0} + z_{d0} \qquad (19)$$

where

$$z_{s0} = B^{-1} f \qquad (20)$$

$$z_{d0} = z_{,\alpha} - z_{s0} \qquad (21)$$

or

$$z_{d0} = (sA + B)^{-1} f - B^{-1} f \qquad (22)$$

From the Equation 5, we obtain

$$Y^T A Z = \begin{bmatrix} \ddots & & \\ & 2s_j & \\ & & \ddots \end{bmatrix} \qquad (23)$$

$$Y^T B Z = \begin{bmatrix} \ddots & & \\ & -2s_j^2 & \\ & & \ddots \end{bmatrix} \qquad (24)$$

where Y and Z is the modal matrix to be formed by the right and left eigenvector, respectively.

Substituting the Equations 23 and 24 into Equation 22, it yields:

$$z_{d0} = Z \begin{bmatrix} \ddots & & \\ & \dfrac{1}{2s_k(s - s_k)}\left(\dfrac{s}{s_k}\right) & \\ & & \ddots \end{bmatrix} Y^T f \qquad (25)$$

From the Equations 20 and 25, we obtain the derivatives of right eigenvectors.

$$z_{j,\alpha} = \left\{ B^{-1} + \sum_{k=1,k\neq j}^{N} \left[\left(\frac{s_j}{s_k}\right) \frac{z_k y_k^T}{2s_k(s_j - s_k)} \right.\right.$$
$$+ \left(\frac{s_j}{s_k^*}\right) \frac{(z_k y_k^T)^*}{2s_k^*(s_j - s_k^*)} \right]$$
$$\left. + \left(\frac{s_j}{s_j^*}\right) \frac{(z_j y_j^T)^*}{2s_j^*(s_j - s_j^*)} \right\} f_j + a_{jj} z_j \qquad (26)$$

By the similar procedure, we can obtain the derivatives of left eigenvectors.

$$y_{j,\alpha} = \left\{ B^{-T} \sum_{m=0}^{M-1} (-s_j A^T B^{-T})^m \right.$$
$$+ \sum_{k=1,k\neq j}^{N} \left[\left(\frac{s_j}{s_k}\right)^M \frac{y_k z_k^T}{2s_k(s_j - s_k)} \right.$$
$$\left. + \left(\frac{s_j}{s_k^*}\right)^M \frac{(y_k z_k^T)^*}{2s_k^*(s_j - s_k^*)} \right]$$
$$\left. + \left(\frac{s_j}{s_j^*}\right)^M \frac{(y_j z_j^T)^*}{2s_j^*(s_j - s_j^*)} \right\} g_j + b_{jj} y_j \qquad (27)$$

3.2 Modal acceleration method (MMA method)

In the modal acceleration method approach, the convergence of the series is speeded up through preliminary calculation of the pseudostatic response z_{s0} to the excitations f. Based on the similar idea, if the pseudostatic response z_{s1} to the combination force of f and inertia force that comes from the response z_{s0} is preliminarily calculated, the convergence would be further improved for including the effects of the inertia. The pseudostatic response is,

$$z_{,\alpha} = z_{s\,n-1} + z_{d\,n-1} \qquad (28)$$

where

$$z_{s\,n-1} = B^{-1} f[I - sAz_{s\,n-2}] f \qquad (29)$$

$$z_{d\,n-1} = z_{,\alpha} - z_{s\,n-1}$$
$$= Z \begin{bmatrix} \ddots & & \\ & \dfrac{1}{2s_k(s - s_k)}\left(\dfrac{s}{s_k}\right)^n & \\ & & \ddots \end{bmatrix} Y^T f \qquad (30)$$

By the similar procedure as the modal acceleration approach, the derivatives of right eigenvectors are given as:

$$z_{j,\alpha} = \left\{ B^{-1} \sum_{m=0}^{M-1} (-s_j AB^{-1})^m \right.$$
$$+ \sum_{k=1,k\neq j}^{N} \left[\left(\frac{s_j}{s_k}\right)^M \frac{z_k y_k^T}{2s_k(s_j - s_k)} \right.$$
$$\left. + \left(\frac{s_j}{s_k^*}\right)^M \frac{(z_k y_k^T)^*}{2s_k^*(s_j - s_k^*)} \right]$$
$$\left. + \left(\frac{s_j}{s_j^*}\right)^M \frac{(z_j y_j^T)^*}{2s_j^*(s_j - s_j^*)} \right\} f_j + a_{jj} z_j \qquad (31)$$

By the similar procedure, the derivatives of left eigen-vectors are given as:

$$
\begin{aligned}
y_{j,\alpha} = &\left\{ B^{-T} \sum_{m=0}^{M-1} (-s_j A^T B^{-T})^m \right. \\
&+ \sum_{k=1,k\neq j}^{N} \left[\left(\frac{s_j}{s_k}\right)^M \frac{y_k z_k^T}{2s_k(s_j - s_k)} \right. \\
&+ \left.\left(\frac{s_j}{s_k^*}\right)^M \frac{(y_k z_k^T)^*}{2s_k^*(s_j - s_k^*)} \right] \\
&+ \left.\left(\frac{s_j}{s_j^*}\right)^M \frac{(y_j z_j^T)^*}{2s_j^*(s_j - s_j^*)} \right\} g_j + b_{jj} y_j
\end{aligned}
\tag{32}
$$

3.3 Multiple modal accelerations with shifted-poles (MMAS method)

For more high convergence rate, the term $(s_j A + B)^{-1}$ is expanded in Taylor's series at the position β as:

$$
\begin{aligned}
(s_j A + B)^{-1} &= [(B + \beta A - (s_j - \beta)(-A)]^{-1} \\
&= (B + \beta A)^{-1}[I + (s_j - \beta)(B + \beta A)^{-1} A]^{-1} \\
&= (B + \beta A)^{-1} \sum_{m=0}^{M-1} [-(s_j - \beta)A(B + \beta A)^{-1}]^m
\end{aligned}
\tag{33}
$$

Through the similar previous procedure using the Equation 33, the j-th right eigenvector derivatives are formulated as:

$$
\begin{aligned}
z_{j,\alpha} = &\left\{ (B + \beta A)^{-1} \sum_{m=0}^{M-1} [-(s_j - \beta)A(B + \beta A)^{-1}]^m \right. \\
&+ \sum_{k=1,k\neq j}^{N} \left[\left(\frac{s_j - \beta}{s_k - \beta}\right)^M \frac{z_k y_k^T}{2s_k(s_j - s_k)} \right. \\
&+ \left.\left(\frac{s_j - \beta}{s_k^* - \beta}\right)^M \frac{(z_k y_k^T)^*}{2s_k^*(s_j - s_k^*)} \right] \\
&+ \left.\left(\frac{s_j - \beta}{s_j^* - \beta}\right)^M \frac{(z_j y_j^T)^*}{2s_j^*(s_j - s_j^*)} \right\} f_j + a_{jj} z_j
\end{aligned}
\tag{34}
$$

By similar procedure, the left eigenvector derivatives are given as:

$$
\begin{aligned}
y_{j,\alpha} = &\left\{ (B + \beta A)^{-T} \sum_{m=0}^{M-1} [-(s_j - \beta)A^T(B + \beta A)^{-T}]^m \right. \\
&+ \sum_{k=1,k\neq j}^{N} \left[\left(\frac{s_j - \beta}{s_k - \beta}\right)^M \frac{y_k z_k^T}{2s_k(s_j - s_k)} \right. \\
&+ \left.\left(\frac{s_j - \beta}{s_k^* - \beta}\right)^M \frac{(y_k z_k^T)^*}{2s_k^*(s_j - s_k^*)} \right] \\
&+ \left.\left(\frac{s_j - \beta}{s_j^* - \beta}\right)^M \frac{(y_j z_j^T)^*}{2s_j^*(s_j - s_j^*)} \right\} g_j + b_{jj} y_j
\end{aligned}
\tag{35}
$$

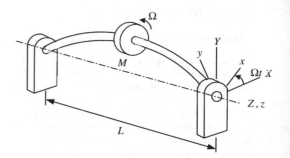

Figure 1. Whirling beam.

4 NUMERICAL EXAMPLES

Whirling beam whose system matrices are asymmetric is considered as numerical example. This example is a gyroscopic system rotating with high speed and has a lumped mass in center of beam as Figure 1.

The equation of motion of gyroscopic system is as follows:

$$
M\ddot{u}(t) + (C + G)\dot{u}(t) + (K + H)u(t) = F(t)
$$

where M, C, K, and F are mass, damping, stiffness and external force matrices respectively, G is gyroscopic matrix and H is circulatory matrix that make system matrix asymmetric. The detailed information of this system is represented in Ref. 3.

The numerical values chosen are as follows:

$$
m_0 = 10 kg/m, \quad M_0 = 10 kg, \quad L = 5m, \quad EI_x = 4L^3/5\pi^2 Nm^2
$$

$$
EI_y = 9L^3/5\pi^2 Nm^2, \quad K_1 = K_2 = L^2/20 Nm
$$

$$
\Omega = \sqrt{21.6\pi} \ rad \ s^{-1}, \quad c = h = 1/4 Nsm^{-1}
$$

Number of DOF: 10, Design Parameter: length of beam

Table 1, 2 and 3 shows exact eigenvalues and eigenvectors and their derivatives with respect to length for design variable.

To demonstrate the effectiveness of modified modal methods, right eigenvector derivative is calculated using six modes. Table 4 shows resulting errors. (MMA: $M = 2$, MMAS: β = eigenvalue $- 1$, $M = 2$)

As you can see in the Table 4, multiple modal acceleration method with shifted poles is very effective.

To demonstrate the efficiency of MMAS, right eigenvector derivative is calculated using fewer modes. Table 5 shows resulting errors. (β = eigenvalue $- 1$, $M = 2$)

Table 1. Eigenvalues and their derivatives.

Mode number	Eigenvalues	Derivatives
1	$-8.4987e-03$ $+2.3563e+00i$	$1.3251e-03$ $+1.5799e+00i$
2	$-2.7151e-03$ $+6.3523e+01i$	$2.2533e-03$ $+8.5934e-01i$
3	$1.6771e-02$ $+1.0548e+01i$	$3.3394e-03$ $+3.4034e-01i$
4	$6.3300e-02$ $+1.2534e+01i$	$8.8052e-03$ $+2.0616e-01i$
5	$2.3092e-01$ $+1.4079e+01i$	$2.1905e-02$ $+1.7729e-02i$
6	$-2.6645e-01$ $+1.5122e+01i$	$-2.3974e-02$ $-1.7731e-02i$
7	$-1.1330e-01$ $+1.6668e+01i$	$-8.8052e-03$ $-2.0608e-01i$
8	$-5.8579e-02$ $+1.8650e+01i$	$-3.7909e-03$ $-3.3918e-01i$
9	$-4.7285e-02$ $+2.2774e+01i$	$-2.2533e-03$ $-8.2215e-01i$
10	$-3.6890e-02$ $+2.6214e+01i$	$-1.2833e-03$ $-1.0644e+00i$

Table 3. First left eigenvector and its derivative.

DOF number	Eigenvector	Derivative
1	$-6.0874e-03$ $+6.2442e-06i$	$-2.2630e-03$ $+1.8636e-05i$
2	$0.0000e+00$ $+0.0000e+00i$	$0.0000e+00$ $+0.0000e+00i$
3	$7.4415e-03$ $-6.7358e-06i$	$2.6937e-04$ $-2.3495e-05i$
4	$0.0000e+00$ $+0.0000e+00i$	$0.0000e+00$ $+0.0000e+00i$
5	$2.8849e-02$ $+2.1839e-05i$	$7.0186e-03$ $-1.0403e-04i$
6	$-1.2500e-05$ $-1.2110e-02i$	$-3.5515e-05$ $-5.3611e-03i$
7	$0.0000e+00$ $+0.0000e+00i$	$0.0000e+00$ $+0.0000e+00i$
8	$1.4785e-05$ $-1.4677e-02i$	$4.3471e-05$ $+6.4573e-03i$
9	$0.0000e+00$ $+0.0000e+00i$	$0.0000e+00$ $+0.0000e+00i$
10	$8.3733e-05$ $-5.7187e-02i$	$1.8429e-04$ $+1.3508e-02i$

Table 2. First right eigenvector and its derivative.

DOF number	Eigenvector	Derivative
1	$6.0874e-03$ $-6.2442e-06i$	$6.3118e-04$ $+6.3342e-06i$
2	$0.0000e+00$ $+0.0000e+00i$	$0.0000e+00$ $+0.0000e+00i$
3	$-7.4415e-03$ $+6.7358e-06i$	$-7.6005e-04$ $-7.1917e-06i$
4	$0.0000e+00$ $+0.0000e+00i$	$0.0000e+00$ $+0.0000e+00i$
5	$-2.8849e-02$ $-2.1839e-05i$	$-6.0508e-03$ $-1.3386e-05i$
6	$-1.2500e-05$ $+1.2110e-02i$	$1.0624e-05$ $-4.8858e-03i$
7	$0.0000e+00$ $+0.0000e+00i$	$0.0000e+00$ $+0.0000e+00i$
8	$1.4785e-05$ $-1.4677e-02i$	$-1.2799e-05$ $+5.9162e-03i$
9	$0.0000e+00$ $+0.0000e+00i$	$0.0000e+00$ $+0.0000e+00i$
10	$8.3733e-05$ $-5.7187e-02i$	$-3.7941e-05$ $+1.6957e-02i$

Table 4. Error comparison of proposed using four modes.

DOF number	MA	MMA	MMAS
1	$8.3063e-01$	$2.0224e-01$	$7.1932e-02$
2	$0.0000e+00$	$0.0000e+00$	$0.0000e+00$
3	$3.8258e+01$	$1.5063e+00$	$4.7845e-01$
4	$0.0000e+00$	$0.0000e+00$	$0.0000e+00$
5	$4.6312e+00$	$1.2077e-01$	$3.5371e-02$
6	$8.0424e-02$	$5.3198e-02$	$1.2030e-02$
7	$0.0000e+00$	$0.0000e+00$	$0.0000e+00$
8	$1.6789e+00$	$5.8813e-01$	$1.1871e-01$
9	$0.0000e+00$	$0.0000e+00$	$0.0000e+00$
10	$5.2018e-01$	$1.5716e-01$	$3.0334e-02$

Table 5. Error comparison of MMAS using fewer modes.

DOF number	MA	MMA	MMAS
1	$7.1932e-02$	$3.4065e+00$	$2.0896e+00$
2	$0.0000+00$	$0.0000e+00$	$0.0000e+00$
3	$4.7845e-01$	$4.5377e-01$	$3.1398e+00$
4	$0.0000e+00$	$0.0000e+00$	$0.0000e+00$
5	$3.5371e-02$	$3.5167e-02$	$5.1810e-02$
6	$1.2030e-02$	$6.2550e-01$	$3.8320e-01$
7	$0.0000e+00$	$0.0000e+00$	$0.0000e+00$
8	$1.1871e-01$	$1.1407e-01$	$5.4249e-01$
9	$0.0000e+00$	$0.0000e+00$	$0.0000e+00$
10	$3.0334e-02$	$3.0189e-02$	$3.8830e-02$

5 CONCLUSION

The modified modal methods for the eigenpair derivatives of asymmetric damped system has been derived. It is assumed that the system does not possess any repeated eigenvalues. By analyzing the numerical example, it is verified that the proposed methods are more effective than previous method.

For accurate result, previous modal method is needed for all eigenvalues and eigenvectors of system. But in practical case, only a few lower modes are available. So the errors may become significant. The modified modal methods are possible to calculate derivatives of eigenvlaues and eigenvectors of asymmetric damped system using a few lower modes.

REFERENCES

Adhikari, S. & Friswell, M.I. 2001. Eigenderivative Analysis of Asymmetric Non-Conservative Systems. *International Journal for Numerical Method in Engineering*. 51: 709–733.

Zeng, Q.H. 1994. Highly Acurate Modal Method for Calculating Eigenvector Derivative in Viscous Damping Systems. *AIAA Journal*. 33(4): 746–751.

Meirovitch, L. & Ryland, G. 1985. A Perturbation Technique for Gyroscopic Systems with Small International and External Damping. *Journal of Sound and Vibration*. 100(3): 393–408.

Efficient eigensolution method of large structural systems with proportional and non-proportional dampers

H.-J. Jung
Sejong University, Seoul, Korea

J.-S. Jo & I.-W. Lee
Korea Advanced Institute of Science and Technology, Daejeon, Korea

M.-G. Ko
Kongju National University, Chungnam, Korea

ABSTRACT: An efficient eigenvalue analysis method for large structural systems with proportional and non-proportional dampers is presented. The proposed method consists of an efficient eigensolution technique and a reliable checking technique for missed eigenvalues. In the method, the part of the eigensolution technique can be obtained by applying the modified Newton-Raphson method and the orthonormal condition of the eigenvectors, and the part of checking technique for missed eigenvalues can be derived by extending the Gleyse's theorem, which can count the number of eigenvalues of a characteristic polynomial inside an open disk on the complex plane. The efficiency and reliability of the proposed method is verified by comparing convergence and solution time for numerical examples with those of the subspace iteration method, the determinant search method and the Lanczos method, and by counting the number of eigenvalues of numerical examples inside an open disk of arbitrary radius on the complex plane.

1 INTRODUCTION

The dynamic equation of motion can be written as:

$$M \ddot{u}(t) + C \dot{u}(t) + K u(t) = f(t) \tag{1}$$

where M, C and K are the mass, damping and stiffness matrices of order n, respectively, $u(t)$ the displacement vector, and $f(t)$, the load vector.

The methods for solving dynamic equation of motion can be divided into the step-by-step integration method and the mode superposition method. If the dynamic analysis is performed by the mode superposition method, the free vibration analysis must be first solved. And most of computational time is required for free vibration analysis. Therefore, an efficient eigensolution technique is necessarily required.

For symmetric and positive definite matrices, the eigenvalues and the associated eigenvectors of the system in Equation 1 may be determined in a straightforward and efficient manner provided that the damping matrix is proportional or, more generally (Caughey & O'Kelly 1965), provided that

$$CM^{-1}K = KM^{-1}C. \tag{2}$$

That is, in case of structures with proportional dampers, we can get easily the desired eigenpairs by analyzing the following eigenproblem of order n not considering the damping matrix C;

$$K \phi_i = \lambda_i M \phi_i \tag{3}$$

where λ_i is the ith eigenvalue and ϕ_i the corresponding eigenvector.

Systems for which Equation 2 is not satisfied are called the non-proportionally damped systems. The eigenanalysis for such systems is traditionally performed in the space extended to $2n$-dimensional such as

$$\begin{bmatrix} -K & 0 \\ 0 & M \end{bmatrix} \begin{Bmatrix} \phi_i \\ \lambda_i\phi_i \end{Bmatrix} = \lambda_i \begin{bmatrix} C & M \\ M & 0 \end{bmatrix} \begin{Bmatrix} \phi_i \\ \lambda_i\phi_i \end{Bmatrix}. \tag{4}$$

2 METHOD OF EIGENVALUE ANALYSIS

We consider an eigenproblem of which the eigenvalue λ_i has multiplicity m. For simplicity let us assume that the first m eigenvalues are equal or close to each other

$$\lambda \equiv \lambda_1 \cong \lambda_2 \cong \cdots \cong \lambda_m.$$ (5)

If the multiplicity of an eigenproblem equals 1, then the eigenvalues of the eigenproblem are not multiple or close, but distinct.

The eigenvalue problem of proportionally and non-proportionally damped system can be presented in matrix form for the m multiple or close eigenvalues as follows:

$$A\,\Psi = B\,\Psi\,\Lambda.$$ (6)

For proportionally damped case, $(n \times n)$ matrices A, B and $(n \times 1)$ vectors ψ_i $(i = 1,\ldots,m)$ can be expressed as follows:

$$A = K, \; B = M \text{ and } \psi_i = \phi_i.$$ (7)

For non-proportionally damped case, $(2n \times 2n)$ matrices A, B and $(2n \times 1)$ vectors ψ_i $(i = 1,\ldots,m)$ can be written like this:

$$A = \begin{bmatrix} -K & 0 \\ 0 & M \end{bmatrix}, \; B = \begin{bmatrix} C & M \\ M & 0 \end{bmatrix} \text{ and } \psi_i = \begin{Bmatrix} \phi_i \\ \lambda_i\phi_i \end{Bmatrix},$$ (8)

where $\Psi = [\psi_1 \; \ldots \; \psi_m]$ is a matrix satisfying the orthonormal condition with respect to matrix B such as

$$\Psi^T B\,\Psi = I_m$$ (9)

and $\Lambda = diag(\lambda_1,\ldots,\lambda_m) = \lambda I_m$ is a matrix of order m.

Let $X = [x_1,\ldots,x_m]$ be the vectors in the subspace Ψ, and X be the orthonormal with respect to B. Then

$$\Psi = XZ$$ (10)

$$X^T BX = I_m$$ (11)

where Z is the unknown rotation matrix of order m.

Introducing Equation 10 into Equation 6, we get

$$AXZ = BXZ\Lambda.$$ (12)

Let

$$DZ = Z\Lambda$$ (13)

where $D = [d_1,d_2,\ldots,d_m] = X^T AX$ and symmetric. Then,

$$AXZ = BXDZ$$ (14)

and

$$AX = BXD$$ (15)

or

$$Ax_i = BXd_i \; (i = 1,\ldots,m).$$ (16)

We obtain the m multiple or close eigenvalues and associated eigenvectors from Equations 10, 13 and 15.

Note when m eigenvalues are multiple ($\lambda_1 = \ldots = \lambda m$), from Equation 13

$$\Lambda = D$$

$$\Psi = X,$$

and when m eigenvalues are close to each other ($\lambda_1 \approx \ldots \approx \lambda_m$), D is not a diagonal matrix. We should solve the small standard eigenvalue problem as in Equation 13. Then we get the eigenvalues Λ from Equation 13 and the eigenvectors Ψ from Equation 10.

Let us assume that initial approximate solutions of Equation 6, $\Lambda^{(0)}$ and $\Psi^{(0)}$, are known. Denoting the approximate eigenvalues and the associated eigenvectors after k iterations by $\Lambda^{(k)}$ and $\Psi^{(k)}$, we can get

$$R^{(k)} = A\,\Psi^{(k)} - B\,\Psi^{(k)}\,\Lambda^{(k)}$$ (17)

and

$$(\Psi^{(k)})^T B\,\Psi^{(k)} = I_m$$ (18)

where the residual matrix $R^{(k)} = [r_1^{(k)} \; \ldots \; r_m^{(k)}]$ denotes the error for each eigenpair, and is not generally zero because of substitution of approximate values into Equation 6.

In order to get the solutions converged to the multiple eigenvalues and the associated eigenvectors of the system, the residual vectors should be removed. For the purpose of that, the Newton-Raphson technique is applied such as

$$R^{(k+1)} = A\,\Psi^{(k+1)} - B\,\Psi^{(k+1)}\,\Lambda^{(k+1)}$$
$$= 0$$ (19)

and

$$(\Psi^{(k+1)})^T B\,\Psi^{(k+1)} = I_m$$ (20)

where

$$\Lambda^{(k+1)} = \Lambda^{(k)} + \Delta\Lambda^{(k)}$$ (21)

$$\Psi^{(k+1)} = \Psi^{(k)} + \Delta\Psi^{(k)}.$$ (22)

Substituting Equation 21 and 22 into Equation 19 and 20, and neglecting the nonlinear terms, $B\Delta\Psi^{(k)}$ $\Delta\Lambda^{(k)}$ and $(\Delta\Psi^{(k)})^T B\Delta\Psi^{(k)}$, we can get the linear simultaneous equations for unknown incremental values, $\Delta\Lambda^{(k)}$ and $\Delta\Psi^{(k)}$ as follows:

$$A\,\Delta\Psi^{(k)} - B\,\Delta\Psi^{(k)}\,\Lambda^{(k)} - B\,\Psi^{(k)}\,\Delta\Lambda^{(k)} = -R^{(k)}$$ (23)

and

$$(\Psi^{(k)})^T B \Delta\Psi^{(k)} = 0. \tag{24}$$

Since the eigenvalue is multiple, the off-diagonal elements of $\Lambda^{(k)}$ are zero or very small compared with its diagonal at kth iteration step, and the diagonal element very close. Thus, the second term in left side of Equation 23 may be approximated by $\lambda_1^{(k)} B\Delta\Psi^{(k)}$, which yields

$$A \Delta\Psi^{(k)} - \lambda_1^{(k)} B \Delta\Psi^{(k)} - B \Psi^{(k)} \Delta\Lambda^{(k)} = -R^{(k)} \tag{25}$$

Writing (24) and (25) in matrix form, we can get

$$\begin{bmatrix} (A - \lambda_1^{(k)} B) & -B\Psi^{(k)} \\ (-B\Psi^{(k)})^T & 0 \end{bmatrix} \begin{bmatrix} \Delta\Psi^{(k)} \\ \Delta\Lambda^{(k)} \end{bmatrix} = - \begin{bmatrix} R^{(k)} \\ 0 \end{bmatrix}. \tag{26}$$

Because the new coefficient matrix should be reformed and refactorized in each iteration step, the above method adopting the Newton-Raphson technique and a side condition, despite of its rapid convergence, is not efficient.

These blemishes may be overcome by applying the modified Newton-Raphson technique to Equation 26 such as

$$\begin{bmatrix} (A - \lambda_1^{(0)} B) & -B\Psi^{(k)} \\ (-B\Psi^{(k)})^T & 0 \end{bmatrix} \begin{bmatrix} \Delta\Psi^{(k)} \\ \Delta\Lambda^{(k)} \end{bmatrix} = - \begin{bmatrix} R^{(k)} \\ 0 \end{bmatrix}. \tag{27}$$

The symmetric coefficient matrix of Equation 27 is of order $(n + m)$ in case of proportional damping system, and of order $(2n + m)$ in case of non-proportional damping system. While singularity occurs in factorization process of the iteration methods such as the inverse iteration method and the subspace iteration method when the shift is close to an eigenvalue of the system, nonsingularity of the proposed method is always guaranteed (Lee et al. 1998). This is the main difference compared with the iteration methods with shift.

3 METHOD OF CHECKING MISSED EIGEN-VALUES

3.1 Characteristic polynomial of a matrix

The characteristic polynomial in Equation 28 can be obtained another way using the matrix $\mathbf{A}$ in standard form of Equation 4 as

$$p(\lambda) = \det(A - \lambda I)$$

$$= \hat{a}_{2n}\lambda^{2n} + \hat{a}_{2n-1}\lambda^{2n-1} + \cdots + \hat{a}_1\lambda + \hat{a}_0 = \sum_{i=0}^{2n} \hat{a}_i \lambda^i, \tag{28}$$

where λ is a complex value and $\hat{a}_i$ $(i = 0, 1, \ldots, 2n))$ are real coefficients. The coefficients a_i $(i = 0, 1, \ldots, 2n)$ in Equation 28 are the same scalar multiples to each $\hat{a}_i$ $(i = 0, 1, \ldots, 2n)$ in Equation 28.

There are several methods for calculating the coefficients of the characteristic polynomial of a real square matrix. The most famous one is Faddeev-Leverrier's method, which is often described as a standard method in text books. Wang & Chen (1982) pointed out the numerical instability and inefficiency of Faddeev-Leverrier's method and proposed a numerically stable method to compute the characteristic polynomial based on Frobenius form of a matrix. This method needs to prescribe a small value to prevent some elements be divided by this small value and this value should be guided by error analysis and/or experience. Recently, Rombouts & Heyde (1998) presented an algorithm for calculating the coefficients of the characteristic polynomial of a general square matrix for the evaluation of canonical traces in determinant quantum Monte-Carlo methods. This algorithm does not include dividing operations, so it is stable and also known as efficient and accurate. In this paper, for calculating the coefficients of the characteristic polynomial of a matrix Rombouts algorithm is used.

A general real square matrix $\mathbf{A}$ of size $2n$-by-$2n$:

$$\mathbf{A} = \begin{bmatrix} a_{11} & a_{12} & \cdots & a_{1,2n-1} & a_{1,2n} \\ a_{21} & a_{22} & \cdots & a_{2,2n-1} & a_{2,2n} \\ \vdots & \vdots & \ddots & \vdots & \vdots \\ a_{2n-1,1} & a_{2n-1,2} & \cdots & a_{2n-1,2n-1} & a_{2n-1,2n} \\ a_{2n,1} & a_{2n,2} & \cdots & a_{2n,2n-1} & a2_{n,2n} \end{bmatrix}, \tag{29}$$

can be transformed to upper Hessenberg form $\overline{\mathbf{A}}$:

$$\overline{\mathbf{A}} = \begin{bmatrix} \overline{a}_{1,1} & \overline{a}_{1,2} & \cdots & \overline{a}_{1,n-1} & \overline{a}_{1,n} \\ \overline{a}_{2,1} & \overline{a}_{2,2} & \cdots & \overline{a}_{2,n-1} & \overline{a}_{2,n} \\ 0 & \overline{a}_{3,2} & \cdots & \overline{a}_{3,n-1} & \overline{a}_{3,n} \\ \vdots & \vdots & \ddots & \vdots & \vdots \\ 0 & 0 & \cdots & \overline{a}_{n,n-1} & \overline{a}_{n,n} \end{bmatrix}, \tag{30}$$

by applying Householder reduction or sequence of Gaussian elimination like similarity transformations. Because the matrix $\overline{\mathbf{A}}$ was obtained by applying similarity transformations to $\mathbf{A}$, the eigenvalues of both $\overline{\mathbf{A}}$ and $\mathbf{A}$ and are same and the characteristic polynomials are scalar multiples to each other. For the purpose of calculating eigenvalues of the system, therefore, the characteristic polynomial can be considered as

$$p(\lambda) = \det(\overline{\mathbf{A}} - \lambda\mathbf{I}). \tag{31}$$

If we define $\bar{p}(\lambda)$ as

$$\bar{p}(\lambda) = \det(\mathbf{I} + \lambda\bar{\mathbf{A}}),\tag{32}$$

then this polynomial is closely related to $p(\lambda)$:

$$\bar{p}(\lambda) = (\lambda)^{2n}\, p(-1/\lambda).\tag{33}$$

The basic idea of the Rombouts' algorithm is to consider $\bar{\mathbf{A}} + \lambda\mathbf{I}$ as a matrix of polynomials in λ. We then calculate the polynomial $\bar{p}(\lambda)$ by evaluating the determinant in Equation 32 using Gaussian elimination, with polynomials instead of scalars as matrix elements. As presented at Equation 33, the coefficients of $\bar{p}(\lambda)$ are closely related to the coefficients of the $p(\lambda)$.

3.2 Number of eigenvalues inside an unit open circle

Gleyse (1999) suggested a method of calculating the number of eigenvalues of a real polynomial inside a unit open circle by a determinant representation as shown in Figure 1.

Let $p(\lambda) = \Sigma_{h=0}^{2n}\,\hat{a}_h\lambda_h$ ($\hat{a}_h$ is a real number) be a characteristic polynomial of a given matrix $\mathbf{A}$, then the number of eigenvalues inside a unit open circle can be determined as

$$N_o = 2n - V\big[1, d_1, d_2, \cdots, d_{2n}\big]\tag{34}$$

where N_0 is the number of eigenvalues in a unit open circle, $2n$ is the degree of the polynomial, $V[k_0, k_1, k_2, \ldots, k_{2n}]$ is the number of sign changes in the sequence k_i ($i = 0, 1, \ldots, 2n$) and d_i ($i = 1, 2, \ldots, 2n$) is the determinants (minors) of the leading principal submatrices of order i in the Schur-Cohn matrix $\mathbf{T}$:

$$\mathbf{T} = \begin{bmatrix} t_{11} & \cdots & t_{1i} & \cdots & t_{1,2n} \\ \vdots & \ddots & \vdots & \ddots & \vdots \\ t_{i1} & \cdots & t_{ii} & \cdots & t_{i,2n} \\ \vdots & \ddots & \vdots & \ddots & \vdots \\ t_{2n,1} & \cdots & t_{2n,i} & \cdots & t_{2n,2n} \end{bmatrix} \begin{matrix} \mathbf{T}_1 & \cdots & \mathbf{T}_i & \cdots & \mathbf{T}_{2n} \end{matrix}\tag{35}$$

$$t_{ij} = \sum_{h=0}^{\min(i,j)}\big(\hat{a}_{2n-i+h}\hat{a}_{2n-j+h} - \hat{a}_{i-h}\hat{a}_{j-h}\big)\ (i,j = 1,2,\cdots,2n)\tag{36}$$

$$d_i = \det(\mathbf{T}_i)\tag{37}$$

The processes of computing the number of eigenvalues inside a unit open circle by the above method requires calculation of the characteristic polynomial of a given matrix $\mathbf{A}$, the construction of the Schur-Cohn matrix $\mathbf{T}$ and the calculation of the determinants (minors) of the leading principal submatrices of order i in the Schur-Cohn matrix $\mathbf{T}$. The coefficients

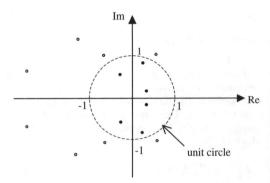

Figure 1.   Eigenvalues inside a unit circle ($\bullet$).

of the characteristic polynomial of a given matrix can be determined by Rombouts' algorithm described at the previous chapter, and each elements of the Schur-Cohn matrix can be obtained using Equation 35.

3.3 Modified Sturm sequence property

Gleyse's theorem (1999) considers only about the number of eigenvalues in a unit open circle. To apply this theorem to an open circle of arbitrary radius ρ, we substitute $\lambda = \rho\bar{\lambda}$ (ρ is a real number) to Equation 28, and then the modified characteristic polynomial can be written as

$$\begin{aligned}P(\bar{\lambda}) &= \hat{a}_{2n}\rho^{2n}\bar{\lambda}^{2n} + \hat{a}_{2n-1}\rho^{2n-1}\bar{\lambda}^{2n-1} + \cdots + \hat{a}_1\rho\bar{\lambda} + \hat{a}_0 \\ &= \tilde{a}_{2n}\bar{\lambda}^{2n} + \tilde{a}_{2n-1}\bar{\lambda}^{2n-1} + \cdots + \tilde{a}_1\bar{\lambda} + \tilde{a} = \sum_{i=0}^{2n}\tilde{a}_i\bar{\lambda}^i,\end{aligned}\tag{38}$$

where $\tilde{a}_i = \hat{a}_i\rho^i$ ($i = 0, 1, \ldots 2n$) are modified coefficients.

Using the modified coefficients $\tilde{a}_i$ ($i = 0, 1, \ldots, 2n$) in Equation 38, this theorem can be extended to calculate the number of eigenvalues inside the open disks of arbitrary radius ρ as shown in Figure 2.

The calculation of d_i ($i = 1, \ldots, 2n$) can be easily performed by the $\mathbf{LDL}^T$ factorization of the Schur-Cohn matrix $\mathbf{T}$. If $\mathbf{T} = \mathbf{LDL}^T$, then:

$$\mathbf{T}_i = \mathbf{L}_i\mathbf{D}_i\mathbf{L}_i^T,\tag{39}$$

$$\mathbf{L} = \begin{bmatrix} 1 & \cdots & 0 & \cdots & 0 \\ \vdots & \ddots & \vdots & \ddots & \vdots \\ l_{i1} & \cdots & l_{ii} & \cdots & 0 \\ \vdots & \ddots & \vdots & \ddots & \vdots \\ l_{2n,1} & \cdots & l_{2n,i} & \cdots & 1 \end{bmatrix},\ \mathbf{D} = \begin{bmatrix} d_{11} & \cdots & 0 & \cdots & 0 \\ \vdots & \ddots & \vdots & \ddots & \vdots \\ 0 & \cdots & d_{ii} & \cdots & 0 \\ \vdots & \ddots & \vdots & \ddots & \vdots \\ 0 & \cdots & 0 & \cdots & d_{2n,2n} \end{bmatrix}$$
$$\tag{40}$$

where the matrix $\mathbf{T}_i$ is the leading principal submatrices of order i in the Schur-Cohn the matrix $\mathbf{T}$, the matrix $\mathbf{L}_i$ is the leading principal submatrices of order

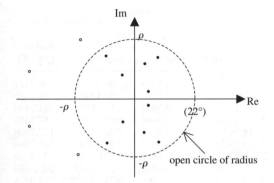

Figure 2. Eigenvalues inside an open circle of radius ρ (•).

i in the factorized lower triangular matrix $\mathbf{L}$ and the matrix $\mathbf{D}_i$ is the leading principal submatrices of order i in the factorized diagonal matrix $\mathbf{D}$ as shown in (40). The value of d_i ($i = 1, \ldots, 2n$) can be evaluated as

$$d_i = \det(\mathbf{T}_i) = \det(\mathbf{L}_i\mathbf{D}_i\mathbf{L}_i^T) = \det(\mathbf{D}_i)$$

$$= \prod_{h=1}^{i} d_{hh} \; .$$

(41)

Therefore, each $d_i = \det(\mathbf{T}_i)$ can be obtained by multiplying from the first diagonal element d_{11} to the i-th diagonal element d_{ii} of the factorized diagonal matrix $\mathbf{D}$.

Considering Equation 34, we only need to know the signs of each d_i because the unknown value of $V[1, d_1, d_2, \ldots, d_{2n}]$ depends on sign changes of each, d_i ($i = 1, \ldots, 2n$) and from (41) the sign change of d_i from $d_{i\text{minus}1}$ occurs when the diagonal element d_{ii} of the factorized diagonal matrix $\mathbf{D}$ is negative. So, the value of $V[1, d_1, d_2, \ldots, d_{2n}]$ is equal to the number of negative element in the matrix $\mathbf{D}$. If we combine this result with Equation 34, the number of eigenvalues inside an open circle of radius ρ and the number of positive elements the factorized diagonal matrix $\mathbf{D}$ has the following relationship:

$$N_\rho = \text{the number of positive elements in } \mathbf{D} \quad (42)$$

where N_ρ is the number of eigenvalues inside an open circle of radius ρ and $\mathbf{D}$ is the diagonal matrix obtained by factorization of Schur-Cohn matrix $\mathbf{T}$ constructed using the modified coefficients in Equation 38. This relation is very similar to the Strum sequence property for undamped systems.

4 NUMEIRCAL EXAMPLE

To show the efficacy of the proposed eigensolution method as well as the applicability of the eigenvalue-counting method (i.e., the modified Sturm sequence

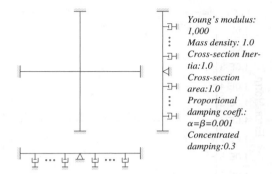

Figure 3. Plane frame structure with lumped dampers.

Table 1. CPU time (in seconds) of the plane frame structure with lumped dampers.

Methods	CPU time (Ratio)
Proposed method	872.69 (1.00)
Subspace iteration method	3096.62 (3.55)

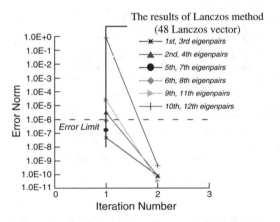

Figure 4. Proposed method.

property), the plane frame structure with lumped dampers is considered as a numerical example.

The geometric configuration and material properties are shown in Figure 3. The model is discretized in 6 beam elements with equal length for each direction resulting in the system of dynamic equation with a total of 18 degrees of freedom. Thus, the order of the associated eigenproblem is 36. The consistent damping matrix is derived from the classical damping given by $\mathbf{C} = \alpha\mathbf{K} + \beta\mathbf{M}$ and concentrated dampers resulting in non-proportional damping matrix.

The CPU time spent for the first twelve eigenvalues of the proposed method is compared with that of the subspace iteration method in Table 1. If we let the

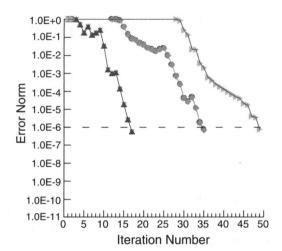

Figure 5. Subspace iteration method.

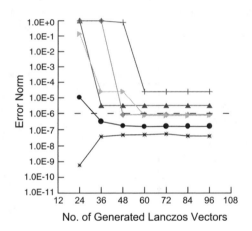

Figure 6. Lanczos method.

solution time for the proposed method be 1, it takes 3.55 times for the subspace iteration method. The variations of the error norms to increasing the iteration step are shown in Figures 5 to 6. The error norms of the initial values obtained by using the $4p$ (48) Lanczos vectors are about 0.7 to 10^{-7}, which are possible to check the multiplicity of the desired eigenvalues. The number of iterations for the proposed method applied to the initial values that do not satisfy the error norm 10^{-6} is only one. The results in Figures 4 to 5 indicate that the convergence of the proposed method is much better than that of the subspace iteration method. The results of the Lanczos method in Figure 6 are not improved in spite of the increase of the number of the Lanczos vectors.

The results for the modified Sturm sequence property are shown in Table 3. As shown at the last column in the table, the number of sign changes is 28. So if we

Table 2. Calculated eigenvalues.

| Mode Number | Eigenvalues (λ) | | Radius ($\rho = |\lambda|$) |
	Real	Imaginary	
1,2/3,4	−1.1369	46.2187	46.2327
5,6/7,8	−1.3731	51.1333	51.1517
9,10/11,12	−3.3902	±81.0872	81.1490
13,14/15,16	−3.9407	±87.4771	87.5659
17,18/19,20	−8.1642	±127.4394	127.7006
21,22/23,24	−10.2629	±142.8367	143.2049
25,26/27,28	−14.8662	±171.7301	172.3720
29,30/31,32	−20.5387	±201.6249	202.6683
33,34/35,36	−23.7699	±216.7332	218.0328

Table 3. Coefficients $\bar{a}_i$, diagonal element d_{ii} of $\mathbf{D}$, and sign of d_i.

$$\rho = 1.005|\lambda_8| = 51.4075$$

I	a_i	d_{ii}	Sign of d_i	V
0	2.5017e + 006	−	+	0
1	2.3595e + 006	−6.2584e + 006	−	1
2	1.8523e + 007	−6.2584e + 006	+	2
3	1.5836e + 007	−6.2584e + 006	−	3
4	6.0360e + 007	−6.2584e + 006	+	4
5	4.6688e + 007	−6.2584e + 006	−	5
6	1.1462e + 008	−6.2584e + 006	+	6
7	8.0016e + 007	−6.2584e + 006	−	7
8	1.4176e + 008	−6.2584e + 006	+	8
9	8.9075e + 007	−6.2584e + 006	−	9
10	1.2111e + 008	−6.2584e + 006	+	10
11	6.8279e + 007	−6.2584e + 006	−	11
12	7.4043e + 007	−6.2584e + 006	+	12
13	3.7327e + 007	−6.2584e + 006	−	13
14	3.3137e + 007	−6.2583e + 006	+	14
15	1.4882e + 007	−6.2576e + 006	−	15
16	1.1017e + 007	−6.2563e + 006	+	16
17	4.3882e + 006	−6.2388e + 006	−	17
18	2.7450e + 006	−6.2202e + 006	+	18
19	9.6439e + 005	−6.0086e + 006	−	19
20	5.1461e + 005	−5.9203e + 006	+	20
21	1.5833e + 005	−4.8338e + 006	−	21
22	7.2533e + 004	−4.7180e + 006	+	22
23	1.9357e + 004	−2.4454e + 006	−	23
24	7.6408e + 003	−2.4029e + 006	+	24
25	1.7448e + 003	−5.4284e + 005	−	25
26	5.9414e + 002	−5.3645e + 005	+	26
27	1.1381e + 002	−6.1754e + 003	−	27
28	3.3379e + 001	−4.1125e + 003	+	28
29	5.1996e + 000	2.4923e + 004	+	−
30	1.3074e + 000	1.3928e + 004	+	−
31	1.5712e − 001	3.0169e + 003	+	−
32	3.3582e − 002	2.8778e + 003	+	−
33	2.8092e − 003	2.5915e + 000	+	−
34	5.0338e − 004	2.5924e + 000	+	−
35	2.2413e − 005	2.8473e − 004	+	−
36	3.2943e − 006	1.6343e − 004	+	−

where V represents the number of sign changes of d_i.

use the Equation 34, the number of eigenvalues inside the circle is $36 - 28 = 8$. Using Equation 42, the number of positive elements in the matrix **D** is 16 as shown at the third column in the table. Therefore, we verify that the methods can exactly check the number of eigenvalues inside some open disk of arbitrary radius for the system with multiple eigenvalues.

5 CONLUSIONS

An efficient method for solving eigenproblems of structures with proportional and non-proportional dampers is presented. It is demonstrated from the numerical analysis that the proposed eigensolution method is very effective for solving dynamic systems with a large number of degrees of freedom because the proposed method converges very fast, and the nonsingularity of the proposed method is always guaranteed, which is proved analytically. In addition, a reliable checking technique for missed eigenvalues is also proposed. The checking technique for missed eigenvalues is derived by extending the Gleyse's theorem, which can count the number of eigenvalues of a characteristic polynomial inside an open disk on the complex plane.

The efficiency and reliability of the proposed eigenvalue-counting method is verified by checking the number of eigenvalues of a numerical example inside an open disk of arbitrary radius on the complex plane.

REFERENCES

Caughey, T.K. & O'Kelly, M.E.J. 1965. Classical normal modes in damped linear dynamic systems. *Transaction on ASME, Journal of Applied Mechanics* 32: 583–588.

Gleyse, B. & Moflih, M. 1999. Exact computation of the number of zeros of a real polynomial in the open unit disk by a determinant representation. *Computers and Mathematics with Applications* 38: 257–263.

Lee, I.-W., Kim, M.-C. & Robinson, A.R. 1998. An efficient solution method of eigenproblems for damped structural systems using the modified Newton-Raphson technique. *ASCE Journal of Engineering Mechanics*, 124(5): 576–580.

Rombouts, S. & Heyde, K. 1998. An accurate and efficient algorithm for the computation on the characteristic polynomial of a general square matrix. *Journal of the Computational Physics* 140: 453–458.

Wang, J. & Chen, C.T. 1982. On the computation of the characteristic polynomial of a matrix. *IEEE Transaction on Automatic Control* 27: 449–451.

On static limit analysis using the *p*-version FEM

F. Tin-Loi & N.S. Ngo

School of Civil and Environmental Engineering, University of New South Wales, Australia

ABSTRACT: A well-known difficulty in solving plane strain and 3D limit analysis problems is that caused by volumetric locking when certain yield criteria, such as von Mises, are adopted. In this paper, we investigate the use of the high order *p*-version finite element method (FEM) within the static approach which, somewhat surprisingly, does not appear to have been proposed in this context before. We focus on the 2D plane strain case and provide an example, modelled with quadrilateral elements, to highlight the robustness and accuracy of the approach.

1 INTRODUCTION

Limit analysis is undoubtedly one of the most powerful and widely used so-called "simplified" methods to assess the safety of structures. It not only avoids a computationally expensive time-stepping analysis but also provides useful information regarding the collapse of plastic structures.

Current research in the area of limit analysis is primarily motivated by two aims: (a) to overcome the volumetric locking behavior encountered in plane strain and 3D problems with such commonly used yield criteria as von Mises', and (b) to solve efficiently practically motivated, often very large size, problems.

The present paper is concerned with the first aim. In particular, the primary objective of the work reported herein is to propose a robust scheme to carry out limit analyses within a static approach (Christiansen 1996) that would avoid the traditional locking behavior exhibited by a number of widely used displacement finite elements.

Towards this end, we investigate the performance of a high order approach, however, not through the standard *h*-version of the finite element method but through the increasingly popular *p*-version. Firmly established in the 1980s (Szabó & Babuška 1991), the *p*-version has a simple mesh requirement, a sound theoretical basis and a reputation for providing robust, accurate and exponentially convergent solutions to (linear elliptic) elastostatic problems. We recall that, as opposed to the traditional *h*-version in which the error in the solution is reduced by refining the mesh of size *h*, a *p*-version reduces the error by increasing, within a fixed mesh, the degree *p* of the polynomials

used. The combination of the two approaches is possible and is known as the *hp*-version.

The organization of this paper is as follows. In Section 2, we review the static principle of limit analysis for a general rigid perfectly-plastic continuum. Section 3 deals with some key concepts of the *p*-version of the finite element method, thereby leading to the formulation of the discrete static limit analysis problem as a constrained optimization problem. We then present in Section 4 one numerical example, dealing with a classical plane strain benchmark problem of a double notched tensile specimen obeying von Mises criterion, to illustrate the performance of the proposed *p*-version approach. We conclude with some pertinent remarks in Section 5.

2 STATIC APPROACH TO LIMIT ANALYSIS

The limit analysis problem is primarily aimed at answering the question: given a load distribution on a rigid perfectly-plastic solid, what is the maximum multiplier of this load that the solid can sustain without collapsing? It is often also of interest to find out information regarding the collapse mechanism and the stresses, although these quantities are not necessarily unique.

The static approach to finding out the collapse multiplier μ^* is now briefly described (see Christiansen 1996 for details). Consider the body with a bounded domain V. Its boundary ∂V consists of a fixed region S, where $\mathbf{u} = \mathbf{0}$ ($\mathbf{u}$ = displacement rates), and of a free and possibly loaded part C. Assume also that surface forces $\mathbf{g}$ and body forces $\mathbf{f}$ are given on C and V, respectively.

The external work rate $W(\mathbf{u})$ of $(\mathbf{f},\mathbf{g})$ and a virtual plastic flow $\mathbf{u}$ is

$$W(\mathbf{u}) = \int_V \mathbf{f} \cdot \mathbf{u}\,dv + \int_C \mathbf{g} \cdot \mathbf{u}\,dc. \quad (1)$$

In turn the internal or dissipation rate $U(\boldsymbol{\sigma},\mathbf{u})$ is given by

$$U(\boldsymbol{\sigma}, \mathbf{u}) = \int_V \sum_{i,j} \sigma_{ij}\varepsilon_{ij}\,dv \quad (2)$$

where the strain rate tensor ε_{ij} at each point $\mathbf{x}$ is defined by

$$\varepsilon_{ij} = \frac{1}{2}\left(\frac{\partial u_i}{\partial x_j} + \frac{\partial u_j}{\partial x_i}\right). \quad (3)$$

We assume that the form of the yield condition is

$$\boldsymbol{\sigma} \in K \quad (4)$$

where K is a convex, but possibly unbounded, function of $\boldsymbol{\sigma}$. For von Mises condition in plane strain K is

$$K = (\sigma_{11} - \sigma_{22})^2 + 4\sigma_{12}^2 \leq \tfrac{4}{3}\sigma_0^2 = 4\tau_0^2 \quad (5)$$

where σ_0 and τ_0 are familiar material constants.

The static principle of limit analysis can now be stated compactly in the form of a nonlinear programming problem (NLP) as follows:

$$\mu^* = \max\left\{\mu \mid \exists \boldsymbol{\sigma} \in K : U(\boldsymbol{\sigma}, \mathbf{u}) = \mu W(\mathbf{u}),\ \forall \mathbf{u}\right\}. \quad (6)$$

Clearly, (6) states the existence of a statically admissible stress tensor $\boldsymbol{\sigma}$ (i.e. one that obeys equilibrium and the traction boundary conditions) that satisfies the yield conditions. It is noted that equilibrium is given by equating internal and external work rates.

Two comments are worthy of note.

Firstly, solution of (6) is typically carried out by suitable space discretization so that a finite dimensional NLP will need to be solved. As presented, a mixed finite element approach (that does not necessarily guarantee, of course, a lower bound solution) is particularly suitable.

Secondly, the admissible set for $\boldsymbol{\sigma}$ is clearly unbounded for plane strain (and 3D) von Mises condition since addition of a hydrostatic pressure does not affect the yield condition. As indicated by Christiansen (1996), this requires that $\mathbf{u}$ is divergence free. To avoid this volumetric locking, it is important that appropriate displacement functions be chosen in a displacement finite element model for use with the static approach, as we intend to do. To ensure "appropriateness", we would need to satisfy the criterion given in the seminal paper of Nagtegaal et al. (1974). In essence, they showed that locking is unlikely to occur for h-elements if, in the limit, the ratio of number of degrees of freedom in the model to the number of incompressibility constraints is greater than or equal to one. Arguably, the most robust and effective means of avoiding locking is through the use of high order elements, as in Sloan and Randolph (1982) for elastoplastic analysis. Our proposal, as described in the following, is the use of p-elements to generate the discretized form of (6).

3 p-VERSION LIMIT ANALYSIS MODEL

In this section, we briefly present some essential features of a p-approach leading to the discrete form of (6). For simplicity of notation, we do not use kinematic quantities in rates. We assume that the quadrilateral p-element is oriented the reference $\xi - \eta$ plane such that element corner nodes and sides are numbered anticlockwise with node 1 at $(-1,-1)$ and side 1 at $\eta = -1$.

3.1 Shape and mapping functions

The shape functions for the generic p-element e are expressed in the same form as for an h-element, namely

$$\mathbf{u}(\xi,\eta) = \begin{bmatrix} u_x \\ u_y \end{bmatrix} = \begin{bmatrix} N_1 & 0 & \cdots & 0 \\ 0 & N_1 & \cdots & N_n \end{bmatrix} \mathbf{a}^e = \mathbf{N}\mathbf{a}^e \quad (7)$$

where $\mathbf{N}$ contains the element shape functions and $\mathbf{a}^e$ collects the unknown parameters to be found. For a p-element, however, n no longer corresponds to physically identifiable h-type number of nodes and $\mathbf{a}^e$ does not solely represent displacements.

The approximation is improved, not by mesh refinement, but by increasing the degree p of polynomials. The polynomial functions used are hierarchical (Szabó & Babuška 1991) in that as p is increased, the new higher order shapes are simply added on to the existing ones. Such functions can be obtained from orthogonal Legendre polynomials.

For $p = 1$, the shape functions are precisely those of a bilinear h-element. For instance, the nodal mode for corner node 1 is

$$N_1 = \tfrac{1}{2}(1-\xi)(1-\eta). \quad (8)$$

For $p \geq 2$, we need to specify $p - 1$ edge modes for each of the element sides. For instance, for side $s1$, this is given by

$$N^{s1,i} = \tfrac{1}{2}(1-\eta)\,\varphi_i(\xi), \quad i = 2,\ldots,p \quad (9)$$

where function $\varphi_i(s)$ is defined, in terms of the Legendre polynomial P_{i-1}, as

$$\varphi_i(\varsigma) = \sqrt{\frac{2i-1}{2}} \int_{-1}^{\varsigma} P_{i-1}(z) \, dz. \tag{10}$$

For $p \geq 4$, there are $(p-2)(p-3)/2$ internal or "bubble" modes constructed from

$$N^{jk} = \varphi_j(\xi)\varphi_k(\eta), \quad j,k \geq 2, \quad j+k \leq p. \tag{11}$$

For example, if $p = 6$ there will be a total of six bubble modes (three added to the current $p = 5$ set).

The following additional remarks are notable.

Firstly, the shape functions as described are hierarchical in that each additional higher order contribution does not change any of the interpolation functions used in previous contributions. This has the advantage of embedding elastic stiffness matrices (previously calculated stiffnesses are retained). Unfortunately, it appears that equilibrium matrices, as we require, cannot be embedded.

Secondly, in the limit as the number of degrees of freedom tends to infinity, the ratio of number of freedoms to number of constraints is one that would prevent incompressibility locking. In accordance with the criterion of Nagtegaal et al. (1974) this ratio needs to be greater than or equal to one. Consequently, for straight sided 2D quadrilateral plane strain p-elements, we would need $p \geq 2$ and for curved sided elements of order two, we would need p ≥ 3.732.

Lastly, since a p-version approach typically involves few elements, special geometric mapping (between $x - y$ and $\xi - \eta$ spaces) requirements are needed. We employ the popular blending function method for this purpose (see details in Campion & Jarvis 1996).

3.2 Equilibrium

The formation of the equilibrium conditions is the same as for a conventional h-approach.

Consider a generic element e of volume Ω and, for simplicity, constant thickness t. We start from the traditional strain-displacement relation given by

$$\varepsilon = \mathbf{B}^e \mathbf{a}^e \tag{12}$$

where the position dependent matrix $\mathbf{B}^e$ can be obtained as usual (e.g. Cook et al. 2002).

For a calculated load vector $\mathbf{f}^e$, the virtual work equation provides, as in (6), the equilibrium relation

$$\int_{\Omega} \mathbf{B}^{eT} \boldsymbol{\sigma} \, d\Omega = \mathbf{f}^e \tag{13}$$

which can be numerically integrated to yield

$$\int_{\Omega} \mathbf{B}^{eT} \boldsymbol{\sigma} \, d\Omega = t \int_{-1}^{1} \int_{-1}^{1} \mathbf{B}^{eT} |\mathbf{J}| \boldsymbol{\sigma} \, d\xi \, d\eta$$
$$= t \sum_{i=1}^{G} (w_\xi w_\eta \, \mathbf{B}^{eT} |\mathbf{J}|)_i \, \boldsymbol{\sigma}_i$$
$$= \mathbf{A}^e \boldsymbol{\sigma}^e \tag{14}$$

where $|\mathbf{J}|$ is the determinant of the 2×2 Jacobian matrix of the mapping functions, w represents a Gauss weight at point i, $\mathbf{A}^e$ is the element equilibrium matrix and $\boldsymbol{\sigma}^e$ is the concatenated stress vector collecting all stresses in order for all G Gauss points.

In turn, the element load vector $\mathbf{f}^e$ can be formed as in Szabó & Babuška (1991). For instance, the r-th freedom contribution to this load vector by a normal traction q_n and a tangential traction q_t on side 1 of the element is given by

$$f_r^e = t \sum_{i=1}^{g} w_{\xi i} \left(\mathbf{N}_{\cdot r}^T \Big|_{\eta=-1} \begin{bmatrix} J_{12}(\xi,-1) \\ -J_{11}(\xi,-1) \end{bmatrix} q_n \right)_{\xi=\xi_i}$$
$$+ t \sum_{i=1}^{g} w_{\xi i} \left(\mathbf{N}_{\cdot r}^T \Big|_{\eta=-1} \begin{bmatrix} J_{11}(\xi,-1) \\ J_{12}(\xi,-1) \end{bmatrix} q_t \right)_{\xi=\xi_i} \tag{15}$$

where g is the number of Gauss points, a (first) subscripted dot associated with $\mathbf{N}$ indicates all of its rows, and the appropriate elements of $\mathbf{J}$ are indicated by the double subscripts.

We use Gauss-Legendre quadrature to carry out all integrations. For the formation of the elastic stiffness, Campion & Jarvis (1996) suggest, for two dimensions, $p + 3$ points to integrate a polynomial of degree p. Banerjee and Suri (1992), however, recommend $p + 1$ points. In our case, we need to evaluate only the equilibrium matrix and the load vector (not the stiffness matrix). Hence, we typically use $p + 1$ points for computational efficiency.

Finally, at the structure level, the following equilibrium equations can be assembled from elemental contributions and with due account for boundary conditions:

$$\mathbf{A}\mathbf{s} = \mathbf{f} \tag{16}$$

where $\mathbf{A}$ is the equilibrium matrix (of full row rank), $\mathbf{s}$ is the stress vector and $\mathbf{f}$ the global load vector.

3.3 Discrete limit analysis

The discrete limit analysis model based on the static principle can now be formulated as the constrained optimization problem

$$\mu^* = \max\{\mu \mid \mathbf{A}\mathbf{s} = \mu\mathbf{f}, \quad \boldsymbol{\Phi}(\mathbf{s}) \leq \mathbf{0}\} \tag{17}$$

where all the yield conditions have been collected through the yield functions $\boldsymbol{\Phi}(\mathbf{s})$, the number of which corresponds to the number of check points (which are Gauss points in our case).

3.4 Implementation

We have implemented the above approach in a pilot scheme with the aim of testing the robustness and accuracy of the approach (rather than its efficiency). Key features of this implementation are: (a) setup of the *p*-version FEM in MATLAB to form **A** and **f**; (b) generation from the MATLAB code of an appropriate data file for use by a generic GAMS (an acronym for General Algebraic Modelling System) (Brooke et al. 1998) model that implements the NLP (17); and (c) solution of the NLP from within the GAMS model using the state-of-the-art optimization solver GAMS/MINOS ver 5.5 (Gill et al. 1998).

The GAMS framework provides several advantages. Of these, we need only mention: the facility it provides in constructing, maintaining and solving large and complex mathematical programming models; its powerful, easy to understand and write language; simplicity and compactness of model construction; an internal efficient sparse data representation; and automatic differentiation capabilities. The GAMS file is written using a standard text editor and solved via a simple "gams foo" command where "foo.gms" is the name of the text file.

4 NUMERICAL EXAMPLE

For paucity of space we present only one illustrative example to highlight the performance of our approach.

The computations were carried out on a 1 GHz WinNT4 Pentium III and the MINOS ver 5.5 GAMS solver.

The example concerns the popular benchmark plane strain test used for elastoplastic procedures (Nagtegaal et al. 1974). However, similar to Christiansen & Andersen (1999) we focus on the limit analysis problem. The structure consists of a rectangular specimen with two thin notches under a reference load consisting of in-plane tensile stresses, as shown in Figure 1.

We took advantage of symmetry and modelled only a quarter of the specimen. Two models were used: one (Figure 2a) with two *p*-elements and the other (Figure 2b) with four *p*-elements. We adopted dimensions of $L = 1$, $W = 1$, and $d = 0.5$.

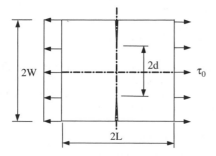

Figure 1. Two notched tensile specimen.

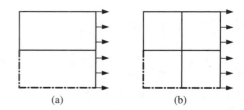

Figure 2. FE models: (a) 2 elements; (b) 4 elements.

Table 1. Limit multipliers for different quadrature rules.

| Degree p | Quadrature rules | | | |
	p	$p + 1$	$p + 2$	$p + 3$
2	1.3158	1.5514	1.5567	1.5600
3	1.3525	1.4394	1.4341	1.4340
4	1.3298	1.3533	1.3528	1.3541
5	1.2930	1.3057	1.3031	1.3040
6	1.2584	1.2629	1.2621	1.2637
7	1.2388	1.2416	1.2404	1.2409
8	1.2165	1.2200	1.2188	1.2183
9	1.2053	1.2075	1.2072	1.2069
10	1.1936	1.1960	1.1952	1.1952

We carried out a series of limit analyses on both models in order to investigate the following key aspects: (a) effect of quadrature rules; (b) variation of μ^* with p; and (c) computational costs.

Table 1 summarizes the results regarding the use of various quadrature rules (p to $p + 3$) on the accuracy of the calculated collapse load multiplier. The 2-element model was used for this purpose.

Clearly, integration using p points is not acceptable for low values of p. Our proposed choice of $p + 1$ points appears justified as it provides about the same accuracy as the computationally more expensive higher integration rules.

The variations of collapse multipliers with increasing p and an integration scheme of $p + 1$ points are displayed in Figure 3 for both 2-element and 4-element models.

As can be seen, good convergence is achieved as p is increased. The estimates of μ^* are all higher than the "reference" value of $\mu^* = 1.136$ predicted by Christiansen & Andersen (1999) which is considered to be very accurate; our best prediction (4-element model with $p = 15$) is $\mu^* = 1.157$ (or about 1.8% higher). Surprisingly, the 4-element model provided only a slight increase in accuracy in collapse load prediction over the 2-element model. This was achieved at a considerably higher computational cost.

A "smoothed" feasible mechanism for the 4-element model with $p = 15$ is shown in Figure 4. This was constructed from the dual values (displacements)

628

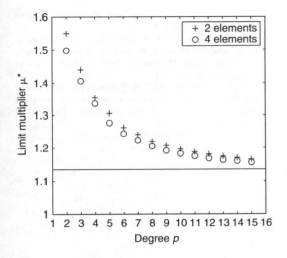

Figure 3. Variation of limit loads with polynomial degree.

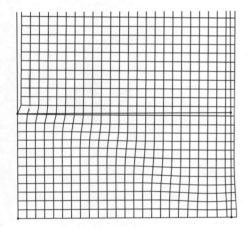

Figure 4. Feasible mechanism (4-element model, $p = 15$).

Table 2. Computational details (4-element model).

p	μ^*	$ncon$	$nvar$	$iter$	t (sec)
2	1.4983	70	109	27	0
3	1.4067	119	193	32	1
4	1.3348	184	301	55	3
5	1.2771	265	433	87	10
6	1.2445	362	589	132	28
7	1.2236	475	769	173	65
8	1.2052	604	973	278	179
9	1.1916	749	1201	546	507
10	1.1829	910	1453	711	1048
11	1.1757	1087	1729	712	1910
12	1.1690	1280	2029	964	3553
13	1.1644	1489	2353	1651	9195
14	1.1609	1714	2701	3346	25038
15	1.1569	1955	3073	8164	89064

corresponding to each equilibrium equation; the displacements were used to generate, from (7), interpolated values on a grid. The resulting representation generally agrees with the mechanism obtained by Christiansen & Andersen (1999).

Finally, it should be noted that the accuracy achieved with $p = 15$ comes at some computing cost. Table 2 provides some statistics concerning the NLPs that were solved. The data presented relate to the 4-element model, $p + 1$ integration and consist of: polynomial degree p, corresponding limit multiplier μ^*, number of constraints $ncon$, number of variables $nvar$, number of major MINOS iterations $iter$, and run time t in secs. As Table 2 shows, it becomes increasingly harder to solve the NLPs directly as the polynomial degree p is increased.

5 CONCLUDING REMARKS

We propose the use of the p-version FEM within a static approach to carry out robustly and accurately the limit analysis of rigid plastic structures.

The high order nature of the FE approximations prevents volumetric locking. Whilst we have specifically illustrated the approach with a plane strain problem, we expect that 3D problems can be similarly solved.

We have not attempted to develop special schemes to solve the NLPs; our current implementation uses a simple MATLAB code to generate appropriate data (equilibrium and yield conditions) which are then passed on to a generic GAMS model for optimization. This direct approach can incur a heavy computational cost for high degree polynomials. Schemes to increase the computational efficiency of the approach certainly deserve study.

Finally, it is worth noting that the approach is also eminently suitable to solve shakedown problems, as we plan to carry out, for which an accurate elastic solution is a prerequisite.

ACKNOWLEDGEMENT

This research was supported by the Australian Research Council.

REFERENCES

Banerjee, U. & Suri, M. 1992. The effect of numerical quadrature in the p-version of the finite element method. *Mathematics of Computation* 59: 1–20.

Brooke, A., Kendrick, D., Meeraus, A. & Raman, R. 1998. *GAMS: A user's guide*. Gams Development Corporation, Washington, DC 20007.

Christiansen, E. 1996. Limit analysis of collapse states. In: P.G. Ciarlet & J.L.Lions (eds), *Handbook of numerical analysis Vol. 4*: 193–312, Amsterdam: North-Holland.

Christiansen, E. & Andersen, K.D. 1999. Computation of collapses states with von Mises yield condition. *International Journal for Numerical Methods in Engineering* 46: 1185–1202.

Cook, R.D., Malkus, D.S., Plesha, M.E. & Witt, R.J. 2002. *Concepts and applications of finite element analysis*. New York: John Wiley & Sons, 4th edition.

Gill, P.E., Murray, W., Saunders, M.A. & Wright, M.H. 1998. MINOS 5.5 user's guide. *Report 83-20R (revised 1998)*, Department of Operations Research, Stanford University, Stanford, CA.

Nagtegaal, J.C., Parks, D.M. & Rice, J.R. 1974. On numerically accurate finite element solutions in the fully plastic range. *Computer Methods in Applied Mechanics and Engineering* 4: 153–177.

Sloan, S.W. & Randolph, M.F. 1982. Numerical prediction of collapse loads using finite element methods. *International Journal for Numerical and Analytical Methods in Geomechanics* 6: 47–76.

Szabó, B.A. & Babuška, I. 1991. *Finite element analysis*. New York: John Wiley & Sons.

System-based Vision for Strategic and Creative Design, Bontempi (ed.)
© 2003 Swets & Zeitlinger, Lisse, ISBN 90 5809 599 1

Analysis of edge and corner column-slab connections with and without stud shear reinforcement

H. Guan & Y.C. Loo
School of Engineering, Griffith University Gold Coast Campus, Queensland, Australia

ABSTRACT: Stud shear reinforcement (SSR) has been widely used in practice to increase the strength of a column-slab connection in flat plate systems. In this paper, a nonlinear layered finite element method (LFEM) is used to investigate the effectiveness of the shear studs in increasing the punching shear strength of edge and corner column-slab connections. The accuracy and effectiveness of the LFEM are verified against two case studies of a total of 14 slab specimens. In case study 1, nine large-scale edge and corner column-slab connections are analysed with varying column sizes and the stud spacing/slab thickness ratios. While in case study 2, five edge column-slab connections are examined with different location and amount of shear studs. In general, the predictions are satisfactory and consistent in both case studies.

1 INTRODUCTION

The flat plate is a very common and competitive structural system in building construction. However, the structural concept of such system is at a great disadvantage. The high shear forces and unbalanced moments around the supporting columns (corner and edge columns in particular) render the flat plate structure susceptible to brittle punching shear failure at a load well below the flexural capacity of the slab.

To increase the shear strength of a column-slab connection, shear reinforcement is usually provided to ensure that a ductile failure caused by yielding of flexural reinforcements occurs at ultimate load. Various types of shear reinforcement in the form of stirrups, bent-up bars and structural shear heads have been developed in the past to strengthen the column-slab connections. Despite being effective to some extent, all the above mentioned types of shear reinforcement have been found to have certain drawbacks. The installation of stirrups in reasonably thin slabs has been found to congest the slab-column connections, adding significant complications to the placement of flexural reinforcement and driving up overall construction costs. Bent-up bars often cannot be used as the reinforcement overcrowds the column region, hence reducing the ability to effectively pour the concrete. Shear heads are quite expensive and interfere with the column steel making it difficult to place. To meet the requirements of strength, ductility and economy, stud shear reinforcement (SSR) was developed by Dilger and Ghali (1981)

in Canada. SSR is comprised of forged steel anchors welded to round bars, which in turn welded to a flat steel strip. The large steel anchor head on top of the bar and the strip on the bottom engage the concrete to prevent any slippage. Various tests on column-slab connections with shear studs (Seible et al. 1985; Mokhtar et al. 1985) revealed that such studs are easy to install and they do not interfere with flexural reinforcement. Most importantly by providing a more efficient anchorage, the full yield strength of the shear studs can be attained, thus enabling a more ductile failure of the slab and a larger load carrying capacity.

Needless to say, laboratory tests are labour-intensive and time-consuming. On the other hand, various empirical methods, based heavily on model test results, inevitably involve gross approximations which are not always reliable and, by nature, their scope of applications is limited. For a rigorous cracking and failure analysis of reinforced concrete flat plates, a nonlinear layered finite element method (LFEM) has been developed (Guan & Loo 1997; Loo & Guan 1997). The degenerate shell elements encompassing concrete and smeared steel layers were used in the LFEM where a smeared crack approach was adopted to model cracked concrete and a strain-hardening plasticity procedure was employed to model concrete compressive behaviour. The effect of tension-stiffening and the deterioration of shear stiffness were also considered after cracking of concrete. The contribution of the smeared reinforcing steel having elasto-plastic behaviour was added to that of concrete to form the total material constitutive matrix. With the shell-element assumption, the transverse shear deformation can be accounted for which is crucial to punching shear analysis.

In this study, the LFEM is applied to analyse the load-carrying capacity and the punching shear strength of column-slab connections with SSR. The accuracy and effectiveness of the LFEM are verified against two case studies of a total of 14 slab specimens. In case study 1, nine large-scale edge and corner column-slab connections tested by Lim & Rangan (1995) are analysed with varying column sizes and the stud spacing/slab thickness ratios. While in case study 2, five edge column-slab connections tested by Mortin (1989) are examined with different location and amount of shear studs. In both case studies, the concrete strength is also a varying parameter.

2   CASE STUDY 1 – LIM & RANGAN (1995)

2.1   Test slabs

Tests on nine large-scale reinforced concrete slabs of a flat plate floor in the vicinity of edge and corner columns have been reported by Lim & Rangan (1995). The purpose of the tests was to study the effectiveness of stud shear reinforcement (SSR) in increasing punching shear strength of column-slab connections. In the experimental work, two parameters were investigated, viz the column size and the ratio of stud spacing to slab thickness. The test specimens were designated as Slab 1, the control specimen; Slabs 2, 3, 4, 5, 6A and 7, the edge-column connections; and Slabs 8 and 9, the corner-column connections. The details of the test slabs are shown in Figures 1 and 3, respectively, for the edge and corner column-slab connections. The slab thickness is 110 mm. Also shown in Figures 1 and 3 are the three locations of dial gauges for deflection measurement (i.e. Points D1, D2 and D3), as well as the positions of 24 (for edge column-slab connections) and 16 (for corner column-slab connections) point loads placed in a symmetric grid on the slab. These point loads were applied in the test to simulate a uniformly distributed vertical load. Each slab contains four layers of flexural reinforcing bars of 8 mm diameter. The column size ($C_1 \times C_2$), the concrete strength (f'_c), the yield strength of steel reinforcement (f_y) and the stud spacing/slab thickness ratio (s/D_s) for each slab are summarised in Table 1. Further details of the test specimens can be found elsewhere (Rangan & Lim 1992; Lim & Rangan 1994).

Slab 1 is a control specimen which has no SSR, whereas Slabs 2 to 9 contain SSR in the vicinity of the column. The arrangements of stud rails in the test slabs are illustrated in Figures 2 and 4, respectively, for edge and corner column-slab connections. In all slabs, two stud rails were located at each face of the column.

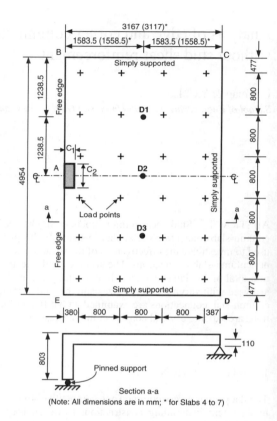

Figure 1.   Layout of Slabs 1 to 7.

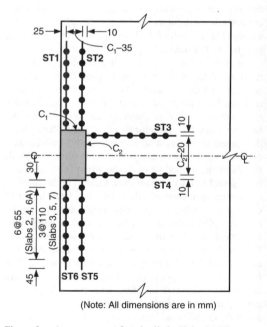

(Note: All dimensions are in mm)

Figure 2.   Arrangement of stud rails in Slabs 1 to 7.

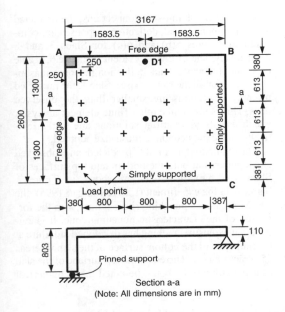

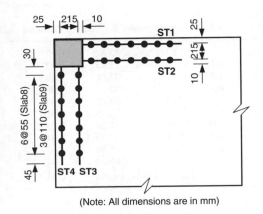

Figure 3. Layout of Slabs 8 and 9.

Figure 4. Arrangement of stud rails in Slabs 8 and 9.

Table 1. Relevant data for test slabs.

Slab No.	Column type	Column size $C_1 \times C_2$ (mm)	f'_c (MPa)	f_y (MPa)	s/D_s	Mesh scheme
1	Edge	250×250	25.0	516	–	12×11
2	Edge	250×250	26.9	516	0.5	15×13
3	Edge	250×250	27.5	516	1.0	15×13
4	Edge	150×600	26.3	546	0.5	15×12
5	Edge	150×600	27.7	546	1.0	15×12
6A	Edge	150×400	35.5	524	0.5	15×13
7	Edge	150×400	27.7	515	1.0	15×13
8	Corner	250×250	32.5	515	0.5	14×13
9	Corner	250×250	33.3	515	1.0	14×13

In Slabs 2 to 7, six stud rails were used whereas four stud rails were used in Slabs 8 and 9. The yield strength of the stud is 365 MPa.

2.2 Modelling approach

For the seven edge column-slab connections, only half of each of the slabs is analysed on account of symmetry whereas the entire slab is modelled for each of the two corner column-slab connections. The finite element mesh scheme used for each slab is also summarised in Table 1. A typical finite element mesh for Slabs 2 and 3 is shown in Figure 5 where unequal-sized meshes are adopted to account for the non-uniformly spaced reinforcement as well as the locations of the dial gauges. In addition, refined meshes are used around the column region where punching failure would occur. In all the slab models, each element is subdivided into eight concrete layers of different thicknesses. The thinnest concrete layers are placed at the bottom and top of the element. The layer thickness gradually increases towards the element mid-surface. This is to provide a more account of the extensive cracking near the bottom and top surfaces. The top and bottom reinforcement meshes are represented by four (smeared) steel layers with equivalent thickness. The out-of-plane shear studs are modelled by adding their contributions to the material matrix that corresponds to the normal strain in the transverse direction. To better simulate the concentrated effect of the shear studs, the meshes at the stud locations are made relatively thin.

An incremental and iterative procedure is used to obtain the nonlinear solution. With the LFEM, the nonlinear behaviour caused by both material and geometric nonlinearities can be reproduced. The load is applied incrementally through the loading points as indicated in Figures 1 and 3. Larger increments are applied at the initial stages followed by gradually decreased increments up to the failure load.

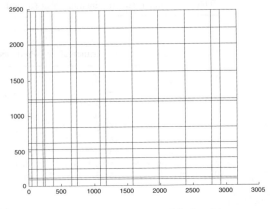

Figure 5. Finite element mesh for Slabs 2 and 3.

633

2.3 Punching shear strength, load–deflection response and crack patterns

A comparison of the values of punching shear strength V_u for all slabs is summarised in Table 2 which includes the test results, the LFEM predictions and the calculated values due to the truss theory (Lim & Rangan 1995). The ratio of the experimental and predicted V_u as well as that of the experimental and calculated V_u are also included in the table. The comparison shows that the LFEM predicts closely the punching shear strengths of edge column-slab connection but overestimates those of the corner column-slab connections. In general, however, both the predictions by the LFEM and the truss theory correlate well with the test results, having mean ratios of 0.98 and 1.02 respectively. The correlation coefficients for the LFEM and the truss theory are 0.99 and 0.97 respectively. Table 2 also reveals that the use of SSR is effective in increasing V_u and, at either stud spacing. However, like the experimental findings, the column size ($C_1 \times C_2$) and the s/D_s ratio do not seem to have significant influence on the punching shear strength.

The failure loads predicted by the LFEM agree remarkably well with the measured values, as evident in Table 3. The ratio of the experimental and predicted failure load varies between 0.92 and 1.07 for the nine slabs, with a mean ratio of 1.01 and a correlation coefficient of 0.94. It is also seen in the table that Slabs 2 to 9 carry significantly more loads than Slab 1 due to the presence of SSR. In addition, the numerical results indicate that Slabs 2 to 7 deflect more than Slab 1 because they carry greater loads which would cause more extensive cracking. This is also in accordance with the experimental findings. Further, the column size does not seem to have significant effect on the failure load. However, the smaller the s/D_s ratio, the greater the failure load, except for Slabs 4 and 5 for which the failure loads are almost identical.

For typical column-slab connections, the predicted and experimental load–deflection responses are compared in Figures 6(b) and 6(c) for Slabs 3 and 8 respectively. The LFEM, as evident in Figure 6, is able to predict the actual load–deflection response reasonably well. For all the slabs, expect Slab 1, the predicted ultimate deflections are smaller than the observed ones. This is not unlike other finite element analyses, which usually yield stiffer solutions due to the relatively coarse but economic mesh size adopted.

The comparisons of the predicted and observed crack patterns at both the bottom and top surfaces of Slabs 3 (symmetrical half) are shown in Figure 7. Same as in the experiment (Lim & Rangan 1995), the LFEM predicts a punching shear failure with the formation of the characteristic punching cone. It is evident that extensive cracking has developed at failure at the mid-span of the bottom surface of the slab whereas 45° cracks have occurred on the top surface of the slab near the column. It should be noted that a numerical

Table 3. Comparison of failure load (kN/m²).

Slab No.	s/D_s	Experimental	Predicted	Experimental / Predicted
1	–	21.92	23.87	0.92
2	0.5	30.81	31.23	0.99
3	1.0	25.76	25.66	1.00
4	0.5	34.17	32.22	1.06
5	1.0	35.27	33.02	1.07
6A	0.5	35.74	35.40	1.01
7	1.0	29.00	31.23	0.93
8	0.5	27.74	27.45	1.01
9	1.0	27.66	25.88	1.07
			Mean	1.01
		Correlation coefficient		0.94

Table 2. Comparison of punching shear strength V_u (kN).

Slab No.	s/D_s	Experimental	Predicted	Truss theory	Experimental / Predicted	Experimental / Truss theory
1	–	105.8	110.4	89.8	0.96	1.18
2	0.5	144.6	147.6	149.2	0.98	0.97
3	1.0	118.5	116.7	116.3	1.02	1.02
4	0.5	161.0	143.7	158.6	1.12	1.02
5	1.0	160.6	146.6	151.4	1.10	1.06
6A	0.5	161.6	151.0	181.5	1.07	0.89
7	1.0	131.8	131.4	146.0	1.00	0.90
8	0.5	60.0	80.79	50.5	0.74	1.19
9	1.0	64.3	81.24	64.8	0.79	0.99
				Mean	0.98	1.02
			Correlation coefficient		0.99	0.97

analysis would normally show more cracks than the experimental observation (Loo & Guan 1997). This discrepancy can however be alleviated when a finer mesh is adopted. Taking this fact into account, the agreement between the predicted and observed crack patterns is considered satisfactory.

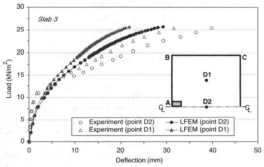

(a) Slab 3 (edge colum-slab connection)

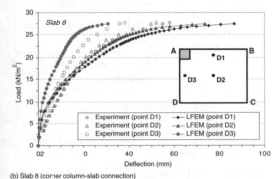

(b) Slab 8 (corner column-slab connection)

Figure 6.   Load–deflection response.

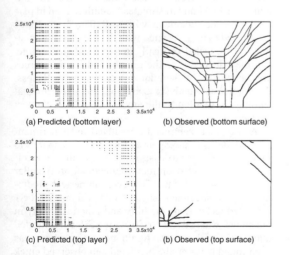

(a) Predicted (bottom layer)   (b) Observed (bottom surface)

(c) Predicted (top layer)   (b) Observed (top surface)

Figure 7.   Crack patterns for Slab 3 (symmetrical half).

3   CASE STUDY 2 – MORTIN (1989)

3.1   *Test specimens*

A total of six edge column-slab connections were tested by Mortin (1989) where the performance and strength of the connections under increasing shear and moment were examined. Each specimen has a dimension of $1380 \times 1900 \times 150\,mm$. A 250 mm square column stub is located at the centre of one of the long sides, flush to the edge of the slab. The column stub extends 700 mm from the top and bottom faces of the slab. All test specimens had uniform compression reinforcement in both directions, while the tension reinforcement varied for each slab. The test variables include: (a) tension steel ratio; (b) location of shear studs in the spandrel strip; (c) distance from the column face to the last stud; (d) spacing of the studs, and (e) concrete strength. Five out of six specimens are studied herein and they are designated as S1, S2, S3, S5 and S6. S1 is a control specimen without any shear reinforcement. The yield strengths of flexural reinforcement and the studs are repsectively 420 MPa and 480 MPa. The layout of the test specimens is shown in Figure 8 where the dial gauge location is indicated as Point D1. The shear force and unbalanced moment were transferred to the connection through the column stub. Relevant test data is summarised in Table 4 and a typical stud rail arrangement in S4 is shown in Figure 9. Further details can be found elsewhere (Mortin 1989).

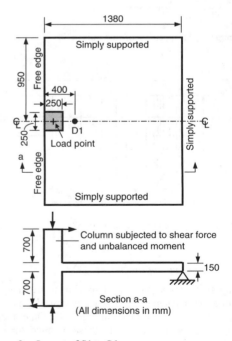

Figure 8.   Layout of S1 to S6.

Table 4. Relevant data for test specimens.

Specimen No.	f'_c (MPa)	Number of studs in a stud rail	Number of stud rails parallel to free edge	s/D_s
1	43.2	–	–	–
2	49.0	5	3	0.4
3	44.7	5	2	0.4
5	35.8	4	3	0.4
6	33.9	4	3	0.6

Table 5. Comparison of failure load (kN).

Specimen No.	s/D_s	Experimental	Predicted	Experimental Predicted
1	—	140	140	1.00
2	0.4	231	192	1.20
3	0.4	212	180	1.18
5	0.4	212	168	1.26
6	0.6	201	160	1.26
			Mean	1.18
		Correlation coefficient		0.93

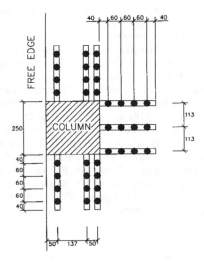

Figure 9. Arrangement of stud rails in S4.

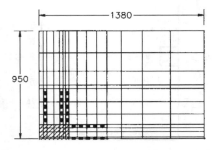

Figure 10. Finite element mesh for S2.

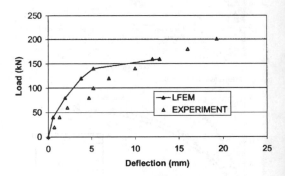

Figure 11. Load–deflection response for S5.

3.2 Modelling approach

Only symmetrical half of all specimens are analysed with a mesh scheme of 15 × 11. A typical finite element mesh for S2 is shown in Figure 10. Other modelling schemes are similar to those adopted for case study 1.

3.3 Failure load, load–deflection response and crack patterns

The failure loads predicted by the LFEM are compared with the measured values in Table 5. The mean ratio of the experimental and predicted failure load is 1.18 and the correlation coefficient is 0.93. In general, the LFEM underestimates the failure load in particular for the specimens with SSR. The discrepancy is believed to be associated with the fact that the specimens were tested vertically in a vertical steel frame, and the effects due to the gravity and friction forces are unable to be simulated exactly. Nevertheless, the numerical analysis confirms the experimental findings in relation to the amount of SSR in the test specimens.

As a typical example, the predicted and experimental load–deflection responses for S5 are compared in Figure 11. Similar to case study 1, for all the specimens the predicted ultimate deflections are smaller than the observed ones. However, numerical predictions for all specimens suggest that without SSR, S1 exhibited virtually no ductility and failed suddenly in punching, whereas S2 to S6 with SSR all exhibited ductile flexural failure. Again good agreement has been found between the predicted and observed crack patterns.

4 CONCLUSIONS

Two case studies are carried out on the punching shear failure behaviour of edge and corner column-slab connections with and without stud shear reinforcement (SSR). The investigation is based on a nonlinear layered finite element method (LFEM) developed previously by the authors. In case study 1, seven edge and two corner column-slab connections under uniformly distributed load are analysed with different column sizes and the stud spacing/slab thickness ratios. While in case study 2, five edge column-slab connections under shear force and unbalanced moment are analysed with different location of shear studs in the spandrel strip, varying distance from the column face to the last stud and the spacing of the studs. The punching shear strengths, the failure loads, the load–deflection responses and crack patterns predicted by the LFEM are compared with the experimental results. The study confirms the experimental findings in that the use of SSR is the most practical and effective means of reinforcing column-slab connections. In addition, the LFEM has shown to be able to satisfactorily and consistently performs for edge and corner column-slab connections with different column dimensions and different location and amount of stud shear reinforcement.

ACKNOWLEDGMENTS

The authors would like to thank Messrs Suphol Boonnoy and Mark Trenchard-Smith for their assistance in preparing some of the input data for the numerical analysis.

REFERENCES

Dilger, W.H. & Ghali, A. 1981. Shear reinforcement for concrete slabs. *Proceedings, ASCE* 107(12):2403–2420.

Guan, H. & Loo, Y.C. 1997. Layered finite element method in cracking and failure analysis of RC beams and beam-column-slab connections. *Structural Engineering Mechanics– An International J* 5(5):645–662.

Lim, F.K. & Rangan, B.V. 1994. *Strength of Concrete Slabs with Stud Shear Reinforcement in the Vicinity of Edge and Corner Columns.* Research Report No.1/94. Perth: Curtin University of Technology.

Lim, F.K. & Rangan, B.V. 1995. Studies on concrete slabs with stud shear reinforcement in vicinity of edge and corner columns. *ACI Structural J.* 92(5):515–525.

Loo, Y.C. & Guan, H. 1997. Cracking and punching shear failure analysis of RC flat plates. *J. Structural Engineering, ASCE* 123(10):1321–1330.

Mokhtar, A., Ghali, A. & Dilger, W.H. 1985. Stud shear reinforcement for flat concrete plates. *ACI J. Proceedings* 82(5):676–683.

Mortin, J.D. 1989. *Connections of Concrete Slabs with Edge Columns.* MSc Thesis. Alberta: The University of Calgary.

Rangan, B.V. & Lim, F.K. 1992. *Tests on Concrete Slabs with Stud Shear Reinforcement in the Vicinity of Edge Columns.* Research Report No.1/92. Perth: Curtin University of Technology.

Seible, F., Ghali, A. & Dilger, W.H. 1980. Preassembled shear reinforcing units for flat plates. *ACI J. Proceedings* 77(1):28–35.

System-based Vision for Strategic and Creative Design, Bontempi (ed.)
© *2003 Swets & Zeitlinger, Lisse, ISBN 90 5809 599 1*

Elastic–plastic large displacement analysis of thin-walled beam type structures

G. Turkalj, J. Brnic & D. Lanc
Faculty of Engineering, University of Rijeka, Rijeka, Croatia

ABSTRACT: This work presents a beam element model for second-order analysis of spaced framed structures with thin-walled cross-sections. Applying the updated Lagrangian incremental formulation and nonlinear displacement field of thin-walled cross-section, which accounts for restrained warping and includes second-order displacement terms due to large rotation effects, equilibrium equations of a straight beam element are firstly developed. Material non-linearity is introduced for an elastic-perfectly plastic material behavior through the plastic hinge formation at finite element ends. For this, a corresponding plastic reduction matrix is determined. The interactions of element forces are taken into account.

1 INTRODUCTION

The main task in any structural design philosophy is to find an optimal solution (Gutkowski 1997). Thin-walled structures as weight-optimised ones, take a very important place in the field of structural engineering. However, such members display a very complex structural behaviour and thus, in their design, an important consideration concerns the accurate prediction of their limit load-carrying capacity. For this purpose, a large-displacement or second-order elastic–plastic analysis should be performed.

The large-displacement analysis is usually carried out using some of the approximate methods (Boresi et al. 2003) and some of the incremental descriptions like the total and updated Lagrangian approaches, respectively or the Eulerian approach (Belytschko et al. 2000). Each description utilizes a different structural configuration for system quantities referring and results in the form of a set of non-linear equilibrium equations of the structure. This set should be solved using some incremental-iterative scheme, which consists of three main phases. The first or predictor phase comprises evaluating the overall structural stiffness and solving for the displacement increments from the approximated incremental equilibrium equations for the structure. Using the standard transformation process displacement increments of each finite element can be determined immediately. The second or corrector phase involves the geometry updating of each finite element and the determination of element nodal forces using some force recovery algorithm. Before choosing an appropriate force recovery algorithm, the rigid-body test should be performed (Yang & Kuo 1994). While the updating of nodal co-ordinates is a trivial task, the updating of nodal space orientations should be based on the large rotation theory (Crisfield 1997, Doyle 2001). The third or checking phase comprises checking if the adopted convergence criterion of iteration is achieved in the current increment by comparing with the pre-set tolerance value.

This work presents a one-dimensional finite element formulation for non-linear analysis of framed structures with thin-walled cross-section. Using the updated Lagrangian (UL) incremental formulation, the assumption of isotropic and linear-elastic material behavior and the non-linear displacement field of thin-walled cross-section based on inclusion of second-order terms of large rotations (McGuire 2000), a tangent stiffness matrix of a two-node space beam element is firstly developed. Due to the nonlinear displacement field, all internal moments occurring in the geometric stiffness are obtained as those of semitangential behavior. In this way, the joint equilibrium of non-collinear elements is provided. External stiffness approach (ESA) is applied in the force recovery phase (Turkalj et al. 2001).

Material non-linearity is introduced for an elastic-perfectly plastic material behavior through the plastic hinge formation at finite element ends (Chen & Sohal 1995, Orbison et al. 1982). For this, a plastic reduction matrix of the element is determined, a function of which is to keep the element incremental forces at a plastic hinge to move tangentially to the yield surface (Conci & Gattas 1990). The interaction of element forces at a hinge and the possibility of elastic unloading are taken into account.

2 BASIC CONSIDERATIONS

2.1 Linearized virtual work principle

In the incremental description, a load-deformation path of a finite element is subdivided into a number of increments where three equilibrium configurations can be recognized: the initial configuration C_0, the last calculated configuration C_1 and current unknown configuration C_2. Adopting the updated Lagrangian formulation, each system quantity occurring in C_2 should be referred to C_1. The index notation adopted in this work is as follows: a left superscript denotes the configuration in which a quantity occurs, while a left subscript denotes the configuration in which this quantity is measured. If the superscript and the subscript are same, the latter one may be dropped.

Neglecting the body forces and applying the UL description, the principle of virtual work for a finite element in the configuration C_2 can be expressed as:

$$\int_{1_V} {}_1^2 S_{ij} \, \delta_1 \varepsilon_{ij} \, {}^1 dV = \int_{1_{A_\sigma}} {}_1^2 t_i \, \delta u_{i \, \text{tot}} \, {}^1 dA_\sigma \tag{1}$$

where S_{ij} and t_i represent the second Piola–Kirchhoff stress tensor and the surface force, respectively, occurring in C_2 but measured in C_1, ε_{ij} and $u_{i \, \text{tot}}$ are the Green–Lagrangian strain and total displacement increments, respectively. The δ means *variation in*.

The variables of Equation 1 can be further decomposed as:

$$\begin{aligned} u_{i \, \text{tot}} &= u_i + \tilde{u}_i \,, \quad \varepsilon_{ij} = e_{ij} + \eta_{ij} + \tilde{e}_{ij} \\ {}_1^2 S_{ij} &= {}_1^1 S_{ij} + C_{ijkl} \, \varepsilon_{ij} \,, \quad {}_1^2 t_i = {}_1^1 t_i + {}_1 t_i \end{aligned} \tag{2}$$

where u_i and $\tilde{u}_i$ = first- and second-order displacement terms, respectively; e_{ij} and η_{ij} = linear and nonlinear strain increments due to u_i, respectively; $\tilde{e}_{ij}$ = linear strain increment due to u_i; C_{ijkl} = incremental constitutive tensor.

After the back-substitution of Equation 2 into Equation 1 and neglecting some higher order terms, follows:

$$\delta U_E + \delta U_G = \delta \, {}_1^2 W - \delta \, {}_1^1 W \tag{3}$$

The δU_E represents the linear behavior of the beam element

$$\delta U_E = \int_{1_V} {}_1 C_{ijkl} \, {}_1 e_{kl} \, \delta_1 e_{ij} \, {}^1 dV \tag{4}$$

The δU_G represents the change in potential energy due to initial stresses and element nodal forces occurring at C_1

$$\begin{aligned} \delta U_G &= \int_{1_V} {}_1^1 S_{ij} \, \delta_1 \eta_{ij} \, {}^1 dV \\ &+ \int_{1_V} {}_1^1 S_{ij} \, \delta_1 \tilde{e}_{ij} \, {}^1 dV - \int_{1_{A_\sigma}} {}_1^1 t_i \, \delta \tilde{u}_i \, {}^1 dA_\sigma \end{aligned} \tag{5}$$

The terms on the right-hand side of Equation 3 represent the virtual work of external forces at the end and beginning of current increment, respectively:

$$\delta \, {}_1^2 W = \int_{1_{A_\sigma}} {}_1^2 t_i \, \delta u_i \, {}^1 dA_\sigma \,; \, \delta \, {}_1^1 W = \int_{1_V} {}_1^1 S_{ij} \, \delta_1 e_{ij} \, {}^1 dV \tag{6}$$

2.2 Cross-sectional displacement field

Displacement field used in this work conforms to the following assumptions: a beam member is prismatic and straight; the cross-section is not deformed in its own plane, but is subjected to warping in the longitudinal direction, displacements and rotations are large but strains are small; the shear center and centroid of the cross-section coincide. A right-handed Cartesian co-ordinate system (z, x, y) is chosen in such a way that axis z coincides with the beam axis passing through the centroid O of each cross-section. The co-ordinate axes x and y are the principal inertial axes of the cross-section.

If the assumption of small rotations is not valid, then the total incremental displacement components $(w_{\text{tot}}, u_{\text{tot}}, v_{\text{tot}})$ of an arbitrary point on the cross-section defined by the position co-ordinates x and y and the warping function $\omega(x, y)$ with respect to the centroid, contain the conventional or first-order displacement terms (Gjelsvik 1981).

$$w = w_o - yv_o' - xu_o' - \omega\varphi_z' \,; \, u = u_o - y\varphi_z \,; \, v = v_o + x\varphi_z \tag{7}$$

and the second-order displacement terms due to large rotation effects (Turkalj et al. 2001).

$$\begin{aligned} \tilde{w} &= 0.5\left(-x\varphi_z \, v_o' + y\varphi_z \, u_o'\right); \, \tilde{u} = -0.5\left\{x\varphi_z^2 + x\left(u_o'\right)^2\right. \\ &\left. + yv_o' \, u_o'\right\}; \, \tilde{v} = 0.5\left\{-xv_o' \, u_o' - y\varphi_z^2 - y\left(v_o'\right)^2\right\} \end{aligned} \tag{8}$$

In Equations 7 and 8, $w_o = w_o(z)$, $u_o = u_o(z)$ and $v_o = v_o(z)$ are rigid-body translations of the cross-section in the z direction at the centroid and in the x and y directions at the centroid, respectively, while $\varphi_z = \varphi_z(z)$, $\varphi_x = -v_o'(z)$ and $\varphi_y = u_o'(z)$ and rigid-body rotations about the centroidal axes z, x and y, respectively; $\theta = -\varphi_z'(z)$ is a parameter defining warping of the cross-section. The superscript "prime" indicates the derivative with respect to z.

2.3 Strain–displacement relations

The Green–Lagrange strain tensor corresponding to the non-linear displacement field, the components of which are given by Equations 7 and 8, can be written in the following form:

$$\varepsilon_{ij} = 0.5\left(u_{i \, \text{tot}, j} + u_{j \, \text{tot}, i} + u_{k \, \text{tot}, i} \, u_{k \, \text{tot}, j}\right) \cong e_{ij} + \eta_{ij} + \tilde{e}_{ij} \tag{9}$$

$$2e_{ij} = u_{i,j} + u_{j,i} \, ; \, 2\eta_{ij} = u_{k,i}u_{k,j} \, ; \, 2\tilde{e}_{ij} = \tilde{u}_{i,j} + \tilde{u}_{j,i} \quad (10)$$

Due to geometrical hypothesis of the cross-sectional in-plane rigidity, the strain components $\varepsilon_{xx} = \varepsilon_{11}$, $\varepsilon_{yy} = \varepsilon_{22}$ and $\gamma_{xy} = 2\varepsilon_{xy} = 2\varepsilon_{12}$ in Equation 9 should be equal to zero. The non-zero strain components are

$$e_{zx} = \frac{\partial w}{\partial z} \, ; \, e_{zx} = \frac{\partial w}{\partial x} + \frac{\partial u}{\partial z} \, ; \, e_{zy} = \frac{\partial w}{\partial y} + \frac{\partial v}{\partial z} \quad (11)$$

$$\eta_{zz} = 0.5\left[\left(\frac{\partial w}{\partial z}\right)^2 + \left(\frac{\partial u}{\partial z}\right)^2 + \left(\frac{\partial v}{\partial z}\right)^2 \right]; \ \eta_{zx} = \frac{\partial w}{\partial z}\frac{\partial w}{\partial x}$$

$$+\frac{\partial u}{\partial z}\frac{\partial u}{\partial x} + \frac{\partial v}{\partial z}\frac{\partial v}{\partial x}; \ \eta_{zy} = \frac{\partial w}{\partial z}\frac{\partial w}{\partial y} + \frac{\partial u}{\partial z}\frac{\partial u}{\partial y} + \frac{\partial v}{\partial z}\frac{\partial v}{\partial y} \quad (12)$$

$$\tilde{e}_{zx} = \frac{\partial \tilde{w}}{\partial z} \, ; \, \tilde{e}_{zx} = \frac{\partial \tilde{w}}{\partial x} + \frac{\partial \tilde{u}}{\partial z} \, ; \, \tilde{e}_{zy} = \frac{\partial \tilde{w}}{\partial y} + \frac{\partial \tilde{v}}{\partial z} \quad (13)$$

2.4 Beam stress resultants

Using the Euler–Bernoulli–Navier theory for bending and Timoshenko–Vlasov theory for torsion, then the cross-sectional stress resultants can be defined as

$$F_z = \int_A \sigma_z \, dA; \, F_x = \int_A \tau_{zx} \, dA; \, F_y = \int_A \tau_{zy} \, dA$$

$$M_z = \int_A \left(\tau_{zy}x - \tau_{zx}y \right) dA; \quad M_x = \int_A \sigma_z y \, dA$$

$$M_y = -\int_A \sigma_z x \, dA; \quad M_\omega = \int_A \sigma_z \omega \, dA \quad (14)$$

where F_z = axial force acting at the centroid; F_x and F_y = shear forces; M_z = torsional moment; M_x and M_y = bending moments with respect to x- and y- axes, respectively; and M_ω = bimoment occurring due to restricted cross-sectional warping. The torsion moment is represented as a sum of T_{sv} = Saint Venant or uniform torsional moment and T_ω = warping or nonuniform torsional moment, respectively. Assuming the linearized incremental stress-strain relations can be defined as $\sigma_z = Ee_{zz}$, $\tau_{zy} = Ge_{zy}$ and $\tau_{zy} = Ge_{zy}$, where E = elastic modulus and G = shear modulus, then from Equations 11 and 14 follows:

$$F_z = EAw'_o \, ; \, F_x = -M'_y \, ; \, F_y = M'_x \, ; \, M_x = -EI_xv''_o$$

$$M_y = EI_yu''_o \, ; \, T_{sv} = GJ\varphi'_z \, ; \, M_\omega = -EI_\omega\varphi''_z \quad (15)$$

$$T_\omega = M'_\omega \, ; \, \overline{K} = F_z\alpha_z + M_x\alpha_x + M_y\alpha_y + M_\omega\alpha_\omega$$

where A = cross-sectional area; I_x and I_y = principal moments of inertia about x and y axes, respectively; J = Saint Venant torsion constant; I_ω = warping moment of inertia, while detailed expressions of α_z, α_x, α_y and α_ω can be found in (Chen & Atsuta 1977).

3 BEAM FINITE ELEMENT

3.1 Nodal vectors

In the present analysis, a two-node space beam element with 7 degrees of freedom (d.o.f.) per node is adopted. The seventh degree at each node describes the cross-sectional warping displacement. The nodal displacement and force vectors, $\mathbf{u}^e$ and $\mathbf{f}^e$, of an arbitrary eth element with the end nodes A and B, are:

$$\mathbf{u}^e = \begin{Bmatrix} \mathbf{u}^e_A \\ \mathbf{u}^e_B \end{Bmatrix} \, ; \, \mathbf{f}^e = \begin{Bmatrix} \mathbf{f}^e_A \\ \mathbf{f}^e_B \end{Bmatrix}$$

$$\left(\mathbf{u}^e \right)^T = \left\{ w_{oi}, u_{si}, v_{si}, \varphi_{zi}, \varphi_{xi}, \varphi_{yi}, \theta_i \right\} \quad (16)$$

$$\left(\mathbf{f}^e \right)^T = \left\{ F_{zi}, F_{xi}, F_{yi}, M_{zi}, M_{xi}, M_{yi}, M_{\omega i} \right\}$$

3.2 Element stiffness matrices

The derivation of the stiffness matrices for the finite element is based upon the assumed approximate displacement field. Applying the linear interpolation for w_o and the cubic one for the u_o, v_o and φ_z (Zienkiewicz & Taylor 2000), and expressing the beam stress resultants at the z-section with those at the element nodes, from Equations 4–6 follows:

$$\delta \mathrm{U}_E = \left(\delta \mathbf{u}^e \right)^T \mathbf{k}^e_E \, \mathbf{u}^e \, ; \quad \delta \mathrm{U}_G = \left(\delta \mathbf{u}^e \right)^T \mathbf{k}^e_G \, \mathbf{u}^e$$

$$\delta^2_1 \mathrm{W} - \delta^1_1 \mathrm{W} = \left(\delta \mathbf{u}^e \right)^T \left({}^2\mathbf{f}^e - {}^1\mathbf{f}^e \right) \quad (17)$$

where $\mathbf{k}_E$ and $\mathbf{k}_G$ are the incremental elastic and geometric stiffness matrices of the beam element, respectively. The $\mathbf{u}^e$ now contains the nodal displacement increments, while ${}^2\mathbf{f}^e$ and ${}^1\mathbf{f}^e$ are the nodal force vectors at the end and beginning of increment, respectively. Substituting Equation 17 into Equation 3, the incremental equilibrium equations can be written in the matrix form as:

$$\left(\mathbf{k}^e_E + \mathbf{k}^e_G \right) \mathbf{u}^e = \mathbf{f}^e \, ; \quad \mathbf{f}^e = {}^2\mathbf{f}^e - {}^1\mathbf{f}^e \quad (18)$$

in which the $\mathbf{f}^e$ contains nodal force increments.

3.3 Predictor phase

At the beginning of each load step, the incremental elastic and geometric stiffness matrices are formed for each beam element. To set up the overall incremental equilibrium equation, those matrices should be transformed from the local co-ordinate system (${}^1z$, ${}^1x$, ${}^1y$) of each element in C_1 configuration to the global co-ordinate system (Z, X, Y). Thereafter, the standard assembling procedure can be performed. The described procedure can be summarized as:

$$\left(\mathbf{K}_E + \mathbf{K}_G\right)\mathbf{U} = \mathbf{P}; \quad \mathbf{P} = {}^2\mathbf{P} - {}^1\mathbf{P}$$

$$\mathbf{K}_E = \sum_e \left({}^1\mathbf{t}^e\right)^{\mathrm{T}} \mathbf{k}_E^e \, {}^1\mathbf{t}^e; \quad \mathbf{K}_G = \sum_e \left({}^1\mathbf{t}^e\right)^{\mathrm{T}} \mathbf{k}_G^e \, {}^1\mathbf{t}^e \quad (19)$$

where ${}^1\mathbf{t}^e$ is the transformation matrix of the eth beam element in C_1 and which should be continuously updated for each new configuration of the element. The $\mathbf{U}$ and $\mathbf{P}$ are the incremental displacement vector and the incremental external loads of the structure, respectively. ${}^2\mathbf{P}$ and ${}^1\mathbf{P}$ are the vectors of external loads applied to the structure at C_2 and C_1 configurations, respectively. The procedure depicted by Equation 19 is to be repeated at every iteration during the loading cycle.

3.4 Corrector phase

Assuming all the restrained degrees of freedom are removed in Equation 19, the overall incremental displacement vector $\mathbf{U}$ can be solved. After extracting the global incremental nodal displacements $\bar{\mathbf{u}}^e$ for an each element from the $\mathbf{U}$, then the $\mathbf{u}^e$ can be obtained by the back-transformation to the local coordinate system of the element, i.e.

$$\mathbf{u}^e = {}^1\mathbf{t}^e \, \bar{\mathbf{u}}^e \quad (20)$$

Finally, for the nodal force vector of the beam element in C_2 configuration, from Equation 24 one obtains:

$$^2\mathbf{f}^e = {}_1^2\mathbf{f}^e = {}^1\mathbf{f}^e + \mathbf{f}^e = {}^1\mathbf{f}^e + \left(\mathbf{k}_E^e + \mathbf{k}_G^e\right)\mathbf{u}^e \quad (21)$$

where, according to the updated Lagrangian formulation, $^2\mathbf{f}^e$ contains the force components acting on the element nodes at C_2 but which are stated in the direction of the element axes at C_1. Thus, these components can be used neither in the checking phase nor in the geometric stiffness matrix forming for the next incremental step.

As the accuracy of a non-linear solution depends primarily on the algorithm used in the corrector phase it should be exact as much as possible. In this work, the ESA is applied, i.e.

$$^2\mathbf{f}^e = {}_2^2\mathbf{f}^e = {}^1\mathbf{f}^e + \mathbf{f}^e = {}^1\mathbf{f}^e + \left(\mathbf{k}_E^e + \mathbf{k}_G^e - \mathbf{k}_{Ext}^e\right)\mathbf{u}^e \quad (22)$$

where $\mathbf{k}_{Ext}$ is the external stiffness matrix of the eth beam element, the purpose of which is to exclude the rigid-body effects from the element nodal forces. The procedure for developing this matrix was presented by Turkalj et al. (2001) and was based on a special variation approach firstly introduced by Yang & McGuire (1986).

3.5 Plastic hinge model

To obtain the plastic reduction matrix, it is assumed that the continuous and convex yielding function of nodal forces obtained by the ESA exists:

$$\Phi = \Phi\left(\mathbf{f}^e\right) = 1 \quad (23)$$

and that the infinitesimal displacement increment $d\mathbf{u}^e$ of a plastic hinge can be additively decomposed into the elastic and plastic parts

$$d\mathbf{u}^e = d\mathbf{u}_{el}^e + d\mathbf{u}_{pl}^e \quad (24)$$

If the normality principle holds, then for beam element ends in a plastic state it can be written:

$$\left(d\mathbf{u}_{pl}^e\right)^{\mathrm{T}} d\mathbf{f}^e = 0 \quad (25)$$

where the $d\mathbf{f}^e$ is the infinitesimal force increment and

$$d\mathbf{u}_{pl}^e = \left\{\begin{matrix} d\mathbf{u}_{plA}^e \\ d\mathbf{u}_{plB}^e \end{matrix}\right\} = \begin{bmatrix} \mathbf{G}_A & 0 \\ 0 & \mathbf{G}_B \end{bmatrix}\left\{\begin{matrix} d\lambda_A \\ d\lambda_B \end{matrix}\right\} = \mathbf{G}\,d\lambda$$

$$\mathbf{G}_i^{\mathrm{T}} = \left\{\frac{\partial \Phi}{\partial F_{zi}}; \frac{\partial \Phi}{\partial F_{xi}}; \frac{\partial \Phi}{\partial F_{yi}}; \frac{\partial \Phi}{\partial M_{zi}}; \frac{\partial \Phi}{\partial M_{xi}}; \frac{\partial \Phi}{\partial M_{yi}}; \frac{\partial \Phi}{\partial M_{\omega i}}\right\} \quad (26)$$

In Equation 26 the $\mathbf{G}$ represents a gradient matrix containing gradient vectors $\mathbf{G}_A$ and $\mathbf{G}_B$ of the yield surface, while $d\lambda$ is a vector of an arbitrarily positive scalar functions or plastic deformation magnitudes. Because the $d\lambda$ is arbitrary, from Equations 25 and 26, it can be written:

$$\left(\mathbf{G}\,d\lambda\right)^{\mathrm{T}} d\mathbf{f}^e = d\lambda^{\mathrm{T}}\mathbf{G}^{\mathrm{T}} d\mathbf{f}^e = 0 \quad \Rightarrow \quad \mathbf{G}^{\mathrm{T}} d\mathbf{f}^e = 0 \quad (27)$$

As for the elastic-perfectly plastic material behavior the infinitesimal force increment consists of an elastic part only, from Equations 22, 24 and 26 follows:

$$d\mathbf{f}^e = \left(\mathbf{k}_E^e + \mathbf{k}_G^e - \mathbf{k}_{Ext}^e\right)d\mathbf{u}_{el}^e = \mathbf{k}_{T,Ext}^e \, d\mathbf{u}_{el}^e$$

$$= \mathbf{k}_{T,Ext}^e \left(d\mathbf{u}^e - d\mathbf{u}_{pl}^e\right) = \mathbf{k}_{T,Ext}^e \, d\mathbf{u}^e - \mathbf{k}_{T,Ext}^e \, \mathbf{G}\,d\lambda \quad (28)$$

and after combining Equations 26 and 28:

$$d\lambda = \left(\mathbf{G}^{\mathrm{T}} \mathbf{k}_{T,Ext}^e \, \mathbf{G}\right)^{-1} \mathbf{G}^{\mathrm{T}} \mathbf{k}_{T,Ext}^e \, d\mathbf{u}^e \quad (29)$$

Substituting Equation 29 into Equation 28, one can finally obtain:

$$d\mathbf{f}^e = \left(\mathbf{k}_{T,Ext}^e - \mathbf{k}_P^e\right)d\mathbf{u}^e \quad (30)$$

where the plastic reduction matrix

$$\mathbf{k}_P^e = \mathbf{k}_{T,Ext}^e \, \mathbf{G} \left(\mathbf{G}^T \, \mathbf{k}_{T,Ext}^e \, \mathbf{G} \right)^{-1} \mathbf{G}^T \, \mathbf{k}_{T,Ext}^e \qquad (31)$$

If a plastic hinge exists at one or both element nodes at the beginning of the incremental step, this matrix should be subtracted from the element stiffness matrices in both the predictor and corrector phases.

4 EXAMPLES

In the numerical examples, the yield function reported by Conci & Gattas (1990) has been adopted in this work

$$\Phi = 1.15 f_z^2 + m_x^2 + m_y^4 + 3.67 p^2 m_x^2 + 3 p^6 m_y^2$$

$$+ 4.65 m_x^4 m_y^2 + m_z^2 + m_\omega^2 \qquad (32)$$

which is a modified version of a yield surface introduced by Orbison et al. (1982), although any continuous function with the continuous first derivatives can be used.

The generalized displacement control method (Yang & Kuo 1994) has been employed as an incremental-iterative solution strategy.

4.1 Plane frame

Figure 1 shows a one-story, two-bay plane frame. Each horizontal member is W 27 × 84 and each column is W 10 × 45, with the yield strength $\sigma_y = 36$ ksi. Modulus of elasticity $E = 29000$ ksi. Obtained results are presented in Figure 2 and compared with those obtained by MASTAN2 (Ziemian & McGuire 2000) for the first- and second-order elastic analysis.

4.2 Space frame

A one-storey, one-bay space frame is presented in Figure 3. The external load is composed of three forces acting at the frame corner A: $F_Z = 100$ kN; $F_X = 25$ kN and $F_Y = 500$ kN. All frame members are HEB 300

with the web lying in the Z–Y plane at columns and normal to the X–Y plane at girders, respectively. The yield strength $\sigma_y = 240$ MPa. Material moduli are $E = 210$ GPa and $G = 80$ GPa, respectively. The length of each beam is 400 cm and column 130 cm. The full warping restrain is assumed at the ends of each frame member.

Elastic and elastic–plastic cases are treated, respectively. The elastic frame behavior is analyzed using different mesh configurations and obtained results are given in Figure 4. To validate the importance of the external stiffness matrix, the results obtained applying Equation 21 in the corrector phase, are also shown. For the analysis of elastic-plastic frame behavior, only one-element mesh model is used and the obtained results are presented and compared in Figure 5.

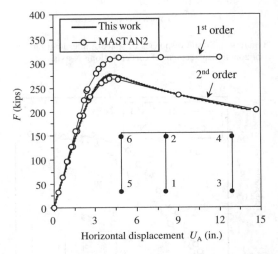

Figure 2. Elastic–plastic behavior of plane frame: applied load vs. horizontal displacement of corner A.

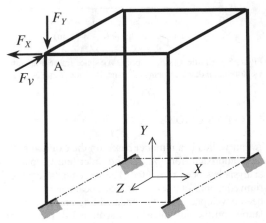

Figure 3. One-storey, one-bay space frame.

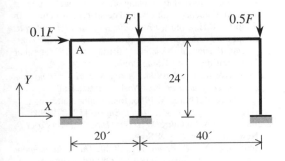

Figure 1. One-storey, two-bay plane frame.

643

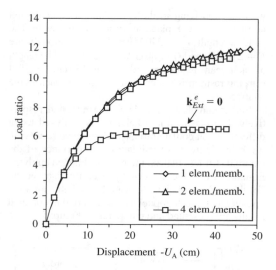

Figure 4. Elastic responses of space frame: load ratio vs. horizontal displacement of corner A along X-axis.

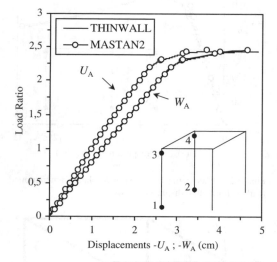

Figure 5. Elastic–plastic responses of space frame: load ratio vs. horizontal displacements of corner A along X and Y-axes.

5 CONCLUSIONS

A thin-walled beam model based on the external stiffness approach for the second-order elastic–plastic analysis has been presented. The incremental equilibrium equations of a two-node space beam element have been developed using the updated Lagrangian formulation and the non-linear crosssectional displacement field accounting for the restrained warping and large rotation effects, respectively. For the force recovering,

the ESA has been adopted by including the external stiffness matrix of the beam element is included in the equilibrium equations in the corrector phase. To model the elastic–plastic material behavior, the plastic-hinge method has been employed. Using the assumption that the continuous and convex yielding function of nodal forces obtained by the ESA exists and applying the normality principle, the element plastic reduction matrix has been developed. Such a matrix has been included in both the predictor and corrector phases, respectively. Presented and compared results have shown that a very good accuracy could be achieved using even one beam element per frame member.

REFERENCES

Belytschko, T., Liu, W.K. & Moran, B. 2000. *Nonlinear finite elements for continua and structures*. Chichester: John Wiley & Sons.

Boresi, A.P., Chong, K.P. & Saigal, S. 2003. *Approximate Solution Methods in engineering mechanics*. New Jersey: John Wiley and Sons.

Chen, W.F. & Atsuta, T. 1977. *Theory of beam-columns* Vol. 2. New York: McGraw-Hill.

Chen, W.F. & Sohal, I. 1995. *Pastic design and second order analysis of steel frames*. New York: Springer-Verlag.

Conci, A. & Gattas, M. 1990. Natural approach for geometric non-linear analysis of thin-walled frames. *Int. J. Num.Meths. Engrg* 30: 207–231.

Crisfield, M.A. 1997. *Non-linear finite element analysis of solids and structures* Vol. 2. New York: John Wiley & Sons.

Doyle, J.F. 2001. *Nonlinear analysis of thin-walled structures: Statics, dynamics and stability*. New York: Springer-Verlag.

Gjelsvik, A. 1981. *The theory of thin walled bars*. New York: John Wiley & Sons.

Gutkowski, W. (ed.) 1997. *Discrete structural optimization*. Wien: Springer-Verlag.

McGuire, W., Gallagher, R.H. & Ziemian, R.D. 2000. *Matrix structural analysis*. New York: John Wiley & Sons.

Orbison, J.G., McGuire, W. & Abel, Y.F. 1982. Yield surface applications in nonlinear steel frame analysis. *Comp. Meths. Appl. Mech. Engrg*. 33: 557–573.

Turkalj, G., Brnic, J. & Prpic-Orsic, J. 2001. Updated Lagrangian formulation using ESA approach in large rotation problems of thin-walled beam-type structures. In Topping, B.H.V. (ed.), *Proceedings of the eight international conference on civil & structural engineering computing*, Eisenstadt – Vienna, Austria, 19–21 September 2001, Stirling: Civil-Comp Press.

Yang, Y.B. & Kuo, S.R. 1994. *Theory & analysis of nonlinear framed structures*. New York: Prentice Hall.

Yang, Y.B. & McGuire, W. 1986. Joint rotation and geometric nonlinear analysis, *J. Struct. Engrg*. 112: 879–905.

Ziemian, R.D. & McGuire, W. 2000. *MASTAN2: Version 1.0*. New York: John Wily & Sons.

Zienkiewicz, O.C. & Taylor, R.L. 2000. *The finite element method: The basis* Vol. 1. Oxford: Butterworth-Heinemann.

A strain based solid element for plate bending

L. Belounar & S. Benmebarek
Civil Engineering Laboratory, Biskra University, Biskra, Algeria

M. Guenfoud
Civil Engineering Laboratory, Guelma University, Guelma, Algeria

A. Charif
Civil Engineering Department, Batna University, Batna, Algeria

ABSTRACT: A solid finite element presented in this work is developed by the use of the strain based approach for the linear analysis of plate bending. This solid element contains three degrees of freedom (u, v and w) at each of the eight corner nodes. The displacements field of the developed element satisfies the exact representation of the rigid body modes of displacements. The performance of this element is evaluated on several problems related to both thick and thin plates in bending. This element is found to be numerically more efficient than the corresponding element based on the displacement model.

1 INTRODUCTION

Considerable research works have been oriented to the Reissner/Mindlin plate theory (Reissner 1945 & Mindlin 1951) which takes into account the shear effects. In consequence the elements based on the Reissner/Mindlin plate theory can be used for the analysis of both thick and thin plates.

Other researchers (Zienkiewicz & Taylor 1977, Gallagher 1976) have used three-dimensional elements (solid elements) for the thick plates in bending. These elements tend to cause undesirable shear locking phenomena when dealing with thin plates. Acharhabi (1978 & 1990) has formulated isoparametric solid elements with several shapes, without any intermediate nodes in their thickness and with a modified elasticity matrix. Venkatesh & Shrinivasa (1996) have developed two hexahedral finite elements based on the Papacovitch Neuber solution to the Navier equation.

As alternative for displacement models, the finite elements based on the strain model were appeared in the early seventies. The first elements developed concerned only with curved elements (Ashwell et al. 1971, Ashwell & Sabir 1972). This approach was later extended to plane elasticity elements (Sabir 1985, Sabir & Sfendji 1995) and three-dimensional elasticity (Belarbi & Charif 1999).

The advantages of the finite elements based on strain model in comparison with the classical elements based on the displacement model have been illustrated on several two-dimensional and three-dimensional elements (Ashwell et al. 1971, Ashwell & Sabir 1972, Sabir 1985, Sabir & Sfendji 1995, Belarbi & Charif 1999).

Belarbi & Charif (1999) have developed a hexahedral solid finite element (SBH8) based on the strain model for the analysis of both thin and thick plates in bending with a modified elasticity matrix. The modification of the constants of the elasticity matrix aims to soften the element stiffness matrix in order to represent the reel behavior of plates in bending, either thick or thin.

In this paper an eight solid finite element which is based on the strain model is presented for plate bending problems. This element is examined and compared with other elements through a deep numerical evaluation which confirms the good performances of the strain based approach.

2 THEORETICAL CONSIDERATIONS

2.1 *Strain displacement relationships and compatibility equations*

Consider a parallelepiped element shown in figure 1. If the displacement at any point in the x, y and z directions are u, v and w respectively then the strain

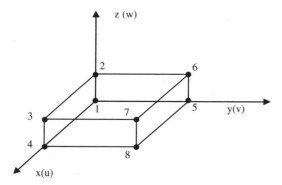

z (w)

2   6

1   7

3   5   y(v)

4

8

x(u)

Figure 1. Parallelepiped element with u, v, and w degrees of freedom at each of the eight corner nodes.

displacement relationships are given by:

$$\varepsilon_x = \frac{\partial u}{\partial x} \qquad \gamma_{xy} = \frac{\partial u}{\partial y} + \frac{\partial v}{\partial x}$$

$$\varepsilon_y = \frac{\partial v}{\partial y} \qquad \gamma_{yz} = \frac{\partial v}{\partial z} + \frac{\partial w}{\partial y} \qquad (1)$$

$$\varepsilon_z = \frac{\partial w}{\partial z} \qquad \gamma_{zx} = \frac{\partial w}{\partial x} + \frac{\partial u}{\partial z}$$

where ε_x, ε_y and ε_z are the normal strains and γ_{xy}, γ_{yz} and γ_{zx} are the shear strains.

The compatibility equations are:

$$\frac{\partial^2 \varepsilon_x}{\partial y^2} + \frac{\partial^2 \varepsilon_y}{\partial x^2} = \frac{\partial^2 \gamma_{xy}}{\partial x \partial y}$$

$$\frac{\partial^2 \varepsilon_y}{\partial z^2} + \frac{\partial^2 \varepsilon_z}{\partial y^2} = \frac{\partial^2 \gamma_{yz}}{\partial y \partial z}$$

$$\frac{\partial^2 \varepsilon_z}{\partial x^2} + \frac{\partial^2 \varepsilon_x}{\partial z^2} = \frac{\partial^2 \gamma_{zx}}{\partial z \partial x}$$

$$\frac{\partial^2 \gamma_{zx}}{\partial x \partial y} - \frac{\partial^2 \gamma_{yz}}{\partial x^2} + \frac{\partial^2 \gamma_{xy}}{\partial z \partial x} = 2\frac{\partial^2 \varepsilon_x}{\partial y \partial z} \qquad (2)$$

$$\frac{\partial^2 \gamma_{yz}}{\partial x \partial y} - \frac{\partial^2 \gamma_{zx}}{\partial y^2} + \frac{\partial^2 \gamma_{xy}}{\partial y \partial z} = 2\frac{\partial^2 \varepsilon_y}{\partial x \partial z}$$

$$\frac{\partial^2 \gamma_{yz}}{\partial x \partial z} - \frac{\partial^2 \gamma_{xy}}{\partial z^2} + \frac{\partial^2 \gamma_{zx}}{\partial y \partial z} = 2\frac{\partial^2 \varepsilon_z}{\partial x \partial y}$$

2.2 Constitutive relationships

For an isotropic material, the stress–strain relationship equations for three-dimensional elasticity are given by:

$$\begin{bmatrix} \sigma_x \\ \sigma_y \\ \sigma_z \\ \tau_{xy} \\ \tau_{yz} \\ \tau_{zx} \end{bmatrix} = \begin{bmatrix} d_{11} & d_{12} & d_{13} & 0 & 0 & 0 \\ d_{12} & d_{22} & d_{23} & 0 & 0 & 0 \\ d_{13} & d_{23} & d_{33} & 0 & 0 & 0 \\ 0 & 0 & 0 & d_{44} & 0 & 0 \\ 0 & 0 & 0 & 0 & d_{55} & 0 \\ 0 & 0 & 0 & 0 & 0 & d_{66} \end{bmatrix} \begin{bmatrix} \varepsilon_x \\ \varepsilon_y \\ \varepsilon_z \\ \gamma_{xy} \\ \gamma_{yz} \\ \gamma_{zx} \end{bmatrix}$$

$$\{\sigma\} = [D]\{\varepsilon\} \qquad (3)$$

where σ_x, σ_y and σ_z are the normal stresses and τ_{zy}, τ_{yz} and τ_{zx} are the shear stresses. The elasticity matrix [D] contains dij terms, which are defined as modified constants:

$$d_{11} = d_{22} = \frac{E}{(1-v^2)} \ , \ d_{12} = v d_{11} \ , d_{13} = d_{23} = 0,$$

$$d_{33} = d_{11} \frac{(1-v)^2}{(1-2v)} \ ,$$

$$d_{44} = \frac{E}{2(1+v)} \ and \ d_{66} = d_{55} = k d_{44}$$

The symbol k represents the "shear factor" which is usually taken as k = 5/6.

2.3 Derivation of the shape functions for the new elements

If these strains given by Equation 1 are equal to zero, the integration of these equations allows obtaining the following:

$$u = a_1 + a_4 y + a_6 z$$
$$v = a_2 - a_4 x - a_5 z \qquad (4)$$
$$w = a_3 + a_5 y - a_6 x$$

Equation 4 represents the displacement field in terms of its six rigid body displacements. The present element is parallelepiped with eight corner nodes and each node has three degrees of freedom. Thus, the displacement field should contain twenty-four independent constants. Having used six (a_1, a_2, ..., a_6) for the representation of the rigid body components, thus it is left eighteen constants (a_7, a_8, ..., a_{24}) for expressing the displacement due to straining of the element. These eighteen independent constants are apportioned among the six strains and the bracketed terms are added in order to satisfy the compatibility conditions Equation 2. We assume the strain field for the developed element in this paper baptized

SBBM8 as follows:

$$\varepsilon_x = a_7 + a_8\, y + a_9\, z + a_{10}\, y\, z$$
$$\varepsilon_y = a_{11} + a_{12}\, x + a_{13}\, z + a_{14}\, x\, z$$
$$\varepsilon_z = a_{15} + a_{16}\, x + a_{17}\, y + a_{18}\, x\, y$$
$$\gamma_{xy} = a_{19} + a_{20}\, z + (\, f_1(x,y,z)\,)$$
$$\gamma_{yz} = a_{21} + a_{22}\, x + (\, f_2(x,y,z)\,)$$
$$\gamma_{zx} = a_{23} + a_{24}\, y + (\, f_3(x,y,z)\,)$$

(5)

where f_1, f_2 and f_3 are defined for the present element.

The Equation 5 is substituted into Equation 1 and then the resulting differential equations are integrated to obtain the displacement functions due to the imposed strain field for the element. The final expressions for u, v and w are obtained by adding these results to Equation 4 to obtain the displacement field for the SBBM8 element.

The strain field for the hexahedral solid finite element (SBH8) given by Belarbi & Charif (1999):

$$\varepsilon_x = a_7 + a_8\, y + a_9\, z + a_{10}\, y\, z$$
$$\varepsilon_y = a_{11} + a_{12}\, x + a_{13}\, z + a_{14}\, x\, z$$
$$\varepsilon_z = a_{15} + a_{16}\, x + a_{17}\, y + a_{18}\, x\, y$$
$$\gamma_{xy} = a_{23} + a_{24}\, z + a_{20}\, z + (-a_{18}\, z^2\,)$$
$$\gamma_{yz} = a_{19} + a_{20}\, x + a_{22}\, x + (-a_{10}\, x^2\,)$$
$$\gamma_{zx} = a_{21} + a_{22}\, y + a_{24}\, y + (-a_{14}\, y^2\,)$$

(6)

3 NUMERICAL EVALUATION

The performance of the developed element presented herein, SBBM8, is evaluated on a set of examples for the linear analysis of thick and thin plates in bending. This element, in addition, can be used in a general three-dimensional problem. It is to be compared with the corresponding solid element based on displacement model (named DBB8), with analytical solutions and with numerical results of other elements.

3.1 Constant strain patch test

For many reasons the constant strain patch test has been considered a necessary and sufficient condition for convergence (Zienkiewicz & Taylor 1989 and 1991). The version given by Wilson & Ibrahimbegovic (1990) of the constant strain patch test as shown in figure 2 is used. The element passes this test and the results are given in Table 1.

3.2 Plate patch tests

If the element passes the plate patch tests, convergence is assured in plate problems. Hence to access the convergence characteristic of SBBM8, the test proposed by White & Abel (1989) is conducted. Loading and boundary conditions, for the constant bending moment, out-of-plane shear load and twist

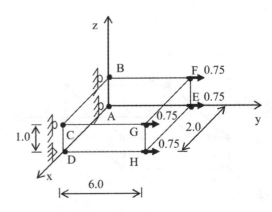

Figure 2. Constant strain patch test.

Table 1. Results for the constant strain patch test.

Mesh	SBBM8	SBH8	PN30*	ANSYS*
Tip deflection w				
1 × 1	6	6	6.779	6
Theory*		6		
Stresses σ_x				
1 × 1	1	1	0.9651	1
Theory*	1			

* Venkatesh & Shrinivasa (1996).

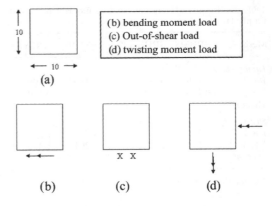

Figure 3. Loading conditions for plate patch tests.

ing constant moment patch tests, are shown in figure 3 and figure 4 respectively.

a) Constant bending moment patch test for plates
The applied load shown in figure 3(b) is a constant bending load of 2 units. The results of the vertical displacement and bending stress at the tip of the plate are presented in Table 2. SBBM8 and SBH8 predict exactly the theoretical values for all two types of meshes.

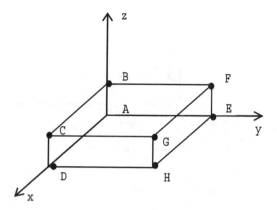

Figure 4.   Boundary conditions for plate patch tests.

Constant bending moment patch test:
   Line AE (u = w = 0) and Line BF (u = 0).
      Faces ABCD and EFGH (v = 0).
Out-of-shear load patch test:
   Line AE (u = w = 0) and Line BF (u = 0).
      Node A (u = v = w = 0).
Constant twisting moment patch test:
   Face ABCD (u = w = 0) and ABEF (v = w = 0).

Table 2.   Results of constant bending moment patch test for plates.

Mesh	SBBM8	SBH8	PN30*	ANSYS*
Tip deflection w($\times 10^{-1}$)				
1×1	0.1092	0.1092	0.1092	0.1092
3×3	0.1092	0.1092	0.1106	0.1092
Theory*		0.12		
Stresses σ_x				
1×1	1.2	1.2	1.2	1.2
3×3	1.2	1.2	1.201	1.2
Theory*		1.2		

* Venkatesh & Shrinivasa (1996).

b) Out-of-plane shear load patch test for plates
The same meshes as for the bending test in the previous problem is used again. The loading corresponds to 4 units in the z direction as shown in figure 3(c), and the results of the vertical displacement at the tip and bending stress are shown in Table 3. The performance of SBBM8 and SBH8 are similar.

c) Constant twisting moment patch test for plates
On the same meshes as the previous problem, a constant twisting moment load of 2 units is applied on

Table 3.   Results of out-of-plane shear load patch test for plates.

Mesh	SBBM8	SBH8	PN30*	ANSYS*
Tip deflection w				
1×1	0.1213	0.1272	0.132	0.121
3×3	0.1465	0.1465	0.151	0.147
Theory*		0.16		
Stresses σ_x				
1×1	12	12	11.61	12
3×3	19.88	20	19.99	19.45
Theory*		24		

* Venkatesh & Shrinivasa (1996).

Table 4.   Results of constant twisting moment patch test for plates.

Mesh	SBBM8	SBH8	PN30*	ANSYS*
Tip deflection w($\times 10^{-1}$)				
1×1	0.312	0.312	0.312	0.312
3×3	0.312	0.312	0.314	0.312
Theory*		0.312		
Stresses τ_{xy}				
1×1	1.2	1.2	1.2	1.2
3×3	1.2	1.2	1.205	1.2
Theory*		1.2		

* Venkatesh & Shrinivasa (1996).

each face (Fig. 3(d)). The results given in Table 4 show that both elements SBBM8 and SBH8 predict similar results to theoretical values for the two types of meshes.

3.3   Simply supported square plate

The simply supported square plate shown in figure 5 is examined with either a uniform loading (q = 1) or with a concentrated load (P = 1) at the center. The quarter of the plate is divided into a mesh of N × N elements, and the hard simple support boundary is used. The convergence tests are carried out on two different L/h ratios of 10 and 100 for thick and thin plates respectively. The results for the central deflection are given in Table 5 and Table 6. The effect of L/h ratio on the deflection at the center w_c for a plate is studied. The results presented in Table 7 are given for the 12 × 12 meshes in terms of w_c/w_k where w_k is the reference Kirchhoff solution (Zienkiewicz & Taylor 1989, 1991) for thin plates.
   The numerical tests show that:

- The strain based element SBBM8 has quite rapid rate of convergence to reference solutions for both thick and thin plates.

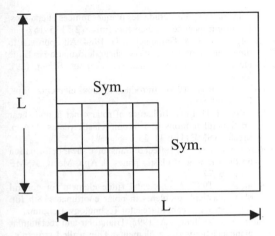

Figure 5. Simply supported square plate (L = 10, h = 1. or 0.1, E = 10.92, v = 0.25).

Table 5. Results for central deflection of a simply supported plate with a uniform load.

	$\frac{wD}{qL^2} \times 100$		
Mesh	SBBM8	SBH8	DBB8
L/h = 10			
2 × 2	0.3799	0.326	0.2283
4 × 4	0.4222	0.4048	0.351
8 × 8	0.419	0.4145	0.3982
12 × 12	0.427	0.4249	0.4171
Exact solution*		0.427	
L/h = 100			
2 × 2	0.0359	0.0523	0.0045
4 × 4	0.2553	0.3081	0.0171
8 × 8	0.3847	0.3883	0.0582
12 × 12	0.4032	0.4029	0.0786
Exact solution*		0.406	

D = $Eh^3/12(1 - v^2)$, * Zienkiewicz & Taylor 1989, 1991.

- The SBBM8 element is free from any shear locking since it converges to the Kirchhoff solution for thin plates, contrarily for the corresponding displacement based element DBB8.
- For thick plates, all results obtained with SBBM8 element are in good agreement with the exact solution (Zienkiewicz & Taylor 1989, 1991) for the plate with a uniform load and with the numerical results given in reference (Bhashyam & Gallagher 1984) for the plate with a concentrated load.
- SBBM8 has similar behavior as the SBH8 element, and it has the advantages to be valid for both thin and thick plates.
- The influence of the transverse shear for the strain based elements is much more important for plates

Table 6. Results for central deflection of a simply supported plate with a concentrated load.

	$\frac{wD}{qL^2} \times 100$		
Mesh	SBBM8	SBH8	DBB8
L/h = 10			
2 × 2	1.164	0.9907	0.7269
4 × 4	1.308	1.243	1.097
8 × 8	1.353	1.333	1.289
12 × 12	1.374	1.364	1.344
Kirchhoff solution*		–	
Ref.**		1.346	
L/h = 100			
2 × 2	0.112	0.1452	0.0134
4 × 4	0.709	0.8387	0.0481
8 × 8	1.106	1.115	0.1636
12 × 12	1.148	1.145	0.2269
Kirchhoff solution*		1.16	
Ref.**		–	

* Zienkiewicz & Taylor 1989, 1991; ** Bhashyam & Gallagher 1984.

Table 7. Influence of L/h on the central deflection for simply supported plate.

	w_c/w_{ref}		
L/h	SBBM8	SBH8	DBB8
Uniform load			
5	1.2075	1.2024	1.2016
10	1.0517	1.0466	1.0273
20	1.0123	1.0074	0.9206
40	1.0018	0.9975	0.7027
50	1.000	0.996	0.6000
100	0.9931	0.9924	0.1936
w_{ref}		$0.406 \times 10^{-2} qL^4/D$	
Concentrated load			
5	1.74	1.7317	1.7338
10	1.1845	1.1759	1.1586
20	1.0446	1.0363	0.9473
40	1.0083	1.0008	0.6987
50	1.0034	0.9959	0.5919
100	0.9896	0.9871	0.1956
w_{ref}		$1.16 \times 10^{-2} PL^2/D$	

with concentrated load than for those with uniform load.

4 CONCLUSION

The solid finite element (SBBM8) for the linear analysis of plate including transverse shear presented here is simple and straightforward with only 24 degrees of freedom. This element passes the constant strain patch test and the three plate patch tests. Numerical results obtained, using this element, agree well with those from other investigations and theoretical results for both thin and thick plates. It has been confirmed that SBBM8 is free from transverse shear locking contrarily for the elements based on displacement model. This solid element has quite rapid rate of convergence to the reference solutions for both thin and thick plates. The performance of the SBBM8 element has been demonstrated in plate bending, and the advantages of using the strain model are again confirmed.

REFERENCES

Acharhabi, A. 1978. Le calcul des plaques minces et épaisses à l'aide des éléments finis tridimensionnels à nombre de nœuds et de forme variable. Thèse de Doctorat 3e cycle, Université de Technologie de Compiègne.

Acharhabi, A. 1990. Calcul des plaques minces et épaisses à l'aide des éléments finis tridimensionnels, Annales de l'ITBTP n° 486.

Ashwell, D.G., Sabir, A.B. & Robert, T.M. 1971. Further studies in the application of curved finite elements to circular arches. Int. J. Mech. Sci. (13): 507–517.

Ashwell, D.G. & Sabir, A.B. 1972. A new cylindrical shell finite element based on independent strain functions. Int. J. Mech. Sci. (14): 171–183.

Belarbi, M.T. & Charif, A. 1999. Développement d'un nouvel élément hexaédrique simple basé sur le modèle en déformation pour l'étude des plaques minces et épaisses. Revue européenne des éléments finis 8(2): 135–157.

Bhashyam, G.R. & Gallagher, R.H. 1984. An approach to the inclusion of the transverse shear deformation in finite element plate bending analysis. Comput. Struct. (19): 35–40.

Gallagher, R.H. 1976. Introduction aux éléments finis. Edition Plurali.

Mindlinn, R.D. 1951. Influence of rotary inertia and shear on flexural motions of isotropic elastic plates. J. App. Mech., ASME (18): 31–35.

Reissner, E. 1945. The effect of transverse shear deformation on the bending of elastic plates. J. App. Mech., ASME (12): 66–77.

Sabir, A.B. 1985. A segmental finite element for general plane elasticity problems in polar coordinates. 8th Int. Conf. Struct. Mech. in Reactor Technology, Belgium.

Sabir, A.B. & Sfendji, A. 1995. Triangular and rectangular plane elasticity finite elements. Thin-walled structures (21): 225–232.

Venkatesh, D.N. & Shrinivasa, U. 1996. Plate bending with hexahedral with PN elements. Comp. Struct. (60): 635–641.

White, D.W. & Able, J.F. 1989. Testing of shell finite element accuracy and robustness. Finite Element Anal. Des. (6): 129–151.

Wilson, E.L. & Ibrahimbergovic, A. 1990. Use of incompatible displacement modes for the calculation of element stiffnesses or stresses. Finite Element Anal. Des. (7): 229–241.

Zienkiewicz, O.C. & Taylor, R.L. 1977. The finite element method. Third edition, McGraw-Hill. 1977.

Zienkiewicz, O.C. & Taylor, R.L. 1989, 1991. The finite element method. McGraw Hill. Vol. 1 & 2.

System-based Vision for Strategic and Creative Design, Bontempi (ed.)
© 2003 Swets & Zeitlinger, Lisse, ISBN 90 5809 599 1

Study of full composite action in slab-beam systems

N. Chikh
Department of Civil Engineering, University of Constantine, Algeria

J. Harrop
Department of Civil Engineering, University of Leeds, UK

ABSTRACT: The structural behaviour of a uniformly loaded slab-beam panel is described considering the effect of varying the supporting beam stiffness for different aspect ratios. The analysis was carried out by means of the finite element package PAFEC. Both the BS8110 slab design and the ACI-318-95 Direct Design Method are used for comparison purposes. The results obtained reveal many interesting aspects of full composite action in slab-beam systems, often ignored in current design practice.

1 INTRODUCTION

Although there is clear evidence from many theoretical and experimental investigations, Wood (1955) and Gamble (1972), that the moment pattern in slabs and beam bending moments are significantly affected by changes in supporting stiffness, it is still customary, in many codes of practice, to design slab and beams as though they were independent elements. The effects of composite action are only acknowledged in the form of allowing a certain width of the slab to be considered as the flange of each of the supporting beams.

An extensive investigation has been carried out by Chikh (1988), studying the influence of supporting stiffness variations on the elastic structural behaviour of fully composite slab-beam systems subject to uniform transverse load. Part of the results from this work is presented in this paper. As shown in Figure 1, a rectangular internal panel with various beam span-to-depth ratios, hence varying beam stiffness, was studied.

The analysis was carried out using the finite element package PAFEC (1978). This latter and other aspects related to the structural modelling are fully described in Chikh (1988). Both the BS8110 (1985) slab design method, which is derived on the assumption of rigid supports, and the ACI-318-95 Direct Design Method (1995), which allows for the stiffness of the supporting beams, are used for comparison purposes.

2 FINITE ELEMENT MODELLING

The element used for the idealisation of the slab is a four-noded flat thin shell element which can carry both bending and membrane loads. Each node of the element has six degrees of freedom. The element used for the modelling of the beam is a simple straight beam element with offset. The element has a node, with six degrees of freedom, at each end of the shear centre, and is connected to the slab by means of offset nodes. Hence full composite action at the slab-beam junction is realised.

Tacking advantage of symmetry, only one quarter of the structure was analysed. Referring to Figure 2, the symmetry conditions are modelled by restraining the following degree of freedom: θx and Uy along axis X, and θy and Ux along axis Y. To establish the boundary conditions of a typical internal panel, zero rotation is imposed along the supporting beams as well as restraint of in-plane displacement in the direction perpendicular to the beams, as indicated in Figure 2.

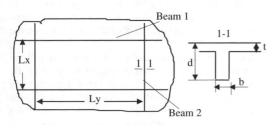

Figure 1. Geometrical dimensions of an internal panel.

	Translations			Rotations		
DOF	Ux	Uy	Uz	θx	θy	θz
Codes in PAFEC	1	2	3	4	5	6

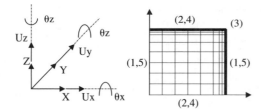

Figure 2. Meshing and boundary constraints used in PAFEC analysis.

The results of an investigation (Chikh 1988) carried out to determine a suitable element mesh size show that a 12 × 12 mesh with a finer division at the edge is quite satisfactory.

3 STUDY OF RECTANGULAR PANELS

The beam relative stiffness in the two directions can be related in many different ways. The present study was confined to the case where all the supporting beams have the span-to-depth ratio (L/d). The resulting combination of the adjacent beam relative stiffness is therefore: $\gamma_1/\gamma_2 = (Ly/Lx)^5$.

In order to assess the effects of beam stiffness and panel shape variations, the results obtained for some typical values of beam span-to-depth ratios L/d are shown in Figures 3–4. Several observations can be made from analysing the different graphs on these figures:

- While in a square panel increasing beam stiffness causes decreases in positive central slab moment and increases in negative central moments, as the panel gets longer the situation is reversed for the short span positive moment Mxc and long span negative moment Hyc. As shown in Figures 3–4, the effects of increasing beam stiffness become less important.
- The influence of beam stiffness variations on both negative slab moment Hxc and positive slab moment Myc remains very important for all panel shapes.
- With an increasing aspect ratio, more load tends to be carried by the short slab span resulting in a continuous increase in the magnitude of both Mxc and Hxc. However, in the long span the negative slab moment Hyc remains appreciable for all beam stiffnesses.
- In all cases, the edge moments, positive and negative, are significantly reduced as the beam stiffness increases.

- As the panel gets longer, edge moments in both directions decrease slowly or ultimately remain constant, indicating thereby that they are influenced by the beam stiffness variations in their particular directions.
- The agreement with ACI-318-95 results is generally less satisfactory. Two main factors contributed to this, the ratio I_1/I_2 and the range of values considered for beam stiffness effects, as explained below:
  1) The various apportioning coefficients given in the ACI-318-95 for the use of the Direct Design Method were derived from elastic studies in which $I_1/I_2 = Ly/Lx$. Where this is not the case, the same coefficients are still used provided some conditions of use are satisfied. For the present study, the theoretical results have been obtained using the same span-to-depth ratio for the two directions, this leads to a relation $I_1/I_2 = (Ly/Lx)^4$ which fulfils these conditions up to an aspect ratio of 1.7. However, the correspondence between the two approaches, as illustrated in Figures 2–3, highlights the inability of the Direct Design Method to cater for all panels situations even though they satisfy its conditions of use.
  2) The range of values specified in the Direct Design Method for which the effects of beam stiffness are allowed for is quite small and needs to be increased so as to improve the presentation of the various moment distributions. Some proposals have been made in this respect for the case of square panels (Chikh & Harrop 2002).
- BS8110 results are fairly close to those obtained with L/d =10 (i.e. rigid beams), particularly for the beam moment distributions. Regarding the slab moments, their trend is in general similar, but the ratio of negative to positive BS8110 slab moments is significantly lower (excessive redistribution).
- Beam moments always increase with increasing beam stiffnesses irrespective of the panel shape.
- Long span beam moments M_1 and H_1, BS8110 and ACI values, converge to a common value as the panel gets longer, illustrating thereby the trend of the panel towards one-way behaviour.
- Short span moments M_2 and H_2 remain essentially constant despite increases of aspect ratio. The amount of the load received by the short beam seems to be mostly dependent on its stiffness and not on the panel shape.
- Regarding the distribution of the transmitted load on the beam, not shown on graphs because of the limitation of space, it was found very dependant on its stiffness. This feature is not reflected in both BS8110 and ACI-318-95 codes where the beam load distributions are set to assumed shapes whatever the actual beam stiffnesses.

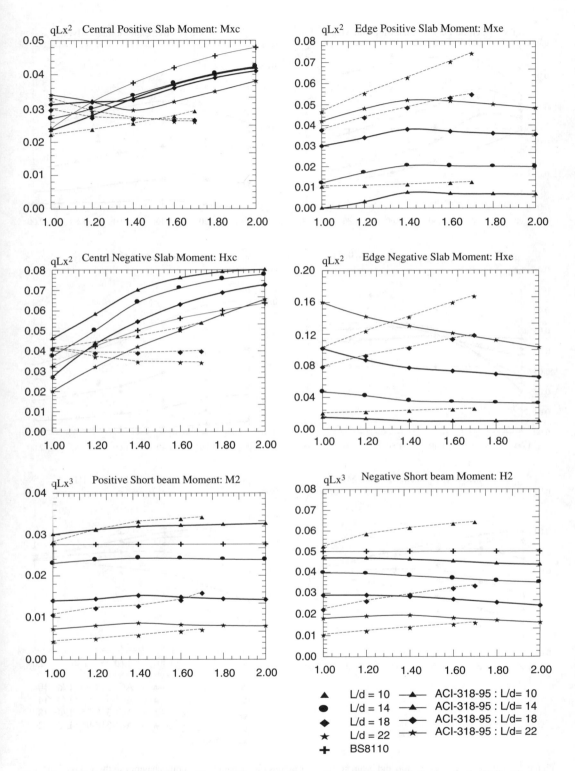

Figure 3.   Effects of the aspect ratio and beam stiffness variations on the panel structural behaviour in the X direction.

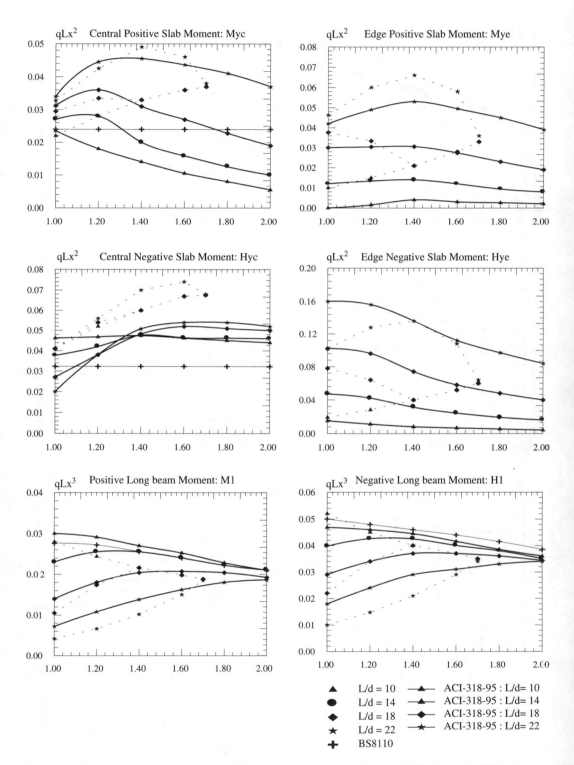

Figure 4. Effects of the aspect ratio and beam stiffness variations on the panel structural behaviour in the Y direction.

Table 1. Twistless case parameters.

Ly/Lx	1.0	1.2	1.4	1.6	1.8	2.0
$\gamma_1 = \dfrac{EI_1}{DL_x}$	0.50	0.80	1.20	1.60	2.10	2.8
$\gamma_2 = \dfrac{EI_2}{DL_y}$	0.50	0.33	0.20	0.15	0.12	0.09
Load factor (i)	0.50	0.63	0.72	0.79	0.84	0.88

3.1 Twistless cases

At some specific beam/slab stiffness ratios, Table 1, the panels were found to exhibit a very particular structural behaviour, whereby the beam load distributions were essentially uniform. In addition to that, the slab was is in a state of no-twist (twistless case) with the bending moments uniformly distributed across the full width of the panel. Thus, the slab was behaving as though it was made of independent strips spanning in both orthogonal directions.

These elastic twistless cases may offer, however, a serious alternative for developing a new slab design procedure, because of the interesting structural behaviour involved. This approach would be similar to the one undertaken by Hillerborg (1974) in developing his Simple Strip Method but it has the advantage of providing the designer with the load distribution factor (i) in the short direction, while considering the effect of supporting beam stiffness.

4 CONCLUSIONS

The influence of varying beam support stiffness on the elastic structural behaviour of rectangular slab panels is considered. The results obtained reveal many interesting features of slab/beam interaction often ignored in current design practice. In this respect, some general conclusions may be formulated:

- For slabs supported on very flexible beams, the sensitivity of the structure to beam stiffness variations is considerable. But such supporting beams are generally too small to be practical, since they introduce significant costs in beam formwork without any real compensating benefits. However, for slabs supported on relatively rigid beams, which is the case of many practical situations, the effects of beam stiffness are quite important and should be considered in design.
- A comparison with BS8110 results indicates that above certain ratios of beam/slab stiffness, whereby the beams may be regarded as rigid, the agreement is fairly good with BS8110 values generally overestimated. But below certain critical beam/slab stiffness ratios, the bending moment distributions as well as

the beam load distribution given by BS8110 are far from representing the likely service situation. Therefore, it seems safer to require a minimum for the beam/slab stiffness ratio before using BS8110 method, and other similar methods, for the design of slab-beam panels.

- The development of a slab design method coping with any beam/slab stiffness ratio is an extremely difficult task. It is also evident that the non-incorporation of important factors, such as the relation between beam stiffness in the two orthogonal directions (I_1/I_2), in the formulation of a design procedure may lead to results far from the actual ones. An example of that is illustrated by the unsatisfactory agreement between the theoretical results and those obtained from using the Direct Design Method.
- The elastic twistless solutions may provide useful landmarks in the study of slab-beam systems.

5 NOTATIONS

q: Intensity of loading on slab

E: Young's modulus of elasticity

ν: Poisson's ratio ($\nu = 0.2$)

I: Second moment of area of beam; $I = \dfrac{bd^3}{12}$

D: Flexural stiffness of slab; $D = \dfrac{Et^3}{12(1 - \nu^2)}$

γ: Beam/slab relative stiffness ratio

REFERENCES

Building code requirements for reinforced concrete 1995. ACI-318-95, American Concrete Institute (ACI), Detroit.
British Standard Institution 1985. *Structural Use of Concrete, Part 1: Code of Practice for Design and Construction*, London.
Chikh, N. 1988. *Full Composite Action In Slab-Beam Systems And The Development Of Design Procedures*, PhD Thesis, University of Leeds, U.K.
Chikh, N. & Harrop, J. 2002 *Aspects of Full Composite Action in the Structural Behavior of Slab-Beams Floors'*, Proceedings of the 6th International Conference on Concrete Technology for Developing Countries, Amman-Jordan, 21–24 October 2002, Vol. 3:863–870.
Gamble, W.L. 1972. *Moments in beam Supported Slabs*, Proc. ACI, Vol. 69:149–157.
Hillerborg, A. 1974, *Strip Method of Design*, London: Viewpoint Publication, Cement and Concrete Association.
PAFEC 75. 1978. *Theory & Results*, Nottingham: PAFEC Ltd, U.K.
Wood, R.H. 1956. *Studies in Composite Action, Part 2: The Interaction of Floor and Beams in Multistorey Buildings*, N.B.S, Paper No. 22, H.M.S.O., London.

9. Advanced modelling and non-linear analysis of concrete structures

System-based Vision for Strategic and Creative Design, Bontempi (ed.)
© *2003 Swets & Zeitlinger, Lisse, ISBN 90 5809 599 1*

Modelling non-linear behavior of shear walls with damage

S. Yazdani
Department of Civil Engineering and Construction, North Dakota State University, Fargo, USA

ABSTRACT: This paper summarizes the theoretical and computational efforts on the modelling of small shear walls. Small scale shear walls are used extensively in research because the construction and testing of full size walls are rather expensive. A finite element code is developed which incorporates nonlinear constitutive relations of damage mechanics. The program is used to obtain nonlinear load–deformation curves and to address the initial loss of stiffness due to shrinkage cracking. The program can also be used to monitor the continuous degradation of fundamental frequency due to progressive damage.

1 INTRODUCTION

Shear walls are important structural members that are designed to resist horizontal forces due to wind or seismic action. Since the full size construction and testing of shear walls are expensive, many studies have been carried on scaled down models. Endebrock et al. (1985) has conducted one such investigation as a part of an on going research program. In their work, shear wall models with high surface to volume ratios were used. The test results show that small scale models exhibits nonlinear behavior with an initial loss of stiffness and lower fundamental frequency than those computed with conventional linear elastic formulation or those observed in prototype walls.

The observed nonlinearity in the behavior of non-homogeneous cementitious materials arises from two distinct microstructural changes. One is the development of plastic flow along preferred planes under high confining pressure. The second pattern involves the nucleation and propagation of microvoids and microcracks. Since the design and behavior of most conventional structural members, including shear walls, are under low to zero confining pressure it is plausible to assume that the nonlinear behavior of shear walls is strongly influenced by microcracking.

The presence of non-homogeneities in the form of aggregate or reinforcement has microstructurally two conflicting effects. It is known for example that weak links develop at the interface of mortar and aggregate due to accumulation of water lenses. These week interface bonds are the sources of nucleation and propagation of microcracks. On the other hand, aggregate particles serve as crack arresters and help improve the strength and apparent ductility of mortar. The idea that aggregate particles act as energy barriers has been used to explain why high strength concrete behaves in a relatively more brittle fashion than normal strength concrete.

It is believed that reinforcement plays similar roles as manifested by numerous experiments. For most effective reinforcing action, it is essential that concrete and reinforcement deform together, which in turn implies the necessity of developing strong bonds between them. The bond strength between the reinforcement and concrete is developed through (a) adhesion, (b) natural roughness of the rebar, and (c) closely spaced rib-shaped deformation that provides a high degree of interlocking of the two materials. The majority of the bond strength develops through the interlocking of the two materials. The experimental investigation of Ervin & Jundi (1969) has shown that bonding of rebars is nonlinear and in particular it losses stiffness with alternating loads. With this nonlinear characterization of the bond and the nonlinear behavior of concrete it is not surprising to see that a finite element program with a linear elastic material model overestimates the response stiffness of a given shear wall. It is therefore proposed here that continuum damage mechanics could be used to predict the associated anisotropic degradation in stiffness of the shear walls.

Another aspect of the behavior that may warrant consideration is the shrinkage cracking of concrete. Shrinkage is caused by the evaporation of the free water over what is needed for the hydration of cement gel. The rate and completeness of drying depends on ambient temperature, humidity, and the surface area that is available for the heat out-flux. The work of Troxell et al. (1958) has shown that, with the geometry of the mold unchanged, a chief factor that determines the amount of final shrinkage is the water content of the fresh concrete. In their investigation the same aggregates were used for all tests, but in addition to and independently of water content, the amount of cement was also varied from four to eleven sacks per cubic yard of concrete. This very large variation of cement content had only very minor effect on the amount of shrinkage, compared with the effect of water content. Similar findings were reported by Mckeen & Ledbetter (1970). On the other hand, Hanssen & Mattock (1966) investigated the shrinkage characteristics of structural members made form the same batch but with different surface areas and volumes. They considered the surface to volume ratio to be a design parameter and concluded that members with high surface to volume ratio showed higher shrinkage deformations.

This paper addresses the issues outlined above. A finite element program incorporating continuum damage mechanics is used to predict non-linear load deformation behavior and to reflect the changes in the fundamental frequency of model shear walls due to damage. The paper also shows that if initial damage attributed to shrinkage cracking is taken into account, a good correlation with experimental data can be obtained.

2 GENERAL THEORY

The general formulations derived in this section come from the widely accepted approach of thermodynamics with internal variables (Lubliner 1972, Coleman & Gurtin 1967). With the assumptions of a purely mechanical theory and isothermal, rate-independent, and infinitesimal deformations in the stress space, one can start with the Gibbs free energy per unit volume, G, as

$$G(\sigma, k) = \frac{1}{2}\sigma : \mathbf{C}(k) : \sigma + \sigma : \varepsilon^i(k) - A^i(k) \qquad (1)$$

where σ represents the total stress tensor and k is the scalar damage variable. The colon (:) represents the tensor contraction operation and ε^i represents the total inelastic strain tensor. The inelastic strains may arise due to a mismatch of the crack surfaces, referred to as an inelastic damage processes (Yazdani & Schreyer 1988). The form of Equation 1 also implies the dependence of the material compliance on the state of microcracking. This is concurrent with the arguments made by several researchers that during the damage process the fourth-order elastic compliance tensor is no longer constant but evolves with

damage (Ju 1989, Ortiz 1985, Horii & Nemat-Nasser 1983). The dependence of $\mathbf{C}$ on damage parameter allows induced anisotropy to be captured through components of the material compliance. The scalar function, A^i, represents an inelastic component of the Helmholtz free energy.

In this work, we assume the following additive decomposition of the material compliance:

$$\mathbf{C}(k) = \mathbf{C}^0 + \mathbf{C}_I^c(k) + \mathbf{C}_{II}^c(k) \qquad (2)$$

in which $\mathbf{C}^0$ is the compliance tensor of an uncracked solid, and $\mathbf{C}_I^c$ and $\mathbf{C}_{II}^c$ denote the added flexibility tensor due to active microcracks in modes I and II, respectively. Similarly, an inelastic damage strain tensor can be separated into two parts as

$$\varepsilon^i = \varepsilon_I^i + \varepsilon_{II}^i \qquad (3)$$

where ε_I^i and ε_{II}^i denote the inelastic strain tensors due to inelastic damage processes in modes I and II, respectively. Note that for infinitesimal deformations and uncoupled theory, such additive decompositions of terms of any order is permissible. Following the Clausius-Duhem inequality and utilizing the standard thermodynamic arguments (Coleman & Gurtin 1967) the dissipation inequality is expressed as:

$$d_s = \frac{\partial G}{\partial k}\dot{k} \geq 0 \qquad (4)$$

where d_s is the dissipation rate and $\partial G/\partial k$ represent the thermodynamic force associated with the conjugate effective flux, $\dot{k}$. For all admissible processes, the inequality presented by Equation 4 must be satisfied. The substitution of Equations 1 to 3 and A^i into Equation 4 yields

$$d_s = \frac{1}{2}\sigma : \dot{\mathbf{C}}_I^c : \sigma + \frac{1}{2}\sigma : \dot{\mathbf{C}}_{II}^c : \sigma + \dot{\varepsilon}_I^i : \sigma + \dot{\varepsilon}_{II}^i : \sigma - \dot{A}^i \qquad (5)$$

To proceed further, let the rates of added flexibility and inelastic strain tensors in Equation 5 be represented by the following rate-independent linear damage evolution laws:

$$\dot{\mathbf{C}}_I^c = \dot{k}\,\mathbf{R}_I(\sigma), \quad \dot{\mathbf{C}}_{II}^c = \dot{k}\,\mathbf{R}_{II}(\sigma) \qquad (6)$$

and

$$\dot{\varepsilon}_I^i = \dot{k}\,\mathbf{M}_I(\sigma), \quad \dot{\varepsilon}_{II}^i = \dot{k}\,\mathbf{M}_{II}(\sigma) \qquad (7)$$

where $\mathbf{R}_I(\sigma)$ and $\mathbf{R}_{II}(\sigma)$ are the fourth-order response tensors, which determine the direction of damage in modes I and II, respectively. Similarly, inelastic deformations in modes I and II are represented by the second-order response tensors, $\mathbf{M_I}(\sigma)$ and $\mathbf{M_{II}}(\sigma)$, respectively. Substitution of Equations 6 and 7 into Equation 5 yield the dissipation as

$$d_s = \dot{k}\left(\begin{array}{c} \dfrac{1}{2}\sigma:\mathbf{R_I}:\sigma + \mathbf{M_I}:\sigma + \dfrac{1}{2}\sigma:\mathbf{R_{II}}:\sigma \\ + \mathbf{M_{II}}:\sigma - A^i,_k \end{array}\right) \geq 0 \qquad (8)$$

where, subscript comma (,) is used to denote the partial differentiation with respect to the variable that follows. Since k is the measure of energy dissipation, by definition, irreversible character of damage implies $k \geq 0$. Further, in the absence of any internal constraints, as indicated by Ortiz (1985), the coefficient of $\dot{k}$ must be nonnegative. Therefore, Equation 8 can be expressed as

$$\left(\begin{array}{c} \dfrac{1}{2}\sigma:\mathbf{R_I}:\sigma + \mathbf{M_I}:\sigma + \dfrac{1}{2}\sigma:\mathbf{R_{II}}:\sigma \\ + \mathbf{M_{II}}:\sigma - A^i,_k \end{array}\right) \geq 0 . \qquad (9)$$

At this point, one can define the damage potential or damage surface by simply introducing a positive valued function to force the right hand side of Equation 9 to zero. Assuming that positive function is H(σ, k), the damage surface Ψ takes on the following form:

$$\Psi(\sigma,k) = \left(\begin{array}{c} \dfrac{1}{2}\sigma:\mathbf{R_I}:\sigma + \mathbf{M_I}:\sigma + \dfrac{1}{2}\sigma:\mathbf{R_{II}}:\sigma \\ + \mathbf{M_{II}}:\sigma - \dfrac{1}{2}t^2(\sigma,k) \end{array}\right) = 0 \qquad (10)$$

where

$$t^2(\sigma,k) = 2\left(A^i,_k + H(\sigma,k)\right) \qquad (11)$$

is identified as the damage function. After employing the standard Kuhn-Tucker loading-unloading criteria (i.e., $k \geq 0$, $\Psi \leq 0$, and $k\Psi = 0$), Equation 10 essentially completes the general formulation of the proposed model; however, the details must be worked out to fully describe a particular solid. Specific expressions for response tensors, $\mathbf{R_I}$, $\mathbf{R_{II}}$, $\mathbf{M_I}$, $\mathbf{M_{II}}$, and particular form of damage function, t, must be specified.

3 LOAD REVERSAL

When concrete is loaded in tension, unloaded, and subsequently reloaded in compression, crack closure becomes an important phenomenon, which exhibits recovery of stiffness in the reversed loading direction.

The experimental works of Mazars et al. (1990) clearly show the stiffening effect of crack closure. These experimental investigations also reveal the presence of a reference pressure where the closing pressure is first noticed. This indicates that the recovery of the original stiffness of the material does not commence at the point where the sign of stress is changed, nor does it begin where the strain becomes compressive. The reference stress should be interpreted as a pressure where the majority of microcracks, in the direction of the applied stress, have become effectively closed. It is not clear at this point what this reference pressure would be under different stress and strain paths and how it would change accordingly. It should be pointed out that the complexities of the testing procedures in load reversals make the determination of the reference pressure a rather formidable task as various loading conditions must be considered. To this end, postulates on the form of the reference pressure must be based on engineering judgment until further results are available.

A number of researchers have made attempts to address these issues (see e.g., Hansen & Schreyer 1995, Chaboche 1993, Ju 1989, Ortiz 1985). Some have used the stress-based approach while other preferred strain-based approach. Chaboche (1992) has produced a rather comprehensive review on the concepts of crack closure effects, which he refers to as unilateral effects.

In this paper, similar to Ortiz (1985), the crack closure effects are addressed by employing the stress-based projection operator in the definition of an effective compliance tensor in mode I, $\mathbf{C_I^{ce}}$, as

$$\mathbf{C_I^{ce}} = \mathbf{P^+}:\mathbf{C_I^{ca}}:\mathbf{P^+} + \left(\mathbf{I} - H(-\underline{\lambda})\,\mathbf{I}\right):\mathbf{C_I^{ch}}, \qquad (12)$$

where $\underline{\lambda}$ is the minimum eigenvalue of σ^-. Note that when all the eigenvalues of σ are positive (tensile), the Projection Operator, $\mathbf{P^+}$, will be the fourth order identity tensor and $H(-\underline{\lambda}) = 0$; therefore, $\mathbf{C_I^{ce}} = \mathbf{C_I^{ca}} + \mathbf{C_I^{ch}}$ Conversely, if all the eigenvalues of σ are negative (compressive), $\mathbf{P^+}$ becomes the null tensor and $H(-\underline{\lambda}) = 1$, which forces $\mathbf{C_I^{ce}}$ to disappear from contributing to the overall material compliance (that does not mean k is necessarily zero). It is assumed that during the crack closing process, the damage in mode I does not decrease or heal but rather is just not active due to the compressive loading condition. The damage in tensile loading direction picks up from where it had left off after the new tensile load exceeds the previously attained load-level. Note that coefficient in the second term of Equation 12 is necessary to deactivate any changes in the apparent Poisson's effect (during mode-I type deformations) under the reversed loading paths, which guarantees the recovery of the original stiffness.

4 INITIAL STIFFNESS

The theoretical and experimental investigations by Picket (1946) have shown that a reasonable agreement between measured shrinkage strains and values calculated from stiffness equation can be achieved. Picket has suggested that shrinkage deformation of concrete follows the approximately the laws of diffusion similar to those expressing the flow of heat. Hanssen & Mattock (1964) followed the approach by Picket and concluded that although volume/surface ratio does not reflect perfectly – variations in both sizes and shapes, nevertheless, the degree of correlation found between the theory and experiment is satisfactory for purposes of engineering modelling and design.

Based on these studies, it is plausible to assume that shrinkage cracking has no preferential direction so that the degradation in the initial stiffness is isotropic. Let $\mathbf{C}^0$ be the initial compliance tensor as to be defined as

$$\mathbf{C}^0 = (\beta_1 + \beta_2)\mathbf{I} - \beta_2\,\mathbf{i} \otimes \mathbf{i} \qquad \text{if } \mathrm{tr}(\varepsilon) > 0 \qquad (13)$$

where, $\mathbf{I}$ and $\mathbf{i}$ are fourth-order and second-order identity tensors as before and β_1 and β_2 denote material parameters to be identified from two different loading paths.

5 CONCLUSIONS

Continuum damage mechanics approach for the modelling of shear walls was presented within the framework of continuum thermodynamics. The approach addresses the continuous degradation of elastic moduli due to damage as well as stiffness losses due to shrinkage cracking. Although the development of such models is relatively new, there is a significant potential for accurately reflecting the behavior concrete structures that display damage. However, for a direct correlation between theoretical and experimental data, the effects of reinforcement should be incorporated.

REFERENCES

Chaboche, J.L. 1993. Development of continuum damage mechanics for elastic solids sustaining anisotropic and unilateral Damage. *Int. J. Damage Mech.*, 2, 311–329.

Chaboche, J.L. 1992. Damage induced anisotropy: on the difficulties associated with the active/passive unilateral conditions. *Int. J. Damage Mech.*, 1, 148–171.

Coleman, B.D. & Gurtin, M.E. 1967. Thermodynamics with internal state variables, *J. Chem. Phys.*, 47(2), 597–613.

Endobrock. E.G., Dove, R.C. & Dunwoody, W.E. 1985. Analysis and tests on small shear walls. Report#LA-10433-MS. Los Alamos National Lab., USA.

Ervin, S.P. & Jundi N. 1969. Pull-out bond stress distribution under static and dynamic repeated loading. *ACI*, 66(28), 377–384.

Hansen, N.R. & Schreyer H.L. 1995. Damage deactivation. *J. App. Mech.*, 62, 450–458.

Horii, H. & Nemat-Nasser, S. 1983. Overall moduli of solids with microcracks: load-induced anisotropy. *J. Mech. Phys. Solids*, 31(2), 155–171.

Ju, J.W. 1989. On energy-based coupled elastoplastic damage theories: constitutive modelling and computational aspects, *Int. J. Solids Struct.*, 25(7), 803–833.

Lubliner, J. 1972. On the thermodynamic foundations of non-linear solid mechanics. *Int. J. Non-Linear Mech.*, 7(3), 237–254.

Mazars, J., Berthaud, Y. & Ramtani S. 1990. The Unilateral Behavior of Damaged Concrete. *Engng. Fracture Mech.*, 35(4/5), 629–635.

Mckeen, R.G. & Ledbetter, W.B. 1970. Shrinkage cracking characteristics of structural light weight concrete. *ACI*, 69(44), 769–775.

Ortiz, M. 1985. A constitutive theory for the inelastic behavior of concrete. *Mech. Mater.*, 4(1), 67–93.

Stankowski, T. 1990. Numerical simulation of progressive failure in particle composites. *Ph.D. Dissertation*, University of Colorado, Boulder.

Troxell, G.D., Rapheal, G.E. & Davis H.E. 1958. Long-term creep and shrinkage tests of plain and reinforced concrete. *ASTM Proc.*, 58, 1101–1120.

Van Mier, J.G.M. 1984. Strain-softening of concrete under multiaxial loading conditions. *Ph.D. Dissertation*, University of Eindehoven, The Netharlands.

Yazdani, S. & Schreyer H.L. 1988. An anisotropic damage model with dilatation for concrete. *Mech. of Mat.*, 7(3), 231–244.

Non-linear analysis of reinforced concrete slabs

B. Belletti, P. Bernardi, R. Cerioni & I. Iori
Department of Civil and Environmental Engineering and Architecture, University of Parma, Italy

ABSTRACT: The progressive behaviour up to failure, with particular attention to the crack pattern development and failure modes, of reinforced concrete slabs subjected to monotonic loading is affected, as demonstrated experimentally, by the arrangement of reinforcement. In this study, a finite element method is presented in order to simulate the effect of different arrangement of bars on the response of R/C slabs. In the analyses the behaviour of the composite material "reinforced concrete" is described by means of a non-linear model, which is based on equivalent uniaxial stress–strain curves in the uncracked stage, and on a recently-proposed physical approach (PARC) in the cracked stage. The resulting material stiffness matrix has been implemented into ABAQUS code which can makes use of a finite element, layered, shell formulation. In order to check the capability of non-linear finite element (NLFE) analyses to describe the behavior of shell elements, ten slabs are analyzed and comparisons between numerical and experimental results are reported.

1 INTRODUCTION

Conventional and simplified analytical methods are insufficient to accurately predict the non-linear behaviour and the limit states of reinforced concrete slabs whose behaviour is characterised by concrete cracking, steel yielding and second order effects. For this reason non-linear finite element analysis is become a practical and powerful tool not only for research purpose but also for ordinary design. Indeed for R/C complex structures (slabs, folded plates, precasted roof elements, bridge decks, etc.), NLFE method represents the main way to take into account mechanical and geometrical nonlinearities and to evaluate local failures, crack opening widths, strain fields, and all the quantities needed for the verifications at the service and ultimate limit states. As a consequence, successful and accurate NLFE analyses depend on the choice of an appropriate constitutive model able to evaluate the non-linear behaviour of the material "reinforced concrete".

Numerous NLFE methods available in the literature (Hand et al. 1973, Hu & Schnobrich 1990, Polak & Vecchio 1994, Cerioni & Mingardi 1996, Bontempi et al. 1997, Cerioni 1997), have considered plate structural elements, subjected to flexural, torsional, shear and axial forces, as benchmarks to prove their capacities of describing the actual response of the R/C structures. A lot of them, based on smeared and rotating crack models similar to the MCFT (Vecchio & Collins 1986), showed obtaining satisfactory results.

Recently, a local behavioural model, named PARC, able of analysing the non-linear behavior up to failure of reinforced concrete membrane elements, was proposed (Belletti et al. 2001). By a local fixed-crack approach, the main phenomena occurring after cracking such as aggregate interlock, tension stiffening, dowel action, compression softening, bridging effect, can be taken into account. In Belletti et al., 2003 via a layered approach, a stiffness matrix which links internal forces to deformations of plate elements is formulated and numerical results are compared with experimental ones relative to slabs tested by Cardenas and Sozen 1968. Cardenas and Sozen slabs are characterized by different reinforcement ratios and different rebar orientations with respect to principal moment axes, and they are subjected to combined uniform torsion and bending moments.

In this paper the effect of rebar arrangement on slab response has been analysed, taking into account ten slabs experimentally tested by Taylor et al. 1966. The decrease in bending capacity and the increase in deflection due to cracking is a consequence of the rigidity of cracked sections, depending mostly on reinforcement, with respect to uncracked sections. So, rebar arrangement affects strongly crack patterns and consequently kinematic failure.

PARC matrix has been implemented into ABAQUS program and non linear finite element analyses have been carried out using multi layered shell elements. With a view to demonstrate the capacity of the proposed NLFE procedure to predict the bending strength and the development of crack pattern as load increases, in this work a numerical study on the behavior of a series of R/C slabs, with varying thicknesses and reinforcement arrangements, is presented. Numerical analyses and their comparison with some experimental results (Taylor et al. 1966) are reported.

2 EXPERIMENTAL TESTS OF TAYLOR ET AL. (1966)

Ten reinforced concrete slabs were tested (Taylor et al. 1966) to obtain data on the effect on behavior of the arrangement of the reinforcing bars, including variable spacing and stopping-off bars.

All slabs were 1981 mm square and were simply supported along each edge to give 182.9 mm spans. The slabs have been classified according to their thickness: 50.8 mm for S1 to S6 slabs, 44.45 mm for S7 and S8 slabs, 76.2 mm for S9 and S10 slabs, resulting span/depth ratios of 41, 36 and 24 respectively.

All the slabs were designed for the same ultimate load (79.68 kN) on the assumption of a uniformly distributed load.

The reinforcement bars were 4.76 mm (3/16 in.) diameter plain round mild steel, annealed to give a long yield plateau. For most of the slabs, the reinforcement steel yield stress and the ultimate stress were of 375.76 N/mm^2 and 486.1 N/mm^2 respectively; only for S5 and S6 slabs the reinforcement steel showed a yield stress and an ultimate stress of 420.6 N/mm^2 and 497.1 N/mm^2, respectively.

The cover to the bottom layer of bar mesh was 4.76 mm (3/16 in.). For concrete, ordinary Portland cement and crushed gravel of 9.52 mm (3/8 in.) maximum size were used.

In Table 1 the main characteristics of the concrete are reported.

Load was applied to the slab through 50.8 mm (2 in.) square plates at 16 uniformly spaced positions by means of hydraulic jacks.

Table 1. Characteristics of tested slabs.

Series	Slabs	Thickness (mm)	Span/depth ratio	Concrete cube strength (MPa)
1	S1	50.8	41	35.02
	S2			36.33
	S3			35.99
	S4			31.09
	S5			33.30
	S6			35.30
2	S7	44.5	36	38.19
	S8			37.99
3	S9	76.2	24	33.23
	S10			31.71

3 NON-LINEAR FE ANALYSIS

Non-linear finite element analyses have been carried out using quadratic multilayered isoparametric shell elements.

These elements (Fig.1) have six degrees of freedom per node: three displacements (u, v and w along x, y and z directions) and three rotations (β_x, β_y, β_z about x, y, and z axes) and use Reissner-Mindlin theory for thick shell which converge to Kirchhoff shell theory as thickness decreases.

Due to the symmetry of the structure and the loading, only a quarter of each slab has been analyzed.

A mesh of 89 elements has been adopted for all slabs: geometrical features, boundary conditions and load positions are shown in Figure 2.

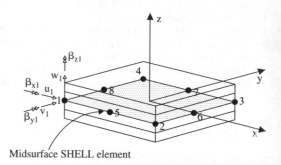

Midsurface SHELL element

Figure 1. Multilayered shell element adopted for NLFE analyses.

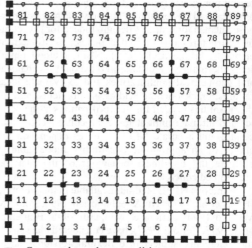

□ Support boundary conditions;
■ Symmetric boundary conditions;
● Load positions.

Figure 2. Mesh adopted for NLFE analyses.

Plain concrete or RC layers, where rebars are smeared in the layer, define the composite shell section. Figure 3 shows, for example, the three-layer element adopted for the analysis of S1 slab.

Material properties, constant thickness and the number of integration points for each layer must be specified.

In the case of non-uniform arrangement of reinforcement, element sets characterized by different layer reinforcement ratios which describe the geometrical and mechanical features of cross section must be determined.

In Figure 4, for example, element sets adopted for NLFE analysis of S5 slab is reported.

The material name of the layer refers to a material behavior which can be defined by implementing the constitutive model into a user subroutine.

In this way PARC stiffness matrix for uncracked and cracked reinforced concrete subjected to plane stresses has been adopted to describe the mechanical non-linear behavior.

The material model which includes compression softening, bridging effects, aggregate interlock, tension stiffening and dowel action, is described in detail in a previous paper (Belletti et al 2001).

Under loading, if the minor principal moment reaches cracking moment values, two sets of primary and secondary cracks may occur. Following the formulation of cracked concrete stiffness matrix proposed in Belletti et al. 2003, doubly cracked concrete is assumed to have zero secant modulus E_c.

In order to form the element stiffness matrix of layer along the thickness, the Simpson's rule with three points in each layer has been chosen and locking problems have been overcome by using, Gaussian reduced integration on the midsurface plane of shell element.

The updated Lagrangian formulation is utilized for tacking into account the effects of changing structural geometry.

The non-linear procedure is based on an iterative secant stiffness formulation which make use of Newton-Raphson convergence method.

4 COMPARISONS BETWEEN NUMERICAL AND EXPERIMENTAL RESULTS

Comparisons between numerical and experimental results are shown in Figures 5–8.

Figure 5 shows the comparison in terms of load-deflection relationships for series 1, Figure 6 for series 2 and Figure 7 for series 3.

The comparison of numerical and experimental crack patterns related to the underside of the S2, S3, S6, S8 slabs at failure is shown in Figure 8.

Numerical results fit well central displacement versus total load experimental curves at all the most significant stages of loading (cracking, concrete crushing, steel yielding).

For the series 1 flexural cracking started on the underside at about 50 kN. In the slabs with uniform reinforcement, cracks appeared first in the central region and spread towards the corners under further load (Fig 9), while in the slabs with variable reinforcement cracks appeared initially near the corners and spread towards the center (Fig 10).

At the design ultimate load, the slabs show clearly signs of the diagonal yield pattern even if in all the cases the collapse was not imminent.

For the slabs with stopped-off bars, the structural stiffness had a quick reduction owing to the formation of the square yield pattern, following approximately the line of the ends of the stopped-off bars.

For the other slabs the maximum applied load was much higher than that of design, showing wide deflections and tensile cracking extending, in the central region, to the top surface.

For the series 3, the numerical simulation have shown that crack occur after the design ultimate load.

Successively, because of the low percentage of reinforcement, the cracks widened very rapidly and extended to the top surface in the central region.

Moreover, it has been observed that the slabs with variable reinforcement had narrower cracks near the slab center than those of the corresponding slabs with uniform reinforcement, resulting the opposite in the corners.

In the slab S6 the maximum crack widths remained smaller than that in the others slabs.

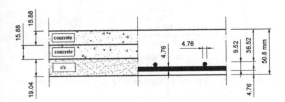

Figure 3. Geometrical features of cross-section of S1 slab.

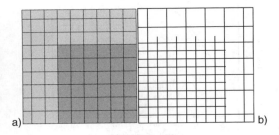

Figure 4. S5 slab: (a) Element sets of the mesh and (b) reinforcement arrangement.

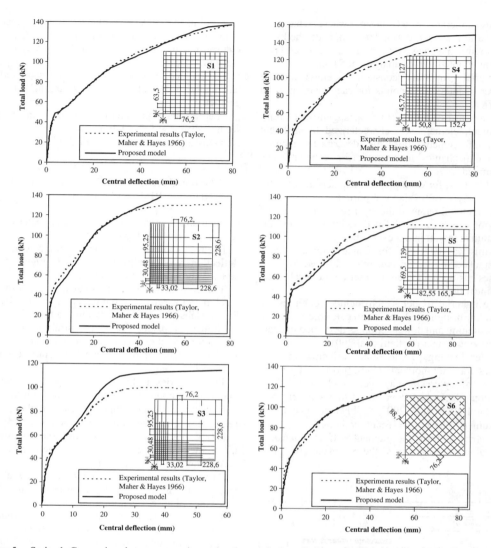

Figure 5. Series 1: Comparison between experimental and numerical results in terms of total load versus central deflection.

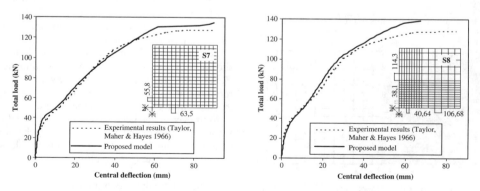

Figure 6. Series 2: Comparison between experimental and numerical results in terms of total load versus central deflection.

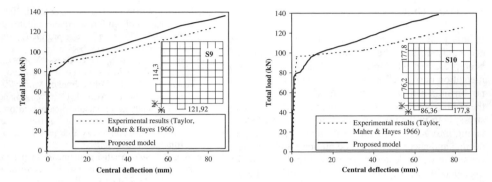

Figure 7. Series 3: Comparison between experimental and numerical results in terms of total load versus central deflection.

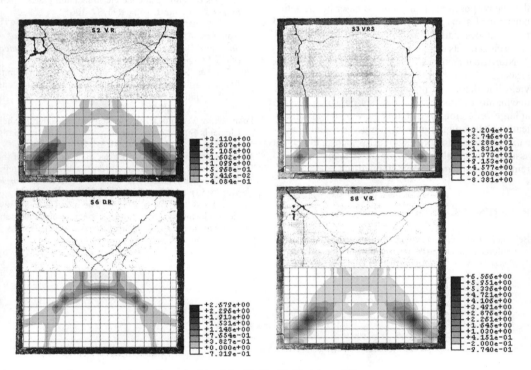

Figure 8. Crack pattern relative to the underside of the S2, S3, S6, S8 slabs at failure.

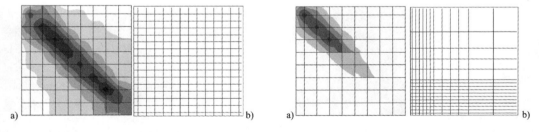

Figure 9. Slab S1: (a) flexural cracking on the underside at 50 kN and (b) reinforcement arrangement.

Figure 10. Slab S2: (a) flexural cracking on the underside at 50 kN and (b) reinforcement arrangement.

5 CONCLUSIONS

In this paper, a numerical method which is able to accurately simulate the structural response of slabs has been presented. The procedure is based on the implementation into a well-known FE code (ABAQUS) of a nonlinear constitutive matrix (PARC), which describes the nonlinear behaviour of reinforced concrete in plane stress, both in the uncracked and in the cracked stage, taking into account all the contributions affecting the normal and shear stiffness. The numerical results were consistent with relevant experimental findings, providing a detailed description of the global and local behaviour, particularly regarding crack opening width and crack pattern development. Such results demonstrate that the proposed method is able to describe the actual behavior of slabs which show a cracking pattern and failure modes markedly affected by the adopted different arrangements of reinforcement.

Numerical analyses have confirmed that the slabs sustained loads higher than that evaluated by the yield-line theory, being increasing carrying capacity due mainly to tensile membrane action which develop at large deflection. In fact, this increment was numerically predicted only introducing geometrical nonlinearity in the solution procedure. Also such an increment assumed high values only for those slabs where all reinforcement bars are non-stopped-off.

REFERENCES

Belletti, B., Cerioni, R. & Iori, I. 2001. A physical approach for reinforced concrete (PARC) membrane elements. *ASCE Journal of Structural Engineering* 127 (12): 1414–1426.

Belletti, B., Bernardi P., Cerioni R. & Iori I. 2003. Nonlinear local analysis of reinforced concrete plates. *Proceedings of EURO-C 2003 Conference, March 17–20*, St. Johann im Pongau, Austria: 635–645.

Bontempi, F., Malerba, P.G. & Grossi, V. 1997. Analisi non lineare di piastre inflesse in cemento armato. *Studies and Researches*, Vol.18, Polytechnic of Milan: 79–106.

Cardenas, A. & Sozen, M.A. 1968. Strength and behaviour of isotropically and nonisotropically reinforced concrete slabs subjected to combinations of flexural and torsional moments. *Civil Engineers Studies*, SRS 336, University of Illinois, Urbana, IL.

Cerioni, R. 1997. Analisi non lineare di piastre in calcestruzzo armato e precompresso. *Proceedings of AICAP '97 Congress*, 23–25 October, Rome.

Cerioni, R. & Mingardi, L. 1996. Nonlinear finite element analysis of reinforced concrete foundation plates. *Computers & Structures*, Vol. 61(1): 87–106.

Hand, F.R., Pecknold, D.A. & Schnobrich, W.C. 1973. Nonlinear Analysis of RC Plates and Shells. *Journal of Structural Division, Proceedings of the American Society of Civil Engineers*, Vol. 99: 1491–1505.

Hu, T.H. & Schnobrich, W.C. 1990. Nonlinear Finite Element Analysis of Reinforced Concrete Plates and Shells Under Monotonic Loading. *Computer & Structures*, Vol. 38(5/6): 637–651.

Polak, M. & Vecchio, F.J. 1994. Reinforced Concrete Shell Elements Subjected to Bending and Membrane Loads. *Aci Structural Journal*, Vol. 91(3) : 261–268.

Taylor, R., Maher, D.R.H. & Hayes, B. 1966. Effect of the arrangement of reinforcement on the behavior of reinforced concrete slabs. *Magazine of Concrete Research*, Vol. 18(55): 85–93.

Vecchio F.J. & Collins, M.P. 1986. The modified compression-field theory for reinforced concrete elements subjected to shear." *Aci Structural Journal*, 83(2), 219–231.

System-based Vision for Strategic and Creative Design, Bontempi (ed.)
© *2003 Swets & Zeitlinger, Lisse, ISBN 90 5809 599 1*

Finite deformation analysis using natural strain (on anisotropy in yield surface under large uni-axial tension and shear)

Y. Kato & Y. Moriguchi
Department of Mechanical Engineering, College of Science & Technology Nihon University, Tokyo, Japan

ABSTRACT: The Natural Strain is obtained by integrating infinitesimal strain increment on an identical line element over the whole process of the deformation path. Consequently, the shear strain becomes pure angular strain, which is obtained by removing the rigid body rotation from the rotating angle of a line element. Since the expression of the Natural Strain is different from the strain expression of ordinary rate type, this theory has merits that can satisfy the additive law of strain on an identical line element. In this paper, the behavior of a plastic deformation is investigated to a large uni-axial tension and the large shear deformation by using the Natural Strain theory. And, a combined hardening model, which the movement and the expansion of the yield surface are considered simultaneously, is suggested. Moreover, the existence of anisotropy is confirmed by investigating the distribution of the elastic modulus G in the yield surface.

1 INTRODUCTION

The A.E. Green and W. Zerna's finite strain has been widely applied to the description of large deformation. However, since this strain expression is associated with the distortion of embedded coordinate in a deforming body and is defined by the difference of metric tensor between an undeformed and deformed state, it cannot exactly express the relation of the stress and the strain which depends on the deformation history such as the plastic deformation. Therefore, the strain expression of rate type, which represents an instantaneous motion on the current condition of a deforming body, i.e., the rate of deformation tensor, is mainly used in the theoretical studies on an elasto-plastic analysis.

However, in the finite deformation analysis, using the rate of deformation tensor as a strain rate and the Jaumann derivative as a stress rate, unexpected result is derived from the numerical calculation of a simple shear deformation for kinematic hardening materials. Namely, the oscillatory normal and shear stress are induced for monotonically increasing simple shear deformation. Assuming that the unexpected result is caused by the spin tensor in a stress rate, many researchers have been tried to solve the finite deformation problem by introducing the various modified Jaumann derivatives based on the modified spin tensor. As a result, monotonically increasing simple shear deformation. However, these modified spin tensors are not always clear for a physical meaning.

Although the many researchers mainly pay attention to the modifications of the spin tensors in the stress rate, it seems that there is an essential problem in the conventional strain expression. As well known, this expression can be obtained by resolving the velocity gradient tensor into symmetric part $\dot{\varepsilon}$ (rate of deformation tensor) and skew-symmetric part ω (spin tensor). However, the rate of deformation tensor dose not express the strain rate on an identical line element in a body. Namely, the rate of deformation tensor is the velocity strain with respect to elements streaming into each orthogonal axis at the moving observation point and replacing one after another. Therefore, an additive law of strain on an identical line element cannot be satisfied, and the physical meaning of the strain, which is obtained by integrating the strain rate, is not clear. Moreover, the shear components of this strain are obtained by taking the average of angular velocity of these coordinate axes and, as a result, the spin is removed from the shearing strain, but the rigid body rotation is not accurately removed from it.

In the theoretical studies, not only the modification of spin tensor in the stress rate but also reconsideration of the formulation of strain rate is tried to solve large deformation problem. For example, the stress analysis using the rotationless strain, which is obtained by removing the rigid body rotation from the strain rate, is suggested by Stören-Rice.

On the other hand, the Natural Strain stated in this paper has also the feature, which can remove the rigid body rotation clearly from the shear strain.

However, the strain expressions of these models have an essential difference. That is, the Natural Strain is obtained on an identical line element in a body, while the rotationless strain by Stören-Rice is not expressed as the strain on an identical line element. Hence, the rotationless strain cannot satisfy an additive law of strain on an identical line element.

In our previous study, the finite deformation analysis of an isotropic elastic body has been discussed about the combined deformation of simple tension and simple shear in the case of the three different deformation paths. In general, if each of the deformation at the final state is the same, the strain at the final state must be given uniquely regardless of the different deformation paths in an isotropic elastic body. And, it was revealed that the analysis using the Natural Strain theory arrived at a reasonable result from the comparison with other strains.

Next problem presented to us is to reveal the relation of the stress and the strain for an elasto-plastic body by using this strain theory, and the final purpose of this study is to verify that the Natural Strain theory is effective in a large plastic deformation. However, not only the material nonlinearity but also a geometrical nonlinearity should be taken into consideration in the elasto-plastic analysis under the large deformation. If the anisotropy is caused in the material, it is necessary to introduce the expression that the line elements of principal axes replace with an increase of the deformation. And, the relation of the stress and the strain under the large deformation is considerably complex, and it seems that these elucidations are not easy. Therefore, considering the features of those large deformation behaviors, a reasonable and simpler formulation is required.

As the first step of this study, we estimate the boundary region of yield (elastic limit in compression side) from the experiment of uni-axial tension (we call it hereafter simple tension) under the large deformation. And, adopting a combined hardening model of the Mises-type in which the kinematic hardening and the isotropic hardening coexist, the formulation of hardening model by the Natural Strain theory is performed based on the experimental result of a ductile metal (pure copper). Moreover, the elasto-plastic analysis of shear deformation, which not only the direction of the principal axis rotates in the space but also the line element of the principal axis replaces with the progression of deformation, are carried out. And in order to verify the rationality of this model, we compare the numerical calculation with experiments of the shear deformation.

Another theme of this paper is to confirm the existence of anisotropy in the yield surface that is newly formed with an increase of the deformation by investigating the distribution of elastic modulus G. In this paper, the above-mentioned two kinds of large

pre-deformations, i.e. the simple tension and the shear deformation, are considered as investigated anisotropy. And using the test piece, which is given these pre-deformations, the proportional loading test in the elastic region is carried out applying the tension and the torsion simultaneously. The directions of the principal axis of the elastic deformation are obtained from the extensional strain component of the triaxial strain gage in consideration of the Natural Strain theory, and the relation between the direction of the principal axis of strain and the direction of the principal axis of stress can be determined. If anisotropy is produced with increase of the deformation, it is expected that the difference occur in the direction of the principal axis of stress and the principal axis of strain. However, it could be confirmed that there were few differences in the direction of both principal axes. Hence, we consider that elastic modulus G can be estimated from the deviatoric strain and the deviatoric stress on the principal axis, and reveal distributions of elastic modulus G.

2 NUMERICAL ANALYSIS OF SIMPLE TENSION AND SHER DEFORMATION

2.1 Hardening model for simple tension

When the tensile load shown in Figure1 is applied to the body, an infinitesimal line element ℓ_0 located at an arbitrary direction changes its length and direction, and turn into the current line element ℓ. In this case, deformation gradient D which defines the relations between initial and the current line element can be decomposed as follows:

$$\ell = \overline{D}\ell_o = M_oM\ell_o \tag{1}$$

$$D = \begin{bmatrix} D_{11} & 0 & 0 \\ 0 & D_{22} & 0 \\ 0 & 0 & D_{33} \end{bmatrix} = \begin{bmatrix} \lambda_1 & 0 & 0 \\ 0 & \lambda_2 & 0 \\ 0 & 0 & \lambda_3 \end{bmatrix} = \begin{bmatrix} m_o & 0 & 0 \\ 0 & m_o & 0 \\ 0 & 0 & m_o \end{bmatrix} \begin{bmatrix} \frac{1}{\sqrt{m}} & 0 & 0 \\ 0 & m & 0 \\ 0 & 0 & \frac{1}{\sqrt{m}} \end{bmatrix} \tag{2}$$

Where M_0 and M in Equation 1, are deformation gradient tensors that define the volumetric deformation and the non-volumetric deformation respectively.

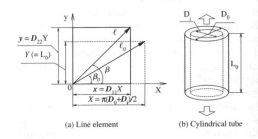

(a) Line element   (b) Cylindrical tube

Figure 1.   Tensile deformation (simple tension).

Here, we assume that the plastic deformation under large deformation is an incompressible material. For large deformation, we proceed with the plastic analysis by using only the deviatoric strain increment without including the volumetric strain.

$$_n\Delta e_2 = {}_{n+1}e_2 - {}_n e_2$$

$$= \int_m^{m+m} \frac{dm}{m} = [ln\, m]_m^{m+m} = ln\, _{n+1}m - ln\, _n m = ln \frac{_{n+1}m}{_n m} = ln\, _n\Delta m_2 \quad (3)$$

Where, Δe is composed of three components $\Delta e_1, \Delta e_2$ and Δe_3, but only the relation of a strain increment to the deformation on the second principal axis that the tensile load applies is shown (The left subscript n means the state of the n-th order in the numerical calculation based on the incremental method).

In the Natural Strain theory that the additive law of the strain can be satisfied, this deviatoric strain increment $_n\Delta e$ is represented easy by the summation form of an elastic component $_n\Delta e_e$ and a plastic component $_n\Delta e_p$.

$$_n\Delta e = {}_n\Delta e_e + {}_n\Delta e_p \quad (4)$$

On the other hand, the deformation gradient in a plastic region can be decomposed into the multiplicative form of elastic component $_n\Delta M_e\, _nM_e$ and plastic component $_n\Delta M_r\cdot_nM_r$.

$$_{n+1}M = {}_nM_e\, _n\Delta M_e\, _n\Delta M_r\, _nM_r = {}_{n+1}M_e\, _{n+1}M_r \quad (5)$$

And, this corresponds to the decomposition suggested by E.H. Lee.

As indicated in Equation 4, a part of total deviatoric strain increment becomes into an elastic strain component by the work hardening $_n\Delta e_e$ and the rest is a plastic strain component $_n\Delta e_p$ Here we define this ratio as the strain hardening modulus $_nh$.

$$_n\Delta e_p = {}_nh\, _n\Delta e_e \quad (6)$$

On the other hand, the relation between the deviatoric strain increment $_n\Delta e$ and the deviatoric stress increment $_n\Delta s$ can be represented as follows:

$$_n\Delta s = 2G_n\, \Delta e_e \quad (7)$$

Substituting Equations 6 and 7 into Equation 4, the hardening modulus $_nh$ is rewritten as

$$_nh = \frac{2\,G}{_n\Delta s\,/\,_n\Delta e} - 1 \quad (8)$$

Further, the elastic component $_n\Delta e_e$ in Figure 2 can be decomposed into two parts.

$$_n\Delta e_e = {}_n\Delta e_e^e + {}_n\Delta e_e^a \quad (9)$$

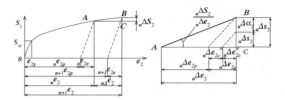

Figure 2. Decomposition of stress and strain.

Where, $_n\Delta e_e^e = \{1 - F(_nm_r)\}_n\Delta e_e$, $_n\Delta e_a^a = F(_nm_r)_n\Delta e_e$.

In above equations, $F(_nm_r)$ is a function which gives the ratio of the movement and the expansion of yield surface ($_nm_r$ is the value of principal stretch of the plastic deformation). And, we formulate this function based on the experimental result as follows:

$$F(_nm_r) = \left\{ a + \frac{(1-a)}{2} ln\, m_r \right\}\left(1 - \frac{1}{_nm_r^b}\right) \quad (10)$$

Where, a and b in Equation 10 are constants decided from the experimental result ($a = 0.42$, $b = 150$).

The stress increment $_n\Delta s$ can also be decomposed into $_n\Delta s^e$ and $_n\Delta\alpha$ (see Figure 2).

$$_n\Delta s = {}_n\Delta s^e + {}_n\Delta\alpha \quad (11)$$

And the stress increment which contribute to the expansion of the yield surface $_n\Delta s^e$ and the movement of the center of the yield surface $_n\Delta\alpha$ (back stress) are expressed as follows:

$$_n\Delta s^e = 2G\,_n\Delta e_e^e = \frac{2G}{1 + _nh^e}\, _n\Delta e\ ,\quad _n\Delta\alpha = 2G\,_n\Delta e_e^a = \frac{2G}{1 + _nh^\alpha}\, _n\Delta e$$

Where, the hardening modulus $_nh^e$ and $_nh^\alpha$ are related to the expansion and the movement of the yield surface respectively.

2.2 Shear deformation

Since the deformation considered here is produced by only the shearing stress without the normal stress, it is essentially different from the ordinary simple shear deformation that the compressive stress occurs under a large deformation. This deformation is analogues to the simple torsion which is free from displacement between both sides of the cylindrical tubular specimen (see Figure 3 (b)).

Since the hydrostatic stress becomes zero and it can be assumed non-volumetric deformation, all stress and strain components are regarded as the state of deviatoric stress and strain. The directions of the principal axis of stress are always fixed at $\pi/4$, and

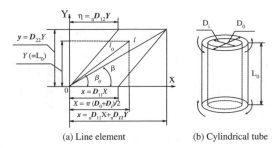

(a) Line element   (b) Cylindrical tube

Figure 3.   Shear deformation.

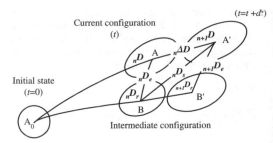

Figure 4.   Initial, current and intermediate configurations in finite deformation.

these principal components are represented as $s_1 = \tau_{xy}$, $s_2 = -\tau_{xy}$, $s_3 = 0$. From the geometrical relation in Figure 3, the deformation gradient tensor is prescribed as Equation 12.

$$D = \begin{bmatrix} D_{11} & D_{12} & 0 \\ 0 & D_{22} & 0 \\ 0 & 0 & D_{33} \end{bmatrix} \qquad (12)$$

Where,

$$D_{11} = \frac{x}{X} = \frac{1}{D_{22}} \quad , \quad D_{12} = \frac{\eta}{Y} = \left\{ \frac{\pi}{180} \frac{(D_i + D_o)}{4L_o} \right\} \varphi_{deg.} \cdot \frac{Y}{y} \quad ,$$

$$D_{22} = \frac{y}{Y} \quad , \qquad D_{33} = 1$$

Here, D_i and D_o are inside and outside diameter of the cylindrical tube, and $\varphi_{deg.}$ is an angle of twist.

The deformation gradient can be decomposed by investigating the principal value of the deformation, and they are expressed as follows:

$$D = H\Lambda H_0^T \qquad (13)$$

Where H is a coordinate system defined by the direction of the principal axis of the deformation θ_m, and H_o is a coordinate system defined by the direction of its undeformed state θ_0, and Λ is a stretch tensor which consists of principal values. Hence, the deformation can be divided into the rigid body rotation $HH_0^T \ (=R)$ and the symmetrical stretch $H_0\Lambda H_0^T \ (=U)$ or $H\Lambda H^T \ (=V)$.

2.3   Elasto-plastic decomposition of deformation gradient for shear deformation

In discussing about the elasto-plastic analysis of the shear deformation based on a strain increment, we use the following notations. The deformation gradient tensor at time **t** with respect to the original configuration at time **0** is represented as $_nD$, where the number of a left subscript n means the referring time of variable. Similarly, the deformation gradient at time $t + dt$ is represented as $_{n+1}D$ (see Figure 4).

When the load is removed from this current state, irreversible deformation exists in the material. And, this irreversible deformation has the character to be generated newly along with the progression of the deformation. Thus, in an elasto-plastic continuum, total deformations at time t can be decomposed into two parts: elastic part of deformation $_nD_e$ and plastic part of deformation $_nD_r$. According to E.H. Lee, this is indicated by well-known multiplicative decomposition of the deformation gradient.

$$_nD = {}_nD_e \ {}_nD_r \qquad (14)$$

Next, we consider the deformation at time $t + dt \ (A')$ which increases slightly by the infinitesimal deformation $_n\Delta D$ from the configuration at time t. As if intermediate configuration (**B**) was considered to be an initial configuration, we newly define the concept of added deformation $_nD_s$ between intermediate configuration and configuration at time $t + dt$ (**B**⇔**A'**). Here, the added deformation $_nD_s$ satisfy following multiplicative elasto-plastic decomposition.

$$_nD_s = {}_{n+1}D_e \ {}_n\Delta D_r = {}_nD_e \ {}_n\Delta D_e \ {}_n\Delta D_r \qquad (15)$$

Further, total deformation gradient at time $t + dt$ is represented by multiplying plastic part of the deformation gradient $_nD_r$ and the added deformation gradient $_nD_s$, and is represented as

$$_{n+1}D = {}_nD_s \ {}_nD_r = {}_nD_e \ {}_n\Delta D_e \ {}_n\Delta D_r \ {}_nD_r \qquad (16)$$

Where $_n\Delta D_e$ and $_n\Delta D_r$ means the elastic and plastic part of newly produced deformation $_n\Delta D$. Furthermore, the elastic increment can be decomposed into two terms which relate to expansion of yield surface $_n\Delta D_e^e$ and movement of yield surface $_n\Delta D_e^\alpha$. That is,

$$_n\Delta D_e = {}_n\Delta D_e^e \ {}_n\Delta D_e^\alpha \qquad (17)$$

672

Where, $_n\Delta D_e^e$ and $_n\Delta D_e^\alpha$ are represented as

$$_n\Delta D_e^e = H_e^*(_n\Lambda_a/_n\Lambda_e^{-1})^{\frac{1}{1+_nh^*}} H_{ee}^{*T} \qquad (18)$$

$$_n\Delta D_e^\alpha = H_\alpha^*(_n\Lambda_a/_n\Lambda_e^{-1})^{\frac{1}{1+_nh^*}} H_{o\alpha}^{*T} \qquad (19)$$

In these equations, $_n\Lambda_a$ means the principal stretch of an added deformation when the line element of the principal axis does not rotate. And, the hardening modulus $_nh^e$ and $_nh^\alpha$ are obtained from the experiment of simple tension under large deformation. Moreover, since the right side of Equation 16 is represented as $_nD_e\,_n\Delta D_e = _{n+1}D_e$ or $_n\Delta D_r\,_nD_r = _{n+1}D_r$, this equation is reduced to the multiplicative elasto-plastic decomposition defined by Equation 14.

3 EXPERIMENT OF FINITE DEFORMATION

3.1 Experimental method

In order to investigate the boundary region of a yield limit under a large deformation, the cylindrical tubular specimens of annealed pure copper (purity 99.999%) is especially adopted in the ductile metal. In the experiment, to decide the yield region for the simple tension, the compressive load is applied to test pieces, which the pre-deformation of the simple tension has already applied from an infinitesimal deformation to large deformations (value of stretch m = 1.03, 1.05, 1.12, 1.16, 1.25, 1.3, 1.38, and 1.43 (3 ~36% strain)), and the value of yield stress on the compression side is investigated to the pre-deformed material of the simple tension. On the other hand, in order to research the yield region of a large shear deformation, the torsional test is carried out within the range of finite deformation (the angle of twist $\varphi = 15 \sim 270$ [deg.], the value of principal stretch $\lambda = 1.04 \sim 1.95$). The reverse shear stress is applied to the cylindrical tubular specimen after pre-deformation, and boundary region of a yield limit is decided in similar experimental method as simple tension.

3.2 Experimental result

Figure 5 shows the experimental results obtained by the simple tension. In this figure, Plots ○ are estimated values of the yield on the compression side in each deformation process. The experimental equation of the deviatoric stress shown in Figure 5 (here, we will call it upper bound eq.) is obtained by determining the strain hardening modulus h from the tensile test. On the other hand, the experimental equation of a yield stress on the compression side (lower bound eq.) has been decided to agree approximately with the plots ○. Thus, we can estimate the stress of isotropic

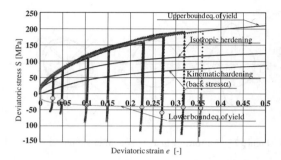

Figure 5. Isotropic and kinematic hardening under tensile load.

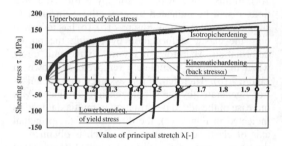

Figure 6. Numerical and experimental result for shear deformation.

hardening which means the expansion of the yield surface and the back stress α which means the movement of a center position of the yield surface by these curves in Figure 5.

Figure 6 indicates the experimental results obtained by the shear deformation. In this figure, these plots in each deformation process ○ are estimated values of the yield on a reverse shear side. Curve of the shearing stress in Figure 6 (upper bound eq.), which is obtained by numerical analysis based on the elasto-plastic decomposition, almost agrees with the experimental values of pre-deformation. Since estimated values of the yield on a reverse shear side (plots ○) agree well with the curve obtained by the analysis (lower bound eq.), we can verify that the result of the numerical calculation based on this combined hardening model to which isotropic hardening and kinematic hardening coexist is appropriate to the large shear deformation.

4 ANISOTROPY IN YIELD SURFACE

4.1 Anisotropy in yield surface caused by deformation

We consider the unit circle embedded in the body in order to explain the anisotropy, which is caused after applying the large deformation (see Figure 7).

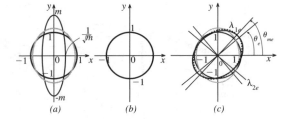

Figure 7. Anisotropy in a material after simple tension.

The unit circle is stretched to m times in the y direction by the large simple tension as shown in Figure 7(a). In this figure, if the anisotropy is formed at that time, it will be indicated by gray ellipse. In order to simplify the description, Figure 7 (b), (c) has indicated only the elastic deformation by erasing the plastic deformation. Therefore, it returns to the unit circle when the load is completely removed, as shown in Figure 7 (b). After that, if it is assumed that the anisotropy generated by the simple tension is induced with increase of the added deformation in multiaxial load as indicated in Figure (c), the direction of the principal axis of elastic deformation θ_{me}, which is obtained by the composition of the ellipse by added deformation and anisotropy ellipse, is different from the direction of principal axis of the added deformation θ_e. Thus, the difference is expected in the direction of the principal axis of the stress and the principal axis of the elastic deformation (the elastic part of deformation gradient).

4.2 Experimental method

The pre-deformation of the simple tension (value of stretch $m = 1.1 \sim 1.44$ (10 ~ 37% strain)) is firstly given to the test piece. Applying the tension and the torsion at the same time after the triaxial strain gages have been bonded to the test piece, the proportional loading tests in the elastic region are carried out under condition that these angles of principal axis of stress are fixed at 0, 20, 30, 40, 45, 50, 60, 75, and 90 degrees respectively. The direction of the principal axis of the elastic deformation (namely, the principal axis of strain) is calculated from the measured value of the extensional strain components of the triaxial strain gauge in consideration of the Natural Strain theory. Firstly, the direction of the principal axis of strain is compared with the principal axis of the stress, and the relation of both principal axis is confirmed. In the next place, we obtain the elastic modulus (shear modulus) G in each loading direction from the measurements of the deviatoric principal strain and the deviatoric principal stress. Moreover, similar experiments are also performed to the shear deformation (value of stretch $\lambda = 1.13 \sim 1.95$ (angle of twist $\varphi = 45 \sim 270[\text{deg.}]$)). Where, although the nonlinear

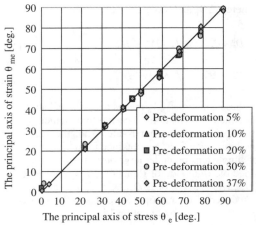

Figure 8. The principal axis of stress and strain (simple tension).

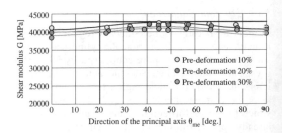

Figure 9. The distribution of elastic modulus G (simple tension).

behavior in elastic region by Bauschinger effect will be considered in measurement of elastic modulus G, we measured it in the unloading process of proportional loading test at which the influence of Bauschinger effect did not occur.

4.3 Experimental results

Figure 8 shows the relation between the direction of the principal axis of the stress and the principal axis of an elastic part of the deformation gradient (principal axis of strain). In this figure, since the direction of principal axis of the deviatoric stress almost agree with the direction of the principal axis of an elastic deformation, contrary to our expectation, it can be confirmed that there is little influence of anisotropy about the direction of the principal axis obtained after the pre-deformation. If the direction of principal axis of the elastic deformation agrees approximately with the direction of the principal stress, we conclude that the elastic modulus G can be determined from both principal values.

Figure 9 shows the distribution of elastic modulus G under the various loading directions. As obviously

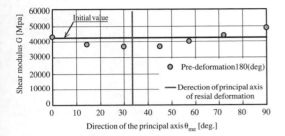

Figure10. The distribution of elastic modulus G (shear deformation).

from this figure, the values of elastic modulus G on the first principal axis of the pre-deformation (90 [deg.]) and on the 2nd principal axis (0 [deg.]) have a tendency to reduce with growth of the magnitude of pre-deformation (residual deformation). Similarly, Figure 10 shows the distribution of elastic modulus G in the large shear deformation (twisting angle 180 [deg.]). It is clear that a minimum value of G exists in the neighborhood of the principal axis of the residual deformation ($\theta_r = 33.5$ [deg.]).

5 CONCLUSION

In order to decide the yield region under large simple tension, the value of a yield stress on the compression side was experimentally investigated to the pre-stretched material. And, the experimental equation of combined hardening model was formulated based on the Natural Strain theory. The concept of an added deformation was introduced into the elasto-plastic analysis in this paper, and since the result of the numerical calculation for large shear deformation coincided approximately with an experimental value, the validity of this hardening model was verified.

Moreover, the existence of anisotropy in the elastic modulus, which is newly formed with increase of pre-deformation, was confirmed by investigating these distributions in the yield surface. As a result, it could be recognized that the anisotropy of elastic modulus G depends on the magnitude of residual deformation and the direction of its principal axis.

REFERENCES

Kato Y. & Nishimura T. 1996. The Stress analysis using the rate type formulation of Natural Strain. ASME PVP & ICPVT. Vol. 326: 159–166.
Lee E.H. 1969. Elastic-Plastic Deformation at Finite Strain. J. A. Mechanica.Vol.36: 1–6.

System-based Vision for Strategic and Creative Design, Bontempi (ed.)
© 2003 Swets & Zeitlinger, Lisse, ISBN 90 5809 599 1

The effective length factors for the framed columns with variable cross sections

S.G. Lee
Department of Architecture, College of Engineering, Chonnam National University, Yongbong-Dong, Puk-ku, Kwangju, Korea

S.C. Kim & Y.J. Moon
Department of Architecture Engineering, Dongshin University, Daeho-Dong, Naju, Chonnam, Korea

ABSTRACT: The elastic critical loads of the framed columns are determined by the finite element method. The frame is a single story-two bay, with the same support conditions at the bases, and the columns are either prismatic or linearly tapered along their axes. In general, the critical load coefficients of the columns with uniform sections show lower bound errors when they are compared with those determined by the slope-deflection method. The changes of the critical load coefficient are represented by algebraic functions of analysis parameters. On the basis of these algebraic functions, the effective length factor (K-factor) formula is proposed. In the cases of the braced frame, K-factors for columns with variable rigidities are less than unity ($K \leqslant 1$), which are consistent with the conventional definition of K-factors for the framed columns with uniform rigidities.

1 INTRODUCTION

Structural engineers are accustomed to the concept of effective length factor (or K-factor) when they are involved in the design of compression members. When the prismatic member exists as an isolated member, the effective length factor is easy to determine. In the cases of framed columns with uniform cross section, the derivation of K-factor is not simple because the frame stability is governed by several parameters. The most widely adopted method for K-factor determination may be the so-called alignment charts found in AISC Manuals. This alignment charts for framed columns, however, are based on some unacceptable assumptions, for which one can not expect the exact K-factors.

In some cases of building frames, the columns are in the form of variable cross sections. The structural engineers who are in charge of the design of these types of frame can experience difficulties in finding the proper design aid information.

In this study, the stability analysis of double span and single story frame with prismatic or linearly tapered columns is performed first by the finite element method. Then the changes of critical load coefficients for each m (see Equation 1) are expressed by an algebraic function of numerical analysis parameters.

Finally the K-factor formula is derived in the form of a simple equation by using the proposed algebraic function. K-factors by the proposed method can play the design aid role because the critical load coefficients estimated by the proposed algebraic equation coincide well with those determined by the finite element stability analysis of the frame.

2 SCOPE OF THE STUDY

Figure 1 shows framed columns with variable cross sections. For the stability analysis of the frame by the finite element method and finally the derivation of K-factor formula, the following items are considered.

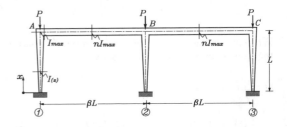

Figure 1. Two bay frame with non-prismatic columns.

Classification of frame

- Braced frame (the frame without side-sway)
- Un-braced frame (the frame with side-sway)

Support conditions

- fixed bases
- hinged bases

Analysis parameters (see Fig.1) column,

$$I(x) = I_0(1 + \alpha \frac{x}{L})^m, \text{ (second moment of area)} \quad (1)$$

- α (=taper parameter): 0.0, 0.2, 0.4, ... 2.0
- m (=sectional property parameter): 1, 2, 3, or 4.

In Equation 1, $\alpha = 0.0$ denotes the prismatic column.
frame,

- n (=second moment of area ratio): 1.0, 1.5, 2.0
- β (=span to height ratio): 1, 2, 3, or 4.

3 ELEMENT STIFFNESS MATRICES

Figure 2 shows a linear element having two degrees of freedom at each node. In the picture, q_is in the parenthesis denote the generalized force components corresponding to the displacement components, o_is.

When the flexural rigidity change within the element is neglected, the displacement function for the above element can be represented by

$$v = v(x) = A_1 + A_2 x + A_3 x^2 + A_4 x^3$$

$$= [N_1 \quad N_2 \quad N_3 \quad N_4] \begin{Bmatrix} \delta_1 \\ \delta_2 \\ \delta_3 \\ \delta_4 \end{Bmatrix} \quad (2)$$

where the shape functions, N_is are easily verified to be given by the following equations.

$$N_1 = 1 - 3(\frac{x}{l})^2 + 2(\frac{x}{l})^3, \quad N_2 = x(1 - \frac{x}{l})^2$$

$$N_3 = 3(\frac{x}{l})^2 - 2(\frac{x}{l})^3, \quad N_4 = -\frac{x^2}{l}(1 - \frac{x}{l}) \quad (3)$$

When one considers only the flexural or bending part, the strain energy of an element is given by

$$U = \frac{1}{2} \int_0^l EI(x) \cdot (\frac{d^2v}{dx^2})^2 dx$$

$$= \frac{1}{2} \{\delta\}^T \cdot \left(\int_0^l EI(x) \cdot [\frac{d^2N}{dx^2}]^T \cdot [\frac{d^2N}{dx^2}] dx \right) \cdot \{\delta\} \quad (4)$$

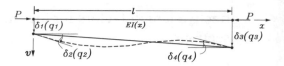

Figure 2. Linear element with 4 D.O.F.

Meanwhile, the external work due to constant axial force, P and due to nodal force component, q_i is expressed by

$$W = \frac{P}{2} \int_0^l \left(\frac{dv}{dx} \right)^2 dx + \frac{1}{2} \{q\}^T \cdot \{\delta\}, \quad (\{q\} = [k] \cdot \{\delta\})$$

$$= \frac{1}{2} \{\delta\}^T \cdot \left(P \int_0^l [\frac{dN}{dx}]^T \cdot [\frac{dN}{dx}] dx + [k] \right) \cdot \{\delta\} \quad (5)$$

Equating Equation 5 to Equation 4 and rearranging terms, one can obtain the following expressions for the element stiffness matrices.

$$[k] = \int_0^l EI(x) \cdot [\frac{d^2N}{dx^2}]^T \cdot [\frac{d^2N}{dx^2}] dx - P \int_0^l [\frac{dN}{dx}]^T \cdot [\frac{dN}{dx}] dx \quad (5a)$$

In the above, the flexural and geometric stiffness matrix corresponding to the first and second part of right hand side are

$$[k_b] = \int_0^l EI(x) \cdot [\frac{d^2N}{dx^2}]^T \cdot [\frac{d^2N}{dx^2}] dx$$

$$\approx \frac{EI(e)}{l^3} \begin{vmatrix} 12 & & & symm \\ -6l & 4l^2 & & \\ -12 & 6l & 12 & \\ -6l & 2l & 6l & 4l^2 \end{vmatrix} \quad (6a)$$

$$P[k_g] = P \int_0^l [\frac{dN}{dx}]^T \cdot [\frac{dN}{dx}] dx$$

$$\approx \frac{P}{30l} \begin{vmatrix} 36 & & & symm \\ -3l & 4l^2 & & \\ -36 & 3l & 36 & \\ -3l & -l & 3l & 4l^2 \end{vmatrix} \quad (6b)$$

The second moment of area of the column element is changing along the element axis. To avoid the complicated integral in Equation 6a, the variable $I(x)$ is replaced by constant $I(e)$. Here $I(e)$ denotes the $I(x)$ at the midlength of each element. The errors due to the replacement of $I(x)$ by $I(e)$ are negligible and the final eigenvalues are affected little by this kind of replacement.

4 CRITICAL LOAD OF THE FRAME

The column with a variable cross section is divided into 10 equal elements, and the prismatic beam into

678

2 equal elements. The element stiffness matrices are obtained by applying Equation 6(a) and (b) to each element. The assembly of element matrices and the application of boundary conditions to them, yields following type of matrix equation

$$([K_b] - P[K_g])\{\Delta\} = \{Q\}, \quad \{Q\} = \{0\} \tag{7}$$

where $\{\Delta\}$ denotes the nodal displacement vector for the structure. Because of the large number of equations, the least eigenvalues (=critical load of the frame) is obtained by commonly used iteration techniques. For this purpose, the above equation is transformed into the following form.

$$\left([K_b]^{-1} \cdot [K_g] - \frac{1}{P}[I]\right)\{\Delta\} = \{0\} \tag{8}$$

in which $[I]$ is the unit(identity) matrix.

Because of the space limit, only a few cases of the critical load changes ($m = 2$) are listed in Table 1 and 2. At the bottom of each table, the regression coefficients appearing in Equation 18 are given.

5 EFFECTIVE LENGTH FACTOR

In Table 1 and 2, the critical load coefficients, corresponding to $\alpha = 0.0$ denote the buckling loads of the frames with prismatic columns. In these cases, the critical loads for the exterior columns can be determined by applying the following modified slopedeflection equations (see Figure 3).

$$M_{AB} = \frac{EI}{L}[\alpha_n \theta_A + \alpha_f \theta_B - (\alpha_n + \alpha_f)\frac{\Delta}{L}] \tag{9a}$$

$$M_{BA} = \frac{EI}{L}[\alpha_f \theta_A + \alpha_n \theta_B - (\alpha_n + \alpha_f)\frac{\Delta}{L}] \tag{9b}$$

where α_n and α_f, the so-called Merchant's stability functions are given by ($kL = \sqrt{PL^2/EI}$)

$$\alpha_n = \frac{\Phi_n}{\Phi_n^2 - \Phi_f^2}, \quad \alpha_f = \frac{\Phi_f}{\Phi_n^2 - \Phi_f^2} \tag{10a}$$

in which

$$\Phi_n = \frac{1}{(kL)^2}(1 - kL \cot kL), \Phi_f = \frac{1}{(kL)^2}(kL \csc kL - 1) \tag{10b}$$

When $kL = 0$, that is, when there is no axial force, $\alpha_n = 4$ and $\alpha_f = 2$. These values of α_n and α_f are used

in the common structural analysis where the axial compression effect on the buckling is neglected.

As the first example, the frame of Figure 1 *with fixed supports* is assumed to have the parameters, $\alpha = 0.0$, $\beta = 2.0$, and $n = 2.0$. For the braced frame, the moment equilibrium at joint A,

$$\sum M_A = M_{A1} + M_{AB} = \frac{EI}{L}(\alpha_n \theta_A) + \frac{EI}{L}(4\theta_A) = 0$$

leads to the buckling equation

$$\alpha_n + 4 = 0 \tag{11a}$$

The least root satisfying this equation and the corresponding critical load for the exterior column are

$$kL \approx 5.3290, \quad P_{cr} = \frac{28.393EI}{L^2}, \quad (K_{)braced} \approx 0.590) \tag{12a}$$

from (Table 1), $P_{cr} = \frac{26.181EI}{L^2}, \quad (K_{)braced} \approx 0.614)$

In the above fem denotes the critical load appearing in Table 1.

When the frame is un-braced, the moment equilibrium at joint A and the column, $\overline{A}1$ itself take the following forms ($\theta_B = \theta_A$)

$$\sum M_A = M_{A1} + M_{AB} = \frac{EI}{L}(\alpha_n \theta_A - (\alpha_n + \alpha_f)\frac{\Delta}{L}) + \frac{EI}{L}(6\theta_A) = 0$$

$$= \frac{EI}{L}[(\alpha_n + 6)\theta_A - (\alpha_n + \alpha_f)\frac{\Delta}{L}] = 0$$

$$\sum M_{column} = M_{A1} + M_{1A} + P\Delta$$

$$= \frac{EI}{L}[(\alpha_n + \alpha_f)\theta_A - 2(\alpha_n - \alpha_F - 0.5(kL)^2)\frac{\Delta}{L}] = 0$$

The above two equations lead to the characteristic equation

$$(\alpha_n + \alpha_f)^2 - 2(\alpha_n + 6)(\alpha_n + \alpha_f) + (kL)^2(\alpha_n + 6) = 0 \tag{11b}$$

From this, one obtains

$$kL \approx 2.7165, \quad P_{cr} = \frac{7.379EI}{L^2}, \quad (K_{)unbraced} \approx 1.156) \tag{12b}$$

from (Table 2), $P_{cr} \approx \frac{6.562EI}{L^2}, \quad (K_{)unbraced} \approx 1.226)$

Now the critical loads of the frame *with the same parameters but hinged supports* are to be determined.

Table 1. Critical load and regression coefficients for braced frames.

- fixed-fixed-fixed bases, ($P_{cr} = C_{fem} \dfrac{EI_0}{L^2}$), $C_{fem} \approx C_{est}$

- hinged-hinged-hinged bases

$m = 2, \beta = 1$	$n = 1.0$		$n = 1.5$		$n = 2.0$		$m = 2, \beta = 2$	$n = 1.0$		$n = 1.5$		$n = 2.0$	
α	C_{fem}	C_{est}	C_{fem}	C_{est}	C_{fem}	C_{est}	α	C_{fem}	C_{est}	C_{fem}	C_{est}	C_{fem}	C_{est}
0.0	26.1802	26.5627	28.1363	27.7166	29.6499	29.2600	0.0	13.4565	13.5718	14.5215	14.2514	15.3154	15.1611
0.2	32.0008	32.2880	34.4207	34.2040	36.2583	36.1790	0.2	16.4715	16.1131	17.7761	16.9707	18.7309	17.8564
0.4	38.0702	38.0133	40.9650	40.6914	43.1292	43.0980	0.4	19.6300	18.6544	21.1780	19.6900	22.2940	20.5517
0.6	44.3883	44.0219	47.7676	47.4124	50.2596	50.2529	0.6	22.9243	21.3509	24.7194	22.5379	25.9970	23.3797
0.8	50.9330	50.3139	54.8055	54.3671	57.6278	57.6435	0.8	26.3552	24.2026	28.3999	25.5145	29.8392	26.3405
1.0	57.7124	56.8892	62.0863	61.5555	65.2412	65.2699	1.0	29.9117	27.2095	32.2100	28.6198	33.8124	29.4342
1.2	64.7062	63.7478	69.5893	68.9775	73.0797	73.1321	1.2	33.5909	30.3716	36.1449	31.8537	37.9110	32.6606
1.4	71.8993	70.8898	77.2998	76.6332	81.1272	81.2301	1.4	37.3870	33.6890	40.2008	35.2163	42.1314	36.0198
1.6	79.3101	78.3151	85.2349	84.5226	89.4031	89.5639	1.6	41.3111	37.1615	44.3868	38.7076	46.4829	39.5119
1.8	86.9243	86.0237	93.3794	92.6456	97.8899	98.1334	1.8	45.3417	40.7892	48.6815	42.3275	50.9439	43.1367
2.0	94.7277	94.0157	101.7217	101.0023	106.5774	106.9388	2.0	49.4716	44.5722	53.0794	46.0760	55.5093	46.8943

$m = 2, \beta = 2$	$n = 1.0$		$n = 1.5$		$n = 2.0$		$m = 2, \beta = 2$	$n = 1.0$		$n = 1.5$		$n = 2.0$	
α	C_{fem}	C_{est}	C_{fem}	C_{est}	C_{fem}	C_{est}	α	C_{fem}	C_{est}	C_{fem}	C_{est}	C_{fem}	C_{est}
0.0	23.6102	23.0456	24.9850	24.1679	26.1802	25.6794	0.0	11.9810	11.6404	12.7817	12.3034	13.4566	13.1964
0.2	28.7489	28.6156	30.4983	30.2859	32.0007	32.0151	0.2	14.6199	14.0845	15.6309	14.8206	16.4715	15.5848
0.4	34.1035	34.1856	36.2479	36.4039	38.0701	38.3508	0.4	17.3875	16.5286	18.6184	17.3378	19.6299	17.9732
0.6	39.6783	39.9123	42.2355	42.6607	44.3883	44.8590	0.6	20.2778	19.0635	21.7371	19.9362	22.9244	20.4636
0.8	45.4531	45.7955	48.4398	49.0561	50.9329	51.5398	0.8	23.2933	21.6892	24.9884	22.6156	26.3551	23.0561
1.0	51.4384	51.8353	54.8697	55.5902	57.7125	58.3931	1.0	26.4228	24.4058	28.3613	25.3762	29.9117	25.7506
1.2	57.6143	58.0317	61.5049	62.2629	64.7059	65.4190	1.2	29.6654	27.2133	31.8534	28.2178	33.5908	28.5471
1.4	63.9687	64.3847	68.3320	69.0743	71.8992	72.6174	1.4	33.0144	30.1116	35.4588	31.1405	37.3870	31.4456
1.6	70.5198	70.8942	75.3687	76.0244	79.3099	79.9884	1.6	36.4827	33.1008	39.1890	34.1444	41.3110	34.4461
1.8	77.2552	77.5603	82.6015	83.1132	86.9238	87.5319	1.8	40.0493	36.1809	43.0228	37.2293	45.3415	37.5487
2.0	84.1622	84.3830	90.0178	90.3406	94.7277	95.2480	2.0	43.7075	39.3518	46.9536	40.3953	49.4717	40.7533

m (= sectional property parameter) = 1

A_0	31.8989	C_0	0.0027	E_0	0.0001	A_0	16.4051	C_0	0.0014	E_0	0.0000
A_1	−5.8145	C_1	17.2177	E_1	−2.1849	A_1	−3.2996	C_1	9.6806	E_1	−1.1016
A_2	7.2578	C_2	−6.2344	E_2	0.8076	A_2	3.9245	C_2	−3.4797	E_2	0.4128
B_0	−6.7223	D_0	1.0103	F_0	0.8995	B_0	−3.6252	D_0	0.5359	F_0	0.5318
B_1	6.5607	D_1	−0.8505	F_1	−3.6998	B_1	3.2923	D_1	−0.4337	F_1	−2.2251
B_2	−3.5152	D_2	0.4716	F_2	1.4960	B_2	−1.7993	D_2	0.2418	F_2	0.8801

m (= sectional property parameter) = 2

A_0	31.6042	C_0	0.0027	E_0	0.0001	A_0	16.2629	C_0	0.0014	E_0	0.0000
A_1	8.2152	C_1	21.1850	E_1	−2.6168	A_1	3.8332	C_1	11.9071	E_1	−1.2996
A_2	10.1304	C_2	−5.2727	E_2	0.7939	A_2	5.4998	C_2	−3.0017	E_2	0.4196
B_1	−6.6431	D_0	0.9997	F_0	0.8823	B_0	−3.5909	D_0	0.5318	F_0	0.5219
B_1	4.3033	D_1	−0.5040	F_1	−4.0810	B_1	2.0662	D_1	−0.2568	F_1	−2.4811
B_2	−3.9181	D_2	0.5133	F_2	1.2949	B_2	−2.0055	D_2	0.2605	F_2	0.7673

m (= sectional property parameter) = 3

A_0	31.2337	C_0	0.0025	E_0	0.0001	A_0	16.0463	C_0	0.0013	E_0	0.0000
A_1	22.0602	C_1	25.0363	E_1	−3.1472	A_1	11.0097	C_1	14.1378	E_1	−1.5479
A_2	19.7356	C_2	−1.9977	E_2	0.8319	A_2	10.3275	C_2	−1.3877	E_2	0.4844
B_0	−6.3661	D_0	0.9535	F_0	0.8715	B_0	−3.4488	D_0	0.5093	F_0	0.5100
B_1	1.5641	D_1	−0.0485	F_1	−4.3372	B_1	0.5541	D_1	−0.0216	F_1	−2.6758
B_2	−5.2285	D_2	0.6189	F_2	0.5560	B_2	−2.6412	D_2	0.3017	F_2	0.3579

m (= sectional property parameter) = 4

A_0	31.1507	C_0	0.0019	E_0	0.0000	A_0	12.5972	C_0	−0.0002	E_0	−0.0001
A_1	32.9455	C_1	27.7973	E_1	−3.9874	A_1	24.5856	C_1	18.4069	E_1	−1.5865
A_2	40.5782	C_2	5.2620	E_2	1.2559	A_2	17.1511	C_2	0.9112	E_2	0.2283
B_0	−5.4895	D_0	0.7914	F_0	0.9262	B_0	−0.4926	D_0	−0.0296	F_0	0.6010
B_1	−2.3439	D_1	0.7269	F_1	−4.1214	B_1	−8.1313	D_1	1.4102	F_1	−3.9419
B_2	−7.6613	D_2	0.6903	F_2	−1.3542	B_2	−0.9380	D_2	−0.1136	F_2	−0.0182

Table 2. Critical load and regression coefficients for unbraced frames.

• fixed-fixed-fixed bases, ($P_{cr} = C_{fem} \dfrac{EI_0}{L^2}$), $C_{fem} \approx C_{est}$

• hinged-hinged-hinged bases

$m = 2, \beta = 1$	$n = 1.0$		$n = 1.5$		$n = 2.0$	
α	C_{fem}	C_{est}	C_{fem}	C_{est}	C_{fem}	C_{est}
0.0	7.0477	6.9280	7.7680	7.5250	8.2226	8.3316
0.2	8.6600	8.5059	9.5306	9.3788	10.0620	10.2528
0.4	10.3076	10.0838	11.3255	11.2326	11.9332	12.1740
0.6	12.0914	11.7507	13.2606	13.1637	13.9488	14.1861
0.8	13.9407	13.5064	15.2649	15.1724	16.0267	16.2889
1.0	15.8686	15.3510	17.3482	17.2585	18.1881	18.4825
1.2	17.8854	17.2845	19.5145	19.4221	20.4377	20.7670
1.4	19.9161	19.3070	21.7025	21.6632	22.6990	23.1422
1.6	22.0606	21.4183	24.0076	23.9818	25.0833	25.6082
1.8	24.3732	23.6186	26.4857	26.3778	27.6424	28.1650
2.0	26.6031	25.9078	28.8837	28.8513	30.1205	30.8126

$m = 2, \beta = 1$	$n = 1.0$		$n = 1.5$		$n = 2.0$	
α	C_{fem}	C_{est}	C_{fem}	C_{est}	C_{fem}	C_{est}
0.0	1.8517	1.6387	2.0184	1.8695	2.1153	2.1855
0.2	2.4735	2.3359	2.6757	2.6222	2.7909	2.9025
0.4	3.1254	3.0331	3.3675	3.3749	3.5038	3.6195
0.6	3.8607	3.7801	4.1422	4.1807	4.2966	4.4010
0.8	4.6882	4.5769	5.0089	5.0395	5.1858	5.2471
1.0	5.5163	5.4235	5.8768	5.9515	6.0723	6.1578
1.2	6.4291	6.3199	6.8359	6.9165	7.0524	7.1331
1.4	7.3240	7.2662	7.7713	7.9346	8.0186	8.1729
1.6	8.3388	8.2623	8.8288	9.0058	9.0886	9.2774
1.8	9.5245	9.3082	10.0564	10.1301	10.3369	10.4464
2.0	10.5669	10.4040	11.1458	11.3074	11.4498	11.6801

$m = 2, \beta = 1$	$n = 1.0$		$n = 1.5$		$n = 2.0$	
α	C_{fem}	C_{est}	C_{fem}	C_{est}	C_{fem}	C_{est}
0.0	5.3138	5.0871	6.0154	5.6727	6.5633	6.4676
0.2	6.4857	6.4085	7.3859	7.2269	8.0742	8.0464
0.4	7.6869	7.7299	8.7941	8.7811	9.6273	9.6252
0.6	8.9852	9.0946	10.3124	10.3788	11.2974	11.2723
0.8	10.3593	10.5026	11.9134	12.0198	13.0538	12.9876
1.0	11.7733	11.9539	13.5669	13.7042	14.8691	14.7711
1.2	13.2478	13.4485	15.2909	15.4320	16.7578	16.6228
1.4	14.7410	14.9865	17.0533	17.2032	18.6876	18.5428
1.6	16.3679	16.5678	18.9465	19.0178	20.7529	20.5310
1.8	18.0849	18.1923	20.9270	20.8758	22.9258	22.5874
2.0	19.7396	19.8602	22.8637	22.7772	25.0432	24.7120

$m = 2, \beta = 1$	$n = 1.0$		$n = 1.5$		$n = 2.0$	
α	C_{fem}	C_{est}	C_{fem}	C_{est}	C_{fem}	C_{est}
0.0	1.4313	1.2833	1.6612	1.5122	1.8095	1.8266
0.2	1.9372	1.8560	2.2276	2.1521	2.4166	2.4423
0.4	2.4710	2.4287	2.8304	2.7920	3.0599	3.0580
0.6	3.0617	3.0435	3.4972	3.4790	3.7701	3.7341
0.8	3.7649	3.7006	4.2720	4.2131	4.5935	4.4706
1.0	4.4394	4.3997	5.0289	4.9945	5.3975	5.2675
1.2	5.1858	5.1411	5.8697	5.8229	6.2878	6.1248
1.4	5.9191	5.9246	6.6878	6.6986	7.1507	7.0425
1.6	6.7953	6.7503	7.6601	7.6214	8.1764	8.0206
1.8	7.7675	7.6181	8.7305	8.5913	9.3011	9.0591
2.0	8.6322	8.5281	9.7009	9.6084	10.3298	10.1580

m (= sectional property parameter) = 1

A_0	9.3673	C_0	0.0008	E_0	−0.0001	A_0	1.9561	C_0	0.0000	E_0	−0.0001
A_1	−2.7244	C_1	7.7947	E_1	−0.5079	A_1	0.4339	C_1	2.4194	E_1	0.0749
A_2	2.4591	C_2	−2.7141	E_2	0.2298	A_2	0.2723	C_2	−0.7228	E_2	−0.0112
B_0	−3.2006	D_0	0.4318	F_0	0.4769	B_0	−0.4794	D_0	0.0385	F_0	0.1893
B_1	1.2704	D_1	−0.2183	F_1	−2.1861	B_1	−0.4275	D_1	0.0307	F_1	−0.9198
B_2	−0.9171	D_2	0.1232	F_2	0.7946	B_2	0.0591	D_2	−0.0071	F_2	0.2985

m (= sectional property parameter) = 2

A_0	9.2949	C_0	0.0008	E_0	−0.0001	A_0	1.9442	C_0	0.0000	E_0	−0.0001
A_1	0.9119	C_1	9.6675	E_1	−0.6021	A_1	1.8047	C_1	3.0083	E_1	0.0901
A_2	3.4973	C_2	−2.1213	E_2	0.2878	A_2	0.9919	C_2	−0.4774	E_2	0.0434
B_0	−3.1771	D_0	0.4302	F_0	0.4682	B_0	−0.4825	D_0	0.0398	F_0	0.1872
B_1	−0.2811	D_1	−0.0191	F_1	−2.4543	B_1	−0.8041	D_1	0.0497	F_1	−1.0367
B_2	−1.3284	D_2	0.1569	F_2	0.6190	B_2	−0.1423	D_2	0.0010	F_2	0.2062

m (= sectional property parameter) = 3

A_0	9.1560	C_0	0.0006	E_0	−0.0001	A_0	1.9305	C_0	−0.0001	E_0	−0.0001
A_1	4.2278	C_1	11.2558	E_1	−0.8111	A_1	3.0803	C_1	3.4249	E_1	0.0721
A_2	6.7254	C_2	0.2773	E_2	0.5431	A_2	3.1588	C_2	0.4702	E_2	0.2350
B_0	−2.8888	D_0	0.3781	F_0	0.4756	B_0	−0.3744	D_0	0.0235	F_0	0.1811
B_1	−2.4847	D_1	0.3356	F_1	−2.5546	B_1	−1.5600	D_1	0.1321	F_1	−1.0474
B_2	−2.0888	D_2	0.1485	F_2	−0.1305	B_2	−0.6068	D_2	0.0083	F_2	−0.1765

m (= sectional property parameter) = 4

A_0	9.0030	C_0	−0.0002	E_0	−0.0002	A_0	2.0722	C_3	−0.0001	E_0	−0.0001
A_1	5.2199	C_1	12.3034	E_1	−1.4378	A_1	3.2299	C_1	4.2552	E_1	0.0030
A_2	15.5223	C_2	4.8842	E_2	1.5159	A_2	7.9407	C_2	1.7869	E_2	0.6399
B_0	−1.6445	D_0	0.1642	F_0	0.4788	B_0	−0.0164	D_0	−0.0209	F_0	0.1087
B_1	−6.9220	D_1	1.1517	F_1	−2.0048	B_1	−3.3491	D_1	0.3453	F_1	−0.9241
B_2	−2.6002	D_2	−0.1149	F_2	−2.0941	B_2	−0.7137	D_2	−0.0724	F_2	−0.9439

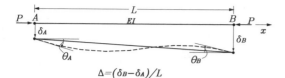

Figure 3.   Deformation of beam-column.

For the braced frame, the moment equilibrium at joint A,

$$\sum M_A = M_{A1} + M_{AB}, \quad (\theta_1 = -(\alpha_f / \alpha_n)\theta_A, \quad \theta_B = 0)$$

$$= \frac{EI}{L}(\frac{\alpha_n^2 - \alpha_f^2}{\alpha_n} + 4)\theta_A = 0$$

leads to the buckling equation

$$\alpha_n^2 - \alpha_f^2 + 4\alpha_n = 0 \qquad (13a)$$

From which, one can obtain the following results

$$kL \approx 3.8288, \quad P_{cr} = \frac{14.660EI}{L^2}, \quad \left(K_{)braced} \approx 0.821\right)$$
$$(14a)$$

from (Table 1), $P_{cr} \approx \dfrac{13.456EI}{L^2}$, $\left(K_{)braced} \approx 0.856\right)$

Finally, for the un-braced frame, the moment equilibrium at joint A and column, $\overline{A1}$ itself lead to the following

$$(\alpha_n^2 - \alpha_f^2)((kL)^2 - 6) + 6\alpha_n(kL)^2 = 0 \qquad (13b)$$

$$kL \approx 1.3496, \quad P_{cr} = \frac{1.821EI}{L^2}, \quad \left(K_{)unbraced} \approx 2.328\right)$$
$$(14b)$$

from (Table 2), $P_{cr} \approx \dfrac{1.903EI}{L^2}$, $\left(K_{)unbraced} \approx 2.277\right)$

It is noticed that the critical load coefficients of Table 1 and 2 show the lower bound errors except the last case.

For the framed columns, the critical loads are usually expressed in terms of K-factor

$$P_{cr} = \frac{\pi^2 EI}{(KL)^2} \qquad (15)$$

where K, the effective length factor, can be determined by Alignment charts of AISC Manual or by

using the following "CM 66 Rules" appearing in the French steel code.

$$K = \frac{3G_A G_B + 1.4(G_A + G_B) + 0.64}{3G_A G_B + 2(G_A + G_B) + 1.28}, \text{ (braced frame)}$$
$$(16a)$$

$$= \sqrt{\frac{1.6G_A G_B + 4(G_A + G_B) + 7.5}{G_A + G_B + 7.5}}, \text{ (unbraced frame)}$$
$$(16b)$$

where the definitions of G_A and G_B are well known to the structural engineers and so are to be abridged. When Equation 16 are applied to the present frame, one obtains for the fixed supports ($G_A = 1.0$, $G_B = 1.0$)

$$K_{)braced} = \frac{6.44}{8.28} = 0.778, \quad K_{)unbraced} = \sqrt{\frac{17.1}{9.5}} = 1.342$$
$$(17a)$$

And for the hinged supports ($G_A = 1.0$, $G_B = 10$)

$$K_{)braced} = \frac{46.04}{53.28} = 0.864, \quad K_{)unbraced} \approx 1.919$$
$$(17b)$$

The above values show a large deviation from those determined by the slope-deflection method but some what closer to those based on the finite element method.

To derive an effective length factor formula applicable to framed columns with constant or variable cross section, the changes of the critical load coefficient for each sectional property parameter, m is assumed to be an algebraic function of analysis parameters of Figure 1.

$$P_{cr} \approx C_{est} \frac{EI_0}{L^2} \qquad (18)$$

$$C_{fem} = C_{est} = A_0 + A_1\alpha + A_2\alpha^2 + (B_0 + B_1\alpha + B_2\alpha^2) \cdot (\beta^{-0.5})$$
$$+ (C_0 + C_1\alpha + C_2\alpha^2) \cdot (n) + (D_0 + D_1\alpha + D_2\alpha^2) \cdot (\beta^{-1})$$
$$+ (E_0 + E_1\alpha + E_2\alpha^2)(\beta^{-0.5} \cdot n) + (F_0 + F_1\alpha + F_2\alpha^2)(n^2)$$

The numerical value of coefficients, $A_0, A_1, \ldots, F_2$ determined by the regression technique are given at the bottom of Table 1 and 2. In these tables, the columns $C_{est}s$ denote the critical load coefficients estimated by the proposed algebraic equation, Equation 18. The correlation coefficient, ρ of C_{fem} and C_{est} is almost unity ($\rho \approx 1.0$) in any case, which suggests the applicability of Equation 18 for the practical calculation of critical load.

Now equating Equation 15 to Equation 18, one can obtain the effective length factor formula for the framed columns with variable rigidities

$$K = \frac{\pi}{\sqrt{C_{est}}} \qquad (19)$$

In the above, C_{est} is easy to calculate when one use Equation 18 and regression constants. For example, one can obtain the following results when the frame shown in Figure 1 has conditions in the parenthesis.

$$(m = 2, \quad \beta = 2.0, \quad n = 1.0, \quad \alpha = 1.0)$$

Bases	K-factors (Un-braced)	K-factors (braced)
Fixed bases	$\frac{\pi}{\sqrt{11.7733}} \approx 0.915$	$\frac{\pi}{\cdot\sqrt{51.8373}} \approx 0.436$
Hinged Based	$\frac{\pi}{\sqrt{4.4394}} = 1.491$	$\frac{\pi}{\sqrt{26.6415}} \approx 0.608$

6 CONCLUSIONS

To derive the effective length factor formula for framed columns with constant or variable flexural rigidity, the stability analysis of the frames is performed by the finite element method and then the changes of the critical load coefficients for the exterior columns are represented by an algebraic function of analysis parameters for each m. The results can be summarized as follows:

The critical load coefficients estimated by the proposed algebraic function show good agreement with those determined by the finite element method. Simple formula for effective length factor is possible to derive by using the proposed algebraic equation. The effective length factors determined by the proposed formula are less than one ($K \leq 1$) when the frames are braced. The K-factors for the unbraced frames, however are incompatible with the conventional definition of K-factors for the framed columns with uniform sections. In other words, K-factors are less than unity in some cases.

As expected, the increase of restraints at column bases results in the decrease of effective length factor. The changes of base conditions from fixed to hinged bases results in a more prominent decrease of K-factor for the unbraced frame than for the braced frame. On the whole, the K-factors for the unbraced frames are more than twice the K-factors of those for the braced frames.

REFERENCES

AISC, 1986. *Specification for Load and Resistance Factor Design*. AISC, Chicago, IL.

Bazant, Z.P. & Cedolin, L. 1991. *Stability of Structures*. Oxford University Press, Inc.

Bleich, F. 1952. *Buckling Strength of Metal Structures*. McGraw-Hill Co.

Chajes, Alexander. 1974. "*Principles of Structural Stability Theory*". Prentice Hall, Inc.

Dumonteil, P. 1999. Historical Note on K-factor Equations. *Engineering Journal, AISC* 39(2): 102–103.

Himat Solanki & Sabni, Gajanan, M. 1989. Buckling Load of Taperd Columns. *Proceeding of Structures Congress*, San Francisco: 436–442.

Moshe Eisenberger & Yoram Reich, 1989. Buckling of Variable Cross Section columns. *Proceeding of Structures Congress*, San Francisco:443–451.

Newmark, N.M. 1949. A Simple Approximate Formula for Effective End-Fixity of Columns. *Journal of Aeronautical Science* 16(2).

Newmark, N.M. 1971. *Fundamentals of Earthquake Engineering*. Prentice Hall, Inc.

Shanmugam, N.E. & Chen, W.F. 1995. An Assessment of K-factor Formulus. *Engineering Journal, AISC* 32(1): 3–11.

Spiegel, Murray, R. 1975. *Probability and Statistics*. Schaum's Outline Series, McGraw-Hill Book Co.

System-based Vision for Strategic and Creative Design, Bontempi (ed.)
© *2003 Swets & Zeitlinger, Lisse, ISBN 90 5809 599 1*

Development of a continuum-mechanics-based tool for 3D finite element analysis of reinforced concrete structures

H. Hartl
Institute for Structural Concrete, Graz University of Technology, Austria

ABSTRACT: A 3D (three-dimensional) finite element program has been developed for reinforced and pre-stressed concrete structures in order to make advanced numerical methods available to engineers. All para-meters needed can be taken from the literature (codes, fib-bulletins). Concrete is modeled in terms of plasticity, employing the Ottosen failure criterion. As flow rule serves the Drucker-Prager surface. A robust return is guar-anteed by the elasto-visco-plastic approach. A rotating crack model based on the cohesive crack concept is pre-sented for tensile failure. Creep is accounted for by integrating the entire stress history. The program has the capability to account for every single rebar at its exact spatial position. The rebars are automatically discretized to the element mesh. A case study presents the interface stresses between two concrete layers due to shrinkage and creep.

1 SIGNIFICANCE OF FEM IN REINFORCED CONCRETE ENGINEERING

If the performance of a reinforced or prestressed con-crete structure needs to be simulated numerically many nonlinear phenomenon will be encountered over the time and load history, even at low service load lev-els: shrinkage & creep, cracking and crushing at the concrete end. The reinforcement which is embedded into the concrete behaves nonlinear due to bond slip and may start to yield at high load levels.

Some tools are able to account for such nonlinear effects within a sectional analysis. Though, discontinu-ous regions cannot be analyzed with such tools and strut and tie models are employed in many situations of prac-tical design. Such models show a possible flux of forces but cannot provide firm information about the service-ability. This is often an issue when an existing structure should be adapted and subjected to higher loads.

A tool for a 3D-analysis of reinforced concrete was developed (Hartl 2002a). It allows studying the inter-action of several nonlinear effects of reinforced and prestressed concrete structures from the engineering point of view. No solid knowledge of the theoretical framework behind is necessary.

A successful introduction of nonlinear methods into practice can be achieved only, if these methods do require only reasonable time in order to prepare the input data. This requires that only easily accessible material parameters, which can be understood by an engineer, need to be provided on the one hand. And on the other hand the laborious work of providing the geo-metric input should be minimized as much as possible.

The advantage of a continuum-mechanics based approach is that nearly no simplification and idealiza-tion of the domain is necessary. Such a computer pro-gram can account by default for every single rebar at its exact spatial position. Hence, the load-bearing mechanism is computed by the program once the geometry of the domain is provided. The computing expenses are high but acceptable for today's standard computers. Considering the fast development in com-puter hardware, it is acceptable to increase the com-puting demand, if the time for preparing the input data can be decreased.

It was a major goal to develop a tool, which gains the capability to investigate soil structure interaction prob-lems as well. In order to be able to combine some of these ideas, it appeared to be necessary that full access to the program code is available and the program should have implemented some features toward these goals. (BEFE 2001) served as a development platform. The geotechnical part is already covered by the program.

2 MATERIAL MODEL FOR CONCRETE

Concrete behavior is complex and shows a significant scatter. Several models are available for describing the constitutive behavior of concrete but none of them can be regarded as the well accepted concrete model. Sophisticated models may be excellent for special purposes but no better results may be expected in general cases where only limited information about the concrete and the loading history is available.

The employed model is simple in concept. All parameters have a physical meaning and are familiar to an engineer.

2.1 Concrete crushing

For the sake of simplicity the compressive behavior is assumed linear elastic up to the failure surface (Ottosen 1977) and perfectly plastic thereafter. This simple approach is able to describe well many engineering situations because the load deformation behavior is indeed nearly linear up to approximately 40% of f_{cm} and even more at high strength concrete. Stresses at service load level will exceed such stress levels rarely. Beyond such stress levels micro-cracks in the concrete matrix induce an anisotropic behavior and the constitutive behavior becomes rather complex. However, the ultimate stress can be described well by a failure surface.

The (Ottosen 1977) surface is described by four parameters. (Dahl 1992) proposed for the four parameters an approximation based on experimental data knowing only the compressive strength f_{cm}. The parameters computed according to Dahl can be employed for normal strength concrete and for high strength concrete. The parameters are

$$x = \frac{f_{cm}}{100[\text{MN/m}^2]} \tag{1}$$

$$A = -1.66 \cdot x^2 + 3.49 \cdot x + 0.73 \tag{2}$$

$$B = -0.19 \cdot x^2 + 0.41 \cdot x + 3.13 \tag{3}$$

$$K_1 = 0.46 \cdot x^2 - 0.97 \cdot x + 11.89 \tag{4}$$

$$K_2 = -0.02 \cdot x^2 + 0.04 \cdot x + 0.974 \tag{5}$$

(Model Code 90 1993) gives recommendations for the Ottosen parameters based on the uniaxial compressive and tensile strength of normal strength concrete ($f_{ck} < 80$ MPa).

If this advice is neglected, contradictory results will be obtained as shown in Figure 1. Although the uniaxial compressive strength ($f_{cm} = 98$ MPa) is an input parameter for the failure envelope, it represents a stress state outside the failure envelope (dotted line in Figure 1). This is a clear contradiction. Therefore, the (Model Code90 1993) recommendations should not be extrapolated for high-strength concrete. But f_{cm} is on the failure envelope if the parameters are

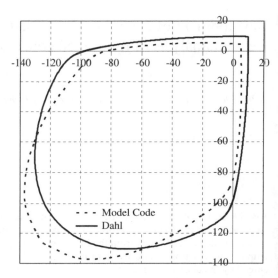

Figure 1. Ottosen envelope for C90/105 ($f_{cm} = 98$ MPa) with parameters according to Dahl vs. Model Code90.

computed according to Dahl as shown by the solid line in Figure 1.

A stress state outside the failure surface is not admissible. Plastic strains will develop instead and the stress state will remain on the failure surface. Therefore the computed strain increment must be split into an elastic part which may yield to another stress state on the failure surface and a plastic part which does not produce stresses. Based on experimental observations at ductile materials, it is assumed that the direction of the plastic strain increment is independent on the loading path leading to the failure envelope and on the current loading direction. Thus, a potential function may be employed as flow rule for determination of the plastic strain increment (Melan 1938). Although real concrete behavior is much more complex, the Drucker-Prager surface is employed as plastic potential function.

2.1.1 Return algorithm

The elasto-visco-plastic approach is employed as return method (Perzyna 1963, 1966) for its robustness. A stress state outside the yield surface is allowed for t ≠ ∞ in this method. The stress at time $t + \Delta t$ is

$$\sigma_{t+\Delta t} = \sigma_t - \mathbf{D} \cdot \frac{\Delta t}{\eta} \langle F \rangle \frac{\partial Q}{\partial \sigma} \tag{6}$$

where $\sigma_{t+\Delta t}$ is the stress at time $t + \Delta t$. $\mathbf{D}$ is the elasticity matrix. Q is the plastic potential function, which is in this case the Drucker-Prager cone and F is the

Ottosen failure criterion. $\langle F \rangle$ indicates a step function where

$$\langle F \rangle = 0 \qquad \text{if} \quad F \leq 0 \qquad (7)$$

$$\langle F \rangle = f_{(F)} \qquad \text{if} \quad F > 0 \qquad (8)$$

No material rheology is considered here. Thus, the viscosity parameter η is set to unity and time has no physical meaning. The time reduces to a mere convergence parameter. The plastic strain rate $\partial Q/\partial\sigma$ is multiplied by $\mathbf{D}$ in order to obtain the stress rate. $\Delta t \cdot \langle F \rangle$ can be interpreted as a rate multiplier $\Delta\lambda$ in order to obtain a stress state on the failure surface. This multiplier $\Delta\lambda$, which results in a limiting stress state on the yield surface, is of interest for a fast computation.

$$F_{\left(\sigma - \mathbf{D}\cdot\Delta\lambda\frac{\partial Q}{\partial\sigma}\right)} = 0 \qquad (9)$$

An analytical approach towards this issue is shown in (Mang & Hofstetter 2000). A numerical approach is shown here. The condition given (Equation 9) can be fulfilled numerically by employing an iterative scheme employing the Newton method. The derivative of F_n is approximated by means of the secant connection of two trial points as shown in Figure 2.

$$\sigma_{n+1} = \sigma_n - \mathbf{D}\cdot\frac{F_n}{\dfrac{F_{n-1} - F_n}{\left\|\sigma_{n-1} - \sigma_n\right\|}}\cdot\frac{\partial Q}{\partial\sigma_0} \qquad (10)$$

The initial trial stress is $\sigma_0 = \sigma_{el}$. Then, a small value is assigned to $\Delta\lambda (= \Delta t \cdot \langle F \rangle)$ and σ_1 is computed by evaluation of Equation 6. For all subsequent steps, Equation 10 applies and a fast convergence is obtained. The final stress is always on the yield surface.

A merit of this elasto-visco-plastic approach is that the derivative of the yield function F is not needed in order to compute σ. This procedure is appealing when the derivative of the yield function is very involved and costly to compute. Only a smooth plastic potential function is required in order to ensure a robust return.

2.2 Concrete cracking

Tensile cracking is a dominant source for nonlinear material behavior in reinforced concrete structures. A review of available crack models can be found in (Hofstetter & Mang 1995).

Cracking is a discrete phenomenon at discrete planes. The first crack plane is initiated perpendicular to the principal axis of any tensile stress higher than f_{ct}. Tensile stresses can be transferred still at any plane perpendicular to the crack plane. Upon subsequent rotation of the principal stress axis, the load transfer mechanism becomes complex: A certain shear stresses can be transferred still over cracks and additional crack planes may develop as well.

At reinforced concrete structures the load transfer mechanism will be controlled dominantly by the reinforcement after cracks have initiated. Hence, a sophisticated model for the shear stress transfer over open cracks seems not to be a primary issue. It is more important that the crack model accounts well for the softening behavior of cracking concrete.

The implemented crack model is formulated within plasticity theory and is based on the smeared crack concept. A crack is assumed to be smeared over the volume represented by the regarding integration point. The model accounts for the introduced anisotropy, unless the user enforces the program to assume an isotropic strength reduction.

In order to account for the anisotropy the plastic strain components (illustrated by the solid Mohr circle in Figure 3) are computed along the principal stress axis and the admissible stress for each principal axis is computed from the regarding plastic strain component. Then, an iterative procedure takes place for the stress update and additional plastic strains may arise along the principal axis. After constitutive

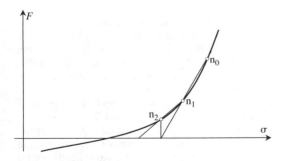

Figure 2. Iterative scheme for obtaining a stress state on the yield surface.

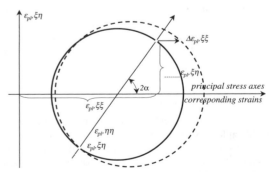

Figure 3. Update of plastic strain.

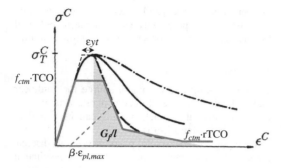

Figure 4. Constitutive behavior of a crack plane at loading and at unloading.

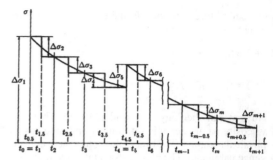

Figure 5. Approximation of the stress history by an implicit integration.

relations are satisfied the updated plastic strain components are rotated back to the global coordinate system and stored as shown by the dashed Mohr circle in Figure 3 (Welscher 1993, Hartl 2002a).

Figure 4 illustrates the behavior at tensile loading. Concrete is assumed to behave linearly elastic up to the tensile limit. The user can provide a tension cut-off factor ($1.0 \geqslant \mathrm{TCO} > 0.0$) in order to scale the maximum allowable tensile stress. After a certain amount of tensile flow ε_{yt} has occurred, strain-softening is accounted for in a bilinear fashion in the context of the cohesive crack concept (Hillerborg et al. 1976). There the developing crack plane is treated as discrete phenomenon. It is assumed that a certain amount of fracture energy G_F is absorbed by the formation of a unit area of crack surface. The tension softening behavior is now described by a stress elongation diagram, which is controlled by the specific crack energy. This ensures results which are independent of the element size. The parameters for the employed model are given in Model Code 90. In the implementation the stress obtained from the model is limited such that $\mathrm{TCO} \cdot f_{ctm} \geqslant f_{ct} \geqslant \mathrm{rTCO} \cdot f_{ctm}$.

At unloading, crack closing is taken into account by reducing the plastic strain increment and a path as illustrated by the dashed line in Figure 4 is followed. The amount of crack closing is controlled by β. An irreversible crack corresponds to $\beta = 1.0$ and a completely recoverable crack corresponds to $\beta = 0.0$. According to (Dahlblom & Ottosen 1990) $\beta = 0.20$ may give realistic results.

2.3 Shrinkage and creep of concrete

The model implemented into this work is that one of (fib bulletin No 1, 1999). This model is able to account for normal strength and for high-performance concrete. Although a model which is based on diffusion theory would be doubtless more appropriate for such a continuum based approach from the physical point of

view, the model of (fib bulletin No 1) is accepted well in the engineering society and the employed parameters are simple to obtain. On the programming end, the differential equation for diffusion theory need not to be implemented. Since shrinkage is a volumetric process, the 3D shrinkage strain is

$$\varepsilon_{sh}^T = \begin{bmatrix} \varepsilon_{sh} & \varepsilon_{sh} & \varepsilon_{sh} & 0 & 0 & 0 \end{bmatrix} \tag{11}$$

The uniaxial shrinkage strain ε_{sh} is dependent on the cement mixture and on the environmental conditions like moisture content of the air and temperature. Creep is additionally dependent on the stress history of the concrete. Procedures which do not require storage of the entire stress history are discussed in (Hofstetter & Mang 1995). However, the respective algorithms are not able to account for the general case and are therefore disregarded. The additional computing expenses (especially storage and CPU) for accounting for the entire stress history are no longer genuine computational challenges.

The stress history is approximated on the basis of an implicit midpoint rule as shown in Figure 5 and in Equation 12 (Walter 1988, Hofstetter & Mang 1995).

$$\varepsilon_{cc}(t_m) = \mathbf{A} \cdot \sum_{i=1}^{m} \frac{\varphi(t_m, t_{i-1/2})}{E_{ci}} \Delta\boldsymbol{\sigma}(t_i, t_{i-1}), \quad m \geq 2 \tag{12}$$

No recommendation could be found in literature for the Poisson's ratio of the creep compliance matrix. According to Bažant/Wittmann (1982), v_{cr} may drop almost to zero. If no better value for v_{cr} is available, $v_{cr} = 0.20$ might serve as an acceptable but crude first approximation.

Figure 6 shows the development of creep coefficients for one concrete loaded at different ages.

At stress levels above a certain limit the relation between stresses and creep strains is no longer linear. For stresses between $0.40 \cdot f_{cm}$ and $0.60 \cdot f_{cm}$, the regarding creep coefficients are modified depending on the current stress level according to Model Code90.

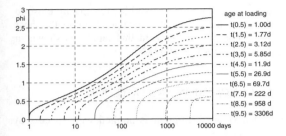

Figure 6. Development of creep coefficients for a generic concrete.

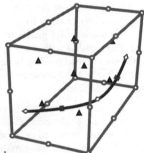

Legend:

O Node of parent element; (DOF, appears in the vector of nodal element displacements)

◇ Rebar point; (does not appear in the vector of nodal element displacements)

▲ Integration point for the parent element; (local coordinates of the Gauss points are known)

Ⅰ Integration point for the rebar; (local coordinates and rebar orientation have to be determined)

Figure 7. Embedded reinforcement bar.

3 MODELLING THE REINFORCEMENT

The reinforcement represents a discontinuity of the stiffness distribution within a reinforced concrete member. Only in very few cases the domain is subdivided into plain concrete elements and steel elements. This will be done only, if details are investigated.

In general, a formulation needs to be employed which is able to account for both, the concrete and the reinforcement in an implicit manner.

The embedded formulation of the reinforcement accounts for the exact geometric position of the reinforcement without giving any restriction to the element mesh of the concrete as shown in Figure 7.

The mesh of the parent domain can be prepared independently of the reinforcement layout. The reinforcement needs to be provided in global coordinates only. A preprocessing routine detects automatically the intersection of the rebars with the parent element faces (Hartl 2002a). And the rebar stiffness is

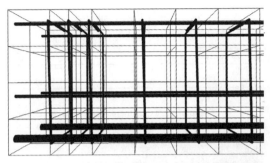

Figure 8. Concrete mesh and embedded reinforcement.

added to the concrete stiffness in the element stiffness matrix.

$$\mathbf{K}^e = \underbrace{\int \mathbf{B}^{eT}\mathbf{D}_c\mathbf{B}^e \cdot dV}_{parent} + \underbrace{\int \mathbf{B}^{eT}\mathbf{T}_{\varepsilon,gl}^T\mathbf{D}_r\mathbf{T}_{\varepsilon,gl}\mathbf{B}^e \cdot dV}_{rebar} \quad (18)$$

The crux in this method is that the integration points of the reinforcement need to be found in local coordinates of the parent elements. This inverse mapping is not straightforward, a Newton root finding algorithm in three dimensions needs to be applied in order to find these integration points for the rebar within the parent element.

Figure 8 shows a concrete mesh with embedded rebars. The effort for preparing the input in this way is small. Modifications can be made in a simple way.

4 CASE STUDY, STRESS AT THE INTERFACE OF TWO CONCRETES

Bridge decks are exposed to traffic and environmental aggression. The concrete cover is removed often during general repair work by high pressure water jetting. In order to enhance the deck for increased traffic loads a new concrete layer with a certain thickness is often cast on top of the existing deck. The load transfer mechanism and the bearing behavior was investigated experimentally by (Kernbichler 2002a, b) and numerically by (Hartl 2002b).

The setup of the test is shown in Figure 9. Let us concentrate here on the development of stresses due to shrinkage and creep of these two concretes with different ages. A considerably tensile stress exists at the bottom after the old concrete has experienced creep and shrinkage over 25 years since the reinforcement obstructs the shorting caused by shrinkage as shown in Figure 10a for the right end of the plate. The normal stresses are almost zero at the top of the old concrete since the reinforcement ratio is much lower at the top. The normal stresses in the newly installed concrete are obviously zero at 25 years.

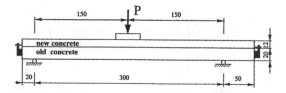

Figure 9.   Setup of the experiment, depth of plate 2.50 m.

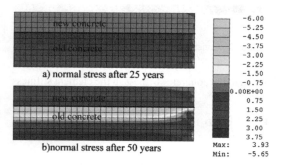

a) normal stress after 25 years

b) normal stress after 50 years

Max: 3.93
Min: -5.65

Figure 10.   Distribution of normal stresses due to shrinkage and creep.

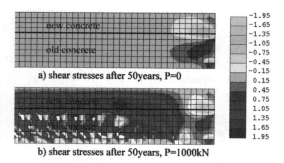

a) shear stresses after 50years, P=0

b) shear stresses after 50years, P=1000kN

Figure 11.   Shear stress after 50 years due to shrinkage and creep.

Figure 10b shows the stress distribution when the new concrete is 25 years old (then the old concrete is 50 years old). The new concrete has high tensile stresses and the old concrete has compressive stresses close to the interface.

Shear stresses up to 2 MN/m² arise after 50 years in the interface between these two concretes without any external load acting as shown in Figure 11 for the right end of the plate. Considering this situation on a Mohr circle, the according principal stress has the same magnitude and is obtained by rotating the axis by 45° since the stress perpendicular to the interface is zero. (Daschner 1976) observed that concrete develops at a well prepared interface almost the same strength as monolithic concrete. Assuming $f_{ctm} \approx 3$ MN/m² for the given situation, the shear stress in the interface is

utilized at about 2/3 of its ultimate capacity close to the outer end of the plate. And upon loading, the shear stress does not increase in this region as shown in Figure 11b for P = 1000 kN.

5   CONCLUSION AND OUTLOOK

The developed program is applied with success in several areas.

–   Laboratory tests are reanalyzed with the program for two purposes. On the one hand to get more insight into the structural behavior especially at parameter variations. And, on the other hand to validate the computer program itself.
–   It is in use as well in teaching for graduate students. The students get fast familiar with the program and they are able to study the load bearing behavior of a detail as part of their advanced concrete class.
–   For consulting in special cases.

Additional non nonlinear phenomena of reinforced concrete are implemented into the code as these phenomena appear to be an issue in a case study. However, an additional plan is to make many of the described and well tested features available to standard FE-codes, like Abaqus or similar ones by means of user routines.

REFERENCES

Bažant Z.P., Wittmann F.H., (eds.) 1982. *Creep and shrinkage in concrete structures*, John Wiley & Sons, New York
BEFE 2001: Beer G., *BEFE user's reference and verification manual*, CSS, Graz
Dahl K.K.B. 1992. *A failure criterion for normal and high strength concrete*, Technical University of Denmark, Lyngby
Dahlblom O., Ottosen N.S. 1990. Smeared crack analysis using generalized fictitious crack model, *Journal of Engineering Mechanics*, 116, pp. 55–76
Daschner F. 1986. *Versuche zur notwendigen Schubbewehrung zwischen Betonfertigteilen und Ortbeton*, Deutscher Ausschuß für Stahlbeton, Heft 372, Ernst & Sohn, Berlin
Elwi A.E., Hrudey T.M. 1989. Finite element model for curved embedded reinforcement, *Journal of Engineering Mechanics*, 115, pp. 740–754
fib bulletin No 1, 1999. *Structural concrete*, vol. 1, International Federation for Structural Concrete (fib), Lausanne
Hartl H. 2002a. *Development of a Continuum-Mechanics-Based Tool for 3D Finite Element Analysis of Reinforced Concrete Structures and Application to Problems of Soil-Structure Interaction*, Doctoral Thesis, Graz University of Technology, Austria
Hartl H., Sparowitz L. 2002b. *A 10 Tauernautobahn, Brückenverstärkung F8/F8a und F9, Numerische Untersuchung des Tragverhaltens nachträglich ergänzter*

Stahlbetonplatten, Institute for Structural Concrete, TU-Graz, Graz

Hillerborg A., Modeer M., Peterson P.E. 1976. Analysis of crack formation and crack growth in concrete by means of fracture mechanics and finite elements, *Cement and Concrete Research*, 6, pp. 773–782

Hofstetter G., Mang H.A. 1995. *Computational mechanics of reinforced concrete structures,* Vieweg, Braunschweig

Kernbichler K. 2002a. *A10 Tauernautobahn/Brückenverstärkung F8/F8A und F9: Bericht über experimentelle Untersuchung des Tragverhaltens nachträglich ergänzter Stahlbetonplatten,* Konstruktive Versuchsanstalt, Graz University of Technology, Graz

Kernbichler K. 2002b. *A10 Tauernautobahn/Brückenverstärkung F8/F8A und F9: Bericht über ergänzende experimentelle Untersuchung des Tragverhaltens nachträglich ergänzter Stahlbetonplatten,* Konstruktive Versuchsanstalt, Graz University of Technology, Graz

Mang H., Hofstetter G. 2000. *Festigkeitslehre*, Springer, Wien

Melan E. 1938. Zur Plastizität des räumlichen Kontinuums, *Ingenieur-Archiv*, **9**, pp. 116–126

Model Code 90, 1993. *CEB-FIP model code 1990,* CEB-FIP Comitè Euro-International du Bèton, Thomas Telford, London

Ottosen N.S. 1977. A failure criterion for concrete, *Journal of the Engineering Mechanics Division*, 103, pp. 527–535

Perzyna P. 1963. The constitutive equations for rate sensitive plastic materials, *Quarterly of Applied Mathematics*, **20**, pp. 321–332

Perzyna P. 1966. Fundamental problems in viscoplasticity, *Advances in Applied Mechanics*, **9**, pp. 243–377

Walter H. 1988. *Finite Elemente Berechnungen von Flächentragwerken aus Stahl- und Spannbeton unter Berücksichtigung von Langzeitverformungen und Zustand II*, Doctoral Thesis, TU-Vienna, Vienna

Welscher S. 1993. *Implementierung und Anwendung eines elasto-plastischen Werkstoffmodells für Beton*, Master Thesis, Institute for Strength of Materials, TU-Vienna, Vienna

System-based Vision for Strategic and Creative Design, Bontempi (ed.)
© 2003 Swets & Zeitlinger, Lisse, ISBN 90 5809 599 1

Stringer Panel Method: a discrete model to project structural reinforced concrete elements

G. Tarquini
Structural Engineer, Rome, Italy

L. Sgambi
University of Rome "La Sapienza", Rome, Italy

ABSTRACT: In this work applications are presented for the design of reinforced concrete structures using the Stringer-Panel Method (S&PM); a discrete model which divided a structure into elementary subsystem working in tension or compression (stringers) and in membrane shear stress (panels). Stringers are dimensioned for normal forces, panels for shear forces. A simple beam and a squat cantilever is studied, and is shown as the S&PM is able to get the right global and local results in this two antithetical cases.

1 INTRODUCTION

1.1 Design and models

Design is the aim of engineers; they studies reality in all aspects using analysis and intuition. Engineers invents models to get the real behavior or real structures. Continuously models are improved to get better results.

Different principles which seems to be contrasting determines the choice of a model or another:

– To get a precise valuation of the behavior,
– Costs of the analysis proportional at the aim that agrees to achieve.

The model must be able to reproduce the real behavior of the structure, however the use must not be complicated.

Into the model, the real structure is simplified and schematized. The fundamental static and dynamic characteristics are put in evidence by a finite number of parameters and the tensional field or the cinematic field are approximately reproduced. The precision of these reproduction depends of the model precision and, in general, if great is the model precision great will be the computational cost of the model.

1.2 Naturally discrete, discrete and continuous models

Models can be divided in three principal categories: naturally discrete, discrete and continuous models.

Reticular systems belongs to the first group as Frame Work, or Strut and Tie. The Stringer Panel Method belongs to the second group. Finally the Finite Element Method belongs to the third group.

Numerically using one of this three type of model is the same thing: you have to be solve a linear system of equations with known coefficients in all cases.

In Figure 1 a simple modellation scheme is shown. In general a modellation method can be gathered in a continuous models or in a discrete models. In the first case the structure is maintained continuous and the solution is found by series development or other method, in the second case a discretization of the structure is need. The Stringer and Panels method belong at

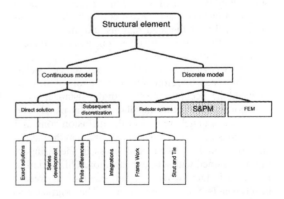

Figure 1. Modellation scheme.

693

the discrete model, whit the finite element method, strut and tie and other.

All the models (FW, S&T, S&PM, FEM) represents a priori discretization of a continuous structure.

2 THE STRINGER PANEL METHOD

2.1 Historical mensions

Since the thirties (Wagner) the S&PM has been applied to wing and fuselage elastic analysis and to many diffusion problems like the shear lag in stiffened box girders, the stresses distribution around framed holes and the behavior of the nodal zones in beam column joints. This projectual technique (Stringer-Panel Method – S&PM), is nowadays used to design aeronautical structures (Curtis 1997 and Megson 1999). Its popularity is based on its easy procedures and for the right correlation between reality and models results.

The S&PM has been introduced on Reinforced Concrete walls design by Nielsen et al. (1979).

Now, the Stringer Panel Method is studied in many European University: at the *University of Denmark* (Prof. Damkilde and Dr. Nielsen), at the *Delft University of Technology* (Prof. Blaauwendraad and Prof. Hoogenboom) and at the *Milan University of Technology* (Prof. Malerba and Prof. Bontempi).

In particular, at the *Delft University of Technology* the *S&PM* has been implemented into the SpanCad Software. This is a very interactive program able to read directly from AutoCAD using its graphic interface.

2.2 The S&PM applied to the r.c. structures

In the aeronautic structures, the presence of stringers and panels is need for the structural required (lightness, great stiffness…) differently from the civil structures. However in the CA/CAP structures the stress field show a natural subdivision in stringers (great concentration of stress) and panels (diffusion stress). In fact one have a great concentration of reinforced steel near the load regions and the supported zones, in other zones (with diffusion stress field) there are a reinforcement meshes.

The S&PM is able to define the resistance mechanisms by zones, therefore it is clear the role of the concrete and the steel into the structural resistance.

A continue structure is subdivided by panels and stringer. The panels represent the diffusion zone and can be considered with constant shear stress during the numerical analysis. The axial stress in the stringers can be assumed with a linear variation. This variation is caused, in fact, by the constant shear stress present in the panels close to the stringer. The original resolution technique is deduced from the force method

but using several matrix transformations one can reformulate the resolution technique in displacement terms.

The dimensioning of the stringer and the panels is executed by the outcomes of the linear elastic analysis. In the original formulation the stringers are designed considering their axial stress while the panels are designed considering only the shear field. The reinforcement steel dimensioning and the verifies, are executed with the Struct-and-Tie criteria.

A double perpendicular reinforcement meshes is need for the presence of the shear stress field, into the panels. Different methods have been proposed for the design of the reinforcement mesh (Nielsen 1984, Gupta 1984, Vecchio e Collins 1986, Fialkow 1990, Hsu 1991). The ratio between the reinforcement stiffness of the two reinforcement meshes characterize the kind of cracking. The cracking can be:

a) ductile–ductile,
b) ductile–brittle,
c) brittle–brittle,
d) balanced rupture.

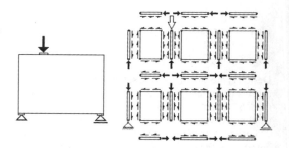

Figure 2.   From the structure to the stringer panel model.

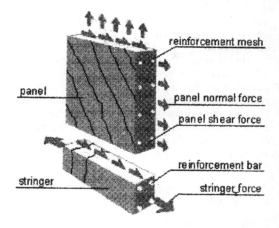

Figure 3.   Panel and Stringer.

For the designer by the S&PM the most common procedure is composed by the following steps:

1. The structural predimensioning;
2. The definition of the loads and the loads combinations;
3. The elastic linear analysis of the discretized structure with the valuation of the stress into all elements under all load combination;
4. The dimensioning of the reinforcement mesh and tensile stringer by ductility design criteria using the plastic resource of the steel;
5. Non linear analysis of the designed structure;
6. Re-design of the reinforcement steel using the non linear analysis outcomes;
7. Structural verification;
8. Non linear analysis under the most important load combination and determination of the ultimate load.

2.3 Typical applications for the S&PM

The S&PM is a natural tool for studying the thin wall structures, as a folded plate covering, concrete tiles, box girders and shells. This is a valid tool for the analysis of the diffusion zone that are present in the design of deep beam or in the anchorage zone of the prestressed concrete beam. In several support zone are present diffusion field, i.e. the Gerber supports, such as deep beam with holes.

3 MATRIX FORMULATION OF THE S&PM

Stiffness matrices for stingers and panels are presented below. More details on the S&PM implementations can be found in Biondini et al. (1999), Hoogenboom (1998) and Simone & Malerba (2001). The original technique was derived from the force method; through suitable matrix transformations, it can be led back to the displacement method (Przemieniecki 1968).

3.1 The stringer

In a stringer the tensile forces are supported entirely by the reinforced steel. The Strut-and-Tie Method is used to design the stringer. The compressed stringer is need only the compression stress in the concrete is greater than effective resistance $f_c^* = \nu_c \cdot f_c$. In this case is necessary to increase the concrete resistance by an adequate confinement reinforcement (longitudinal reinforcements and stirrups).

$$K = N^T \cdot F^{-1} \cdot N = \frac{2EA}{l} \cdot \begin{bmatrix} 2 & -\frac{3}{l} & 1 \\ -\frac{3}{l} & \frac{6}{l^2} & -\frac{3}{l} \\ 1 & -\frac{3}{l} & 2 \end{bmatrix} \qquad (1)$$

3.2 The panel

The rational design of a CA bidimensional element with plane stress field has been studied since the 1940. Many methods find their explanation into the Static Theorem of the Limit Analysis.

$$\begin{bmatrix} f_1 \\ f_2 \\ f_3 \\ f_4 \end{bmatrix} = \frac{G \cdot t}{A_p} \cdot \begin{bmatrix} 1 & \frac{1}{r} & -1 & -r \\ \frac{1}{r} & \frac{1}{r^2} & -\frac{1}{r} & -1 \\ -1 & -\frac{1}{r} & 1 & r \\ -r & -1 & r & r^2 \end{bmatrix} \cdot \begin{bmatrix} u_1 \\ u_2 \\ u_3 \\ u_4 \end{bmatrix} \qquad (2)$$

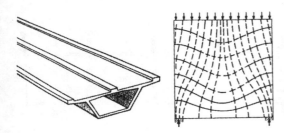

Figure 4. Box girder and deep beam structure.

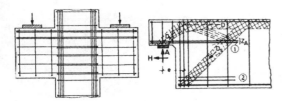

Figure 5. Gerber supports.

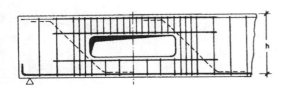

Figure 6. Beam with a hole.

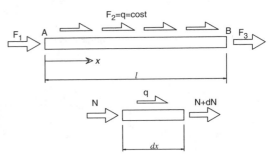

Figure 7. Stringer forces: linear variability of axial stress.

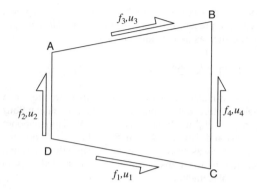

Figure 8.   Generic panel.

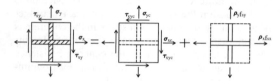

Figure 9.   Panel element a) reinforced concrete; b) concrete matrix; c) reinforcement mesh.

In fact, the reinforcement mesh dimensioning has usually executed considering an hypothetic stress distribution in equilibrium with the external load in the respect of the constitutive law.

The stress field into the panel can be separated into two contributions:

– the stress field into the concrete matrix,
– the stress into the reinforcement mesh.

4   APPLICATIONS

Some applications are now discussed. The analysis are executed using the SpanCAD software.

4.1   *The project of a simple beam*

The next step is the design of the one span beam loaded by uniform load. We have assumed one discretization with 8 elements (see Fig. 12).

The span is 10 meters, the height is 1 meter, and the uniform load is 50 kN/m. The dimensions of the current are: longitudinal current (bottom and top) 35 cm $\times$ 7.5 cm = 262.5 cm^2; external transversals current – 10 cm $\times$ 15 cm = 150 cm^2; internal transversals current – 10 cm $\times$ 10 cm = 100 cm^2;

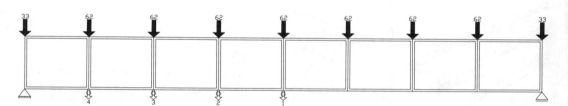

Figure 10.   8 element discretization for the S&P model.

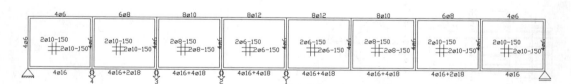

Figure 11.   Dimensioning of the reinforcement steel.

Figure 12.   Stringer force (elastic linear analysis).

696

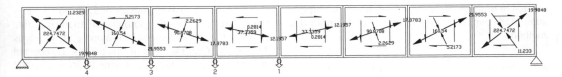

Figure 13. Shear stress in the panels and principal directions (elastic linear analysis).

Figure 14. Stringer force (non linear analysis).

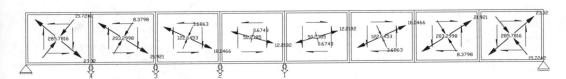

Figure 15. Shear stress in the panels and principal directions (non linear analysis).

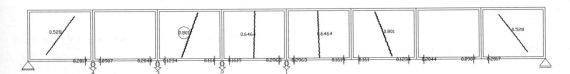

Figure 16. Cracking directions and entity of the crack.

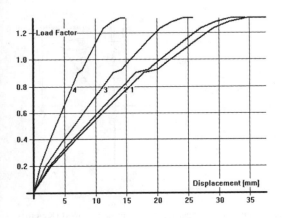

Figure 17. Load/Displacement multiplayer.

panels – 100 cm × 500 cm = 50000 cm²; thickness – 15 cm. Material characteristics: Concrete with Rck = 50 N/mm², steel FeB44K f_y = 400 N/mm².

In the Figure 13 and 14 one shown the outcomes of the analyses in terms of the current force and tensional field into the panel.

Again the non linear analysis and re-design, the outcomes are:

The load factor at the rupture is about 1.30, this indicate that the rupture occur when the load is 30% grater than the designed load. The maximum displacement in the middle span is 3.8 cm.

Naturally, this analysis must be executed with an adequate number of stringer and panel elements, because the behavior of the structures must be reproduced with sufficient accuracy for the design. Moreover one remember that the S&PM has been created in order to study the diffusion zones, a simple supported beam is, of course, a limit problem for this methods.

4.2 *Progetto di una mensola corta*

In Figure 23 one show the reinforcement of a squat cantilever designed by traditionally methods. In this paragraph the design of this squat cantilever is reproposed using the S&PM. The material characteristics are: concrete: Rck $=50\,\text{N/mm}^2$, steel: FeB44K, $f_y = 400\,\text{N/mm}^2$; load P = 200 kN.

The squat cantilever is discretized by 4 panels (thickness = 30 cm, dimensions = 40 × 40 cm) and 13 stringers (length = 40 cm, area = 135 cm²). As one can see from Figure 24 the pier is discretized too. In this study we have considered the only load on the squat cantilever, because the purpose was his design.

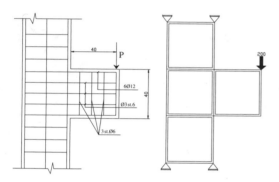

Figure 18. Mensola corta e relativo schema.

By the linear elastic analysis one design the reinforcement steel, therefore a non linear analysis is able to verify the reinforcement and improve the previous design. The final outcome of this process is reported in Figure 25, where the reinforcements are uniformed

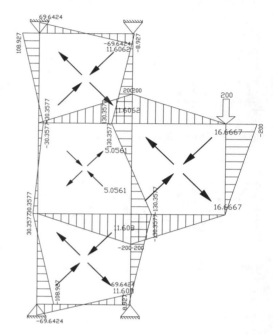

Figure 19. Linear analysis: Stringer force (kN), principal stress (Kg/cm²).

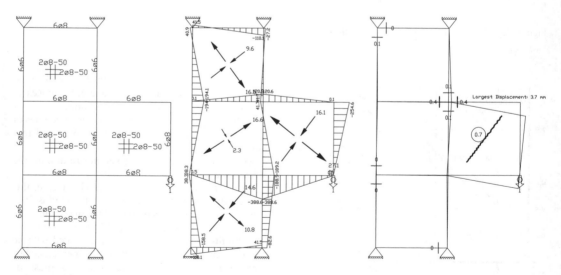

Figure 20. Non linear analysis: Reinforcement steel into the squat cantilever, Stringer force (kN), principal stress (Kg/cm²), shear force into the panel (kN/m) and cracking orientation again the non linear analysis.

698

with the maximum quantity of steel necessary in one of the four panels.

The load factor at the rupture is about 1.25, this indicate that the rupture occur when the load is 30% grater than the designed load. The maximum displacement is 3 mm.

Now, is interesting to confront the reinforcement design derived from the Stringer and Panel Method with the same reinforcement quantity derived from traditional Strut-and-Tie methodology of design. Naturally one must considering both concentrated and diffusion reinforcement.

While with the traditional methodology are necessary 6Ø12 in the tensile zone, in the Stringer and Panel Method the quantity of the concentrated reinforcement one reduced at 6Ø8. In opposite the diffusion reinforcement designed by traditional method foreseen 3 stirrups Ø6 (or Ø6 #100 mm) while the Stringer Panels Method Ø8 #50 mm.

The design with the Stringer and Panels Method provide a quantitative of diffusion steel 4.8 times greater than the same quantitative calculate by the traditional method (in terms of weight).

The concentrated reinforcement designed by the traditional method is 2.2 times greater than the same quantity designed by Stringer and Panels Method. The Table 1 summarize this results.

The traditional method, based on Strut-and-Tie, concentrate the reinforcement in tensile zone of the squat cantilever unlike the Stringer-Panels Method that carry at diffusion reinforcement most important. In this case one can used the reinforcement mesh with constant step in both directions X and Y. However, from the Table 1 one note that the total reinforcement designed by Strut-and-Tie is the same of the total reinforcement designed by Stringer-Panels Method.

5 CONCLUSIONS

With the Stringer and Panels Method one analyze a structure using a subdivision into stringer (in compression or in tension) and panels (diffusion stress). This numerical method can be considered an optimum tool for analysis and design of civil structure in reinforced concrete or in prestressed reinforced concrete. This tool produce a reinforced design very different respect the traditional method of design. In fact, using the Stringer and Panels Method the reinforcement are very distributed, however the total quantity of steel not change respect a the traditional method of design. This is evident from the second application shown in the 4 paragraph.

The Stringer and Panels is a rational method for the design of the concrete structure where the diffusion regions are presents.

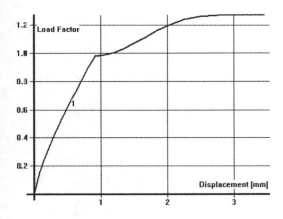

Figure 21. Load/Displacement multiplayer.

Table 1. Reinforcement resultant from S&PM and S&T.

Kind of reinforcement (Kg)	Kind of analysis	
	S&PM	S&T
Concentrate reinforcements	1.9	4.2
Diffusion reinforcements	3.2	0.9
Total	5.1	5.1

REFERENCES

Azar, J. 1972. Matrix Structural Analysis. Pergamon Press

Blaauwendraad, J. & Hoogenboom, P.C.J. 1996. Stringer Panel Model for Structural Concrete Design, *ACI Structural Journal*

Chen H.C. 1992. A simple quadrilateral shear panel elment, *Communications in applied numerical methods*

Biondini, F., Bontempi, F., Dolora, E. & Malerba, P.G. 1999. Modellazione di zone diffusive in elementi in c.a. mediante modelli discreti, *AICAP '99*

Biondini, F., Bontempi, F., Malerba, P.G. & Simone A. 1999. Stringer Panel Modellization of R. C. Elements. *Proceedings of the First International Conference on Advances in Structural Enginnering & Mechanics (ASEM)*, Seoul

Biondini, F., Bontempi, F., Malerba, P.G. & Simone A. 2000. Optimal reinforcement layout in concrete elements by using the stringer and panel method, *Proceeding of the Fourth International Colloquium on Structural Morphology*, Delft, The Netherlands

Biondini, F., Bontempi, F. & Malerba, P.G. 2001. Validità e calibrazione dei motodi statici per l'analisi di elementi in cemento armato, *Atti del Workshop S&T-2001* Università degli Studi di Firenze

Bontempi, F. & Malerba, P.G. 1997. *Analisi matriciale non lineare di telai in c.a./c.a.p.*, Politecnico di Milano & Università di Udine

Bontempi, F. 2001. Fondamenti teorici dei modelli avanzati di calcolo, *Seminario Tecnico 16 novembre 2001*, Università degli Studi di Roma "La Sapienza"

Curtis, H.D. 1997. *Fundamentals of Aircraft Structural Analysis*, Richard D. Irwin, Chicago, Illinois

Hoogenboom, P.C.J. 1998. *Discrete Elements and Nonlinearity in Design of Structural Concrete Walls*, Delf University of Technology

Megson, T.H.G. 1999. *Aircraft Structures for Engineering Students*, 3rd Edition, Hodder Headline Group, London

Przemieniecki, J.S. 1968. *Theory of Matrix Structural Analysis*, McGraw-Hill Book Company Ltd., New York

Robinson, J.S. 1996. *Structural Matrix Analysis for Engineer*, Jhon Wiley & Sons, London

Simone, A. & Malerba, P.G. 2001. Schemi discreti nel progetto di strutture piane in c.a., il modello stringer panel. *Atti del Workshop S&T-2001*. Università degli Studi di Firenze

Simone, A., Malerba, P.G. & Bontempi F. 1999. Modellazione di zone diffusive in elementi in c.a. mediante il modello a pannelli e correnti. *Atti Giornate A.I.C.A.P. '99*, Torino

Vecchio, F.J. 1989. Nonlinear Finite Analysis of Reinforced Concrete Membranes, *A.C.I. Structural Journal*

Design of reinforced structures with Strut-and-Tie model

S. Arangio
Structural Engineer, University of Rome "La Sapienza", Rome, Italy

L. Catallo
University of Rome "La Sapienza", Rome, Italy

A. Rago
"P.&A. S.R.L.", Rome, Italy

ABSTRACT: The design of reinforced concrete load bearing elements needs the knowledge of the stress state and so the development of a structural analysis. This is a complex task in the part of the structure characterized by static or geometrical discontinuities (D-Regions), in which it is not possible to apply the Bernoulli's hypothesis. A *Strut-and-Tie Model* is a rational criteria obtained through a generalization of the chord truss analogy. In this model, the complex flow of internal forces is idealized with a scheme that consists of struts and ties interconnected at nodes like a real truss.

This paper deals with the Strut-and-Tie Model for the design of reinforced concrete elements and explains in some detail.

1 INTRODUCTION

The structural analysis is a basic task for the right design of a reinforced concrete element. In order to achieve a realistic analysis, one should consider the nonlinearities in the real material behavior and the complexity in the causes of the failure. Some hypothesis on the material's behavior are made to use computing models. In order to verify that the idealization of the behavior agrees with the basic mechanics principles, equilibrium and congruence conditions have to be checked.

The type of analysis is connected to the typology of the problem.

In selecting the appropriate design approach for structural concrete, it is useful to classify portions of the structure as either B- (Beam or Bernoulli) Regions or D- (Disturbed or Discontinuity) Regions.

B-Regions are part of structure in which Bernoulli's hypothesis of straight-line strain profile applies. D-Regions are parts of a structure with a complex variation in strain. D-Regions include geometrical discontinuities (portions near abrupt changes in geometry) or statically discontinuities (concentrated forces).

Most design practices for B-Regions are based on model of behavior. As examples, the design for shear is based on the truss analogy. By contrast, the most familiar types of D-Regions, such as deep beams, corbels, are currently still designed by empirical approaches or by using common detailing practices.

The Strut-and-Tie Method is a methodology for the design of all types of D-Regions in structural concrete. Using this method the complex flow of stresses has been transformed in an equilibrated scheme. This methodology comes from the criteria of the Limit Analysis and can represent in a rational and synthetic way the capacity of the structure.

The structural concrete has then been idealized by a material with a perfectly plastic behavior underlining, in this way, the resisting mechanism of the element.

2 STRUT AND TIE MODEL

2.1 *General features*

In the Strut-and-Tie Method (STM) the complex flow of internal forces in the D-Regions is idealized as a truss carrying the imposed loading through the region to its support. This truss is called a Strut-and-Tie Model. Like a real truss, consists of struts and ties interconnected at nodes.

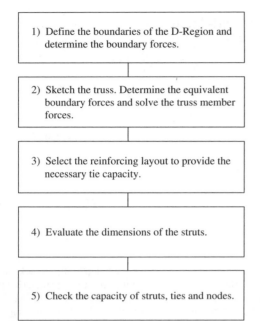

1) Define the boundaries of the D-Region and determine the boundary forces.

2) Sketch the truss. Determine the equivalent boundary forces and solve the truss member forces.

3) Select the reinforcing layout to provide the necessary tie capacity.

4) Evaluate the dimensions of the struts.

5) Check the capacity of struts, ties and nodes.

Figure 1.   Flow chart of the design process.

Struts are the compressed members and represent concrete stress fields whose principal compressive stresses are predominantly along the centreline of the strut. The idealized shape of concrete stress field can be prismatic, bottle shaped or fun-shaped.

2.2   Design process

The design process involves five major steps (Fig. 1).

Since equilibrium of the truss with the boundary forces must be satisfied and stresses everywhere must be below the limits, one can see the Strut-and-Tie Model as an application of the Lower-Bound Theorem of the Limit Analysis.

3   APPLICATION

3.1   Description

The analysis of a post-tensioned prestressed R.C. beam, characterized by a parabolic profile and a I middle crosssection with a rectangular extremity cross-section, will be presented in the following (Figs. 2 and 4). The length of the beam is 20.70 m. The depth changes with parabolic law from 1 m at the beam end to 1.8 m in the middle. The thickness of the core is 14 cm. The bearing section has been enlarged for a length of 135 cm from the beam end using a rectangular section, 42 cm wide. Four post-tensioned cables have been used (Fig. 3).

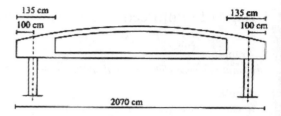

Figure 2.   Post-tensioned concrete beam.

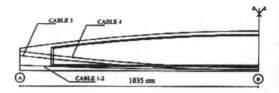

Figure 3.   Configuration of the cables.

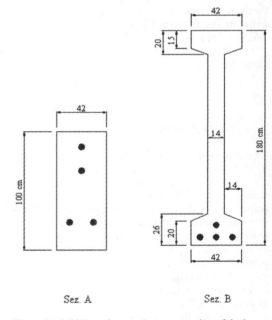

Sez. A   Sez. B

Figure 4.   Middle and extremity cross-section of the beam.

3.2   Design process

3.2.1   Define the boundaries of the D-Regions

A double discontinuity takes place at the beam end: a geometrical discontinuity is due to the sudden change of beam section; a statical one is due to the concentrated reaction at the bearing.

In order to determine the length of the D-Region, results of an elastic analysis can be used: the diffusive

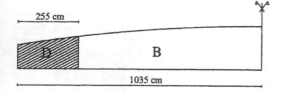

Figure 5. D-Region and B-Region.

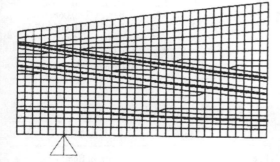

Figure 6. Discretization of the D-region.

zones are the ones with stress concentration that reduces going away from the discontinuity (Fig. 5).

According to the De Saint Venant's principle, stressing the validity of Bernoulli's hypothesis in a region as long as the depth of the beam end, one can assume this measure as the length of the D-Region.

The length of the region, using this criteria, is 255 cm from the beam end: 135 cm due to the cables and 120 cm is the depth of the beam where the section changes shape.

3.2.2 Sketch the truss

The simply supported beam scheme is the static scheme used in the analysis.

Afterwards, the structure has been split in finite elements and an elastic linear analysis has been carried out. The objective of the preliminary finite element analysis is to determinate the direction of the principal stresses. The results are shown in Figures 6, 7, 8 and 9.

To obtain a first basic truss restrains and loads have been replaced by a scheme with consistent restrains and statically equivalent loads. In this way the boundary forces are taken into account by forces applied as equivalent forces that are self-equilibrated. The trajectories of the principal compressive stresses can be used to select the orientation of the strut members. The Strut-and-Tie Model is then completed by placing tie members in order to furnish a stable load-carrying structure (*load path method*).

Obviously, there is no unique truss model associated with a particular problem. The model has been

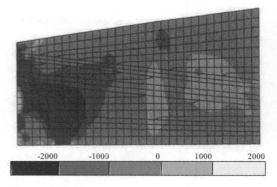

Figure 7. Transversal stress.

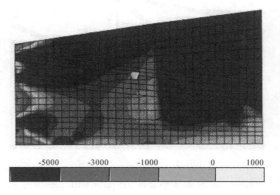

Figure 8. Longitudinal stress.

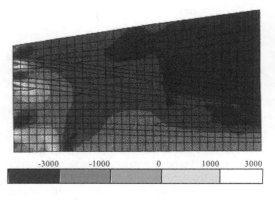

Figure 9. Shear stress.

chosen in a way so that the ultimate load value was the higher. In fact, the values obtained through the Lower-Bound Theorem of the Limit Analysis are always connected with safe situations.

In selecting the model two criteria have been used. to choose. The first one has been an energetic

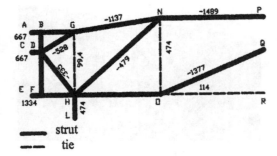

strut
tie

Figure 10. Strut-and-Tie model: model 1.

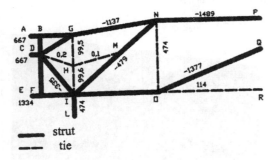

strut
tie

Figure 11. Strut-and-Tie model: model 2.

criteria: loads will follow the path with least forces and deformations. The energy can be calculated with the equation:

$$\sum_i F_i \cdot l_i \cdot \varepsilon_i = \min \qquad (1)$$

where F, l and ε are the axial stress, the length and the deformation of the i element, respectively. Since reinforcement ties are more deformable than concrete struts, the model with the least and shortest ties is the best.

In the second criteria also the practical point of view has been considered. In case of same energy, a model with orthogonal ties has been chosen to permit an easier arrangement of the reinforces that they represent.

The two last models obtained have the same strain energy but the second has been chosen because it is more sensible to recognize the little tensile regions near the cables.

In searching an optimum truss scheme using an iterative procedure, a more realistic Strut-and-Tie Model has been obtained.

3.2.3 Select reinforcing to provide the necessary tie capacity

Reinforcing have been calculated using the internal forces of the tensile members. The reference stress

Table 1. Energy comparison.

Ties	F [kN]	l [m]	ε	Energy [kN m]
Model 1				
NO	474.00	0.77	0.002	0.73000
OR	114.30	1.20	0.002	0.27000
GH	99.50	0.64	0.002	0.13000
			Total energy =	1.13000
Model 2				
NO	474.00	0.77	0.002	0.73000
OR	114.30	1.20	0.002	0.27000
GH	99.48	0.33	0.002	0.06600
HI	99.57	0.31	0.002	0.06200
DH	0.15	0.37	0.002	0.00011
HM	0.14	0.51	0.002	0.00014
			Total energy =	1.12800

Table 2. Global comparison.

	Model 1	Model 2
Energetic aspect	Strain Energy = 1,13 KN m	Strain Energy = 1,128 KN m
Ties position	Horizontal + vertical	Horizontal + vertical
Constructive aspects	Horizontal and vertical reinforcement	Horizontal and vertical reinforcement + diffused reinforcement
Connection with reality	Good design for shear action and local detailing.	One can understand the necessity of more/ different reinforcement in order to assure the ductile behavior of the overall structural element, including the possibility of development of the hypothesized collapse mechanism.

state used has been the serviceability limit state. In this way one can be sure that an equilibrium condition establishes and this one can be considered valid until the ultimate limit state. It is worth to note that it will be necessary to consider also the service situations, to guarantee anyway the reachment of the ultimate configuration.

In order to calculate the stirrups has been considered the internal forces of the tie GH and HI:

$$A_{HI} = \frac{N_{HI}}{\phi \cdot f_{yd}} \qquad (2)$$

$$A_{GH} = \frac{N_{GH}}{\phi \cdot f_{yd}} \qquad (3)$$

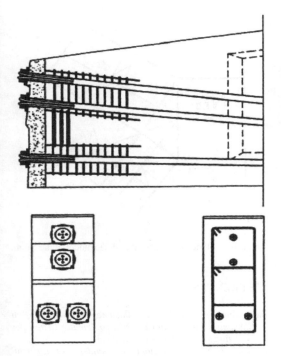

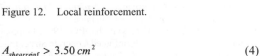

Figure 12.   Local reinforcement.

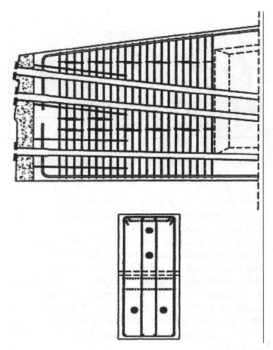

Figure 13.   Shear reinforcement.

$$A_{shearreinf} > 3.50 \, cm^2 \qquad (4)$$

Using $8 \, \phi6$ with two arms, one obtains:

$$A = 4{,}52 \, cm^2 > 3{,}50 \, cm^2 \qquad (5)$$

The shear reinforcement has been calculated using the same process. The arrangement is shown in Figures 12, 13 and 14.

3.2.4   *Evaluate the dimension of the strut*

The compressive members of the truss represents uniform stress areas. The length of the struts is the length of the truss members. The width can be computed using the following equation:

$$h_{strut} = \frac{N}{f_{cd}^* \cdot b}$$

where N is the axial internal force of the strut, b is the thickness of the beam (in this example is $42 \, cm$ for the rectangular section and $14 \, cm$ for the core of the beam) and f_{cd}^* is the stress limit modified through an effective reduction factor v ($f_{cd}^* = f_{cd} \cdot v$).

Using this factor it is possible to consider that the real stress state is not only axial but also crosswise stresses exist. The factor v has been used with two purposes: it can minimize the shifting from the theoretical

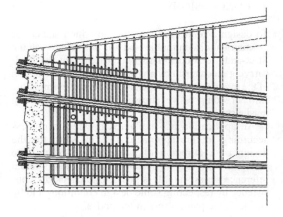

Figure 14.   Total reinforcement.

results and it leads to a lower value of capacity in accordance with the Lower Bound Theorem. In this case one has been used the value of 0.6 as suggested by Collins and Mitchell.

3.2.5   *Check the capacity of struts and nodes*

Struts have been checked by computing the strut widths and by controlling their fitness in the available space.

Truss members represent uniform stress zones. In order to check that the tensional field is statically

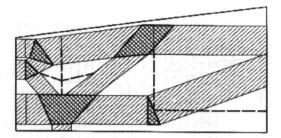

Figure 15.   Node *D* of the Strut-and-Tie model of the beam.

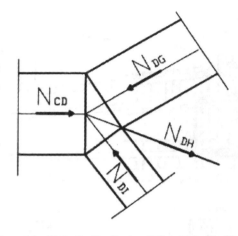

Figure 16.   Node *D* of the Strut-and-Tie model of the beam.

allowable, that is equilibrated and admissible, the conformity condition has to be checked also in the nodes that are in a plan stress situation.

For example, the node *D* has been considered. First the equilibrium between the internal forces has been checked. Afterwards the stress state has been calculated through a graphic construction of the circles of Mohr for each member. This node represents a particular situation: the struts have been computed with uniform stress state represented by a circle of Mohr collapsed in a point. It is an hydrostatic stress state.

4   CONCLUSIONS

To design a reinforced structure in which statical or geometrical discontinuities exist is possible to use the Strut-and-Tie Model. This model represent the load-carrying mechanism by approximating the distribution of the internal forces by mean of struts representing the flow of compressive stresses and ties representing tensile stresses.

An application has explained the design process according to this approach, step by step, for the design of a D-region of a prestressed beam. The assumed truss has to be consistent with the actual reference stress state. It is possible to check the consistence by respecting some design conditions and by checking the plane stress in the nodes.

REFERENCES

Baldassino, N. 2002. *Modellazione Strut-and-Tie di Elementi Strutturali in Calcestruzzo Armato: Criteri per la Definizione del Modello a Traliccio.*

Baldassino, N., *Modellazione Strut-and-Tie di Elementi Strutturali in Calcestruzzo Armato: Meccanismi Elementari e Criteri di Dimensionamento.*

Biondini, F., Bontempi, F. & Malerba, P.G. 1999. Optimal Strut-and-Tie Models in Reinforced Concrete Structures. *Computer Assisted Mechanics and Engineering Sciences*, 6(3–4), 279–293.

Malerba, P.G. 1999. Modellization of the Diffusion Zones in R.C. Elements through Discrete Schemes. *Proceedings of the First International Conference on Advances in Structural Engineering & Mechanics (ASEM)*. Keynote lecture, August 23–25. Seoul: Korea.

Schlaich, J. & Schäfer, K. 1991. Design and Detailing of Structurale Concrete using Strut-and-Tie Models. *The Structural Engineer*, 69(6), 113–125.

Schlaich, J. & Anagnostou, G. 1990. Stress Fields for Nodes of Strut-and-Tie Models. *ASCE Journal of Structural Engineer*, 116(1), 13–23.

Schlaich, J. & Schäfer, K. & Jennewin, M. 1987. Towards a Consistent Design of Structural Concrete. *PCI Journal*, 32(3), 72–150.

System-based Vision for Strategic and Creative Design, Bontempi (ed.)
© *2003 Swets & Zeitlinger, Lisse, ISBN 90 5809 599 1*

Approximate methods for analysis of viscoelastic behavior of concrete structures

D. Veglianti
Structural Engineer, Rome, Italy

L. Sgambi
University of Rome "La Sapienza", Rome, Italy

ABSTRACT: This paper describes the viscoelastic behavior of concrete structures and especially the approximate methods for estimation of creep. In particular it studies the so-called Degenerate Kernel Method. This method approximates the creep function with a Dirichlet series. As comparison, creep has been estimated also with Eurocode 2.

1 INTRODUCTION

1.1 *Viscosity and creep*

A system of forces has been applied in a concrete structure of elastic material. In this situation, structure assumes a deformed configuration, but when forces have been removed, their effects have been removed too.

Experimentally, it has been demonstrated that hypothesis of elastic material is acceptable if the system of forces has been applied on the structure for a limited time. In fact, if forces remain on the structure for a long time, there is also a new kind of strain besides the elastic one. The new strain increases with time. If forces have been removed, this strain does not disappear, but it decreases with time until a determinate value that is different from zero. Therefore it is partially irreversible.

Increment of strain respect to elastic strain is called creep. The property of material to have increments of strain caused by stress that remains on the structure for a long time is called viscosity.

1.2 *Effects of creep*

Creep and shrinkage cause strain and new stress distribution. There are some cases in which this phenomena are very important: (1) in non-homogenous sections formed by material with different rheologic characteristics, for example precast sections with cast-in-place parts, sections with more types of steel, mixed-sections (concrete-steel); (2) if there are different behaviors in the structure, in structures built for progressive erection, if structure endures restrains variations; (3) if this situations are contemporary.

Another effect of creep is reduction of stress in concrete, but at the same time there is an increase of stress in steel. In precast concrete, creep generates a loss of prestress.

1.3 *Linear viscoelasticity theory*

In this work concrete is a material characterized by linear viscoelastic behavior therefore creep generated from a constant load is linear function of stress. This hypothesis on concrete behavior is suitable for a practice study of structure, moreover with it is possible to apply superposition principle.

For a specimen of concrete subjected to a constant monoaxial state of stress σ_c, with application of stress since t_0, in the generic time t, strain is:

$$\varepsilon_C(t,t_0) = \sigma_C J(t,t_0) \tag{1}$$

where $J(t,\ t_0)$ = creep function (Fig. 1). Creep function is the strain history for unitarian constant stress applied in a determined time. Generally it is formulated by:

$$J(t,t_0) = \frac{1}{E(t_0)} + \frac{\varphi(t,t_0)}{E(t_0)} \tag{2}$$

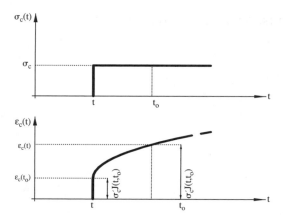

Figure 1. Strain history deriving by the application of a constant stress.

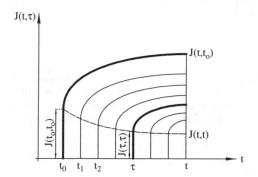

Figure 2. Creep functions for different load's times.

where $E(t_0)$ = elastic modulus in the time of application of load; $\varphi(t, t_0)$ = creep coefficient that defines the shape of creep function. The first component of creep function is an elastic one, the second component represents creep. The shape and the evolution in time of creep function for different time of application of load is visible in Figure 2.

If stress is variable in time, with superposition principle is possible to obtain:

$$\varepsilon(t,t_0) = \int_0^t J(t,\tau)d\sigma(\tau)$$ (3)

that is Stieltjes integral.

Dual of creep function is relaxation function. With it is possible to calculate a stress history generated from a strain history.

Fundamental theorems of the linear viscoelasticity reassume the theory of viscoelasticity. The first theorem

says that in an homogenous structure with rigid restrains and constant Poisson's ratio, elastic stress caused by a variable system of forces is not influenced from creep, but the state of elastic strain is modified in accord to Equation 3. The second theorem says that in an homogenous structure with rigid restrains and constant Poisson's ratio, elastic strain caused by yielding of restrains is not influenced from creep, but the state of elastic stress is modified in accord to Equation 4:

$$\sigma(t,t_0) = \int_0^t R(t,\tau)d\varepsilon(\tau)$$ (4)

where $R(t, t_0)$ = relaxation function.

2 STRESS–STRAIN RELATIONSHIP AND APPROXIMATE METHODS

2.1 Stress–strain relationship: creep models

In general creep analysis needs automatic programs of calculation. In practice design are used approximate formulations. Integral stress–strain relationship has been transformed in an approximate algebraic form, but in this time physical phenomenon hasn't been simplified. Actually, general formulation based on mathematic algorithms for analysis of integral equations is oriented to search and it is a reference for approximate formulations. These approximate methods represent a typical approach of engineering to structural analysis in viscoelastic field.

Principal creep models are formulated by *Comitè Euro-International du Beton* (C.E.B. code) and by *American Concrete Institute* (A.C.I. code). In both cases, for creep function is proposed an expression type (2), but with different creep coefficients. From C.E.B. code derives also Eurocode 2 model (EC2) for creep analysis. In particular, in appendix 1 of EC2, creep coefficient is calculated with expression:

$$\varphi(t,t_0) = \varphi_0 \beta_C(t-t_0)$$ (5)

where φ_0 = nominal creep coefficient; $\beta_c(t - t_0)$ = coefficient that describes the development of load. Expression of φ_0 is:

$$\varphi_0 = \varphi_{RH}\,\beta(f_{cm})\beta(t_0)$$ (6)

instead for the second:

$$\beta_C(t-t_0) = \left(\frac{t-t_0}{\beta_H + t - t_0}\right)^{0.3}$$ (7)

Terms in Equations 6 and 7 are functions of more parameters, for example compressive mean strength

f_{cm}, relative humidity RH, time of application of load t_0, equivalent dimension h_0. For the expressions of particular functions is possible to see EC2.

2.2 Approximate methods

Approximate methods for determination of creep can be divided in three groups: (1) general character methods; (2) algebraic methods; (3) simplified methods. Through the first is possible to obtain solutions of elevated accuracy and with it is possible to analyze complex structures. Algebraic methods lead to approximate solutions, but suitable for technical problems. They approximate integral equations with simpler expressions. Finally, with the third type of methods that used particular formulations for the stress–strain relationship, is possible to resolve the integral equations in closed form. This type of methods are important because they permit to study simply characteristic behavior of structure.

A general character method is based on quadrature formulas. Strain is calculated as a sum of rectangular or trapezoidal areas that approximate effective area defined by Stieltjes integral (Fig. 3). This method has a disadvantage, in fact, is necessary to know all load history. This problem does not exist with Degenerate Kernel Method that approximates creep function with a Dirichlet series:

$$J(t,\tau) = \sum_{i=1}^{n} a_i(\tau)\left[1 - e^{-\frac{(t-\tau)}{\lambda_i}}\right] \qquad (8)$$

where n = number of elements of series; $a_i(\tau)$ = multiplicative coefficient of series; λ_i = generic retardation time. The single terms of series have a shape of a step. The sum of all exponential terms is the curve in the first diagram of Figure 4. A third method to general character is the Reduct Relaxation Function Method (R.R.F.M.) to study homogeneous viscoelastic structures with elastic restrains, but it is applicable also for structures with non-homogeneous behavior in time.

Also algebraic methods use quadrature formulas, but in this case there is only one period of time. In other words, the period of time considered is not divided in subparts. The solutions are approximate through a rectangular with width defined by the variation of stress and with height depending from the particular algebraic method in use. In Effective Modulus Method (E.M.M.) height is the maximum value of creep function; in Mean Stress Method (M.S.M.) height is the arithmetical mean between maximum and minimum of creep function; in Age Adjusted Effective Modulus Method (A.A.E.M.M.) height is such that rectangular area is equal to exact area defined by the curve, in other words, height is such that S_1 area in Figure 5 is equal to S_2 area.

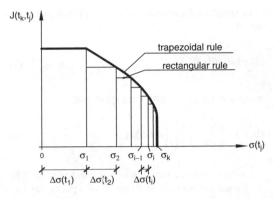

Figure 3. Determination of the strain with quadrature formulas.

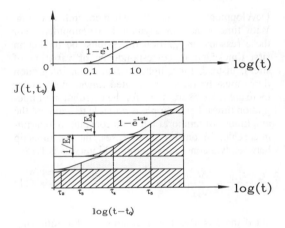

Figure 4. Degenerate Kernel Method: creep function.

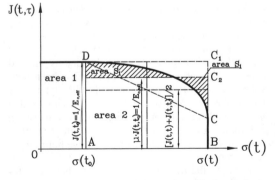

Figure 5. Determination of the strain with the algebraic methods.

In simplified methods, when is defined the creep kernel:

$$\phi(t,\tau) = -E(\tau)\frac{\partial J(t,\tau)}{\partial \tau} \tag{9}$$

creep is determined with the expression:

$$\varepsilon(t,t_0) = \frac{\sigma(t)}{E(t)} + \int_{t_0}^{t}\frac{\sigma(\tau)}{E(\tau)}\phi(t,\tau)d\tau \tag{10}$$

Creep kernel is a function of temporal transfer. The simplification consists in adoption of a particular formulation of creep kernel, for example an aging kernel.

3 APPLICATION OF CREEP MODELS

3.1 *Temporal discretization*

Development of creep is fast when concrete is young. With time it has an asymptotic development. For these reasons, integration times must be thicker in first times and in correspondence of variation of stress, instead, for a lighter calculation, integration times must be rarer for elevated times. In literature there are more expressions for the calculation of integration times. For example is possible to maintain the amplitudes of temporal intervals constant in logarithmic scale. In one of these cases, the relationship between two consecutive temporal intervals is 1.15:

$$\frac{t_k - t_{k-1}}{t_{k-1} - t_{k-2}} = \frac{\Delta t_k}{\Delta t_{k-1}} = 1.15 \tag{11}$$

but if there is a variation of stress, in the following period, there is a temporal interval of 0.05 days (Mola 1981).

3.2 *Application of normative models*

Considering an isostatic structure when is applied a force that generates a normal stress. Strain history has been estimated with EC2 and A.C.I. code. The force of traction applied since $t_{01} = 30$ days, till $t_{02} = 1730$ days. For calculation of strain history is applied superposition principle. Load history has been considered as sum of two constant loads with equal value in modulus: first load is of traction and it is imposed in t_{01}, second load is of compression and it is imposed in t_{02}. Total load is 360,000 N, stress reachs 6 N/mm², concrete class is C25/30 of EC2, relative humidity is $RH = 50\%$.

For both the models creep function has instantaneous increment that is elastic strain at the time of application of load; with time creep function has an asymptotic development. Maximum difference between creep function estimated with EC2 and A.C.I. code is about 14%.

3.3 *Application of degenerate kernel method*

For application of this method is necessary a correct determination of parameters.

First parameter is the number of elements of Dirichlet series n: (1) the approximation with creep function and Dirichlet series increases; (2) also the onerosity of calculation increases; (3) numeric instability increases. Moreover successive terms of series are less important. An optimal compromise between good solutions and minimum onerosity of calculation is $n = 3$.

Retardation times are calculated with an expression proposed by Bazant (1973):

$$\lambda_i = 10^{i-1}\lambda_1 \tag{12}$$

where $i = 1, 2, \ldots, n$; λ_1 = first retardation time. If it is 0.1, the other two are 1 and 10 respectively.

Multiplicative coefficient of series has been calculated with least squares method to diminish difference between creep function and Dirichlet series.

Increments of creep have been calculated with the expression:

$$\Delta\varepsilon_k = \sum_{i=1}^{n} A_{k,i}\left(1 - e^{-\frac{\Delta t_k}{\lambda_i}}\right) \tag{13}$$

where:

$$A_{k,i} = A_{k-1,i}e^{-\frac{\Delta t_k}{\lambda_i}} + \Delta\sigma_{k-1}a_i(t_{k-1}) \tag{14}$$

and in particular:

$$A_{i,2} = \Delta\sigma_1 a_i(t_1) \tag{15}$$

The first structure considered is the same as that in the preceding paragraph, but with a different load history. Three forces of traction have been applied on the structure, their values are 12,000 N for each force; time of application of load are to 8, 14 and 28 days. Total force, from 28th day, generates a stress of 6 N/mm².

Creep is shown in Figure 6. Total strain history is shown in Figure 7. Maximum difference between the two models is 5% to 10,000 days.

Instead, in a continuos beam with two equal spans of 3 m, with the same geometric, mechanics and ambiental behaviors of preceding case, a uniformly distributed load is applied. Load is applied to 8th, 14th and 28th days and in an instant of load is added

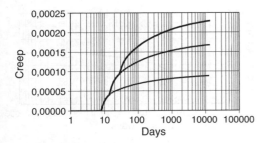

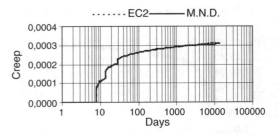

Figure 6. Creep calculated with the Degenerate Kernel Method.

Figure 8. Strain history for a continuos beam calculated with the Degenerate Kernel Method.

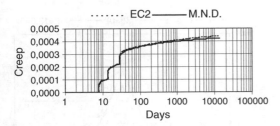

Figure 7. Strain history calculated with the Degenarate Kernel Method and comparison with EC2.

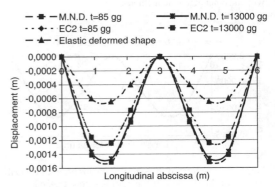

Figure 9. Deformed shape in a continuos beam calculated with Degenerate Kernel Method and for comparison with EC2.

a load that is 50% of preceding applied load. To 28th day load is 20,000 N. In this case, stress is variable with longitudinal axis and it reachs 4.2 N/mm^2 in span and 7.5 N/mm^2 in correspondence of the central restrain. Strain history calculated in the point of span with maximum stress is shown in Figure 8. Figure 9 shows deformed shape calculated with Degenerate Kernel Method to 85 and 13,000 days; as comparison they are calculated also with EC2 model and also elastic deformed shape is shown. Difference between the two models are minimum to 85 days, instead, to 13,000 days they are about 3%.

3.4 Application of age adjusted effective modulus method

Creep has been determined also with algebraic methods and in particular with Age Adjusted Effective Modulus Method. For comparison, solutions calculated with quadrature formulas method (it is indicated in figures with F.Q.) and with EC2 model are also shown.

For isostatic structure, load is a traction and it is applied in six different times. In every time of application of load, it is increases of 50% of load relatives to preceding time. After 56 days load is constant and its value is 360,000 N. The relative stress is 6 N/mm^2.

With the method considered, creep has been calculated in different time (for example to 13,000 days in

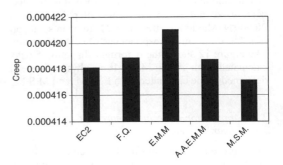

Figure 10. Strain calculated with A.A.E.M.M. to 85 days and comparison with the other algebraic methods.

Fig. 10). If the solutions are reported in a temporal scale, is possible to obtain the strain history (Fig. 11). Differences between creep calculated with A.A.E.M.M. and EC2 model are minimal: they are inferiors than 1%. This result derives by creep function used for algebraic methods that is calculated with EC2 model. Moreover A.A.E.M.M. is potentially exact. The solutions calculated with other algebraic

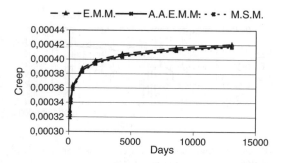

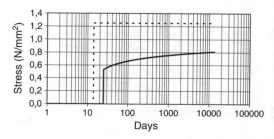

Figure 11. Strain history calculated with A.A.E.M.M. and with the other algebraic methods.

Figure 13. Stress history in a continuos beam built for union of a series of isostatic beams (solid curve). As comparison beam diretly continuos built is shown (dashed curve).

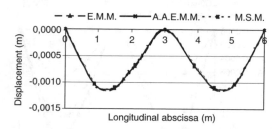

Figure 12. Deformed shape in a continuos beam calculated with A.A.E.M.M. and with the other algebraic methods.

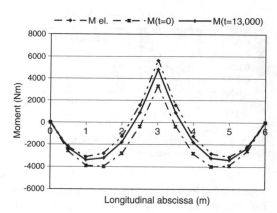

Figure 14. Bending moment in a continuos beam with a displacement in correspondence of the central restrains.

method are approximate above (E.M.M.) or below (M.S.M.) respect to the exact value (Figs. 10, 11).

For continuos beam, the same load function has been used, but the final value after 56 days is 20,000 N. Maximum stress is 4.2 N/mm^2 in span and it is 7.5 N/mm^2 in correspondence of central restrain. The Figure 12 shows the deformed shape to 85 days calculated with A.A.E.M.M. It is always between deformed shape calculated with E.M.M. and M.S.M.

3.5 Application of Second theorem of linear viscoelasticity

In the preceding examples the First theorem of linear viscoelasticity has been applied. In fact, after the application of a constant load a strain history has been calculated. Instead, for Second theorem of viscoelasticity, after the application of a perturbation (variation of static configuration, application of a prestress, restrain displacement, etc.) there is a variation of stress state in structure. In particular have been studied the following cases: (1) union of a series of isostatic beams in a iperstatic beam (continuos beam); (2) restrain displacement in central restrain of a continuos beam with two equal spans; (3) stress state variation caused by creep in a prestressed concrete beam. The solutions of some cases are show in Figures 13–15.

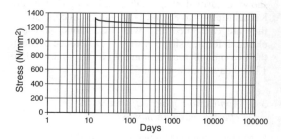

Figure 15. Stress history caused by creep in a prestressing steel.

4 CONCLUSION

In Degenerate Kernel Method, creep function is approximate with a Dirichlet series. This method has same advantage respect the other exact methods: (1) it uses a relative low parameter number; (2) the solutions are quiet accuracy; (3) it is not necessary to know all the load history, but only the increase of stress from two consecutive steps to calculate the strain in a particular time. Respect to EC2 model there are difference of 5% in strains. After all Degenerate Kernel Method results reliable and solutions supplied are next to real for a greater number of elements of series.

Another method considered for calculation of creep is Age Adjusted Effective Modulus Method.

It is potentially exact. Its difference respect EC2 model are inferior than 1%. However it is convenient to determinate strain in a particular time, but it is more complex to determinate all strain history.

REFERENCES

A.C.I. Committee 209/11 1971. Prediction of Creep, Shrinkage and Temperature effects in Concrete structures. A.C.I.-SP27 *Designing for effects of Creep, Shrinkage and Temperature.*

Bazant, Z.P. 1972. Numerical Determination of Long-Range Stress history from Strain history in Concrete. *Material and Structures* 5.

Bazant, Z.P. 1975. Theory of Creep and Shrinkage in Concrete structures, a precis of recent development. *Mechanics today* 2.

Bazant, Z.P. 1982. Inelasticity and Failure of Concrete. *Mathematical models of Creep and Shrinkage of Concrete* 1.

Bazant, Z.P. & Wu, S.T. 1973. Dirichlet Series Creep function for aging Concrete. *Journal of Eng. Mech. Div.* 99.

F.I.P./C.E.B. 1984. CEB Design manual on structural effects of the time dependent behavior of concrete. *Bullettin d'information* 142-142bis.

Mola, F. 1979. Metodo Generale e Metodo Approssimato per la risoluzione di strutture non omogenee a comportamento elastoviscoso lineare. *Studi e Ricerche* 1.

Mola, F. 1981. Metodi di analisi di strutture in c.a. e c.a.p. a comportamento elastoviscoso lineare. *Studi e Ricerche* 3.

UNI ENV Eurocodice 2 1992. Progettazione delle strutture di calcestruzzo.

System-based Vision for Strategic and Creative Design, Bontempi (ed.)
© 2003 Swets & Zeitlinger, Lisse, ISBN 90 5809 599 1

Studying of elastic–plastic behavior of concrete ceiling, joints, supports by live loading of concrete ceiling

A. Turk
Supervisor Engineer, Water division, KWPA (khuzestan water and power authority), Ahwaz, Kuzestan, IRAN

ABSTRACT: In Asemaneh building, steel structure and concrete slab has occurred misfit steel members and unknown quality of concrete slab sections. Steel long plate connections in supports were replaced by angle shapes connection in joints. New Kormit concrete ceiling was executed and we did not have any theoretical criterion for concrete acceptation. Two main problems were solved by Loading Test on ceiling concrete.

a) We made a strip line of live load (wet bricks) parallel the axial of concrete slab beams.
b) Live load settlement was measured by accurate instrument before and after loading.
c) Computer drew deflection 3D map.

Qualification of ceiling was obtained by support condition movements and maximum settlement at mid point and zero slope in support.
3D map of live load test have concluded the right shape of angel ∟ connection. Therefore this method could be used in conditional structure, where we need an easy way to know quality of members and joints.

1 INTRODUCTION

Quality control of concrete ceiling is the more controversial discussion in workshop when the concrete was executed. In addition, steel connection behavior should be tested especially in modified members and re-welded connections. In steel frame with concrete ceiling, supervisor should be selected the best way to quality control of critical points and it shall be recognized economical and fast method. With aci318 building code, live load test could be used to explaining the new method of ceiling load. Sometimes in steel frame is needed to fit members by extra cable tension in misfit members for erecting frame. In this case, nuts and bolts steel plates should be modified by new welding connection and it is necessary to check the new replacement connection by live load test. The more advantage was produced by this method of live load test that it could be recognized every desired point of concrete to need quality control of concrete steel frame. It is mentioned that the tension is not allowed by extra cable tensional instruments because the frame should be acted to absorb misfit members. The torsion and deflection were occurred by extra cable force in frames it should be return to initial position to omit the residual stresses.

2 WARPING AND MODIFICATION CRITERION

2.1 *Steel frame*

In steel frame building Asemaneh some misfit and warping were occurred with below items:

1. One miss-fit of main steel beam, $\Delta x = -5\,cm$
2. One miss-fit of main steel beam, $\Delta x = -6\,cm$
3. Tensile instruments acted extra tension on frame.

Consideration above item can be resulted below:

1. steel skeleton torsion
2. undesired bending moments in columns and beams
3. warping in steel members (columns)

2.1.1 *Modification method of steel frame*

Modify processing is needed to add an L-shape steel connection (steel angel) where the members were cut by supervisor engineer to return in the initial shape and the residual deflection (or torsion movement) should be absorbed to erect column plump line. It is mentioned that un-symmetry torsion was created by misfit displacement in the steel structure. Modifying steps are recommended below:

1. Center of gravity and stiffness should be found.

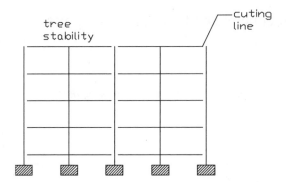

tree
stability

cuting
line

Figure 1. Tree stability by cutting connections.

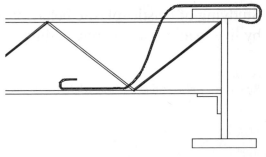

Figure 3. Hook steel bars in end. In computation notebook, lateral beam support is designed by rigid joint but in the workshop, it is fitted to execute by simple joint. Therefore hooks bar should be placed to guarantee rigidity conditions.

Figure 2. Tree stability.

2. Measuring the torsion & displacement (θz, Δx, Δy).
3. Warping columns should be cut to separate frame into tree static stability that it is rigidity fixed at the foundation (refer to Figure 1).
4. Measuring the member's deflections shall be necessary advised again to control (θz, Δx, Δy).
5. Plastic deformation of beams and columns must be recognized. It should be declared to modify decreasing resistance of live load.
6. Un-justify displacement (θz, Δx, Δy) could be fixed again by opposite tension force against desired columns (by using step 1).
7. Adding L-shape or angel 90 degree in cutting connection. Rigidity behavior should be guaranteed by this connection.

Above Steps could be guaranteed the final test of steel frame. Notification, in each odd span, beams constrains should be released where the span is needed to convert a tree shape structure by unconstraint freedom degrees (the one main column and links cantilever beams, refer to Figure 2).

2.2 Concrete ceiling

Another problems were obtained simultaneously by uncertainly concrete design that it had been made for new Kormit ceiling. Main problem could be defined with below items:

1. Notebook design has not been matched with characteristics of concrete member's especially steel I-beams dimensions when supervisor engineer measures it to control in the workshop.
2. Concrete mix design is differed where it should be used in ceiling with aggregate limitations (aci).
3. Unknown ultimate loads, live and dead.

2.2.1 Concrete modification

Suggestion methods are set below to modify problems that it is occurred by three items above:

1. Compulsory end beam rigidity; it is obtained by adding two bend hook steel bars that it is placed between main girder steel beam and end of each lateral I-beam (Figure 3).
2. Cement increasing; C in C/W ratio was increased in constant ratio.
3. In lateral beams, Adding required steel bars in positive moment.
4. Adding T-shape steel support in each end of lateral steel beams of ceiling.

2.3 Simultaneously modification

After above, a criterion behavioral is needed to control deflection and plumb-lines when the modification steps are exerted on structure to fix movement. The load test based on aci318 could be verified operations by new method of live load test that it will be explain in the body of this text. Flexibility and randomly of loading test point produce more advantage.

3 NEW LIVE LOAD TEST AND VALUE MEASUREMENT METHOD

Safe and complete test should be recognized the three steps below:

3.1 At rest condition

The concrete surface is clear against any live load and allowable resistance is started by during 45 days. Concrete with type 5 is used to serve at least 45 days.

3.1.1 Bench mark
A bench mark point should be determined in special part of structure that this point must be keep away from any settlement or influence radius (deflection is zero). A suitable point shall be determined away from test span and the point position is determined to consider by member stiffness notebook.

3.1.2 Nailing
Steel nails ($l = 50$ mm, $d = 2$ mm) should be driven in concrete ceiling where it is needed to determine the deflection curve of load span. Accurate surveying instruments can be used to measure the nail deflections.

3.2 Measuring value, live load test with specific material (wet bricks)

Live load is defined to carry by wet bricks comfortably. Dry Brick loads to set easy on span and it will be damped to wet by water.

3.2.1 Load condition and boundary
Live load boundary is limited by supervisor engineer which the deflection should be measured for conclusion and interpretations. It is mentioned that square nailing areas (14×14 cm^2) have been getting used in blanked space surveying measurements.

3.2.2 Studying of parameters
Importance notice, the main opinion could be clarified parameters to choose the load span that it is contained a two meters width stripe live load and it should be parallel the beam axes. Wet bricks are used to complete loading and all dry bricks should be set in desired boundary to starting measurements. After they are set in place it should be added to weight dry into wet bricks. It may be contained the below items:

1. The steel members misfit
2. Concrete ceiling bending stiffness
3. Maximum concrete settlements
4. verifying steel connection in critical frames
5. torsion behavior of side span
6. needs to control the allowable movements

3.3 Measuring value, Un-loading condition

During 24 hours, if the q_{ult} or live load has been chosen less than elastic load in σ-ε graph, residual deflection is return again to the initial point (elastic behavior). It is mentioned, the maximum load could be acted on concrete members less than 75% of total ultimate load (aci318). In this case, the load is exerted up on the members by plastic condition and the residual deflection is remained in near the initial point by test load. Notification on concrete ceiling elements, the concrete ceiling is named one-side by one side resistance in lateral ceiling beam. Therefore the loading test should be made in strip line.

4 INTERPRETATION OF 2 & 3D DEFLECTION

Two-dimensional deflection maps (2DDM) is set by a group of curves which they shall be explained with below steps:

4.1 Longitudinal sections

It can be shown the deflection points that they have been settled under live load lines with support specific conditions. The maximum deflection is appeared in the mid point of span in rigid and symmetrical supports. Also, another advantage will be obtained to determine below items:

1. Determining the slopes in each end, zero in fixed supports. Non-zero slop could be interpreted to consider low fixate
2. Deflection curve
3. beam symmetrically considerations
4. bending moments in each ends
5. Earthquake engineering parameters, stiffness matrix K, it is obtained by $P = K \cdot \Delta$ (Equation 1)
6. Rigidity percentage (steel frames end)
7. Verifying of steel connections, actual and theoretical resistance comparison
8. Kormit concrete design criterion and replacement steel joints

Notification, items 6,7, and 8 had discussed to clear replacement connection that it was installed by supervisor engineer and designed clam. Designer (Tazand, consulting engineering co. ltd.) has been believed to prove the not sufficient rigidity of L-connection that supervisor engineer in the workshop places it. The Figure 4 could be defined the correct behavior.

$$M_A = \frac{2EI}{L}\left(2\theta_A + \theta_B - \frac{3\Delta}{L}\right) - M_{fixed}$$

Symmetrical Conditions:

$$M_A = M_{fixed} \Rightarrow 2EI/L = 2M_A/\left(2\theta_A + \theta_B - \frac{3\Delta}{L}\right)$$

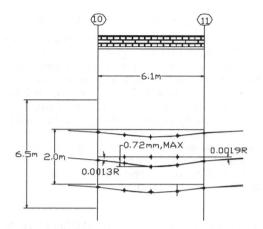

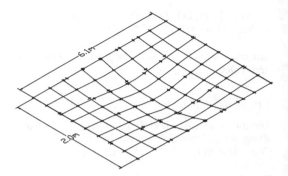

Figure 5. Space deflection is shown by contour map of curves. Slopes in end should be notified to calculate stiffness matrix. The live loading will be acted on concrete ceiling to recognize steel plate girder behavior where it is down in misfit conditions. Inertia

Figure 4. Loading span and deflection with curve branches. It is a clear notification when maximum deflection will be occurred near the mid point of span and zero slop in ends.

$$\Rightarrow \frac{EI}{L} = \frac{M_{fixed}}{(2\theta_A + \theta_B - \frac{3\Delta}{L})} \qquad (1)$$

4.2 Widthwise sections

In theoretical concepts, the one-side beam could be elected the total bending moment in lateral axes; therefore using lateral curve in limited to produce bellow items:

1. Side-way deflection curve (Figs 4 , 5)
2. Lateral behavior

4.3 Plan or contour map

These kinds of maps are used to interpret the resistance of steel members in pointed joints and it could be ordinary determined to approve safety of test load. Some advantages have been resulted during the test:

1. Vectors displacement
2. Scalar displacement
3. Distribution displacement

4.4 Space deflection

4.4.1 Steel frame
It is used specially to determine connection reactions in each end of steel plate girders, in safety concepts, the final check could be assessed by compatibility curve.

4.4.2 Concrete ceiling
Main purpose was decided by uncertainly safety design. It could be tested to result the maximum

deflection of the settlement curve that it should be determined good or no-good results.

5 DRAWING CURVES

By Referring to Figure 4, actual settlement and slope are shown to compute by Equations 2 and 3. Supports rigidity condition could be taken to prove modification processing by slope at each end of the lateral beams.

$\theta_a = (Twisting \quad Angel\,by \quad live \quad load \quad test)_a$

$\theta_b = (Twisting \quad Angel\,by \quad live \quad load \quad test)_b$

$E = Elastisity \quad Moduls \quad = 2 \times 10^5 \quad (\frac{kg}{cm^2})$

$I = Moment \quad of \quad Inertia \quad = 10^4 \quad (cm^4)$

$L = Length \quad of \quad beam \quad (m)$

$M_a = Bending \quad Moment \quad at \quad a$

$M_b = Bending \quad Moment \quad at \quad b$

$q = \alpha \times \beta(1.4q_{Dead} + 1.7q_{Live})$

$\alpha = 0.75(ACI318)$

$\beta = Effective \quad Width\,of \quad Beam \quad = 0.72 \, m$

$q = 0.75 \times 0.72(1.4q_{Dead} + 1.7q_{Live})$

$q = 0.75 \times 0.72(1.4 \times 550 + 1.7 \times 500) = 875 \frac{kg}{m}$

$\frac{qL^2}{12} = \frac{875 \times 6.1^2}{12} = 2.713 \quad t.m$

$\theta_a = 0.0013^R \quad ; \theta_b = -0.0019^R$

$\Delta = 3.1 - 2.5 = +0.6 \quad mm \qquad ; L = 610 \quad cm$

$$M_a = \frac{2EI}{L}\left(2\theta_a + \theta_b - 3\frac{\Delta}{L}\right) - \frac{qL^2}{12} \qquad (2)$$

718

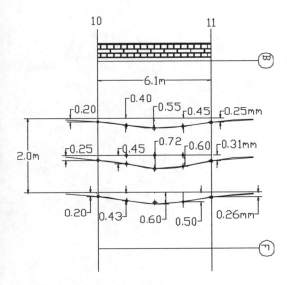

Figure 6. Live load values.

$$M_b = \frac{2EI}{L}\left(2\theta_b + \theta_a - 3\frac{\Delta}{L}\right) + \frac{qL^2}{12} \qquad (3)$$

$$2\theta_a + \theta_b - 3\frac{\Delta}{L} = 2\times.0013 - .0019 - \tfrac{3\times0.6}{610} = .0007$$

$$2\theta_b + \theta_a - 3\frac{\Delta}{L} = -2\times.0019 + .0013 - \tfrac{3\times0.6}{610} = -.0025$$

$$M_a = \tfrac{2\times(2\times10^5)\times(10^4)}{610}(0.0007) - 2.71\times10^5 = -2.66 \ \ t.m$$

$$M_b = \tfrac{2\times(2\times10^5)\times(10^4)}{610}(-0.0025) + 2.71\times10^5 = +2.55 \ \ t.m$$

$$\Rightarrow M_a = -2.66 \ \ t.m \qquad \leq \frac{qL^2}{12} = -2.71 \, t.m$$

$$\Rightarrow M_b = +2.55 \ \ t.m \qquad \leq \frac{qL^2}{12} = -2.71 \, t.m$$

6   POINTS ABOUT STIFFNESS (EI/L)

By using Equation 1, it is possible to access the real value EI/L that it is related the actual stiffness of concrete members. First, the desired span should be fined to loading by symmetrical position and conditions. Therefore the M_a could be evaluated to substitute in Equation 1 by Equation 4 that it could be clear the symmetric phenomena symmetrical condition is used to determine stiffness EI/L. It is mentioned that the twist values should be equal both point M_a and M_b.

$$\theta_a = \theta_b \cong 0$$
$$\Delta_a = \Delta_b$$
$$\Rightarrow M_a = M_b = M_{fixed} = \frac{ql^2}{12}$$

$$\frac{EI}{L} = \frac{\frac{ql^2}{12}}{(2\theta_a + \theta_b - \frac{3\Delta}{l})} \qquad (4)$$

$$\vec{P} = K.\vec{\Delta}$$

7   CONCLUSION

The misfit steel members could be solved simultaneously with uncertain concrete design if the project is used new live load on ceiling concrete. Also, stiffness of concrete members could be completed to use in earthquake and dynamic engineering design (Equation 4). Important notice should be considered to evaluate EI/L, that it is experimental value and it could be compared with theoretical EI/L in unsafe structure, in addition, new live load test shall be suggested to release the problems.

REFERENCES

Aci318, Building code requirements for Structural concrete and Commentary.
Keynia, A.M. 1995. Analyses and Design of concrete structures.10th edn.
Popov, I.P. 1996. Engineering Mechanics of Solids 2nd edn.
Road & Transportation Laboratory, 1996. Report of Asemaneh concreting Building.
Salmon, C.G.1996. Steel Structures: Design and Behavior.
Turk, A & Zakerynia, M. 1996. Report of live load test on concrete ceiling Asemaneh into technical office.

System-based Vision for Strategic and Creative Design, Bontempi (ed.)
© 2003 Swets & Zeitlinger, Lisse, ISBN 90 5809 599 1

Crack width control in two dimensional reinforced concrete elements

G. Bertagnoli, V.I. Carbone, L. Giordano & G. Mancini
Politecnico di Torino, Italy

ABSTRACT: Physical models for two dimensional reinforced concrete elements design at ultimate limit state verification can be considered sufficiently well tested from both the scientific and normative viewpoint. It is still unsatisfactory, on the contrary, the study of serviceability behaviour of two dimensional elements designed at the ultimate limit state, especially as regards expected crack width control. This aspect of the issue is of particular interest also for D-regions in order to define the secondary reinforcement, that is not strictly necessary to ensure the equilibrium in the estimated ultimate condition. In this paper we aimed to find dimensioning criteria for secondary reinforcement in r.c. two dimensional elements, in order to ensure cracks of predetermined width in serviceability conditions. This aim can be achieved by a detail analysis of the structure behaviour that arises on the crack opening and following evolution, validating the obtained results by design procedures consolidated in international codes.

1 INTRODUCTION

Crack width evaluation in two dimensional reinforced concrete elements with two orthogonal reinforcement layers can be easily performed by the application of well known normative procedures (C.E.B.–F.I.P. 1990), (Eurocode 2 2002) based on through experimental studies (Bhide 1989), (Vecchio 1982), (Marti 1992), once known the internal actions in each element.

However, two dimensional elements can be commonly seen as parts of non slender structures as deep beams, that are dimensioned according to the typical theory of D-regions, that is applying the static theorem of plasticity.

Such a method brings to a correct ultimate dimensioning and allows to verify the opening of cracks near the main tie, but is useless in to draw an outline of the crack pattern in the regions controlled by secondary reinforcement, whose size is chosen according to empirical methods.

The throughout evaluation of the crack pattern would require a non linear step by step analysis after a first dimensioning and a following iterative optimizing procedure. This operating way doesn't seem to be reasonable almost in every case in structural engineering.

In this paper is presented a procedure that allows to know crack opening just after their formation, and, if the results of a linear FEM analysis are available, to follow the crack-width evolution subsequent to external actions variation. This procedure is surely conservative, as internal actions redistribution from cracked regions to stiffer ones are not taken into account.

2 MODEL DEFINITION

Let's consider a two dimensional reinforced concrete element with orthogonal reinforcement, where a crack pattern with a (inclination from the x axis (Fig. 1) has taken place.

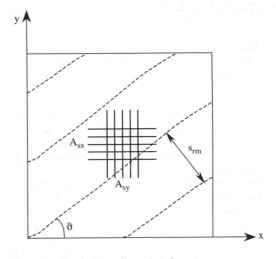

Figure 1. Cracked two dimension element.

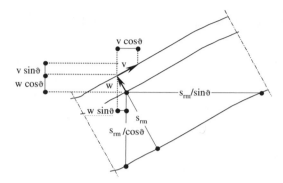

Figure 2. Displacement components along the crack.

$$\Delta\varepsilon_{sy} = \beta_t f_{ct}\left(\frac{1}{\rho_y E_s} - \frac{1}{E_c}\right) = \frac{\beta_t f_{ct}}{E_s}\left(\frac{1}{\rho_y} - n\right) \qquad (4)$$

where ρ_x and ρ_y are the geometrical ratios of reinforcement in directions x and y and β_t is an empirical coefficient for the evaluation of average strain between two adjacent cracks.

It is then possible to calculate the stresses in reinforcement along the crack:

$$\sigma_{sx} = E_s\left(\overline{\varepsilon}_{sx} + \Delta\varepsilon_{sx}\right) \le f_{sy} \qquad (5)$$

$$\sigma_{sy} = E_s\left(\overline{\varepsilon}_{sy} + \Delta\varepsilon_{sy}\right) \le f_{sy} \qquad (6)$$

Furthermore the average distance between cracks can be evaluated as (C.E.B.–F.I.P. 1990):

$$s_{rm} = \left(\frac{\sin\vartheta}{s_{rmx}} + \frac{\cos\vartheta}{s_{rmy}}\right)^{-1} \qquad (7)$$

where s_{rmx} and s_{rmy} can be calculated with the expressions (C.E.B.–F.I.P. 1990):

$$s_{rmx} = \frac{2}{3}\frac{\phi_x}{3.6\rho_{eff,x}} \qquad (8)$$

$$s_{rmy} = \frac{2}{3}\frac{\phi_y}{3.6\rho_{eff,y}} \qquad (9)$$

where ϕ_x and ϕ_y are bar diameters in x and y directions, $\rho_{eff,x}$ and $\rho_{eff,y}$ geometrical reinforcement ratios referred to concrete areas controlled by each bar and 2/3 a coefficient to shift from characteristics to average values.

It is furthermore necessary to specify that as a consequence of the displacement components v and w arises along the crack a tangential stress that can be estimated according to (Bazant 1980) and (Gambarova 1983) as:

$$\sigma_{ct} = \tau_0\left(\frac{a_0}{a_0 + w^2}\right)\frac{v}{w}\frac{\left[a_3 + a_4\left|\frac{v}{w}\right|^3\right]}{\left[1 + a_4\left(\frac{v}{w}\right)^4\right]} \qquad (10)$$

where $\tau_0 = 0.245 \cdot f_c$, $a_0 = 0.01 \cdot d^2$, $a_3 = 2.45/\tau_0$, $a_4 = 2.44 \cdot (1-4/\tau_0)$ and d is the maximum aggregate diameter.

In effect together with σ_{ct} a σ_{cn} arises, that is a tension orthogonal to the crack, that isn't taken into account in the following process both because has

Following a typical approach to this subject (Iori 1985), after a detail analysis of the element behaviour nearby the crack, we can assume that a point lying on the crack undergoes through two displacement components w and v, respectively orthogonal and parallel to the crack (Fig. 2).

The average steel deformations in the x and y directions can be then calculated using the following expressions:

$$\overline{\varepsilon}_{sx} = \frac{w^* \sin\vartheta - v\cos\vartheta}{s_{rm}/\sin\vartheta} =$$
$$= \frac{w^* \sin^2\vartheta - v\sin\vartheta\cos\vartheta}{s_{rm}} \qquad (1)$$

$$\overline{\varepsilon}_{sy} = \frac{w^* \cos\vartheta + v\sin\vartheta}{s_{rm}/\cos\vartheta} =$$
$$= \frac{w^* \cos^2\vartheta + v\sin\vartheta\cos\vartheta}{s_{rm}} \qquad (2)$$

where w^* is the displacement component orthogonal to the crack reduced by concrete lengthening between two adjacent cracks, that is, in first approximation, $w^* = w - f_{ct} \cdot s_{rm}/2 \cdot E_c$.

On the other hand, can be observed that the term referring to concrete is by one order of magnitude smaller than the minimum expected for w, so its contribution can be left out and w^* can be confused with w.

When in the uncracked element the principal tesile stress, inclined of ϑ from the x axis, reaches the value of concrete tensile strength f_{ct}, the strain increment in steel along the crack can be evaluated (C.E.B.–F.I.P. 1990) as:

$$\Delta\varepsilon_{sx} = \beta_t f_{ct}\left(\frac{1}{\rho_x E_s} - \frac{1}{E_c}\right) = \frac{\beta_t f_{ct}}{E_s}\left(\frac{1}{\rho_x} - n\right) \qquad (3)$$

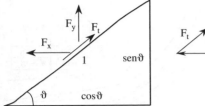

Figure 3. Strengths along the crack.

almost no effect in the engineering field of cracks opening ($w \geq 0.2\,\mathrm{mm}$), and because its small contribution works on the safety side.

By analogy the residual tensile strength, present in the same direction along the crack, isn't taken into account because its effect is completely negligible in the research field of the present work.

Along the crack takes place the following force system (Fig. 3):

$$F_x = \sigma_{sx}\rho_x \sin \vartheta \qquad (11)$$

$$F_y = \sigma_{sy}\rho_y \cos \vartheta \qquad (12)$$

$$F_t = \sigma_{ct} \cdot 1 \qquad (13)$$

The resultant of this system when the crack takes place must be orthogonal to the crack and assume the value:

$$R = f_{ct} \cdot 1 \qquad (14)$$

At the end we have:

$$R_x = F_x - F_t \cos \vartheta = \left(\sigma_{sx}\rho_x - \frac{\sigma_{ct}}{\tan \vartheta}\right)\sin \vartheta \qquad (15)$$

$$R_y = F_y + F_t \sin \vartheta = \left(\sigma_{sy}\rho_y + \sigma_{ct} \tan \vartheta\right)\cos \vartheta \qquad (16)$$

$$\frac{R_x}{R_y} = \tan \vartheta \qquad (17)$$

$$R = \sqrt{R_x^2 + R_y^2} = F_x \sin \vartheta + F_y \cos \vartheta =$$
$$= \sigma_{sx}\rho_x \sin^2 \vartheta + \sigma_{sy}\rho_y \cos^2 \vartheta = f_{ct} \qquad (18)$$

Equations system made of (17) and (18), where the implicit unknown values are v and w, can be uncoupled introducing the following simplifications:

• In equations (3) and (4) n can be neglected in comparison to $1/\rho_x$ and $1/\rho_y$, getting

$$\Delta\varepsilon_{sx} = \frac{\beta_t f_{ct}}{E_s \rho_x} \qquad (21)$$

$$\Delta\varepsilon_{sy} = \frac{\beta_t f_{ct}}{E_s \rho_y} \qquad (22)$$

As a consequence inequalities (5) and (6) become

$$\sigma_{sx} = E_s\left(w\sin^2 \vartheta - v\sin \vartheta \cos \vartheta\right) +$$
$$+ \frac{\beta_t f_{ct}}{\rho_x} \leq f_{sy} \qquad (23)$$

$$\sigma_{sy} = E_s\left(w\cos^2 \vartheta + v\sin \vartheta \cos \vartheta\right) +$$
$$+ \frac{\beta_t f_{ct}}{\rho_y} \leq f_{sy} \qquad (24)$$

• In equation (10) the term $a_0/(a_0 + w^2)$ may be considered to assume unit value when $d = 30\,\mathrm{mm}$ and w less than $0.4\,\mathrm{mm}$.

Supposing that both reinforcements aren't yielded, by substitution of equations (23) and (24) in (18) we get

$$v = Aw - B \qquad (25)$$

with

$$A = \frac{\rho_x \sin^4 \vartheta + \rho_y \cos^4 \vartheta}{\rho_x \sin^3 \vartheta \cos \vartheta - \rho_y \sin \vartheta \cos^3 \vartheta} \qquad (26)$$

$$B = \frac{(\gamma - \beta)f_{ct} s_{rm}}{E_s \sin \vartheta \cos \vartheta\left(\rho_y \sin^2 \vartheta - \rho_y \cos^2 \vartheta\right)} \qquad (27)$$

where γ is a coefficient that assumes unit value at the crack formation.

By substitution of equations (23), (24) and (25) in (17) can be found the following expression that is only function of w:

$$wD + F = \tau_0 \frac{(Aw - B)\left(a_3 w^3 + a_4|Aw - B|^3\right)}{w^4 + a_4(Aw - B)^4} \qquad (28)$$

with

$$D = \frac{E_s \sin \vartheta \cos \vartheta}{s_{rm}}\left[\rho_x \sin \vartheta(\sin \vartheta - A\cos \vartheta)\right.$$
$$\left. - \rho_y \cos \vartheta(\cos \vartheta + A\sin \vartheta)\right] \qquad (29)$$

$$F = \frac{E_s B \sin^2 \vartheta \cos^2 \vartheta}{s_{rm}}\left(\rho_x + \rho_y\right) \qquad (30)$$

723

Equation (28) can be numerically solved to obtain w. In any case it has to be checked that inequalities (23) and (24) are satisfied.

If reinforcement in the x direction turns out to be yielded the computation has to be repeated replacing equations from (25) to (30) with the following ones.

$$v = A_1 w - B_1 \tag{31}$$

$$A_1 = -ctg\,\vartheta \tag{32}$$

$$B_1 = \frac{\left[(\gamma - \beta\cos^2\vartheta)f_{ct} - \rho_x f_{sy}\sin^2\vartheta\right]s_{rm}}{E_s\rho_y\sin\vartheta\cos^3\vartheta} \tag{33}$$

$$wD_1 + F_1 = \tau_0\frac{(A_1 w - B_1)\left(a_3 w^3 + a_4|A_1 w - B_1|^3\right)}{w^4 + a_4(A_1 w - B_1)^4} \tag{34}$$

$$D_1 = 0 \tag{35}$$

$$F_1 = \sin\vartheta\cos\vartheta\left(\rho_x f_{sy} + \right.$$
$$\left. + E_s\rho_y B_1\frac{\sin\vartheta\cos\vartheta}{s_{rm}} - \beta f_{ct}\right) \tag{36}$$

Instead, if reinforcement in y direction is yielded, equation from (25) to (30) have to be replaced with the following ones:

$$v = A_2 w - B_2 \tag{37}$$

$$A_2 = tg\,\vartheta \tag{38}$$

$$B_2 = \frac{\left[(\gamma - \beta\sin^2\vartheta)f_{ct} - \rho_y f_{sy}\cos^2\vartheta\right]s_{rm}}{E_s\rho_x\sin^3\vartheta\cos\vartheta} \tag{39}$$

$$wD_2 + F_2 = \tau_0(A_2 w - B_2)\cdot$$
$$\frac{\left[a_3 w^3 + a_4|A_2 w - B_2|^3\right]}{w^4 + a_4(A_2 w - B_2)^4} \tag{40}$$

$$D_2 = \frac{E_s\rho_x\sin^2\vartheta\cos\vartheta}{s_{rm}}(\sin\vartheta - A_2\cos\vartheta) \tag{41}$$

$$F_2 = \sin\vartheta\cos\vartheta\left(-\rho_y f_{sy} + \right.$$
$$\left. + E_s\rho_x B_2\frac{\sin\vartheta\cos\vartheta}{s_{rm}} + \beta f_{ct}\right) \tag{42}$$

If both reinforcements are yielded the equilibrium cannot be reached.

The group of equations written above can be read in adimensional terms, assuming, $W = w/s_{rm}$, $V = v/s_{rm}$.

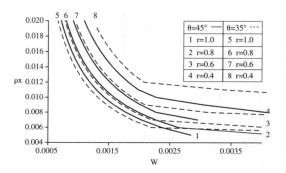

Figure 4. W as a function of ρ_x.

Then equations (25) and (28) become

$$V = AW - B' \tag{43}$$

$$WD' + F' = \tau_0\frac{(AW - B')\left(a_3 W^3 + a_4|AW - B'|^3\right)}{W^4 + a_4(AW - B')^4} \tag{44}$$

where

$$B' = \frac{(\gamma - \beta)f_{ct}}{E_s\sin\vartheta\cos\vartheta(\rho_y\sin^2\vartheta - \rho_y\cos^2\vartheta)} \tag{45}$$

$$D' = E_s\sin\vartheta\cos\vartheta\left[\rho_x\sin\vartheta(\sin\vartheta - A\cos\vartheta)\right.$$
$$\left. - \rho_y\cos\vartheta(\cos\vartheta + A\sin\vartheta)\right] \tag{46}$$

$$F' = E_s B'\sin^2\vartheta\cos^2\vartheta(\rho_x + \rho_y) \tag{47}$$

We can proceed in the same way for adimensionalization when reinforcement yields.

Equation (44) and the corresponding ones for yielding situations, allows to evaluate non dimensional crack opening W, once known $r = \rho_y/\rho_x$, ϑ, f_{ct} e f_{sy}, for a given value of ρ_x.

In Figure 4 is indeed drawn the relation $W = f(\rho_x)$ for different r values (0.4 , 0.6 , 0.8 , 1.0) and for two ϑ values (35°, 45°) once chosen $f_{ct} = 2.37\,\text{MPa}$ and $f_{sy} = 430\,\text{MPa}$.

It's interesting to see that ϑ has a secondary and not monotone role. Besides it turns to be more significant the r parameter.

This diagram can be used in design, having fixed the crack opening, to obtain the geometrical reinforcement ratio to be introduced in the two orthogonal directions x and y.

In this way it is possible to obtain the reinforcement amount necessary to ensure an established crack opening when the principal tensile stress is equal to

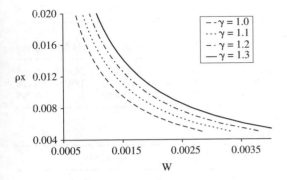

Figure 5. Relation $W = f(\rho_x)$ for different (values for $\theta = 45°$.

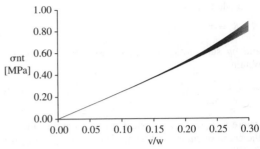

Figure 6. Tangential stress in function of v/w for f_c values variable between 30 and 50 MPa.

the corresponding concrete resistance f_{ct} reached in ϑ direction.

If we'd rather know crack opening beyond the first stabilized cracking, can be assumed that, as a first approximation, the tensile resistance $f_{ct,fict}$ would be increased against the real one.

This amounts to saying that the panel, uniformly loaded along the edges, would behave as if it was isostatically bounded and so it hadn't the chance to take advantage of the favorable effect of redistributions toward stiffer zones of the structure.

In practice this operation implies the assignment of the value $f_{ct,fict}/f_{ct,real}$ to γ in equations (27) (33) (39) and (45).

Diagram in Figure 5 shows the known function $W = f(\rho_x)$ for $\vartheta = 45°$ and four different γ ratios between fictious tensile resistance and real one (1.0, 1.1, 1.2, 1.3).

It's therefore possible to evaluate the increase of crack width after first cracking. Needless to say the results of a FEM elastic analysis allow to know the real ratio between external actions at a time t and at first cracking.

It is then possible to calculate the proper geometrical reinforcement ratio ρ_x to keep cracks width within a given fixed value in serviceability conditions. As already said this method is conservative as it doesn't take into account internal redistributions.

3 SIMPLIFIED PROCEDURE

It can be also observed that within the range of the parameter $v/w \leqslant 0.2$ equation (10) is considerably linear and independent by concrete grade (Fig. 6). Moreover, assuming this simplifications, it comes out that $\sigma_{ct} = 0$ for $v/w = 0$ and $\sigma_{ct} = 0.51$ for $v/w = 0.2$. As a result equation (10) can be simplified in:

$$\sigma_{ct} = 2.55\frac{v}{w} = 2.55\frac{V}{W} \qquad (48)$$

and equation (28) is substituted by

$$wD + F = 2.55\frac{v}{w} \qquad (49)$$

Then, taking into account (25) yields

$$w^2 D + w(F - 2.55A) + 2.55B = 0 \qquad (50)$$

This equation has only one positive root, which is the desired crack opening value. Needless to say v is given by (25) as before.

As seen in the general procedure it has to be verified that both the reinforcement orders aren't yielded, otherwise this simpler method can't be followed.

The error anyhow entailed by the application of this procedure can be evaluated verifying if the resultant R assumes f_{ct} or $f_{ct,fict}$ value as seen in equation (18).

4 VALIDATION PROCEDURE

The validation of the proposed procedure would require the experimental knowledge of the cracking pattern when the first cracks arise in wall elements isostatically restrained and loaded with uniform loads at the edges.

As at the present moment these data are not available in literature because of the objective experimental difficulties (e.g. advanced optical systems are indeed required) the validation will be performed with a limit analytical operation, transferring the two dimensional approach to the monodimensional one and checking the subsequent analytical issues with the ones known in bibliography.

Setting then $\vartheta = 90°$, from equation (17) we get $R_y = 0$; moreover, from equation (16) with $\sigma_{sy}\rho_y = 0$ we obtain $\sigma_{ct} = 0$ and from (10) $v/w = 0$ that is $v = 0$.

No slip is thus present along the crack plane as expected in one dimensional elements subjected to cracking transverse to their main direction.

In addition equation (18) reads:

$$R = R_x = \sigma_{sx}\rho_x = f_{ct} \qquad (18a)$$

and by substitution of (1) in (5) with $\vartheta = 90°$ we obtain:

$$\sigma_{sx} = E_s \frac{w}{s_{rm}} + \Delta\varepsilon_{sx} \qquad (19)$$

where $f_{ct}/E_s \cdot \rho_x = \varepsilon_{sx}$ is steel strain along the crack at the crack opening, and from (7) results $s_{rm} = s_{rmx}$ for $\vartheta = 90°$.

As a conclusion we get that:

$$w = (\varepsilon_{sx} - \Delta\varepsilon_{sx})s_{rm} \qquad (20)$$

matching the well known expression proposed in the Model Code for the evaluation of crack opening in beam elements.

5 APPLICATION EXAMPLES

The proposed procedure is now used to investigate some typical cracking cases in two dimensional reinforced concrete elements 100 mm thick.

The following parameters are assumed common to all cases: $f_{ct} = 2.37$ MPa, $f_{sy} = 430$ MPa, $\vartheta = 30°$ (longitudinally prestressed web).

In Table 1 is shown the crack width for $\gamma = 1$ in function of different values of the ratio $r = \rho_x/\rho_y$ obtained keeping constant the horizontal reinforcement (x axis) (1ϕ18/150) and changing the vertical one (from 1ϕ12/150 to 1ϕ18/150).

In Tables 2 and 3 the same crack width is calculated in the same elements, but with γ values variable from 1 to 1.9. In order to get a clearer comprehension the tabular data are also shown in Figure 7 diagram.

It can be clearly seen how cracks width has an almost linear behaviour till one of the two reinforcements yields; from that point the opening rises with an over-proportional law.

6 CONCLUSIONS

Crack width control in two dimensional reinforced concrete elements can be performed following the proposed procedure, that, starting from completely general hypothesis on materials behaviour nearby the crack and introducing some acceptable engineering simplifications, leads to a handy design and verification tool.

The extension of this procedure to elements taking place in an hyperstatic environment brings to a surely conservative evaluation of the cracking state, as no stress redistributions are taken into account.

Table 1.

A_{sx}, A_{sy}	r [−]	s_{rm} [mm]	σ_{sx} [MPa]	σ_{sy} [MPa]	w [mm]
ϕ18, ϕ14	0.60	156.3	117.1	243.15	0.166
ϕ18, ϕ16	0.79	147.11	108.03	189.99	0.126
ϕ18, ϕ18	1.00	138.94	100.69	152.71	0.098

Table 2.

	ϕ18, ϕ18			ϕ18, ϕ16		
γ	σ_{sx} [MPa]	σ_{sy} [MPa]	w [mm]	σ_{sx} [MPa]	σ_{sy} [MPa]	w [mm]
1.0	100.69	152.71	0.098	108.03	189.99	0.126
1.1	109.83	168.30	0.116	118.26	209.23	0.148
1.2	119.31	183.76	0.133	128.78	228.35	0.170
1.3	129.09	199.13	0.150	139.57	247.35	0.192
1.4	139.13	214.41	0.168	150.58	266.26	0.214
1.5	149.40	229.62	0.186	161.80	285.09	0.236
1.6	159.89	244.75	0.203	173.20	303.83	0.260
1.7	170.57	259.82	0.221	184.77	322.51	0.284
1.8	181.42	274.83	0.239	196.48	341.13	0.309
1.9	192.42	289.79	0.257	208.32	359.69	0.334

Table 3.

	ϕ18, ϕ14		
γ	σ_{sx}[MPa]	σ_{sy}[MPa]	w [mm]
1.0	117.10	243.15	0.166
1.1	128.54	267.61	0.194
1.2	140.21	291.95	0.222
1.3	152.07	316.18	0.250
1.4	164.11	340.32	0.278
1.5	176.30	364.37	0.307
1.6	188.62	388.35	0.337
1.7	201.05	412.26	0.368
1.8	213.60	436.12	0.455
1.9	226.24	459.92	0.806

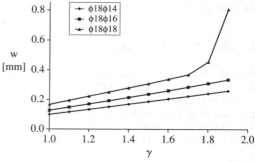

Figure 7. Relation $W = f(\rho_x)$ for different horizontal and vertical reinforcement ratios.

REFERENCES

Bazant Z.P., Gambarova P.G. 1980. Rough cracks in reinforced concrete, Journal of structural division, ASCE, Vol. 105, April 1980

Bhide S.B., Collins M.P. 1989. Influence of Axial Tension on the Shear Capacity of Reinforced Concrete Members, ACI Structural Journal, vol. 86, pp. 570–581, 1989

C.E.B.–F.I.P. Model code 1990. Thomas Telford Editor, 1993

Eurocode 2 – Design of concrete structures – Final Draft – November 2002

Gambarova P.G. 1983. Sulla trasmissione del taglio in elementi bidimensionali piani di c.a., Atti delle Giornate AICAP 1983

Iori I. 1985. Analisi di alcuni parametri significativi della torsione di elementi in conglomerato armato precompresso, testimonianze e note scientifiche in onore del settantesimo compleanno di Sandro Dei Poli, Ottobre 1985

Marti P., Meyboom J. 1992. Response of prestressed concrete elements to in-plane shear forces, ACI Structural Journal, Vol. 89, pag 503–514, 1992

Vecchio F.J., Collins M.P. 1982. Response of Reinforced Concrete to In-Plane Shear and Normal Stresses, Publication N. 82–03, Department of Civil Engineering, University of Toronto, Mar 1982

System-based Vision for Strategic and Creative Design, Bontempi (ed.)
© *2003 Swets & Zeitlinger, Lisse, ISBN 90 5809 599 1*

Effect of cracking and material non-linearities on the dynamic behavior of reinforced concrete beams

K.S. Numayr & S.K. Jubeer
Jordan University of Science & technology, Irbid, Jordan

ABSTRACT: In the present study, an analytical approach is proposed for the dynamic analysis of reinforced concrete beams taking into consideration the effect of cracking and material non-linearities. This approach is based on discretization the beam into a number of uniform finite elements, and satisfying the boundary conditions at the ends of the beam and the continuity conditions at the junctions of the elements. For nonlinear analysis, the normalized deflected shape function for each element at every load step is used for computing the parameters of an equivalent single degree-of-freedom dynamic system. A restoring forcedisplacement model is developed in this study and used in the equivalent single degree-of-freedom analysis. The response of reinforced concrete beams subjected to dynamic loading was determined using the approach developed herein and found to be in good agreement with experimental results. This proposed approach can be adopted for the determination of dynamic properties of reinforced concrete beams.

1 INTRODUCTION

It is well known that concrete is a non-homogenous nonlinear material composed of different types of aggregates with different grading bonded into a solid mass by cement. Concrete tension strength is very small compared to its compressive strength. Hence, a reinforced concrete beam would crack under service loads. The characteristic and spread of formed cracks in a reinforced concrete beam depend mainly on concrete properties, and dimension as well as the size and physical properties of used reinforcing steel.

Any structural system may be subjected to dynamic loading during its lifetime. For this reason, it is necessary to know the stiffness rigidity (EI) of concrete structures to calculate their response to dynamic loads. Concrete exhibits a nonlinear stress–strain relationship; therefore, the modulus of elasticity cannot be uniquely assigned. The moment of inertia is considered to be constant (I_g) for only small applied moments, where (I_g) is the gross moment of inertia of a cross section. When the service loads are applied, moments might exceed the cracking moment (M_{cr}), and the problem will be further complicated. The amount of cracking and stress variation along the length of a concrete beam varies considerably, hence E and I. In the analysis of reinforced concrete beams, different sections along the span of the beam would have different flexural rigidities proportional with the moment level (M) at the section and depends on concrete compressive strength, steel area and yield stress, area of steel, and cross section dimensions. Other factors such as nonlinear stress–strain relation of concrete and non-linearity associated with cracking and tension stiffening effect significantly the flexural rigidity.

In the present work, the main objective is to investigate the effect of cracking and material nonlinearity on the natural frequency and deformed configuration of reinforced concrete beams, and to employ this information to compute the nonlinear dynamic response of these beams due to different type of dynamic loading. A new analytical approach is proposed to analyze reinforced concrete beams subjected to dynamic loading. This approach is based on the principles of satisfying the boundary conditions at both ends of the beam and the continuity conditions at the junctions between elements. This is accompanied by using a reliable moment-curvature model to calculate the effective moment of inertia for each section along this beam under the load concern.

During the past century different models, were proposed for the moment-curvature relationship or developed different formulas to calculate the dynamic stiffness for concrete beams. Johns & Belanger (1981); developed a formula for the dynamic stiffness (EI_{dyn}), similar to that of the ACIcode (1989) expression for static effective modules of elasticity. (Nam et. al. 1977); suggested using the dynamic modulus of elasticity

729

(E_d), that is roughly 30% higher than the static value. Jerath & Shibani (1984); found that the average difference between the values of dynamic modulus (E_d), and the modulus of elasticity (E_c) given by ACI-code (1989) is 9.5%. (Soroushian, et. al. 1986); developed an empirical model for confined and unconfined concrete subjected to dynamic compression. The effect of strain rate on wet and dry concrete also was considered. It was found that at higher strain rate, the compressive and secant modulus of elasticity of concrete increases. (Krauthammer, et. al. 1990); proposed a numerical approach for the nonlinear analysis of reinforced concrete beams and one-way slabs under severe dynamic loads. That approach is based on the principles of equilibrium and compatibility combined with reliable material models and failure criteria, to compute the deformed configuration of the structural element at every load step and to employ that information for computing the parameters of an equivalent dynamic model. A number of reinforced concrete structural elements, which were tested by other investigators such as Feldman & sisess (1957), have been analyzed to evaluate the validity and demonstrate the effectiveness of this approach. It has been shown that the analytical results were very accurate.

2 MOMENT-CURVATURE RELATION

The model proposed by AL-Jalamdah (1997) for describing moment-curvature relationship for singly reinforced concrete beams was used in the present study after being modified to consider compression reinforcement. The modified model takes into consideration the effect of cracking and material non-linearities for any load levels. In this model, curvature at an uncracked section, where moment is less than cracking moment, is evaluated using properties of uncracked section. For a cracked section, additional curvature due to difference between the moment at the section and the cracking moment is evaluated using properties of cracked section.

3 DYNAMIC ANALYSIS

3.1 *Free vibration analysis*

Figure 1 shows two views of a simply supported reinforced concrete beam loaded at center with a concentrated static load (p). The first view shows the effective sectional properties due to cracking and material non-linearities, the second assumes that the beam is divided into a number of finite elements, each of which has constant sectional properties obtained by analyzing the section as a partially cracked transformed section which is dependent on the moment level. The origin

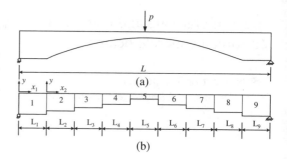

Figure 1. (a) Effective sections due to effect of cracking and material non-linearities. (b) Discretization using finite elements.

of the coordinates of each element is located at the left end of the element.

The equation of the free vibration for each element can be written as:

$$EI_i \frac{\partial^4 \varphi_i}{\partial x_i^4} + m_i \frac{\partial^2 \varphi_i}{\partial t^2} = 0 \qquad (1)$$

where E is the modulus of elasticity, m_i, I_i, $\phi_i (x_i)$ are mass, moment of inertia and transverse deformation of element i respectively, $i = 1$, NE is the element number as shown in Figure 2b, and NE is the number of elements. The general solution of Equation 1 is

$$\varphi_i(x_i) = A(i,1)\sin a_i x_i + A(i,2)\cos a_i x_i$$
$$+ A(i,3)\sinh a_i x_i + A(i,4)\cosh a_i x_i \qquad (2)$$

where $A(i,1), A(i,2), A(i,3), and A(i,4)$ are constants of integration,

$$a_i = \sqrt[4]{\frac{m_i \omega^2}{EI_i}} \qquad (3)$$

and (ω) is the natural frequency. The natural frequencies and corresponding mode shapes can be evaluated by satisfying Equation 1, the boundary conditions at the ends of the beam and the continuity conditions at the junctions between elements. The boundary conditions of zero deflection and zero moment at the ends of the beam, that is :

$$\varphi_i(0)=\varphi''_i(0)=\varphi_{NE}(L_{NE})=\varphi''_{NE}(L_{NE})=0 \qquad (4)$$

The continuity conditions at junction j between element j and element $j + 1$ can be expressed by the following set of equations:

$$\varphi_j(L_j) = \varphi_2(0) \qquad (5a)$$

$$\varphi_1'(L_1) = \varphi_2'(0) \tag{5b}$$

$$EI_1\varphi_1''(L_1) = EI_2\varphi_2''(0) \tag{5c}$$

$$EI_1\varphi_1'''(L_1) = EI_2\varphi_2'''(0) \tag{5d}$$

Using Equation 2 and the set of boundary and continuity conditions, the deflected shape function for each element is defined, that is :
For the first element, $i = 1$;

$$\varphi_1(x_1) = A(1,1)\sin a_1 x_1 + A(1,3)\sinh a_1 x_1 \tag{6}$$

for other elements, $i = 2, NE$ and $j = i-1$

$$\begin{aligned}
\varphi_i(x_i) = &\left[Z_{8j-7}A(1,1) + Z_{8j-3}A(1,3)\right]\sin a_i x_i \\
&+ \left[Z_{8j-6}A(1,1) + Z_{8j-2}A(1,3)\right]\cos a_i x_i \\
&+ \left[Z_{8j-5}A(1,1) + Z_{8j-1}A(1,3)\right]\sinh a_i x_i \\
&+ \left[Z_{8j-4}A(1,1) + Z_{8j}A(1,3)\right]\cosh a_i x_i
\end{aligned} \tag{7}$$

and for the last element, $i = NE$;

$$\begin{aligned}
\varphi_{NE}(x_{NE}) = &\left[Z_{8NJ-7}A(1,1) + Z_{NJ-3}A(1,3)\right]\sin a_{NE} x_{NE} \\
&+ \left[Z_{8NJ-6}A(1,1) + Z_{8NJ-2}A(1,3)\right]\cos a_{NE} x_{NE} \\
&+ \left[Z_{8NJ-5}A(1,1) + Z_{8NJ-1}A(1,3)\right]\sinh a_{NE} x_{NE} \\
&+ \left[Z_{8NJ-4}A(1,1) + Z_{8NJ}A(1,3)\right]\cosh a_{NE} x_{NE}
\end{aligned} \tag{8}$$

where $NJ = NE - 1$ the number of junctions, and Z_i are constants that can be found in Jubeer (1999).
Using Equations 6, 7, and 8 and rewriting the equations in a matrix form yields;

$$\begin{bmatrix} K_{11} & K_{12} \\ K_{21} & K_{22} \end{bmatrix} \begin{Bmatrix} A(1,1) \\ A(1,3) \end{Bmatrix} = \begin{Bmatrix} 0 \\ 0 \end{Bmatrix} \tag{9}$$

where;

$$\begin{aligned}
K_{11} = &Z_{8NJ-7}\sin\alpha_{NE} + Z_{8NJ-6}\cos\alpha_{NE} \\
&+ Z_{8NJ-5}\sinh\alpha_{NE} + Z_{8NJ-4}\cosh\alpha_{NE} \\
K_{12} = &Z_{8NJ-3}\sin\alpha_{NE} + Z_{8NJ-2}\cos\alpha_{NE} \\
&+ Z_{8NJ-1}\sinh\alpha_{NE} + Z_{8NJ}\cosh\alpha_{NE} \\
K_{21} = &-Z_{8NJ-7}\sin\alpha_{NE} - Z_{8NJ-6}\cos\alpha_{NE} \\
&+ Z_{8NJ-5}\sinh\alpha_{NE} + Z_{8NJ-4}\cosh\alpha_{NE} \\
K_{22} = &-Z_{8NJ-3}\sin\alpha_{NE} - Z_{8NJ-2}\cos\alpha_{NE} + \\
&Z_{8NJ-1}\sinh\alpha_{NE} + Z_{8NJ}\cosh\alpha_{NE}
\end{aligned}$$

and $\alpha_{NE} = \alpha_{NE} L_{NE}$. The eigen problem, Equation 9, is then solved, and the fundamental natural frequency is defined, and also the corresponding mode shape is defined since $A(1,1)$ and $A(1,3)$ are already being evaluated. To summarize, the employment of the proposed procedure, in a computer program developed for this purpose, is done as follows:

(1) Dividing the beam into a number of finite elements.
(2) For each element, an average value of the moment is found, $M_{avg} = (M_i + M_j)/2$ where (M_i) and (M_j) are the values of the moments at each end of the element.
(3) The corresponding value of the curvature for each element is found using the moment-curvature relationship Al-Jellamdeh (1997). From these values a new estimation for equivalent EI for each element is obtained.
(4) Assume $\omega = 0$ and select suitable incremental for natural frequency $\Delta\omega$.
(5) Set $\omega = \omega + \Delta\omega$ and calculate (a_i) from Equation (14).
(6) Calculate (Z_k) where $k = 1,8\,NJ$, Jubeer (1999)
(7) Determine $[K]$ and check Equation 9.
(8) (a) Repeat steps (5–7) If Equation 9 is not satisfied.
  (b) When Equation 9 is satisfied, the eignvalue resulted from it will represent the fundamental natural frequency of the reinforced concrete beam.

3.2 Equivalent single degree of freedom model

In the present approach, the continuous system is represented by an Equivalent single degree of freedom system. The equivalent single degree of freedom system may be defined as the system for which the kinetic energy, potential energy (strain energy) and work done by external forces have the same values as the continuous system. Equating the kinetic energy, potential energy, and the work done by external forces of the discretized continuous system to the kinetic energy, potential energy, and the work done by external forces of the equivalent single degree of freedom system and solving the resulting equation for the equivalent mass (M), equivalent stiffness K, and equivalent force $(F(t))$ respectively, yields;

$$M = \int_0^l m(x)\{\varphi(x)\}^2 dx = \sum_{i=1}^{NE} \int_0^{l_i} m_i(x_i)\{\varphi_i(x_i)\}^2 dx_i \tag{10}$$

$$K = \int_0^l EI(x)\{\varphi(x)\}^2 dx = \sum_{i=1}^{NE} \int_0^{l_i} EI_i(x_i)\{\varphi_i(x_i)\}^2 dx_i \tag{11}$$

$$F(t) = \int_o^L p(x,t)\varphi(x)dx = \sum_{i=1}^{NE} \int_o^{L_i} p_i(x_i,t)\varphi_i(x_i)dx_i$$

(12)

The differential equation of motion for the equivalent single degree of freedom system;

$$M\ddot{Y}(t) + KY(t) = F(t)$$ (13)

The nonlinear transverse dynamic response of the equivalent model is determined for different dynamic loading using linear acceleration and step-by-step integration method.

3.3 Dynamic restoring model

The proposed restoring-displacement model in Figure 2 is similar to the model used by (Krauthmer et al. 1990). The portion OAB of the curve shown in this figure is a load-deflection function. Unlike the model proposed by (Krauthmer et al. 1990), the present non-linear function includes all cracking and materials non-linearties discussed above.

When the maximum dynamic displacement does not exceed the yield point A, where at this point the applied moment is equal to cracking moment for considered beam, the behavior of the beam is elastic and oscillation will occur about the zero displacement position. But, if the maximum dynamic displacement exceeds the yield point A, the behavior of the beam is inelastic. In this case, the beam will come to rest with a residual displacement after all energy is dissipated by the internal hysteretic damping mechanism. Upon dynamic loading, the deflection increases along the restoring-displacement function (R-Y), and reaches a maximum deflection at point B as shown in the figure. At point B the displacement begins to decrease and positive unloading of the beam is assumed to occur along a straight line BD parallel to line OA. Once point D is reached, negative unloading follows along line DB'. The slope of the negative unloading segment is the same as that proposed by krauthamer [9] to choose point B' to be the mirror image of point B on the negative R-Y curve. Negative unloading continues until the point of minimum displacement E is reached. After point E, the displacement begins to increase, and negative reloading occurs along a straight line EF parallel to line OA. Once point F is reached, marks the end of the first complete hysteretic cycle, the positive reloading follows along line FB and reaches a new maximum deflection at point G. The process of reloading and unloading cycles continuous until the beam comes to rest with a residual deflection.

The model shown in the figure is constructed for a beam with a cross section that is symmetrically reinforced only. In this study another computer program is developed to compute the nonlinear dynamic response of reinforced concrete beams.

4 RESULTS AND DISCUSSIONS

In the first place, a comparison of the proposed approach for free vibration analysis is presented with experimental results available in the literature. These results are obtained from Johns & Belanger (1981), and Jearth & Shibani (1985) who investigated the natural frequency of reinforced concrete beams for different load levels. Details of the beams studied here are presented in Tables 1 & 2 and Figure 3 below.

Table 1. Details and properties of reinforced concrete beams.

Bm. No.	A_s mm^2	$A_s^\backslash$ mm^2	f'_c MPa	f_y MPa	d mm	d$^\backslash$ mm
3	568	–	32	414	295	–
4	568	–	40	141	295	–
1A,B	258	–	41.4	276	209	–
2A,B	568	–	48.3	276	206	–
3A,B	852	258	42.1	276	206	44.5

Table 2. Details and properties of reinforced concrete beams.

Bm. No.	Lengths (mm)			Dimensions (mm)	
	L_t	L_s	a	b	H
3	6553	6096	2286	203	356
4	6553	6096	2286	203	356
1A,B	3353	3048	1143	127	254
2A,B	3353	3084	1143	127	254
3A,B	3353	3084	1143	127	254

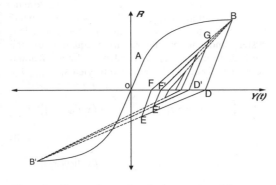

Figure 2. Proposed restoring-displacement model.

Figure 4 present the variation of natural frequency with static load levels on one hanger for beam number 4. The experimental results are obtained from Johns & Belanger (1981). The solid line represents the natural frequency-load curve obtained using the proposed approach. These figures show that the trend of the curve obtained using the proposed approach agree well with that of the experimental results.

Figure 5 presents the variation of natural frequency with static load levels on one hanger for beam number 1 (A&B). The experimental results are obtained from Jearth & Shibani (1985). This figure shows that the trend of the curve obtained using the proposed approach also agree well with the trend of the experimental results for singly or doubly reinforced concrete beams.

Figure 6 presents a comparison of the moment-curvature model considered in this study for free vibration analysis with the models representing the uncracked and cracked transformed sections, and with the common model proposed by Branson[3] by studying the variation of natural frequency with static load levels on one hanger for beams number 3 (A&B) shown in Figure 3 and Tables 1 & 2. The solid line represents the natural frequency-load curve obtained using the proposed approach, the other lines represents the same relation obtained using uncracked section model, cracked section model, and Branson model. From this figure it can be noticed that the curve representing the proposed approach coincides with that representing the uncracked section model until the applied moment reaches cracking moment (M_{cr}), and the gab between the curve representing the uncracked section model and that representing the Branson model in this region, exists due to neglecting the reinforcement effect of calculating the gross moment of inertia (I_g) considered in Branson model. When applied moment becomes greater than cracking moment, the curves representing the proposed approach and the Branson model move from that represents the uncracked section model due to the cracking effect and approache that represents the cracked section model. This response indicates that the Branson model takes into account the effect of tension stiffening, but it still under estimates this effect when compared with the moment-curvature model considered here, especially for high load levels where this curve coincides with that representing the cracked section model. Furthermore, it can be noticed from this figure, that the curve representing the moment-curvature model considered in this study agrees well with the experimental results when compared with other curves, which makes it a powerful tool for estimating the dynamic properties of reinforced concrete beams.

Figure 7 presents the normalized deflected shape of reinforced concrete beam for different load levels. This beam has $2.69\,m$ simply supported clear span, and loaded by a distributed static load along the span length, with $f_c^\backslash = 45\,MPa$, $f_y = 414\,MPa$, $A_s = 765\,mm^2$, $A_s^\backslash = 558.5\,MPa$, $b = 150\,mm$, $h = 300\,mm$, $d = 225\,mm$, and $d^\backslash = 45\,mm$.

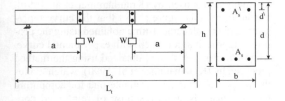

Figure 3. Beam setup with two points load (W).

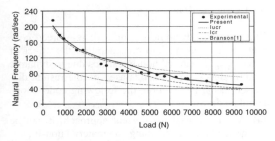

Figure 4. Natural frequency versus load on one hanger for beams No.4 (Johns & Belanger 1981).

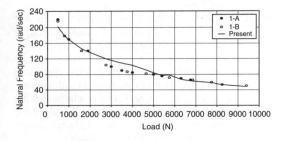

Figure 5. Natural frequency versus load on one hanger for beams No.1(A&B) (Jearth & Shibani 1985).

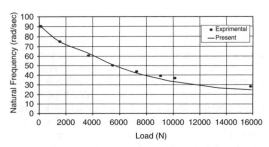

Figure 6. Natural frequency versus load on one hanger for beams number 1 (A&B).

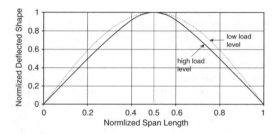

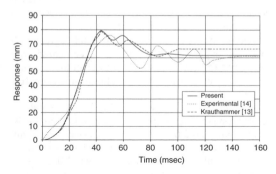

Figure 7. The deflected configuration of reinforced concrete beam for different load levels.

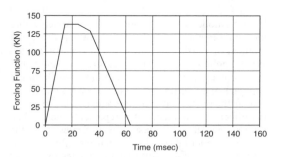

Figure 8. Dynamic Force function applied to beam C-1.

Figure 9. Mid span displacement versus time for beam C-1 (Feldman[4]).

Figure 8 and Figure 9 shows the experimental dynamic load applied to beam C-1 and the variations of mid span displacement with time of reinforced concrete beam number C-1. This beam has 2.69 m simply supported clear span, and loaded by a concentrated dynamic load at mid span shown in Figure 8 below, with $f_c^\backslash = 45$ MPa, $f_y = 414$ MPa, $A_s = 765$ mm^2, $A_s^\backslash = 558.5$ MPa, $b = 150$ mm, $h = 300$ mm, $d = 225$ mm, and $d^\backslash = 45$ mm. The solid line represents the mid span displacement-time curve obtained using the proposed approach, while the other

lines represent the same relation obtained using the method proposed by (Krauthammer et al. 1990), and the experimental results obtained by Feldman & Siess (1957). The peak experimental displacement response of 76.2 mm which was recorded at 50 msec, agrees with that by analytical results, where the peak displacement response computed using the proposed approach of 79.3 mm is reached at 44 msec, and that computed using the method proposed by Krauthammer of 78.8 mm is also reached at 44 msec. The permanent experimental displacement recorded of this beam was 61 mm agrees well with that computed using the proposed approach than that computed using the method proposed by (Krauthammer et al. 1990), where the permanent displacement resulted using the proposed approach is 61.7 mm, while that resulted using the method proposed by (Krauthammer et al. 1990), is 66.5 mm. It can be noticed from Figure 9, that the trend of the displacement-time curve obtained using the proposed approach agrees with that obtained using the method proposed by (Krauthammer et al. 1990). Furthermore, this figure shows that the curve representing the displacement-time obtained using the proposed approach agrees well with experimental curve, when compared with that obtained using the method proposed by (Krauthammer et al. 1990), which makes the proposed approach a reliable one for computing the nonlinear dynamic response of reinforced concrete beams.

5 CONCLUSIONS

The nonlinear dynamic response of reinforced concrete beams, taking into consideration the effect of cracking and material non-linearities due to dynamic loading, has been studied. Based on the results discussed in the last section, the following conclusions could be drawn;

(a) When we used the present approach, it can be noticed that the cracking and material non-linearities have significant effects on the dynamic behavior of reinforced concrete beams, while using the other methods have the same effects but with much less.

(b) The dynamic properties of reinforced concrete beams are affected by different variables such as; steel ratio, section dimensions, concrete cover, and material properties.

(c) The well agreement between the proposed approach in the free vibration case (with concentrated masses) and experimental results makes it a powerful method for calculating the dynamic properties of any doubly and singly reinforced concrete beams subject to static loads.

(d) The comparison of results obtained using the proposed approach for nonlinear dynamic analysis of reinforced concrete beams subject to dynamic loading with experimental and other analytical ones indicate that the accuracy of the proposed approach is good.

REFERENCES

ACI, Building Code Requirements for Reinforced Concrete, and Commentary. 1989 ACI, Detroit, Michigan.

Al-jellamda, S.A. 1997. Modeling the effect of cracking and material non-linearities in reinforced concrete beams to be used in the finite element method for structural analysis. MSc thesis, Department of Civil Engineering, Jordan University of Science and Technology. Irbid, Jordan.

Branson, D.E. 1977. Deformation of concrete structures. Mcgraw Hill. pp. 546.

Feldman, A. & Siess, E. 1957. An investigation of resistance and behavior of reinforced concrete members subjected to dynamic loading, Part III. SRS Report No. 165, Department of civil Engineering, University of Illinois at Urbana-Champaign, Urbana.

Jerath, S. & Shibani, M. 1985. Dynamic stiffness and vibration of reinforced concrete beams. ACI journal, V. 82, No. 18, pp. 196–202.

Jerath, S. & Shibani M. 1984. Dynamic Modulus for Reinforced Concrete Beams. Journal of structural engineering, V. 110, No. 6, pp. 1405–1410.

Johns, K.C. & Belanger, M.D. 1981. Dynamic stiffness of Concrete beams. ACI journal, V. 78, No. 3, pp. 201–205.

Jubeer, S.K. 1999. Effect of cracking and material non-linearities on the dynamic behaviour of reinforced concrete beams. MSc thesis, Department of Civil Engineering, Jordan University of Science and Technology, Irbid, Jordan.

Krauthammer, T. Shahriar, S. & Sahana, H.M. 1990. Response of reinforced concrete elements to severe impulsive loads. Journal of Structural Engineering, V. 116, No. 4, pp. 1061–1079.

Loo, Y.C. & Santos, A. P. 1986. Impact deflection analysis of concrete beams. Journal of Structural Engineering, V. 112, No. 6, pp. 1297–1312.

Nam, C.H. Campomanes, N. V. & Kim, Y. K. 1977. Design of farmed foundation subjected to vibration. Computers and Structures journal, V. 7, pp. 103–107.

Soroushian, P. Chio, K.B. & Al-Hamad, A. 1986. Dynamic constitutive behavior of concrete. ACI journal, V. 83, No. 26, pp. 251–259.

System-based Vision for Strategic and Creative Design, Bontempi (ed.)
© 2003 Swets & Zeitlinger, Lisse, ISBN 90 5809 599 1

Continuous-discontinuous failure analysis in a rate-dependent elastoplastic damage model

A. Simone & L.J. Sluys
Faculty of Civil Engineering and Geosciences, Delft University of Technology, the Netherlands

ABSTRACT: This paper illustrates the use of displacement discontinuities in a rate-dependent damage elastoplastic model. Rate-dependency is considered in the framework of Perzyna viscoplasticity. Displacement discontinuities are incorporated using the partition of unity property of finite-element shape functions. Various examples illustrate the flexibility of the approach.

1 INTRODUCTION

Failure representation in quasi-brittle materials can be enhanced by techniques in which displacement discontinuities stem as a consequence of material failure processes. A displacement discontinuity can be considered as originating either from complete material failure in quasi-brittle materials, representing genuine material separation, or from failure of the cementitious matrix in some steel fibre-reinforced concrete (SFR-concrete), representing crack bridging. In this paper, degradation in the continuum is described by means of a rate-dependent damage elastoplastic model in which rate-dependency is considered in the framework of Perzyna viscoplasticity. The coupling to damage is crucial for the subsequent introduction of a discontinuity as it allows the necessary narrowing of the width of the localisation zone (converging to a discrete surface) which preludes the discontinuity in the displacement field. Further, it allows full stress relaxation at the integration point level response. In describing the behaviour of SFR-concrete, the discontinuity is given cohesive forces to describe the crack bridging effect of the fibres. The detailed description of the continuum constitutive model is followed by three applications in failure mechanics problems.

2 DISCONTINUOUS INTERPOLATION

The discrete representation of a discontinuity can be rigorously achieved through a discontinuous interpolation of the problem fields. For the portion $\bar{\Omega}_d$ of the body $\bar{\Omega}$ depicted in Figure 1, which is divided into two

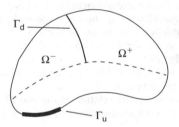

Figure 1. Body $\bar{\Omega}$ crossed by a discontinuity Γ_d.

sub-domains ($\Omega_d = \Omega^+ \cup \Omega^-$) by a discontinuity surface Γ_d, the displacement field is given by

$$\mathbf{u} = \hat{\mathbf{u}} + \mathcal{H}_{\Gamma_d} \tilde{\mathbf{u}}, \qquad (1)$$

where $\mathcal{H}_{\Gamma_d}$ is the Heaviside function centred at the discontinuity surface ($\mathcal{H}_{\Gamma_d} = 1$ if $\mathbf{x} \in \bar{\Omega}^+$, $\mathcal{H}_{\Gamma_d} = 0$ if $\mathbf{x} \in \bar{\Omega}^-$) and $\hat{\mathbf{u}}$ and $\tilde{\mathbf{u}}$ are continuous functions on $\bar{\Omega}_d$. The discrete counterpart of Equation 1 reads

$$\mathbf{u}_h = \mathbf{Na} + \mathcal{H}_{\Gamma_d} \mathbf{Nb}, \qquad (2)$$

with $\mathbf{N}$ a matrix containing standard finite-element shape functions and $\mathbf{a}$ and $\mathbf{b}$ vectors containing global degrees of freedom.

The inclusion of displacement discontinuities represents, in this context, either genuine separation of material or the formation of cohesive surfaces. In the former case, a discontinuity is extended when damage in at least one of the integration points in the element ahead of the discontinuity tip is above a critical value; in the latter case this condition has to be fulfilled in all the integration points in the element ahead of the discontinuity tip. The critical damage value, close to unity for quasi-brittle materials, will be specified in the application to SFR-concrete. The discontinuity direction is aligned with the direction of maximum dissipation. This is achieved performing a non-local averaging of the equivalent plastic strain, the quantity driving damage evolution, ahead of the discontinuity tip. The characteristic length for the non-local averaging equals three times the average element size ahead of the discontinuity tip. When the discontinuity is close to a boundary, the discontinuity extension direction is aligned to the previous discontinuity segment. Details on the finite-element technology can be found in Wells & Sluys (2001).

3 A MODEL FOR BULK DEGRADATION

Bulk degradation is described by a rate-dependent isotropic elastoplastic damage model derived from the class of models proposed by Ju (1989). The coupling of damage and plasticity is introduced by adopting the effective stress concept and the hypothesis of strain equivalence. In such a framework, a simple algorithmic formulation can be derived. The algorithmic procedure for the coupled model hinges on the knowledge of the stress tensor $\tilde{\sigma}$, of the algorithmic tangent moduli $\tilde{\mathbf{D}}^p$ and of the equivalent plastic strain κ in the effective space.

The stress update relation at the end of the time step for the elastoplastic damage model reads

$$\sigma_{n+1} = \left(1 - \omega_{n+1}\right) \tilde{\sigma}_{n+1} \tag{3}$$

where the plastically induced damage value is updated through

$$\omega_{n+1} = \alpha \left(1 - e^{-\beta \kappa_{n+1}}\right), \tag{4}$$

with α and β parameters influencing the asymptotic value of damage and the slope of the damage evolution law, respectively, and κ_{n+1} the equivalent plastic strain in the effective space for the elastoplastic problem.

The algorithmic tangent stiffness tensor $\mathbf{D}^{pd}$ is defined by $d(\Delta\sigma) = \mathbf{D}^{pd}: d(\Delta\varepsilon)$ for variations $d(\Delta\varepsilon)$ of the current strain increment $\Delta\varepsilon$ To derive the consistent tangent operator, Equation 3 is differentiated at t_{n+1} (note that $d(\square_n) = 0 \rightarrow d(\square_{n+1}) = d(\Delta\square)$) to obtain (dropping the subscript $n+1$):

$$d(\Delta\sigma) = (1 - \omega) d(\Delta\tilde{\sigma}) - d(\Delta\omega) \tilde{\sigma} \tag{5}$$

The variation $d(\Delta\omega)$ of the damage variable can be related to $d(\Delta\varepsilon)$ by

$$d(\Delta\omega) = \frac{\partial\omega}{\partial\kappa} d\kappa = \frac{\partial\omega}{\partial\kappa} \tilde{\mathbf{a}} : d(\Delta\varepsilon), \tag{6}$$

where $d\kappa = d\lambda$ for the yield functions used in this study (smoothed Rankine and J2 yield functions) and $\tilde{\mathbf{a}}$ is a second order tensor which depends on the plasticity model in the effective stress space and which will be specified later. Substituting $d(\Delta\omega)$ from the above expression in Equation 5, and recalling that $d(\Delta\tilde{\sigma}) = \tilde{\mathbf{D}}^p : d(\Delta\varepsilon)$, yields the consistent tangent operator for the elastoplastic damage model:

$$\mathbf{D}^{pd} = (1 - \omega) \tilde{\mathbf{D}}^p - \frac{\partial\omega}{\partial\kappa} b \, \tilde{\sigma} \otimes \tilde{\mathbf{a}}. \tag{7}$$

Note that no restriction has been placed on the nature of the plastic moduli $\tilde{\mathbf{D}}^p$, of the stress tensor $\tilde{\sigma}$ and of the equivalent plastic strain κ which are computed in the effective stress space. However, to preserve well-posedness of the governing equations when softening constitutive relationships are used, a rate-dependent response in the effective stress space must be used.

The Perzyna viscoplastic model has been conveniently chosen for its robustness. In presence of plastic flow ($\tilde{f} \geq 0$, where $\tilde{f}$ is the yield function in the effective stress space), the viscoplastic strain rate for the Perzyna model is expressed in the associative form

$$\dot{\varepsilon}^{vp} = \frac{1}{\tau} \tilde{\phi} \, \tilde{f}_{\sigma}, \tag{8}$$

where τ is the relaxation time, $\tilde{f}_{\sigma} = \partial\tilde{f}/\partial\tilde{\sigma}$ and the overstress function is given the following power-law form

$$\tilde{\phi}(\tilde{f}) = \left(\frac{\tilde{f}}{\bar{\sigma}_0}\right)^N, \tag{9}$$

with $\bar{\sigma}_0$ the initial yield stress and N ($N \geq 1$) a real number. After standard manipulations, the algorithmic treatment of the constitutive equations for Perzyna viscoplasticity in the effective stress space yields the differential of the incremental plastic multiplier

$$d(\Delta\lambda) = \frac{\tilde{f}_{\sigma} : \tilde{\mathbf{R}} : d(\Delta\varepsilon)}{\tilde{f}_{\sigma} : \tilde{\mathbf{R}} : \tilde{f}_{\sigma} - \tilde{f}_{\tilde{\kappa}} \tilde{\kappa}_{\tilde{\lambda}} + \tau/\left(\Delta t \tilde{\phi}_{\tilde{f}}\right)}, \tag{10}$$

with $d(\Delta\lambda) = d\lambda$, and the consistent tangent

$$\tilde{\mathbf{D}}^p = \tilde{\mathbf{R}} - \frac{\tilde{\mathbf{R}} : \tilde{f}_{\sigma} \otimes \tilde{f}_{\sigma} : \tilde{\mathbf{R}}}{\tilde{f}_{\sigma} : \tilde{\mathbf{R}} : \tilde{f}_{\sigma} - \tilde{f}_{\tilde{\kappa}} \tilde{\kappa}_{\tilde{\lambda}} + \tau/\left(\Delta t \tilde{\phi}_{\tilde{f}}\right)}, \tag{11}$$

where

$$\tilde{\mathbf{R}} = \left(\mathbf{I} + \Delta\lambda \mathbf{D}^e \tilde{f}_{\sigma\sigma}\right)^{-1} \mathbf{D}^e, \tag{12}$$

$\square_i = \partial\square/\partial_i$, $\tilde{f}_{\sigma\sigma} = \partial\tilde{f}_{\sigma}/\partial\tilde{\sigma}$, $\mathbf{I}$ is the fourth-order identity tensor and $\mathbf{D}^e$ is the fourth-order elastic stiffness tensor. After employing the symmetry of $\tilde{\mathbf{R}}$, the second order tensor $\tilde{\mathbf{a}}$, required for the evaluation of the consistent tangent operator for the elastoplastic damage model in Equation 7, reads as

$$\tilde{\mathbf{a}} = \frac{\tilde{\mathbf{R}} : \tilde{f}_{\boldsymbol{\sigma}}}{\tilde{f}_{\boldsymbol{\sigma}} : \tilde{\mathbf{R}} : \tilde{f}_{\boldsymbol{\sigma}} - \tilde{f}_{\tilde{\kappa}} \tilde{\kappa}_{\tilde{\lambda}} + \tau / \left(\Delta t \tilde{\phi}_{\tilde{f}} \right)}. \tag{13}$$

The consistent tangent operator for the elastoplastic damage model is readily available by direct substitution of the above expressions into Equation 7. It is noted that the consistent tangent operator is not symmetric. The step-by-step integration procedure is very similar to that of standard plasticity, the difference being the presence of the damage update which requires only the evaluation of Equations 3 and 7.

Unlike classical rate-dependent plasticity, where full stress relaxation in the load–displacement response cannot be achieved, due to the coupling to damage the load-displacement response converges to a response with no residual load-carrying capacity. When localisation is completed, the strain profile mimics the Dirac-delta function and the displacement field is better represented by a discontinuous function. An analysis of the properties of the model can be found in Simone et al. (2003). A similar model, based on Duvaut-Lions viscoplasticity, was developed by Georgin et al. (2002).

4 COMPACT-TENSION SPECIMEN

The failure characterisation of the compact-tension specimen depicted in Figure 2 has been investigated with the combined continuous/discontinuous failure strategy. The specimen is placed on two loading pins whose action has been modelled by applying two vertical forces in the uppermost and lowermost node of the

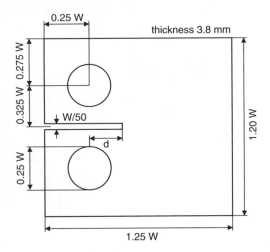

Figure 2. Compact-tension specimen (W = 50 mm; dimensions in mm).

pinholes via deformation control. In the simulations, indirect displacement control has been used, with the displacement (crack mouth opening displacement, cmod) measured between two markers placed 25 mm from the left edge and 14 mm from the symmetry axis of the specimen. The total cmod (5 mm) has been applied in 200 steps. The vertical displacement of the mid-side point on the right central part of the specimen has been restrained, as well as the horizontal displacement of the right lowermost and uppermost corners. The simulations are performed using unstructured meshes of bilinear quadrilateral elements with average element sizes h in the central part of the specimen equal to 2, 1, 0.5 mm with 438, 1243 and 3918 elements, respectively.

Plastic flow is described by a smoothed Rankine yield criterion with a yield stress equal to 35.2 MPa under the assumption of a plane stress situation. The softening rule governing the cohesion capacity of the material is given by an exponential form according to

$$\sigma_y(\kappa) = \bar{\sigma}_0 \left((1+a) \, e^{-b\kappa} - a \, e^{-2b\kappa} \right), \tag{14}$$

with $a = 1.5$ and $b = 13$. Damage growth is expressed via the exponential law in Equation 4 with $\alpha = 1$ and $\beta = 20$. Other model parameters have been chosen as follows: $N = 1$ and relaxation time $\tau = 20$ s for the viscous regularisation of Equations 8 and 9, Young's modulus $E = 3200$ MPa and Poisson's ratio $\nu = 0.28$. Of the above model parameters, the Young's modulus, the Poisson's ratio and the yield stress have been adopted from Geers et al. (1999). The remaining parameters have been chosen to ensure a qualitative fit at the global and local levels in terms of load-cmod curve and damage profile, respectively, with the data reported by Geers et al. (1999). To avoid damage growth in the elements around the the pinholes, a higher value of the yield stress $\bar{\sigma}_0$ has been given to elements in these areas. The critical damage value for discontinuity extension (traction-free) has been set to 0.99. An initial horizontal traction-free discontinuity has been placed in the notch zone as starting point for the discontinuity extension. This has no effect on the global/local response since the traction-free discontinuity mimics the real notch.

The load-cmod response is shown in Figure 3. The marked drop in the load-cmod curve for the coarsest of the discretisations relates to the high residual stress in the element at the moment of the first extension of the discontinuity – only one integration points had damage values larger than 0.99 while in the remaining integration points damage was around 0.7. The following discontinuity extensions are characterised by a smooth global response as a consequence of similar damage values in the elements. The failure pattern at cmod = 5 mm is shown in Figure 4. The combined continuous/discontinuous failure strategy provides a clear indication of the extent of the real discontinuity and of the zone of plastic/damage activity.

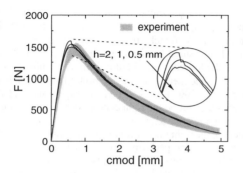

Figure 3. Load-cmod diagrams for the compact-tension specimen for different mesh resolutions (h indicates the average element size in the central part of the specimen).

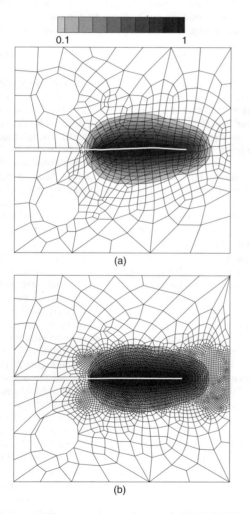

(a)

(b)

Figure 4. Failure state at cmod = 5 mm: damage contour plot for (a) coarse ($h = 2$ mm) and (b) fine ($h = 0.5$ mm) mesh. The thick white line indicates the traction-free discontinuity.

5   STRIP FOOTING NEAR A SLOPE

A more interesting failure pattern can be observed from the numerical analysis of the rigid and rough strip footing resting on the crest of a slope depicted in Figure 5. A 0.6 m deep initial traction-free discontinuity is located on the right side of the footing. The domain has been discretised by using 8-node quadrilateral elements with reduced integration scheme – 930 elements for the coarse mesh and 3720 elements for the fine mesh. Plane strain J2 softening plasticity with cohesive capacity according to Equation 14 with initial cohesion $\bar{\sigma}_0 = 0.00005$ MPa, $a = 1$ and $b = 100$ and with damage growth according to Equation 4, with $\alpha = 0.9999$ and $\beta = 200$, has been used to describe the material behaviour. The remaining model parameters have been chosen as follows: $N = 1$ and relaxation time $\tau = 1000$ s, Young's modulus $E = 0.1$ MPa (the strip is assumed to be elastic and one hundred times stiffer) and Poisson's ratio $\nu = 0.2$. The above model parameters have been chosen for numerical convenience. The high value of the relaxation time allows a meaningful width of the localisation band. The rigid footing has been loaded in displacement control and the total vertical displacement (100 mm) has been applied in 50 steps. The critical damage value for discontinuity extension (traction-free) has been set to 0.99. A traction-free discontinuity has been used to describe the tension crack.

The failure of the slope develops in the typical curved shape depicted in Figures 6b and 6d and is accompanied by localised deformations which are well described by the continuous model and by the following discontinuity. The direction of the discontinuity is properly described even with the coarse mesh due to the significant extension of the equivalent plastic strain beyond the discontinuity tip. No significant

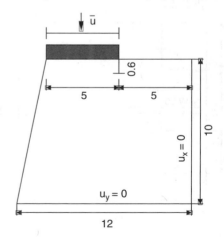

Figure 5. Geometrical configuration and boundary/loading conditions of the slope (dimensions in m).

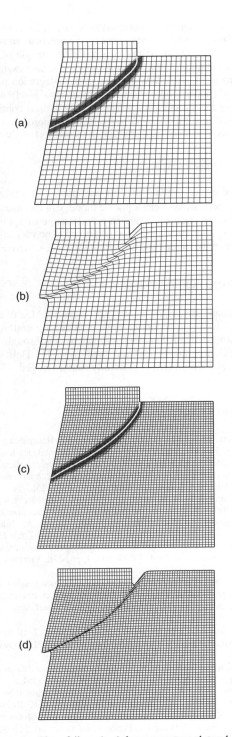

differences have been observed with respect to computations performed in a continuous framework only. The use of traction-free discontinuities does not improve failure representation when bulk degradation obeys the rate-dependent damage elastoplastic model described in Section 3.

6 STEEL FIBRE-REINFORCED CONCRETE

Discontinuities can be better employed for the description of SFR-concrete. Numerical modelling of SFR-concrete is based on the use of stress-crack opening relationships. Within the stress-crack opening approach, a reasonable approximation of the tensile behaviour of SFR-concrete can be obtained by using a bilinear relationship of the type depicted in Figure 7a. According to Stang & Olesen (1998), "the first part of the bilinear relationship reflects a combination of the concrete contribution and the initial fibre bridging action, while the second part reflects the fibre bridging action only". For normal strength concrete and low fibre content, the first branch of the bilinear relationship can be taken equal to that of plain concrete, so that the effect of the fibres is reflected only by the second branch. The numerical strategy proposed for the modelling of SFR-concrete consists in the use of the model for bulk degradation, presented in Section 3, to describe, in a continuous fashion, the initial degradation of the cementitious matrix, represented by the first part of the curve in Figure 7a. A cohesive discontinuity is introduced at a specified level of damage of the cementitious matrix, corresponding to a residual stress $f_{t\omega}$ (cf Figure 7b), and represents the second part of the curve in Figure 7a. The constitutive model for the cohesive discontinuity is described by a linear decreasing relationship between the stress σ and the crack opening w for which $\sigma = f_{t\omega}$ at $w = 0$ and $\sigma = 0$ for $w \geqslant w_{max}$ where w_{max} is related to the fibre length.

A notched beam in four point bending with a 150 mm × 150 mm cross section, a 550 mm span and a 25 mm notch is analysed. The load is applied via displacement control at a distance of 75 mm from the

Figure 6. Slope failure: (a, c) damage contour plot and discontinuity at failure and (b, d) deformed state (magnified 100 times) for different mesh resolutions. The thick white line indicates the discontinuity.

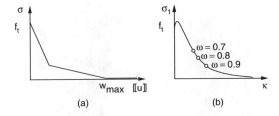

(a)   (b)

Figure 7. Constitutive models: (a) bilinear constitutive relationship for SFR-concrete (not to scale) and (b) qualitative stress-equivalent plastic strain plot with critical damage values for the activation of the cohesive discontinuity.

midspan and the total deflection (0.4 mm) has been applied in 160 steps. The beam was discretised with bilinear quadrilateral elements with element size, in the central part of the beam, of 2.73 mm × 3.125 mm. Bulk degradation is described by plane stress Rankine plasticity with $f_t = \bar{\sigma}_0 = 2$ MPa and with softening parameters $a = 0$, $b = 200$, $\alpha = 0.99$ and $\beta = 400$. The other model parameters have been chosen as follows: $N = 1$ and relaxation time $\tau = 20$ s, Young's modulus $E = 30$ GPa and Poisson's ratio $\nu = 0.2$. The notch has been described by a traction-free discontinuity. Plain and SFR-concrete are differentiated by the introduction of a cohesive discontinuity related to the fibre action at three different damage values, $\omega = 0.7$, 0.8 and 0.9. For plain concrete, the traction-free notch was extended at $\omega = 0.989$.

The values of $f_{t\omega}$ at which damage reaches the above values are depicted in Figure 7b in the qualitative plot of the first principal stress *versus* the equivalent plastic strain for an integration point in the element ahead of the notch. The value of w_{max} was chosen equal to 25 mm for all the simulations. Figures 8 and 9 clearly indicates the effect of the cohesive discontinuity on the global and local response, respectively. A cohesive discontinuity allows a more ductile response which correspond to a wider damage zone. The damage values for

the activation of the fibre and the shape of the cohesive relationship have been chosen for numerical convenience – they can be related *e.g.* to the strength of the cementitious matrix. The aim of this academic example was to illustrate how changes at the integration point level (understood as changes at the material level) influence the structural response in a regularised continuous/discontinuous model. Note that this approach is not feasible in a nonlocal continuum (Simone et al. 2003).

7 CONCLUSIONS

The use of displacement discontinuities in a ratedependent damage elastoplastic model can enhance the representation of failure in a wide range of applications. In particular, the model proved to be very effective in the qualitative description of SFR-concrete.

ACKNOWLEDGEMENTS

Valuable discussions with G.N. Wells (TU Delft) and A. Meda (Università di Brescia, Italy) are gratefully acknowledged. Financial support to AS through the BEO programme (special fund from TU Delft for excellent research) is gratefully acknowledged.

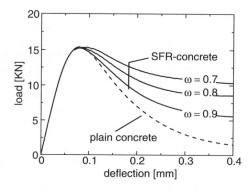

Figure 8. Load–deflection curve for plain and SFR-concrete.

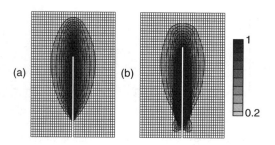

Figure 9. Damage contour plot for (a) plain and (b) SFR concrete ($\omega = 0.8$), deflection = 0.4 mm.

REFERENCES

Geers, M. G. D., R. de Borst, W. A. M. Brekelmans, & R. H. J. Peerlings 1999. Validation and internal length scale determination for a gradient damage model: application to short glass-fibre-reinforced polypropylene. *International Journal of Solids and Structures 36*, 2557–2583.

Georgin, J. F., W. Nechnech, L. J. Sluys, & J. F. Reynouard 2002, July 7–12. A coupled damage-viscoplasticity model for localization problems. In H. A. Mang, F. G. Rammerstorfer, & J. Eberhardsteiner (Eds), *Proceedings of the Fifth World Congress on Computational Mechanics (WCCM V)*, Volume I, pp. 428. Vienna University of Technology, Austria.

Ju, J.W. 1989. On energy-based coupled elastoplastic damage theories: constitutive modeling and computational aspects. *International Journal of Solids and Structures 25*(7), 803–833.

Simone, A., G. N. Wells, & L. J. Sluys 2003, 7–10 April. Discontinuities in regularised media. In D. R. J. Owen, E. Oñate, & B. Suárez (Eds), *Proceedings of the 7th International Conference on Computational Plasticity*, pp. 90. CIMNE, Barcelona, Spain. On CD-ROM.

Stang, H. & J. F. Olesen 1998. On the interpretation of bending tests on frc-materials. In H. Mihashi & K. Rokugo (Eds), *Fracture Mechanics of Concrete Structures, FramCoS 3*, Volume 1, Freiburg, Germany, pp. 511–520. Aedificatio Publishers.

Wells, G. N. & L. J. Sluys 2001. A new method for modelling cohesive cracks using finite elements. *International Journal for Numerical Methods in Engineering 50*(12), 2667–2682.

10. Concrete and masonry structures

System-based Vision for Strategic and Creative Design, Bontempi (ed.)
© 2003 Swets & Zeitlinger, Lisse, ISBN 90 5809 599 1

Cracking around the interface joint between masonry panels and their supporting reinforced concrete beams in buildings

J.L. Miranda Dias

Research officer of LNEC (National Civil Engineering Laboratory), Lisbon, Portugal

ABSTRACT: In the following paper, the matter of cracking around the interface between building masonry walls and concrete beams is discussed. It is well known the inconvenience of that cracking in buildings especially due to the possibility of rain penetration through the cracks and to negative aesthetic aspect. Here, a description is made of the wall-beam behaviour, with special consideration of the zone around the interface joint between masonry walls and their supporting beams when subjected to vertical load, mainly in terms of the cracking susceptibility of that zone for the particular case of solid lightweight concrete blocks (blocks of aerated autoclaved concrete and blocks of lightweight concrete with expanded clay aggregates).

1 INTRODUCTION

Cracking around the interface between building masonry walls and concrete beams is often a problem in buildings based on reinforced concrete frames with infilled masonry walls. It is well known the inconvenience of that cracking in buildings especially due to the possibility of rain penetration through the cracks and to negative aesthetic aspect.

Usually, in case if buildings based on reinforced concrete frames with infilled masonry walls, the interaction between beams and masonry walls is often neglected. This type of building is frequently associated with different construction materials (clay bricks, concrete blocks, etc.), components and workmanship, and where masonry is, generally, considered a non-structural element. In some types of construction systems, where masonry is accepted as a material with significant resistance, (CEN – Eurocode n°6), the composite behaviour of the wall-beam element can be considered, as, for example, in the case of reinforced concrete lintels in the openings, (Davies & Ahmed 1976, Stafford Smith & Pradolin 1978, Page 1979).

It must be stressed the considerable influence, in the construction overall behaviour, of the differences in the characteristics of masonry construction techniques and the constituent parts (units, mortar, workmanship, etc.). The most important effects to be studied require extensive testing, with the investigation of characteristic properties of the constituent elements.

Here, a description is made of the wall-beam behaviour, focusing on the zone around the interface joint between masonry walls and their supporting beams, when the assemble is subjected to vertical load, mainly in terms of the cracking susceptibility of that zone. The analysis is referred to the particular case of solid lightweight concrete blocks – blocks of aerated autoclaved concrete and blocks of lightweight concrete with expanded clay aggregates.

So, mention is made of the principal results and conclusions of an experimental study that mainly concerned the determination of masonry blocks and mortar joints mechanical properties as well as the conduction of masonry wall-beam tests, (Miranda Dias 1997a, Miranda Dias 1997b). In these latter tests, the panel wall is supported by a reinforced concrete beam that spans between supports and a uniformly distributed vertical load, applied on the top of the wall, was produced using hydraulic jacks and a load spreader mounted in a reaction frame. The displacements of the wall and the beam were recorded with special regard to the deflections of the beam at mid span for the load corresponding to the initial cracking around the wall-beam interface and for the maximum vertical load reached.

2 MECHANICAL PROPERTIES OF MASONRY

The experimental determination of masonry properties involved the assessment of the behaviour of solid blocks of aerated autoclaved concrete (material X – dry density of $560kg/m^3$) and solid blocks of lightweight concrete with expanded clay aggregates (material Y – dry density of 1040kg/m^3), through the determination of the compressive strength of the blocks with uniaxial compression test normal to bed joint orientation and uniaxial compression test parallel to bed joint orientation; analysis of the behaviour of mortar joints (block/block for common joint and block/concrete for wall-beam joint) with the study of the most significant types of joint failure.

Block masonry is a composite material, which consists of elastic brittle blocks linked through mortar joints. Due to their low bond strength, particular in tension, these joints act as planes of weakness. Depending on the degree of compression present, failure can occur in the joints alone or as a combined block-joint failure. So the influence of joint strength and orientation must be considered in the failure of masonry (Page 1979).

The elastic properties of the blocks refers to the determination of the modulus of elasticity for load parallel to the bed joint E_b. The elastic properties and the resistance of the lightweight concrete blocks were estimated from uniaxial and triaxial compression tests (see Table 1).

The blocks of aerated autoclaved concrete (material X) and the blocks of lightweight concrete with expanded clay aggregates (material Y) had a nominal compressive strength respectively of 3,9 MPa and 10,1 MPa. The mean values of the elastic modulus were, for material X and Y, at low levels of load, respectively 930 MPa and 8500 MPa (see Table 1). A thin mortar layer was used for material X, while a medium strength mortar, of a 1:1:6 mix by volume of cement, lime and sand, was used for material Y.

The mortar joint properties cannot be defined from simple uniaxial tests performed on the mortar alone, because the state of stress within the joint is complex due to the influence of the surrounding blocks. So the mortar properties were estimated taking in account the results of uniaxial compression tests, flexure tension tests, triaxial compression tests on mortar samples (mortars for material X and Y), and triaxial compression and direct shear tests on blockwork couplets (block/block), which incorporated a mortar joint (see results on Table 1).

So, the strength of the joint under tension was estimated from a series of flexure strength tests on solid blockwork couplets (with a vertical joint in the middle of the specimen). The influence of bond pattern was not considered, as it was desired to define failure for an individual joint rather than masonry as a whole.

The estimated tensile strength was 0,6 and 0,2 MPa, respectively for material X and Y (see Table 1 – block/block joint), which illustrates the low value of masonry tensile bond strength, a value that is well bellow the tensile strength of the respective mortar (respectively 2,9 and 2,5 – Table 1).

The initial shear strength, f_{bvko} obtained from linear regression of triaxial tests of each type of block/block joint were 0,9 MPa and 0,3 MPa respectively.

From the triaxial compression (ratio of lateral stress/vertical stress, (σ_L/σ_V), of the specimens ranging generally between 0,05 and 0,30) and direct shear tests (constant normal stress load, σ_N, applied on the specimens with values ranging generally between 0,50 MPa and 2,00 MPa) on block material and on blockwork couplets that incorporated a mortar joint, average mortar joints stress–strain curves were derived and a Coulomb type failure criterion for those block material and joints was approximately obtained (estimated values of initial shear strength, f_{bvko}, and of friction coefficient tgϕ, maximum and residual value from regression analysis of tests – Table 1). The mortar shear strain, at shear-stress level, can then be estimated for the maximum load (through maximum horizontal displacement, δ_{tm}, direct shear tests, see Table 1), and it was evident the low stiffness of the mortar when compared to that of the block.

The results of this experimental study on both materials X and Y suggests that if failure in the block/block joints occurs under a combination of shear and low compressive stress, a shear bond failure can be considered and some residual capacity will remain in the joint. When the compressive stress is high, the residual shear stiffness can be estimated from the final slope of the shear stress-shear strain curve obtained in direct shear tests on blockwork couplets (block/block – Table 1) that incorporated a mortar joint. The results allow to suppose that the shear resistance can be assumed to reduce approximately to zero between the situation of high compressive stress and tensile stress. So, these results indicate that the joint elements have relatively high compression capacity (see, in Table 1, values of maximum and residual vertical strain ε_{vmax} and ε_{vr} from triaxial tests) and low tensile capacity (flexure tensile stress, f_{tbj} – Table 1), and a shear capacity which is a function of the imposed compression and the bond strength. Similar conclusions can be drawn from results of direct shear tests in couplets of block/concrete (shear behaviour of wall-beam interface joint – Table 1), with mortar joint of the same material as that used in the correspondent block/block joint. In fact, the complex triaxial stress state produced by mortar-block and mortar-concrete interaction and the influence of bonding pattern of the wall makes difficult the understanding of the effective behaviour of the block and the mortar in the masonry and this last with the concrete beam. The non-linear characteristics of this type of blockwork result most probably from the local failure and slip that occur in the joints and the non-linear deformation typical of the joints under shear and compression. So, these characteristics must be taken in account when estimating the mechanical

Table 1. Test material properties of masonry constituents and joints: blocks of material X (wall-beam MX) and Y (wall-beam MY) and associated mortar.

Type of material	Blocks, mortar and masonry — Compressive and tensile strength, modulus of elasticity (1), triaxial compression test (blocks, mortar), direct shear tests (blocks)					Joints — Block/Block Joint — Triaxial compression test, direct shear tests and flexure tensile test (resistance and deformations)					Joints — Block/Concrete Joint — Direct shear tests		
	f_{cb} block / f_{cm} mortar / f_{vk} masonry (MPa)	f_{tb} block / f_{tb} mortar (MPa)	E_b block / E_m mortar / E masonry (MPa)	f_{bvko} triaxial peak blocks (2) / f_{bvko} triaxial peak mortar (MPa)	$tg\phi_p$ triaxial peak blocks (σ_L/σ_V) / $tg\phi_p$ triaxial peak mortar (σ_L/σ_V)	f_{bvko} triaxial peak / f_{tbj} flexural tensile (MPa)	f_{bvko} direct shear peak (σ_N) / f_{bvko} direct shear residual (MPa)	$tg\phi_p$ triaxial peak (σ_L/σ_V) / $tg\phi_p$ triaxial residual	$tg\phi_p$ direct shear peak / $tg\phi_r$ direct shear residual	ε_{vmax} máx.vert. triaxial / ε_{vres} residual mm/m (×10⁻³) $\delta_{tm},(\delta_{tr})$ máx.,(resid) horizontal direct shear (mm)	f_{bvko} direct shear peak (σ_N) / f_{bvko} direct shear residual (MPa)	$tg\phi_p$ direct shear peak / $tg\phi_r$ direct shear residual	δ_{tm} máx.hor.dir.shear (mm) / δ_{tr} residual (mm)
MATERIAL X *Blocks*: of aerated autoclaved concrete	3,9	1,3	930	0,9	0,8 (0,05-0,30)	0	0,2 (0,50-1,25)	0,4 (0,50-1,25)	1,2	5,8	0,3 (0,50-1,25)	0,9	0,1
	5,2	2,9	1580							6,5			
Mortar: thin layer	2,0		1300	0	0,6 (0,05-0,30)	0,6	0,5	0,2	0,4	0,1 (1,1)	0	0,9	1,4
MATERIAL Y *Blocks*: light-weight concrete with expanded clay aggregates	10,1	2,7	8500	2,3	0,9 (0,03-0,30)	0	0,5 (0,75-2,00)	0,1 (0,50-1,25)	0,8	4,1	0,8 (0,75-1,25)	0,7	0,2
	2,6	2,5	1300							22,4			
Mortar: lime, cement, sand	4,5		5070	0	0,6 (0,03-0,30)	0,2	0,2	0,2	0,7	1,8 (7,0)	0,3	0,9	1,9

(1) Estimate of elasticity modulus E_b, E_m and deformations, ε_{vmax}, ε_{vres} of block/block specimen were based on triaxial compression tests (σ_L/σ_V =0,075);

(2) Estimate of initial shear strength f_{bvko} (maximum and residual value) and the friction coefficient $tg\phi_p$, $tg\phi_r$ (maximum and residual value) obtained by linear regression of the triaxial and direct shear test results; δ_{tm}, δ_{tr}, maximum and residual horizontal displacement, are a mean values obtained in the direct shear tests

parameters for numerical simulations of wall-beam behaviour.

A series of uniaxial compression tests in a compressive test machine, for the determination of masonry compressive strength, was also carried out on panels of solid blockwork: panels of aerated autoclaved concrete blocks (material X – 1000 mm high, 900 mm wide and 15 mm thick) and lightweight concrete with expanded clay aggregates blocks (material Y – 1000 mm high, 750 mm wide and 15 mm thick).

The uniaxial compression tests on this masonry panels were performed with compression normal to bed joint. Vertical and horizontal strains were measured on both sides of the panel, and were averaged to eliminate bending effects. The mode of failure of the panels was typical for this type of loading, with vertical tensile splits, generally, propagating through masonry. Splitting of blocks occurred at a load close to the ultimate load.

The elastic properties of blockwork, can be estimated taking 1300 MPa and 5070 MPa as representative values for elastic modulus respectively for material X and material Y (see Table 1).

3 THE BEHAVIOR OF INTERFACE JOINT BETWEEN THE WALL AND THE BEAM

3.1 Description of wall-beam test

In the wall-beam test, an approximating uniformly distributed load was applied in the top of the wall using a hydraulic jack and a load spreader mounted in a reaction frame. The panel is simply supported, and both the supports of the reinforced concrete beam were on rollers.

With a data logging system to monitor the transducers mounted in the panel, vertical and horizontal displacements (absolute and relative) were measured

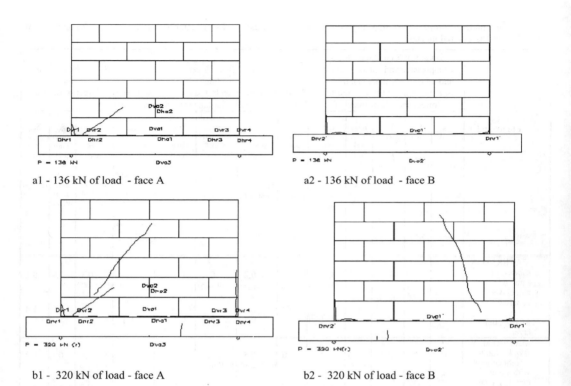

a1 - 136 kN of load - face A

a2 - 136 kN of load - face B

b1 - 320 kN of load - face A

b2 - 320 kN of load - face B

Figure 1.   Cracking pattern of specimen MX (a1, a2 – 136 kN of load (unloading after the relative peak of load); b1, b2 – 320 kN of load (step of reloading – peak load)).

Table 2.   Dimensions and elastic characteristics of the wall-speciments.

Test.	DIMENSIONS AND ELASTIC CHARACTERÍSTICS										
	Geometry and rigidity of the wall				Geometry and rigidity of the beam				General characteristics of the wall-beam specimen		
	length L (mm) (H_w/L)	height H_w (mm)	thickness B (mm)	El. Mod. E_w MPa	height d (mm)	width b (mm)	El. Mod E MPa	Inertia I_v (cm^4) x 10^{-3}	height. H_t (mm)	Ratio H_t/L	bottom reinforcement (cm^2)
MX	1800 (0,67)	1200	150	1500	200	175	29000	11,70	1400	0,78	3,14
MY	2000 (0,70)	1200	150	4500	200	175	29000	11,70	1400	0,70	3,14

(1) Top and bottom reinforcement of the beam (beams MX e MY: bottom reinforcement = 4ϕ10 and top reinforcement = 3ϕ8);

in the middle vertical axis of the wall, along the wall-beam interface, and in the bottom of the beam, at the mid-span. The panels were loaded to failure with the displacements being continuously recorded.

The general arrangement of the specimen MX for the wall-beam test can be seen in Figure 1 (a1, a2). The blockwork panel, MX and MY, was supported by rectangular section reinforced concrete beam (0,175 m – width; 0,20 m – high; 2,40 m – length). The concrete material of the beam had an average crushing compressive strength of 30 MPa at 28 days. The top and the bottom longitudinal reinforcement of

the beam consisted of, respectively, 3 steel bars (8 mm diameter) and 4 steel bars (10 mm diameter), with an average ultimate tensile strength of 646 MPa. The shear reinforcement consisted of 6 mm diameter stirrups. The size of the beam was selected to give a typical wall to supporting beam stiffness ratio. The overall depth to span ratio of the wall-beam specimen was approximately 0,78 for MX and 0,70 for MY. The main parameters related with the wall-beam test are presented in Table 2, in particular the geometry and rigidity of the wall and the beam and other general characteristics.

748

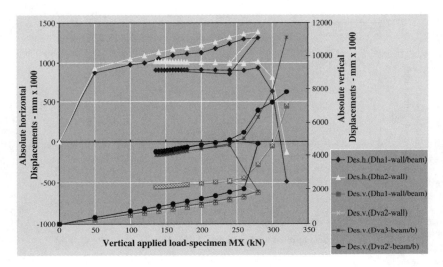

Figure 2. Variation, in the specimen MX, of the absolute horizontal displacements Dha1, Dha2 (Peekel B20 transducers), absolute vertical displacements Dva1, Dva2 (Peekel B2 transducers) in the wall, absolute vertical displacements in the bottom of the beam Dva3, and absolute vertical displacements Dva1' in the face B.

The test instrumentation of the specimen on face A, consisted of "Peekel" displacement transducers set along the interface between the wall and the beam for purpose of vertical relative displacements readings (Dvr1,Dvr2 – left support; Dvr3,Dvr4 – right support) and horizontals (Dhr1,Dhr2 – left support; Dhr3, Dhr4 – right support), and in the vertical central axis for purpose of vertical absolute displacements readings (Dva1,Dva2), horizontal (Dha1,Dha2) and vertical displacements of the beam bottom central point (Dva3). The test instrumentation of the specimen on face B, consisted of digital displacement transducers set along the interface between the wall and the beam for purpose of horizontal relative displacements readings (Dhr1' – right support, in accordance with Dhr1 in face A; Dhr2' – left support in accordance with Dhr4 in face A) and in vertical central axis for purpose of vertical absolute displacement reading of a wall point (Dva1' – in the bottom of the wall and in accordance with Dva1) and vertical absolute displacement of a point in the bottom of the wall (Dva2' – in accordance with Dva3).

3.2 Results of the wall-beam test

Two consecutive phase-loads were performed on the MX wall-beam test. The load was applied in 10 kN increments. In run 1, the load was gradually applied after reaching a load of 280 kN, then it was released till 136 kN of load. At this point of the test a significant cracking was observed on the wall rendering, in the interface between the wall and the beam, particularly in the region near the supports where the cracking

developed more extensively. In run 2, the wall-beam was reloaded from a 240 kN of load till failure, with an ultimate load of 320 kN in the jack being achieved (corresponding to a uniformly distributed load of 156 kN/m – Fig. 2 and Fig. 3). Final failure occurred in a manner typical of this type of test, with a shear crack in the beam near the right support (face A) and the crushing of the blockwork adjacent to one of the supports and near the wall-beam interface, followed by the discharge of the specimen (see cracking pattern of the specimen MX in Fig. 1). Horizontal and vertical displacements in the wall-beam element are presented in Table 3. The cracking sequence is shown in Figure 1. The first cracks appeared at a load level of 280 kN with shear bond and tensile bond failures towards the mid-span adjacent to the supporting beam. As the level of load was increased, predominantly crushing failure in the blocks and shear bond failure occurred in the region of the panel above the support, with an inclined crack propagating up the panel. It seems that stress redistribution, at this loading phase, was taking place due to progressive joint failure and non-linear mortar properties.

At a load of 280 kN (i.e. 88% of ultimate load), there is little difference between the displacements of the two faces (A and B). The differences become more pronounced for greater loads.

In the case of the wall-beam test MY, only one phase-load was performed. The load was applied in 10 kN increments and, at a load of 200 kN, significant cracking was observed on the wall rendering, particularly in the interface between the wall and the beam (Fig. 4).

In MY wall-beam test, the load was gradually applied till a maximum load of 420 kN (corresponding

749

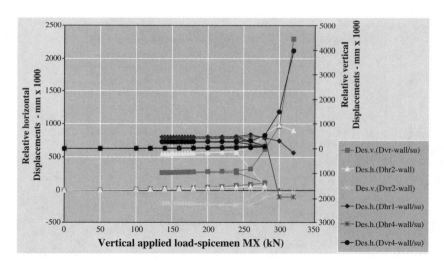

Figure 3. Variation, in the specimen MX, of the relative vertical displacements Dvr1, Dvr2 and relative horizontal displacements, Dhr1, Dhr2, (Peekel transducers B2) in the left extreme zone (support) of the interface wall-beam face A of the specimen, and of the relative vertical displacements Dvr4 and relative horizontal displacements, Dhr4 in the right extreme zone (support) of the interface wall-beam face A of the specimen.

Table 3. Results of the wall-beam test (specimen MX aerated autoclaved concrete blocks and lightweight concrete with expanded clay aggregates blocks with traditional rendering).

Load kN	DIMENSIONS OF THE SPECIMEN (1) length, width, height (mm)			FACE A Vertical and Horizontal displacements μ (mm x 10⁻³) Absolute displacement (Peekel transducers B2/hor. e B20/vert.)					FACE A Relative displacement (Peekel transducers B2/hor. e vert.)								FACE B Absolute displacement (digital deflect.)		FACE B Relative displacement (digital deflect.)	
	Lp Bp Hp	Lv Bv Hp	Lt Bt Ht	Dha1 (wall) hor.	Dva1 (wall) vert.	Dha2 (wall) hor.	Dva2 (wall) vert.	Dva3 (beam) vert.	Dhr1 (w/b-ext) hor.	Dvr1 (w/b-ext) vert.	Dhr2 (w/b-left) hor.	Dvr2 (w/b-right) vert.	Dhr3 (w/b-left) hor.	Dvr3 (w/b-ext) vert.	Dhr4 (w/b-ext) hor.	Dvr4 (w/b-right) hor.	Dva1' (beam) ver.	Dva2' (beam) ver.	Dhr1' (w/b-ext) hor.	Dhr2' (w/b-ext) hor.
50 kN	Lp= 1836	Lv= 2500	Lt= 1836	881	237	935	229	270	6	8	6	3	3	-4	5	2	610	400	0	0
100	Bv= 175	Bv= 175	Bt= 175	979	537	1050	528	584	15	17	14	8	7	-5	11	5	950	740	0	0
200	Hp= 1220	Hv= 200	Ht= 1420	1122	1064	1219	1057	1134	54	44	38	12	24	-11	41	19	1630	1420	0	-30
280				1308	1764	1386	1758	1849	106	111	66	18	43	-18	99	74	3280	4680	940	-
136				913	2118	1017	2137	4012	446	261	549	-199	180	-297	391	258	2890	4210	1350	-
260				908	2686	991	2731	5004	551	319	642	-224	230	-366	476	304	3510	5390	2770	-
320				-486	6930	-132	7041	11111	-165	2284	893	-20	-	234	-	3976	7800	7800	-	-

(1) Lp, (dimensions of the wall); Lv (dimensions of the beam); Lt (global dimensions); others dimensions with analogous meaning

to a uniformly distributed load of 190 kN/m), and at that moment the test ended. At this end point of the test, a shear crack in the beam near the right support (face A) and a vertical crack at mid-span was observed on the wall rendering, as well as cracking around the interface between the wall and the beam, particularly in the region near the supports where crushing of the blockwork adjacent to both the supports also occurred.

The observed horizontal and vertical displacements in the wall-beam, MY, are presented in Table 4.

The wall-beam was loaded till failure, with an ultimate load of 420 kN in the jack being achieved (corresponding to a uniformly distributed load of 210 kN/m). Final failure occurred similarly as in the specimen MX with a shear crack in the beam near the end of the support and the crushing of the blockwork adjacent to one of the supports, followed by the discharge of the specimen.

Based on the results of the specimen MX and MY tests, it seems that significant stress redistribution

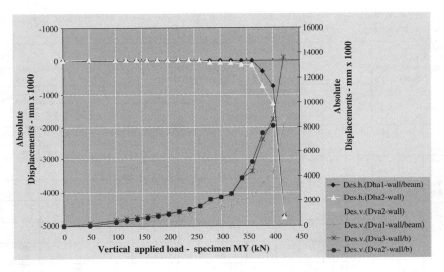

Figure 4. Variation, in specimen MY, of the absolute horizontal displacements Dha1, Dha2 (Peekel transducers B20), absolute vertical displacements Dva1, Dva2 (Peekel transducers B2) in the panel; the absolute vertical displacement in the base of the beam Dva3; and the absolute vertical displacement Dva1′ on face B.

Figure 5. Wall-beam test – specimen MX.

occurs, as well as a reduction in the stresses in the lower half of the panel. The high horizontal relative displacements near the interface between the wall and the beam correspond presumably to the increase in

arching between the supports due to gradual loss of composite action. At higher loads, significant bond and crushing failures occurred in the zone adjacent to the supporting beam, with a consequent reduction in horizontal shear capacity.

The changing behaviour of the wall-beam composite element is also shown by the displacement variations in the supporting beam and in the base of the wall at middle span (see Table 3 and 4, and Figs. 2 to 4). Once wall-beam separation occurred there was presumably a marked change in the stress distribution within the supporting beam. The supporting beam acts as a beam separated from the wall when there is loss of composite action. Complementing these bending stresses there is a uniform tensile stress produced by tension tie action in the beam. With the wall-beam separation, a higher bending moment is supposed to be induced in the beam.

4 CONCLUSIONS

The relative weakness of the wall-beam joint of MX and MY tests produced early wall-beam separation and cracking extended to almost the full length of the wall and the beam. A considerable part of the wall-beam joint failed in shear, but it still maintained its capacity to transmit normal stress, although composite action was lost.

It can therefore be concluded that the properties of the wall-beam joint are significant for the overall behaviour of the wall-beam element, and the achievement of adequate strength for this joint is a crucial

Table 4.   Results of the wall-beam test (specimen MY – wall of lightweight concrete with expanded clay aggregates blocks with cement-lime rendering).

Load kN	DIMENSIONS OF THE SPECIMEN (1) length, width, height (mm)			FACE A — Vertical and Horizontal displacements μ (mm x 10⁻³) — Absolute displacements (Peekel transducers B2/hor. e B20/vert.)					FACE A — Relative displacement (Peekel transducers B2/hor. e vert.)								FACE B — Vertical and Horizontal displacements μ (mm x 10⁻³) — Absolute displacement (digital deflect.)		FACE B — Relative displacement (digital deflect.)	
	Lp Bp Hp	Lv Bv Hp	Lt Bt Ht	Dha1 (wall) hor.	Dva1 (wall) vert.	Dha2 (wall) hor.	Dva2 (wall) vert.	Dva3 (beam) vert.	Dhr1 (w/b-ext) hor.	Dvr1 (w/b-ext) vert.	Dhr2 (w/b-left) hor.	Dvr2 (w/b-right) vert.	Dhr3 (w/b-left) hor.	Dvr3 (w/b-ext) vert.	Dhr4 (w/b-ext) hor.	Dvr4 (w/b-right) hor.	Dva1' (w/b-right) ver.	Dva2' (beam) ver.	Dhr1' (w/b-ext) hor.	Dhr2' (w/b-ext) hor.
50 kN	Lp=2000	Lv=2500	Lt=2000	7	176	25	172	176	18	19	14	5	11	1	13	15	2	2	0	0
100	Bv=175	Bv=175	Bt=175	6	374	16	392	436	33	27	24	3	23	-7	24	19	280	280	0	-10
200	Hp=1220	Hv=200	Ht=1420	6	792	16	823	936	69	38	49	-13	57	-37	62	17	830	880	30	-70
300				-2	1448	-54	1503	2296	184	51	151	-104	240	-191	230	-17	1530	2270	90	40
400				-740	4345	-293	4379	8610	501	160	694	-800	1036	-535	-522	1121	4730	8100	-	-
420				-4735	8137	-4752	8570	13586	715	208	777	-807	-791	1495	-	97	-			

(1)   Lp, (dimensions of the wall); Lv (dimensions of the beam); Lt (global dimensions); others dimensions with analogous meaning

(2)   Maximum load was close by 420 kN, so it was adopted this latter load as the maximum load

Figure 6.   Specimen MX after 320 kN of load level, with cracking at the interface between the wall and the beam.

task. The changing stress distributions caused by non-linear material characteristics, joint failure in localized areas and wall-beam separation also has important implications.

Finally, it is expected that a better understanding of products characteristics and of wall-beam performance, and, in particular, of the behaviour of the interface joint between beam and wall, under certain conditions, can lead to savings in costs, and possibly reduce the situations of cracking of masonry caused, mainly, by the excessive deflections of masonry supporting element.

ACKNOWLEDGEMENTS

LNEC Programmed Research has funded the present study. The assistance and help in the experimental tests of Mr. António Nunes and Mr. Deodato Sanches is gratefully acknowledged

REFERENCES

CEN – Eurocode n°6 – Design of masonry structures – Part. 1–1: General rules for buildings. Rules for reinforced and unreinforced masonry. CEN, prENV 1996-1-1, 1995.

EUROPEAN COMMITTEE FOR STANDARDIZATION (CEN) – Eurocode n°2: Design of concrete structures. Part 1, CEN, ENV 1992-1-1, 1991.

Davies, S.R. & Ahmed, A.E. 1976. Composite action of wall-beams with openings. Proceedings of 4th International Brick and masonry conference, pp. 4b 6.1–6.5, Brugge, 1976.

Stafford Smith, B. & Pradolin, L. 1978. A contribution towards the design of heavily loaded masonry walls on reinforced concrete beams. Proceedings of North American masonry conference, 1, Boulder, Colorado, August, 1978.

Page, A.W. 1979. A non-linear analysis of the composite action of masonry walls on beams. Proceedings of Instn. Civ. Engrs., Part 2, 67, pp. 93–110, Mar., 1979.

Miranda Dias, J.L. 1997a. Composite action between masonry panels and their supporting beams. ENBRI Newsletter (European Network of Building Research Institutes, Issue 6, Spring 1997.

Miranda Dias, J.L. 1997b. Composite action between lightweight concrete masonry blocks and their supporting beams – PhD Thesis, IST. LNEC, July 1997.

Restoration and repair of existing masonry structures

W.C. Bracken
Bracken Engineering Inc, Tampa, Florida, USA

ABSTRACT: Masonry structures, whether reinforced, partially reinforced or unreinforced, when subjected to wide spread foundation failure or increases in rational loading requirement, often require innovate methods of repair and strengthening. Therefore, when masonry structural systems become damaged, an evaluation of both the structural system and the damaged components must be conducted. This evaluation should not begin with the assumption that replacement is the only option but should include identifying the condition and viability of the damaged component, the impact of removal versus restoration, and the development and implementation of supplemental structural measures.

1 RESTORATION ENGINEERING PROCESSES

1.1 Overview

The restoration engineering process can be simplified into five basic steps; data collection, assessment of the structure's components & systems, identification of restoration constraints, engineering of the most appropriate solution, and implementation of that solution. Depending upon the complexity of the structure and the extent of the damage additional iteration may be required but is typically determined on a case-by-case basis.

1.2 Data collection

The data collection phase involves the identification, collection and compilation of all available information. Such information would include reports of previous damage, drawings, design criteria, calculations, and any other pertinent information. Once compiled this data should be reviewed first with respect to its accuracy and second with respect to relevance. When possible, such information should be assembled prior to commencing the assessment and on-site inspection phase. In the absence of this information or in the face of woefully inadequate documentation, the engineer should attempt to obtain as much information as possible during on-site inspections.

1.3 Assessment

The assessment phase serves to physically examine and numerically evaluate the structure's components and/or systems. Due to logistical requirements as well as the impact of a comprehensive assessment, a graduated approach is recommended. This approach begins with a preliminary assessment, followed by an interim assessment followed by more detailed assessments of those portions deemed necessary to the success of the restoration process. Because the scope of the investigation normally encompasses a large portion of the structure, refinement criteria should be established with a focus on adequately identifying that portion of the structure to be addressed by the restoration. Refinement criteria should focus on structural criticality, age, and materials used.

1.4 Identification of constraints

The identification of restoration constraints begins during the data collection phase and is carried through the assessment phase. Restoration constraints typically include material degradation, material compatibility, time limitations, access of construction equipment, budget restrictions, and building code upgrade requirements. Proper identification and continued reevaluation of these restoration constraints is required throughout the restoration process.

1.5 Engineering

The engineering phase begins by establishing whether the structure and/or its components has adequate capacity to withstand both the increased structural demands as well as the constriction activities associated with the restoration process. This evaluation is conducted by first identifying structural deficiencies and then calculating capacities with respect to increased requirements. Engineering judgment and experience along with simplified analysis techniques should be utilized when determining structural demands and capacities. Environmental, aging and compatibility effects should also be considered within this phase.

1.6 *Implementation*

The actual construction and the engineering in support of that construction realize the implementation phase. It should be noted that no matter how extensive or sophisticated the data collection, assessment and engineering is, a successful restoration project requires engineering input and often times adaptation based on unanticipated as-discovered conditions.

2 CASE STUDY: FAILED FOUNDATION DUE TO EXPANSIVE SOILS

2.1 *Overview*

This case study examines a 1-year old concrete masonry structure that was damaged by expansive clay

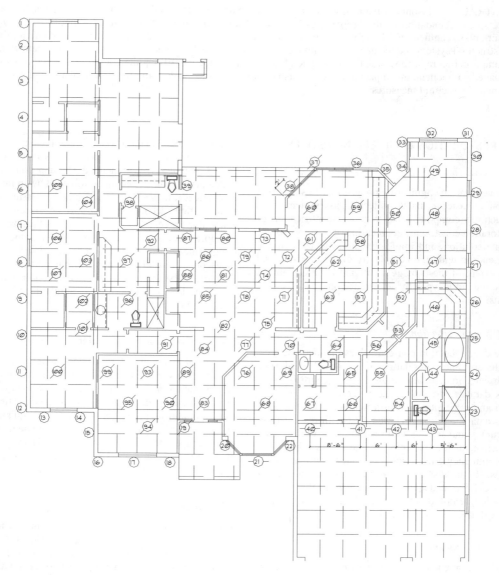

Figure 1.   This graphic depicts the tendon layout as well as the interior & exterior pin pile layout.

soils. This structure consisted of exterior concrete masonry walls sitting atop a cast-in-place monolithic footing and slab along with interior wood frame bearing walls sitting atop interior thickened footings. These walls acted to support a wood frame roof structure. Expansive clay soils are defined, for the purpose of this paper, as a surface layer of highly plastic cohesive clay. These types of soils are found to be capable of expansion when hydrated and contraction when dehydrated. The result of this expansion and contraction is the undulation of the soil's surface topography. The impact of this undulation on a shallow foundation system is the cyclic inducement of unanticipated stresses throughout the entire structure.

2.2 Data collection

Given that this structure was only 1-year old, the data collection portion of this case study included the compilation and evaluation of the original design plans. This portion of the case study also included an interview of the original owner supplement by visual observations.

2.3 Assessment

The assessment portion of the restoration engineering began with a topographic mapping of the surface of the slab. This topographic mapping was performed so as to identify those areas of the structure that were most affected by the undulations resulting in differential displacements. Once these areas were identified and the displacements quantified the scope of the restoration was established. The scope was determined to encompass nearly 60% of this 5000 square foot footprint. With the scope of the restoration established and those areas most affected by the displacements identified, the structure's components & systems were evaluated. This evaluation found that due to the extent of the differential displacement experienced, both integral & secondary structural components & systems had been affected. Namely the roof and interior wall systems had been affected.

2.4 Identification of constraints

Concurrent with these phases, identification of restoration constraints was made. The constraints included the amount of time that the structure was to be out of service, the type of foundation restoration system to be used and the limitations on type & size of construction equipment to be used.

2.5 Engineering

The engineering found the most appropriate solution to be the introduction of pin piles to the interior &

Figure 2. This photo depicts the installation of the interior pin piles.

exterior load bearing components as well as the interior non-load bearing slab. The use of pin piles was selected so as to isolate the structure from those soils experiencing the most pronounced undulation and resulting differential displacements.

2.6 Implementation

The implementation of this solution involved the placement, installation and manipulation of the pin piles. The implementation of this solution however proved challenging in that the original design plans were not adhered to during the construction of the foundation and slab on grade. It was discovered upon commencement of the construction that the slab, originally designed to be a mildly reinforced slab on grade, was in fact a pre-tensioned mat foundation. The engineering approach was adapted to these conditions and the structure was successfully restored.

3 CASE STUDY: FAILED FOUNDATION DUE TO SINKHOLE ACTIVITY

3.1 Overview

This case study examines a 100-year old terra cotta masonry structure that was damaged by sinkhole activity. This structure consisted of exterior terra cotta masonry walls sitting atop a cast-in-place strip footing. The floor system was an elevated conventionally framed wood system. This system was also found to contain interior wood frame bearing walls all that acted to support upper wood frame floor and roof systems. Sinkhole activity is defined, for the purpose of this paper, as the development of a void within a relatively deep surface layer of non-cohesive and mildly cohesive sands. The result of this subsurface void is the development of depressions within the soil's surface topography. The impact of these depressions on a shallow foundation system is the loss of supporting soils and the inducement of unanticipated stresses throughout the entire structure.

3.2 Data collection

Given that this structure was nearly a century old original plans and specifications were not available. The data collection portion of this case study did however include thorough investigative and partially destructive testing. This phase also included historical research on the materials, methods and craftsman of the time.

3.3 Assessment

The assessment portion of the restoration engineering began with a topographic mapping of the surface of the various floor levels. This topographic mapping enabled the identification of those areas of the structure that were most affected by the differential displacements. Evaluating the topographies of the various floors and separating out the foundation displacements from anticipated material aging effects accomplished this identification. Once the areas exhibiting foundation displacements were identified and the displacements quantified the scope of the restoration was established. The scope was determined to encompass nearly 40% of this 2000 square foot footprint. With the scope of the restoration established and those areas most affected by the displacements identified, the structure's

components & systems were evaluated. This evaluation found that due to the extent of the differential displacement experienced by the structure, both integral and secondary structural components and systems had been affected. This evaluation also found significant structural deficiencies resulting from the materials used, their age and the impact of the displacement induced stresses.

3.4 Identification of constraints

Concurrent with these phases, identification of restoration constraints was made. The constraints encountered included the types of foundation restoration system that could be used, the limitations on type & size of construction equipment to be used and the amount of time that the structure was to be out of service. The most significant constraint encountered was found to be the amount of vertical recovery that could be achieved without causing significant or catastrophic collateral damage to the structure's systems and/or components.

3.5 Engineering

The engineering found the most appropriate solution to be a combination of supplemental piering to the field of the interior floor, supplemental piering below the interior load bearing walls, pin piles to the exterior load bearing walls, partial reconstruction of the exterior wall, and the introduction of supplemental internal post and beams. Perhaps the greatest challenge of this engineering effort was the successful introduction & integration of these systems into the existing structure without significantly impacting the characteristic or makeup of this structure.

3.6 Implementation

The implementation of this solution proved challenging in that additional systems, not previously discovered,

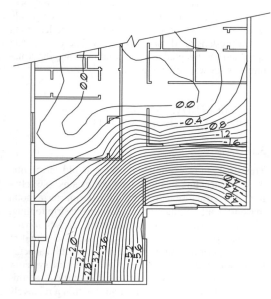

Figure 3. This graphic depicts typical sinkhole related differential displacements measured in 1/10-inch increments.

Figure 4. This photo depicts the partial reconstruction of the front right exterior corner.

were encountered. The implementation of this system was further challenged as severe aesthetic constraints were imposed subsequent to design and prior to construction. The engineering approach was adapted to these conditions and the global process was iterated three complete times. The length of time required to successfully restore the structure was nearly two years.

4 CASE STUDY: STORM RESISTANCE STRENGTHENING BY EXTERNAL MEASURES

4.1 Overview

This case study examines a 30-year old concrete masonry structure that required strengthening so as to meet increased loading requirements imposed by a change in use. The structure was originally constructed as a school building and remains in service as a school building. The change in use was brought about when this structure was recently designated as a hurricane storm shelter. As such, this structure was required to meet or exceed loads resulting from a 140 mile per hour wind speed gust. The structural system consisted of exterior and interior concrete masonry walls sitting atop cast-in-place strip footings. This structural system acted in turn to support precast pre-stressed concrete tee floor and roof structures.

4.2 Data collection

The data collection portion of this case study included the compilation and evaluation of the original design plans. Given that this structure had undergone years of remodelling and updating, structural changes from the design plans were anticipated. Therefore this portion of the case study also included thorough investigative and partially destructive testing.

4.3 Assessment

The assessment portion of the restoration engineering began with a numeric evaluation of the exterior walls

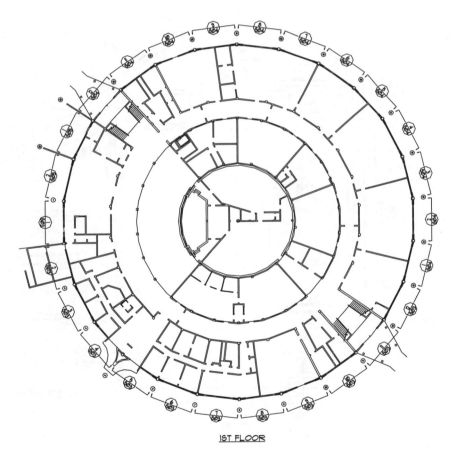

IST FLOOR

Figure 5. This graphic depicts the configuration of the structure as well as the layout of the structural steel tube strengthening.

757

intended to establish existing capacities. This numeric evaluation was then refined based on the as-built modifications and physical constraints encountered. This evaluation found that the existing structural components & systems failed to provide sufficient out of plane bending resistance. It was at this point that the restoration constraints were established, strengthening options identified and one strengthening method selected. Once the strengthening method was established the scope of the storm resistance strengthening was established. The scope was determined to encompass 100% of the exterior of this 25000 square foot footprint. With the scope of the storm resistance strengthening established, engineering of the method and its details was completed.

4.4 Identification of constraints

As previously stated, within the assessment phase the identification of restoration constraints was made.

The constraints included the fact that the structure was not to be taken out of service, the fact that the masonry walls had been filled with mechanical and telecommunications wires, the existence of a brick veneer and the limitations on type & size of construction equipment to be used. Based on these constraints internal reinforcing was not an option. Therefore, external reinforcing combined with limited internal fastening techniques were employed.

4.5 Engineering

The most appropriate solution found was the introduction of exterior structural steel tubing to the exterior face of the exterior load bearing walls. The use of exterior structural steel tubing was selected so as to provide the requisite out of plane bending strength. The attachment of this tubing required integral connection to the exterior concrete masonry walls as well as integral connection to floor and roof slabs.

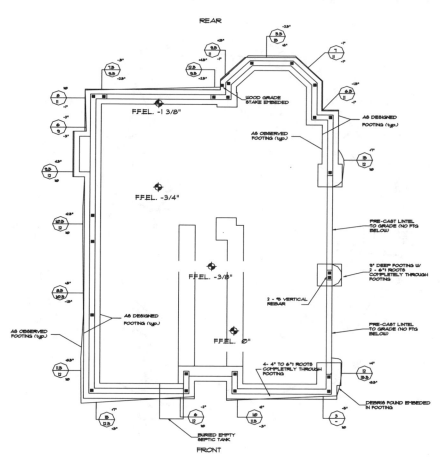

Figure 6.   This graphic depicts the as-discovered conditions encountered.

4.6 Implementation

The implementation of this solution involved the placement and installation of the structural steel tubing. The implementation of this solution proved challenging from a geometry control point given that the existing structure was build out of level and out of plumb. The engineering approach required only slight adaptation and the structure was successfully restored.

5 CASE STUDY: POST-CONSTRUCTION STRENGTHENING BY INTERNAL MEASURES

5.1 Overview

This case study examines a 3-year old concrete masonry structure that required strengthening so as to meet minimum building code requirements. This strengthening resulted from the discovery of original design and construction deficiencies. This structure was required to not only to sit atop an expansive clay soil but also to resist loads resulting from a 110 mile per hour wind speed gust. The structural system consisted of exterior concrete masonry walls sitting atop cast-in-place strip footings. This system was also found to contain interior wood frame bearing walls and columns. These exterior & interior walls and columns acted to support upper wood frame floor and roof systems.

5.2 Data collection

The data collection portion of this case study included the compilation and evaluation of the original design plans. This portion of the case study also included an interview of the original owner supplement by visual observations. Based on these findings exploratory and partially destructive testing was utilized. This testing included X-raying of the exterior walls, partial deconstruction and a topographic mapping of the surface of the slab.

5.3 Assessment

The assessment portion of the restoration engineering began with a numeric evaluation of the exterior walls

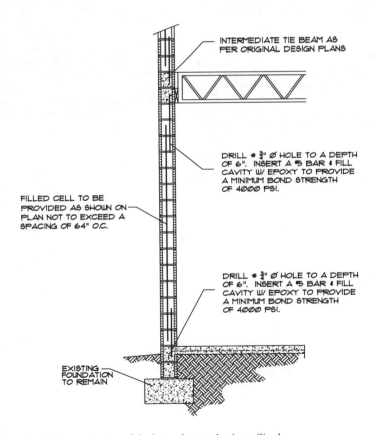

Figure 7. This figure depicts the application of the internal strengthening utilized.

intended to establish existing capacities. This numeric evaluation was then refined based on the as-built and as-discovered deviations. This evaluation found that the existing structural components & systems failed to provide sufficient in-plane sheer and out of plane bending resistance. The topographic mapping of the surface of the slab also found the structure incapable of resisting or accommodating the cyclic inducement of unanticipated stresses resulting from this expansion and contraction of the soil's surface topography. Once the strengthening method was established and the displaced areas quantified, the scope of the restoration was established. The scope was determined to encompass nearly 100% of this 2000 square foot footprint and nearly 100% of the structure's exterior walls. With the scope of the strengthening established, engineering of the method and its details was completed.

5.4 Identification of constraints

Concurrent with these phases, identification of restoration constraints was made. The constraints included the amount of time that the structure was to be out of service, the type of foundation restoration system to be used and the limitations on type & size of construction equipment to be used.

5.5 Engineering

The engineering found the most appropriate solution to the foundation issues was the introduction of pin piles to the exterior load bearing walls. The use of pin piles was able to isolate the structure from those soils experiencing the most pronounced undulation and resulting

differential displacements. The most appropriate solution found for strengthening the exterior walls was the introduction of internal structural steel reinforcing and grout. The use of internal structural steel reinforcing and grout was selected so as to provide the requisite in-plane and out of plane strengths.

5.6 Implementation

The implementation of this solution involved the placement, installation and manipulation of the pin piles first and then the internal structural steel reinforcing and grout. The implementation of this solution however proved challenging in that the original construction contained significantly worse deviations than were originally contemplated. The engineering approach was adapted to each condition as encountered and the structure was successfully restored.

6 CONCLUSION

As originally stated, the evaluation of an existing masonry structure should not begin with the assumption that replacement is the only option but should include identifying the condition and viability of the damaged components, the impact of removal versus restoration, and the development and implementation of supplemental structural measures. This paper served to clearly outline and illustrate procedures which, when followed, enable the engineer to restore masonry structural systems when they become damaged or require increases in resistance capacities.

System-based Vision for Strategic and Creative Design, Bontempi (ed.)
© 2003 Swets & Zeitlinger, Lisse, ISBN 90 5809 599 1

Mechanical response of solid clay brick masonry reinforced with CFRP strips under eccentric loading

A. Brencich, C. Corradi & E. Sterpi
*DISEG Department of Structural and Geotechnical Engineering, Faculty of Engineering,
University of Genova, Genova, Italy*

G. Mantegazza
RUREDIL s.p.a., Milan, Italy

ABSTRACT: The problem of eccentric loading of CFRP-reinforced solid clay brick masonry is addressed in this paper. Experimental tests have been performed on both unreinforced (URM) and CFRP-reinforced masonry (CFRP-RM) being the loads applied with moderate-to-high eccentricities. The comparison between the mechanical response of URM and CFRP-RM shows a significant increase in the compressive strength of reinforced specimen some 40–50% on the average; in many cases the recorded inelastic strains where significantly higher in CFRP-reinforced prisms. The analysis of the cracking processes inside the masonry prisms gives way to some considerations on the internal collapse mechanisms of URM and CFRP-RM masonry.

1 INTRODUCTION

The stress distribution in masonry structures is non uniform due to its intrinsic non homogeneous structure. Nevertheless, in most technical applications, when the units and the mortar joints are periodically distributed, it is accepted to refer to the mean stress field, such as in the case of load bearing walls. This approach cannot be extended to other masonry structures, such as arch bridges, vaults and pillars because the stress gradient through the masonry thickness, due to the eccentricity of the load, make any periodicity to be lost.

A large number of tests have been performed on concentrically loaded masonry prisms (Hilsdorf 1969 and Drysdale & Hamid 1982 among the others) giving some information on the collapse mechanisms under uniform loading. The developed theoretical models assume masonry as an unlimited layered medium (Hilsdorf 1969, Francis et al. 1971) in which the collapse mechanism is that of a tensile-tensile-compressive stress limit due to the compatibility conditions at the brick/mortar interface. These models, along with more detailed ones relying on proper homogenizing techniques of the periodical units (Biolzi 1989, Pietrusczac & Niu 1992), are not applicable to eccentrically loaded masonry since the local stress and displacement fields are not uniform through the thickness and cannot be described by their mean value only.

Many assessment procedures for arch-type structures assume a No-Tensile-Resistance model with unbounded compressive strength (Heyman 1982, Gilbert & Melbourne 1994) or a perfectly elasto-plastic response without any limit to inelastic strains (Smith et al. 1990, Clemente et al. 1995); only in few cases an ultimate limit is set to the inelastic strains assuming elasto-plasto-softening constitutive models (Crisfield 1985, Boothby 2001). These approaches need, at least, the compressive strength of masonry to be given, but few experimental tests on eccentrically loaded masonry have been performed (Hatzinikolas et al. 1980, Drysdale & Hamid 1982, Maurenbrecher 1983, Taylor & Mallinder 1993); besides, some of the code approaches to the strength of eccentrically loaded masonry (FICHE-UIC 1994) seem to be of uncertain origins and not referring to well known mechanical models.

The large number of masonry bridges in service in the European transportation system, the need for their upgrading to higher loads and the degradation of the materials ask for a detailed knowledge of the mechanical response of masonry and for reliable strengthening techniques, putting forward the need of reliable models for eccentrically loaded masonry. In this paper a series of tests on masonry prisms representing an arch voussoir loaded by an eccentrical axial thrust are discussed. $6 \times 12 \times 24$ cm solid clay bricks, and 1 cm thick 1:1:5

cement:lime:sand mortar joints are used to represent a medium-to-high strength clay brick masonry.

Some of the prisms have been reinforced by CFRP strips and tested under the same loading conditions as un-reinforced prisms, showing an increase of both the collapse load (40–50% on the average) and the inelastic strains. This technique is somehow similar to near-surface reinforcement (Garrity 2001) and has been recently studied by experimental tests (Triantafillou 1998, Valluzzi et al. 2001).

Simple mechanical models are developed for both URM and CFRP-RM prisms taking into account the limited inelastic strains exhibited by solid clay brick masonry. The results of the tests show that the masonry compressive strength might be almost independent on the load eccentricity provided that the masonry ductility is taken into account. Even though more experimental research and more refined mechanical models are needed, this paper presents a first step towards the analysis of eccentrically loaded URM and CFRP-RM masonry.

2 SPECIMENS AND EXPERIMENTAL SETUP

The generic section of an arch may be represented by the central joint of four $5.5 \times 11 \times 24$ cm bricks and five 10 mm thick mortar joints (global height 270 mm), Figure 1, the load being applied by of 60 mm thick steel plates. Two series of ten prisms each, cured for 60 days in air at constant conditions, have been produced in different days differing in the cement/water ratio of mortar only (3.9 for series n. 1 and 6.6 for series n. 2).

Bricks and mortar have been tested in direct displacement-controlled compressive tests and in 3PB tests (EN196); the load has been measured with a 0.01% accuracy (50 kN C5 class *AEP-TCE* load cell), Table 1. The 1:1:5 cement-lime mortar, intended to represent a medium strength European mortar, showed a high compressive strength; also the tensile strength for mortar was higher than the expected value of 1/10 of the compressive strength. This is probably due to two factors: (1) the indirect flexural tensile strength measured by a 3 PBT is higher than the direct tensile strength, to which a mechanical model usually refers; (2) the mortar specimens are produced and cured in better conditions than the mortar joint (in the steel box water cannot be absorbed and the vibration of the specimen is much more careful than the disposal of the mortar joint onto the brick surface).

The CFRP reinforcing system, consisting of two parallel strips of Mitsubishi/Ruredil Replark© fabric, each one 4 cm wide, is glued to the prism by an epoxy resin once a thin layer (2–3 mm thick) of a fiber reinforced mortar had been used to make plane the masonry surface. The mechanical parameters of the CFRP strip are listed in Table 2 as provided by the producer.

The upper and lower joints of the prisms are in direct contact with the steel plates, where steel cylinders allow the load to be applied with desired eccentricity, the load being applied above the load cell (1000 kN C5 class *HBM-RTN* device, 0.01% accuracy), located just above the upper plate, the bottom one being connected to a stiff frame. The loading process is controlled through the vertical global displacement. The steel cylinders are free to rotate (ϕ_1 and ϕ_2); secondary out-of-plane rotations, due to bad workmanship, are controlled by the transversal cylinders and are not directly corrected by the experimental setup.

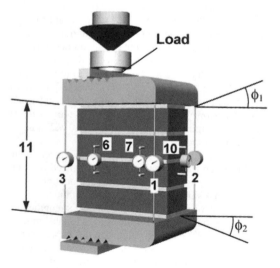

Figure 1. Masonry prism and experimental setup.

Table 1. Mechanical characteristics of bricks and mortar.

BRICKS	
Compressive strength	19.90 ± 4.37 MPa
Tensile strength	3.39 ± 0.26 MPa
1:1:5 MORTAR	**Series n. 1**
Compressive strength	11.39 ± 0.11 MPa
Tensile strength	3.30 ± 0.22 MPa
1:1:5 MORTAR	**Series n. 2**
Compressive strength	14.72 ± 0.76 MPa
Tensile strength	4.19 ± 0.62 MPa

Table 2. Mechanical characteristics of the CFRP fabric.

Thickness	0.167 mm
Weight	300 gr/m^2
Elastic modulus E	>230000 MPa
Tensile strength	>3400 MPa
Ultimate strain	>1.3%

The relative displacement and the absolute rotation between the specimen ends are measured in four different points directly on the plates (bases 1, 2, 3 and 4), whilst six sections are used to control the position of the central joint, two at the extremities (5 and 10) and two on each side of the specimen at 1/4th and 3/4th of the brick length (6 and 7 on one side, 8 and 9 on the other one). The absolute displacement of the upper plate has been measured on the 11th base, Figure 1. Other details are given in (Brencich et al. 2002).

3 TEST RESULTS

3.1 *URM prisms*

Figure 2 shows the load-displacement response of the URM prisms for the two series of specimen. The higher strength, referred to concentric loading, shows inelastic strains beyond the peak load; the non linear response and the inelastic strains are much more evident for eccentric loading. Due to the different water content of mortar, the two series performed differently: higher strength leads to lower inelastic strains, i.e. to higher brittleness. The main mechanical properties are summarized in Table 3, where ductility δ is assumed as the ratio of the ultimate strain ε_{ul} vs. the strain at the

end of the linear behaviour ε_{el}: $\delta = \varepsilon_{ul}/\varepsilon_{el}$. The elastic modulus of the masonry assemblage under concentric loading (1260–1620 MPa) fits reasonably well with some laboratory and other *in-situ* tests on Italian historical railway bridges (Rabaioli 1993).

Figure 3 represents the position of the central joint for an 8 cm eccentricity, the highest value allowed by URM. The lines refer to different steps of the load history: the "100%" line refers to the maximum load, while the "125%" and "150%" lines refer to a global strain which is 1.25 and 1.5 times the strain at the peak load. The position of the central joint shows that, for URM masonry, the standard Navier hypothesis of plane section, is verified.

The typical collapse mechanism of URM masonry is shown in Figure 4, where it is clear that cracking activates close to the external border, some 10 mm inside the brick. This result, typical of this kind of URM (Brencich et al. 2002), shows that the collapse mechanism of brickwork is ruled by local stress concentrations close to the brick boundary.

3.2 *CFRP Reinforced Masonry prisms*

Figure 5 shows the load-displacement response of CFRP-RM specimens. The CFRP-RM with a 4 cm eccentric load showed the same behavior as for the

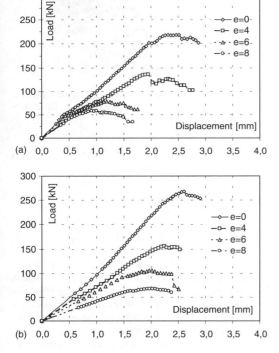

(a)

(b)

Figure 2. Load-displacement response of the URM prisms: a) series n. 1; b) series n. 2.

Table 3. Mechanical parameters of masonry.

	Series n. 1	Series n. 2
Compressive strength f_c [MPa]	9.9	13.5
Elastic modulus E [MPa]	1260	1620
Elastic strain ε_{el}	0.0074	0.0088
Ultimate strain ε_{ul}	0.105	0.107
Ductility $\delta = \varepsilon_{ul}/\varepsilon_{el}$	1.42	1.20

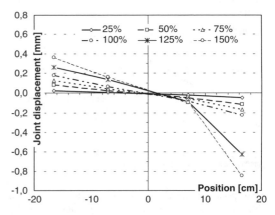

Figure 3. Position of the central joint as a function of the axial average strain (eccentricity = 8 cm).

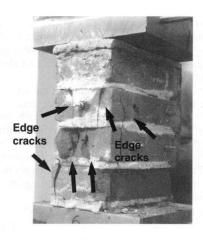

Figure 4. Edge cracks due to local concentration of tensile stresses close to the brick external sides in URM prisms. Concentric loading.

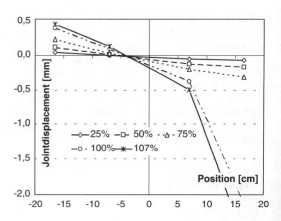

Figure 6. Position of the central joint as a function of the axial average strain (eccentricity = 8 cm).

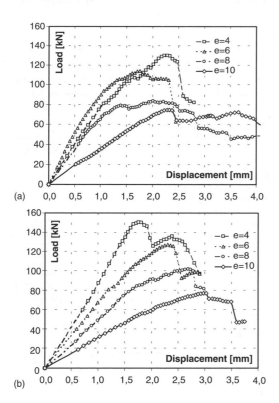

(a)

(b)

Figure 5. Load-displacement response of CFRP-RM prisms: (a) series n. 1; (b) series n. 2.

corresponding URM prisms being the section still entirely compressed. Reinforced specimens could be tested also at a 10 cm eccentricity, which has no comparison in URM prisms being this eccentricity too

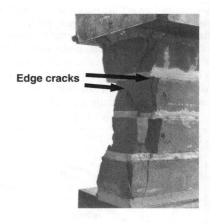

Figure 7. Edge cracks due to local concentration of tensile stresses close to the brick external sides in CFRP-RM prisms. Eccentricity 10 cm.

high. At collapse, also a CFRP-RM prism shows cracks parallel to the external surface of the brick, Figure 7. In all the tests there was no sign of delamination of the CFRP reinforcement.

4 A SIMPLE MECHANICAL MODEL

The comparison between the load-displacement response of URM and CFRP-RM prisms is shown in Figure 8 for prisms of the first series. Some effects of reinforcements need to be underlined: (1) the specimen strength is increased some 40%; (2) the specimen ductility is not reduced by increase in strength; in some cases it is significantly enhanced; (3) the stiffness of the specimen remains the same. Similar results have been obtained for the second series of specimens.

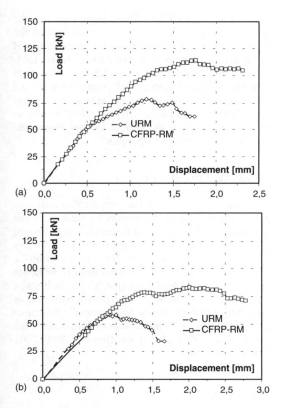

(a)

(b)

Figure 8. CFRP-RM vs. URM: load-displacement response of the specimens with load eccentricity of: (a) 6 cm; (b) 8 cm. Series n. 1.

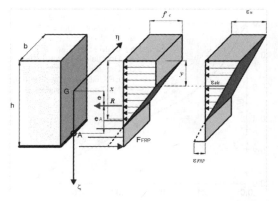

Figure 9. Elasto-plastic, No-Tensile-Resistant model with ductility control model for the section response.

Let us assume the plane section hypothesis, which has been found to be verified during the tests, and an elasto-perfectly plastic constitutive model for masonry in which the maximum allowable strain is limited to the ultimate strain found in the concentric loading test, Figure 9. The equilibrium equations at collapse are given:

$$N_{EP} = f'_c by + f'_c b \frac{x-y}{2} + \sigma_{CFRP} A_{CFRP};$$ (1)

$$M_{EP} = N_{EP} e = f'_c by \left(h - \frac{y}{2} \right)$$

$$+ f'_c b \frac{x-y}{2} \left[(h-y) - \frac{1}{3}(x-y) \right].$$ (2)

where f'_c is the compressive strength measured in the concentric loading test, σ_{CFRP} and A_{CFRP} the tensile stress and the net area of the reinforcement; other symbols are given in Figure 9. For the moment, masonry compressive strength is assumed as independent on the load eccentricity. Given the ultimate strain ε_{ul}, the

plastic part of the section can be calculated $y = x(\delta - 1)/\delta$. Being known the CFRP effective elastic modulus E_{CFRP}, the tensile stress may be expressed as $\sigma_{CFRP} = E_{CFRP} \varepsilon_{CFRP} = E_{CFRP} \varepsilon_{ul} (h - x)/x$. Equations 1 and 2 may be thus written in a non-dimensional form:

$$n = \frac{N_{EP}}{N_0} = \frac{N_{EP}}{f'_c bh} = \frac{x}{h} \frac{2\delta - 1}{2\delta} - \rho_{CFRP} \, \eta \, \delta \frac{1 - x/h}{x/h};$$ (3)

$$n \frac{e}{h} = \frac{N_{EP}}{N_0} \frac{e}{h} = \frac{N_{EP}}{f'_c bh} \frac{e}{h}$$

$$= \frac{1}{2} \frac{x}{h} \left[2 - \frac{1}{\delta} + \frac{1}{3} \frac{x}{h} \left(3 - \delta - \frac{2}{\delta} + \frac{1}{\delta^2} \right) \right],$$ (4)

where $\rho_{CFRP} = A_{CFRP}/bh$ stands for the mechanical percentage of CFRP reinforcement and $\eta = E_{CFRP}/E_{MAS}$ for the ratio between the effective elastic modulus of the CFRP and of masonry.

Equations 3 and 4 allow the limit domain of the masonry section to be represented in a normalized $N/N_0 - e/h$ plane ($N_0 =$ compressive strength under concentric loading; $h =$ section height). Figures 10 and 11 compare of the limit curves predicted by Equations 3 and 4 and the experimental data. It can be seen that the relatively simple mechanical models of Figure 9 fit rather well the experimental points, particularly for CFRP-RM specimens.

5 CONCLUSIONS

Some procedures for the assessment of masonry bridges and arches (Smith et al. 1990 among the others), assume that collapse takes place when hinges are formed in masonry in a number large enough to transform the structure into a mechanism. This approach

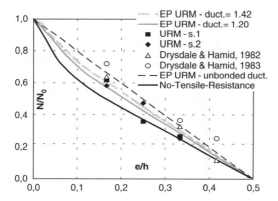

Figure 10. Limit domain for URM and experimental data.

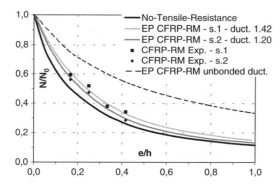

Figure 11. Limit domain for CFRP-RM and experimental data.

assumes implicitly that masonry may exhibit a substantially unbounded ductility in compression. Also some approach setting a limit to the ultimate compressive strain (Crisfield 1985) assumes rather high values for the masonry ductility. The experimental tests on URM and CFRP-RM specimens showed that masonry exhibits rather limited ductility, even though non vanishing, raising major objections to the classical limit analysis approach.

A common approach to eccentric loading of masonry assumes a NTR material perfectly brittle ($\delta = 1$); the interpretation of experimental data requires the compressive strength of masonry to be assumed an increasing function of the load eccentricity (Drysdale & Hamid 1979, Hatzinikolas et al. 1980). The present results and the proposed mechanical approach does not need to vary the compressive strength and puts forward the need for further experimental and theoretical investigation.

FRP overlay strips are a retrofitting technique able of raising the load carrying capacity of a bridge. The

tests showed that CFRP reinforcement may rise the compressive strength of masonry up to 40% of the unreinforced value. This happens for eccentricities of the axial thrust that are typical of the most severe loading conditions on the bridges, which shows the great efficiency of this technique. Further research is needed to enlighten the collapse mechanisms of both URM and CFRP-RM and on the effect of CFRP reinforcement on brickwork with different mortars, bricks and mortar joints of different thickness.

ACKNOWLEDGMENTS

This research was carried out with the financial support of the (MURST) Department for University and Scientific and Technological Research in the frame of the PRIN 2002/2003 "*Safety and Control of Masonry Bridges*" project, and of the National Earth-quake Defense Group (GNDT) of the National Institute for Geophysics and Vulcanology (INGV) inside the *VIA* research project "*Seismic vulnerability reduction of infrastructural systems and environment*" (*Riduzione della vulnerabilità sismica di sistemi infrastrutturali e ambiente fisico*), a part of the Biennial 2000–2002 Research Program.

REFERENCES

Biolzi, L. 1988. Evaluation of Compressive Strength of Masonry Walls by Limit Analysis, *Journal of Structural Engineering ASCE*, 114, 2179–2189.

Brencich, A., Corradi, C., Gambarotta, L., Mantegazza, G. & Sterpi, E. 2002. Compressive Strength of Solid Clay Brick Masonry under Eccentric Loading, *Proc. of the 6th Iny. Mas. Conf.*, London, England.

Boothby, T.E. 2001. Load Rate of Masonry Arch Bridges, *Journal of Bridge Engineering ASCE*, 6, 79–86.

Clemente, P., Occhiuzzi, A. & Raithel, A. 1995. Limit Behaviour of Stone Arch Bridges, *Journal of Structural Engineering ASCE*, 121, 1045–1050.

Crisfield, M.A. 1985. Finite Element and Mechanism Methods for the Analysis of Masonry and Brickwork Arches, *Transport and Road Research Laboratory, Department of Transport*, Research Report 19, TRL, Crowthorne.

Drysdale, R.G. & Hamid, A.A. 1979. Capacity of Concrete Block Masonry Prisms under Eccentric Compressive Loading, *ACI Journal*, 80, June 1979.

FICHE-UIC 778-3E 1994. Recommandations pour l'evaluation de la capacite portante des ponts-voutes existants en maçonnerie et beton.

Foraboschi, P. 2001. Fiber-Reinforced-Polymer Composites (FRP) for Strengthening Masonry Arch Bridges, *Proc. of Arch '01, 3rd Int. Arch Bridges Conf.*, Paris, 2001, Ecole Nat. des Ponts et Chaussées, 283–288.

Francis, A.J., Horman, C.B. & Jerkems, L.E. 1971. The Effect of Joint Thickness and other Factors on the Compressive Strength of Brickwork, *Proc. of the 2nd I.B.Ma.C.*, Stoke on Kent, England, 1971, British Ceramic Res. Ass., 31–37.

Garrity, S.W. 2001. The Strengthening of Single Span Masonry Arch Bridges Using Near-Surface Reinforcement, *Proc. of Arch, '01, 3rd Int. Arch Bridges Conf.*, Paris, Ecole Nat. des Ponts et Chaussées, 301–307.

Gilbert, M. & Melbourne, C. 1994. Rigid-Block Analysis of Masonry Structures, *The Structural Engineer*, 72, 356–361.

Hatzinikolas, M., Longworth, J. & Warwaruk, J. 1980. Failure Modes for Eccentrically Loaded Concrete Block Masonry Walls, *ACI Journal*, 77, 258–263.

Hilsdorf, H.K. 1969. Investigation into the Failure Mechanism of Brick Masonry under Axial Compression, in *Designing, Engineering and Construction with Masonry Products*, Gulf Publ., Houston, Texas, 34–41.

Maurenbrecher, A.H.P. 1983. Compressive Strength of Eccentrically Loaded Masonry Prisms, *Pro. of the 3rd Can. Mas. Symp.*, Edmonton, Canada, 1983, 10.1–10.13.

Pietrusczac, S. & Niu, X. 1992. A Mathematical Description of Macroscopic Behavior of Brick Masonry, *International Journal of Solids and Structures*, 29, 531–546.

Rabaioli, R. 1993. Control Methods for Masonry Arch Bridges: an Example (in italian), *Ingegneria Ferroviaria*, August 1993, 531–537.

Smith, F.W., Harvey, W.J. & Vardy, A.E. 1990. Three Hinge Analysis of Masonry Arches, *The Structural Engineer*, 68, 203–213.

Triantafillou, T.C. 1998. Strengthening of masonry structures using epoxy-bonded FRP laminates, *Journal of Composites for Construction*, 2, 96–104.

Valluzzi, M.R., Valdemarca, M. & Modena, C. 2001. Behaviour of brick masonry vaults strengthened by FRP laminates, *Journal of Composites for Construction*, 5, 163–169.

System-based Vision for Strategic and Creative Design, Bontempi (ed.)
© 2003 Swets & Zeitlinger, Lisse, ISBN 90 5809 599 1

On the numerical analysis of localized damage in masonry structures

J. Alfaiate & A. Gago
Instituto Superior Técnico, Lisboa, Portugal

J.R. de Almeida
Faculdade de Ciências e Tecnologia, Universidade Nova de Lisboa, Monte da Caparica, Portugal

ABSTRACT: In this paper, two masonry structures are analyzed: a wall and an arch bridge. The description of the fracture behaviour of the joints between bricks is taken into account by means of a discrete approach. In the former example, different limit surfaces are adopted. In these surfaces, the shear strength of the joints under compressive stresses is made to vary in order to study its influence on the structural behaviour. In the second example, the description of the soil behaviour is investigated with two different models: i) a simplified model, in which the soil is modelled as a boundary condition, and ii) a more sophisticated model, in which the soil is discretized in the mesh and a non-linear behaviour for both the soil and the interface between the soil and the arch is adopted. In the latter case, non linear geometric effects are also taken into account. The numerical results obtained from both groups of tests are compared with the corresponding experimental results.

1 INTRODUCTION

In this paper, non-linear bidimensional finite element models are used to simulate fracture in masonry structures. Masonry consists of bricks, considered as linear elastic, and joints which are modelled as interfaces with initial zero thickness. A discrete approach is used to simulate both the localized behaviour of the joints, as well as cracking across the bricks.

Two groups of tests are numerically studied and compared to the experiments. In the first group, a masonry wall with an opening is first compressed and afterwards submitted to a horizontal load at the top. Due to this fact, different crack mechanisms develop, both under tension, in mode I, and under shear in mixed mode and mode II. Furthermore, some cracks also develop across the bricks under mode I fracture. Different yield criteria are tested in order to evaluate the shear resistance of the joints. For this purpose, different localized limit surfaces in the traction space are proposed, which deviate more or less from the Coulomb friction law, giving rise to a decrease of shear strength under strong compression. The failure mechanisms and the peak loads obtained clearly depend on the surfaces adopted, allowing to draw interesting conclusions related to the influence of the shear strength on the overall response of the structure.

The second structure analyzed is a single span arch bridge, which was submitted to full scale load tests to

collapse. In this case, it is found that the soil plays a very important role on the global behaviour of the structure. Two finite element models are used: i) a simplified one where the soil behaviour is simulated with non linear springs acting in the horizontal direction and ii) a more refined model where the soil is discretized in the finite element mesh and modelled using a plasticity model. In these tests the joints open according to mode I fracture. The numerical results are compared to the data obtained in situ and the mechanical behaviour of the masonry arch bridges is examined. Finally, the numerical implementation is discussed and a new method is proposed based on a total formulation. The numerical results obtained with this method are compared to the results obtained with the incremental Newton-Raphson algorithm. It is found that the total formulation presents important advantages over the incremental one. In particular, with non-proportional loading, in which case some cracks tend to close and new crack mechanisms develop, it is always very difficult to obtain convergence with the incremental procedure.

2 MASONRY WALL

In this section a masonry wall with an opening is analyzed. These walls were tested in Vermerltfoort and Raijmakers (1993), and the experiments were performed under monotonous load gradually increasing until failure. First, the constitutive model adopted is described. Next, the numerical results are presented and compared to the experimental ones.

2.1 Material model

Bricks are assumed to behave linear elastically until the tensile strength is reached; subsequently, a fictitious crack initiates in mode I fracture and a softening behaviour is adopted. Crushing under strong compression is simulated by a plasticity model with a Von Mises failure criterion.

A non-associative plasticity model is adopted to model the behavior of the mortar joints. These joints are approximated by interfaces with initial zero thickness. Denoting the normal and shear traction components at the interface respectively by t_n and t_s, a limit surface is defined in the traction space (t_n, t_s) such that both tensile mode I cracking and a modified Coulomb friction envelope are taken into account. Different limit surfaces are considered, as shown in fig. 1; the corresponding analytical expression can be found in Alfaiate & de Almeida (2000).

The limit surface f_1 is a tensile cap corresponding to mode I crack evolution. Surface f_2 represents the Mohr-Coulomb friction law. These two surfaces have been used in Lourenço and Rots (1997). Surfaces f_3 and f_4 are continuous with continuous derivatives in the traction space. Both these surfaces correspond to modified Coulomb friction laws in which the shear tractions remain bounded. In surface f_4, a more severe limitation for the shear strength under strong compression is adopted.

Both the tensile strength f_t and the cohesion c are assumed as functions of an internal scalar variable κ according to the following exponential softening flow rules:

$$f_t = f_{t0} \exp\left(-\frac{f_{t0}}{G_F}\kappa\right), \quad c = c_0 \exp\left(-\frac{c_0}{G_F^{II}}\kappa_s\right) \quad (1)$$

where f_{t0} is the initial tensile strength and c_0 is the initial cohesion value. In general, equations (1) can be regarded as independent (Alfaiate & Pires 1999); here, an isotropic softening criterion is adopted, leading to:

$$c = \frac{c_0}{f_{t0}} f_t. \quad (2)$$

2.2 Numerical results

The walls analyzed had a thickness of 100 mm, were approximately square ($990 \times 1000\,\text{mm}^2$) and were composed of clay bricks and cement mortar joints. The base and top were fixed against steel beams. In addition to the dead weight, the walls were first loaded by a vertical uniformly distributed pressure of 0.30 MPa applied to the top, after which a horizontal load F was progressively applied at a top corner while keeping the bottom and top boundaries fixed along the vertical direction. Load–displacement diagrams and crack patterns were registered. The material parameters adopted in the computational simulations were taken from Lourenço and Rots (1997); in surface f_4, a maximum value of the shear traction equal to 2.6 MPa is adopted.

In fig. 3, load-displacement curves obtained at the point where the horizontal load F was applied are shown. These curves are compared to the ultimate loads determined from two experiments where different failure modes occurred. Each curve corresponds to a

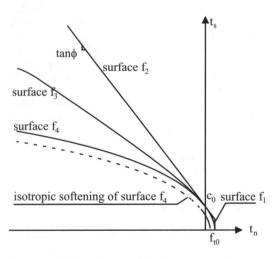

Figure 1.   Yield surfaces used for the mortar interfaces.

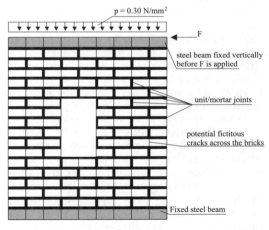

Figure 2.   Masonry wall with an opening: boundary conditions.

different formulation. In curve i), an elastic perfectly plastic behavior is adopted for the bricks and cracking at the joints is not allowed. In curve a), cracking at the mortar joints is allowed and the behavior of units is taken as linear elastic. In curve ii), cracking is allowed, both along the mortar interfaces (using the multi-surface model for joints) and across the units (assuming mode I fracture); once more, compressive plastic behavior is adopted for the bricks. Using this approach, the load–displacement curve reached a plateau, although the corresponding maximum load was much higher than the experimental values. With respect to the

evolution and extent of cracking, it is found that cracks propagate in a stepwise manner, being predominantly oriented along the diagonal that passes through the point of application of the lateral load (see fig. 4). The wall collapses only when the clay units fail under compression. Curve iii) is obtained using the same approach as in curve ii) with limit surface f_3. Cracking is only allowed along the mortar interfaces since it is found that, in this test, cracking across the bricks does not introduce significant changes in the structural response. The differences between the results in curves ii) and iii) are due to the decrease in the shear strength under high compressive stresses. Hence, we conclude that the shear strength of the joints has a major influence on the value of the maximum load. Curve iv) is obtained with limit surface f_4. Again, the influence of the shear strength on the results is quite noticeable since the peak load is considerably smaller than the one determined using surface f_3. Furthermore, it is interesting to observe that the resultant failure mechanism is different from the one associated to curve ii). In fig. 5, the deformed mesh near the collapse obtained with surface f_4 is presented. In this case the plastic hinges were not reached; instead, the wall collapses due to slippage along some mortar joints. As reported in Lourenço (1996), experimentally, one of the walls also collapsed due to shear, at approximately the same load as the peak value of curve iv), i.e., about 35 kN.

Finally, it is interesting to verify that, as expected, the collapse mechanism found in test iii) (see fig. 4) corresponds to a transition between the mechanisms found in tests ii) and iv). In this case, plastic hinges can still form, although an increase in deformation induced by shear is also obtained.

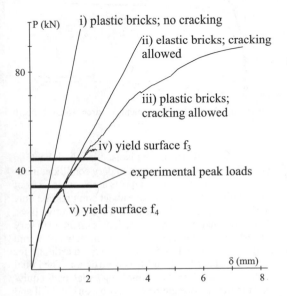

Figure 3. Load–displacement curves.

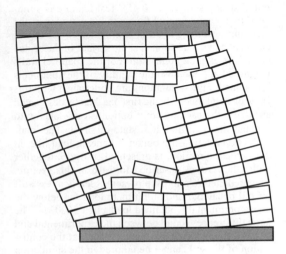

Figure 4. Deformed mesh obtained with envelope surface f_3 near the collapse.

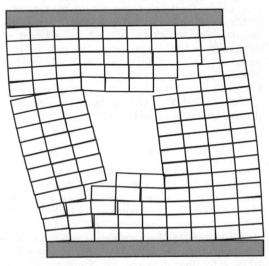

Figure 5. Deformed mesh obtained with envelope surface f_4 near the collapse.

3 ARCH BRIDGE

In this section, the case studied is Bargower bridge, a semi-circular arch bridge with cut-to shape stone voussoirs. This bridge was submitted to full-scale load tests by the Transport and Road Research Laboratory (Hendry et al. 1986).

The essential features of an arch behaviour are: i) the fracture at the joints between stone voussoirs and ii) the backing contribution of the arch springings, which is found to play a major role in the overall structural response of arch bridges. The former feature is simulated in the finite element models using a discrete approach with non tensile strength interface elements. For the contribution of the backing two levels of discretization are adopted. First, as a simplified procedure, non-linear springs acting horizontally are used. Next, a more refined finite element model is adopted, where the fill soil and the interface arch-soil are discretised in the mesh. The non-linear behaviour of both soil and interface is modelled using plasticity Mohr-Coulomb yield criteria.

A more complete description of the experimental test performed on Bargower bridge can be found in Hendry et al. (1986). The dimensions are: span 10.0 m, skew span 10.36 m, rise at midspan 5.18 m, arch thickness 0.558 m, total width 8.68 m and depth crown 1.20 m. In the finite element models the adopted span is 10.36 m. Experimental data on sandstone specimens allowed to determine a compressive strength of 33.3 MPa and a Young modulus of 14.1 GPa. The evaluated stone self-weight is 26.8 kN/m³ and the fill self weight adopted in the present work is 20.0 kN/m³. The test procedure consisted of the incremental application of load, by means of hydraulic jacks, to a concrete strip cast in the road surface across the full width of the bridge and located at a third span, where the minimum failure load was expected. Ground anchors, set through the bridge deck, supplied the jack reactions against steel beams. During the test, the first visible sign of damage (material falling out of the longitudinal crack) occurred at 3400 kN. The maximum load applied was 5600 kN. Failure occurred by crushing of the arch beneath the load line.

3.1 Numerical simulations

Fracture is allowed only at the masonry joints by means of a tension free model prescribed at the interfaces. Penalty functions are introduced under compression in order to prevent overlapping at crack closure. The units or blocks are represented by continuum plane stress isoparametric 4-node elements and the joints by 4-node interface elements. The material parameters adopted for the interfaces are: joint normal and tangential stiffness equal to 1012 kN/m³ and tensile strength of joint equal to 0 MPa.

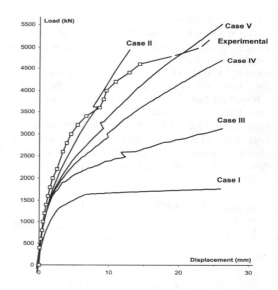

Figure 6. Vertical displacement of arch soffit beneath load line.

First, a simplified model is used in which backing contribution is assumed as a boundary condition, introducing horizontal spring supports at the outer faces of the arch. These springs behave under compression only with either linear or bilinear elastic constitutive laws. The horizontal subgrade coefficient is assumed to vary linearly along the depth of the arch, between 0 and 3 MNm^{-2}/m, which is considered a good estimate for the material used in the bridge construction. The initial state of stress is introduced applying nodal loads equivalent to the self-weight of stone voussoirs and fill and to the lateral earth pressure, which is considered due to initial steady-state ($k_0 = 0.45$). Test loading is simulated by means of nodal forces at the extrados of the arch ring, according to the approximated elastic degradation of a line load applied at the surface of the bridge deck. The explicit contribution of the spandrel walls is ignored and the absolute rigidity of the abutments is assumed. Five simulations are undertaken with this finite element model. In the first one, hereby designated as Case I, the backing contribution is only taken into account through the initial state of stress. The load-deflection relationship obtained beneath load line, in the vertical direction, is presented in fig. 6, together with other curves described forward in this section. The predicted relationship presents clearly a less stiff overall behaviour and an ultimate load far below the one experimentally obtained load, circa 5600 kN. The large differences found between the experimental and numerical results clearly demonstrate that the contribution of the soil cannot be ignored in the simulation of the arch behaviour. In the second simulation, designated Case II, the interaction between the backing and

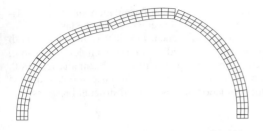

Figure 7. Case III deformed mesh.

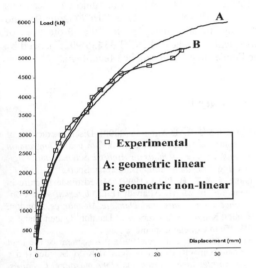

Figure 8. Vertical displacement of arch soffit beneath load line using the refined model.

the arch ring is modelled by horizontal linear-elastic springs. This result confirms the long known dependency of semicircular arches from the sustaining effect of backing passive thrusts at springings (Crisfield & Page 1990). However, the global structural stiffness does not decrease significantly at the later stage of the deformation curve, giving rise to a much higher load than the maximum load obtained in the experimental test. In the remaining three cases studied, bilinear elastic law responses are adopted at the spring supports. The constitutive relations adopted for the springs share the same inflection point at a predetermined contraction displacement limit and their common initial elastic stiffness is subsequently reduced to one-tenth (Case III), one-third (Case IV) and finally one-half (Case V). In all the analysis performed, the maximum compressive reaction in the springs is found to be always below the passive lateral pressure of the haunching material. The best agreement with the experimental curve is achieved in the last situation. It is observed that the non-linear soil behaviour has an important

contribution to approximate the actual behaviour of the arch bridge. The experimental results could be better approximated by adjusting the parameters involved, both the inflection point in the bilinear constitutive relation of the springs and the reduction of the elastic stiffness afterwards. Instead, similar to the work presented in Gago et al. (2002), a more sophisticated model was used to obtain a better agreement between numerical and experimental results. In this model, a Mohr Coulomb plasticity model was adopted for the fill soil which was discretized in the mesh and the interface between the soil and the arch was modelled by interface elements; for these interfaces, an associated plasticity friction model with a Mohr Coulomb yield criterion and a near zero cohesion value was adopted. Moreover, non-linear geometric effects were also investigated. Two load displacement curves obtained with this second model are presented in fig. 8: in curve A geometric linearity was assumed, whereas in curve B non-linear geometric effects were taken into account.

3.2 Incremental versus total formulation

The use of non-linear stress-strain relationships requires an incremental iterative solution procedure, i.e., the loads are applied step by step and equilibrium iterations are carried out at each increment until equilibrium is reached within acceptable limits. The arc-length method was used in the tests presented, in which a monotonic increase of the main crack mouth opening displacement (CMOD) was enforced. However, numerical convergence was always difficult to achieve. This is due the fact that the loading is non-proportional: first the self weight is introduced, which gives rise to some initial cracking and next the external load is applied, leading to a change in crack systems: the former cracks closed whereas new cracks opened. This is very often the case with masonry structures and also happened in all the tests presented. Different numerical schemes were used to overcome this difficulty, namely by changing the constraint equation in the arc length method and/or adjusting the step size (Alfaiate & de Almeida 2000).

Here, a different numerical technique is introduced, which is inspired on a lattice formulation (van Mier 1997; Lilliu & van Mier 2000): whenever the strength of an element of the lattice is attained, this element is removed giving rise to a more compliant structure; then the material is reloaded and a new critical point is reached *elastically*. In Rots (2001), a similar idea was applied to a continuum: a decrease of the global structural stiffness is enforced whenever a limit surface is reached at the most critical point. In section 3, a sequentially linear localized model is introduced, in which changes in the stiffness are allowed only at the mortar joints. In this numerical model, the evaluation of the structural response is not obtained incrementally; instead, the stiffness of the structure is reduced according to a material law, and equilibrium points on the structural response are obtained by sequentially linear analyses. As a consequence, no convergence algorithm is necessary.

For each step, the following algorithm is performed:

1. increment the loading parameter λ;
2. solve the global system of equations: $\mathbf{Ka} = \mathbf{f}_{ext}$, where $\mathbf{a}$ are the total nodal displacements and $\mathbf{K}$ is the total (secant) stiffness matrix;
3. at each integration point check if the limit surface f is attained:
   (a) if $f < 0$, evaluate λ such that $(\max f = 0)$;
   (b) if $f > 0$,
       i. evaluate λ such that $(\max f = 0)$;
       ii. update internal variables;
       iii. reduce the secant stiffness matrix: $\mathbf{T}_{sec}$;
4. obtain the tractions at the discontinuities, the stresses in the bulk and the internal forces;
5. for each discontinuity confirm if, due to the final loading parameter λ evaluated, $f = 0$; in this case adopt the updated internal variables and corresponding stiffness matrix, otherwise adopt the previous stiffness matrix;
6. form the global stiffness matrix;
7. go to 1.

Although the algorithm presented can be applied in general, the procedure adopted to reduce the stiffness of the material in (iii.) still remains to be defined. However, in the examples of section 3, the condition $f = 0$ in the joints corresponds to a free normal opening, i.e., the corresponding secant stiffness matrix $\mathbf{T}_{sec}$ becomes a null matrix. Note that, in the examples presented in fig. 6, both the incremental approach and the sequentially linear approach gave rise to the same load displacement curves. However, the results obtained with the incremental approach were far more difficult to achieve, leading to several runs of the code.

4 CONCLUSIONS

In this paper, two masonry structures were analyzed: a wall and an arch bridge. In the former case, it was concluded that the shear resistance of the mortar joints had a big influence both in the peak load and in the failure mechanism. In particular, it was observed that plastic hinges under compression formed if the shear strength was sufficiently high, whereas a decrease in the shear strength led to a different failure mechanism due to sliding of the joints. Both types of mechanism were observed experimentally.

In the second group of tests, the structural response on an arch bridge was analyzed. It was observed that the surrounding soil played a crucial role in the resistance and deformation of the bridge. Proposal of a new total numerical formulation was made as an alternative

to the usual incremental formulation, due to the difficulty in obtaining convergence with the latter.

As a general conclusion, it was found that both structures exhibited a rather complex behaviour, demanding for sophisticated non-linear analyses, both physically and numerically, in order to obtain a good approximation of the observed structural response.

ACKNOWLEDGEMENTS

The work was developed within the research projects "Protecção do Património Construido da Acção dos Sismos", PRAXIS I & D 3/3.1/CEG2606/95 and "Computational Strategies for the Protection of Historical Churches", POCTI 33435/99, financed by the Fundação para a Ciência e Tecnologia.

REFERENCES

Alfaiate, J. & J. R. de Almeida (2000). Discrete cracking of masonry walls. In E. Oñate (Ed.), *European Congress on Computational Methods in Applied Science and Engineering – Eccomas 2000*, Barcelona, Spain.

Alfaiate, J. & E. B. Pires (1999). Mixed mode fracture in concrete. In M. H. Aliabadi (Ed.), *International Conference on Fracture and Damage Mechanics*, London, United Kingdom. University of London, Queen Mary & Westfield College London.

Crisfield, M. A. & J. Page (1990). Assessment of the load carrying capacity of arch bridges. In A. M. Sowden (Ed.), *The maintenance of brick and stone masonry structures*, pp. 81–113. E. & F.N. Spon.

Gago, A. S., J. Alfaiate, & A. Gallardo (2002). Numerical analyses of the bargower arch bridge. In J. Rots (Ed.), *3rd DIANA World Conference on Finite Elements in Civil Engineering Applications*, Tokyo, Japan.

Hendry, A. W., S. R. Davies, R. Royles, D. A. Ponniah, M. C. Forde, & F. Komeyli-Birjandi (1986). Test on masonry arch bridge at bargower. Technical report, Crowthorne, Berks.

Lilliu, G. & J. G. M. van Mier (2000). Simulation of 3D crack propagation with the lattice model. In http://www.materials week.org/proceedings (Ed.), *Materials Week 2000*.

Lourenço, P. & J. G. Rots (1997). A multi-surface interface model for the analysis of masonry structures. *ASCE Journal of Engineering Mechanics 123*(7), 660–668.

Lourenço, P. B. (1996). *Computational strategies for masonry structures*. Ph. D. thesis, Delft University of Technology.

Rots, J. G. (2001). Sequentially linear continuum model for concrete fracture. In R. de Borst, J. Mazars, G. Pijaudier-Cabot, & J. G. M. van Mier (Eds.), *Fracture Mechanics of Concrete Structures – FRAMCOS4*, Paris, France, pp. 831–840.

van Mier, J. G. M. (1997). *Fracture Processes of Concrete*. CRC Press, Inc.

Vermerltfoort, A. T. & T. Raijmakers (1993). Deformation controlled meso shear tests on masonry piers, part 2. Technical report, TU Eindhoven, Eindhoven, The Netherlands.

System-based Vision for Strategic and Creative Design, Bontempi (ed.)
© *2003 Swets & Zeitlinger, Lisse, ISBN 90 5809 599 1*

Load carrying capacity of masonry arch bridges

A. Brencich, A. Cavicchi, U. De Francesco, L. Gambarotta & A. Sereno
DISEG Department of Structural and Geotechnical Engineering, Faculty of Engineering,
University of Genova, Genova, Italy

ABSTRACT: This paper presents some aspects of the approach to the assessment of masonry arch bridges developed by the Italian National Railway Authority (RFI) and the University of Genova. Being the non linear response of masonry a crucial issue in the evaluation of the load carrying capacity of a bridge, a No Tensile Resistance approach, with limited inelastic compressive strains (controlled ductility), has been formulated to allow an incremental non linear analysis of the bridge up to collapse in the frame of a simplified 2-D geometry. 3-D FEM models give a general overview of the structural response, provide detailed information on the stress state but need simplified non linear constitutive models for masonry and are not able of giving a synthetic description of the bridge response. For this reason, 3-D analyses assuming either elastic material models, meaningful if the tensile stresses are limited, and non linear perfectly brittle ones are used in the procedure as a comparison with 2-D estimates of the limit load.

1 INTRODUCTION

The European transportation system still relies on a large number of masonry bridges; the railway systems alone account for more than 100000 of them. Masonry bridges, though among the first engineered structures, had been designed according to some rule of practice and simplified design criteria; for this reason reliable estimates of their load carrying capacity nowadays are needed to face the increase of the travelling loads.

A widely used approach to the assessment of masonry bridges relies on the analysis of a single arch assuming simplified mechanical and kinematic assumptions. The kinematic approach takes into account a collapse mechanism activated by an adequate number of plastic hinges (Heyman 1982); more complicate collapse mechanism have been considered for twin-span models (Hughes 1995). Such an approach is somehow objectable because it does not take into account the non-linear response of masonry and the complex load settings, for which non linear F.E. analyses are needed (Criesfield 1985, Criesfield & Packham 1988, Molins & Roca 1998). The single-arch approach to multi-span bridges is even more questionable since the geometry of the bridge, the actual position of the loads and the global compliance of the arch system greatly affect its structural response (Harvey & Smith 1991). Besides, the kinematic approach implicitly assumes for masonry unbounded inelastic strains or, at least, a ductility never less than 3, whilst

experimental results (Brencich et al. 2002) show that this assumption may be not fulfilled by ordinary masonry, so raising the need for more accurate structural analyses.

A multi-level approach to the evaluation of the load carrying capacity of a masonry arch bridges is discussed in this work. Assuming for masonry an elasto-plastic model with controlled ductility in compression and No Tensile Resistance (NTR) in traction, a two-dimensional model (Brencich et al. 2001) is formulated in order to evaluate the load carrying capacity of the arch barrel, a lower bound to the capacity of the entire bridge. This simplified model allows the estimation of many important structural effects: masonry ductility, adjacent span interaction and pier flexibility, among the others. Detailed two-dimensional non linear FE analyses allow some estimate of the arch/fill interaction effect and its contribution to the global load carrying capacity. Three-dimensional linear and non linear FE models are used to assess the bridge in service conditions and close to the collapse load. The load carrying capacity of the bridge can thus be estimated by comparison of the values foreseen by the different models.

The seismic response of masonry bridges is a still open issue of great importance with respect to the vulnerability of transportation systems in seismic prone areas. The non linear response of masonry bridges makes this problem a challenging issue that is still under development.

The procedure is applied to a multi-span case study pointing out: (a) the difference between the estimates given by classical procedures and by the presented approach; (b) the effect of structural compliance, load distribution and bridge geometry on the collapse mechanism.

2 THE ASSESSMENT PROCEDURE

Classical approaches to the load carrying capacity of a masonry arch bridge are mainly based on basic two assumptions: (1) the bridge response can be deduced from the analysis of a single arch, corrected by some reducing factors; (2) the load carrying capacity of an arch, i.e. the collapse load, can be estimated on the basis of a limit analysis approach. The first hypothesis is somehow questionable since it does not take into account the interaction between spans and of the spans with the piers. The second assumption asks for unlimited inelastic strains in compression, which is clearly not admissible for masonry. Besides, in arch-type structures, masonry experiences strong stress gradients, so that all the approaches to the compressive strength of masonry, relying on a periodic distribution of stresses, are not applicable. From this point of view, the response of eccentrically compressed masonry is still an open issue only partially dealt with in codes (Fiche-UIC 1994) and that should not be considered of secondary importance.

The developed procedure is divided in several steps.

- On the basis of a No Tensile Resistant model for masonry, with limited inelastic compressive strains, a 2-D approach allows the estimation of the load carrying capacity of the arch barrel. The synthetic description of the inelastic behavior of the arch at collapse allows a comprehensive analysis of the bridge and of the influence of the different mechanical parameters on the global response of the structure. The limits to the inelastic strains are assumed on the bases of several experimental tests (Brencich et al. 2002).
- Assuming for the fill a Coulomb cohesive law, 2-D analyses allow an estimate of the arch-fill interaction and of its contribution to the load carrying capacity of the bridge.
- 3-D elastic FEM models allow the analysis of the bridge under the service loads. Such an approach is of some importance if the foreseen tensile stresses are limited and extended in small areas.
- 3-D No Tensile Resistant perfectly brittle models allow an estimate of the collapse load and show the effect of the spandrel walls on the mechanical behavior of the whole bridge.

In the following this procedure will be briefly outlined and applied to a real 6 span viaduct making use

of a commercial FEM code, and its library constitutive models, for 3-D analyses.

3 THE BI-DIMENSIONAL MODEL

A non linear constitutive model for the masonry section may be formulated on the basis of the plane section hypothesis (Navier), which seems to be experimentally verified (Brencich et al. 2002). Assuming a vanishing tensile strength, the non linear compressive response assumes that inelastic strains are allowed when the compressive strength σ_c is attained, Figure 1. Since experimental tests show that the inelastic strains are quite limited, retaining the common definition of ductility δ as the ratio between the strain at crushing ε_{ul} and the strain at the end of the linear response ε_{el}, $\delta = \varepsilon_{ul}/\varepsilon_{el}$, masonry can be represented as a quasi-brittle material with maximum ductility of approximately 1.5 (Brencich et al. 2002).

Under these hypotheses, the constitutive equations for the elasto-plastic, ductility controlled section are given as:

$$N^{EP} = \sigma_c \frac{b}{2}(x+y) \tag{1}$$

$$M^{EP} = \sigma_c \frac{b}{2}\left[\frac{h}{2}(x+y) - \frac{1}{3}\left(x^2 + xy + y^2\right)\right] \tag{2}$$

$$\delta = \frac{\varepsilon_{ul}}{\varepsilon_{el}} = \frac{\sigma_c'}{\sigma_c} = \frac{x}{x-y} \leq \delta_{max}, \tag{3}$$

where δ_{max} is the maximum ductility of masonry, y is the extension of the plastic plateau and σ_c' stands for the maximum compressive stress that would be recorded by a NTR model, Figure 1.

Once the constitutive model for the cross section is given, a beam type model of the arch, i.e. assuming a unit width, can be formulated. This approach allows

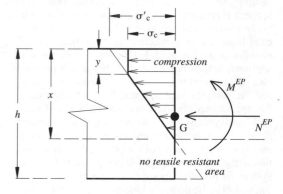

Figure 1. Constitutive No Tensile Resistance model with strain control (limited ductility) for the masonry section.

an iterative procedure to be set up on the basis of a standard predictor-corrector algorithm so that an elastic analysis in performed and than the section height is corrected to drop down the tensile part of the section and external fictitious forces are added to take into account the plastic response of masonry. For the details see Brencich et al. (2001).

Let consider the arch of Figure 2, typical of many single-and multi-span bridges. For the moment we can consider the fill as a dead weight distributing the load over a 80° cone in order to take into account the distribution effect of the rails.

Several models for masonry have been considered: (a) a No Tensile Resistance model without any limit to compressive strength; (b) an NTR model with elastic-perfectly plastic response and unlimited ductility, i.e. no limit is set to the inelastic strains; (c) an NTR model with elastic-perfectly plastic response with decreasing values of ductility (2.5, 2.0, 1.4, 1.0). The latter value of the ductility represents a perfectly brittle material, whilst the compressive strength is assumed as 5 MPa.

The limit load, represented in Figure 3 for different positions, can be greatly overestimated by simplified constitutive models: the elasto-perfectly plastic, ductility controlled model foresees limit loads that are half the value predicted by a NTR model in the weakest position but up to some six times less in other positions.

The limit load vs. load position diagrams for the two-span model of Figure 4, and a similar three-span bridge, considering both short and long piers, are represented in Figure 5; all the models assume a 5 MPa compressive strength and a 1.4 ductility. It can be seen that the span interaction is responsible for a dramatic reduction of the load carrying capacity. The limit load estimated by the discussed 2-D model is six times less than the estimate given by a single arch No Tensile Resistant approach, raising objections to some of the classical approaches to arch bridge assessment.

Besides, when a limit is set to the inelastic strains, it is found that the collapse mechanism cannot activate: the collapse of some sections is met far before a collapse mechanism of the entire arch is activated by plastic hinges. From this point of view, the collapse of a masonry arch should not be identified with the activation of a mechanism but with either the activation of a mechanism or the collapse of a single section, whatever the first.

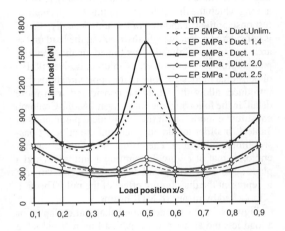

Figure 3. Limit load vs. load position and masonry ductility for the shallow single-arch model of Figure 2.

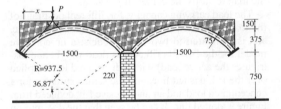

Figure 4. Load position in two-span models.

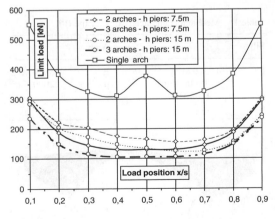

Figure 5. Limit load vs. load position and masonry ductility for a shallow two- and three-arch model. Ductility $\delta = 1.4$.

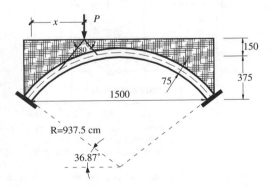

Figure 2. Geometry of the single arch model.

4 THE CONTRIBUTION OF THE FILL

The contribution of the fill is known to be of great importance in the collapse mechanism of a bridge on the basis of experimental grounds (Royles & Hendry 1991). Nevertheless, the mechanical modelling of the fill is rather complex due to many reasons, among which the difficulty in coupling the mechanical response of the fill and that of the arch. Usually, the fill is considered a dead weight distributing the load on the arch extrados, as already mentioned in the previous paragraph, i.e. it is assumed as an un-cohesive fill. Bi-dimensional models, in spite of the approximations they introduce, allow the fill to be considered with more detail. In the following, the fill is given a Mohr-Coulomb constitutive model, with the mechanical parameters of Table 1, in order to take into account the effect of passive limit equilibrium. The bridge model under consideration is that of Figure 2 assuming a unit width and a plane strain state and a load distributed over a 3 m area to represent the distributing effect of the rails. The arch is modelled by means of NTR beams.

Figure 6 shows the deformed shape at collapse for a load located at $x/s = 0.13$, whilst Figure 7 plots the inelastic strains in the fill for a cohesive model. It can be seen that below the load a kind of column is formed (arrow in Fig. 7) which deviates a large part of the load towards the center of the arch.

The load carrying capacity, for different positions of the load, is plotted in Figure 8, continuous bold line, and is compared to two other models: a un-cohesive model for the fill (the fill acts as dead weight and distributes the active load) with a distributed load applied over the fill, dashed line, and the same estimates for a concentrated load and an un-cohesive fill, deduced from Figure 3, dotted line. It can be seen that the distribution of the load over 3 m raises the limit load as much as not less than 50%. The effect of the fill is mainly that of

Table 1. Mechanical characteristics for the fill.

Fill		Arch	
E	300 MPa	E	15000 MPa
ρ	19000 N/m³	ρ	22000 N/m³
c	0.02 MPa		
φ	25°		

Figure 6. Deformed mesh of the single-span model of Figure 2.

shifting the weakest position as a result of the inclined fill columns, Figure 7, and of raising the limit load. The minimum limit load, that is the bridge load carrying capacity, is raised some 15% by a cohesive fill. Parametric analyses showed that these results are not affected by the boundaries of the fill, i.e. by the lateral surfaces of the fill.

5 A CASE STUDY

The described procedures refers to simplified loading conditions, i.e. a single concentrated force or a short distribution of load, to enlighten some of the structural phenomena typical of masonry arch bridges. The assessment of a real bridge shpuld refer to more realistic loading conditions. In the following these procedures are applied to an existing one-way 6 span viaduct, the *Cantalupo* bridge on the Genova-Ovada-Aqui Terme

Figure 7. Inelastic strains in the fill.

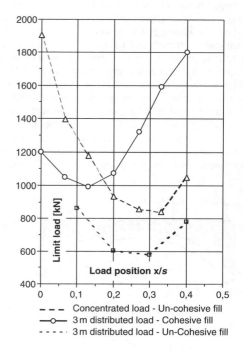

Figure 8. Limit load vs. load position for a single-arch model with un-cohesive and cohesive fill and concentrated and distributed forces.

line. The main geometric and mechanical characteristics of the model are summarized in Table 2; more details are given in (Brencich & De Francesco, 2002).

The schematic of the bridge is represented in Figure 9 along with the considered loading condition (train of D4 carriages, 12 m long, with 90 tons/carriage and 22.5 tons/axle). Figure 10 shows the load-displacement response whilst in Figure 11 the deformed shape of the viaduct and its effective sections are displayed at the point A of the loading history, where the bridge stiffness suddenly drops down, and at the end of the loading process, point B.

The collapse is attained when the maximum allowed ductility ($\delta = 1.4$) is reached in a section, i.e. when a section crushes. From Figure 11b it can be seen that this phenomenon takes place when many hinges are active but their number, three hinges per arch, is still far from activating a mechanism. Nevertheless the viaduct collapses because of crushing of some sections (crown of span 3). This fact raises severe objections to the kinematic approach to the collapse of arches, mainly referring to the assumption that masonry can exhibit large inelastic compressive strains. It can be seen that the simplified model foresees a limit per carriage load that is approximately 4 times the service loads, even though the assumed compressive strength (5 MPa) is rather low. Besides, in Figure 10 the comparison with an equivalent distributed load shows that the effective load distribution and the equivalent ones do not always give the equivalent results.

Table 2. Geometric and mechanical (assumed) characteristics of the *Cantalupo* bridge.

Geometry		Mechanics	
Arch span s [cm]	1850	E [MPa]	5000
Rise r [cm]	925	Masonry dens. [kN/m³]	22
r/s	1/2	Compr. strength [MPa]	5
Arch thck. d [cm]	107	Masonry ductility δ	1.4
Fill in crown f [cm]	75	Fill density [kN/m³]	24
f/d	0.7	Load diffusion in the fill	80°
Arch width [cm]	500	Type of load	knife-type
Backfill height [cm]	700		
Piers:	1068–		
$h_{min}-h_{max}$ [cm]	3105		
Pier inclination p [%]	3.5		

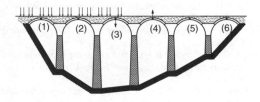

Figure 9. Schematic of the bridge, of the loads and of the reference points – spans (3) and (4).

This procedure presents the limits of a small displacement approach: the diagrams of Figure 10 should be considered reliable only for small displacements, i.e. for crown displacements below 1/300th of the arch span, and the results for larger displacements should be considered with great attention. In the case of the *Cantalupo* bridge, such displacements are reached for loads that are higher than the service ones.

Figure 12 presents the compressive stresses distribution on the arch extrados as deduced from 3-D models for (a) an elastic model and (b) a NTR perfectly brittle ($\delta = 1$) model and (c) a detailed stress distribution on the central arch. In the elastic case, Figure 12a, the maximum tensile stresses are found close to 0.5 MPa, low enough to assume that the elastic model is able of giving some valuable information, while the maximum compressive stress is something more than 1.2 MPa. These results are in agreement with the simplified analysis.

The NTR brittle model of Figure 12b shows that the compressive stresses under the service loads are not higher than 1.5 MPa, in this way corroborating the results of the elastic analysis. The 3-D NTR model

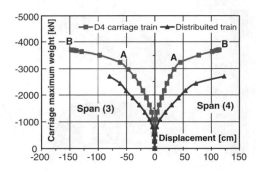

Figure 10. Load–displacement response of the bridge.

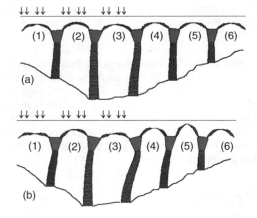

Figure 11. Deformed shape and effective sections of the bridge. (a) at point A and (b) at point B of Figure 10.

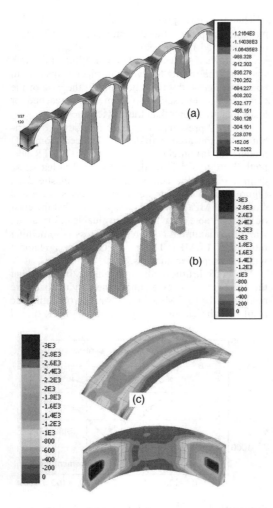

the influencer of the mechanical parameters. Besides, they allow both synthetic and detailed information on the bridge structural response.

In the presented case study, the 2-D and 3-D models gave coherent results in terms of stresses and limit loads, showing that the collapse load is expected to be not less than four times the service loads.

The dynamic response of the viaduct, i.e. its seismic vulnerability, is still an open issue that deserves further research.

ACKNOWLEDGMENTS

This research was carried out with the partial financial support of the (MURST) Dept. for Univ. and Sc. and Tech. Res. in the frame of the PRIN 2002/2003 "*Safety and Control of Masonry Bridges*" project, and of the Nat. Earthq. Def. Group (GNDT) inside the *VIA* research project "*Seismic vulnerability reduction of infrastructural systems and environment*", a part of the Biennial 2000–2002 Research Program.

Figure 12. Principal compressive stresses at the arch extrados for (a) an elastic model; (b) an NTR perfectly brittle ($\delta = 1$) model; (c) detailed principal compressive stress distribution in the central arch at collapse. Same load as that of Figure 9.

would foresee a limit load that is 7.2 times the service loads, almost twice the estimate of the simplified 2-D model. This is due to the three-dimensional response of the viaduct, i.e. to the contribution of the spandrel walls. In Figure 12c the compressive stress distribution on the central arch shows a clear concentration of stresses, close to the arch edges, due to the arch/spandrel interaction.

6   CONCLUSIONS

Different mechanical models allow the analysis of many aspects of the structural response of a bridge and

REFERENCES

Brencich, A. & De Francesco, U. 2002. Simplified approaches to the assessment of railway masonry bridges, *Railway Engineering 2002*, London, 3–4 July 2002.
Brencich, A., Corradi, C., Gambarotta, L., Mantegazza, G. & Sterpi, E. 2002. Compressive strength of solid clay brick masonry under eccentric loading, *Proc. Brit. Mas. Soc.*, 9, November 2002, 37–46.
Brencich, A., De Francesco, U. & Gambarotta, L. 2001. Non linear elasto-plastic collapse analysis of multi-span masonry arch bridges, *Arch '01, 3rd Int. Conference on Arch Bridges*, Paris, 19–21 September 2001.
Crisfield, M.A. 1985. Finite element and mechanism methods for the analysis of masonry and brickwork arches. *Transport and Road Research Laboratory, Dept. of Transport*, Research Report 19, TRL, Crowthorne.
Crisfield, M.A. & Packham, A.J. 1988. A mechanism program for computing the strength of masonry arch bridges, *Transport and Road Research Laboratory, Dept. of Transport*, Research Report 124, TRL, Crowthorne.
FICHE-UIC 778-3E. Recommandations pour l'evaluation de la capacite portante des ponts-voutes existants en maçonnerie et beton (1994).
Harvey, W.E.J. & Smith, F.W. 1991. The behaviour and assessment of multi-span arches, *The Structural Engineer*, 69, 411–417.
Heyman, J. 1982. *The masonry arch*, Ellis Horwood, Chichester.
Hughes, T.G. 1995. Analysis and assessment of twin-span masonry arch bridges, *Proc. Instn. Civ. Engrs.*, 110, 373–382.
Molins, C. & Roca, P. 1998. Capacity of masonry arches and spatial frames, *J. Str. Eng.rg*, 124, 653–663.
Royles, R. & Hendry, A.W. 1991. Model tests on masonry arches, *Proc. Instn. Civ. Engrs.*, 91, 299–321.

System-based Vision for Strategic and Creative Design, Bontempi (ed.)
© 2003 Swets & Zeitlinger, Lisse, ISBN 90 5809 599 1

Limit analysis of masonry domes: two case studies

P. Foraboschi & M. Nart
Dipartimento di Costruzione dell'Architettura – Istituto Universitario di Venezia, Venezia, Italy

ABSTRACT: This paper aims at defining the tools to interpret and quantify the mechanical behavior of masonry domes. The analysis is based on geometrical parameters only, while constitutive laws are not taken into account. No-tension assumption is made. Accordingly, membrane theory does not hold true and the dome splits into slices, so that it behaves like a set of arches with variable section, i.e., a thrusting behavior is considered for the dome. By limit analysis the collapse mechanisms are analyzed in relation to the load and shell geometry. This approach introduces an analytical method to predict the collapse and the associated horizontal limit thrust at the springing. This would suggest the possibility of adopting a geometrical safety factor Φ to define the condition acceptable for the equilibrium of the structure and the tool to lead the decisions when we must strengthened the dome.

1 INTRODUCTION

The particular nature of the static behavior of masonry domes makes it difficult to consider them as functioning purely as shells in order to explain their stress regime.

The features of both the structure and the material contrast with the hypotheses on which membrane analysis is based.

While there is no problem concerning their compressive strength – which is generally far greater than the structure needs to cope with the loads involved – the same cannot be said in the case of tensile stresses. The mechanical characteristics of the material strongly contradict the membrane solution. The thicknesses typical of domes, moreover, can hardly be defined as slender, making any reference to a simple curved surface an oversimplification. Such considerations cannot be disregarded in any attempt to analyze the stability of masonry structures.

In addition, historical domes generally coexist with a number of other building elements that interact in the way they work. The fact that local moments can occur in relation to particular loading conditions or by faulty workmanship or the physical or chemical effects does not weaken the dome. But there may be other effects, such as the opening of cracks, that may not reduce the load-bearing capacity of the structure, but may nonetheless dramatically alter its behavior.

Considering the incompatibility between tensile stresses (developing due to the self weight and any outside load brought to bear on the structure) and the features of the building material, it is easy to conclude that, once the weak tensile strength of the masonry has been exceeded, the first signs of damage develop along the meridians and then propagate towards the top, dividing the dome into segments that converge towards the center and tend to splay out, altering the stress–strain diagram and making the compressed zone shift upwards.

While the shell produces no thrust due to the tie effect of the parallels, this is not so for the cracked dome.

Such a cracking situation is typical of the masonry dome, however, the presence of meridian cracks is physiological to the functioning of the dome as a whole. But when this meridian cracking occurs, the thrust line is displaced: if it touches certain points in the intrados and extrados, it can trigger the formation of dangerous circumferential fractures, that can be schematically represented as hinges. While the meridian lesions may merely indicate that a slight widening of the dome and cracking of the drum has occurred, any parallel lesions mark the onset of a failure mechanism.

Considering the dome as being divided into segments, as the meridian cracks suggest, enables a single element to be analyzed and, in the light of the *safe theorem*, if the stability of this one element is demonstrated, then the structure as a whole must be stable.

The model, already proposed by Heyman (1966), is based on three essential assumptions: no tensile strength; virtually infinite compressive strength; virtually infinite shear strength.

Moreover the material is assumed to be stiff, so no elastic constant is specified.

This assumption enables the masonry to be represented schematically as set of one-dimensional stiff elements held together by compressive forces – a model according to which failure is characterized by the formation of non-dissipative hinges and can occur only when the number of hinges suffices to convert the structure into a mechanism.

The building can collapse if the structural elements needed to prevent any movement of the springing are lacking or inadequate, i.e. due to inadequate or excessive thrust. These two mechanisms are associated with the corresponding minimum and maximum thrust values, which define the range of values within which the real condition of the dome necessarily lies.

Assuming a no-tension material for the dome implies, however, that the thrust developing along the entire meridian section is only constant in the band of parallels under tensile stress, while it grows proportionally with the angular coordinate in the area above it, due to the compressive stresses.

Considering the structure as being capable of transmitting compressive stresses complicates the definition of the collapse mechanism, making it necessary to determine the portion of dome that behaves like a shell – a difficult line to draw because it is impossible to predict how the meridian crack will develop.

In the proposed model (Nart 2003), the uncertainty is eliminated by starting from the structural hypothesis of a completely cracked dome. In this case, neither the tensile nor the compressive forces are transmitted and the thrust is constant all over the meridian section. The only unknown quantity is represented by the form of the collapse mechanism; once this has been defined, all we have to do is apply the static equilibrium.

The values of the minimum and maximum thrusts can also be correlated to assess the amplitude of the range of values in which the real state of the building will lie. We can thus define a geometric factor Φ that enables an assessment of the actual safety of the dome.

The present analytical model focuses on the limit analysis, whereas tensile stress analysis would prove scarcely significant, even if the considerable uncertainty in estimating the acting and resisting forces were overlooked. In fact, if the geometric safety factor Φ (Blasi & Foraboschi 1994), or the relationship between the real thickness and the limit thickness, and also the relationship between the minimum thrust needed by the dome and the maximum thrust supported by the drum are known, it becomes feasible to objectively assess the building's condition. On the other hand, the relationship between the maximum stress reached in the masonry and the stress allowable for masonry buildings is scarcely relevant because failure due to crushing is highly unlikely and, in terms of any collapse due to a mechanism, this relationship

provides only marginal and sometimes deceptive information.

The theoretical tools that have been fine-adjusted facilitate a rational management of masonry domes, suggesting when action is needed, in which case the same tools can also point to the most suitable restoration strategy.

2 CASE STUDIES

Based on the above-described logic, the following is an analysis of two dome shapes, the hemispherical and the ogival, loaded by their self weight, by a lantern and by buttressing elements, taking by way of example two real domes, i.e. the one in the Tempietto at Villa Barbaro in Maser and the one in the Church dedicated to Santa Maria delle Querce in Lucignano.

2.1 *The Tempietto at Villa Barbaro in Maser*

The Tempietto has a circular floor plan with a central body about 35 feet in diameter (Vicenza foot = 35.7 cm), divided into eight equal spaces by eight Corinthian columns supporting the round cornice on which the dome rests.

The dome is made entirely of bricks and forms a hemispherical profile, surrounded at its springing by four large steps.

Visual inspections and endoscopic investigations performed during restoration work revealed the masonry fabric and the arrangement of the materials forming both the dome and the surrounding steps. In particular, the latter are composed of a rubble wall whose outer surface was made with large solid bricks in three different sizes, while the inner surface (which pursues the hemispherical profile of the intrados) shows a face on which the bricks are placed with the headers alternating with the stretchers. Finally, the rubble wall is an infill of common lime and aggregate of various sizes to guarantee the maximum vertical load in line with the springing of the dome.

The lantern, made entirely of wood protected with lead sheet, is attached to the dome by means of two continuous circular brackets that distribute its weight evenly around the two circumferences.

The present damage includes the evidence of cracking and the walls that are bent, probably due partly to anthropic action in the past, the construction of the building standing alongside and the environmental strains related to the road traffic, but above all to subsidence of the ground on which the Tempietto stands.

A settlement of the foundations was, in fact, detected in the south-eastern part of the Tempietto, which caused a translation and rotation of the building's central body (Fig. 1).

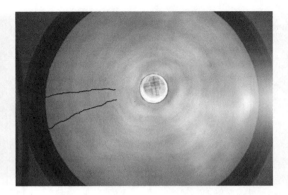

Figure 1.   Tempietto at Villa Barbaro in Maser, cracks.

Figure 2.   Santa Maria delle Querce in Lucignano, cracks.

2.2   The Santa Maria delle Querce church in Lucignano

The church has three naves and a Latin cross floor plan. The central nave is separate from the cross-vaulted side naves and covered with a barrel vault interrupted in the transept by a dome standing on cruciform pillars and topped by a heavy masonry lantern.

The dome has a pointed arch profile and is made so that only the surface of the intrados is visible. On the extrados there are eight buttresses contained by a cylindrical tiburio supporting the roofing structure that protects the dome from the weather.

The dome is 7 m in diameter and 26 cm thick, and bears the weight of the eight one-header-thick brick-work buttresses supporting the roof. The pointed arch is topped with a heavy lantern weighing approximately 7200 kg, i.e. 1/8th of the weight of the dome. The tiburio, made using masonry two headers thick, seems to be separate from the vaulted structure, coming to bear directly on the drum, which coincides with the 4 large arches forming the perimeter from which the whole dome springs.

The main reason for the damage recorded on several occasions seems to be poor workmanship.

The building's condition is made even more precarious by the nature of the ground. Only the original structure, a small chapel constructed for the worship of a sacred image, rests on a rocky outcrop, whereas the extension has its foundations on backfill material coming from the hill that was flattened for the occasion and there are water channels passing right through the building's foundations.

In particular, the foundations under the pillar to the right of the high altar (one of the elements supporting the dome) appear to have subsided and there are signs of meridian cracks on the intrados that start at the springing and run vertically upwards, nearly reaching the lantern (Fig. 2).

Figure 3.   Tempietto at Villa Barbaro, lantern.

2.3   Critical comparison of the results

The result of membrane analysis immediately emphasize the different influence of the structural elements, in relation to the shape of the dome, on the distribution of the meridian and parallel stresses.

In the dome over the Tempietto in Maser, it was thanks to the decision to build a lightweight wooden lantern (Figs 3–4), and above all to the particular type of connection used to attach it (avoiding the load being concentrated on a single parallel ring) that enabled the maximum tensile stress to be achieved in line with the eye, and kept below the admissible stress (0.3 N/mm^2), bearing in mind that the dome was built using good-quality materials and careful construction methods. The reaction of the ogival dome in Lucignano is very different, where the analysis revealed that the lantern (Figs 5–6), though heavy (1/8th of the weight of the dome instead of 1/20th in the case of the Palladian building), has a negligible influence on the elastic behavior of the dome and induces a maximum tensile stress in the ring at the springing of just 0.045 N/mm^2.

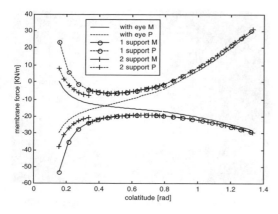

Figure 4. Tempietto at Villa Barbaro, membrane solution.

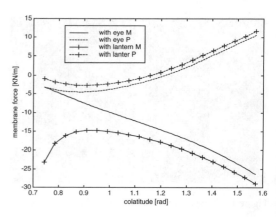

Figure 6. Santa Maria delle Querce, membrane solution.

Figure 5. Santa Maria delle Querce, lantern and buttresses.

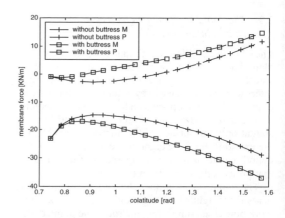

Figure 7. Santa Maria delle Querce, membrane solution.

Conversely, the stress due to the load of the buttresses (Fig. 7) in Vasari's work is amplified by their shape, which affects the distribution of the parallel and meridian stresses over the entire cross-section, particularly determining a considerable increase in the area under tensile stress, which includes almost all the parallel rings. The maximum stress nonetheless remains below the presumable admissible stress bearing in mind the good-quality building materials and construction methods used to build the dome, unlike the church's other structures. Moreover, the tiburio and roof protecting the dome's extrados have meant that the mortar joints have not suffered from deterioration due to the effects of weather.

In both cases, therefore, it seems logical to assume that the main cause of the structural damage probably lies in the differential subsidence, though in the case

of Lucignano there is the additional problem relating to the rough-and-ready methods and poor-quality materials used in the supporting structures.

Limit analysis, on the other hand, demonstrated the fundamental role of the design choices behind the construction of the Tempietto, unlike the situation observed in the Santa Maria (Fig. 8). In particular, the stepped buttresses of the Tempietto is made using materials, shapes and positions capable of reducing the minimum thrust needed for the dome, while also providing a static contribution to the drum. The decision to construct a lightweight lantern, whose presence contrasts with the geometry of the dome, also proved right since it avoids excessively influencing the minimum thrust value.

The findings emerging for Vasari's pointed arch dome were diametrically opposite: analyzing the failure mechanism due to minimum thrust emphasized the negative effect of the buttress on the definition of

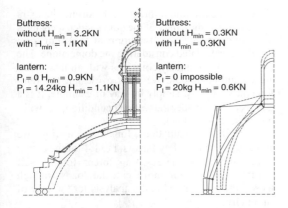

Buttress:
without H_{min} = 3.2KN
with H_{min} = 1.1KN

lantern:
P_l = 0 H_{min} = 0.9KN
P_l = 14.24kg H_{min} = 1.1KN

Buttress:
without H_{min} = 0.3KN
with H_{min} = 0.3KN

lantern:
P_l = 0 impossible
P_l = 20kg H_{min} = 0.6KN

Figure 8.   Lower mechanism and minimum thrust.

the kinematism characterizing failure, influenced particularly by the distribution of the additional load that comes to bear on the very block that tends to rotate inwards, accentuating its movement. The presence of the buttress also induces a two-fold increase in the minimum thrust, despite the increment in the load being relatively limited; said thrust does not seem to pose particular problems for the supporting elements, however, and the stability is improved by the presence of the tiburio.

The significance of the lantern also proved quite the reverse of the situation in the dome of the Tempietto. The pointed arch shape and the dimensions of Vasari's cross-section make the load concentrated at the top particularly important. The lantern produces a peak in the weight distribution diagram, making the shape of the thrust line pointed. The limit condition for the dome depends on the link between the geometric characteristics of the segment and the weight of the lantern. Assuming the same acuteness and thickness of the section, the range defined by the maximum and minimum thrust varies as a function of the concentrated load. Unlike the situation for the hemispherical dome, the amplitude of said range diminishes reducing the value of the variable involved.

The static importance acquired by the collapse mechanism due to minimum thrust prompts the definition – for both profiles, the hemispherical and the ogival – of an upper limit attributable to the weight of the lantern, which is defined after establishing the appropriate limit for the amount of thrust transmitted to the drum.

For Lucignano, moreover (like all ogival shapes), there is also the further constraint given by the minimum allowable value of the load considered, i.e. there is a ratio of the weight of the lantern to the weight of the dome below which the structure is no longer in equilibrium. When the lantern is too light, the minimum thrust becomes greater than the maximum.

Both the domes analyzed revealed an adequate safety condition that demands no particular reinforcement measures. However, should we wish to increment the real thickness to minimum thickness ratio in the case of Lucignano, it would be important to pay particular attention in the design of any measures, especially as regards the lantern, which cannot be removed without taking the necessary precautions, otherwise the thickness would become lower than the calculated minimum and this would lead to the dome's collapse due to pure rotation. The required result can be achieved by increasing the thickness of the dome or modifying the loads due to the structural elements interacting with the dome, though this might put the architectural value of the work at risk. The most straightforward alternative, however, would be to provide tie reinforcement, not at the springing (where it would be absolutely ineffectual because it would be unable to prevent the kinematism), but at the reins. In the specific case of Lucignano, moreover, such a measure is easily achievable, for instance, by gluing fiber-reinforced polymer (FRP) composite strips or fabric onto the dome's intrados, which is not frescoed and therefore of no particular historical-artistic value (attaching the reinforcement to the extrados would be more effective, but impossible to achieve in this particular case due to the presence of the buttresses and tiburio).

3   DESIGN AND ASSESSMENT OF THE REINFORCEMENT MEASURE

The widespread use of FRP composite strips or fabrics as reinforcement in the consolidation and restoration field makes it necessary to develop guidelines for the design and assessment of any such measures based on the use of this innovative material.

In the specific case in point, we are interested in tie reinforcement measures in line with the reins to improve the safety of a masonry dome. Previous articles (Nart 2001) have dealt with the design of how FRP strips should be attached to the springing to inhibit the failure mechanism triggered when the supporting structure is no longer capable of withstanding the minimum thrust needed for the dome.

Following the logic outlined in the previous paragraphs, the aim of the measure is to counter the mechanism of pure rotation; in fact, the tie prevents the activation of the intrados hinge characterizing said mechanism, stopping any opening of the corresponding parallel.

Starting from a condition of failure due to pure rotation, we can calculate the external work L_e after assuming the allowable virtual displacement $\delta = 1$. For the dome to be in equilibrium, it must hold that:

$$L_e \leq L_{FRP} \tag{1}$$

where L_{FRP} is the work performed by the reinforcement provided in line with the point most susceptible to displacement during the activation of the mechanism. Thus, if we define the maximum displacement coinciding with the imposed virtual unit displacement as δ_{max}, the circumference of the parallel involved becomes:

$$C_f = 2\pi\left(r + \delta_{max}\right) \qquad (2)$$

where r is the internal radius of the parallel.

Once said circumference is known, the strain (dilation) suffered by the tie due to the effect of the maximum displacement δ_{max} is given by:

$$\varepsilon = \frac{\Delta l}{l} = \frac{\left(2\pi r + 2\pi\delta_{max}\right) - 2\pi r}{2\pi r} = \frac{\delta_{max}}{r} \qquad (3)$$

Now, applying Clapeyron's theorem, the deformation work LFRP becomes:

$$L_{FRP} = \frac{\delta_{max}^{\;2}}{r} \cdot E_{FRP} \cdot S_{FRP} s_{FRP} n_{FRP} \pi \qquad (4)$$

where E_{FRP} is the reinforcement's modulus of elasticity, S_{FRP} is the height of the attached strip or fabric, s_{FRP} is its thickness and n_{FRP} is the number of overlapping layers of thickness s. If we now pose Equation 1, we can obtain S_{FRP} after setting $n_{FRP} = 1$ and choosing the type of reinforcement we intend to use, for which we know E_{FRP} and s_{FRP} because they are specified in the technical data sheets on the commercially-available products and given by the characteristics of the fibers and the manufacturing method. It is nonetheless advisable to consider the maximum height of the strip as 10 cm, beyond which it is best to overlap several layers in order to guarantee the efficacy of the measure. In fact, the height S_{FRP} depends on the shape of the dome and the corresponding installation problems and bonding difficulties due to the double curvature of the dome.

In the specific case of Lucignano, and in all the cases in which we decide to take action on the intrados, it is also necessary to check the characteristic tearing resistance of the system used to guarantee the bonding of the strips.

The end result then depends exclusively on the selected composite's modulus of elasticity and the dependability of the measure is fundamentally a matter of the strips' stiffness.

The case of Lucignano is characterized by two different conditions that influence the determination of the failure mechanism and the real thickness to minimum thickness ratio: in fact, it proves necessary to distinguish between the structure's behavior with and without the buttresses. In the former case, though it

increases the minimum thrust on the drum, the extra load improves the safety of the dome, since it changes the minimum thickness requirement to 12 cm from the 17 cm calculated considering the dome alone. The real situation obviously coincides with an intermediate condition. Should we wish to design the reinforcement anyway, simply by way of example, it is a good idea to consider the weakest condition, i.e. without the additional load.

According to regulations, for the calculations we adopted the usual safety factors, i.e. 1.4 for the acting forces and 1 for the resisting forces for the self weights, and 1.5 for the accidental loads (though these were disregarded in the analysis for the sake of simplicity).

For the reinforcement measure, we chose to attach strips made of fabric reinforced with one-directional glass fibers (VV 320 U-HT beton tex FTS), given the drastically prevalent direction of the work, which had an elastic modulus $E_{FRP} = 74000$ N/mm^2 and a fiber thickness s_{FRP} of 0.17 mm. With this data we obtain $S_{FRP} = 2.1$ cm.

4 CONCLUSIONS

Structural assessments and any consolidation measures on a masonry dome must focus on limit analyses rather than stress analysis. This is not only because it is difficult to ascertain the strength of the masonry and stress analyses suffer from a significant degree of uncertainty, but also and above all because the comparison between an acting force (expressed in terms of peak stress) and a resisting force (expressed in terms of admissible stress) is scarcely representative in the cases considered: suffice it to mention the role of structural elements such as the lantern or buttresses. Stress analysis associates their presence with an increase in the peak stress and a consequently lower margin vis-à-vis the allowable stress, whereas limit analysis demonstrates, for instance, that the addition of a lantern on an ogival dome is associated with a greater load at failure and consequently with a greater margin of safety. Where such a duality of behavior exists, only the information deriving from limit analysis is reliable.

To be more specific, in order to emphasize the importance of the geometric safety factor, the displacement needed at the springing to trigger collapse is all the smaller, the narrower the thickness of the dome. Considered as a function of the ratio of real thickness to limit thickness, when the latter tends virtually to 1, the displacement tends virtually to 0. If the ratio is less than 1, the condition is impossible and the structure collapses. But it is not enough to say that it is greater than 1, because there is a difference between a situation where it is 1.02 and one where it is

1.5 in the former, minimal displacements are sufficient to cause collapse, while larger displacements are needed in the latter. So this, albeit geometric, factor can provide essential information even from the point of view of civil protection requirements, indicating which structural elements need to be assessed.

REFERENCES

Blasi, C. & Foraboschi, P. 1994. Analytical approach to collapse mechanisms of circular masonry arch. *J. Structural Engineering, ASCE*, 120.

Heyman, J. 1966. The stone skeleton. *Intern. J. of solids and structures*, 2.

Nart, M. 2001. Cupole in muratura: il rinforzo in FRP per il consolidamento. *L'Edilizia*, 5.

Nart, M. 2003. Limit analysis of masonry domes. *Masonry International*, 1.

System-based Vision for Strategic and Creative Design, Bontempi (ed.)
© 2003 Swets & Zeitlinger, Lisse, ISBN 90 5809 599 1

ACI shear reinforcement for flat slabs

R.L. Vollum & U.L. Tay
Department of Civil and Environmental Engineering, Imperial College London, UK

ABSTRACT: This article is concerned with the development of an improved method for the design of ACI shear reinforcement for flat slabs that is compatible with EC2. Research at Cardington compared material and labour costs for various forms of punching shear reinforcement including traditional stirrups, shear studs, shear hoops, shear ladders, structural steel shear heads and ACI shear stirrups. Of all these systems, the ACI shear reinforcement was the most economic and quickest to fix. This article describes a load test on the full scale multi-storey concrete building at Cardington which included a slab with ACI shear reinforcement. The article also reviews the limited test data available for ACI shear reinforcement and shows that current EC2 guidelines are overly conservative and severely restrict the use of ACI shear reinforcement. An improved method is suggested for calculating the maximum possible shear strength for specimens with ACI shear reinforcement that is consistent with EC2. Finally, details are given of a test program that is being carried out at Imperial College on ACI punching shear reinforcement to verify/improve the proposed design method.

1 BACKGROUND

Research into punching shear reinforcement at Cardington by Goodchild (2000) showed that ACI shear reinforcement (see Figure 1) was the most economic and quickest to fix. The Cardington building is a seven-storey building with flat slabs spanning 7.5 m in each direction. The building was built for research and was intended to be representative of a typical office building. The structure was generally designed using EC2 (1992) but ACI 318 (1992) was used to design the ACI shear reinforcement. Subsequent analysis by the authors showed that it is impossible to justify the design of the ACI shear reinforcement at Cardington with EC2 (2002). It is instructive to compare the maximum possible design imposed loads allowed by each code at a concentrically loaded internal column. ACI 318 (2002) limits the maximum possible design shear strength with ACI shear stirrups to $1.5 V_{cdesignACI}$ (where $V_{cdesignACI}$ is the design shear strength without stirrups) whereas EC2 (2002) limits the maximum strength to:

$$V_{EC2\,max} = \frac{U_{out}}{U_1} V_{cdesignEC2} \qquad (1)$$

where U_1 and U_{out} are the control perimeters used to calculate shear strength within and outside the shear reinforced zone. For internal columns:

$$U_1 = U_{col} + 4\pi d \qquad (2)$$

and for ACI shear reinforcement

$$U_{out} = 4x + 3\pi d + 8d \qquad (3)$$

where U_{col} is the column perimeter and x is the width of the stirrups which was 280 mm at Cardington.

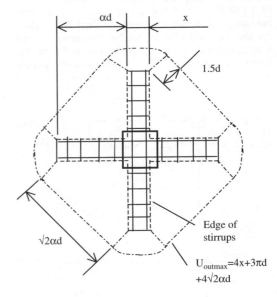

Figure 1. ACI shear reinforcement.

The slabs at Cardington were 250 mm thick flat slabs with an average effective depth d of 215 mm. The internal columns were 400 mm square giving $V_{EC2max} = 1.13\,V_{cEC2design}$. The tension reinforcement in the column strips was T16.175 in each direction over the columns where ACI shear reinforcement was provided. The mean concrete cylinder strength was 43 MPa. According to EC2 (2002) the maximum possible design shear resistance at these columns is 702 kN whereas ACI 318 (2002) gives a much greater limiting design shear strength of 1466 kN. These capacities are not directly comparable since EC2 (2002) and ACI 318 (2002) use different load factors and material factors of safety. It is more useful to compare the maximum possible design imposed loads permitted by each code for a typical internal bay. The design shear force at internal columns was assumed to be $1.15\,V_{max}$ where $V_{max} = 1.1\,nL^2$ where n is the design ultimate load and L is the span of 7.5 m. The maximum possible characteristic design imposed load (over and above the slab self-weight of 6 kN/m²) for slabs with ACI shear reinforcement is 1.2 kN/m² according to EC2 (2002) but 7.2 kN/m² according to ACI 318 (2002). This analysis shows that EC2 severely restricts the use of ACI shear reinforcement.

2 CARDINGTON LOAD TEST

The Building Research Establishment (BRE) carried out a full-scale load test for Imperial College on a corner bay (see Figure 2) of the Cardington in-situ concrete building in September 2001 to investigate the robustness of flat slabs designed in accordance with EC2 (2002). A steel frame was bolted to the corner column at D5 between ground and first floor before the test. Subsequently, the load in the corner column was transferred into the frame by four jacks and the column was cut through below the bolted connection.

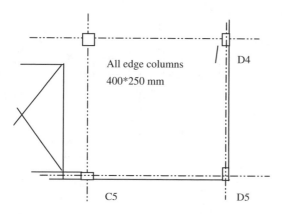

Figure 2.   Plan on corner bay at Cardington.

The slabs were loaded with a superimposed load of 4.5 kN/m² before the test in which the corner of the 7-storey building was gradually released until it hung freely. Before the load test, BRE carried out a 3-dimensional non-linear finite element analysis of the complete structure with the finite element code DIANA. The aim of the analysis was to predict (a) the load deformation response at the corner column, (b) the column moments and (c) the failure mechanism in the heave and settlement tests. The slab was modelled with curved shell elements with embedded reinforcement. The finite element analysis predicted that the structure could just hang freely carrying the imposed load of 4.5 kN/m² with the corner column unsupported. Deflections were monitored throughout the test and were found to be close to the predicted values.

Vollum used EC2 (2002) to estimate the shear strengths V_{uEC2} of the slab-column connections corresponding to the maximum column bending moments predicted by the finite element analysis. The most critically loaded connections were the edge column connections at columns D4 and C5 (see Figure 2). EC2 (2002) was used to calculate an effective shear force V_{eff} for the connections which were loaded in biaxial bending. The shear strengths V_{uEC2} were calculated using the measured concrete strengths with a material factor of safety $\gamma_c = 1$. The analysis to EC2 (2002) predicted that shear failure could occur in the test ($V_{uEC2}/V_{efftest}$ ranged between 0.96 and 1.34 with a mean value was 1.17) and if it did failure would occur outside the shear reinforcement in all cases. EC2 (2002) predicts that ACI shear reinforcement can only increase the shear strength of connection C5 by up to 10% and that the connection was overloaded by 4% in the test with $\gamma_c = 1$ (or 56% with $\gamma_c = 1.5$). The predicted shear force at column D4 exceeded the EC2 (2002) design capacity (with $\gamma_c = 1.5$) by 25%. In reality, the corner of the building hung freely in the test and failure did not occur at any of the slab-column connections. The test clearly demonstrated that EC2 (2002) gives conservative estimates of the strength of bi-axially loaded connections with and without ACI shear reinforcement if failure outside the shear reinforced zone is critical.

3 REVIEW OF EXISTING TEST DATA

A literature review showed a remarkable lack of data on slabs reinforced with ACI type shear reinforcement. The only data found on tests with ACI type shear stirrups were those of Hawkins (1989) (eccentrically loaded internal connections) and Unnikrishna (1982) (edge connections). More data were found on interior slab-column specimens with shear studs arranged in the ACI pattern (the axially loaded specimens of Gomes & Regan (1999), Marzouk & Jiang

(1997) Mokhtar et al. (1985) Seible et al. (1980)) and the eccentrically loaded specimens of Elgabry & Ghali (1987). These data were analysed to determine whether the limit on the maximum possible design shear strength given in EC2 (2002) is justified for ACI shear reinforcement. The increase in strength due to shear reinforcement was determined by dividing the measured effective shear strength by the EC2 (2002) shear strength without stirrups V_{cEC2} (evaluated with the material factor of safety for concrete $\gamma_c = 1.0$). The effective shear strength was taken as the failure load for the axially loaded specimens of Gomes & Regan (1999), Marzouk & Jiang (1997) Mokhtar et al. (1985) and Seible et al. (1980) but was increased as described in EC2 (2002) for the eccentrically loaded specimens of Hawkins et al. (1989) and Elgabry & Ghali (1987). In EC2 (2002), the shear resistance with stirrups is given by:

$$V = 0.75 V_{cEC2design} + V_{sEC2} \qquad (4)$$

where $V_{cEC2design}$ is the design shear strength without stirrups which is given by $V_{cEC2}/(\gamma_c = 1.5)$ where:

$$V_{cEC2} = 0.18k(100\rho_l f_{ck})^{1/3} U_1 d \qquad (5)$$

$$k = 1 + \sqrt{\frac{200}{d}} \leq 2.0 \quad \text{and}$$

$$\rho_l = \sqrt{\rho_x \rho_y} \leq 0.02 \quad \text{where} \quad \rho_x = \frac{A_{sx}}{bd} \text{ and } \rho_y = \frac{A_{sy}}{bd}$$

V_{sEC2} is the contribution from the stirrups which is taken as:

$$V_{sEC2} = 1.5 \frac{d}{s} A_{sw} f_{ydef} \qquad (6)$$

where $f_{ydef} = 250 + 0.25d < f_{yd}$

Throughout this paper in the analysis of test data, mean measured concrete strengths f_{cm} have been used in Equation 5 instead of characteristic strengths f_{ck}. Strength ratios $V_{efftest}/V_{cEC2}$ are plotted against the stirrup contributions V_{sEC2}/V_{cEC2} in Figure 3 which suggests that there is an upper limit to the maximum possible mean shear strength of specimens reinforced with shear studs in an ACI pattern of $\sim 1.5\,V_{cEC2}$ (evaluated with $\gamma_c = 1$ and f_{cm}). Figure 3 suggests that the upper limit on shear strength of $2\,V_c$ proposed by Ghali & Megally (1999) for shear studs arranged in the ACI pattern is excessive. The effect of increasing the distance to the last row of shear reinforcement is investigated in Figure 4. For comparison, Figures 3 and 4 include specimens 6 to 9 of Gomes & Regan (1999) which were reinforced with steel I-section beams

arranged in a radial pattern around the column and failed outside the shear reinforced zone. Figures 3 and 4 show that ACI shear reinforcement is less effective at increasing shear strength than radially distributed shear reinforcement. Figure 4 also shows that there appears to be little benefit in terms of increased strength in extending the last row of ACI shear reinforcement beyond around 1.5d from the column face. The tests of

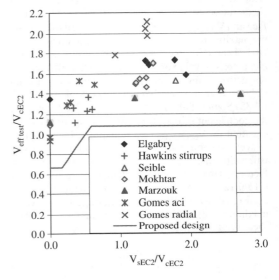

Figure 3. Influence of shear reinforcement on strength of specimens with ACI shear reinforcement.

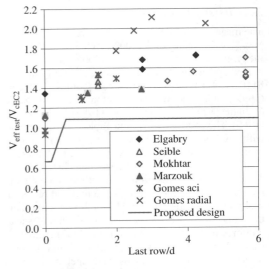

Figure 4. Influence of distance to last row of shear reinforcement on shear strength.

Hawkins et al. (1989) are inconclusive since only one failed in shear. Of the remainder, four tests were stopped due to excessive deflection and in one case failure was attributed to loss of stirrup anchorage.

3.1 Proposed limit for maximum possible shear strength

The data from the tests on axially loaded specimens with ACI shear reinforcement with the last row of shear reinforcement at least 1.5d from the column face and $V_{sEC2}/V_{cEC2} > 0.42$ were analyzed to estimate the maximum possible increase in shear strength with ACI shear reinforcement. The mean and 5% lower characteristic value of $V_{efftest}/V_{cEC2}$ are 1.50 and 1.36 respectively for specimens of Gomes & Regan (1999), Marzouk & Jiang (1997) Mokhtar et al. (1985) Seible et al. (1980). Walraven (2002) justified the coefficient of 0.12 ($=0.18/\gamma_c$) in the EC2 (2002) equation for $V_{cEC2design}$ (see Equation 5 for V_{cEC2}) by a level 2 reliability analysis. The 5% lower characteristic value of the coefficient was 0.15 which gives a factor of safety on the lower characteristic strength of $0.15/0.12 = 1.25$. The same safety factor of 1.25 is used in BS 8110 (1997). A similar approach gives a maximum possible design shear strength for ACI shear reinforcement of:

$$V_{max} = \frac{1.36}{1.25} \times 1.5V_{cEC2design} = 1.6V_{EC2design} \quad (7)$$

Analysis suggests that the full outer perimeter U_{outmax} (see Figure 1) can be considered effective if V_{max} is limited to 1.6 $V_{cEC2design}$ as suggested.

3.2 Assessment of proposal

The mean and standard deviation were calculated for $V_{predicted}/V_{test}$ using EC2 (2002), ACI 318 (2002) and the proposed amendment to EC2 (2002) for 36 axially loaded specimens tested by Chana (1992) (with BS 8110 (1997) type shear stirrups), Gomes & Regan (1999), (radial and ACI shear reinforcement), Marzouk & Jiang (1997) Mokhtar et al. (1985) Seible et al. (1980). The results are given in Table 1 for specimens with ACI shear reinforcement (including parallel control tests on specimens without shear reinforcement) and Table 2 for all the specimens listed above. Table 1 shows that the proposed method is more economic than EC2 (2002) and gives a notional factor of safety $(1/(\mu + 1.64\sigma))$ of 1.31 which is greater than the value of 1.25 used for specimens without shear reinforcement in EC2 (Walraven 2002). Table 2 shows that the proposed method gives similar factors of safety for all specimens and specimens with shear studs arranged in the ACI pattern. Figure 3 shows that Hawkins' specimens were significantly

Table 1. Comparison of design methods for specimens with ACI shear reinforcement.

V_{pred}/V_{test}	Mean μ	st dev σ	$1/(\mu + 1.64\sigma)$
EC2	0.57	0.05	1.51
Proposed	0.64	0.07	1.31
ACI	0.64	0.12	1.19

Table 2. Comparison of design methods for all specimens.

V_{pred}/V_{test}	Mean μ	st dev σ	$1/(\mu + 1.64\sigma)$
EC2	0.64	0.10	1.25
Proposed	0.68	0.08	1.23

weaker than Gomes' specimens with similar values of V_{sEC2}/V_{cEC2}. This is consistent with Ghali's proposal (Ghali & Megally 1999) that the ACI 318 (2002) shear strength should be increased from $V = 0.5 V_c + V_s$ for stirrups to $V = 0.75 V_c + V_s$ for shear studs. Adopting this approach, the authors suggest that the EC2 shear strength should be reduced to $V = 0.5 V_{cEC2} + V_s$ for ACI shear stirrups.

EC2 (2002) and ACI 318 (2002) were used to calculate maximum possible design imposed loads (unfactored) for flat slabs with square panels spanning between 7.5 m and 9 m assuming the strength was limited by punching shear failure at an internal column. Slab depths were determined using the BS 8110 (1997) span to depth rules with reinforcement stress $f_s = 288$ MPa assuming a design imposed load of 5 kN/m². A square column was used with cross-sectional area chosen to give an axial stress of 6 MPa per floor under the design ultimate load for a design imposed load of 5 kN/m². The effective depth was taken as the slab depth less 40 mm and the concrete cube strength taken as 40 MPa. The dead load was taken as the slab self-weight. The flexural reinforcement was designed using the equivalent frame method given in BS 8110 (1997) for a design imposed load of 5 kN/m². The effective shear force V_{eff} was taken as 1.15 V where V is the shear force at the internal column which was taken as $V = 1.09 nL^2$ and n is the factored design load. The results of the parametric study are shown in Figure 5 in which the maximum possible design imposed load w_i is plotted against span. Figure 5 shows that the proposed upper limit of 1.6 $V_{cEC2design}$ is not overly restrictive for lightly loaded slabs (e.g. domestic loading) but is conservative compared with ACI 318 (2002).

The maximum design imposed load can be increased, in the proposed method, by increasing the flexural reinforcement index (unlike ACI 318) or the concrete strength both of which increase V_{cEC2}. Figure 5 confirms that EC2 (2002) can be very conservative compared with ACI 318 (2002).

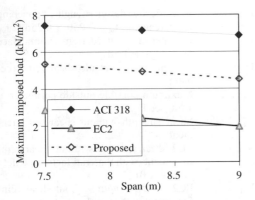

Figure 5. Comparison of maximum possible design imposed loads for flat slabs with ACI shear reinforcement.

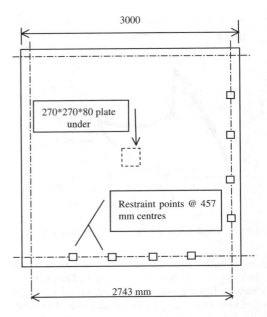

Figure 6. Test specimen in loading rig.

4 TEST PROGRAM AT IMPERIAL COLLEGE

A series of 6 tests are being undertaken at Imperial College to investigate the strength of slabs reinforced with shear stirrups arranged in the ACI pattern. The test specimens are 3 m square by 220 mm thick and are centrally loaded through a 270 mm square plate as shown in Figure 6. The load was applied in displacement-controlled mode and deflections were measured at 14 points with transducers. Four steel rods were used to restrain each slab edge as shown in Figure 6. The average effective depth of the tension reinforcement was about 170 mm. The main flexural reinforcement in the slabs was T16 bars at 90 mm centres. The first perimeter of shear reinforcement was placed at 90 mm from the face of the loaded area and the stirrup spacing was 90 mm. The external width of the stirrups was 150 mm. The specified characteristic yield strength of all the reinforcement was 460 MPa. The concrete target concrete cube strength was 30 MPa and the maximum aggregate size was 20 mm. The slab depth was chosen to comply with the BS 8110 (1997) requirement that stirrups should only be used in slabs of thickness greater than 200 mm.

The flexural failure load of the slabs was estimated with yield line theory to be around 1200 kN. The aims of the tests are to determine: (a) the maximum possible shear capacity of internal slab-column connections with ACI shear stirrups, (b) whether shear strength or more likely ductility is increased by extending the last perimeter of stirrups far enough from the column to ensure shear failure occurs entirely within the shear reinforced zone and (c) the contribution of stirrups to shear strength. To date, two tests have been carried out. Table 3 gives details of the shear reinforcement in each slab and the measured concrete strengths where available. Table 4 gives the measured and predicted

Table 3. Details of authors test specimens.

Test	Stirrup diameter (mm)	Last stirrup/d	Cube strength (MPa)	$P_{test}/$ $P_{design\ proposed}$ (kN)
1	–	–	30	1.49
2	10	5	30	1.28
3	10	3	–	–
4	8	3	–	–
5	8 in pairs	5	–	–
6	To be decided			

Table 4. Comparison of predicted and measured failure loads for the authors test specimens.

Test	ACI (kN)	EC2 in (kN)	EC2 out (kN)	Proposed (kN)	Test (kN)
1	483	617	617	617	614
2	724	980	683	826	843
3	620	980	683	826	–
4	589	794	683	640	–
5	724	1125	683	839	–

failure loads according to EC2 (2002) (at the inner and outer control perimeters with $\gamma_c = 1$), ACI 318 (2002) (with a capacity reduction factor of 1) and the authors' proposal (in which the shear strength with stirrups was taken as $V = 0.5 V_{cEC2} + V_{sEC2}$ and the maxi-

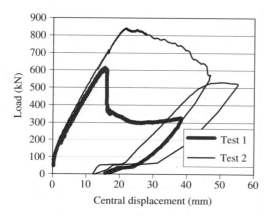

Figure 7. Load–displacement diagram for tests 1 and 2.

mum possible shear strength was assumed to be $1.36 V_{cEC2} = 839 \, kN$ for $f_{cu} = 30 \, Mpa$). The predicted failure loads are given for cube strengths of 30 MPa where measured strengths are not available. The material factor of safety for the concrete γ_c was taken as 1.0. The load–displacement diagrams are compared for specimens 1 and 2 in Figure 7 that shows specimen 2 with ACI shear reinforcement had significant residual strength and ductility post-failure. The area of stirrups will be increased in test 5 to determine whether the area of stirrups provided or the maximum possible shear capacity governed the strength of specimen 2.

5 CONCLUSIONS

EC2 (2002) underestimates the maximum possible shear strength of slabs with ACI shear reinforcement. Analysis of test data suggests that the design punching shear strength can be increased to $1.6 V_{cEC2design}$ by shear studs arranged in the ACI pattern. Tests are being carried out at Imperial College to develop a design method for specimens with ACI stirrups that is compatible with EC2 (2002). It is tentatively proposed that the shear strength of specimens with ACI stirrups should be reduced to $V = 0.5 V_{cEC2} + V_{sEC2}$ instead of $V = 0.75 V_{cEC2} + V_{sEC2}$ in EC2 (2002). It is concluded that ACI shear reinforcement is an economical solution for connections where the design ultimate shear force is close to the actual shear strength without stirrups.

6 NOTATION

A_{sw}	Area of shear reinforcement in each perimeter around the column
d	Effective depth
f_{yd}	Design yield strength

f_{ydef}	EC2 effective design strength of punching reinforcement; $f_{ydef} = 250 + 0.25d < f_{yd}$
U_1	EC2 perimeter at 2d from column face $U_1 = U_{col} + 4\pi d$
U_{out}	EC2 perimeter outside shear reinforcement
U_{outmax}	Maximum possible outside perimeter at 1.5d (see Figure 1)
V_c	Shear strength without shear reinforcement
V_{cEC2}	EC2 shear strength without shear reinforcement (with material factor of safety of $\gamma_c = 1.0$)
$V_{cEC2design}$	EC2 shear strength without shear reinforcement with $\gamma_c = 1.5$
V_{eff}	Effective shear force $V_{eff} = \beta V$ where β is a factor to increase shear force for eccentric loading
V_{max}	Maximum possible design shear force
x	Stirrup width

ACKNOWLEDGEMENTS

The authors would like to acknowledge the financial support of the Engineering and Physical Science Research Council UK, the British Cement Association and the Reinforced Concrete Council. The contribution of the Building Research Establishment to the work at Cardington is also gratefully acknowledged as is the work of the Concrete Structures Laboratory at Imperial College.

REFERENCES

ACI Committee 318. 1992. Building Code Requirements for Reinforced Concrete (ACI 318-89 revised 1992) American Concrete Institute, Detroit.

ACI Committee 318. 2002. Building Code Requirements for Reinforced Concrete (ACI 318-02) American Concrete Institute, Detroit.

BS 8110: Part 1. 1997. *Structural use of concrete: Code of practice for design and construction*, London, British Standards Institution.

Chana, P.S. & Desai, S.B. 1992. Design of shear reinforcement against punching, *The Structural Engineer* 70 No. 9 May 1992, 159–164.

Elgabry, A.A. & Ghali, A. 1987. A Tests on concrete slab-column connections with stud-shear reinforcement subjected to shear moment transfer, *ACI Structural Journal* 433–442.

European Standard 1992. Design of concrete structures, Part 1, General rules and rules for buildings, CEN, 2001, Eurocode 2, ENV.

European Standard 2002. Design of concrete structures, Part 1, General rules and rules for buildings, CEN, Eurocode 2, prEN 1992-1 (Final Draft).

Ghali, A. & Megally, S. 1999. Design for punching shear with ACI 318-95, *ACI Structural Journal* 539–549.

Goodchild, C.H. 2000. Rationalisation of flat slab reinforcement, *British Cement Publication* 97.376.

Gomes, R. & Regan, P. 1999. Punching strength of slabs reinforced for shear with offcuts of rolled steel I-section beams *Magazine of Concrete Research* **51** No. 2 April 121–129.

Hawkins, N., Bao, A. & Yamazaki, J. 1989. Moment transfer from concrete slabs to columns, *ACI Structural Journal* 705–716.

Marzouk, H. & Jiang, D. 1997. Experimental investigation on shear enhancement types for high-strength concrete plates *ACI Journal* 49–58.

Mokhtar, A-S, Ghali, A. & Dilger W. 1985. Stud shear reinforcement for flat concrete plates, *ACI Journal* 676–683.

Seible, F., Ghali, A. & Dilger, W. 1980. Preassembled shear reinforcing units for flat slabs, *ACI Journal* 28–35.

Unnikrishna, P., Kirk, W. & Scavuzzo, L. 1982. Shear reinforcement at slab-column connections in a reinforced concrete flat plate structure, *ACI Journal* 36–42.

Walraven, J.C. 2002. Punching shear Background document for prENV 1992-1-1:2001.

System-based Vision for Strategic and Creative Design, Bontempi (ed.)
© 2003 Swets & Zeitlinger, Lisse, ISBN 90 5809 599 1

Shear behavior of prestressed concrete beams reinforced by CFRP grids bonded on the web surface

A. Yonekura, H. Ito & U. Idehara
Hiroshima Institute of Technology, Hiroshima, Japan

Y. Kawauti, K. Era & T. Mihara
Kyokuto Corporation, Hiroshima, Japan

K. Zaitsu
Sato Benec Company Limite, Oita, Japan

ABSTRACT: Specimens of prestressed concrete beams of life-size (H = 1.0 m, L = 10.0 m) are reinforced with CFRP grids bonded by spraying polymer cement mortar on the surface, and shear behavior of PC beams was investigated by static loading tests. Reinforcing effect was compared in terms of arranging angle of CFRP grids (90°, 45°) and fixation method (anchor fixation, bonding by epoxy resin), and it was confirmed that the highest reinforcing effect was found in the case where the CFRP grids are arranged at an angle of 45° and anchor fixation method is employed. The mode of shear crack initiation and toughness of fracture were found to be better under this condition.

1 INTRODUCTION

Life-span of concrete structure is rapidly decreasing now due to the defects of material or to changes of social situations or natural environment, which had not been foreseen at the time of erection. That is why it is urged to study the methods of repairing or reinforcing the already erected structures to improve their life-span. However, experimental verification of shear reinforcement is one of the still unsolved problems, and further studies are needed in order to make sure the effectiveness of the reinforcement.

There are many kind of reinforcing materials, among which carbon fiber reinforced plastic (CFRP) recently received much attention because of its light-weight, high strength and easiness of handling. Especially, concerning the reinforcing methods where CFRP grids (CFRP assembled in the form of grids) is combined with polymer cement mortar, the reinforcing effect of flexure and fatigue endurance are studied.

So, the purpose of this study is to clarify the shear reinforcing effect of the method where CFRP grids and polymer cement mortar spraying are employed. Prestressed concrete (PC) beams of pretensioning system of life-size are shear reinforced with CFRP grids and polymer cement mortar spraying, and effectiveness of this reinforcing method and validity of reinforcement are shown. And the influence of the difference of both arranging angle of CFRP grids and fixation method on the reinforcing effect has also been examined.

2 EXPERIMENTAL

2.1 *Kinds and properties of materials tested*

Figure 1 shows dimensions of a specimen used for testing. Four specimens of PC beam of girder height H = 1.0 m, girder length L = 10.0 m, and web thickness T = 150 mm (due to the old JIS A 5316) was prepared. Design strength of concrete is assumed to be 50 N/mm², and stirrup D10 (SD 295) were arranged at a pitch of 350 mm. 22 PC strand tendons of 12.7 mm were arranged.

Table 1 shows the kinds of reinforcement for specimens used in the experiments. Two ends of each specimen is referred to as edge A and edge B, respectively, and because on one specimen, the loading test was conducted at the ends of A and B respectively, number of total experimental cases were eight.

Specimen No.1-A corresponds to the case of no reinforcement. In case of specimen No.2-A, 2-B, 3-A, and 3-B, CFRP grids are fixed on both sides of the web by rivet anchoring or bonding by epoxy resin, and

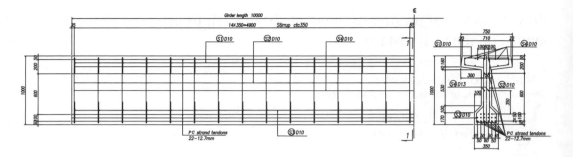

Figure 1. Shape and dimension of specimen.

Table 1. Reinforcing methods for specimens.

Specimens	Reinforcing method	Arranging angle of CFRP grids	Method of fixing CFRP grids
1-A	Not reinforced	–	–
1-B	CFRP grid only	90°	Epoxy resin
2-A	CFRP grids + polymer cement mortar	90°	Rivet anchor
2-B		90°	Epoxy resin
3-A	CFRP grids + polymer cement mortar	45°	Rivet anchor
3-B		45°	Epoxy resin
4-A	Polymer cement mortar only	–	–
4-B	CFRP sheet	–	–

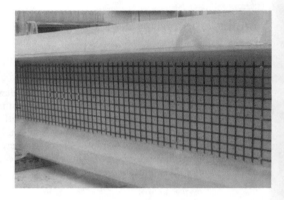

Photograph 1. CFRP grids matched at 90°.

polymer cement mortar was sprayed onto the surface to a thickness of 10 mm to form a composite structure. Angle of arranging CFRP grids (90°, 45°) and method of attaching CFRP grids to the sides of PC girders (rivet anchoring, bonding by epoxy resin) are assumed to be the major factors. Photograph 1 and Photograph 2 show how the CFRP grids are arranged.

In case of specimen No.1-B, only CFRP grids are just attached on the web, and in case of specimen No.4-A, only polymer cement mortar was sprayed on the web without CFRP grids. In case of No.4-B, shear reinforcement by attaching CFRP sheet was tried for comparison.

Physical properties of the materials used in the experiment are shown in Table 2.

2.2 Static loading test

Span of specimens is 7.4 m, and load was applied at the point where the shear span ratio is a/d = 2.5. Because the loading test was to be conducted at the B edge of a specimen, after loading at A edge, the supporting point was moved in order to repeat the test at the other edge as shown in Figure 2. Monolithic loading tests were conducted.

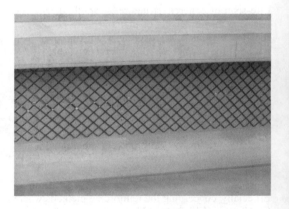

Photograph 2. CFRP grids matched at 45°.

Items of measurements are initial cracking load for flexural and shearing, ultimate load at the shear failure, deflection of the specimen and strain of concrete, steel bars and reinforcing material. Deflection and strain were measured at every load increment. And crack propagation was traced by visual observations and recorded.

Table 2.   Properties of material.

Mix proportion of concrete

	Unit content (kg/m³)				
W/C (%)	W	C	S	G	Chemical admixture
35.5	151	425	721	1128	5.1

Mechanical properties of concrete

Compressive strength (N/mm²)	Tensile strength (N/mm²)	Young's modulus (N/mm²)
62.8	7.9	37,500

Mechanical properties of CFRP grids

Nominal cross-sectional area (mm²)	Tensile strength (N/mm²)	Young's modulus (N/mm²)
17.5	1,591	109,800

Mechanical properties of polymer cement mortar

Compressive strength (N/mm²)	Tensile strength (N/mm²)	Young's modulus (N/mm²)
26.0	2.4	18,100

Properties of CFRP sheet

Mass per unit area (g/mm²)	Tensile strength (N/mm²)	Young's modulus (N/mm²)
200	3,400	230,000

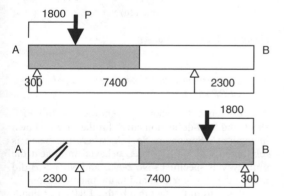

Figure 2.   Loading procedure at two edges A and B of a specimen.

3   EXPERIMENTAL RESULTS AND DISCUSSION

3.1   Initial cracking load and ultimate load

Initial cracking load at flexure, initial cracking load at shear, and ultimate load (load at shear failure) of each specimen are shown in Figure 3. In case of No.4-B, visual observation of crack initiation was not possible because surface of the specimen is covered by CFRP sheet.

The ultimate load of No.2-A, 2-B where CFRP is arranged at an angle of 90° was about 25% greater than that of unreinforced specimen (No.1-A).

But initial cracking load at flexure and shear were about 10%–15% lower than those of unreinforced concrete surface, because the polymer cement mortar sprayed on the web of beams was not prestressed.

In case of specimen No.3-A, 3-B where CFRP grids are arranged at an angle of 45°, the ultimate load at shear failure was about 35% larger than that of the unreinforced specimen. And initial cracking load of polymer cement mortar was also about 5%–10% higher than that of the unreinforced one.

The ultimate load of specimen No.1-B, which is reinforced only by CFRP grids, became about 20% greater than that of the unreinforced specimen. In this case, initial cracking load of the reinforced specimen was almost the same as that of the unreinforced one.

In case of specimen No.4-B, where reinforcement was done only by spraying polymer cement mortar onto the surface, ultimate load was 25% greater than the unreinforced specimen, but initial cracking load was about 5%–10% lower.

3.2   Influence of the arranging angle and the method of fixing CFRP grids

The ultimate load of specimen No.3-A and 3-B, where CFRP grids are arranged at an angle of 45°, is about 10% greater than that of specimen No.2-A and 2-B, where the angle is 90°.

And when the arranging angle is 90° (specimen No.2-A, 2-B), the two fixing methods, namely, anchor fixation and bonding by epoxy resin, gave almost the same reinforcement effect, but when the angle is 45° (specimen No.3-A, 3-B), the ultimate load of the specimen, where the anchor fixation method was employed, was about 10% larger than that for the specimen where bonding by epoxy resin was employed.

Figure 4 shows the load-displacement curves for the case where the PC beams are reinforced with CFRP grids + polymer cement mortar by various ways.

Load-deflection curves of all the reinforced cases were identical in the elastic region where crack is not yet initiated, and deflection of them is smaller than that of the unreinforced case at the same load. It is recognized that deflection is restrained to almost the

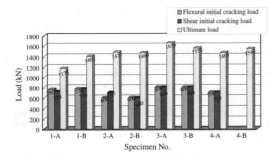

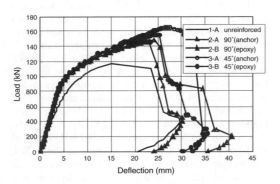

Figure 3.   Initial cracking load and ultimate load.

Specimen	Reinforcing methods
1-A	unreinforced
1-B	CFRP grids only
2-A	CFRP grids 90°(anchor)
2-B	CFRP grids 90°(epoxy)
3-A	CFRP grids 45°(anchor)
3-B	CFRP grids 45°(epoxy)
4-A	Polymer cement mortar only
4-B	CFRP sheet

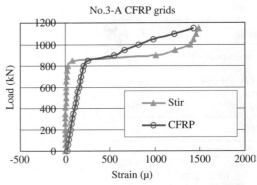

Figure 4.   Dependence of load-deflection curves on CFRP grids arranging angle and fixation method.

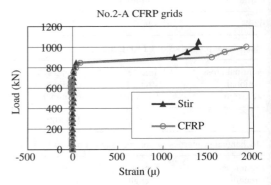

Figure 5.   Load-strain curves.

same extent, or in other words, these reinforcement technique gave rise to the rigidity effect to the structure, whatever the arranging angle or fixation method of CFRP grids might be.

However, there is a definite difference between load-strain curve of stirrup within the specimen and that of CFRP grids on the surface, if the grids arranging angle is different. Figure 5 shows the load-strain curves of stirrup and CFRP grids for the arranging angle of 90° and 45°. Stirrup holds the load after cracks initiated in the beams. In case where CFRP grids are arranged at an angle of 90°, grids hold the load after the cracks initiate just as the stirrup does, but when the grids are arranged at an angle of 45°, it is clear that the grids starts to hold the load at the beginning of loading.

In the plastic region after crack initiation, there are differences of displacement restraint effect among different reinforcement cases. Figure 6 shows displacement of specimens of each case at the moment when the ultimate load of the unreinforced specimen was applied. It is shown that in the plastic region, displacement restraint effect is greater for the case where CFRP grids are arranged at an angle of 45° than for the case where the angle is 90°.

3.3   Comparison with PC beams reinforced with CFRP sheet

As a reference, PC beam was reinforced with CFRP sheet, and load-deflection curve for the case is shown in Figure 7. Specimen No.4-A, where the beam is reinforced with CFRP sheet, behaved in almost the same way as specimens No.2-A,B and No.3-A,B did both in the elastic region and in the plastic region.

Judging from the fact that both CFRP sheet bonding technique which is already reported as a shear reinforcement method and CFRP grids + spraying

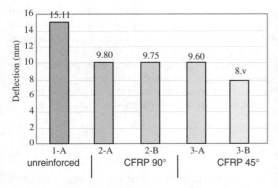

Figure 6. Deflection of specimens when the ultimate load for the unreinforced beam is applied.

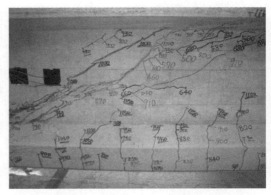

Photograph 3. Unreinforced, failure mode.

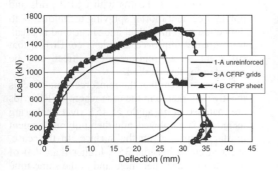

Figure 7. Comparison with CFRP sheet.

Photograph 4. CFRP + mortar, failure mode.

polymer cement mortar technique gave identical behaviors, the technique stated in this paper must be a highly reliable one.

3.4 Crack propagation and modes of fracture of PC beams

In all the cases after bending crack and shear crack initiated, shear crack propagated until finally shear fracture occurred. Peeling between the matrix concrete and polymer cement mortar in the specimens occurred within a limited area prior to fracture, which means the bonding of the two materials was excellent.

In case of no reinforcement (specimen No.1-A), three large shear cracks initiated, and one of them propagated with increasing crack width. And at the moment of maximum load application, brittle fracture occurred (Photograph 3).

In the case of No.4-A, where reinforcement was done only by spraying polymer cement mortar, fracture mode was almost the same as that of unreinforced case. Shear cracks appeared on the surface of both polymer cement mortar and the matrix concrete of the specimen. Two remarkable cracks initiated at the same place. Because the ultimate load is greater, impact at fracture is also larger than the case of the unreinforced specimen, and the sudden failure of this case was higher than any other cases.

In case of specimen No.2-A,B and No.3-A,B where beams are reinforced with CFRP grids + polymer cement mortar, many shear cracks appeared separately on the surface of polymer cement mortar. Especially in case where grids are arranged at an angle of 45° (specimen No.3-A,B), this disperse distribution was remarkable (Photograph 4). Even after the load reached its maximum value, deflection kept on increasing gradually without any brittle fracture which was observed in case of the unreinforced material. This means that this type of specimens are mechanically tough. Among them, specimen No.3-A, where CFRP grids are rivet anchored and arranged at an angle of 45°, showed the most remarkable toughness.

After the loading test is over, polymer cement mortar is removed from the surface in order to observe the situations around the interface, and it became clear that fracture mode is different if the arranging angle of

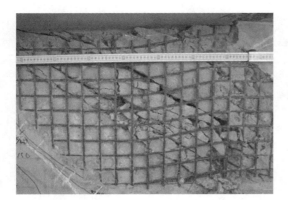

Photograph 5.   CFRP grids, 90°.

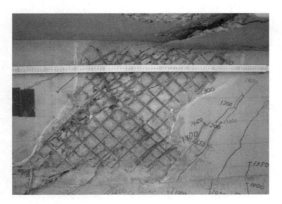

Photograph 6.   CFRP grids, 45°.

CFRP grids is different. When the angle is 90°, the square pattern of CFRP grids are deformed to rhombic pattern (Photograph 5). Fracture of the grids was not observed there. The CFRP grids arranged at an angle of 45° were broken at the cross-links (Photograph 6). High tensile strength of CFRP were made use of almost up to its limit, and this is the reason why the ultimate strength of shear failure could be extremely improved.

3.5   Comparison with results of shear tests for small-sized specimens

Prior to this experiment with life-size specimens, the authors tried some elementary experiments using small-sized specimens (H = 0.27 m, L = 2.0 m). By this elementary experiment, superiority of shear reinforcement method using CFRP grids + polymer cement mortar could be confirmed, but the dependence of reinforcement effect on grids arranging angle could not be clarified.

In the experiment with life-size specimens, the load at break, deflection restraint effect and failure modes are definitely better in case the arrangement angle is 45° than in case the angle is 90°. This means the fact that specimens of big dimension must be used in order to get accurate and reliable engineering information, because the similarity principle does not hold true for this kind of model experiments on shear failure.

4   SUMMARY

In order to clarify the shear reinforcement effect of CFRP grids and polymer cement mortar, static loading experiments were conducted out using PC beams of life-size, and the following information are obtained.

(1) By reinforcing PC beams with CFRP grids and polymer cement mortar spraying technique, both deflection restraint effect and shear load at break were greatly improved, and it is confirmed that sufficient shear reinforcement effect can be expected for this method.

(2) It became evident that the reinforcement effect is mostly remarkable in the case where CFRP grids are matched at an angle of 45°, rivet anchoring technique is employed, and then polymer cement mortar is sprayed on the surface. In this case, shear strength became 35% higher than that of the unreinforced specimen, and at the same time both the situation of shear crack initiation and toughness at fracture were superior to those of the other cases.

REFERENCES

Civil Engineering Research Institute, Ministry of Land, Infrastructure and Transport, Japan et al.: *Reports of the cooperative research on the development of the evaluation methods of fatigue endurance of bridge slab for vehicle weight passage tests.* (No.5) Evaluation Part, pp.40–59, 2002.3.

Civil Engineering Research Institute, Ministry of Land, Infrastructure and Transport, Japan et al.: *Reports of the cooperative research on the repair and reinforcement of concrete members (III)*, pp.69–72, 1999.12.

Era, K., Yonekura, A. et al. 2002. The shear reinforcement effect of PC beams by CFRP grids and polymer mortar blowing. *Proceedings of the 14th Technology & Research Symposium on Inspection and Reinforcement of structures*, pp.129–137, 2002.11.

Okada, S., Yonekura, A. et al. 1999. Reinforcement of PC beams by adhering CFRP grids on the surface of reinforced concrete beams. *Proceedings of the 9th Symposium (60) of Japan Prestressed Concrete Engineering Association*, pp.309–312, 1999.10.

System-based Vision for Strategic and Creative Design, Bontempi (ed.)
© 2003 Swets & Zeitlinger, Lisse, ISBN 90 5809 599 1

Rotation capacity in shear crack hinges of R.C. beams

S. Coccia, M. Como & U. Ianniruberto
Department of Civil Engineering, University of Rome "Tor Vergata", Rome, Italy

ABSTRACT: In this paper we present a theoretical model which provides the ultimate plastic rotation available in shear crack hinges. The rotation capacity is evaluated by integrating the mean curvature across the cracks over the distance from the critical section, where the ultimate moment is reached, to the section where the yielding moment occurs. The influence of the shear in evaluating this distance is taken into account.

A simple formula that gives the rotation capacity of shear crack hinges taking into account all the main parameters of the problem is the main contribution of the paper. This formula is compared with some analytical models and code provisions available in literature.

1 INTRODUCTION

The problem of evaluating the rotation capacity in plastic hinges of reinforced concrete beams has been widely analyzed in literature. Many experimental and theoretical papers have been published on this subject (Bigaj 1999, Bosco & Debernardi 1991, Calvi et al. 1990, CEB 1998, Como 2002a, Cosenza et al. 1990, Cosenza et al. 1991, Eligehausen & Langer 1987, Rinaldi 1998, Riva & Cohn 1994, Sigrist & Marti 1994, Siviero 1976)

Tests showed that the formation of diagonal shear cracks improves the rotation capacity of the hinges because the plastic deformation in the steel rebars spreads over a much larger zone than in flexural crack hinges (see for instance Corley 1966 and Bachmann 1970).

The inclined shear cracks play an important role as the shear slenderness ζ becomes lower than a limit value ζ_{lim} defined as:

$$\zeta_{lim} = \frac{M_{sy}}{Vd} \tag{1}$$

where d is the depth of the section, M_{sy} is the yielding moment and V is the shear at the inclined crack formation, given by:

$$V = \tau_r \kappa (1 + 50\rho_l) bd \tag{2}$$

with:

$$\kappa = 1.6 - d \geq 1 \quad (d \text{ in mts.}) \tag{3}$$

$$\rho_l = \frac{A_{sl}}{bd} \geq 0.02 \tag{4}$$

where A_{sl} is the area of the tensile longitudinal reinforcement and b the width of the cross section.

This formula is currently used to define the load at which shear cracks begin to develop according to the CEB Manual on Cracking and Deformation, (1985).

Even if the ultimate rotation capacity evaluated neglecting the shear forces is always on the safe side, it is very interesting to known the actual value of the plastic rotation available in reinforced concrete structural elements in presence of shear. The problem involves especially beams of r.c. frames.

In this paper we present a theoretical model which extends to the case of diagonally cracked hinges the model for vertical crack hinges proposed by Como, (2002a). It provides the plastic rotation available in a shear crack hinge by integrating the mean curvature across the cracks over the distance between the sections where the ultimate bending moment and the yielding moment occur. The shear influence in evaluating this distance is taken into account.

2 THE ANALYTICAL MODEL

Let us consider a reinforced concrete element whose shear slenderness ζ is lower than the limit value given by Equation 1. The constitutive laws assumed in this model are sketched in Figure 1. The concrete is assumed to have the well-known Kent and Park constitutive law and the steel has a bilinear σ-ε law with strain-hardening ratio Ψ_{sr}. The bond-slip relationship is assumed to be the same of the model DARMSTADT-LEIPZIG shown in CEB Ductility of Reinforced Concrete Structures, (1998). It is the piece-wise

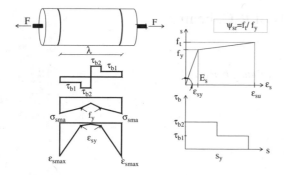

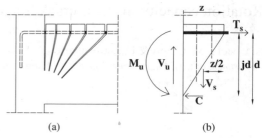

Figure 1. Distribution of steel stresses, strains and bond stresses between two adjacent cracks.

Figure 2. (a) Beam-column connection (b) Free body (after Park & Paulay 1975).

constant function drawn in Figure 1 with τ_{b1} and τ_{b2} given by:

$$\tau_{b1} = 0.6 f_c^{\frac{2}{3}} \quad \text{(MPa)} \tag{5}$$

$$\tau_{b2} = 0.3 f_c^{\frac{2}{3}} \quad \text{(MPa)} \tag{6}$$

being f_c the cylindrical compressive strength of the concrete. The reduction of the shear stress from τ_{b1} to τ_{b2} occurs as soon as the yield strain in the steel is reached.

Moreover it is assumed that the cross sections of the beam remain plane only where vertical cracks occur. This is the case, for instance, of the sections under concentrated loads of beams in three or four points bending tests, or the beam-column interfaces in reinforced concrete frames.

Furthermore, we assume that the shear strength of the beam is always larger than the flexural one; thus the failure is always reached when the maximum bending capacity is attained.

We focus our attention to the zones of the r.c. beams where shear crack plastic hinges form. It is well known that, in these regions, the shear cracks strongly modify the stress distribution in the steel rebars corresponding to flexural hinges where only vertical cracks are present (Bachman 1970). If we consider the beam-column connection of Figure 2(a), the stresses in the steel rebars at flexural failure of the beam can be easily obtained by the rotational equilibrium equation of the free body of Figure 2(b):

$$M_u = T_s(z) jd + \frac{z}{2} V_s(z) \tag{7}$$

where:

$$V_s(z) = \eta V_u \frac{z}{d} \tag{8}$$

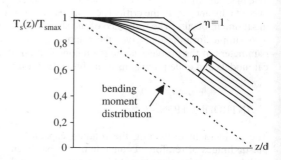

Figure 3. Steel stresses at a shear crack hinge (after Bachmann 1970).

and η is the ratio

$$\eta = \frac{V_s}{V_u} \tag{9}$$

where V_u is the ultimate total shear force and V_s the corresponding share of the web reinforcement. Thus we get

$$T_s(z) = \frac{1}{jd}\left(M_u - z^2 \eta \frac{T_u}{2d}\right) = A_s \sigma_s(z) \tag{10}$$

and the steel stress is given by:

$$\sigma_s(z) = \sigma_{so}\left(1 - \frac{\eta}{2\zeta}\left(\frac{z}{d}\right)^2\right) \tag{11}$$

where σ_{so} is the steel stress at the failure section.

In Figure 3 the force in the bar versus the distance from the failure section is reported for different values of η (Bachman 1970). The differences between the case of flexural and shear cracks are shown by plotting the straight line, sketched in the same figure, which reproduces the bending moment diagram.

The length L_p of the plastic zone can be easily evaluated, with some approximation, by the condition:

$$\sigma_s(L_p) = f_y \qquad (12)$$

We get:

$$L_p = \sqrt{\frac{2\zeta}{\eta}\left(1 - \frac{1}{\Psi_{sro}}\right)}d \qquad (13)$$

with:

$$\Psi_{sro} = \frac{\sigma_{so}}{f_y} \qquad (14)$$

2.1 The crack distance

The evaluation of the crack distance is a crucial point because it has a great influence on the mean curvature and, consequently, on the rotation capacity of the beam.

According to the MC90, crack spacing at the ultimate state can be represented by the stabilized crack pattern occurring in the beam soon afterwards the first cracking. Elastic stresses thus will be considered acting both in the concrete and in the steel when evaluating this stabilized crack distribution.

Figure 4 gives a picture of these stresses acting in the neighbourhood of the cracked section, where $z = 0$, of a beam element. To describe this state of stress, used only to evaluate crack spacing, we will refer to the case of a bending moment M that we assume, for sake of simplicity, constant along the beam.

Following the same approach used in Como, (2002b), the state of stress at the distance z from the crack can thus be obtained by the sum of two different contributions: the primary and the secondary stress states which are equivalent to the couples $M^{(p)}(z)$ and $M^{(s)}(z)$ respectively. We have:

$$M = M^{(p)}(z) + M^{(s)}(z) \qquad (15)$$

The primary state reflects mainly the stress distribution occurring at the cracked section, but with a tensile steel stress $\sigma_s(z)$ that gradually reduces because of the tension stiffening effect. The equilibrium of the bars gives:

$$\sigma_s(z) = \sigma_s(0) - \frac{4\tau_{b2}}{\phi}z \qquad (16)$$

Thus the primary bending moment $M^{(p)}(z)$ is given by:

$$M^{(p)}(z) = \frac{\sigma_s(z)}{n}\frac{J_n}{x_s} = (\sigma_s(0) - \frac{4\tau_{b2}}{\phi})\frac{J_n}{nx_s} \qquad (17)$$

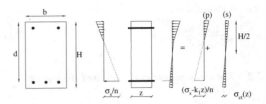

Figure 4. The model to evaluate the crack distance.

where n is the modulus ratio, J_n the moment of inertia of the cracked section with respect to the neutral axis and x_s the distance of the centroid of the tensile steel area from this axis.

The secondary stress distribution develops only within the concrete core and represents the stresses which produce the stiffening effect. It can be approximately represented by a linear distribution with a neutral axis passing through the centroid of the concrete section. The maximum tensile stress $\sigma_{ct}(z)$ in the concrete is thus given by:

$$\sigma_{ct}(z) = \frac{M^{(s)}(z)}{J}\frac{H}{2} \qquad (18)$$

where J is the moment of inertia of the whole concrete section.

The secondary moment $M^{(s)}(z)$ is obtained subtracting from the bending moment M the primary moment $M^{(p)}(z)$ given by (17):

$$M^{(s)}(z) = M - M^{(p)}(z) = \frac{4\tau_{b2}}{\phi}\frac{J_n}{nx_s}z \qquad (19)$$

Thus from (18) and (19) we get:

$$\sigma_{ct}(z) = \frac{2\tau_{b2}}{\phi}\frac{H}{x_s}\frac{J_n}{nJ}z \qquad (20)$$

A new crack occurs at a distance λ_{min} from the section $z = 0$ when the maximum tensile stress in the concrete reaches the tensile strength f_{ct}. Thus we have:

$$f_{ct} = \frac{2\tau_{b2}}{\phi}\frac{H}{x_s}\frac{J_n}{nJ}\lambda_{min} \qquad (21)$$

and:

$$\lambda_{min} = f_{ct}\frac{\phi}{2\tau_{b2}}\frac{x_s}{H}\frac{nJ}{J_n} \qquad (22)$$

λ_{min} represents the minimum distance between cracks and occurs at the midsection of a beam element of length $2\lambda_{min}$. The maximum distance λ_{max} is equal to $2\lambda_{min}$. The average crack distance thus can be assumed as:

$$\lambda = \frac{3}{2} f_{ct} \frac{\phi}{2\tau_{b2}} \frac{x_s}{H} \frac{nJ}{J_n} \qquad (23)$$

2.2 *The mean plastic curvature and the plastic rotation*

Let us consider the small beam element in between two adjacent cracks. If we define the local curvature as:

$$\rho(z) = \frac{\varepsilon_s(z)}{d - x_n(z)} \qquad (24)$$

with $x_n(z)$ the neutral axis position, the mean plastic curvature in the i-esime beam element is given by (Fig. 5):

$$\rho_{m_i} = \frac{1}{\lambda}\left(\int_0^{x_{li}} \frac{(\varepsilon_{sli}(x) - \varepsilon_{sy})}{d - x_n(x)} dx + \int_0^{x_{ri}} \frac{(\varepsilon_{sri}(x) - \varepsilon_{sy})}{d - x_n(x)} dx \right) \qquad (25)$$

By assuming $x_n(z)$ constant and equal to x_{nu}, the neutral axis position at the failure section, we get:

$$\rho_{m_i} = \frac{1}{(d - x_{nu})\lambda}\left(\frac{(\varepsilon_{sli} - \varepsilon_{sy})}{2} X_{li} + \frac{(\varepsilon_{sri} - \varepsilon_{sy})}{2} X_{ri} \right) \qquad (26)$$

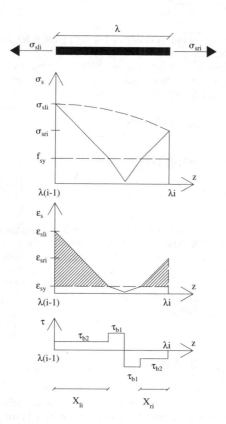

Figure 5. Stress, strain and bond steel distributions over a single element.

where:

$$X_{li} = \frac{\sigma_{sli} - f_y}{k_1} = \frac{\sigma_s(\lambda(i-1)) - f_y}{k_1} \qquad (27)$$

$$X_{ri} = \frac{\sigma_{sri} - f_y}{k_1} = \frac{\sigma_s(\lambda i) - f_y}{k_1} \qquad (28)$$

$$\varepsilon_{sli} - \varepsilon_{sy} = \left(\frac{\varepsilon_{su} - \varepsilon_{sy}}{f_t - f_y} \right)\left[\sigma_s(\lambda(i-1)) - f_y \right] \qquad (29)$$

$$\varepsilon_{sri} - \varepsilon_{sy} = \left(\frac{\varepsilon_{su} - \varepsilon_{sy}}{f_t - f_y} \right)\left[\sigma_s(\lambda i) - f_y \right] \qquad (30)$$

Thus we have:

$$\rho_{m_i} = \left(\frac{\varepsilon_{su} - \varepsilon_{sy}}{f_t - f_y} \right)\left[\frac{(\sigma_s(\lambda(i-1)) - f_y)^2}{2\lambda k_1(d - x_{nu})} + \frac{(\sigma_s(\lambda i) - f_y)^2}{2\lambda k_1(d - x_{nu})} \right] \qquad (31)$$

The ultimate plastic rotation is given by the sum of the mean relative rotations occurring between cracks:

$$\Theta_{pl} = \sum_{i=1}^{N_{tot}} \rho_{m_i}(i)\lambda = \left(\frac{\varepsilon_{su} - \varepsilon_{sy}}{f_t - f_y} \right)\frac{1}{2k_1(d - x_{nu})}\sum \sigma_p \qquad (32)$$

where:

$$\sum \sigma_p = \sum_{i=1}^{N_{tot}} \left[(\sigma_s(\lambda(i-1)) - f_y)^2 + (\sigma_s(\lambda i) - f_y)^2 \right] \qquad (33)$$

$$N_{tot} = \frac{L_p}{\lambda} \qquad (34)$$

The Equation 28 provides:

$$\Theta_{pl} = \left[16 - \left(\frac{\lambda}{L_p} \right)^4 \right]\frac{L_p}{\lambda}\frac{(\Psi_{sro} - 1)^2}{(\Psi_{sr} - 1)}\left(\frac{\varepsilon_{su} - \varepsilon_{sy}}{d - x_{nu}} \right)\frac{f_y}{30 k_1} \qquad (35)$$

where:

$$k_1 = \frac{4\tau_{b1}}{\phi} \qquad (36)$$

Thus, the ultimate rotation capacity Θ_{pl} vanishes when the hardening ratio Ψ_{sr} approaches 1.

3 RESULTS

Here we show the results obtained by applying Equation 35 to the case of a beam with rectangular cross section whose width and height are respectively 300 mm and 500 mm. The assumed material properties are reported in Table 1.

It must be pointed out that the model doesn't account for the fixed end rotation. However it can be easily added when a comparison with experimental results is performed.

Table 1.	Assumed material properties.

Material properties	
Steel	
f_y	500 MPa
ε_{su}	7%
Ψ_{sr}	1.15
Concrete	
f_c	30 MPa
f_{ct}	3 MPa
ε_{co}	2‰
ε_{cu}	7‰

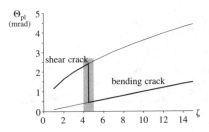

Figure 8. Plastic rotation as a function of ζ ($\mu = 1\%$).

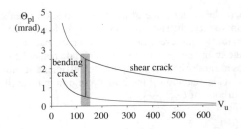

Figure 9. Plastic rotation as a function of V_u ($\mu = 1\%$).

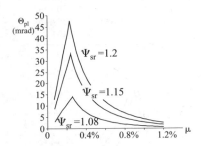

Figure 6. Plastic rotation as a function of μ for different value of Ψ_{sr} with $\alpha = 0$.

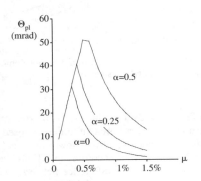

Figure 7. Plastic rotation as a function of μ for $\alpha = 0, 0.25$ and 0.5.

In Figure 6 the plastic rotation versus the geometrical percentage of tensile steel, μ, is reported for three different values of the strain-hardening ratio Ψ_{sr}. Here $\alpha = \mu'/\mu$ with μ' the compression steel percentage. Figure 7 shows the curves obtained varying the ratio α in the range 0–0.5.

4 COMPARISONS

4.1 Comparison with the case of vertical cracks

The available rotation capacity is now evaluated in the whole interval of slenderness ratios in both cases of

shear and flexural plastic hinges (Fig. 8). The rotation capacity available in flexural hinges is evaluated according to the model proposed by Como, (2002a). As expected the plastic rotation accounting for the inclined cracks is always larger than that evaluated in flexural crack hinges. The thickest line is the reference diagram to evaluate the ultimate plastic rotation. Indeed, for ζ lower than ζ_{lim} the upper curve must be used to evaluate the rotation capacity whilst for $\zeta > \zeta_{\text{lim}}$ the vertical cracks formulation is valid.

Figure 9 shows the curve Θ_{pl} versus the shear force at the flexural failure of the beam, V_u, given by:

$$V_u = \frac{M_u}{\zeta d} \qquad (37)$$

The curves obtained show a qualitative agreement with that provided by Langer and reported in CEB Ductility of Reinforced Concrete Structures, (1998).

In Figure 10 the plastic rotation Θ_{pl} is plotted versus the tensile steel percentage μ for a slenderness ratio equal to 3. For low values of μ the plastic rotation Θ_{pl} must be evaluated by the lower curve which corresponds to the case of vertical cracks. As the percentage μ increases, the limit slenderness ζ_{lim} of the beam increases and, for $\mu = 0.547\%$, it reaches the actual slenderness of the beam. Further increases of μ modify the behaviour of the beam. Indeed for μ larger than 0.547% shear cracks form and then the plastic rotation must be evaluated by the corresponding upper curve.

In Figures 8–10 the transition zone from shear to flexural crack pattern is grey filled to remind that

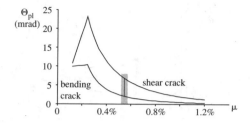

Figure 10. Plastic rotation as a function of μ.

there the actual value of the plastic rotation is uncertain. Indeed, the sudden drop in the plastic rotation is, obviously, incorrect because the crack pattern passage from one type to the other is gradual and the proposed model cannot predict with sufficient accuracy the real behaviour of the hinging region in the neighbourhood of ζ_{lim}.

4.2 Comparison with MC 90

The CEB-FIB MODEL CODE 1990 gives a simplified steel constitutive law that takes into account the tension stiffening effect. The steel behavior is subdivided into four phases and for each of them the expression of the mean steel strain is provided.

The plastic rotation capacity is given by:

$$\Theta_{pl} = \int_0^{L_p} \frac{1}{d - x_n(a)} \left(\varepsilon_{s,mr}(a) - \varepsilon_{s,my} \right) da \qquad (38)$$

where $\varepsilon_{s,mr}$ and $\varepsilon_{s,my}$ are the mean steel strain at failure and at yielding, respectively.

Equation 38, with the modified expression of the steel stress given by the code, becomes:

$$\Theta_{pl} = \int_0^{L_p} \frac{\delta}{d - x_{nu}} \left(1 - \frac{\sigma_{crack}}{\sigma_{sy}} \right) \left(\varepsilon_{s2} - \varepsilon_{sy} \right) da \qquad (39)$$

where σ_{crack} is the steel stress in the crack when the first crack has formed, ε_{s2} is the strain of the reinforcement in the crack and δ (≈ 0.8) is a coefficient that takes into account the hardening ratio Ψ_{sr} and the value of the yield stress f_y.

To understand the difference between the proposed and the CEB models, we analyze the case of a type S steel whose properties are reported in Table 2.

Figure 11 shows the results of this comparison. The curves are quite close each other especially when the steel fails. From the numerical analysis worked out, it essentially appears that the crack spacing is similar in the two models for $\mu \geqslant 0.5\%$. For lower tensile steel percentage the proposed model provides a larger crack spacing than that of the MC 90. Then, for $\mu \geqslant 0.5\%$,

Table 2. Assumed material and geometrical properties.

Material properties	
Steel	type S
f_y	500 MPa
ε_{su}	6%
Ψ_{sr}	1.15
Concrete	
f_c	30 MPa
ε_{cu}	7‰
Geometrical parameters	
b	300 mm
H	500 mm
c (concrete cover)	30 mm
ϕ	16 mm

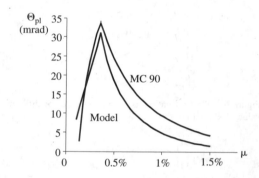

Figure 11. Comparison between the proposed model and the MC 90: case of type S steel.

the differences are especially due to different values of the mean plastic curvature that in the proposed model is, with few exception, always lower than that evaluated by MC 90. Indeed, according to MC 90, the mean plastic curvature is the difference between the mean ultimate and the mean yielding curvatures (see Equation 38) whilst in the proposed model it is related only to the plastic strains which accumulate close to the cracks (see Equation 26) at the ultimate state. Therefore one of the reasons of the distance between the curves in Figure 11 is that the MC 90 accounts for the elastic rotation, occurring between the failure and the yielding sections, which is not considered in the proposed model.

5 CONCLUSIONS

A model able to predict the plastic rotation capacity in shear crack hinges is presented in this paper. The main advantage of the model is to provide a simple equation to evaluate the available plastic rotation which accounts for the main mechanical and geometrical parameters of the problem. Even if further research is needed to verify the reliability of the model against test results available in literature, some parametric enquires show good qualitative results. The comparison with the model proposed in MC 90, in the examined case, gives satisfactory results.

REFERENCES

Bachmann, H. 1970. Influence of shear and bond on rotational capacity of reinforced concrete beams. *IABSE*, Vol. 30, Part. II, pp.11–28, Zurich.

Bigaj, A. J. 1999. *Structural Dependence of Rotation capacity of Plastic Hinges in RC Beams and Slabs*, Delft University Press.

Bosco, C., Debernardi, P. G. 1991. Influenza della duttilità degli acciai sulla capacità di rotazione plastica, *Atti Congresso A.I.C.A.P.*, Spoleto, Italy, 16–18 Maggio.

Calvi, G. M., Cantù, E., Macchi, G., Magenes, G. 1990. *Experimental Investigation on the Rotation Capacity of Concrete Slabs Reinforced with Welded Wire Meshes*, Rapporto N. 34, Dipartimento di Meccanica Strutturale dell'Università Di Pavia.

CEB Design Manual on Cracking and Deformation, 1985. Bulletin d'Information N. 158E, Lausanne.

CEB-FIB MODEL CODE 1990, 1993. Bulletin d'Information N. 213/214, Lausanne.

CEB Ductility of reinforced Concrete Structures, 1998. Bulletin d'Information N. 242:, Part 1 and Part 2, Lausanne.

Como, M. 2002a. On the rotation capacity of reinforced concrete structural elements. *Proc. of the Calladine Conference, Cambridge*, 9–11 September.

Como, M. 2002b. Sulla flessione elastica delle travi in c.a. in presenza di fessurazione, *Atti Congresso A.I.C.A.P.*, Bologna.

Corley, G. 1965, Rotational Capacity of Reinforced Concrete Beams. *ASCE Journal of the Structural Division*, N. ST5.

Cosenza, E., Greco, C., Pecce, M. 1990. Rotazioni plastiche e duttilità richieste nelle travi continue in c.a., *L'industria Italiana del Cemento*, Gennaio.

Cosenza, E., Greco, C., Manfredi, G. 1991. La valutazione teorica delle rotazioni plastiche nelle travi in cemento armato: influenza del legame costitutivo dell'acciaio e dello schema di carico, *Atti Congresso A.I.C.A.P.*, Spoleto, Italy, 16–18 Maggio.

Eligehausen, R., Langer, P. 1987. Rotation capacity of plastic hinges and allowable degree of moment redistribution, CEB Bulletin d'Information N. 175, Lausanne.

Park, R., Paulay, T. 1975. *Reinforced Concrete Structures*. John Wiley & Sons, USA.

Rinaldi, Z. 1998. *Duttilità e resistenza di elementi in c.a.: influenza della localizzazione delle deformazioni nell' acciaio*, PHD Thesis, University of Rome "Tor Vergata".

Riva, P., Cohn, M.Z. 1994. Rotation capacity of structural concrete members, *Magazine of Concrete research*, 46, 223–234.

Sigrist, V., Marti, P. 1994. Ductility of Structural Concrete: A Contribution, Workshop on Development of EN 1992 in Relation to New Research Results and the CEB-FIB Model Code 1990, Czech Technical University, Prague.

Siviero, E. 1976. Rotation Capacity of Monodimensional Members in Structural Concrete, CEB Bulletin d'Information N. 105, Lausanne.

System-based Vision for Strategic and Creative Design, Bontempi (ed.)
© *2003 Swets & Zeitlinger, Lisse, ISBN 90 5809 599 1*

Bond recovery in reinforced high strength concrete after post-fire recuring

R.H. Haddad & L.G. Shannis
Civil Engineering Department, Jordan University of Science and Technology, Irbid, Jordan

ABSTRACT: The potential of bond recovery in reinforced high strength concrete, damaged by fire and recured in water or air, was investigated. Pullout specimens, incorporated natural pozzolan (NP) at contents from 0 to 25% (by cement wt), were used to evaluate bond behavior. Standard cubes ($100 \times 100 \times 100$ mm) were also prepared to evaluate compressive strength. After being cured for 40 days, specimens were heated at 600 and 800°C, then they were re-cured in water or air for another 40 days. Bond behavior and compressive strength were evaluated before, and after heating and after re-curing. The results indicated high potential of bond and compressive strengths recovery after water re-curing, especially at NP contents of 10 and 15%. Air re-cured specimens achieved limited strength and bond recoveries.

1 INTRODUCTION

Reinforced concrete structures are designed to withstand static and dynamic loads and to resist physical, chemical, and physiochemical attacks. During its service life, some of these structures may be subjected to an aggressive fire or high temperatures reaching as high as 1000°C. This would weaken and crack concrete due to (a) undesirable changes in chemistry; (b) destruction of internal structure; and (c) generation of tensile stresses due to thermal gradient. The chemistry changes are represented in destruction of major binding materials at temperatures above 500°C, namely calcium hydroxide and calcium silicate hydrate (C-S-H) (Bazent & Kaplan 1996). Physical changes are represented in an increase in porosity and coarsening of pore structure by vapor pressure action of pore water. These lead to the formation of cracks in concrete in a random manner (Bazent & Kaplan 1996).

Studies conducted on the effect of fire on reinforced concrete mechanical behavior indicated dramatic reduction in its strength (Poon et al. 2001a), especially at temperatures as high as 800°C, accompanied by partial to full loss in bond between reinforcement and concrete (Reichel 1978; Diederichs & Shcneider 1981; Haddad & Shannis, in press). The loss of bond would be devastating to structural stability, as stresses imposed on concrete would be partially (if none) transferred to reinforcing steel; resulting in a sudden-type failure of parts of or the entire structure. Regaining the structural integrity and the serviceability of fire-damaged concrete structures requires extensive repair and rehabilitation works. These would be

very expensive and demand a considerable time to be accomplished. Of course, the more the resulting damage is, the higher would be the cost of rehabilitation.

The possibility of self-healing of damaged concrete through the resumption of cement hydration has been a subject of many investigations (Abdel-Jawad & Haddad 1992; Whitlan 1954; Jacobesn et al. 1995). The findings indicated that self-healing (occurs through filling of cracks) had resulted in effective strength and durability recovery. The percentage of recovery was dependent upon concrete age (at time of damage), causative factor of damage (mechanical or physical), and whether concrete incorporated pozzolanic matter or not.

The potential of self-healing, hence strength and durability recovery, for concrete damaged by fire before re-cured in water was reported to be high (Poon et al. 2001b). The findings indicated that the percentage in strength and permeability recovery of concrete upon re-curing in water was dependent upon temperature reached (amount of damage) and pozzolan type and content used in concrete. The investigators referred the recovery in strength and permeability to the rehydration of decomposed hydration products (Calcium Hydroxide, and C-S-H) and to the filling of cracks by different hydration products. Based on this, self-healing is expected to contribute to regaining, considerably, structural integrity and bond between reinforcement and concrete. In light of this, the amount of overall damage would be reduced and hence the cost of structural rehabilitation.

The above outlined discussion indicates that the potential of bond recovery in reinforced high strength concrete (HSC) members after post-fire curing was overlooked. Therefore, a comprehensive experimental program was designed to investigate this potential, while considering the contribution of pozzolan to the healing process. To achieve the study objectives, pullout high strength concrete specimens (82 × 150, and 100 × 150 mm) were prepared at natural pozzolan contents from 0 to 25% (by cement wt) in order to evaluate bond behavior. Specimens were cured for 40 days at 23°C before subjected to heat treatment at temperatures of 600 and 800°C. Then, they were subjected to two different re-curing regimes for 40 days; immersion in water, and curing in laboratory air. Standard cubes (100 × 100 × 100 mm), prepared to evaluate compressive strength, were subjected to similar treatments. The effect of exposure to heat treatment on mechanical properties and bond behavior was reported by Haddad & Shannis (in press). In this paper, the effect of re-curing (in water or in air) on mechanical properties and bond behavior is presented and discussed.

2 EXPERIMENTAL WORK

2.1 Materials, mix proportions, and specimen preparation

Four HSC mixes were prepared at a w/c ratio of 0.35 with natural pozzolan (NP) at contents of 0, 10%, 15%, and 25% (by wt of cement). Limestone coarse aggregate with a maximum aggregate size of 19 mm and a mixture of equal proportions of two different siliceous sands were used in preparing the HSC mixes. The NP used consists of 37% SiO_2, 12% CaO, 10% Fe_2O_3, and 12.4% Al_2O_3. Mixing was performed according to ASTM testing method C192 using a tilting drum mixer of $0.04 \, m^3$.

Pullout cylindrical specimens at two sizes (82 × 150 and 100 × 150 mm) were cast using the above HSC mixes and grade 60 reinforcing deformed steel rebars of 18 mm diameter. Specimens were stored under moist conditions for 24 hours before being demolded and submerged in water for 40 days until the day of testing. Cube specimens (100 × 100 × 100 mm) were also cast for evaluating compressive strength.

2.2 Heat treatment

Specimens were placed in an electrical high-temperature furnace, after being cured in water at 23°C for 40 days. They were then heated to temperatures of 600 and 800°C for one hour before left to cool down inside the furnace. Later, specimens were taken out and were left to cool further in the laboratory air. The rate of heating was kept constant at 20°C/minute for all specimens.

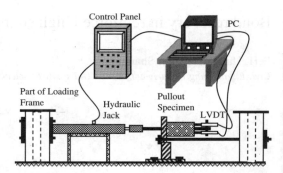

Figure 1. Schematic of the pullout-setup used in the experiments.

2.3 Re-curing process

Heat-treated (HT) specimens were subjected to two re-curing regimes; in water and in air. Those designated to undergo water re-curing (WR) were placed in a water bath at a temperature of 23°C for 40 days. Others designated to undergo air re-curing (AR) were soaked in water for two hours before left on the laboratory shelves for 40 days.

2.4 Pullout testing

Bond behavior of pullout specimens was evaluated by a specially designed concentric pullout setup, shown in the schematic of Figure 1. Pulling-out was carried out at a constant displacement rate of 0.01 mm/sec. The hydraulic jack has a maximum load capacity of 100 kN and a measuring precision of 0.1 kN. The pullout rate was chosen so that bond failure took place within 3 to 5 minutes. The pullout loads versus slippage readings were collected by an electronic panel and a computer setup, as shown schematically in Figure 1. The results presented are the average of two specimens, of which performance was quite similar. The pullout test (ASTM C234) is the most widely used by researchers because of its simplicity. Yet, it is important to mention that obtained results are of value only when comparing bond behaviors of different concrete mixtures or investigating the effect of certain treatments, as is the case herein.

2.5 Evaluation of strength

The compressive strength of heat-treated and re-cured HSC cubes was determined according to BS 8181: Part 5. The average of three to four specimens was taken for each test.

3 RESULTS AND DISCUSSION

Compressive and bond strengths as well as bond behavior recovery after WR and AR were evaluated. The percentage of strength recovery was calculated as the ratio of strength after re-curing to that at 40 days of curing in water.

3.1 Effect of re-curing on recovery of compressive strength

This effect can be understood by referring to Figures 2–3, which show the ratio of compressive strength versus NP content for specimens heated at 600 and 800°C, respectively, and underwent WR or AR. As can be noticed, WR has results in recovering, partially, the compressive strength for HSC specimens after heat treatment, whereas AR imparted limited contribution to strength recovery. Specimens heated to 600°C before WR recovered 69.7, 75.4, 69.5, and 66.3% of the compressive strength for mixes at NP contents of 0, 10, 15, and 25%, respectively. The corresponding percentages after WR of specimen heated at 800°C were 65.4, 76.1, 81, and 55.5%, respectively. On the other hand, AR resulted in much lower strength recovery of 43.4, 45.7, 41.5, and 33.1%, respectively. As

can be noticed, HSC mixes with NP at intermediate contents of 10 and 15% attained the highest strength regains.

3.2 Effect of re-curing on bond stress and free-end slip relationship

Figures 4–5 show bond strength versus free-end slip (for pullout specimens at concrete to cover (c/d) ratio of 1.78 and 15% NP) before and after heating to 600 or 800°C and after WR or AR. The trend behavior of curves pertaining to WR or AR was similar to that of those pertaining to heat treatment. This means that recuring, although enhanced strength and bond, did not contribute to recovering bond stress trend behavior. Nevertheless, the free-end slip at failure (FESF) was substantially reduced, whereas the critical bond stress increased after re-curing as compared to that after exposure to heat. Similar behaviors were observed for other HSC specimens prepared without NP or at 10 and 25% NP and for those prepared at the larger c/d ratio of 2.28 without and with 15% NP.

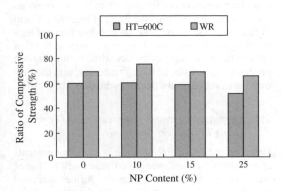

Figure 2. Ratio of compressive strength versus NP content (HT = 600°C).

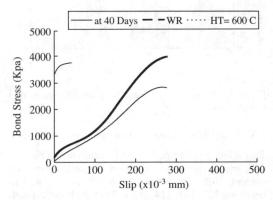

Figure 4. Bond stress versus free-end slip for HSC pullout specimens prepared at 15% NP (c/d ratio = 1.78).

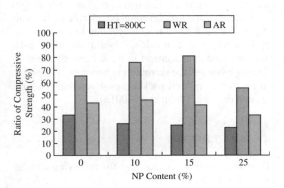

Figure 3. Ratio of compressive strength versus NP content (HT = 800°C).

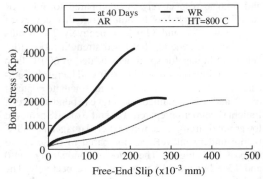

Figure 5. Bond stress versus free-end slip for HSC pullout specimens prepared at 15% NP (c/d ratio = 1.78).

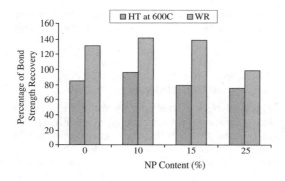

Figure 6. Ratio of bond strength versus NP content (c/d ratio = 1.78).

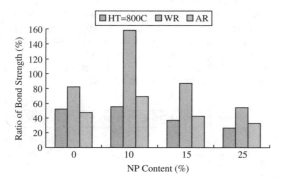

Figure 7. Ratio of bond strength versus NP content (c/d ratio = 1.78).

3.3 Effect of re-curing on bond strength recovery

This effect can be understood by referring to Figures 6–7, which show ratio of bond strength versus NP content. WR after heating to 600°C contributed to regaining 127, 141, 114, and 81% of the bond strength for HSC at NP contents of 0, 10, 15, and 25%, respectively. The corresponding percentage regains after WR of specimen treated at 800°C were 82.2, 158.2, 87.1, and 54.6%, respectively. As compared to WR, AR contributed much less to bond strength recovery of 47.6, 69.4, 42.7, and 32.9%, respectively. The results also show, in general, that bond strength ratios after WR were higher for specimens heated to 600°C than corresponding ones heated to 800°C. The results indicate that HSC mixes with NP at intermediate contents of 10 and 15% attained the highest bond recovery. Pullout specimens prepared at c/d ratio of 2.28 achieved lower bond strength recovery when damaged at 600°C before underwent WR, as compared to those at c/d ratio of 1.78 (Fig. 8). The ratios of bond strength at 0 and 15% NP are 114.5, and 90.9, respectively. The higher damage specimens with the larger c/d ratio received explains the lower recovery percentages. As expected, AR of pullout specimens at c/d ratio of 2.28

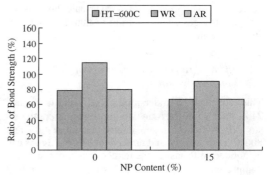

Figure 8. Ratio fo bond strength versus NP content (c/d ratio = 2.28).

results in lower percentage recovery of strength as compared to corresponding ones underwent WR.

Regardless the sever reduction in compressive, and bond strengths after 800°C, HSC specimens were able to heal to a greater extent of that achieved by those heat-treated at 600°C. This is based on the higher vertical deviation between the histogram bars (corresponding to cases before and after WR) of Figures 2–3 and Figures 6–7. Of course, one should discriminate here between self-healing and strength recovery, as the first reflect: the percentage of cracks filled with hydration products, the density of filling materials, and the percentage of rehydrated calcium hydroxide and C-S-H.

2.4 Correlation between compressive and bond strengths recovery potentials

Based on the above discussion, it is clear that percentage recovery in bond strength correlate well to that of compressive strength, although the former achieved higher values. This suggests that the recovery in concrete bond strength upon re-curing is not related only to the recovery of compressive and tensile strengths but also to the enhancement of the bond between concrete and reinforcing steel. The regain of concrete strength (compressive and tensile) could be referred to the healing of cracks, formed in concrete due to temperature, and the rehydration of calcium hydroxide and C-S-H. Whereas, the enhancement in bond between the reinforcing rebar and the surrounding concrete may be due to deposition of well packed new hydration products around the rebar (Poon et al. 2001b).

4 CONCLUSIONS

Based on the above discussion, the following conclusions can be made:

1. The results showed high potential of bond recovery after WR of heat damaged specimens.

2. Water re-cured specimens damaged at 800°C healed more than those damaged at 600°C.
3. The highest strength and bond recovery after water re-curing was at pozzolan contents of 10 and 15%.
4. Air re-cured specimens damaged at high temperatures showed much less compressive and bond strengths recovery as compared to water re-cured ones.
5. The percentage of bond recovery was much higher than that of compressive strength.
6. Although enhanced compressive strength and bond, water or air re-curing did not contribute to recovering bond stress trend behavior.

REFERENCES

Abdel-Jawad, Y. & Haddad, R. 1992. *Effect of early overloading of concrete on strength at later ages*. Cement and Concrete Research 22: 927–936.

Bazant, Z.P. & Kaplan, M.F. 1996. *Concrete at High Temperature: Material Properties and Mathematical Models*. London: Longman Group Limited.

Diederichs, U. & Schneider, U. 1981. *Bond strength at high temperatures*. Magazine Concrete Research, 33 (115): 75–84.

Jacobsen, S., Marchand, J. & Hornain, H. 1995. *SEM observation of the microstructure of frost deteriorated and self-healed concretes*. Cement and Concrete Research 25 (8): 1781–1790.

Poon, C.S., Azhar, S., Anson, M. & Wong, Y-L. 2001a. *Comparison of the strength and durability performance of normal-and high-strength pozzolanic concretes at elevated temperatures*. Cement Concrete Research 31: 1291–1300.

Poon, C.S., Azhar, S., Anson, M. & Wong, Y-L. 2001b. *Strength and durability recovery of fire-damamged concrete after post-fire-curing*. Cement and Concrete Research 31: 1307–1318.

Haddad, R.H. & Shannis, L.G. *Post-fire behavior of bond between high strength pozzolanic concrete and reinforcing steel*. Construction & building Materials. In press.

Reichel, V. 1978. *How Fire affects steel-to-concrete bond*. Building Research Practice 6 (3): 176–187.

Whitlan, E.F. 1954. *Autogenous healing of concrete in compression*. The Structural Engineering 32: 235–243.

Ultimate strength of rectangular CFT column

R.V. Jarquio
New York City Transit, USA

ABSTRACT: This paper presents the analytical method for predicting the ultimate strength of rectangular concrete filled tube column section. It is based on the concept that the concrete core develops its ultimate strength as a reference for determining the corresponding steel forces. The concrete forces for a rectangular section has already been presented at the ISEC-01 conference. Hence, this paper describes only the method of determining the steel forces to be added to the concrete forces for the ultimate strength of rectangular CFT column. Variables considered are concrete strain, ultimate concrete stress, steel yield strength, length and width of the rectangular concrete core, wall thickness of steel tube and position of the column capacity axis. At ultimate condition of stress/strain, the resulting steel stress volumes on the CFT shell area are thus determined. Comparison of results with published data showed divergent values of the customary methods from this analytical method.

1 INTRODUCTION

The current method of calculating the ultimate strength of CFT columns employs the concept of the column interaction formula for steel and reinforced concrete sections subjected to bi-axial bending. In contrast, the analytical method illustrated in this paper will eliminate the need to use the column interaction formula. This is done by using the column capacity axis not only as the reference for equilibrium of internal and external forces but also to determine the capacities of the column section at every position of this axis.

This analysis involves the calculations of concrete and steel forces separately and then combining these to determine the ultimate strength of CFT columns. The concrete forces are determined using the true parabolic stress method of analysis presented in ISEC-01 and SEMC2001. Hence, the calculation of the steel forces is the main focus of this paper. The same assumptions used in the ultimate strength of reinforced concrete columns are also applicable in the analysis for ultimate strength of CFT column section. Similar equations for the determination of the centroid of internal forces and factors for external loads are also applicable in this case.

At ultimate condition of stress/strain, the concrete strain usually assumed equal to 0.003 by the ACI method and 0.0035 by Canadian practice, is the reference point for determining the steel stress/strain. The concrete and steel elements in a CFT column section undergo common deformation when resisting external loads.

This deformation is assumed linear with respect to the neutral axis, whose location is the concrete compressive depth "c". As the concrete compressive depth "c" is varied from the concrete edge it will generate a steel stress/strain diagram consisting of a triangular and rectangular shape. This steel stress/strain diagram will define the steel forces to be added to concrete forces to obtain the ultimate strength of a CFT column section. The compressive and tensile steel stress is limited to the yield strength "f_y" of the material.

The resulting stress volumes on the CFT column section is the measure of the steel forces for every position of "c" and each inclination "θ" of the column capacity axis with the horizontal axis. The integration of these volumes involves 8 limiting ranges of "c" defined by the shape of the steel strain diagram and the corners of the rectangular CFT section. There are 163 equations to be written for the outer and inner rectangular section to obtain the total steel forces at ultimate strength of the CFT section. In particular, the capacity is determined when "θ" falls along the diagonal of the rectangular CFT section. This presentation is limited to the basic formulations since the complete derivation requires more pages than allowed.

The derived equations are programmed using Microsoft Excel'95 and a sample printout for a square CFT section and a comparison with other methods is included in this presentation.

2 DERIVATION

In Figure 1, from the equilibrium conditions of external and internal forces acting on the column section, the following relationships become apparent i.e.,

$$\Sigma F = 0: P = C_c + C_s - T_s \qquad (1)$$

$$\Sigma M = 0: \ M = C_c x_c + C_s x_s + T_s x_t \qquad (2)$$

However, in this analysis only the steel forces C_s, T_s, $C_s x_s$ and $T_s x_t$ will be covered since the concrete forces C_c and $C_c x_c$ have already been determined in papers presented in ISEC-01 and SEMC2001 conference in structural engineering.

To solve for the steel tensile and compressive forces, divide the area of the rectangle into three main sections such as V_1, V_2 and V_3 in which V_1 is the steel stress volume whose limits are from $-x_m$ to x_m, V_2 is the steel stress volume whose limits are from x_m to R_o and V_3 is the steel stress volume whose limits are from $-R_o$ to $-x_m$. These volumes will vary as a function of the value of the compressive concrete depth "c".

Plot the stress/strain diagram such that the concrete reaches its assigned value of strain and the steel reaches the maximum yield stress, f_y. Write the governing equations for the stress/strain lines (one triangular loading and another a uniform loading) for the compressive and tensile steel forces. The intersection of the triangular and rectangular loading will require 8 limiting ranges for "c" to solve V_1, V_2 and V_3 steel force values. The equations for the outer rectangular section is first derived followed by the inner

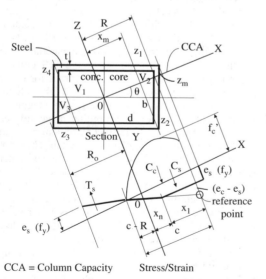

CCA = Column Capacity   Stress/Strain

Figure 1.   Rectangular CFT Column.

rectangular section. From analytic geometry, the equations of the sides of the outer rectangular column section is as follows:

$$z_1 = - \tan \theta \ (x - R_o) + z_m \qquad (3)$$

$$z_2 = \ \cot \theta \ (x - R_o) + z_m \qquad (4)$$

$$z_3 = - \tan \theta \ (x + R_o) - z_m \qquad (5)$$

$$z_4 = \ \cot \theta \ (x + R_o) - z_m \qquad (6)$$

in which,

$$R_o = (1/2) \ \{ (d + 2t) \cos \theta + (b + 2t) \sin \theta \} \qquad (7)$$

$z_m = (1/2) \ \{ (b + 2t) \cos \theta - (d + 2t) \sin \theta \}$ when θ

$$< [(\pi/2) - \alpha] \qquad (8)$$

$z_m = (1/2) \ \{ (d + 2t) \sin \theta - (b + 2t) \cos \theta \}$ when

$$\theta > [(\pi/2) - \alpha] \qquad (9)$$

in which,

$$\alpha = \arctan (b/d) \qquad (10)$$

The equation of steel stress is given by

$$y = k \ \{ x + (c - R) \} \ \text{for triangular shape} \qquad (11)$$

in which, $k = k_1$ or k_3 depending on the position of "c" from the compressive concrete edge of the CFT column section and the balanced condition (simultaneous development of ultimate concrete and steel stress).

$$k_1 \ = 29000 \ e_c \ / \ c \qquad (12)$$

$$k_3 \ = f_y \ /(R + R_o - c) \qquad (13)$$

$$y = k_2 = f_y \ \text{for uniform shape} \qquad (14)$$

The intersection of uniform with triangular loading is given by

$$x_1 = (1/e_c) \ c \ (e_c - e_s) \qquad (15)$$

$$x_n = R - x_1 \qquad (16)$$

in which,

$$R = (1/2) \ [\ d \cos \theta - b \sin \theta \ ] \qquad (17)$$

For limits of pressure volume,

$$x_m = (1/2)\{(d + 2t) \cos \theta - (b + 2t) \sin \theta\} \qquad (18)$$

in which, e_c = concrete strain, f_y = steel yield stress, t = wall thickness, θ = inclination of the column capacity axis with respect to the horizontal axis, "b" and "d" are the width and length of the rectangular section.

Using calculus, V_1, V_2 and V_3 are evaluated within their respective limits defined by 8 limiting ranges of "c" from the compressive concrete edge. These ranges are influenced by the limits of the strain diagram for uniform and triangular shape. The integration process should yield 72 equations for the outer rectangular section and another 72 equations for the inner rectangular section. The difference in values between the outer and inner section is the measure of the steel forces. Add to this the concrete forces to obtain the ultimate strength of the CFT column. The ultimate strength capacity when $\theta = \alpha$ is recommended to resist biaxial bending since the capacity is less than at other position of θ. Plot the values of "P" and "M" to yield the ultimate strength capacity curve of the CFT column section.

Due to page limitations we can only list the following derived equations for the outer rectangular section of the CFT column. However, the rest of the equations for the inner rectangular section can be obtained easily by suitable substitutions.

I. When $0 < c < (R - x_m)$

$$V_{1a} = -4k_3(R_o\tan\theta + z_m)(c-R)x_m \tag{19}$$

$$V_{2a} = -(k_1/6)(\cot\theta + \tan\theta)\{x_n[2x_n^2 + 3(c - R - R_o)x_n$$
$$- 6R_o(c - R)] - (c - R)^2(c + 3R_o - R)\} \tag{20}$$

$$V_{2b} = (k_2/2)(\cot\theta + \tan\theta)\{R_o^2 + x_n(X_n - 2R_o)\} \tag{21}$$

$$V_{2c} = (k_3/6)(\cot\theta + \tan\theta)\{(R - c)^2[c + 3R_o - R] -$$
$$x_m[2x_m^2 + 3(c - R - R_o)x_m - 6R_o(c - R)] \tag{22}$$

$$V_{3a} = -(k_3/6)(\cot\theta + \tan\theta)\{x_m[-2x_m^2 + 3(c - R +$$
$$R_o)x_m - 6R_o(c - R) - R_o^2[3R + R_o - 3c]\} \tag{23}$$

$$C_s = V_{2a} + V_{2b} \tag{24}$$

$$T_s = V_{1a} + V_{3a} + V_{2c} \tag{25}$$

$$V_{1a}x_{1a} = (4/3)k_3(R_o\tan\theta + z_m)x_m^3 \tag{26}$$

$$V_{2a}x_{2a} = -(k_1/12)(\cot\theta + \tan\theta)\{x_n^2[3x_n^2 + 4(c - R -$$
$$R_o)x_n - 6R_o(c - R)] - (R - c)^3[c + 2R_o - R]\} \tag{27}$$

$$V_{2b}x_{2b} = (k_2/6)(\cot\theta + \tan\theta)\{R_o^3 + [2x_n^3 - 3R_ox_n^2]\} \tag{28}$$

$$V_{2c}x_{2c} = (k_3/12)(\cot\theta + \tan\theta)\{(R - c)^3[c + 2R_o - R]$$
$$- x_m^2[3x_m^2 + 4x_m(c - R - R_o) - 6R_o(c - R)]\} \tag{29}$$

$$V_{3a}x_{3a} = (k_3/12)(\cot\theta + \tan\theta)\{x_m^2[3x_m^2 - 4(c - R +$$
$$R_o)x_m + 6R_o(c - R)] - R_o^3[2c - R_o - 2R]\} \tag{30}$$

$$C_sx_s = V_{2a}x_{2a} + V_{2b}x_{2b} \tag{31}$$

$$T_sx_t = V_{1a}x_{1a} + V_{2c}x_{2c} + V_{3a}x_{3a} \tag{32}$$

II. When $(R - x_m) < c < C_1$. V_{3a} = Eq. (26), $V_{2b}x_{2b}$ = Eq. (28), $V_{3a}x_{3a}$ = Eq. (30) and

$$C_1 = [e_c/(e_c - e_s)](R - x_m) \tag{33}$$

$$V_{1b} = k_1(R_o\tan\theta + z_m)\{x_m[x_m + 2(c - R)] +$$
$$(R - c)^2\} \tag{34}$$

$$V_{1c} = k_3(\cot\theta + \tan\theta)\{(R - c)^2 + x_m[x_m - 2(c - R)]\} \tag{35}$$

$$V_{2a} = -(k_1/6)(\cot\theta + \tan\theta)\{x_n[2x_n^2 + 3x_n(c - R - R_o)$$
$$- 6R_o(c - R)] - x_m[2x_m^2 + 3x_m(c - R - R_o) -$$
$$6R_o(c - R)]\} \tag{36}$$

$$V_{2b} = (k_2/2)(\cot\theta + \tan\theta)\{R_o^2 + x_n(x_n - 2R_o)\} \tag{37}$$

$$C_s = V_{2a} + V_{2b} + V_{1b} \tag{38}$$

$$T_s = V_{1c} + V_{3a} \tag{39}$$

$$V_{1b}x_{1b} = (k_1/3)(R_o\tan\theta + z_m)\{x_m^2[2x_m + 3(c - R)] +$$
$$(R - c)^2\} \tag{40}$$

$$V_{1c}x_{1c} = -(k_3/3)(R_o\tan\theta + z_m)\{(R - c)^3 + x_m^2[3(c -$$
$$R) - 2x_m]\} \tag{41}$$

$$V_{2a}x_{2a} = -(k_1/12)(\cot\theta + \tan\theta)\{x_n^2[3x_n^2 + 4x_n(c - R$$
$$- R_o) - 6R_o(c - R)] - x_m^2[3x_m^2 + 4x_m(c - R - R_o) -$$
$$6R_o(c - R)]\} \tag{42}$$

819

$$C_sx_s = V_{2a}x_{2a} + V_{2b}x_{2b} + V_{1b}x_{1b} \tag{43}$$

$$T_sx_t = V_{1c}x_{1c} + V_{3a}x_{3a} \tag{44}$$

III. When $C_1 < c < C_B$. V_{1c} = Eq. (35), V_{3a} = Eq. (23), $V_{1c}x_{1c}$ = Eq. (41), $V_{3a}x_{3a}$ = Eq. (30) and

$$C_B = [e_c/(e_c + e_s)](R + R_o) \tag{45}$$

$$V_{1b} = k_1(R_o \tan \theta + z_m)\{x_n[x_n + 2(c - R)] + (c - R)^2\} \tag{46}$$

$$V_{1d} = 2k_2(R_o \tan \theta + z_m)(x_m - x_n) \tag{47}$$

$$V_{2(max)} = (k_2/2)(\cot \theta + \tan \theta)\{R_o^2 - [2R_ox_m - x_m^2]\} \tag{48}$$

$$C_s = V_{1b} + V_{1d} + V_{2(max)} \tag{49}$$

$$T_s = V_{1c} + V_{3a} \tag{50}$$

$$V_{1b}x_{1b} = (k_1/3)(R_o \tan \theta + z_m)\{x_n^2[2x_n + 3(c - R)] - (c - R)^3\} \tag{51}$$

$$V_{1d}x_{1d} = k_2(R_o \tan \theta + z_m)(x_m^2 - x_n^2) \tag{52}$$

$$V_2x_{2(max)} = (k_2/6)(\cot \theta + \tan \theta)\{R_o^3 - [3R_ox_m^2 - 2x_m^3]\} \tag{53}$$

$$C_sx_s = V_{1b}x_{1b} + V_{1d}x_{1d} + V_2x_{2(max)} \tag{54}$$

$$T_sx_t = V_{1c}x_{1c} + V_{3a}x_{3a} \tag{55}$$

IV. When $C_B < c < (R + x_m)$. V_{1b} = Eq. (34), V_{1d} = Eq. (47), $V_{2(max)}$ = Eq. (48), $V_{1b}x_{1b}$ = Eq. (51), $V_{1d}x_{1d}$ = Eq. (52), $V_2x_{2(max)}$ = Eq. (53) and

$$V_{1c} = k_1(R_o \tan \theta + z_m)\{(c - R)^2 + x_m[x_m - 2(c - R)]\} \tag{56}$$

$$V_{3a} = -(k_1/6)(\cot \theta + \tan \theta)\{x_m[-2x_m^2 + 3x_m(c - R + R_o) - 6R_o(c - R)] - R_o^2[3R + R_o - 3c]\} \tag{57}$$

$$C_s = V_{1b} + V_{1d} + V_{2(max)} \tag{58}$$

$$T_s = V_{1c} + V_{3a} \tag{59}$$

$$V_{1c}x_{1c} = (k_1/3)(R_o \tan \theta + z_m)\{(c - R)^3 - x_m^2[-2x_m + 3(c - R)]\} \tag{60}$$

$$V_{3a}x_{3a} = (k_1/12)(\cot \theta + \tan \theta)\{x_m^2[3x_m^2 - 4x_m(c - R + R_o) + 6R_o(c - R)] - R_o^3[2c - R_o - 2R]\} \tag{61}$$

$$C_sx_s = V_{1d}x_{1d} + V_2x_{2(max)} + V_{1b}x_{1b} \tag{62}$$

$$T_sx_t = V_{1c}x_{1c} + V_{3a}x_{3a} \tag{63}$$

V. When $(R + x_m) < c < (R + R_o)$. V_{1d} = equation (47), $V_{2(max)}$ = equation (48), $V_{1d}x_{1d}$ = equation (52), $V_2x_{2(max)}$ = equation (53) and

$$V_{1b} = k_1(R_o \tan \theta + z_m)\{x_n^2 - x_m^2 + 2(c - R)(x_m - x_n)\} \tag{64}$$

$$V_{3b} = -(k_1/6)(\cot \theta + \tan \theta)\{x_m[-2x_m^2 + 3(c - R + R_o)x_m - 6R_o(c - R)] - (c - R)^2[c - R - 3R_o]\} \tag{65}$$

$$V_{3c} = -(k_1/6)(\cot \theta + \tan \theta)\{(c - R)^2[c - R - 3R_o] - R_o^2[3R_o + R_o - 3c]\} \tag{66}$$

$$C_s = V_{1b} + V_{1d} + V_{2(max)} + V_{3b} \tag{67}$$

$$T_s = V_{3c} \tag{68}$$

$$V_{1b}x_{1b} = -(k_1/3)(R_o \tan \theta + z_m)\{2[x_m^3 - x_n^3] + 3(c - R)[x_n^2 - x_m^2]\} \tag{69}$$

$$V_{3b}x_{3b} = -(k_1/12)(\cot \theta + \tan \theta)\{x_m^2[-3x_m^2 - 4(c - R + R_o)x_m + 6R_o(c - R)] - (c - R)^3[R + 2R_o - c]\} \tag{70}$$

$$V_{3c}x_{3c} = -(k_1/12)(\cot \theta + \tan \theta)\{(c - R)^3[2R_o + R - c] - R_o^3[2c - R_o - 2R]\} \tag{71}$$

$$C_sx_s = V_2x_{2(max)} + V_{1d}x_{1d} - V_{1b}x_{1b} - V_{3b}x_{3b} \tag{72}$$

$$T_sx_t = V_{3c}x_{3c} \tag{73}$$

VI. When $(R + R_o) < c < C_2$. V_{1b} = Eq. (46), V_{1d} = Eq. (47), $V_{2(max)}$ = Eq. (48), $V_{1b}x_{1b}$ = Eq. (51), $V_{1d}x_{1d}$ = Eq. (52), $V_2x_{2(max)}$ = Eq. (53) and

$$C_2 = [e_c/(e_c - e_s)](x_m + R) \tag{74}$$

$$V_{3b} = (k_1/6)(\cot \theta + \tan \theta)\{x_m[-2x_m^2 + 3(c - R + R_o)x_m - 6R_o(c - R)] - R_o^2[3R + R_o - 3c]\} \tag{75}$$

$$C_s = V_{1b} + V_{1d} + V_{2(max)} + V_{3b} \tag{76}$$

$$V_{3b}x_{3b} = (k_1/12)(\cot \theta + \tan \theta)\{x_m^2[3x_m^2 - 4x_m(c - R + R_o) + 6R_o(c - R)] - R_o^3[2c - R_o - 2R]\} \tag{77}$$

$$C_s x_s = V_2 x_{2(max)} + V_{1d} x_{1d} - V_{1b} x_{1b} - V_{3b} x_{3b} \qquad (78)$$

VII. When $C_2 < c < C_3$. $V_{2(max)} = $ Eq. (48), $V_2 x_{2(max)} = $ Eq. (53) and

$$C_3 = [e_c/(e_c - e_s)](R + R_o) \qquad (79)$$

$$V_{1(max)} = 4k_2(R_o \tan \theta + z_m)x_m \qquad (80)$$

$$V_{3b} = (k_1/6)(\cot \theta + \tan \theta)\{x_n[-2x_n^2 + 3x_n(c - R + R_o)$$

$$- 6R_o(c - R)] - R_o^2[3R + R_o - 3c]\} \qquad (81)$$

$$V_{3d} = (k_2/2)(\cot \theta + \tan \theta)\{(x_m^2 - x_n^2) - 2R_o(x_m - x_n)\} \qquad (82)$$

$$C_s = V_{1(max)} + V_{2(max)} + V_{3b} + V_{3d} \qquad (83)$$

$$V_{3b} x_{3b} = -(k_1/12)(\cot \theta + \tan \theta)\{x_n^2[3x_n^2 - 4x_n(c - R$$

$$+ R_o) + 6R_o(c - R)] - R_o^3[2c - R_o - 2R]\} \qquad (84)$$

$$V_{3d} x_{3d} = -(k_2/6)(\cot \theta + \tan \theta)\{2(x_n^3 - x_m^3) + 3R_o(x_m^2$$

$$- x_n^2)\} \qquad (85)$$

$$C_s x_s = V_2 x_{2(max)} - V_{3b} x_{3b} - V_{3d} x_{3d} \qquad (86)$$

VIII. When $c > C_3$. $V_{2(max)} = $ equation (48), $V_{1(max)} = $ equation (80) and

$$V_{3(max)} = (k_2/2)(\cot \theta + \tan \theta)\{x_m(x_m - 2R_o) + R_o^2\} \qquad (87)$$

$$C_s = V_{1(max)} + V_{2(max)} + V_{3(max)} \qquad (88)$$

$$V_3 x_{3(max)} = -(k_2/6)(\cot \theta + \tan \theta)\{x_m^2[-2x_m + 3R_o] - R_o^3\} \qquad (89)$$

$$C_s x_s = V_2 x_{2(max)} - V_3 x_{3(max)} \qquad (90)$$

Equation (19) to (90), which is a total of 72 formulas, will determine the capacity of the outer rectangular section.

To derive the set of equations for the inner rectangular section of the CFT column, replace x_m by x_2, replace R_o by R and replace z_m by z_o in which

$$x_2 = (1/2)[d \cos \theta - b \sin \theta] \qquad (91)$$

$$z_o = (1/2)[b \cos \theta - d \sin \theta] \qquad (92)$$

These substitutions will generate another 72 equations for the inner rectangular section.

3 COLUMN CAPACITY CURVES

Using Microsoft Excel, program the equations for the outer rectangular area followed by the equations of the inner rectangular area. Obtain the difference to yield the steel strength capacity of the CFT column section. Following examples illustrate the results of this analysis.

Figure 2 shows the steel strength capacity curve for a rectangular CFT column in which b = 254 mm, d = 305 mm, t = 13 mm, f'_c = 32 Mpa, f_y = 345 Mpa and θ = 0.69 radian (column capacity axis along diagonal).

Figure 3 shows the column capacity curve of this example when the concrete forces are added to the steel forces.

3.1 Comparison of methods

Figure 4 shows the column capacity curve of a square CFT column with b = d = 234 mm, t = 8 mm, θ = 0.7854 radian, f_y = 373 Mpa and f'_c = 38 Mpa. This CFT column is taken from the 1997 September/October issue of the ACI Structural Journal.

Table 1 shows the comparison of the different methods with the new method for this particular CFT column.

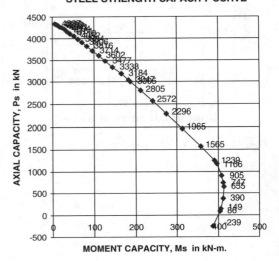

Figure 2. Steel Forces.

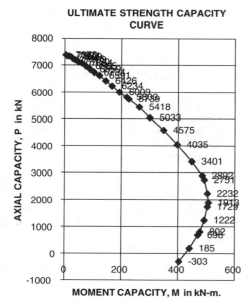

ULTIMATE STRENGTH CAPACITY CURVE

Figure 3. Rect. CFT Column Capacity Curve.

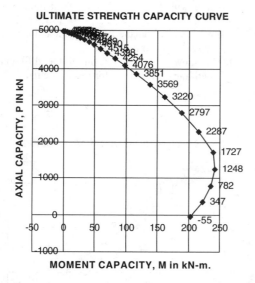

ULTIMATE STRENGTH CAPACITY CURVE

Figure 4. Square CFT Column Capacity Curve.

Table 1.

Axial load (kN)	Moment (kN-m)				
	LRFD	SSLC	NEW	ACI	EXP
1500	163	213	240	304	408
2500	114	172	204	241	423
3500	64	126	143	165	308

4 CONCLUSIONS

1. This paper showed an analytical solution is possible for rectangular and square CFT columns which is consistent with the analysis for ordinary reinforced concrete columns.
2. This analytical method yields the complete range of values of the ultimate strength as compared to the present state of the art presented in the September/October 1997 issue of the ACI Structural Journal, in which the current methods do not yield values at higher eccentricities.
3. This analysis showed the divergence of values by the current methods from the analytical method. In particular, the ACI method yields higher values while the other methods yield lower values.
4. That the column capacity axis must be considered not only for equilibrium of external and internal forces but also to determine the minimum capacity of the CFT column section.

REFERENCES

Singh, A. 2001, *Creative Systems in Structural and Construction Engin*eering, 675–680 & 777–781. AA.Balkema.

Zingoni, A. 2001 *Structural Engineering, Mechanics and Computation, Volume 1,* 319–326 & 343–350. ELSEVIER.

Beyer, W.H. *Handbook of Mathematical Sciences, 6th edition*: 31–32.

System-based Vision for Strategic and Creative Design, Bontempi (ed.)
© 2003 Swets & Zeitlinger, Lisse, ISBN 90 5809 599 1

Bonded-in reinforcement for frame node connections

J. Kunz & F. Muenger
Hilti Corp., Principality of Liechtenstein

H. Kupfer & A. Jaehring
Munich University of Technology, Munich

ABSTRACT: As a result of the increasing need for rehabilitation and strengthening of existing structures, post installed reinforcing bars in concrete are becoming more important.

Some of the tested injection systems – available for post installed bars – have proved to be reliable and to provide behavior at least equivalent to cast in place connections. Approvals for such systems have been released in Germany on the basis of the European Standard EC 2.

For post installed connections, only bars with straight ends can be used in drilled holes instead of bars with hooks or bends. Therefore, careful strut-and-tie modelling in the concrete including the check of splitting forces is necessary for the transfer of bending moments.

A detailed design concept has been developed by means of the strut-and-tie model and the design fundamentals of Eurocode 2. The model has been verified by tests on one in one scale specimens for the transfer of opening and closing moment of the frame.

1 INTRODUCTION

Concrete construction joints and the design of their crossing reinforcement are subjects which arise every day in the course of planning and work execution. If the connecting reinforcement in an existing frame corner does not meet requirements, it can be subsequently bonded in to be rigidly connected using the Hilti HIT injection system (Fig. 1). This is the well-proven method of subsequently anchoring reinforcement which is suitable for use on construction sites and has obtained the first DIBt approval (DIBt 2000). The necessary design work can be carried out in accordance with the reinforced-concrete standard Eurocode 2. The method has proven to be very reliable and economical. Rebars with lengths of up to two meters can be anchored. Rebars subsequently bonded in using the Hilti HIT injection system can be regarded as those normally cast in concrete. In cases where the tensile forces have to be redirected, the cast-in connecting bars are bent in the pertaining direction. Bonded-in reinforcement, however, can only be installed with straight bar ends in drilled holes (Fig. 2).

It is necessary for suitable modelling of the flow of forces in the existing building member to be carried out so that the ultimate and serviceability limit states can be verified. Among the most frequent applications are, for example, the rigid connection of retaining walls or piers (Fig. 1) to existing base plates or of cantilever slabs or corbels to existing reinforced-concrete walls or columns.

2 DESCRIPTION OF TESTS

Two full-scale tests with the test specimens R1 and R2 (Fig. 3) were carried out by the Department for Concrete Construction of the Munich University of Technology. First, the two base plates were cast and later two vertical additions were cast on each base plate. The connecting reinforcing bars where subsequently installed by means of the Hilti HIT injection system using Hilti HIT-HY 150 for R1/1 and R2/1 and Hilti HIT-RE 500 for R1/2 and R2/2.

The reinforcement (Fig. 4) in the base plates and additions was distributed according to the forces calculated with the strut-and-tie model. Two vertical conduits were built in each concrete addition to the test specimens. This made it possible for compressive forces to be superimposed in each addition using two Dywidag prestressing bars. As a result of vertical pretensioning, it was possible, once one of the two connections had failed, to load the stronger one until failure.

Figure 1.   Injection of adhesive to bond reinforcement.

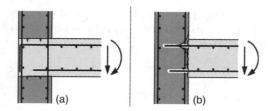

Figure 2.   (a) Cast-in place.   (b) Bonded-in.

The following were recorded during the test: horizontal displacement of the additions, vertical displacement of the base plate, slip of three of the ten bonded-in bars in each addition. Two measuring bars, Dywidag GS 885/1080, $d_s = 15$ mm, each with four strain gauges attached in the core, were installed with the bonded-in bars for each concrete addition to measure the strain in the steel.

The test specimens were loaded with displacement control until failure. This was characterized by a clearly disproportional increase in displacement of the concrete additions without any significant increase in force from the loading equipment (Fig. 5).

At the time of testing, the cube compressive strength of the base plate concrete was approx. $f_{cm} = 25$ N/mm^2

Figure 3.   Test set-up R1 for the opening moment (top) and R2 for the closing moment (bottom).

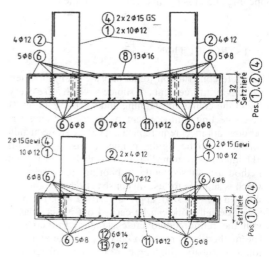

Figure 4.   Reinforcement in the base plates and bonded-in bars. (Top: R1, bottom R2).

and that of the concrete additions approx. $f_{cm} = 39$ N/mm^2.

When the loading jack indicated a force of 318 kN with test specimen R1, it was decided that the superimposed prestressing should be applied to the wall R1/1 due to large widening of the cracks. Afterwards, a maximum loading jack force of 398 kN (yield of

824

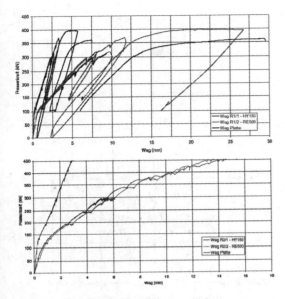

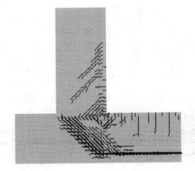

Figure 7.   Crack pattern.

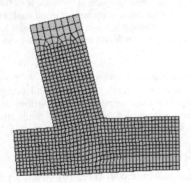

Figure 5.   Load-displacement diagrams for opening moment (R1, top) and closing moment (R2, bottom).

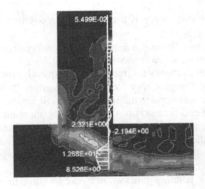

Figure 8.   Bond in compressive strut.

Figure 6.   Deformed system.

R1/2) was reached. After relieving the force and changing the prestressing bar for R1/2 again, the maximum jack force arrived to 361 kN (yield of R1/1). A maximum jack force of 468 kN was achieved when testing specimen R2. It was not necessary for the superimposed prestressing to be applied to the concrete additions (Fig. 5).

3   COMPUTER SIMULATION

The tests were simulated using the finite element program ATENA (ATENA 2000) to depict the internal forces. The bond of the post-installed vertical bars was modelled using a linear bond-slip law on the basis of tests. Figure 6 shows the deformed system for the opening moment in the ultimate limit state. The

computed crack situation at the end of the tests is depicted in Figure 7. The diagonal crack in the base plate and also the cracking in the upper zone of the post-installed bars can be clearly seen. Thus, the bond stress of the vertical bars is shown in Figure 8. It is clear from this that effective anchoring takes place in the diagonal compressive strut and, therefore, the bond strength of the adhesive can take effect.

4   MODELLING AND DESIGN WITH THE STRUT-AND-TIE MODEL

4.1   Fundamentals

Strut-and-tie models are used for design work in the ULS (ultimate limit state) of continuity and discontinuity regions of reinforced-concrete structures (EC 2 (Borgstede 2002), section 2.5.3, or in greater detail: prEN 1992-1, section 5.6.4). The tensile splitting forces must be given attention in the case of the concrete compression members and, if they cannot be taken up by the concrete, reinforcement must be installed to do so. In the case of statically indeterminate structures, the sectional forces may be calculated in accordance with

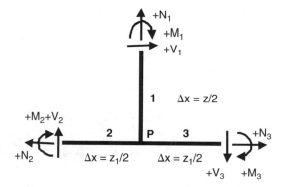

Figure 9. Signs and symbols for section.

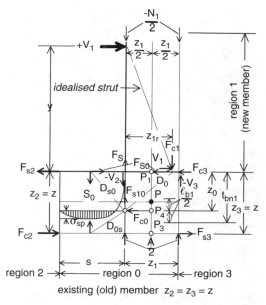

Figure 10. Strut-and-tie model of the frame node for $V_1 > 0$; Ties shown by full lines, struts and idealized cords by dashed line; V_1, V_2, V_3 are shear forces at end-face sections 1, 2, 3; F_{s1}, $F_{c1}, F_{s2}, F_{c2}, F_{s3}, F_{c3}$ are forces in chords at end-faces 1, 2, 3.

the plastic theory if the ductility requirements have been met.

In the following, a frame node of reinforced concrete has been looked at more closely (Fig. 9).

Here, a member, 1, has been subsequently connected at right angles to a continuous member 2–3. The shown signs and symbols were selected for the forces at the end-face sections. The bending moments M_{10}, M_{20} and M_{30} at node P are larger by $V\Delta x$ in each case then the end-face section moments if M and $V\Delta x$ are larger than 0 and Δx is the distance of the respective end-face section from point P.

The bending tension and compression forces F_s and F_c are derived from the section (internal) forces N and M at the end-face section. It may be assumed that in members 2 and 3 the distances of these two forces from the neighboring member edge are roughly the same and, consequently, the axis of elements 1 and 2 halves the lever arm, z, of the internal forces. This means that the following applies to elements 2 and 3:

$$F_s = \frac{|M|}{z} + \frac{N}{2} \text{ and } F_c = \frac{|M|}{z} - \frac{N}{2} \qquad \text{(1a and 1b)}$$

As shown by the tests and confirmed by the computer simulation, the lever arm of the internal forces in member 1 must be set at a reduced figure, $z_{1r} = k \cdot z_1$, owing to strain-induced uplift of the break-out cone of concrete in the upper zone of the drilled hole. Consequently,

$$F_{s1} = \frac{|M_1|}{z_{1r}} + N_1\left(1 - \frac{z_1}{2 \cdot z_{1r}}\right), \text{ and } F_{c1} = \frac{|M_1|}{z_{1r}} - N_1 \cdot \frac{z_1}{2 \cdot z_{1r}}$$

$$\text{(1c and 1d)}$$

Where: $M_1 = V_1 \cdot y$ (Fig. 10).

Forces F_s and F_c are, therefore, local forces which have the same effect as those of the section forces M and N. They are used in the following for the

strut-and-tie model and are defined as positive in each case as the tensile force, F_s, and compressive force, F_c. The most important designations and symbols used are shown in chapter 7 and others are explained in the text.

4.2 Strut-and-tie model

The strut-and-tie model (Fig. 10) consists primarily of the tension cords formed by the bending tension forces, F_s, the compression cords formed by the bending compression forces, F_c, and the inclined compression struts formed by forces D. The tensile splitting force, S_0, is also acting.

The forces in the node can be determined using the following equilibrium relationships:

Rotation of the strut triangle with height $y + z_0$ about

$$F_{c0} \cdot z_0 = V_1 \cdot y + (V_2 + V_3) \cdot \frac{z_1}{2}$$

point P_1:

Rotation of the same triangle about point P_2:

$$(F_{s0} + F_{c3}) \cdot z_0 = V_1 \cdot (y + z_0) + (V_2 + V_3) \cdot \frac{z_1}{2}$$

Rotation of the entire frame about point P_1:

$$(F_{s3} + F_{c2}) \cdot z = V_1 \cdot y + (V_2 + V_3) \cdot \frac{z_1}{2}$$

Rotation of the entire frame about point P_3:

$$\left(F_{s2} + F_{c3}\right) \cdot z = V_1 \cdot \left(y + z\right) + \left(V_2 + V_3\right) \cdot \frac{z_1}{2}$$

Displacement of the entire frame in direction V_1:

$$V_1 = F_{s2} - F_{c2} - F_{s3} + F_{c3}$$

Displacement of entire frame in direction N_1:

$$N_1 + A = V_3 - V_2$$

The horizontal component of strut force, D_0, corresponds to F_{c0}:

$$D_0 = F_{c0} \cdot \frac{1}{\cos\theta}$$

where

$$tg\theta = \frac{z_0}{z_{1r}}$$

with the strut inclination:

$$0.5 < \cot\theta < 2.0$$

(in keeping with EC2 (CEN: Eurocode2, 1991), Section 4.3.2).

4.3 Design

According to EC2 (CEN: Eurocode2, 1991), section 2.3.2 it must be verified that the design value of the acting section force, S_d, remains smaller than the design value of resistance, R_d:

$$S_d < R_d \qquad (2)$$

The lever arm, z_0, of the internal forces in the node region (Fig. 10) results as:

$$z_0 = t_{bn} - \frac{\ell_{b1,d}}{2} \qquad (3)$$

where

$$t_b = h_2 - a_b$$

depth of drilled hole with distance of hole bottom, a_b, from slab edge,

$$t_{bn} = t_b - c_s$$

net depth of drilled hole with axis cover, c_s, of the uppermost reinforcement

$$\ell_{b1,d} = \frac{F_{s10}}{f_{bd} \cdot \Sigma u}$$

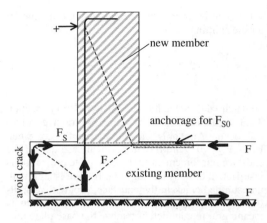

Figure 11. Closing moment at end-face of base plate. Anchorage of tensile forces, F_{s3} and F_{so}, and taking up of splitting force, S_0.

effective length of bond, $\ell_{b1,d}$, of connecting bars (bar total Σu).

The anchorage length, ℓ_{b1}, can be ascertained from the information given by Hilti (Hilti 2002). The design value of the bond includes a partial safety factor, $\gamma_m = 2.16$, compared to the characteristic test value (ETAG 2001, Section 3.2.3). The anchorage length can also be determined in accordance with the DIBt approval (DIBt 2000).

A distinction must be made between two cases when ascertaining the tensile splitting force, S_{0d}, in the discontinuity region, $s = z$:

a) Adjacent end-face reinforcement or shear reinforcement is taking up the tensile splitting force, S_{0d}, in the base plate. Attention must be paid to adequate anchorage of forces F_{s0} and F_{s3} (Fig. 11).
b) End-face is not adjacent: when ascertaining the tensile splitting stresses, $\sigma_{sp,d}$, the characteristic tensile strength of the concrete, $f_{ctk;0.05}$ (CEN: Eurocode2, 1991, table 3.1), is used. The partial safety factor for concrete in tension should be set at $\gamma_m = 1.8$. Internal stresses and those set up by constraint due to shrinkage and temperature do not occur because of the direction of the tensile stresses (perpendicular to the slab axis). In view of this, the tensile strength may be estimated with this conservative figure provided that no progressive failure can occur.

Borgstede showed in his work (Borgstede 2002), based on Leonhardt's recommendations (Leonhardt 1981) for a design allowing for splitting forces in the case of two-dimensional transfer of concentrated forces, and the work done by Jyengar, that, assuming $s = z$ for the discontinuity region, is on the safe side in the case of this application and that the following value may be used when calculating the maximum tensile splitting stresses:

$$\sigma_{sp} = \frac{M_{sp}}{W_{sp}} = 0.39 \cdot \frac{F}{b \cdot d} \approx 0.43 \cdot \frac{F}{b \cdot z} \qquad (4)$$

Schlaich and Schaefer (Leonhardt 1981), section 3.5.3, explain the cases in which progressive failure can occur. An "only closing moment", i.e. when $F_{c2} = F_{s2} = 0$, can present a critical case only if the end-face reinforcement in the base plate projection is insufficient or missing (Fig. 11). If there is an initial, unrestrained crack in the end-face, progressive splitting of the base plate must be expected. It can then be meaningful to completely remove the base plate projection and to splice the bending reinforcement of the new wall with the lower slab reinforcement.

5 DISCUSSION OF TEST RESULTS

The test results are discussed and compared to the design model:

Test specimen R1, opening moment, concrete additions R1/1 and R1/2:

The greatest value of the loading jack force for R1/1 (Hilti HIT-HY 150) was $V_{1,u} = 361\,kN$ and $V_{1u} = 398\,kN$ for R1/2 (Hilti HIT-RE 500).

At the time of stopping the test, the bonded-in connecting bars (10 ϕ 12 only, without measuring bars)

had already suffered plastic deformation ($f_y = 535$ N/mm², Fig. 12).

The clear increase in deformation under jack force V_{1u} can be attributed foremost to the steel slipping in the adhesive. When the steel yields this effect can be often observed during tests with chemical anchors. The ductile behavior, however, is not impaired by this. The test had to be stopped due to the large change in angle of the loading jack support. The upper rebars in the base plate had also virtually reached the yield point.

A follow-up calculation of the reduced lever arm, z_{1r}, gave the reduction factor for R1/1:

$$k = z_{1r} / z_1 = 25.1 / 30 = 0.84$$

and for R1/2:

$$k = z_{1r} / z_1 = 27.5 / 30 = 0.92$$

Lever arm, z_0, at the node:

A recalculation of the anchorage length gave $\ell_{b1,u} = 13.8\,cm$ and $10.8\,cm$ for R1/1 and R1/2 respectively.

The appearance of the cracking (Fig. 13) confirms this anchorage length if it is assumed that the upper inclined crack in the node restricts the anchorage length because the cone of concrete above it is unaffected by the bonding forces due to uplift. The lever arm $z_{0,u}$ calculated from this for R1/1 is 22.1 cm and 23.6 cm for R1/2.

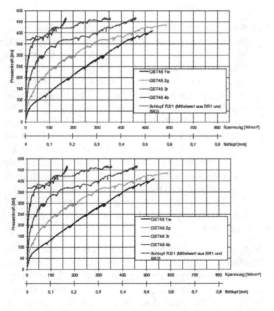

Figure 12. Stress in measuring bars and slip of bonded-in bars: R1/1 top and R1/2 bottom.

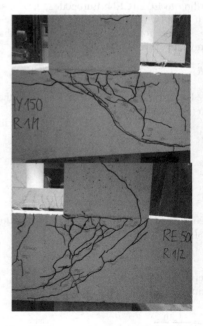

Figure 13. Crack pattern in node: top R1/1, bottom R1/2.

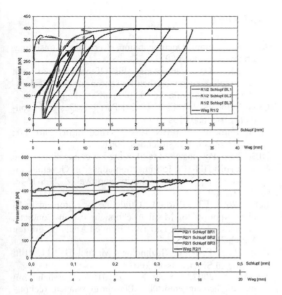

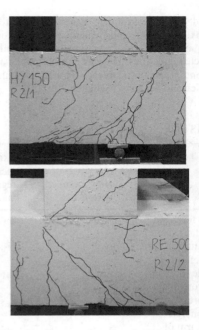

Figure 14. Stress in measuring bars and slip of bonded-in bars: R2/1 top and R2/2 bottom.

Figure 15. Crack pattern in top: node R2/1, bottom: node R2/2.

In the discontinuity region, s, the highest theoretical tensile splitting stress under the maximum load for R1/1 was 0.98 Mpa and for R1/2, 0.93 MPa. The measured tensile splitting strength at specimens was 1.57 Mpa and, thus, splitting was not critical.

The calculated compressive stresses in the immediate zone of the node were also not critical, as a corresponding follow-up calculation showed.

Propagation of the lowest inclined crack in the node zone in the discontinuity region and branching off of the inclined crack in a horizontal direction from $V_1 \sim 200$ kN can be explained as gradual activation of the bottom area of the anchorage length (Fig. 13). At R1/2, the thickness of the split-off layer is considerably smaller than at R1/1. Spalling of this layer does not impair the supporting effect, however, because its effect is not required for the equilibrium of forces.

For test specimen R2, closing moment, again considering concrete addition R1/1 using Hilti HIT-HY 150 and R1/2 using Hilti HIT-RE 500, the highest loading jack force reached was $V_{1,u} = 468$ kN.

The yield point was exceeded in the connecting reinforcement (A_{s1}) (Fig. 14). The tensile stresses in the upper slab reinforcement (A_{s2}) remained within the elastic range, whereas those in the bottom slab reinforcement (A_{s3}) virtually reached the yield.

No reduction in the lever arm, z_1, could be determined due to the closing moment. The calculated ratio was:

$$k = z_{1r}/z_1 = 32.0/30 = 1.07$$

According to Figure 14, the slip, of the connecting bars, was insignificant up to a test load of approx. 380 kN and, at the time of stopping the test, it had reached 0.4 to 0.5 mm. Probably, this slip can be attributed foremost to opening of the inclined crack below the holes (see crack pattern Figure 15).

Compressive failure of the inclined struts in the node was not critical, as a corresponding follow-up calculation showed, and the tensile splitting force, S_0, is taken up by the bent-over upper and lower bars in the base plate projection in the case of test specimen R2 with closing moment. This bending over of the bars was necessary for design reasons with this test specimen to anchor forces F_{s0} and F_{s3}.

6 CONCLUSIONS

The presented tests and computer simulations confirm the previously explained strut-and-tie model with the design rules resulting from it. The method opens up new economical possibilities for upgrading reinforced-concrete structures. In particular, bent-up, frame-like, reinforced-concrete members can be rigidly connected with straight bar ends within the scope of the German approval for a rebar connection made with the Hilti HIT injectable adhesive (DIBt, 2000). The tests also showed that the properties of the adhesive play a major role in the behavior of the connections and cannot, therefore, be simply applied without second thoughts to other systems. The presented design rules are in keeping with EC2 (CEN: Eurocode 2, 1991) and other already or shortly valid reinforced-concrete regulations. They are, furthermore, based on the long-proven principles of frame modelling by Schlaich and Schaefer (Schlaich 2001).

7 LIST OF NOTATIONS

	New member, region 1	Existing member, regions 2 and 3	
Shear force at end-face section	V_1	V_2	V_3
Longitudinal force at section	N_1	N_2	N_3
Tensile force in reinforcement	F_{s1}	F_{s2}	F_{s3}
Compressive force in concrete	F_{c1}	F_{c2}	F_{c3}
Lever arm of internal forces	$z_1; z_{1r}$	$z_2 = z_3 = z$	

Region 0, node and discontinuity	
Tensile force in existing, upper reinforcement	F_{s0}
Clamping force at right angles to connecting bar	F_{c0}
Principal diagonal strut in node	D_0
Diagonal struts indiscontinuity region	D_{s0}, D_{0s}
Tensile splitting force in discontinuity region	S_0
Tensile splitting stresses in discontinuity region	σ_{sp}
Net hole length	t_{bn}
Anchorage length effective in hole	ℓ_{b1}
Lever arm of internal forces in node	z_0
Support reaction in axis of new member	A

REFERENCES

ATENA Program Documentation, Cervenka Consulting, Prague, Edition 2000.
Borgstede, D.: Bemessung für Rahmenknoten mit nachträglich eingemörtelten Bewehrungsstäben; Technische Universität München, Diplomarbeit, August 2002.
CEN: Eurocode 2: V ENV 1992-1 Part 1-1; Design of concrete Structures, 1991.
CEN: Eurocode 2. prEN 1992-1 (final draft) Part 1-1: Design of concrete structures, 2001.
DIBt, 2000. Post installed reinforcing bar connections made with Hilti HIT-HY 150 injection adhesive; General construction supervisory authority approval Z 21.8-1648, 22.11.2000.
EOTA, 2001. ETAG No 001, Guideline for European Technical Approval of Metal Anchors for use in Concrete, Annex C, 1997 and Part five: Bonded Anchors, Edition March 2001.
Hilti, 2002. Fastening Technology Manual B 2.11, Hilti Technical Service, Issue 2002.
Jähring, A. 2002. Bericht Nr. jg2101570, Versuche mit nachträglich eingemörtelten Bewehrungsstäben, Technische Universität München, Lehrstuhl für Massivbau, April 2002.
Jyengar, K.T.S.R., Two-dimensional theories of anchorage zones stresses in post-tensioned prestressed concrete beams., Journ. ACI, Proc. Vol. 59, No 10, p 1443–1466.
Kupfer, H., Muenger, F., Kunz, J. & Jaehring, A. 2003 Nachträglich verankerte Bewehrungsstäbe bei Rahmenknoten. Bauingenieur 01/2003. Springer Verlag.
Leonhardt, F. 1981. Vorlesung über Massivbau, Teil 2, Sonderfälle der Bemessung im Stahlbetonbau, 3. Auflage, Springer Verlag Berlin.
Schlaich, J. 2001. Schäfer, K.: Konstruktion im Stahlbetonbau, Betonkalender, Teil II.

11. Steel structures

System-based Vision for Strategic and Creative Design, Bontempi (ed.)
© *2003 Swets & Zeitlinger, Lisse, ISBN 90 5809 599 1*

Minimum stiffness requirements of intermediate transverse stiffeners in plate girders

Y. Ogawa & K. Fujii
Department of Civil and Environmental Engineering, Hiroshima University, Japan

ABSTRACT: Intermediate transverse stiffener of plate girder should be designed to ensure enough shear strength of the web, but for economical and rational design, it is desirable to make the stiffener small and place it long interval. By elasto-plastic nonlinear finite element analysis, we investigate ultimate behavior and strength of web panels with transverse stiffeners. The results show that the effect of transverse stiffener is different with web thickness. Minimum stiffness requirement of intermediate transverse stiffener is discussed from a view of ultimate limit state.

1 INTRODUCTION

Because the intermediate transverse stiffeners seriously influence to shear strength of plate girder, many researchers have investigated about diagonal tension field of plate girder. E.g. the model proposed by Basler (1961) is used in AASHTO (1994), and Rockey's model (1981) is used in Eurocode3 (2001).

According to the past studies, specifications revised in late years have taken diagonal tension field into account, in the case of strength limit state of plate girders. In these designs, diagonal tension field is modelled by the form similar to pratt truss, and transverse stiffener is designed as a column that supports the axial force caused by diagonal tension field. For example, the cross sectional area of transverse stiffener is prescribed by the following Equation in AASHTO.

$$A_{st} \geq \left(0.15 D A_w (1-C) \frac{V}{V_u} - 18 t_w^2 \right) \frac{\sigma_{yw}}{\sigma_{yst}} \qquad (1)$$

where, V = shear due to factored loads at the strength limit state, V_u = factored shear resistance, σ_{yw} = minimum specified yield strength of web, σ_{yst} = minimum specified yield strength of stiffener, A_w = cross sectional area of web, t_w = web thickness, C = ratio of the shear buckling stress to the shear yield strength, D = 1.0 for stiffener pairs, 1.8 for single angle stiffeners, 2.4 for single plate stiffeners.

However, the dealing with the diagonal tension field theory is different for each specification. The reason of this fact may be unclear interaction of flange, web and transverse stiffeners. In this study, by

using nonlinear finite element analysis, we investigate the relationship between transverse stiffener stiffness and the ultimate shear strength of web, then, propose the stiffness requirements of the intermediate transverse stiffener, based on the stiffness of stiffener when the ultimate strength of web panel with the stiffeners is equal to that of a same size web panel simply supported.

2 ANALYSIS OF WEB PANELS WITH TRANSVERSE STIFFENERS

2.1 *The formulation for non-linear finite element analysis*

The formulation for finite element method was done according to virtual work principle, incremental method, and updated Lagrangian method considering with geometrical and material nonlinearity. Isoparametric shell elements with four nodal points were used.

2.2 *Model for analysis of the ultimate shear strength*

Web panel model with transverse stiffeners used in this study is shown in Figure 1. A lot of studies focusing intermediate transverse stiffeners, ordinarily adopted the web panel model which is a simply supported web plate with a stiffener at center. However, this model can not so obviously represent the effect of the stiffener preventing the deflection caused by web buckling. Therefore, we adopted the model which is free along two web-stiffener connection edges, and simply supported along flange-web connections, as shown in Figure 1. Moreover, in order to consider the effects of

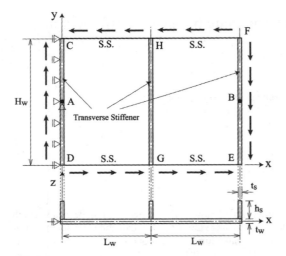

Figure 1. Analytical model.

Table 1. Dimensions and plate slenderness ratio of model.

Hw (m)	α	Lw (m)	λ	tw (mm)	Number of elements x, y-direction
	0.20	0.40	0.5	12.1	8 × 40
			0.7	8.6	
			1.0	6.1	
			1.2	5.1	
			1.5	4.0	
	0.33	0.66	0.5	19.5	16 × 50
			0.7	14.0	
			1.0	9.8	
			1.2	8.1	
			1.5	6.5	
2.00	0.50	1.00	0.5	28.2	8 × 16
			0.7	20.2	
			1.0	14.1	
			1.2	11.8	
			1.5	9.4	
	0.66	1.32	0.5	35.3	16 × 25
			0.7	25.2	
			1.0	17.6	
			1.2	14.7	
			1.5	11.8	
	1.00	2.00	0.5	46.5	16 × 16
			0.7	33.2	
			1.0	23.3	
			1.2	19.4	
			1.5	15.5	

axial force of the stiffener caused by diagonal tension field after web buckling, the analytical model has 2 web panels and 3 transverse stiffeners, and we paid attention the center stiffener of analytical model, particularly.

Web plates are subjected to pure shear force in the direction of arrow in Figure 1. Displacement control of y direction at B was used as incremental control.

The shape of initial deflection of web was given in Equation (2) with respect to x, y-coordinates, as shown in Figure 1, and the maximum deflection $w_{0\,max}$ is taken as $H_w/250$ of which corresponding to the fabrication tolerance in Japanese Specifications for Highway Bridges (JSHB) (1996).

$$w_0(z) = w_{0\,max} \cdot sin\left(\frac{2\pi x}{L_w}\right) sin\left(\frac{2\pi y}{H_w}\right) \quad (2)$$

where, H_w = web depth, L_w = transverse stiffener spacing.

For material properties, yielding stress $\sigma_Y = 235.2$ MPa, yield shear stress $\tau_Y = 135.8$ MPa, elastic modulus $E = 205.8$ GPa, and Poisson's ratio $\nu = 0.3$. Perfect elasto-plastic material, and von Mises's yield criterion are assumed here.

2.3 Parameters

The following parameters are used in discussions: web aspect ratio α, web plate slenderness ratio λ, and the ratio of stiffness of intermediate transverse stiffener to the stiffness of web $\gamma \cdot \alpha$ and λ are:

$$\alpha = L_w/H_w \quad (3)$$

$$\lambda = \frac{H_w}{t_w} \sqrt{\frac{\sigma_Y}{E} \cdot \frac{12(1-\nu^2)}{k \cdot \pi^2}} \quad (4)$$

where, t_w = web thickness, k = buckling coefficient of simply supported plate under pure shear. Value of k is calculated from the following Equation.

$$\left. \begin{array}{ll} k = 4.0 + 5.34/\alpha^2 & : \alpha < 1 \\ k = 5.34 + 4/\alpha^2 & : \alpha \geq 1 \end{array} \right\} \quad (5)$$

For dimensions of the model, shown in Figure 1, $H_w = 2.0$ m. By changing the value of L_w, parameter, $\alpha = 0.2, 0.33, 0.5, 0.66, 1.0$ are investigated. And $\lambda = 0.5, 0.7, 1.0, 1.2, 1.5$ are investigated respectively. Web dimensions and elements of the model are shown in Table 1.

As analytical parameter related to the intermediate transverse stiffeners, we used only γ, which is calculated from Equation (6).

$$\gamma = \frac{E \cdot I_v}{D \cdot H_w} \quad (6)$$

where, I_v = moment of inertia of the transverse stiffener, D = flexural rigidity of web plate.

$$D = \frac{E \cdot t_w^3}{12(1-\nu^2)} \quad (7)$$

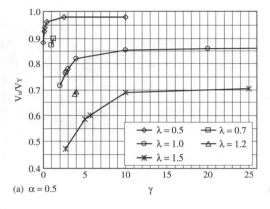
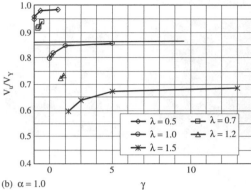

(a) α = 0.5   γ

(b) α = 1.0   γ

Figure 2.   The ultimate strength v.s. γ curve.

When the stiffener is attached on a side of web, the moment of inertia I_v is expressed by Equation (8).

$$I_v = t_s h_s^3/3 \tag{8}$$

where, h_s = width of transverse stiffener, t_s = thickness of transverse stiffener in Figure 1. Since the ratio of t_s to h_s is fixed $t_s/h_s = 13$, in this paper, h_s and t_s can be calculated uniquely, by applying parameters α, γ and λ. The elements for stiffener width divided for z-direction is 4 shown in Figure 1.

3   RESULTS AND DISCUSSIONS

3.1   The effect of transverse stiffener on ultimate shear strength of web panel

The relation between stiffness ratio γ and ultimate shear strength is shown in Figure 2a, b, for the model of α = 0.5 and 1.0, respectively. The ordinate indicates the ratio of the ultimate strength of web V_u to shear yield stress V_Y ($=\tau_Y \cdot H_w \cdot t_w$). From these figures, it can be found that the ultimate strength of web increases with increase of value of γ, but the inclination of γ–V_u/V_Y curve becomes small with increase of value of γ. This fact shows that, the ultimate strength of web panel cannot be enhanced by the stiffener even if the stiffness becomes large beyond the certain value.

The ultimate strength at γ = 0 and λ = 0.5 are V_u/V_Y = 0.88 (α = 0.5) and V_u/V_Y = 0.95 (α = 1.0). These results show the ultimate strength of web without stiffeners (width $2L_w$, depth H_w) that boundary conditions on web-stiffener connections are free, and simply supported along other 2 edges. Thus, in the case of thick plate such as λ = 0.5, web plate approximately ensures shear yield stress, without transverse stiffeners. Moreover, increasing of the ultimate strength is little when value of γ becomes large, comparing with thin web model (λ = 1.5), α = 0.5, 1.0 respectively.

Therefore the effect of transverse stiffener is little for thick web plate such as plastic buckling occurs.

On the other hand, at the thin web model of α = 0.5 and λ = 1.5 in Figure 2, value of V_u/V_Y increases over 20%, in the range of γ = 2.7 to 10.0. This result shows that transverse stiffener greatly contributes to the ultimate strength of web.

For the model of α = 0.5 and λ = 1.5, Mises's stress and principal stress at the ultimate states is illustrated Figure 3 and 4, respectively. As the stiffness of the stiffener γ become large, the diagonal tension field of web progresses and compressive stresses increase along the center stiffener. Corresponding to the progress of diagonal tension field, the ultimate strength V_u/V_Y enhances, as shown in Figure 2a. Especially, it is noticed from Figure 2 that when λ = 1.5 and γ < 10, the effective enhancement of the strength can be obtained by the increse of the stiffness of stiffner γ.

However, as is shown in Figure 3c and d. both figures of Mises's stress distribution is alomost the same, regardless of the increase of γ, because the stress of web is getting larger and the web yileds when γ is larger than a certain value. That is, such large stiffener stiffness γ > 10, in the case of α = 0.5 and λ = 1.5, is not necessary to ensure the ultimate shear strength which the plate girder has, because of web yielding due to diagonal tension field. Thus, it is concluded that the effect of transverse stiffener will not be able to be expected beyond the minimum stiffness requirement γ_{req}, though it can enhance the ultimate shear strength of a plate girder.

3.2   Minimum stiffness requirements of intermediate transverse stiffeners

If the transverse stiffeners in Figure 1 have infinite large stiffness, by the edge CD, GH, and FE with transverse stiffeners, the web panel will be divided into two individual panels each which behaves as simply supported panel with nodal lines at the location of transverse

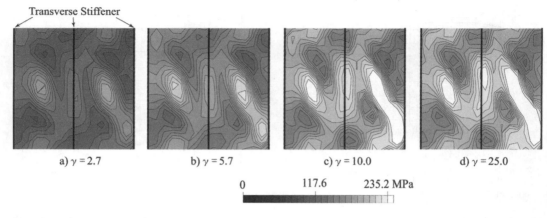

Transverse Stiffener

a) $\gamma = 2.7$ b) $\gamma = 5.7$ c) $\gamma = 10.0$ d) $\gamma = 25.0$

0   117.6   235.2 MPa

Figure 3.   Mises's stress distribution ($\alpha = 0.5$, $\lambda = 1.5$).

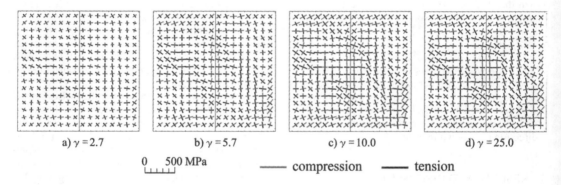

a) $\gamma = 2.7$ b) $\gamma = 5.7$ c) $\gamma = 10.0$ d) $\gamma = 25.0$

0   500 MPa   —— compression   —— tension

Figure 4.   Principal stress of membrane in web ($\alpha = 0.5$, $\lambda = 1.5$).

stiffener attached. In order to decide the minimum stiffness required to ensure the ultimate shear strength of the individual panel mentioned above, firstly, the ultimate shear strength (V_{SS}) was obtained by nonlinear finite element analysis for a simply supported rectangular plate with the same dimensions of the individual web.

If the ultimate strength of the analytical model with transverse stiffeners shown in Figure 1 (V_u) is equal to that of the individual web (V_{SS}), the stiffener stiffness at that strength will be regarded as the minimum stiffness of intermediate transverse stiffener required in the plate girder. However, because it is difficult to get a complete nodal line along the stiffener, judgement for ensuring the ultimate strength of the plate girder is according to the following Equation (9) herein:

$$V_u = 0.98 V_{SS} \tag{9}$$

Thus, the relation between γ and ultimate shear strength V_u/V_{SS} is illustrated in Figure 5, as an example, for the model with stiffener ($\alpha = 0.5$). Using Figure 5, the minimum stiffness for each λ can be obtained

by the intersection point of γ–V_u/V_{SS} curve and broken line ($V_u/V_{SS} = 0.98$).

It is also noticed from Figure 5 that transverse stiffener is much more effective but the larger stiffness will be required to ensure V_{SS}, when the web thickness is thinner (λ is larger). This is caused by the progress of effective diagonal tension field of web panel after web buckling.

Figure 6 shows the minimum stiffness requirements γ_{req} of intermediate transverse stiffener for each λ. The required stiffness regulated by JSHB, DIN4114, AASHTO and Eurocode3 are also shown, where γ_{req} for AASHTO and Eurocode3 is lead out from moment of inertia given in them by Equation (6).

As shown in Figure 6, a typical feature of γ_{req} in this research is that γ_{req} is given as a function of web slenderness ratio λ as well as web aspect ratio α. The values of γ_{req} are also quite different between this research and above-mentioned specifications.

And the figure shows that quite small stiffness is enough to ensure $V_u = 0.98\, V_{SS}$, comparing with that of JSHB based on elastic web buckling.

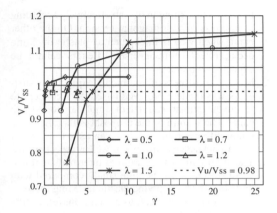

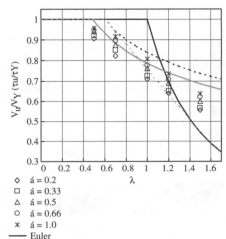

Figure 5. The ultimate strength (V_u/V_{SS}) v.s. γ curve ($\alpha = 0.5$).

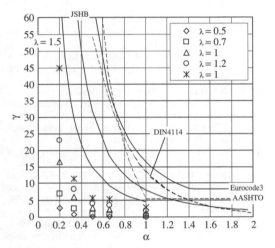

Figure 6. γ_{req} v.s. α curve.

◇ á = 0.2
□ á = 0.33
△ á = 0.5
○ á = 0.66
✳ á = 1.0
—— Euler
- - - - Design Code for Steel Structures Part A (1997)
- - - - Guidelines for Stability Design of Steel Structures (1987)
——— Ultimate Strength and Design of Steel Structures (1994)

Figure 7. Buckling strength curve.

3.3 Web thickness without transverse stiffeners

From Equation (10), the value of γ_{req} becomes negative in the range of $\lambda < 0.53$. This shows that the web plate of $\lambda < 0.53$ does not need transverse stiffener any longer, without concerning of α. It is necessary to discuss whether $\gamma_{req} = 0$ is good considering, in the area where α and λ are small concurrently, because web thickness becomes small, with value of α, about the value of same λ. The buckling strength curve of rectangular plate under shear stress is shown in Figure 7. Buckling strength V_u/V_Y approximates 1.0 adequately, in the range of $\lambda < 0.6$, as shown in Figure 7.

Therefore, plate girder will collapse due to web plastic buckling when $\lambda < 0.6$. Substituting $\lambda = 0.6$ to Equation (3), and α to buckling coefficient k shown in Equation (5), and considering γ_{req} expressed by Equation (10), the following criteria of web which ensures $V_u/V_Y = 1$ is derived out.

$$\left.\begin{array}{l} \dfrac{H_w}{t_w} < 0.6 \cdot \sqrt{\dfrac{E}{\sigma_Y} \dfrac{\pi^2}{12(1-v^2)}} \cdot \sqrt{4.0 + \dfrac{5.34}{\alpha^2}} \quad : \alpha < 1 \\[3mm] \dfrac{H_w}{t_w} < 0.6 \cdot \sqrt{\dfrac{E}{\sigma_Y} \dfrac{\pi^2}{12(1-v^2)}} \cdot \sqrt{5.34 + \dfrac{4.0}{\alpha^2}} \quad : \alpha \geq 1 \end{array}\right\} \quad (11)$$

The criteria for web without transverse stiffener can be obtained from substituting $\alpha = $ infinity to Equation (11):

$$\frac{H_w}{t_w} \sqrt{\frac{\sigma_Y}{E} \frac{12(1-v^2)}{5.34 \cdot \pi^2}} < 0.6 \qquad (12)$$

Finally it is noticed from Figure 6 that the minimum stiffness requirements is nearly 0, when web thickness is thick such like $\lambda < 0.5$ and $\alpha > 0.5$. This fact means that no intermediate transverse stiffener will be needed, when the web is thick.

Based on above consideration, we would like to propose a following design formula on the minimum stiffness requirement of intermediate transverse stiffener, according to regression analysis by numerical results in Figure 6.

$$\gamma_{req} = \frac{(1.43\lambda^2 + 0.218\lambda - 0.508)}{\alpha^{1.7}} \quad : 0.2 \leq \alpha \leq 1.0 \qquad (10)$$

The curve of minimum stiffness requirement for $\lambda = 1.5$ is shown in Figure 6.

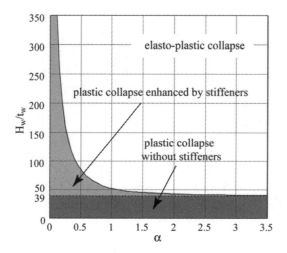

Figure 8. H_w/t_w v.s. α curve.

By the way, substituting $\sigma_Y = 235.2\,\text{MPa}$ and $E = 205.8\,\text{GPa}$ to Equation (11), the following Equation (13) is obtained.

$$\left.\begin{array}{ll} \dfrac{H_w}{t_w} < 16.873 \cdot \sqrt{4.0 + \dfrac{5.34}{\alpha^2}} & : \alpha < 1 \\[3mm] \dfrac{H_w}{t_w} < 16.873 \cdot \sqrt{5.34 + \dfrac{4.0}{\alpha^2}} & : \alpha \geq 1 \end{array}\right\} \qquad (13)$$

Figure 8 shows the relationship of H_w/t_w v.s. aspect ratio α due to Equation (13). This figure shows that web in the area below curve can sustain $V_u/V_Y = 1$ by attaching transverse stiffener. And from Equation (12), Equation (14) is lead out.

$$\frac{H_w}{t_w} < 39.0 \qquad (14)$$

Equation (14) is shown in Figure 8 by broken line, and the web in the area below this line can ensure $V_u/V_Y = 1$ without attaching stiffener.

4 CONCLUSIONS

1. When web is thin such as elastic buckling occur, intermediate transverse stiffener can enhance the ultimate shear strength of web effectively according to progress of web diagonal tension. On the other hand, when web is thick such as plastic buckling occur, effect of transverse stiffeners cannot be expected so much.
2. Minimum stiffness of intermediate transverse stiffeners was made a proposal based on a concept to secure the ultimate strength of simply supported web panel. The feature of the proposal is that the minimum stiffness ratio γ_{req} is given as a function of width-thickness parameter λ as well as aspect ratio α.
3. The minimum stiffness ratio of intermediate transverse stiffeners γ_{req} is quite small, compared with that obtained by applying elastic buckling theory.
4. Web thickness not need to attach transverse stiffeners was shown.

REFERENCES

Japan Road Association. Japanese Specifications for Highway Bridges. 1996.

BS5400 Steel, Concrete and Composite Bridges. Part 3. Code of Practice for Design of Steel Bridges. British Standards Institution. 1982.

AASHTO LRFD Bridge Design Specifications. 1994.

Eurocode3 Design of Steel Structures Part 1.5 Plated structural elements. 2001.

S. Lynn, Beedle. 1991 Stability of Metal Structures A WORLD VIEW Second Edition.

K. Basler, 1961 Strength of Plate Girders in Shear, *Jour. of Structural Division. ASCE.* Vol. 87. No.ST7. 151–180.

K. C. Rockey, Gvaltinat, & K,H,Tang. 1981 The design of transverse stiffeners on webs loaded in shear an ultimate load approach. *Proc. Instn. Civ. Engrs.* Part 2. 71. 1069–1099.

G. S. Stanway, J. C. Chapman, & P. J. Dowling. 1993. Behaviour of a web plate in shear with an intermediate stiffener. *Proc. Instn Civ. Engrs Structs & Bldgs.* Vol. 99. 327–344.

J. C. Chapman, P. C. Davidson. 1987 Behaviour and design of full-depth web panels in shear. *The Structural Engineer.* Vol. 65B. No.4. 65–71.

A. W. Davis, & D. S. C. Griffith. (1999) Shear strength of steel plate girders. *Proc. Instn Civ. Engrs Structs & Bldg.* Vol. 134. 147–157.

Japan Society of Civil Engineers. Guidelines for Stability Design of Steel Structures. 1987.

Japan Society of Civil Engineers. Design Code for Steel Structures Part A; Structures in General. 1997.

Japan Society of Civil Engineers. Ultimate Strength and Design of Steel Structures. 1994.

System-based Vision for Strategic and Creative Design, Bontempi (ed.)
© 2003 Swets & Zeitlinger, Lisse, ISBN 90 5809 599 1

Experimental noise improvement and vibration attenuation of an old steel-bridge

R. Geier & P. Furtner
Vienna Consulting Engineers – VCE, Vienna, Austria

G. Magonette & F. Marazzi
Joint Research Center – JRC, Ispra, Italy

ABSTRACT: Concern for the environmental and the quality of life of citizens forces policy-maker to transfer the transportation of goods from the traditional heavy trucks to railways. However, railway companies are subjected to tremendous resistance and objections to build new railway lines until the problem of vibration exposure to citizens is solved. An innovative method is required to notably reduce noise and vibration, at the same time minimizing energy and material use. For these ambitious goals it was necessary to perform some studies on an existing old steel structure in Austria. Numerous in-field tests have been performed including the measurements of structural vibration on the one hand and noise radiation on the other hand. Tests with an experimental train have also been performed, gathering signals under well-known boundary conditions. Testing existing as well as new developed noise reducing technologies at the Joint Research Centre will be the main outcome of this project.

1 INTRODUCTION

The concept of structural control originated in the early 1970s. Passive methods utilise the system response to dissipate energy without requiring an external power source. Active control, on the other hand, refers to methods that require a large power supply to operate large size actuators. Between passive and active control a very promising area is developing based on semi-active control laws. A very promising class of semi-active control devices uses advanced materials as for example rheological fluids (http://www.samco.org).

Starting point for this extensive research is the CaSCo project (Consistent Semi-active System Control) supported by the European Commission in the frame of their current research programme FP 5. The basic project idea is to develop advanced damping technologies in order to reduce noise and vibration of railway lines. A rather simple, compact and very robust technology is required which can be used for upgrading existing systems as well as achieving better vibration attenuation for future projects. An interesting and powerful method is the application of semi-active damping devices. Some research has been performed in the past concerning active control in civil engineering, which was not really applicable for practical solutions due to extensive space and energy requirements. The semi-active approach is based upon miniaturised equipment that is designed to work as stand alone unit with only less power consumption and less maintenance required.

The innovative aspects are to apply magneto-rheological fluid technology for the real-time control of forces and increase energy dissipation, while at the same time minimise geometric dimensions of individual devices.

2 PROBLEM STATEMENT

Due to their high transport capacity and effective use of energy with lowest damage to the environment, railways are one of the most important means of transportation for the future. In spite of the advantages of railways in comparison with other transport systems as for example motorcars, the acceptance of new railway lines is very low especially by potential neighbours. One of the most important reasons for that is the fear of irritations from noise and vibrations induced by modern high-speed trains. These problems especially occur in densely populated areas as in towns, where railway routes are in tunnels with low overburden and very close to residential buildings (Geier & Wenzel 2001). Due to maintenance reasons ballast less permanent ways become more and more important, especially for such tunnel lines. With regard to load carrying capability and to long-time stability of the track these solid roadways show a lot of advantages. Nevertheless the most important disadvantages of most kinds of permanent ways are the additional increasing noise and vibration emissions caused by such superstructures.

The source of noise and vibration emissions of railway lines is the rough contact area of the wheel-rail-system. The roughness causes vibrations that are induced into the superstructure and propagate through the soil to buildings in the neighbourhood. For the further remarks vibrations are defined as perceptible low frequency oscillations between 1 Hz and 80 Hz, whereas structure or ground borne noise are mechanical vibrations in an audible frequency range between 16 Hz and 20 kHz. Both kinds of emissions are propagated through the soil by mechanical wave propagation. Noise and vibration caused by rail traffic can be transmitted through the air (railway lines at ground level) and trough the soil (railway lines at ground level and underground). In adjacent structures the induced vibrations in the frequency range of around 8 to 20 Hz mainly affect timber-ceiling structures or steel girder construction. Excitation frequencies of railway induced vibrations between 40 Hz and 80 Hz may cause significant acoustic phenomena that are called structure born sound.

For the reduction of vibration, sufficient results have been obtained so far by application of Mass-Spring-Systems. The audible noise emission mainly from old steel bridges is a problem that has to be solved in future. This paper focuses on reduction measures of audible noise that is emitted during train passage. Generally speaking there is only little knowledge about the noise emission from railway bridges up to now.

The main target for the development is shown in figure 1, where the results of a sound level measurement is presented during train passage on a steel bridge and on the free track. The noise emission difference was in the range of $\Delta L \approx 10$ dB(A) which corresponds to a doubling of the noise emitted on free track. This ambitious goal should be achieved in the development in order to upgrade extensive steel bridges successfully.

3 STATE OF THE ART

The concept of control for engineering applications originated in the early 1970. In the three decades, much progress has been made toward exploiting the potential benefits offered for protection of structures when subjected to high level of noise, earthquakes, high wind, blast and other internal of external dynamic excitations. Recently, the use of so-called "Smart Materials" allows an improvement in vibration control techniques (Marazzi 2002).

Passive control refers to methods that utilize the system response to dissipate energy without requiring an external power source for their operation. Examples are metallic dampers, friction dampers, viscoelastic dampers, viscous fluid dampers, tuned mass dampers and tuned liquid dampers. Their effectiveness has clearly proven by laboratory and in field experiments and observations, but their performance has intrinsic limitations due to the fact that they must be tuned once for all before encountering the vibration phenomenon.

Active control, on the other hand, refers to systems that require a large power source to operate large actuators that dissipate energy and supply control forces. Such systems are used to control the response of system components to internal or external excitation, where the safety or comfort level of the occupants is of concern. Active control makes use of a wide variety of actuators, including active mass dampers, hybrid mass dampers, tendon controls, which may employ hydraulic, pneumatic, electro-magnetic actuation. The need for an external power supply makes this system vulnerable to power failure, especially for earthquakes.

Semi-active control combines the best features of active and passive systems. According to presently accepted definitions, a semi-active control device is one that has properties that can be adjusted in real time but cannot input energy into the system being controlled. These methods require a small power source (a battery, for example) to operate and utilize the system response to dissipate energy. Preliminary studies have shown that semi-active control laws can potentially achieve the performance of fully active systems. Two systems are generally included in this category: (1) variable stiffness and (2) variable dampers. In the first category, the stiffness of the system components is adjusted to establish a non-resonant condition. In the second category, supplemental energy dissipation devices, such as fluid, friction, and rheological dampers are used. Modifications are made to

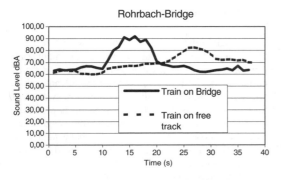

Figure 1.   Noise emission on free track and on a bridge.

allow adjustments in their mechanical properties to achieve significant reductions in the response. A comparison among these methods from an experimental point of view is furnished for example in (Magonette et al. 2000). It must be notice that no control technique is – a priori – better than another, because the final choice depends on several design constrains and requirement as for example:

– Performance
– Maintenance
– Robustness
– Manufacturing
– Energy Consumption
– Reliability
– Installation
– Cost

For these reasons, semi-active devices based on magnetorheological fluids seems to be more appropriated for mechanical vibration at relatively low frequency (up to 20 Hz), for example and high amplitude (up to some millimetres). On the contrary, passive devices similar to Tuned Mass Dampers can be successfully used for acoustic noise reduction on the web plates of the main beams.

However, as mentioned above, it is very difficult to give answer before considering a wide spectrum of possible devices. For this reason in the CaSCo Project different solutions will be tested in order to properly compare them experimentally on a real bridge.

Further details about the state of the art in the field of control of structures can be found in the proceeding of the Third World Conference on Structural Control (Spencer & Soong 1999).

4 AMBIENT VIBRATION TESTS

Ambient Vibration Testing does not require a controlled excitation of the structure. The structure's response to ambient excitation is recorded in a large number of points. By the application of system identification (SI) technologies the frequency response functions are determined and analysed. For large and flexible structures, such as suspension bridges, cable-stayed bridges and high-rise buildings it becomes too difficult and costly to provide controlled excitation (forced testing) at levels that are significantly higher than the excitation provided by ambient sources. The method only requires the measurement of the response to ambient excitation that might be caused by wind, traffic, waves or micro-seismic activity. It is assumed that the excitation is relatively smoothly distributed in the frequency band of interest (white noise). Then the natural frequencies and mode shapes of the structures as well as the other remaining modal parameters can be identified.

The main advantage of this method is that normal operation, such as traffic, does not have to be influenced or interrupted during testing. Traffic is a welcome source of excitation that usually provides good wide-band excitation but also deserves attention on additional effects. The bases for the assessment of structures by the ambient vibration method are the so-called modal parameters, i.e. natural frequencies, mode shapes, damping values and vibration intensities. In addition a new development, the trend cards, are a very good indicator for assessment because interesting information about damage locations can be obtained and eventually on the severity of this damage.

These ambient tests have been performed on the bridge in order to identify the basic modal parameters of the whole structure as well as the frequencies of some single elements. Therefore an extensive measurement campaign was performed and the structural elements such as rails, sleepers, transversal and longitudinal girders have been instrumented. In addition some sensors have been applied to the web of the main girder to quantify the vibration intensity.

The data from the sound measurements have also been treated by a Fast Fourier Transformation (FFT)

Figure 2.   Rohrbach-bridge built in Austria 1903.

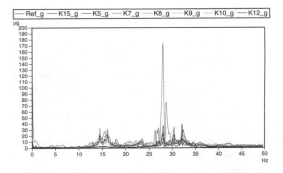

Figure 3.   Frequency spectrum in vertical direction measured on the deck.

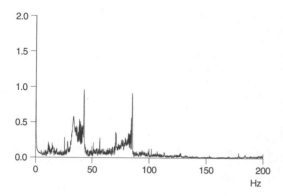

Figure 4. Frequency spectrum obtained from the sound level measurement.

Figure 5. Rohrbach-bridge in the laboratory.

in order to obtain a signal in the frequency domain. The emitted noise (air transmitted noise) from the train has been eliminated before detailed assessment took place in order to show the structural response only. This step is important to carry out the comparison between disturbing noise emission of the train and natural frequencies of the structural elements.

Matching frequencies point to the element which is mainly responsible for the noise origination. From the data shown in figure 4 the bandwidth of interest is between 40 Hz and 100 Hz.

Main outcome of this tests was, that the web-plate of the main girder have shown a matching of frequencies in the range of 75 Hz (second dominant frequency in figure 4) that is already the audible frequency range. Thus, the web-plate is working as a huge loudspeaker-membrane. Changes of the dynamic parameters of this element will also lead to a change in the audible noise emission.

Currently some state of the art techniques are existing, which are accessed for the laboratory tests in Ispra in order to quantify their efficiency.

5 LABORATORY TESTS

After the bridge was dismantled in Austria and moved to the Joint Research Centre JRC by truck, a detailed investigation programme took place. The first step was system identification according to the field tests to carry out a comparison between the dynamic behaviour in the laboratory and in the field. This test is necessary to calibrate the results obtained by the extensive tests. A permanent monitoring equipment was installed to the bridge to enable an accurate determination of the noise attenuating effects obtained by the different damping devices. Several very accurate accelerometer are applied to the structure.

Average frequency spectra of transfer function (H1) - Preliminary measurements

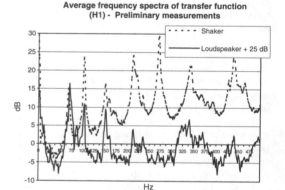

Figure 6. Preliminary results obtained by the laser.

The testing procedure follows up to basic lines, which are (i) integration of additional elements especially to vibrating parts (web-plate of main beam) and (ii) changes of the structure itself.

Until now extensive tests have been performed using of a Laser Doppler Vibrometer (LDV) from the University of Ancona in order to determine accurate values for the frequencies as well as for identification of mode shapes of the web plate. This investigation serves as base for application of counter measures to reduce the vibration intensity and the audible noise emission. Figure 6 show the preliminary results obtained by these measurements, based upon an input-output identification. The first "bending" mode of the web-plate was identified at 73 Hz, which correspond to the measured values during the field tests very well.

The basic idea to meet the targets defined is to introduce additional elements to the vibrating web-plate to reduce the vibration intensity of the element at the same time changing the structural response drastically. For example forced vibration nodes or counter waves introduced by a well tuned Mass-Spring-System lead to good results. This can be achieved by replacing the wood sleepers by a thin concrete slab on semi-active or rubber bearings. One of the main restraints for this operation is the fact that the final level of rails must be the same after the substitutions and this implies that the bearings must be very flat to be arranged in such a small gap.

In addition very simple solutions such like stiffening of the web were tried in order to study the effect to the audible noise. Preliminary calculations performed on a finite element model have showed very good results for the proposed techniques.

6 CONCLUSIONS

The Main outcome until now was the identification of the main noise-radiating element, which is the web-plate of the main girder. This has been assumed earlier, a sound proof of this effect was not done until now. The frequency connected to this effect has been obtained both with ambient vibrations techniques on the field and laser Doppler vibrometer techniques in laboratory, the results matching very well.

The current work focuses on the change of vibration behaviour of the web-plate, which will be investigated for state of the art solutions (additional masses which are correctly applied) as well as semi-active devices developed during this project. Moreover an uncoupling of the rail (vibration source) from the structure by semi-active devices will achieve very good results, as the finite element calculations have already shown.

The research project is still under progress and currently in the very busy testing phase. Moreover due to the strict regulations of this project the main technical details are strictly confidential and cannot be presented in this paper extensively.

REFERENCES

Bachmann, H. 1996. *Vibration problems in structures – Practical guidelines*. ETH Zürich. Birkhäuser Verlag.
Beards, C.P. Structural vibration, analysis and damping. *Halsted Press,* ISBN 0 470 23586 1.
Geier, R. & Wenzel, H. 2001. Noise and vibration attenuating measures for modern railway superstructures. *Proceedings of the 4th European Conference on Noise Control*. Patras. Euronoise.
Magonette, G., Marazzi, F., Molina, J. & Renda, V. 2000. Structural control: experimental activity at ELSA. *Workshop on Mitigation of Seismic Risk Support to Recent Affected European Countries*. Belgirate. Verbania.
Marazzi, F. 2002. Semi-active control of civil structures: implementation aspects. *Ph. D. thesis*. Pavia.
Spencer, B.F. & Soong, T.T. 1999. New applications and development of active, semi-active and hybrid control techniques for seismic and non-seismic vibration in the USA. *Proceedings of the International Post-SMiRT Conference Seminar on Seismic Isolation, Passive Energy Dissipation and Active Control of Vibration of Structures.*, Korea.
Third World Conference on Structural Control, Como, Italy, April 7–12, 2002.
http://www.vce.at
http://www.samco.org

System-based Vision for Strategic and Creative Design, Bontempi (ed.)
© 2003 Swets & Zeitlinger, Lisse, ISBN 90 5809 599 1

Elasto-plastic response of a bar structure to oscillatory external agency

K. Hasegawa, T. Nishimura & N. Kayama

Department of Mechanical Engineering College of Science & Technology, Nihon University, Tokyo, Japan

ABSTRACT: Elastic dynamic problems such as a vibration of beam have been fully investigated by many researchers. However the dynamic plastic analysis is hardly seen except impact problem. Since the materials, which are used in the structure, are generally elasto-plastic, the plastic analysis is also important. Some kinds of structures are allowable to have plastic deformation, if the produced plastic deformation does not induce serious accidents. Although the structure should be safe against an oscillatory external agency such an earthquake, if the structure is able to stand without collapse against the enormous earthquake, which may occur once in several hundreds, the small amount of plastic deformation is permissible. In this study, the elasto-plastic vibration of a bar, which is submitted to bending and twisting moment simultaneously, is discussed. Consequently, it is cleared that the re-elastic region exists on the oscillatory behavior of a bar, where pure elastic motion is recovered in the steady state, although the plastic deformation is observed in the early stage of the transient motion. This re-elastic region may be applicable for the actual structural design, and the restriction of design condition can be expanded for saving construction cost.

1 INTRODUCTION

Dynamic problems in elastic have been fully investigated by many researchers. However there are several studies in plastic, including a impact problem (Stronge & Yu, 1995, Palmov 1998). A usual structure is composed of steel, and if an excessive external agency is applied to the structure, plastic deformation may be induced to the structure. Therefore the elasto-plastic analysis is useful for the sake of saving the construction cost, because a certain kind of structure is permissible a small amount of plastic deformation. For instance, it is not reasonable that the structure should be safe against any enormous earthquake, which may occur once in several hundreds years. The structure is allowable to have a slight plastic deformation for saving money, unless the induced plastic deformation causes fatal damages for human.

In the former study of the elasto-plastic vibration of a beam (T. Nishimura 1999), it is cleared that even if a small plastic deformation occurs in the transient state, the elastic response is recovered in the steady state (this motion is called the re-elastic motion in this study) under the certain external oscillatory agency. Then the allowable condition of structural design can be expanded by the permission of plastic deformation.

In this study, the elasto-plastic response of a bar structure is discussed under the combination of bending and twisting moment. A cantilever discussed here has a concentrated mass, which is attached laterally apart from the axis of bar at the free end. Therefore, the bending and twisting moment are induced simultaneously along the bar by the forced oscillatory displacement at the fixed end. The induced internal moment depends on the frequency and magnitude of the given external displacement. The excessive external agency will cause plastic deformation in the bar. In the paper, the pure elastic limit and re-elastic limit in oscillatory motion is investigated, and the accumulated plastic deformation in re-elastic motion is estimated.

Analysis is performed for evaluate the following terms.

(1) Marginal limit of elastic motion
(2) Alternate elastic and plastic motion
(3) Re-elastic motion

2 EQUATION OF ELASO-PLASTIC VIBRATION

2.1 *Discrete model*

The investigated cantilever is shown in Figure 1, where the concentrated mass is installed at the free end and another concentrated mass is attached laterally apart at the tip. If the cantilever is subjected to the

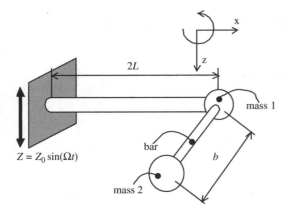

Figure 1. Cantilever structure.

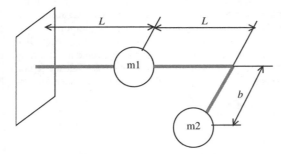

Figure 2. Discrete model.

harmonic external displacement at the fixed end, the bending and twisting oscillatory motion is induced in the bar structure. Although the dynamic behavior is affected by the given frequency, in this study the structural behavior is discussed under the relatively low frequency, because the frequency of earthquake is relatively low compared to the natural frequency of the actual structure.

It is imagined that the induced internal moment becomes maximum at the fixed end for the relatively low frequency. Then plastic deformation occurs at the fixed end over the elastic limit by the excessive external agency and the plastic hinge appears at the plastic portion.

The well-known differential equation can be introduced for the elastic vibration of a bar structure shown in the figure. However the discrete model shown in Figure 2 is convenient to facilitate the motion analysis rather than the continuous model, because the aim of this study is to clear the dynamic response to the relatively low frequency. The cantilever shown in Figure 1 is replaced by the discrete model composed of the two-mass with massless bars. The replaced model is a four-degree-of-freedom.

The motion equation in elastic phase is derived as equation 1. The detail of derivation is omitted for saving space.

$$\mathbf{M\ddot{W} + C\dot{W} + KW = A\dot{Z} + BZ + PW}_p \qquad (1)$$

This is the well-known equation of oscillatory motion. The nomenclature of $\mathbf{M}$, $\mathbf{C}$ and $\mathbf{K}$ in the equation are the mass matrix, the damping matrix and the stiffness matrix. They are represented as below,

$$\mathbf{M} = \begin{bmatrix} -m_1 & 0 & 0 & 0 \\ 0 & -m_2 & 0 & -m_2 b \\ 0 & 0 & -J_1 & 0 \\ 0 & -m_2 b & 0 & -J_2 \end{bmatrix}$$

$$\mathbf{C} = \begin{bmatrix} -2c_B & c_B & 0 & 0 \\ c_B & -c_B & 0 & 0 \\ 0 & 0 & -2c_T & c_T \\ 0 & 0 & c_T & -c_T \end{bmatrix}$$

$$\mathbf{K} = \begin{bmatrix} -\dfrac{96EI}{7L^3} & \dfrac{30EI}{7L^3} & 0 \\ \dfrac{30EI}{7L^3} & -\dfrac{12EI}{7L^3} & 0 & 0 \\ 0 & 0 & -\dfrac{2GI_P}{L} & \dfrac{GI_P}{L} \\ 0 & 0 & \dfrac{GI_P}{L} & -\dfrac{GI_P}{L} \end{bmatrix}$$

and $\mathbf{W}$ is the displacement vector,

$$\mathbf{W} = \{w_1 \ w_2 \ \varphi_1 \ \varphi_2\}^T$$

Z denotes the oscillatory external displacement

$Z = Z_0 \sin \Omega t$.

$\mathbf{W}_p$ is the plastic displacement vector at the hinge, that is residual plastic displacement,

$$\mathbf{W}_p = \{i \ 0 \ \theta \ 0\}^T$$

And also another vectors in the equation can be denoted as,

$$\mathbf{A} = \{c_B \ 0 \ 0 \ 0\}^T$$

$$\mathbf{B} = \left\{ -\dfrac{66EI}{7L^3} \ \dfrac{18EI}{7L^3} \ 0 \ 0 \right\}^T$$

$$
\mathbf{P} = \begin{bmatrix} \dfrac{36EI}{7L^3} & 0 & 0 & 0 \\ -\dfrac{6EI}{7L^3} & 0 & 0 & 0 \\ 0 & 0 & \dfrac{GI_P}{L} & 0 \\ 0 & 0 & 0 & 0 \end{bmatrix}
$$

Another nomenclature are:

m_1 and m_2 : Concentrated mass
J_1 and J_2 : Moment of inertia about x axis
c_B and c_T : Damping factor
EI : Flexural stiffness
GI_p : Torsional stiffness

Equation 1 explains the ordinary oscillatory motion with including the residual plastic deformation at the fixed end. The relation between the plastic deformation and displacement of particles, and the internal moments at the fixed end can be explained with the aid of elementary knowledge of strength of materials as follows:

$$
M_0 = -\dfrac{6EI}{7L^2}\{6(w_1 - Z - Li) - (w_2 - Z - 2Li)\}
$$

$$
T_0 = \dfrac{GI_P}{L}(\varphi_1 - \theta) \tag{2}
$$

Hence, if the oscillatory motion terminates without any plastic deformation, the last term in Equation 1 vanishes. Under the excessive external agency, the internal bending and twisting moment tends to attain the elastic limit state, and the plastic deformation is induced in the bar.

In this study, it is assumed that the cantilever is composed of the elastic and perfectly plastic bar. Then, the internal moments must satisfy the following equation (interaction curve represented by the generalized forces)

$$
f = (M/M_P)^2 + (T/T_P)^2 = \overline{M}^2 + \overline{T}^2 \le 1 \tag{3}
$$

where M and T = induced bending and twisting moment, and M_p and T_p = the corresponding fully plastic moment. In the elastic phase, the internal moment varies within the inside region of the interaction curve, and at the elastic limit, the moment attains the interaction curve. In the plastic phase, the plastic hinge is produced in the bar, and the plastic deformation proceeds at the plastic hinge with remaining the internal moment along the interaction curve. The internal moment cannot exceed the interaction curve, that is, in plastic phase the instantaneous oscillatory motion occurs under the constant reaction moment at the fixed end. In other words, the inclination and twisting angle at the fixed end instantaneously increases under the constant internal moment.

Let introduce the motion equation in plastic phase. Assuming that the internal moments in the plastic hinge at the fixed end are denoted by M_{0p} and T_{0p}, and the plastic displacements at the fixed end are i and θ, the following equation is derived in plastic phase from Equation 4.

$$
\begin{bmatrix} i \\ \theta \end{bmatrix} = \begin{bmatrix} \dfrac{7L}{24EI} & 0 \\ 0 & -\dfrac{L}{GI_P} \end{bmatrix} \begin{bmatrix} M_{0p} \\ T_{0p} \end{bmatrix}
$$

$$
+ \begin{bmatrix} \dfrac{3}{2L} & -\dfrac{1}{4L} & 0 \\ 0 & 0 & 1 \end{bmatrix} \begin{bmatrix} w_1 \\ w_2 \\ \varphi_1 \end{bmatrix} + \begin{bmatrix} -\dfrac{5}{4L} \\ 0 \end{bmatrix} X \tag{4}
$$

The motion equation in plastic phase is obtained by substituting Equation 4 into Equation 1.

$$
\mathbf{M\ddot{W}} + \mathbf{C\dot{W}} + \mathbf{K}_p\mathbf{W} = \mathbf{A\dot{Z}} + \mathbf{BZ} \tag{5}
$$

It should be noted that the stiffness matrix $\mathbf{K}$ is replaced by $\mathbf{K}_p$ in Equation 5, and the detail of stiffness matrix is

$$
\mathbf{K}_p = \begin{bmatrix} -\dfrac{96EI}{7L^3} & \dfrac{30EI}{7L^3} & 0 & 0 \\ \dfrac{30EI}{7L^3} & -\dfrac{12EI}{7L^3} & 0 & 0 \\ 0 & 0 & -\dfrac{2GI_P}{L} & \dfrac{GI_P}{L} \\ 0 & 0 & \dfrac{GI_P}{L} & -\dfrac{GI_P}{L} \end{bmatrix} \tag{6}
$$

It is clear from Equations 1 and 5 that the natural frequency in elastic phase is different from that in plastic phase, because of different stiffness.

2.2 General internal forces and deformation

Since the plastic deformation depends on the loading history, in order to resolve the plastic deformation, the strain increment theory should be applied. When resolving Equation 5, we have to know the incremental displacement during the infinitesimal time interval in order to obtain the increment plastic deformation and internal moment at the plastic hinge. Then let introduce the following equations.

$$
\Delta\Gamma = -\Delta\left[\dfrac{6EI}{7L^2 M_P}\{6(w_1 - Z) - (w_2 - Z)\}\right]
$$

$$
\Delta\Pi = \Delta\left\{\dfrac{GI_P}{LT_P}\varphi_1\right\} \tag{7}
$$

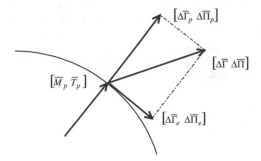

Figure 3. Interaction curve.

These expressions give the total increment of displacements during the infinitesimal time interval. It is required to resolve the elastic and plastic component from the total increment. To perform the resolution, let introduce the generalized deformation. The generalized deformation is defined so as to coincide the generalized force in elastic. Therefore the generalized deformation is defined by the following equation.

$$\bar{\Gamma} = -\frac{6EI}{7L^2 M_p}\{6(w_1 - Z) - (w_2 - Z) - 4Li\}$$

$$\bar{\Pi} = \frac{GI_p}{LT_p}(\varphi_1 - \theta)$$

(8)

Here, the normal flow rule is adopted for the plastic deformation. The normal component of the increment of deformation to the interaction curve gives the plastic deformation (see Fig. 3), that is the increment of inclination and twisting angle. The generalized plastic deformation is obtained by

$$\begin{bmatrix} \Delta\bar{\Gamma}_p \\ \Delta\bar{\Pi}_p \end{bmatrix} = \begin{bmatrix} \bar{M}_{0p} \\ \bar{T}_{0p} \end{bmatrix}\{\bar{M}_{0p} \quad T_{0p}\}\begin{bmatrix} \Delta\bar{\Gamma} \\ \Delta\bar{\Pi} \end{bmatrix}$$

(9)

After incremental calculation, the calculated result is added to the previous plastic deformation. And the remaining tangential component is the elastic, and is identical with the increment of the generalized force. It is given as follows,

$$\begin{bmatrix} \Delta\bar{\Gamma}_e \\ \Delta\bar{\Pi}_e \end{bmatrix} = \begin{bmatrix} \Delta\bar{\Gamma} \\ \Delta\bar{\Pi} \end{bmatrix} - \begin{bmatrix} \Delta\bar{\Gamma}_p \\ \Delta\bar{\Pi}_p \end{bmatrix} = \begin{bmatrix} \Delta\bar{M} \\ \Delta\bar{T} \end{bmatrix}$$

(10)

This component is added to the current internal moment.

3 NUMERICAL CALUCULATION

The dimension and the property of the structure, discussed here, are shown in Table 1. Under the given

Table 1. Physical and mechanical property.

Matter of property	Symbol dimension	Value
Young's modulus	E [GPa]	198.00
Shearing modulus	G [GPa]	76.154
Length of bar	L [10^{-1}m]	1.00
Mass	m_1 [10^{-2}kg]	4.6874
	m_2 [10^{-1}kg]	3.5714
Moment of inertia	J_{p1} [10^{-6}kg·m^2]	2.1301
	J_{p2} [10^{-3}kg·m^2]	3.2773
Inertia moment of cross area	I [10^{-11}m^4]	3.0191
Centroid moment of inertia	I_p [10^{-11}m^4]	6.382
Shifted length	b [10^{-1}m]	1.05
Damping coefficient	c_B [kg/s]	0.37
	c_T [kg/s]	0.001

Table 2. Natural frequency.

	Natural frequency [Hz]	
Mode	Elastic	Plastic
First	9.3879	0.0
Second	39.1414	0.0
Third	217.4844	944.9907
Fourth	346.7362	4630.1986

boundary condition, the natural frequency is numerically calculated as in Table 2.

It should be noted that the natural frequency in plastic phase differs from the elastic natural frequency (see Table 1). It is characterized by that the first and second natural frequency is zero, because the plastic hinge at the fixed end allows to rotate the bar structure. Not only the oscillatory motion but also rotary motion around plastic hinge is brought like a pin joint. The restriction at the fixed end is temporally reduced. However the reverse motion causes unloading and the elastic motion resumes. Then it is imagined that the elastic and plastic motion will be repeated alternately by the large external agency. This fact makes the motion analysis complicated.

The time-varying displacement and twisting angle at the tip are shown in Figures 4, 5. From the figure it is known that the oscillatory motion converges steady state after adequate time duration because of damping factor. The displacement and internal moment produced by the oscillatory external motion depend on the magnitude of external displacement and its frequency. The trajectory of internal moment at the fixed end is shown in Figures 6, 7 as the examples. The circle in the figure denotes the interaction curve, and the abscissa and ordinate denote the generalized twisting moment and bending moment, respectively. If the frequency of external displacement is cross to the natural frequency, the variation of internal moment is

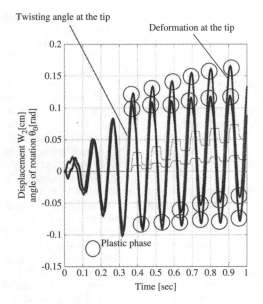

Figure 4. Displacement & angle given amplitude 2 [mm] and frequency 9.4 [Hz].

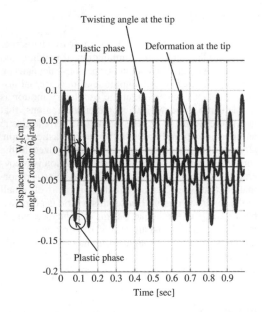

Figure 5. Displacement & angle given amplitude 10 [mm] and frequency 15 [Hz].

Figure 6. Trajectory of moment at fixed end given amplitude 0.9 [mm] and frequency 9.4 [Hz].

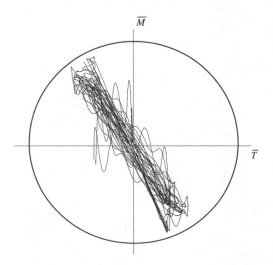

Figure 7. Trajectory of moment at fixed end given amplitude 9 [mm] and frequency 15 [Hz].

relatively simple (see Fig. 6), while, if the given frequency is apart from the natural frequency, the trajectory of moment is very complex (see Fig. 7). The examples shown in the figure indicate the pure elastic motion, because the whole trajectory does not exceed the interaction curve. Since the induced pure elastic moment is proportional to the given amplitude of external displacement under the constant external frequency, it is easy to obtain the elastic limit condition. The magnitude of external displacement, which is brought the elastic limit motion, is determined by magnifying the given external displacement so that the maximum moment on trajectory contacts to the interaction curve. The numerically obtained elastic limit is shown by the solid line in Figures 8, 9.

On exceeding the elastic limit, the plastic hinge is brought at the fixed end by the proceeding deformation. After experienced plastic deformation, if the reverse deformation is induced at the plastic hinge, the elastic motion is recovered till the internal moment

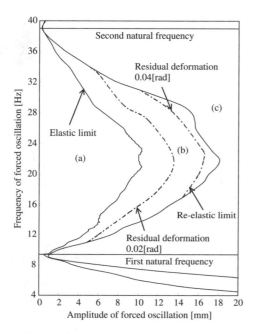

Figure 8.   Characteristic behavior on bending moment.

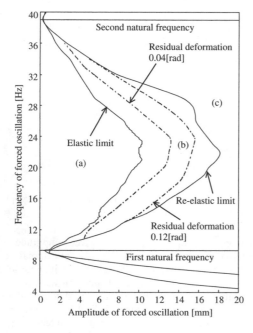

Figure 9.   Characteristic behavior on twisting moment.

attains the interaction curve again. If the frequency of external agency is apart from the natural frequency, the amplitude of oscillatory motion tends to reduce in the steady state by the effect of damping factor. Then

the result of numerical calculation shows that the oscillatory elastic motion is assured in the steady state, although the plastic deformation is recognized in the transient state. In this study, such region is called the re-elastic region. In Figures 8, 9 the result of numerical calculation is summarized. Figures 8, 9 show the characteristic behavior of bending and twisting deformation, respectively. The abscissa indicates the amplitude of external displacement, and the ordinate denotes the given frequency. In the figures, region (a), (b) and (c) indicate the pure elastic, re-elastic and alternate elastic and plastic region, respectively. In the region (c), the elastic and plastic deformation occurs alternatively. Then the motion may not be stable. However, in region (b) the steady state motion is in elastic and is stable, even if the bar structure is subjected to the plastic deformation several times in the transient state and the residual deformation remains at the fixed end (see Fig. 5). The accumulated plastic deformation (inclination angle) at the fixed end dose not exceed 0.08 radian, that corresponds to 16 mm deflection at the free end of the cantilever (200 mm length). And the accumulated plastic twisting angle is less than 0.03 radian.

4   CONCLUSIONS AND DICUSSION

The elasto and plastic dynamic response of a bar structure is studied under the combination of bending and twisting moment. The oscillatory response depends on the given frequency and amplitude of the external displacement. It is cleared that the oscillatory motion is divided into three typical characteristic regions, that is (a) pure elastic, (b) re-elastic and (c) alternate elastic and plastic region. Especially, in the re-elastic region, although the plastic deformation is recognized in the early transient state, the elastic stable motion is recovered in the steady state. The accumulated plastic deformation, that is residual deformation, is relatively small in the re-elastic region. Hence, this region is permissible to apply to the actual design of structure, which is allowed to have small plastic deformation unless the fatal damage is brought to human. Consequently allowable design condition can be expanded, and it will contribute for saving the construction cost.

REFERENCES

Stronge, W.J. & Yu, T.X. 1995. *Dynamic Models for Structural Plasticity*, Springer-Verlag.
Palmov, V. 1998. *Vibrations of Elasto-Plastic Bodies*, Springer-Verlag.
Nishimura, T. & Murakami, N. 1999. Study of Dynamic Response in an Elaso-Plastic Beam, *Advances in Mechanics of Structures and Materials*. A.A. Balkema, 569–574.

System-based Vision for Strategic and Creative Design, Bontempi (ed.)
© 2003 Swets & Zeitlinger, Lisse, ISBN 90 5809 599 1

Water filled steel structures

J.P. Paoluccio

Paoluccio Paoluccio Associates/PWNA, San Diego, California, USA

ABSTRACT: Discusses a new model for steel caged high-rise structures that employ the use of hollow steel sections (HSS) for the structural system. It integrates fire protection by filling the HSS sections with water to absorb heat generated by fire within the building. The means of heat rejection is varied, including the use of the HVAC system's cooling tower and relief valves strategically placed within the system. Pumps or available utility provide the water supply. Fire sprinklers are also part of the design, allowing sprinklers to be placed anywhere in the building by tapping into the HSS. Lastly, architects are free to expose the structure as part of the design, were this desired. The reader is left with the challenge to find how this integration can be successful by refining various concerns, including internal water pressure, economic structural connections, fire sprinkler design approval and basic acceptance by the design community.

1 INTRODUCTION

The notion of using hollow steel sections, HSS, for mid and high-rise structures would generally cause an experienced structural engineer to scratch his head and wonder, "why ponder such an idea." And when one suggests that the tubes be filled with water, one could be taken as a serious candidate for a long rest. The use of water filled HSS is not a technical challenge, although conventional standards would be challenged, it is more a concern of cost and practicality. When would such a structure be preferred? When would it be cost effective? We will explore these questions, in part, and leave the reader to reach his own conclusions. In the meanwhile, some advantages of the proposed integrated structural system are apparent, these include:

- Better Protection: Has the potential to protect the structure from a higher than normal external heat source.
- Aesthetics: Expands opportunities to express structure as part of the architecture.
- Fire Protection Flexibility: Integrates the automatic fire sprinklers using the building structure as the conduit.
- Building systems Integration: Use HVAC for fire heat rejection purposes.
- Variety of water sources: City utilities, nearby lakes or landscaping water features.

It has been about 118 years since the American engineer/architect William Le Baron Jenney designed the first steel caged high-rise building, the Home Insurance Building in Chicago, Illinois, and set the pace for today's high-rise buildings (White, 1976). Both the English and the French involved iron and steel into their structures long before this. The first iron bridge in the world was built at Coalbrookdale in Shropshire on the river Serern in 1779, and, of course the Eiffel Tower in Paris in 1889. Also in 1851, Joseph Paxton proposed his Crystal Palace for the Great Exhibition (Yarwood, 1974). Much has been accomplished throughout the world since then to improve upon the technical and safety issues for tall buildings. Our work will never be finished as long as new and better products and developments become available and innovative persons pursue that spark of genius that causes change. Have high-rise steel structures achieved optimum safety? Do we need to re-examine our design approach? This paper is written to challenge engineers and architects to push the cage structure to an even higher level than it is now.

2 CURRENT PRACTICE

Contemporary steel structures are protected from heat by coating the steel with approved insulating materials. The coatings are designed to provide insulation between the heat source and the structural steel allowing for two or more hours of fire exposure without causing the steel structure to lose its ability to carry the load. Structural steel becomes unstable at temperatures above approximately 800F (427° C), subjecting the structure to partial or total collapse depending upon many other factors. This fact combined with other events can be catastrophic in terms of human life and property loss. No better example exists than the tragic events resulting in the loss of the World Trade Center Towers. In this instance, it was reported that the impact of the aircraft destroyed the protective coating on the structural steel and exposing the steel to prolonged high temperature produced by the building materials and contents. Had the remaining structural steel stayed within relatively normal temperatures, perhaps the structure would not have failed. In the final analysis, protecting the basic structure is all-important, first in terms of life safety and then in terms of property value.

At this point, I would like to comment that the introduction of using water filled tubes for protecting structural steel is not a reaction to this recent disaster. Lally columns or pipe columns filled with cement have been used in the past for fire proofing on the inside rather than on the outside (White, 1976). There are recorded instances of water filled steel columns designed to avoid the use of exterior coatings. There is at least one building in the United States that utilized water filled structural tubes as a means of supplying water to the building's automatic fire sprinkler system. In this example, the structural steel was protected in the usual manner. In any case, these reported applications are few, and little is known about them. The theory of using water to carry away the heat external to the steel is sound and bears a closer look in terms of technology today. This paper explores beyond what has been done and pushes creativity to include the integration of architecture, structural, mechanical and fire protection engineering to seek a higher standard of design.

It may be concluded that contemporary coatings combined with other life safety design elements are considered standard practice and offer a practical approach to life safety with respect to normal fire threat within steel structures. With the aforementioned WTC as an example and as a reminder of the complex social problems dealing with global terrorism, it may be prudent to explore alternative methods of building structure protection. This paper is presented as an opportunity to discuss and evaluate superior alternative methods of protecting structures from fire with an extreme fuel source – fires that challenge fire sprinkler systems and conventional protection.

3 WATER FILLED STEEL TUBE STRUCTURES

The idea of designing with steel tubes has advantages and disadvantages when compared to standard water filled and other standard structural steel sections for building design. It is obvious that standard sections have a long history based on available strength per unit weight, economics and standard practices employed by steel fabricators and erectors. These standard shapes can be considered limited, however, when it comes to other possibilities, including:

3.1 Better protection

Hollow steel sections, HSS, when filled with water, have potential for high capacity to carry away heat generated by an extreme fire threat. Steel structures can remain safe for sustained period of time without the fear of failure due to overheating when integrated with a circulating or replenishable water source. Depending on the building structure design, each column might be arranged as a water circuit, independent of other column circuits. Within each column circuit, beams would also be provided with water, forming a protected cage for vertical and horizontal loads. Together, they could provide a complete network of steel tubes, all filled with water, and with different and isolated circuits from each other. In this manner, physical failure from an external and unnatural force may damage individual circuits but would preserve the remaining structure without significant water loss. There are a number of available water sources including municipal supply or a local body of water, preferably fresh water. Pump(s) or available external pressure can introduce water through the system. Outlets can be automatic and operation can be based on pressure/temperature relationships. Automatic relief valves would be strategically placed at the high point of each column circuit.

A typical fire pump might be employed to boost water pressure. The typical fire pump is usually designed to provide 2500 gallon per minute at a pressure of not less the 100 psi (690 kPa). This flow rate is sufficient to absorb about 45,120 Btu/Sec of heat. It is very difficult to anticipate where a fire might concentrate its heat release, but assuming the worse case scenario, this amount of heat absorption could carry away the heat of a typical office fire on a continuous basis without the fire fighting effects of the sprinkler system. In other words, with a fire concentrated in as little as 250 SF and generating maximum heat, the water filled steel tubes would not be in danger of overheating. Additional pumps or larger pumps could easily be incorporated to mitigate almost any foreseeable heat source, as the column and beam sizes are extremely large when compared to traditional pipe sizes utilized in hydraulically calculated sprinkler systems.

3.2 Aesthetics

At times, it may be desirable to expose the building's steel cage as an aesthetic or style creating space that suites the need of a particular tenant. Minimalism might be preferred and considered an inducement for creativity. Architects may prefer this design aesthetic when their clients are looking for a "bare bones" environment considered from a cost standpoint. This style is currently in vogue for many young high-tech industries, providing them with a casual and less traditional work place.

3.3 Fire protection

Steel tubes, when filled with water, may become the source for fire sprinklers. Major columns and beams, when filled with water, can easily become the water supply source for fire sprinkler systems with a hydraulically sound circuit arrangement providing for equal distribution of pressure and volume to each sprinkler. The water filled tube is a superior conduit in terms of water volume and pressure considerations. Each tributary piping extension, serving one or more sprinklers from either a water filled steel column or beam, will be served with a dependable source of water. Unlike the conventional piping systems, there would be practically no water pressure drop within the water filled steel tubes compared with standard piping. The heat absorbed by the typical office fire sprinkler system is also very efficient. Approximately 342 Btu/Sec/SF of heat absorption is afforded by a properly designed and functioning fire sprinkler system in addition to the water's smothering effect. By comparison, a 62-pound (28.15 kg) chair with an extended heat growth time of about fifty seconds and rated as a fast heat release material would produce about 303 Btu/Sec/SF based on test No. 19 of 2002 National Fire Alarm Code, Table B.2.3, Furniture Heat Release Rates. On the lower side, the same chair with a growth time of three minutes would produce about 53 Btu/Sec/SF. There are many factors that must be taken into consideration in controlling a fire. Early detection and activation of the sprinklers produce very good control. However, once a fire has exceeded the capacity of the sprinklers, the steel frame and building construction may be impacted, depending on how much heat capacity the building contents contribute. When the capacity is sufficient to heat the steel above 800 F (426.67° C) then collapse and failure is probable. The higher the steel temperature the weaker the steel. The water carrying capacity of HSS used for a building frame is considerably greater than that of a traditional piping system. Therefore delivering water to sprinklers anywhere in the building is accomplished with very low pumping head due to friction loss.

3.4 Integration of other building systems

Water filled steel tubes can be integrated with HVAC system's cooling tower(s). Cross connections can be utilized to carry away a significant quantity of heat generated by the building contents during a fire event. The amount of heat varies, but there are standards, the National Fire Alarm Code among them, that can provide the heat propagated by various building contents. In addition, any given cooling tower will reject significantly more heat when the inlet water temperatures are elevated above those specified for the HVAC system. In any case, a cooling tower can help reject heat absorbed into the water filled steel tubes at a rate of approximately twice that of its air conditioning load or about .03 Btu/Sec/SF based on nominal conditions. In other words, a 36,000 SF (3,346 SM) system would be able to carry away about 1000 Btu/Sec. This would be considered a small local fire and it would, most likely, not present a threat to the steel. A larger fire would require a more abundant volume of water.

3.5 Integrate with local water sources

Local utility or any local source of water can be incorporated with or without pumps depending on the source. When using the local utility source, there are at least two possible designs: use the normal fire sprinkler source piping or design with a larger piping system. The decision on how to size the water source depends on many factors, including the building's use and its probable contribution as a fuel source – how big a fire to expect. A regular office environment would allow the usual criteria for sizing water supply, but a special use facility within a building may require higher water use to combat a greater heat source. In addition to the use of the building's cooling tower for heat transfer and rejection, relief valves at each column may be incorporated. In this way, heated water would be allowed to escape at the column near the fire source and cooler water would automatically be routed to the fire source.

There are many combinations for a fire event: it can occur with or without sprinklers; it may generate normal heat; it may be a fire that has gone beyond the capability of the sprinkler system. This last event would be the more challenging and would require more circulation and heat rejection. The means to accomplish this added heat rejection from within the water filled tube construction can incorporate automatic control features that locate and manipulate valves to direct water flow to the fire source. There are many contemporary and standard control technologies that can accomplish this requirement.

This paper postulates that changes in our standards for building design may bring about a more positive and safe environment when experiencing threatening fires within large buildings. For the most part, our current technology is adequate, but protection of steel when used as the basic building frame lacks certainty. When fires occur that go beyond the control of automatic sprinklers, the building's framework is in danger of either collapse or in need of replacement after the fire has been contained. In either case, water filled steel tubes may provide a higher assurance against the loss of life. Lastly and in the words of John A. Roebling (1806–1869), Civil Engineer for the Brooklyn Bridge, "It will no longer suit the spirit of the present age to pronounce an undertaking impracticable, nothing is impracticable which is within the scope of natural laws."

REFERENCES

2002. *National Fire Alarm Code*: 72 - 172 - 72 - 175.
Yarwood, D. 1974. *The Architecture of Europe*. Great Britain: B.T. Batsford Limited.
White, N. 1976. *The Architecture Book*. New York: Knopf.

System-based Vision for Strategic and Creative Design, Bontempi (ed.)
© *2003 Swets & Zeitlinger, Lisse, ISBN 90 5809 599 1*

Moment-rotation relationships of single plate connections

X. Sun & T.H. Tan
Nanyang Technological University, Singapore

ABSTRACT: The advantage of single plate connection is due to its simplicity in fabrication and erection. However, the single plate connection is always assumed to carry the shear load only in agreement with the simply support assumption in practice. Limited investigations were carried out to study the moment capacity and ductility of single plate connections. An experimental program was set up to study the moment-rotation relationships of single plate connection with HSFG bolts under monotonic loading. An analytical model was developed based on the experimental observations and the results of an advanced finite element investigation.

1 INTRODUCTION

Single steel plate connection, also known as the "fin" connection, consists of a length of plate, which is welded to the supporting member in the work-shop, and then bolted to the steel beam web on site. The advantage of this type of connection is that they are simple to fabricate and easy for site assembly and installation. The single plate connections derive their rotational capacity from the bolt deformation in shear and the hole distortion in bearing of the weaker of the steel plate and beam web. However, the single plate connection is always assumed to carry the shear load only in agreement with the simply support assumption in practice. Limited investigations were carried out to study the moment capacity and ductility of single plate connections. Tests and studies carried out by Lipson (1977) indicate that the single plate connection can develop a significant end moment in the beam and supporting member. The magnitude of the moment is generally dependent upon the number, size, configuration of bolt pattern, the thickness of the plate or beam web, etc. In this research, the behaviour of single plate connection with High Strength Friction Grip (HSFG) bolts has been studied. The purpose of using HSFG bolts is to prevent the initial slip between the bolts and connected parts under load increment.

2 EXPERIMENTAL PROGRAM

The aim of the experiment is to study the moment-rotation relationship of single plate connection with HSFG bolts under monotonic loading. Two bare steel sub-frames BSC1 & BSC2 were tested. Each bare steel sub-frame consisted of two universal beams, which were connected to the universal steel column via single plate connection. The details of the specimens are given in Table 1. The configuration of single plate connection is shown in Figure 1.

The single steel plates were welded to the flange of steel column first, and then the steel beams were connected to the steel plate using the HSFG bolts. All HSFG bolts were pre-tensioned to 170 kN by applying

Table 1. Details of specimens.

Specimen (BSC1 & BSC2)	Details
Steel universal beam	356 × 171 UB 45
Steel universal column	356 × 171 UB 67
Single steel plate	130 × 300 × 10 mm
HSFG bolts	ϕ20 mm
Welds	8 mm fillet weld

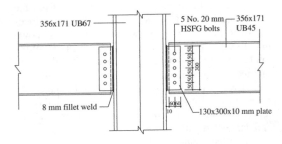

Figure 1. Configuration of single plate connection.

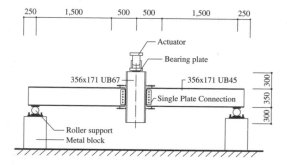

Figure 2. Test set-up for monotonic loading.

a torque of 380 N.m on each bolt. The torque-pretension relationship was found to be linear and can be expressed in a simple form:

$$N = \frac{T}{d_b x K} \qquad (1)$$

where N = bolt pretension (kN); T = applied torque (N·m); d_b = bolt diameter (mm); K = torque coefficient (average value is 0.112).

The connection rotations were measured by two pairs of LVDTs, as shown in Figure 2. Each pair of LVDTs were mounted on the top and bottom of the beam flanges. The connection rotation was obtained by averaging the sum of the top left and right LVDT displacements and subtracting this value from the average of the sum of the bottom left and right LVDT displacements. This value was divided by the beam depth to obtain the connection rotation value.

The test set-up was shown in Figure 2. The test set-up consisted of 30T hydraulic jack and loading rig with 2000 kN capacity. The load was applied at the centre of the connection in steps of 5 kN throughout of the test. At each load increment, the displacement and load were recorded to a computer. After slip, the loading was continued until the shear failure of bottom bolts.

3 EXPERIMENTAL RESULTS

After failure, the connection was removed from the testing machine and inspected. The fractured surfaces and distortion of the holes were observed. As shown in Figure 3, investigation of the faying surfaces of the joints indicated that the areas immediately adjacent to the holes were the areas of highest contact pressure, and therefore provided most of the slip resistance. As expected, the distortions of the holes followed the pattern according to the respective bearing between bolts and connected parts.

The tested results for BSC1 and BSC2 are quite close (Fig. 4). It should be noted that the moment-rotation

Figure 3. Inspection of tested specimen.

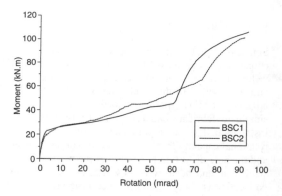

Figure 4. Test results of BSC1 & BSC2.

curve of single plate connection with HSFG bolts consists of four stages. The first stage is almost linear until the slip occurs due to the high friction between contacted components. This high friction is caused by the pre-tension force inside the HSFG bolts. As the load increases, the major slip behaviour occurs at a moment about 25 kN·m. The connection slips rapidly with little increase in moment capacity until all the HSFG bolts go into bearing. The rotation of steel connection at the end of this stage is about 20 mrad. This is considered as the second stage. At the third stage, all the HSFG bolts bear against the single plate as well as beam web similar as the ordinary bolted single plate connection. At this stage, the top beam flange moves towards the column flange and the bottom beam flange moves away from the column flange. The moment capacity keeps on increasing until the top beam flange contacts the column flange. The rotation at the end of this stage is about 60 mrad. At the finial stage, the bearing force between HSFG bolts and connected parts increases rapidly due to the top beam flange bearing against the column flange. This results in rapid increase of moment capacity. The connection rotates about the top beam flange and eventually failure occurs due to shear failure of bottom bolts.

4 ANALYTICAL MODEL

The analytical model is proposed to simulate the moment-rotation relationship of single plate connection with HSFG bolts. The model consists of three stages: the first stage is before the slip occurs; the second stage is after the slip and before the HSFG bolts bearing against the connected parts, and the third stage is that all HSFG bolts fully bear against the connected parts. As discussed above, at the third stage, the behaviour of single plate connection with HSFG bolts is similar as those with ordinary bolts (without pre-tension). Therefore, the third stage simulation is carried out through the finite element modelling of single plate connection with ordinary bolts.

4.1 First and second stage of the model

At the first stage, the initial portion of the moment-rotation curve is linear up to the slip load. There are two parameters needed to be defined, the displacement slip stiffness K_{slip} and the slip resistance P_{slip}. The slip resistance prediction is based on the BS5950 and is given as:

$$P_{slip} = 1.1 K_s \mu. P_0 \tag{2}$$

where $K_s = 1.0$ for bolts in clearance holes; $\mu = $ slip factor; $P_o = $ minimum shank tension.

The displacement slip stiffness K_{slip} is determined as functions of the slip displacements Δ_{slip} as:

$$K_{slip} = \frac{P_{slip}}{\Delta_{slip}} \tag{3}$$

Based on previous researches (Swanson 1999), the value of Δ_{slip} was determined as 0.0076 inch (0.193 mm) by conducting a statistical analysis of tested data.

The horizontal displacement of bolt hole Δ and the corresponding force P are shown in Figure 5. Based on kinematics and equilibrium considerations, the relationships between rotation θ and connection moment M can be described as follows:

$$\Delta = \frac{P}{K_{slip}} \tag{4}$$

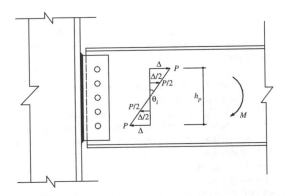

Figure 5. Single plate connection with 5 bolts.

$$\theta = \frac{\Delta}{\left(\dfrac{h_p}{2}\right)} \tag{5}$$

$$M = \left(P.\frac{h_p}{2} + \frac{P}{2}.\frac{h_p}{4} \right) x2 = \frac{5P.h_p}{4} \tag{6}$$

where $h_p = $ height of the bolt pattern.

Therefore, from Equation 4 to Equation 6, the initial rotational stiffness of single plate connection can be derived as:

$$K_{slip-R} = \frac{M}{\theta} = \frac{5.h_p^{2}.K_{slip}}{8} \tag{7}$$

It is assumed that slip occurs when all HSFG bolts (except centre bolt) reach the slip resistance. The slip moment can be given as follows:

$$M_{slip} = \left(P_{slip}.\frac{h_p}{2} + P_{slip}.\frac{h_p}{4} \right) x2 = \frac{3P_{slip}.h_p}{2} \tag{8}$$

where $P_{slip} = $ slip resistance of each HSFG bolt .

The moment capacity of second stage keeps constant until all HSFG bolt bear against connected parts.

4.2 Third stage of the model

At the third stage, the single plate connection with HSFG bolts becomes a bearing type similar as those with ordinary bolts. A three-parameter analytical model is proposed to predict the moment-rotation relationship of single plate connection with ordinary bolts. In the proposed model, the moment-rotation relationship is represented as follows:

$$\theta = \frac{M}{K_{si}\left[1 - \left(\dfrac{M}{M_u}\right)^{n}\right]} \tag{9}$$

where K_{si} = initial stiffness of single plate connection with ordinary bolts; M_u = moment capacity of single plate connection with ordinary bolts; n = shape parameter.

4.2.1 Initial stiffness of single plate connection with ordinary bolts

The single plate connection will rotate about the centroid of bolt group when a moment is applied. The rotation of the connection is mainly due to the bolt hole distortion in bearing against the beam web. The horizontal displacement of bolt hole Δ and the corresponding force P are shown in Figure 5. The stiffness of bolt hole under horizontal force P can be considered as follows:

$$K_b = \frac{E_s.d_b.(t_{web} + t_{plate})}{L_b} \tag{10}$$

where E_s = elastic modulus of structural steel; d_b = bolt diameter; t_{web} = thickness of beam web; t_{plate} = thickness of steel plate; L_b = distance between the centroid of bolt group and column face.

As discussed before, the relationships between rotation θ and connection moment M can be described as follows:

$$\Delta = \frac{P}{K_b} = \frac{P}{\left(\frac{E_s.d_b.(t_{web} + t_{plate})}{L_b}\right)} \tag{11}$$

$$\theta = \frac{\Delta}{\left(\frac{h_p}{2}\right)} \tag{12}$$

$$M = \left(P.\frac{h_p}{2} + \frac{P}{2}.\frac{h_p}{4}\right)x2 = \frac{5P.h_p}{4} \tag{13}$$

where h_p = height of the bolt pattern.

Therefore, from Equation 11 to Equation 13, the initial rotational stiffness of single plate connection with ordinary bolts can be derived as:

$$K_{si} = \frac{M}{\theta} = \frac{5E_s.h_p^2.d_b.(t_{web} + t_{plate})}{8L_b} \tag{14}$$

4.2.2 Ultimate moment capacity of single plate connection with ordinary bolts

Because the thickness of beam web is always less than the thickness of single plate, therefore, the bearing strength between bolt and beam web controls the overall behaviour of single plate connection. Hence, the ultimate moment capacity is defined as the moment which allows all connected beam web being

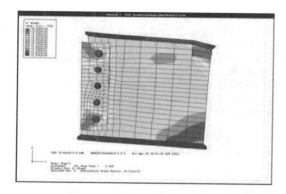

Figure 6. Numerical modelling of single plate connection with ordinary bolts.

loaded up to their bearing capacities. The connection moment capacity may be given as follows:

$$P_b = \frac{d_b.\pi}{2}.t_{web}.P_{web} \tag{15}$$

$$M_u = \left(P_b.\frac{h_p}{2} + P_b.\frac{h_p}{4}\right)x2 = \frac{3P_b.h_p}{2} \tag{16}$$

where P_b = bearing capacity of connected beam web at bolt hole; M_u = ultimate moment capacity of single plate connection.

4.2.3 Shape parameter of single plate connection with ordinary bolts

The ABAQUS finite element package is used to model the behaviour of single plate connection with ordinary bolts (Fig. 6). The 3D solid model incorporates the contact surface between contacting component and nonlinear material properties. Since the shape parameter is affected by many variables, therefore, a parametric study is necessary to be carried out to gain an insight into the behaviour of single plate connection.

Parametric studies has been conducted to investigate the variations in shear span, bolt size, bolt pitch, thickness of steel plate as well as thickness of beam web. As shown in Figure 7, the moment-rotation relationships of single plate connection with different shear spans of 0.3 m, 0.5 m, 1.0 m and 1.5 m are plotted. It is observed that the differences between them are insignificant. Therefore, it may be concluded that the shear deformation is insignificant and the moment-rotation relationship is insensitive to the shear span. The moment-rotation relationships of single plate connection with different bolt sizes are plotted in Figure 8. It can be founded that the bigger the bolt size, the higher are the moment capacity and initial stiffness.

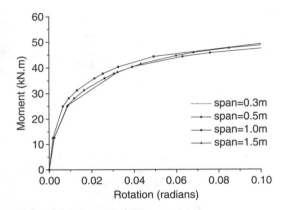

Figure 7. Moment-rotation relationships with different shear spans (5-bolt, bolt dia = 20 mm, bolt pitch = 50 mm, plate thk = 10 mm, beam web thk = 6.9mm).

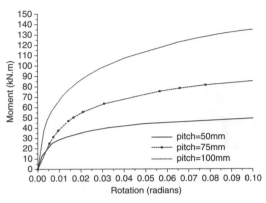

Figure 9. Moment-rotation relationship with different bolt pitches (5-bolt, bolt dia = 20 mm, plate thk = 10 mm, beam web thk = 6. 9 mm).

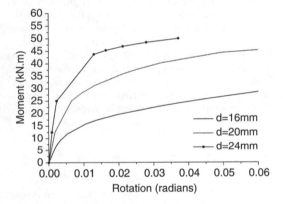

Figure 8. Moment-rotation relationships with different bolt diameters (5-bolt, bolt pitch = 50 mm, plate thk = 10 mm, beam web thk = 6.9 mm).

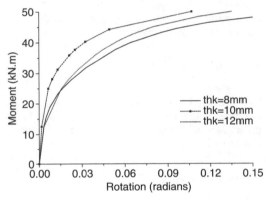

Figure 10. Moment-rotation relationships with different single plate thickness (5-bolt, bolt dia = 20 mm, bolt pitch = 50 mm, beam web thk = 6. 9 mm).

This is primarily due to the higher bearing from the bigger bolt size. The moment-rotation relationships of single plate connection with different bolt pitches are shown in Figure 9. The bolt pitches are 50 mm, 75 mm and 100 mm respectively. Because the increasing in bolt pitch increases the length of level arm about the centroid of bolt group, therefore, resulting in a higher initial stiffness and moment capacity. In Figure 10, the moment-rotation relationships of single plate connection with different thickness of single plate are plotted. No noticeable changes of moment capacity are observed although the initial stiffness are slightly different. In Figure 11, the moment-rotation relationships of single plate connection with different web thickness are plotted. It is important to note that the moment-rotation relationships are dependent on the thickness of beam web. The thicker the beam web, the higher initial

stiffness and moment capacity can be achieved. This can be explained that the thicker beam web can provide larger bearing area between beam web and bolts, which increases the stiffness of the single plate connection as well as the moment capacity. In practice, the thickness of the single plate is always greater than the thickness of beam web. Therefore, it can be considered that the bearing strength between bolt and the beam web is the critical component, which controls the overall behaviour of single plate connection.

Based on the parametric study, it can be summarised that the shear span and thickness of single plate are insignificant variables for the moment-rotation relationships of single plate connection, however, the bolt size, bolt pitch and beam web thickness can affect the behaviour of single plate connection significantly.

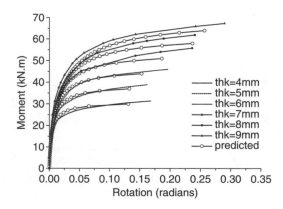

Figure 11. Comparison between finite element model prediction and test results for single plate connection with ordinary bolts.

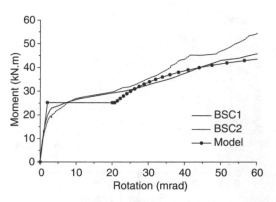

Figure 12. Comparison between analytical model prediction and test result for single plate connection with HSFG bolts.

Based on the regression of numerical data, the shape parameter n for single plate connection with ordinary bolts can be given as:

$$n = -72.842 - 106 \ln\left(\frac{M_u}{K_{si}} + 0.5\right) \qquad (17)$$

The predicted moment-rotation relationships are compared with the numerical results in Figure 11. In general, the predicted results fit well with the numerical curves.

5 CONCLUSIONS

Based on experimental observations and finite element modelling, a three stage analytical model has been proposed to simulate the moment-rotation relationship of single plate connection with HSFG bolts. At the first stage, the moment-rotation relationship is linear up to the slip moment M_{slip}. The moment keeps constant at the second stage until the all the bolts bear against the sides of the bolt holes. At the third stage, the moment-rotation relationship becomes non-linear due to the bearing between bolts and connected components. The predicted result agrees well with test results as shown in Figure 12. However, the research conducted so far is for single plate connection under monotonic loading only. Further research will be carried out for this type of connection under cyclic loading condition as well.

REFERENCES

Lipson, S. L. 1977. Single-Angle Welded-Bolted Connections, *Journal of the Structural Division, ASCE*, Vol. 103, No. ST3, Proc. Paper 12813, March 1977, pp. 559–570.

Swanson, J. A. 1999. *Characterization of the Strength, Stiffness, and Ductility Behaviour of T-stub Connections*, Ph.D. thesis, Georgia Institute of Technology.

Chen, W. F. 1987b. *Joint flexibility in steel frames*, Elsevier Applied Science Publishers, Essex, U.K.

Prestressed steel structures: historical and technological analysis

A. Masullo
Marigliano, Napoli, Italy

V. Nunziata
Studio Nunziata, Palma Campania, Napoli, Italy

ABSTRACT: This paper deals with the historical development of the technique of prestressing; from prestressed concrete (P.C.) to prestressed steel (P.S.). The latter is described in terms of its realization. In addition, several Italian cases are reviewed, which have adopted this technique and finally some experimental work is presented which shows the advantages that the widespread use of P.S. can bring to the sphere of the construction sector.

1 INTRODUCTION

Although seemingly recent, prestressed steel is a material whose origins date back a long way. The adoption of the technique of prestressing is attributed to Paxton, who in 1851, utilized this technique for the realization of Crystal Palace (Fig. 1), unaware of the great discovery he had made.

Koenen was the first to propose prestressing steel bars. He suggested doing this in 1907, before applying concrete, in order to avoid the formation of cracks and thus stumbled across the innovation of reinforced concrete (R.C.). Unfortunately however, his attempts failed because at that time the phenomena of fluage and shrinkage were unknown. In fact, the real "father" of prestressing is Eugène Freyssinet (Fig. 2), who in 1928 defined prestressing as a technique which consists in subjecting a material, in his case reinforced concrete, to loads which produce stresses opposed to those in operation, through the use of cables which have first been laid in the stressed mass.

The reasons which gave rise to this material may be found in the mechanical characteristics of concrete which, in fact, shows great ability to absorb forces of compression but a low resistance to tension which is allowed to be absorbed by the metallic reinforcement. The latter, in its turn, under the effect of tension tends to lengthen and, on account of the phenomenon of bonding, pulls the concrete along with it.

Consequently, if the stresses of tension are high, the concrete will crack. The cracks do not destabilize the structure but could lead to possible further deformation and expose the reinforcement to the danger of

Figure 1. Crystal Palace.

Figure 2. Eugène Freyssinet.

oxidization which in turn produces a reduction of its own resistance. It can be deduced that R.C. can tolerate loads up until the cracking limit. Unlike R.C., steel is a material which has high resistance both to tension and to compression. As a consequence, by making a comparison between prestressed steel and reinforced concrete, we can immediately note that in the first place,

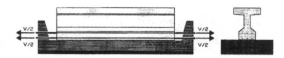

Figure 3.　Prestressing with bonding cables.

Figure 4.　Prestressing with sliding cables.

this technique further raises both the quality and the resistance to tension and compression characteristics of the steel (the technique actually manages to create a state of co-action in which the tensions and deformations are opposed to those induced by the loads which will subsequently act upon the structure). In the second place however, it raises the resistance to tension of reinforced concrete which is, in fact, negligible.

1.1　*The technologies*

The technique for realizing prestressed steel is achieved through external cables.

Here too we notice a further difference with reinforced concrete, which employs different techniques for its realization:

1. Bond cables (Fig. 3), in which the reinforcements are anchored due to bonding between steel and concrete;
2. Sliding cables (Fig. 4), in which the reinforcements are placed within plastic sheaths, allowing them to slide.

As has already been stated, a steel beam adopts prestressing with external cables (Fig. 5), which foresees the use of a type of steel with elevated mechanical characteristics ($f_{ptk} = 1800 \, \text{N/mm}^2$) and which is available on the market in the form of stabilizing seven-thread strands, spiraled around a central thread with a pitch of 12–16 times the diameter. Normal steel of type Fe-430 and Fe-510 is used.

This procedure requires a preliminary phase of preparation which include the following operations:

1. Preparation of the girder through the insertion of contrast elements to the cable which define the passage along the girder (deflectors);
2. Formation of the cable;
3. Placing the cables in position and their subsequent anchoring;
4. Applying tension to the reinforcements with jacks and tightening them;
5. Eventual re-tightening.

All this must be done with maximum care and requires a specialized workforce.

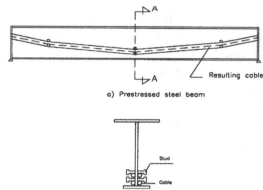

a) Prestressed steel beam

b) Section A–A

Figure 5.　Technique of prestressing with external cables.

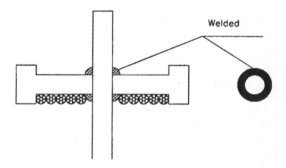

Figure 6.　Details of the deflector stud.

The first operation to carry out is to single out the line of the resulting cable and then to position the contrasts, made up of symmetrical studs which define the line of the cables themselves whose barycentric line is known as the "resulting cable". Technically, the contrasts are realized through symmetrical studs with regard to the web of the girder. The studs are capped at one end to keep the cable in position and are welded to the web. Their number depends on the length of the girder and the stresses in play (Fig. 6).

Once this operation is completed, the next stage is the formation of the cables. During this operation the strands are laid symmetrically in relation to the web and are freely left to run around the deflectors which have been greased or lubricated to avoid friction. The strand, which is made of high tensile steel is more susceptible by nature to corrosion than normal steel and is therefore protected against this risk. The protection is done through zinc-plating (galvanized strand) or through sheathing (sheathed strand) which consists in placing the strand (often zinc-plated) in a high density polyethylene sheath in which it can slide freely due to the presence of grease or wax which also act as

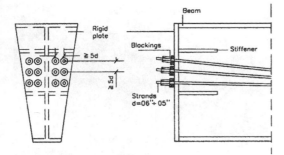

Figure 7. System of anchoring.

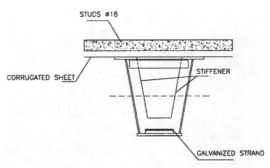

Figure 9. Box girder.

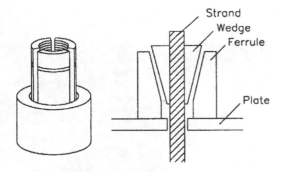

Figure 8. Ferrule for anchoring strands.

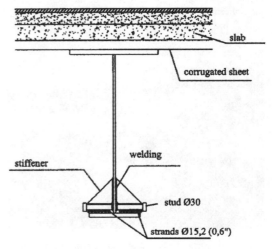

Figure 10. Di-symmetrical double T girder.

protection against corrosion. With this technique it is also possible to replace strands which turn out to be unsuitable. Protection against corrosion can also be obtained by using a sheath of HDPE into which the strands are inserted. The sheath will subsequently be injected with cement paste as occurs with reinforced concrete.

The next phase is anchoring which is the most delicate phase of the entire operation. A very simple system of anchoring is shown in Figure 7. It is made up of :

– A rigid plate
– blockings
– steel stiffeners.

In particular, anchoring the strands foresees the use of conical-trunk ferrules inside of which are toothed wedges of the same shape that hold the steel before tensioning (Fig. 8). Indeed, tightening is assured precisely because of the contact between the strand and the wedge since the strand, tending to pull in on itself, drags the wedge with it and thus self-blocks.

After the preparation phase, the next step is to determine the action acting upon the girder, as well as those associated with those induced by pre-tensioning.

It must be added that the sections most adapted to prestressing are those boxed beams (Fig. 9) and those with a plate girder (a di-symmetrical double T) (Fig. 10) since these are the ones that most suit this

technique, allowing for maximum exploitation of the material.

2 THE REALIZATIONS

Even though structures in P.S. offer many advantages, both economically and technically, unfortunately, at least in Italy, their use has been limited to a very few cases.

Recently in Rome, two roof covers have been constructed, belonging to two different typologies: a commercial center and a multiplex.

The first is the Gulliver commercial center (Fig. 11).

Here, a flat roof cover has been realized with the use of prestressed reticular girders of 21.90 meters, centered apart at 3.00 meters. A slab of concrete on predalles was cast between them. Prestressing was carried out with eight 15 mm diameter strands, raised linearly towards the supports. Protection of the strands was achieved with a controlled jet of mortar

Figure 11. Detail of the roof cover of the Gulliver commercial center.

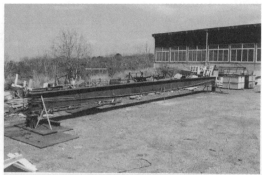

Figure 13. View of the girder.

Figure 12. View of the roof cover of the La Lucchina multiplex.

Figure 14. Sliding bearing.

that fills the U-profile in which they were lodged. The girders were constructed in two parts and put together with bolts and pre-tensioning of the strands.

The second roof cover was realized for the Lucchina multiplex (Fig. 12).

In its construction, 17.20 meter transversal girders were used. These were centered apart at 3.60 meters and laid on main girders which were supported on columns of concrete. Between these and the secondary girders, corrugated sheets were positioned onto which a collaboration slab of reinforced concrete was cast. Prestressing of the transversal girders was done in a workshop using four 15 mm waxed-type strands and then mounted with bolted joints.

2.1 Experimentation

Having described the techniques for employing prestressed steel and described two of the works carried out in Rome, it would be useful to present the results of an experiment which started in April '99 under the guidance of the engineer, Mr Nunziata. The test consisted in observing and studying the behavior of a 21.40 meter pre stressed steel girder.

It goes without saying that the girder had first been studied theoretically to determine its dimensions, loads and other characteristics, after which it was realized. The girder is shown in Figure 13.

The girder has the following characteristics:

It has a height of 80 cm, and is prestressed with ten strands, foreseeing a total capacity of 21.6 kN/m, (equal to 10.2 kN/m for dead loads and 11.4 kN/m for imposed loads) excluding its own weight which is equal to 1.72 kN/m. The beam was positioned in an outdoor courtyard and rested on two supports, one of which was a sliding bearing and the other a hinge (Fig. 14).

The strand deflectors were positioned, which in turn, were anchored at the ends of the girder with blockings (Fig. 15). Finally, we proceeded to the distribution of the load with blocks of cement of 25 kN (Fig. 16) and to the tightening of each strand with a force of an intensity equal to 151 kN.

After this, we passed to the measurement of the deflection in the middle span with a fiftieths caliber

Figure 15. Anchoring the ends.

Figure 16. Distribution of load.

a) Initial

b) Loaded

Figure 17. a) measurement of the deflection at transfer phase; b) measurement of the deflection at loading phase.

for the three fundamental phases (Fig. 17). The following results were obtained:

1. In the transfer phase, the deflection is equal to 54.54 mm
2. In the loading phase, taking into account the climatic conditions, the following values were recorded:
   - −68.32 mm immediately after loading phase;
   - −76.04 mm after three days;
   - −76.00 mm after one week;
   - −77.80 mm after twelve days;
   - −78.70 mm after thirteen days;
   - −79.84 mm after about a month;
   - −79.64 mm after over two months.
3. In the unloading phase, we recorded an elastic return and the final deflection was 37.84 mm

Through this experiment, even though it was carried out under difficult conditions, the results obtained were significant and underline two particular facts:

1. The superiority in terms of resistance and deformation of structures in prestressed steel compared to analogous structural typologies;
2. The economy and simplicity of execution of the proposed technology which can be realized with simple elements and is accessible to all.

3 CONCLUSIONS

Although this paper presented information in a very concise manner, it has illustrated some structures in prestressed steel and a technology which is very simple. This is in the hope that such a technique will become more widely used since prestressed steel is a material which can bring both economic benefit (since the realization of a girder in P.S. brings a savings of 15% compared to a normal one) and technical benefit (being a lightweight material that has great resistance) to the sphere of the construction industry.

BIBLIOGRAPHY

Nunziata, V. 1999. *Strutture in acciaio precompresso.* Palermo, Dario Flaccovio, Editore.

System-based Vision for Strategic and Creative Design, Bontempi (ed.)
© 2003 Swets & Zeitlinger, Lisse, ISBN 90 5809 599 1

Collapse and buckling of sheet piles, modification solution in Mared pump station, ABADAN

A. Turk
Water division, KWPA (Khuzestan Water and Power Authority), Ahwaz, IRAN

ABSTRACT: The original side-dam was drawn by circular cell cofferdam at 1995. Contractor changed the design into straight sheet piles, tie-rods in two levels for each span. Changing the original design, make some characters to ignore. Tie-rods were tensed by inside material. Straight steel sheet piles were collapsed. During of modification, changing the initial design appears some main wrong.

First, there is not solution for tensile member in depth sheets (-10 m about -5 m).

Second, number of tie-rods could not be satisfied the exerted stress upon the bars.

Third, horizontal earth pressure coefficient (Kx) computed less than real value.

The most important coefficient was Kx in designing of sheet piles cofferdam. In modification steps the Kx is chosen 0.5 in active soil. Sheet piles were modified by adding anchorage in two levels for each span and filling material depth were reduced by 2 m decrease from top and 2 m increasing embankment out side.

1   INTRODUCTION

End of Karon river, the Mared is the biggest pump station in south-west of Iran with 120 CMS and it was designed by sowden consulting engineering at 1975 for KWPA's contractors (Jean co. LTD). Mared's sides dams had been chosen to circular cell cofferdam but it was changed to review by inability of contractor condition into wall straight steel sheet piles and tie-rods. Wall straight steel sheets and steel tie-rods anchorage in two level for each span made new structure. Inside the walls were filled by aggregated material with internal friction angel 35 degree. Unfortunately after 6-month, inside material was effected to settle by weather condition therefore extra lateral forces were acted to deform walls by compaction materials which it is occurred by real exerted force that it should be recognized to compute components before installation. In sever exposure, tie-rods were tensed to collapse by above ultimate tensions. Many suggestions were sent into project's office desk to modify by contractor, consulting engineer and KWPA's supervisor engineer. only solution of supervisor engineer (A. Turk) has accepted to modify walls. Execution method will be explained in this text that it is based on new Kx value of lateral earth forces and decreasing potential.

2   MAIN MISTAKE IN NOTE-BOOK DESIGN AND STEEL SHEET PILES COLLAPSE

Referring on notebook design, Kx figure was determined by (Jean Eng. LTD) designer 0.3 in active zone. In each span, two level tie-rods were installed by 4 steel bars on each joint (8 bars in each span). All forces exerted upon the walls should be fixed to resist by members that it is based on figure Kx = 0.3 but the tie-rods could not be received the ultra tensions on their section areas. Figure Kx = 0.3 will produce a set of M (bending moment) and V (shear forces) that they have been designed to determine the numbers of tie-rods (AIII steel grade) and span distances. It is mentioned, the original layout of circular cell cofferdam was replaced to install by wall straight steel sheet piles. Replacement processing could not be satisfied to stable steel walls therefore main illegal designing explain with below items:

1. Low anchorage of tie-rods against real forces.
2. AII steel grade replaced with AIII.
3. Kx = 0.3 in designing and more in workshop.
4. Unlock walls in deep driving.
5. Wall and bars stability comparison with circular cell cofferdam.

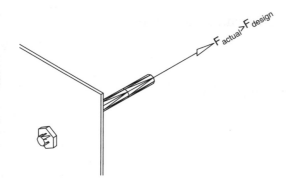

Figure 1. Force on section bars.

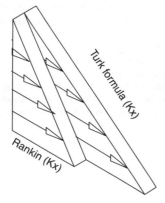

Figure 2. Comparison Kx by Turk formula.

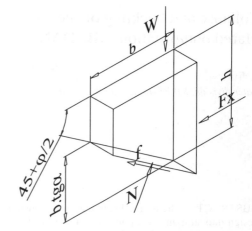

Figure 3. Explaining the A.Turk method and free body diagram of rupture volume in wall straight steel sheet piles. Where F = horizontal force exerted on wall (t/m); W = total weight of volume (t/m); f = friction force on rupture surface (t/m); N = normal force on rupture face (t/m); b = ½ wall distance (m). $\alpha = 45 + \varphi/2$ = soil rupture angel; φ = internal friction angel.

figure and it is mentioned that in the wall sheet piles omitted cohesiveness soil force on vertical plan but it must be determined on rapture surface in two cases.

Two conditions are belonged the below items:

1. Walls straight steel sheet piles with tie-rods.
2. Circular cell cofferdam sheet piles.

3 COLLAPSE AND BUCKLING OF WALL STEEL SHEET

Spaces between walls were filled by aggregated materials that it was compacted to settle by 6-month raining. After time duration, the nearest tie-rod into concrete wall (Mared pump station) was tensed by lateral movement that the sections of steel bars could not exerted to resist by undesired tension more than safety factor (Fig. 1). Another unreal problem is occurred when the AIII steel grade of tie-rods replaced by AII. Also, the Kx figure of notebook design belonged the at rest natural soil condition in active zone but the Kx should be advised to study by author in the next (Fig. 2).

4 Kx ANALYZING AND COMPARISON

Referring to soil mechanic and foundation engineering handbook, basic formulas could be used to determine a new relation for Kx. In this next formula is tried to explain a rupture volume as defined by Turk formula. Two conditions should be determined to produce the Kx

4.1 Straight wall Kx

It is defined by rupture volume in Figure 3 and series of formulas that it is started by Equation 1 and the figure of lateral forces (Kx) could be obtained by c = 0. It is mentioned that vertical cohesiveness must be neglected on rupture surfaces.

$$\sum F_N = 0 \Rightarrow F.\cos\alpha = W.\sin\alpha - N.tg\varphi \qquad (1)$$

$$\sum F_t = 0 \Rightarrow N = W.\cos\alpha + F.\sin\alpha \qquad (2)$$

$$\Rightarrow N/A = \sigma_n = \frac{\gamma.h/2}{(1+tg\alpha..tg\varphi)\sin\alpha}$$

$$h=0 \rightarrow \sigma_n = 0 \quad ; h=H \rightarrow \sigma_n = \frac{\gamma.H/2\sin\alpha}{(1+tg\alpha..tg\varphi)}$$

$$\bar{\sigma}_n(0) = \left(0 + \frac{\gamma.H/2}{2\sin\alpha(1+tg\alpha..tg\varphi_-)}\right) = \frac{\gamma.H/4\sin\alpha}{1+tg\alpha..tg\varphi}$$

$$\sigma_n(h) = \frac{\gamma.H/4\sin\alpha}{1+tg\alpha..tg\varphi}(H+h)$$

$$N = \int_{h_1=H-b.tg\alpha}^{h_2=H} \sigma_n \,.dh = \frac{\gamma(h^2/2+H.h)}{4\sin\alpha.(1+tg\alpha.tg\varphi)}\Big|_{H-b.tg\alpha}^{H}$$

$$H/b = tg\beta \quad ;and \quad M = tg\alpha/tg\beta$$

$$\Rightarrow F_X = \frac{\gamma H^2}{2}\left(2M-M^2+\frac{tg\varphi.(M^2-4M)}{2\sin 2\alpha(1+tg\alpha.tg\varphi)}\right)$$

$$C_k = tg\varphi/(2\sin 2\alpha(1+tg\alpha.tg\varphi))$$

$$\Rightarrow K_X = \left(M^2.(C_k-1)+M(2-4C_k)\right) \quad (3)$$

4.2 Kx, circular cell cofferdam sheet piles

The Kx could be determined by using Figures 4 and 5 that it is modelled to compute by soil rupture volume that the sector space could be defined to analyse by rupture plane with angel $\alpha = (45 + \varphi/2)$ and sector horizontal area with θ degree. It is mentioned that two cases should be recognized to calculate the Kx value and it is belonged to the height of rupture in centerline that it may be more or less than h of circular cell.

4.2.1 Rupture plane under top surface
It is the ordinary case that the maximum height of rupture could not be exceeded more than the total effective h of circular cell cofferdam sheet.

$$N = \sigma_n A_\alpha$$

$$\Rightarrow \sigma_n.\frac{R^2.\theta}{2\cos\alpha} = \frac{W(\cos\alpha+\sin\alpha.tg\alpha)}{1+tg\alpha.tg\varphi} \quad (4)$$

$$W = \gamma.\frac{R^2.\theta}{2}(H-\frac{R}{3}tg\alpha)$$

$$\alpha = 45+\frac{\varphi}{2} \quad ; \quad H/R = tg\beta; \quad M = tg\alpha/tg\beta$$

$$F_{X(volume)} = \gamma.\frac{R^2.\theta}{2}(H-\frac{R}{3}tg\alpha)\left[tg\alpha-\frac{tg\varphi(1+tg^2\alpha)}{1+tg\alpha.tg\varphi}\right]$$

$$F_{X(per\ meters)} = F_{X(volume)}/R.\theta$$

$$\Rightarrow F_X = \frac{\gamma.H^2}{2}(M-\frac{M^2}{3}).\left(1-\frac{tg\varphi(1+tg^2\alpha)}{tg\alpha(1+tg\alpha.tg\varphi)}\right)$$

$$K_{X_0} = \frac{F_X}{W} = (M-\frac{M^2}{3}).\left(1-\frac{tg\varphi(1+tg^2\alpha)}{tg\alpha(1+tg\alpha.tg\varphi)}\right)$$

$$\Rightarrow K_{X_0} = (M-\frac{M^2}{3}).\left(1-\frac{tg\varphi(1+tg^2\alpha)}{tg\alpha(1+tg\alpha.tg\varphi)}\right) \quad (5)$$

4.2.2 Rupture plane above top surface
When the radius of circular cell cofferdam is designed by limited conditions then the cell height of embankment will be equaled with virtual height of rupture volume. In this case, Equations 6 and 7 could be solved the problems and Figure 5 should be recognized during computations.

$$if \quad h_\alpha = R.tg\alpha \quad \rangle h$$

$$then: \quad u = \frac{h_\alpha - H}{H} = \frac{x}{r-x}$$

$$x = \frac{r.u}{u+1}$$

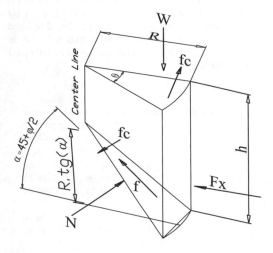

Figure 4. Rupture volume is shown to consider forces by vectors and there is tried to transfer limited rupture volume. Where W = total weight of rupture volume; Fx = horizontal force; N = normal forces on rupture plane; f = friction forces by cohesiveness and normal stress; fc = forces on side faces; R = radius of circular cell cofferdam; h = height of cell.

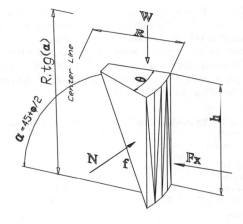

Figure 5. Rupture volume is shown to complete sector analyzing of circular cell cofferdam. Small part of virtual height is set above H of cell and Equations 6 and 7 will be taken Kx value that all of them are bigger than Kx Rankin and Bowels. It is mentioned that the W is considered by section volume in Figure 5.

$$\Delta h = R.tg\alpha - H$$

$$V_1 = \frac{1}{2}x^2.\theta.\frac{1}{3}\Delta h = \frac{1}{6}\theta.x^2.\Delta h$$

$$V_2 = \frac{1}{6}r^2.\theta.h_\alpha - V_1$$

$$V_3 = \frac{1}{2}r^2.\theta.H$$

$$\Rightarrow V = V_3 - V_2$$

$$W = \gamma.V \quad ; \quad W' = W/R.\theta \quad (tons/m)$$

$$F_X = W.K_{X_0}$$

$$F_X = \left(\frac{\gamma.H^2}{2}\right)K_X \tag{6}$$

$$\Rightarrow K_X = \frac{W.K_{X_0}}{\dfrac{\gamma.H^2}{2}}$$

$$K_X = \frac{2W}{\gamma.H^2}.(M - \frac{M^2}{3}).\left(1 - \frac{tg\varphi(1+tg^2\alpha)}{tg\alpha(1+tg\alpha.tg\varphi)}\right) \tag{7}$$

5 COMPARISION FORCES AND MODIFICATION METHODS

The rupture volume could be produced to consider Kx values in Table 1 for wall sheet piles (Equation 3) and Table 2 will be presented to comparison by using the Equation 5 and Bowels formula.

5.1 Kx wall straight steel sheet piles

There is tried to show difference relations by using Turk formula and Rankin in Table 1 and Equation 5. The H is height of embankment cell that it is influenced by inside active zone pressure and the b is ½ width wall sheets in meters unit. The internal friction angel is chosen by collapse condition at 35 degrees (topic of this article, Mared).

Table 1. Fx and Kx value for Turk and Rankin formulas.

H (meters)	10	12	15	17
b = 5 m				
Kx (Turk)	0.47	0.49	0.48	0.46
Fx (Turk)	23	35.5	53.8	66
Fx (Rankin)*	13.5	19.44	30.40	39.16
b = 6 m				
Kx (Turk)	0.38	0.47	0.50	0.49
Fx (Turk)	18.9	33.6	55	70.2
Fx (Rankin)*	same above			

* Kx (Rankin), Equation 8; Fx = t/m; unit weight of soil = 1 t/m³/m.

5.2 Kx circular cell cofferdam sheet piles

Table 2 also could be presented to compare by Turk Kx formula and Bowels's Kx lateral pressure. The H is height of embankment cell that it is influenced by inside active zone pressure and the R is the radius of circular cell cofferdam sheets in meters unit. Filling materials, The internal friction angel is chosen by arbitrary condition at 35 degrees.

$$K_{X(Rankin)} = tg^2(45 - \tfrac{\varphi}{2}) = tg^2(45 - \tfrac{35}{2}) = 0.27 \tag{8}$$

$$K_{X(Bowels)} = \frac{\cos^2\varphi}{2 - \cos^2\varphi} = \frac{\cos^2(35°)}{2 - \cos^2(35°)} = 0.51 \tag{9}$$

$$F_{X(bowels)} = \gamma\frac{(0.5H)^2}{2}K_{X(bowels)}$$

5.3 Mared sheet piles forces

Referring to Table 1, the Kx will be considered to modify tie-rods with Kx (5.5 m, 10 m, 35°) and the main problem is remained in structure until select another modification methods. Adding tie-rods will be solved the lateral forces but the unconstraint sheet piles in depth could be made to collapse again the structure. For this resign new drawn was based on this fact that the head decreasing should be resistance to bearing by added tie-rods. Therefore inside material have been removed to decrease soil potential head to resist by passive zone ($H_{inside} = 16.75$ m into $H_{new} = 14.75$ m) and passive forces should be increased to resist by passive zone against active zone. Finally, 2 m-head soil removed from body of filling material and in depth -12 m, cohesiveness clay soil could be balanced in equilibrium level.

Table 2. Fx and Kx value for Turk and Bowels formulas.

H (meters)	12	17	25
R = 5 m			
Kx (Turk)	0.16	0.12	0.91
Fx (Turk)	11.45	18.00	28.40
Fx (Bowels)*	9.10	18.24	39.45
R = 10 m			
Kx (Turk)	0.22	0.19	0.16
Fx (Turk)	15.45	27.61	48.40
Fx (Bowels)*	same above bowels		
R = 15 m			
Kx (Turk)	0.23	0.22	0.19
Fx (Turk)	16.80	31.46	60.20
Fx (Bowels)*	same above bowels		

* Kx (Bowels), Equation 9; Fx = t/m; unit weight of soil = 1 t/m³/m.

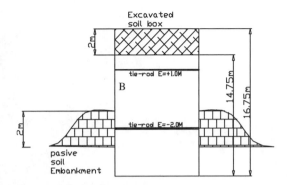

Figure 6.   Final design with modification order.

6   FINAL SOIL HEAD POTENTIAL

Figure 6 could be presented the final map that all details are determined to reconstruct wall sheet piles. It is mentioned that tie-rod capacity could be changed to modified by extra steel bars but the extra movement in depth should be constrained to stable by potential decreasing method. In Figure 6, area A is excavated two meters and area B was filled to increase passive zone embankment (+2 m).

7   CONCLUSION

After collapsing, Mared wall straight sheet piles must be advised to modify by Figure 6 and Equation 3. The steel bars (d = 32 mm) are tensed to release by extra active forces that they could not be considered by ordinary formulas. By using Equation 3, it is possible to modify new design. Also new Fx lateral load is needed to apply on circular cell cofferdam.

REFERENCES

Bowels, J.E. 1968. *Foundation Analysis & Design*, 3nd ed., Mc Graw Hill, New York, USA.
Jean.Co.Ltd. 2000. Collapse and buckling of wall sheet piles in Mared, based on old notebook.
Jean.Co.Ltd. 2000. Collapse and photo report based on views.
Jean.Co.Ltd. 2000. 1-New design, based on old notebook.
Jean.Co.Ltd. 2000. 2-New design, based on KWPA's Supervisor Engineer A.Turk repot. Workshop 202.
SES 1992. Soil Engineering Services, *Technical Report of Soil Mechanic in Mared pump Station Foundation.*
Turk, A. 2000. KWPA's Supervisor Engineer, especially report based on new formula.
Turk, R. & Delbakhsh, B. 2000. Mahab-Ghods Consulting Engineering, photo and document archive.
Vafayean, M. 1995. *Foundation Analyze and Design*. Isfahan University of Technology. 2nd Edition.

System-based Vision for Strategic and Creative Design, Bontempi (ed.)
© 2003 Swets & Zeitlinger, Lisse, ISBN 90 5809 599 1

Effect of number of bay on sway of building frames

B. Ahmed & M. Ashraf
Department of Civil Engineering, BUET, Dhaka, Bangladesh

ABSTRACT: Currently available design methods do not provide necessary information's for the estimation of sway of semi-rigid steel frames. The present paper describes the studies conducted on such frames to explore the effect of number of bays on its sway response. A set of parametric study has been conducted using the developed numerical models. These models are verified against the previous experimental and numerical results. From the obtained results of numerical study attempts have been made to relate the sway of frames having different numbers of bay.

1 INTRODUCTION

Ahsan (1997), proposed a simplified method for estimating sway of semi-rigid "medium-rise" steel frames. Ahsan studied 5 to 8 story high frames and finally proposed a nomograph concluding that: a characteristic straight line can be derived for all medium-rise steel frames having the same ratio of beam to column stiffness. This relation holds true for frames covering a very narrow range. In this chapter frames ranging from 5 to 30 story have been studied and it was observed that sway behavior changes with a change in number of stories and a single straight line could not represent the sway of all regular semi-rigid steel frames.

Ashraf (2001) proposed an equation to calculate sway of semi-rigid frames without using any nomographs. This equation provides satisfactory results. The proposed equation eliminates the use of any FE packages and design charts and has no limitation regarding number of stories or beam span to story height (L_b/L_c) ratio. This equation can be readily used to calculate the sway of semi-rigid steel frames.

A graphical method has been proposed by Ashraf (2001) to determine sway of semi-rigid stepped frames. In this connection, a method for calculating sway of rigid stepped frames has also been proposed using design charts for the evaluation of step factors. Detailed step by step calculation has been provided in the worked examples by Ashraf (2001).

Guidelines have been proposed by Ashraf (2001) to estimate the sway of semi-rigid steel frames having sectional irregularities. These guidelines have been described using worked example. All these proposals provide satisfactory results when compared with the sway values as obtained from FE analysis. The proposed methods eliminate the necessity of using FE packages for the estimation of sway of semi-rigid steel frames.

The effect of non-linear M-φ behavior of beam-to-column connections on the sway response of the semi-rigid steel frames has been studied by Ashraf (2001). From the numerical studies it was observed that in case of semi-rigid steel connections maximum moment occurs at the 2nd story level. A simplified formula has been proposed by Ashraf (2001) to estimate moment at second story level (M_2) and finally it was observed that if M_2 for a given frame is smaller than the maximum linear moment of the connection (M_L) for the connection, the initial slope of the M-φ curve can be considered as the linear stiffness (K_j) for hand calculation. Finally the method has been illustrated by Ashraf (2001) using a worked example.

Effect of base flexibility has been studied by Ashraf (2001) and it was observed that for medium-rise buildings, ranging from 5 to 15 story high, base flexibility significantly increases the overall sway of the frame. For high rise building frames its effect is almost negligible. A nomograph has been proposed to estimate "*base flexibility factor's*" for frames ranging from 5 to 30 story high. A simplified approach has been described to estimate linear stiffness from the non-linear moment rotation behavior of flexible bases. Finally the proposal has been verified using a worked example by Ashraf (2001).

Design proposal has been made by Ashraf (2001) to estimate sway of semi-rigid steel frames. The proposal shall enable the designers to calculate sway by hand calculation. If the overall sway of a frame can be estimated at the early stage of a design process by simple hand calculation necessary measures can be taken to limit the sway. Finally sway of a stepped frame with sectional irregularities has been calculated by Ashraf (2001) and it was observed that the design proposals give quite satisfactory results even for highly irregular frames.

The present paper reports the effect of number of bays on the sway of semi-rigid steel frames.

2 SELECTION OF PARAMETERS

This section describes the parameters selected to study the sway response of semi-rigid steel frames.

2.1 Geometric dimensions and member properties

Braced frames normally give sway well within the allowable limit. In case of un-braced frames sway is often reported as the main concern rather than ultimate strength. The present study intends to look into the behavior of semi-rigid frames ranging from 5 story to 30 story high. Bay numbers are varied from 2 to 5. Each story has a height of 3 meters while the size of each bay as well as frame spacing is 6 meters.

Table 1 shows the standard beam and column sections used in the present study. Beam and column sections have been chosen from an extensive analysis carried out as per BNBC. As the frame becomes higher, columns experience higher axial loads. The lateral pressure also increases with an increase in number of story and hence column axial force is also increased. On the other hand, lateral pressure induces moments at the beam-ends, which in case of semi-rigid connections, is controlled by the moment capacity of the connection.

Considering all these factors various sets of beam and column sections are selected for different frames.

2.2 Connection details

A wide spectrum of joint stiffness has been considered in the analysis. Beam stiffness (k_b) was kept to be constant while joint stiffness (k_j) has been varied so that k_b/k_j ranges between 0.125 to 4.0. For the present case the connections are assumed to have a constant stiffness k_j expressed in kN-m/rad. The base of the frames is considered as rigid.

2.3 Loading on frames

The present study is intended to examine the sway of semi-rigid frames under working load. Frames have been analyzed for gravity and wind loads at working level as per BNBC. The type of occupancy of the building is considered as general office room, banking hall (F). For the determination of wind load the building was considered as a standard occupancy structure for which the structure importance coefficient (C_I) was equal to 1.0. The basic wind speed considered is 210 km/h. Load intensities have been calculated for the highest elevation of a particular story and applied uniformly on that storey.

2.4 Material properties

The materials are assumed to behave elastically throughout the whole range of analysis. Modulus of Elasticity (E) is taken to be $2.07 \times 10^8 \, kN/m^2$.

Table 1A. Sectional properties of beam sections used in analysis.

No of stories	Beam section	Area (cm²)	Depth (mm)	Moment of inertia (cm⁴)	Moment capacity (kN-m)
5	254X102 UB 25	32.1	257	3404	93.84
10	254X102 UB 25	32.1	257	3404	93.84
15	305X127 UB 37	47.4	303.8	7143	166.55
20	305X127 UB 37	47.4	303.8	7143	166.55
25	305X127 UB 37	47.4	303.8	7143	166.55
30	305X127 UB 37	47.4	303.8	7143	166.55

Table 1B. Respective sectional properties of column sections used in analysis.

Column section	Area (cm²)	Depth (mm)	Moment of inertia (cm⁴)	Moment capacity (kN-m)	Kc/Kb for $L_b/L_c = 2.0$
203X203 UC 46	58.8	203.2	4564	159.11	2.68
203X203 UC 71	91.1	215.9	7647	251.67	4.50
203X203 UC 86	110.1	222.3	9462	303.2	2.64
254X254 UC 132	167.7	276.4	22416	578.04	6.28
254X254 UC 167	212.4	289.1	29914	737.6	8.38
305X305 UC 240	305.6	352.6	64177	1296.7	17.97

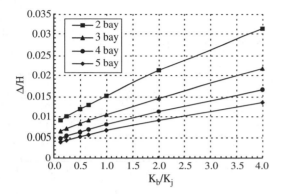

Figure 1. Sway behavior of 5 story frames.

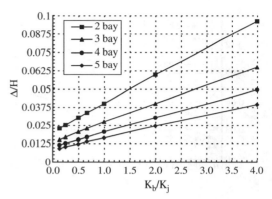

Figure 3. Sway behavior of 15 story frames.

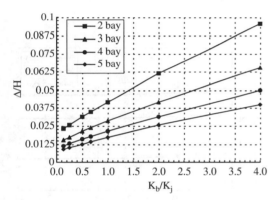

Figure 2. Sway behavior of 10 story frames.

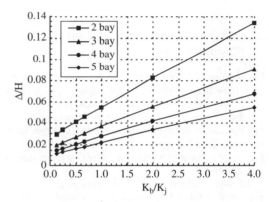

Figure 4. Sway behavior of 20 story frames.

3 SWAY BEHAVIOR OF MULTI-STORIED FRAMES HAVING DIFFERENT NUMBER OF BAY

Sway of frames having same number of stories but of different numbers of bay has been studied. Figures 1 to 6 show the graphical representation of the obtained results. In the present analysis for a particular number of story all frames have the same beam and column sections. Thus these figures give indication about change in sway behavior due to change in number of bay as well as change in connection stiffness.

The ratio of beam to connection stiffness (k_b/k_j) has been taken as abscissa while the ratio of sway to the total frame height (Δ/H) has been considered as the ordinate. Both the ordinate and abscissa are made dimensionless to represent the results in a more general form.

From these figures it is observed that Δ/H values for a frame increases with an increase in the value of k_b/k_j. The relationship between Δ/H and k_b/k_j is linear in nature. But from the results it is observed that this relationship does not maintain any certain order. For 10

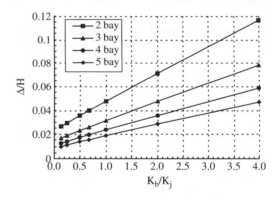

Figure 5. Sway behavior of 25 story frames.

and 15 story frames the values of Δ/H are almost the same. While Δ/H values for 25 story frames are rather smaller than those from 20 story frames. So no specific pattern can be identified for frames having different number of stories.

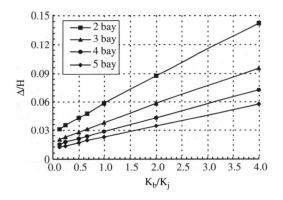

Figure 6. Sway behavior of 30 story frames.

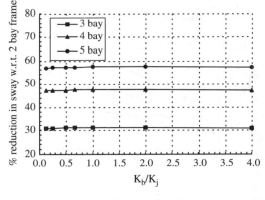

Figure 7. Reduction in sway for 5 story frames.

4 CHANGE IN SWAY DUE TO A CHANGE IN NUMBER OF BAY

Sway values of frames ranging from 5 to 30 story high have been analyzed to get a specific pattern in sway behavior of multi-storied frames. For a specific number of story, sway values for different number of bay have been observed and the relative changes have been calculated. Figures 7 and 8 represent the typical pattern of changes occurring in sway due to change in number of bay.

Results obtained from the numerical analysis are presented in Table 2. In both the cases sway of a 2 bay frame has been considered as the basis and the corresponding reduction (expressed as a percentage of 2 bay frame) in sway has been calculated (this calculation process is explained in Table 2). Increase in bay number reduces sway, from Figures 7 and 8 it is observed that this reduction does not depend on the ratio of beam to connection stiffness. Thus irrespective of the connection stiffness, change in sway will be constant for a specific change in number of bay as long as the beam and column properties remain the same. This reduction is very close for both the 5 to 30 story frames. If the number of bay is increased from 2 to 3, the relative reduction in sway for 5-story frame is almost 31% while that for 30-story frame is nearly 32%.

From the results shown in Table 2, it is observed that while other parameters are kept constant, a change in number of bay causes a constant change (relative) in sway; and this relative change is almost independent of number of stories.

The average results as obtained from Table 2 representing change in sway for different number of bay is shown in Table 3. This table can serve as a basis to compare the sway of frames having different number of bay and can also be used to predict the extent of change in sway if the number of bay is changed keeping all other parameters to be the same.

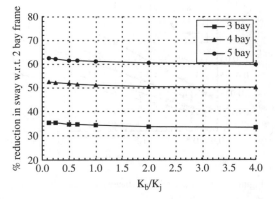

Figure 8. Reduction in sway for 30 story frames.

5 CONCLUSION

The present paper investigates change in sway behavior of multi-storied semi-rigid frames with a special emphasis to the number of bay. As the number of bay increases the sway decreases while other parameters are constant. Studies carried out in this paper shows that this relative change in sway due to a change in number of bay depends neither on the connection stiffness nor even on the number of stories if other parameters are kept constant. The outcomes of the present study can be summarized as: if the number of bay is increased from 2 to 3, without changing the properties of beam and column, sway is reduced by 31~32%; and similarly if the number of bay is increased to 4 and 5 the corresponding reductions (with respect to a 2 bay frame) will be 47~48% and 57~58% respectively. These relationships can be used to predict sway of building frames and to compare the sway of different frames.

Table 2. Change in sway (cm) due to a change in number of bay.

Stories	K_b/K_j	2 bay Δ_{s-r}	3 bay Δ_{s-r}	4 bay Δ_{s-r}	5 bay Δ_{s-r}	Reduction in sway (%) 3 bay	4 bay	5 bay
5	4.00	46.99	32.5	24.86	20.14	30.84	47.10	57.14
	2.00	31.83	21.94	16.76	13.57	31.07	47.35	57.37
	1.00	22.78	15.69	11.99	9.72	31.12	47.37	57.33
	0.67	19.44	13.4	10.25	8.31	31.07	47.27	57.25
	0.50	17.69	12.21	9.34	7.58	30.98	47.20	57.15
	0.25	14.97	10.35	7.93	6.44	30.86	47.03	56.98
	0.125	13.55	9.38	7.19	5.85	30.77	46.94	56.83
10	4.00	286.5	195.5	148.4	119.7	31.76	48.20	58.24
	2.00	183.1	124.5	94.33	75.97	32.00	48.48	58.51
	1.00	124.8	84.72	64.16	51.65	32.12	48.59	58.61
	0.67	104.0	70.62	53.48	43.06	32.10	48.58	58.60
	0.50	93.37	63.38	48.00	38.65	32.12	48.59	58.61
	0.25	76.93	52.24	39.58	31.88	32.09	48.55	58.56
	0.125	68.5	46.54	35.28	28.43	32.06	48.50	58.50
15	4.00	431.4	291.1	219.8	176.5	32.52	49.05	59.09
	2.00	267.6	180.2	135.9	109.1	32.66	49.22	59.23
	1.00	180.7	121.6	91.7	73.6	32.71	49.25	59.27
	0.67	150.75	101.5	76.54	61.45	32.67	49.23	59.24
	0.50	135.58	91.31	68.86	55.3	32.65	49.21	59.21
	0.25	112.6	75.83	57.21	45.96	32.66	49.19	59.18
	0.125	100.9	68.0	51.33	41.24	32.61	49.13	59.13
20	4.00	802	540.4	407.6	327.2	32.62	49.18	59.20
	2.00	493.7	331.2	249.2	199.8	32.91	49.52	59.53
	1.00	328.6	219.6	164.9	132.1	33.17	49.82	59.80
	0.67	271.4	181.0	135.8	108.7	33.31	49.96	59.95
	0.50	242.3	161.4	121.1	96.9	33.39	50.02	60.01
	0.25	198.1	131.6	98.6	78.9	33.54	50.23	60.17
	0.125	175.6	116.6	87.3	69.77	33.63	50.28	60.27
25	4.00	875.5	585.6	440.0	352.5	33.11	49.74	59.74
	2.00	536.3	356.6	267.2	213.6	33.51	50.18	60.17
	1.00	358.4	236.8	176.8	141.2	33.93	50.67	60.60
	0.67	297.5	195.8	146.0	116.2	34.18	50.92	60.94
	0.50	266.7	175.1	130.4	103.9	34.35	51.11	61.04
	0.25	220.0	143.8	106.8	85.02	34.64	51.45	61.35
	0.125	196.4	128.0	94.92	75.48	34.83	51.67	61.57
30	4.00	1283	858.6	645.4	517.0	33.08	49.70	59.70
	2.00	786.0	522.5	391.2	312.7	33.52	50.23	60.22
	1.00	523.4	344.7	257.0	205.0	34.14	50.90	60.83
	0.67	432.7	283.6	211.0	168.0	34.46	51.24	61.17
	0.50	386.7	252.6	187.4	149.3	34.68	51.49	61.39
	0.25	316.8	205.6	152.2	120.9	35.10	51.96	61.84
	0.125	281.4	181.8	134.3	106.5	35.39	52.27	62.15

Table 3. Average reduction in sway due to an increase in number of bay.

Frame type	Reduction in sway (%) (with respect to 2 bay frame) 3 bay	4 bay	5 bay
5 story	31	47	57
10 story	31	47	57
15 story	31	47	57
20 story	31	48	58
25 story	32	48	58
30 story	32	48	58

REFERENCES

Ahsan, R. 1997. *Semi-rigid Joint Action in Sway Steel Frames*, M.Sc. Thesis, Department of Civil Engineering, Bangladesh University of Engineering and Technology, Dhaka.

ANSYS 5.4, Operational guide, SASIP Inc, 201 Johnson road, Houston, PA15342-1300.

Ashraf, M. 2001. "*Sway Estimation of Semi-Rigid Steel Frames*", M. Sc. Thesis, Department of Civil Engineering, Bangladesh University of Engineering and Technology, Dhaka.

"Bangladesh National Building Code (BNBC)", 1993, Part 6 (Structural Design), Chapter 2 (Loads).

System-based Vision for Strategic and Creative Design, Bontempi (ed.)
© *2003 Swets & Zeitlinger, Lisse, ISBN 90 5809 599 1*

CFRP reinforcement design of steel members damaged by fatigue

P. Colombi

Department of Structural Engineering, Technical University of Milan, Milan, Italy

ABSTRACT: Bonded composite patch, eventually prestressed prior to bonding, is an innovative technique to reinforce steel member damaged by fatigue. Experimental results showed the significant increment of the fatigue life of cracked steel plate. The reduction of the fatigue crack growth rate is due to a *global effect* (produced by prestress) and a *local effect* (produced by the reinforcement stiffness). This paper introduces a simplified model to capture the local effect and to study the influence of the main design parameters (such as the reinforcement stiffness and adhesive properties) with reference to riveted steel members. Moreover, an efficient design procedure is introduced in order to select the appropriate reinforcement and to reduce, or eventually to stop, crack propagation in fatigue damaged steel elements.

1 INTRODUCTION

Fatigue crack growth in steel elements is a process influenced by the phenomena acting at the crack tip (Suresh 1991), and it is mainly governed by the stress intensity factor range, ΔK. At crack tip, at the maximal load of the fatigue cycle, plastic deformations (plastic zone) are generated. As the load is released, the elastic material next to the crack tip recovers its original shape and it squeezes the plastic zone. As the crack propagates, a zone of residual tensile deformation is left in the wake of the advancing crack tip. The permanent elongation in these plastic strips produces premature contact between crack faces (crack closure) that results in slower crack propagation (Suresh 1991). In order to take into account crack closure effects, the effective stress intensity factor range concept, ΔK_{eff}, must be introduced.

Then, to reduce or to stop crack propagation, one of the following strategies has to be adopted (Broek 1986):

- reduce the stress range $\Delta\sigma$,
- reduce the stress intensity factor ΔK by reducing the crack opening displacement;
- reduce the effective stress intensity factor ΔK_{eff} by promoting crack closure effects.

Application of bonded prestressed carbon fibers reinforced plastic (CFRP) strips to fatigue damaged steel members makes use of all these three principles in order to contrast crack propagation (Bassetti 2001). High stiffness of CFRP strips results, in fact, in some reduction of the stress range $\Delta\sigma$. Moreover, CFRP strips bonded perpendicular to the crack path limit

crack opening at crack tip and then the stress intensity factor. Eventually, the prestress of the CFRP strips prior to bonding promotes crack closure effects. In other words, prestressed CFRP strips act on cracked section in two different ways. First, a *local effect* is achieved by patching the crack (local reduction of crack opening displacement and stress range). Second, a *global effect* is induced by compressive stresses applied on the whole element. CFRP patches can also be applied as preventive measures to stop crack propagation of small crack which are not detectable by conventional inspection techniques.

2 FATIGUE BEHAVIOR OF OLD STEEL STRUCTURES AND REINFORCEMENT TECHNIQUES

2.1 *Fatigue behavior of old steel structures*

The evaluation of the remaining fatigue life of old steel structures (consider, for instance, riveted steel bridge built up at the beginning of last century) is a difficult task. The following points must be considered in order to produce a reliable estimation of the remaining fatigue life:

- fatigue reliability evaluation technique;
- fatigue resistance of a given structural detail;
- reinforcement techniques;

The evaluation of the fatigue life is usually performed by the well known Miner's rule, i.e. by assuming a linear damage accumulation:

$$d_i = \frac{1}{N_i} = \frac{1}{2 \cdot 10^6} \left(\frac{\Delta \sigma_i}{\Delta \sigma_c} \right)^m$$

$$D = \sum_{i=1}^{k} n_i d_i \leq 1 \tag{1}$$

where N_i is the number of cycles to failure for a given stress range $\Delta \sigma_i$, $\Delta \sigma_c$ is the detail fatigue class, m is the slope of the relevant fatigue resistance curve and n_i is the number of applied load cycles for the stress range $\Delta \sigma_i$. Experimental results showed (Bassetti 2001) that the linear damage accumulation rule (Eq. 1) produces a very conservative fatigue lifetime estimation, in particular under variable amplitude loading.

Alternatively, the fatigue lifetime could be evaluated by fracture mechanics concepts. Stable fatigue crack growth is usually studied by well known Paris' law:

$$\frac{da}{dN} = C \cdot \Delta K^n \tag{2}$$

where ΔK is the stress intensity factor range and C, m are materials parameters. The stress intensity factor range is usually computed as:

$$\Delta K = Y \cdot \Delta \sigma \sqrt{\pi a} \tag{3}$$

where Y is a corrector factor depending from crack and element geometry and applied load, $\Delta \sigma = \sigma_{max} - \sigma_{min}$ is the stress range and a is the crack length.

In order to introduce crack closure effects, the concept of effective stress intensity factor range, ΔK_{eff}, must be introduced in Equation 2 instead of ΔK:

$$\Delta K_{eff} = Y \cdot \Delta \sigma_{eff} \sqrt{\pi a} \tag{4}$$

where $\Delta \sigma_{eff}$ is the effective stress intensity factor range:

$$\Delta \sigma_{eff} = \sigma_{max} - \sigma_{op} \tag{5}$$

Different models are available in the literature to evaluate the "opening stress" σ_{op}. For instance, consider the model proposed by Veers (1987):

$$\sigma_{op} = \max \left[R; \frac{1}{1+\alpha} (1 + R \cdot R_y) \right] \cdot \sigma_{max} \tag{6}$$

where $R = \sigma_{min}/\sigma_{max}$ is the stress ratio, α is the constraint factor and $R_y = \sigma_{max}/\sigma_y$ (σ_y is the yield stress). The constraint factor α is function of stress state at crack tip and it is function of the plastic zone size. In Broek (1986) it is proposed $\alpha = 1.68$, while experimental results indicated $\alpha = 1.5$ for plain stress and

$\alpha = 2$ for plain strain. The fracture mechanics approach produces accurate estimation of the fatigue lifetime of old steel structures but requires the calibration of the fatigue crack growth material parameters (C and m) and the evaluation of the stress intensity factor range.

2.2 Reinforcement techniques

Standard repair techniques of old steel structures make use of welding (if the steel is weldable), stop hole, bolted cover-plate, high strength bolts, cold expansion of rivet hole and external prestressed cables. The last three techniques introduce compressive stresses in the cracked element which reduces the effective stress intensity factor range. Crack welding and stop hole modify crack geometry at crack tip reducing then the stress intensity factor. Finally, bolted cover-plate, reduce the stress range at crack tip and modify the crack geometry. Note that some of the above repair techniques (bolted cover joint and crack welding) introduce additional stress concentration in the repaired element. Moreover, they act on a single visible crack, i.e. on a crack, for instance, which is greater than the rivet head of riveted bridge members.

CFRP-laminates have the following properties, particularly interesting for the repair and strengthening of old riveted steel members under fatigue loading:

- high fatigue resistance;
- high stiffness ($E = 155$–300 GPa);
- high tensile strength ($f_{tk} = 1400$–2400 MPa);
- low self weight ($\gamma = 1.6$ t/m^3);

High fatigue resistance and high stiffness of CFRP materials allows the use of these materials as reinforcement elements. A patch bonded on the crack reduces crack opening displacement and then the stress intensity factor. High fatigue resistance of patch material is mandatory in order to avoid a crack propagation from the cracked steel section into the patch. High stiffness helps to reduce the stress amplitude in the cracked steel section. Finally, the low self-weight of CFRP plates limits the increase of dead load of the structure and simplifies significantly the execution of strengthening work. In order to increase the effectiveness of the composite patch on thicker steel section, the patch could be prestressed. Compressive stresses at crack tip produced by the prestressed patch generate crack closure effects, which reduce or stop fatigue crack propagation.

3 STRESS INTENSITY FACTOR EVALUATION OF REINFORCED STEEL MEMBERS

The application of the fracture mechanics approach to evaluate the fatigue lifetime of a structural element requires the integration of the fatigue crack propagation law (Eqs. 2–4). The stress intensity factor range

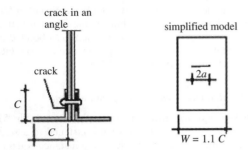

Figure 1. Simplified model for a crack in an angle.

(Eqs. 3–4) must then be evaluated first in order to compute the relevant fatigue crack growth rate. To this end in a general situation, numerical methods, such as finite element method, must be implemented (Bassetti et al. 2003). This task is very time consuming since a detailed mesh is required close to the crack tip in order to get reliable numerical results. Special techniques (Owen & Fawkes 1983) must then be implemented to reduce the total number of nodal points and finite elements of the model.

Bassetti (2001) proposed a simplified method to evaluate the stress intensity factor in a riveted cracked structural element, based on the work performed by Hensen (1992). The cracked component (flanges, web, angles) is replaced by a cracked plate. This approach simplify significantly the stress intensity factor evaluation and produces conservative estimation of the fatigue crack growth rate. The proposed simplified model, for a crack in an angle of a riveted cross section, is illustrated in Figure 1. Hensen (1992) computed, on a numerical basis, the equivalent length W (see Fig. 1) in order to get the same fracture mechanics parameters (typically the J integral) in the real cracked element and plate.

Consider now a cracked plate reinforced by composite (CFRP) patch (see Fig. 2). The intact CFRP layers bridge the cracked metal and the stresses in the reinforced plate are called bridging stress, σ_{br}. The bridging stress must then be determined first in order to compute the stress intensity factor and to predict fatigue crack growth under cycling loading. The bridging stress is, in general, non-uniform (Guo & Wu 1999) since it depends on many factors such as the delamination shape and size and the shear deformation of the adhesive.

The bridging stress must be computed for a given boundary condition, crack length and geometry. It is assumed that delamination exists on each interface between the metal and the CFRP-adhesive layers (Fig. 2). With reference to Figure 2, the bridged area was totally divided into N bar elements and the element width at a distance of x_j, is $2w_j$. Bridging stress acting on the boundary of the delaminated area reduce the crack opening (Fig. 3).

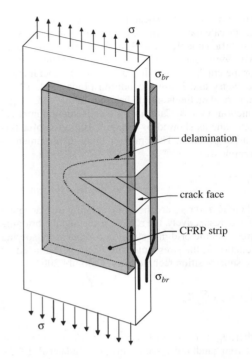

Figure 2. A fiber-bridged crack with delamination at the interfaces between the metal and the adhesive layers.

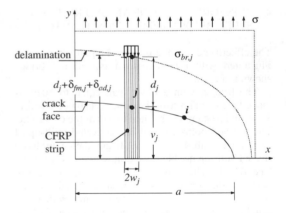

Figure 3. Bridging stress and crack opening displacement of the j-th element of the bridged area.

The extension of the intact bridging fibers, $\delta_{fm,j}$, plus the shear deformation, $\delta_{ad,j}$, of the adhesive in the boundary of the delaminated area, should be equal to the crack opening displacement, v_j, contributed by both the applied, σ, and the bridging stress, $\sigma_{br,j}$. At any point x_j of the crack faced one has (Guo & Wu 1999):

$$v_j = \delta_{fm,j} + \delta_{ad,j} \qquad (7)$$

An estimation of the shear deformation of the adhesive can be calculated from the interlaminar shear stress of a modified double cracked lap shear specimen (Guo & Wu 1999). Because there is no closed form solution for the crack opening displacement for general crack geometry and loading condition (Tada et al. 1974), numerical methods should be used. To this end, weight functions (Wu & Carlsson) is a convenient numerical technique as showed by Wang & Blom to solve this kind of problem. The crack opening displacement is computed as:

$$v_j = v_{\sigma,j} - v_\sigma \tag{8}$$

where v_σ and $v_{\sigma,br}$ are the crack opening displacement due to, respectively, the remote stress and the bridging stress. As the bridging stress is computed by solving Equation 7, the stress intensity factor is evaluated by the superposition technique as (Colombi 2003):

$$K = K_\sigma + \sum_j^N K_{\sigma,br,j} \tag{9}$$

where K_σ is the contribution due to the remote stress σ (from handbooks, see for instance Tada et al. 1973), while $K_{\sigma,br,j}$ is the contribution due to the bridging stress (from weight function technique).

4 REINFORCEMENT OF AN OLD RIVETED STEEL BRIDGE BY COMPOSITE PATCH

The effectiveness of the proposed repair technique is illustrated with reference to a typical rail bridge shown in Figure 4.

The bridge, with a clear span equal to 70 m, is made by two main truss beam at a distance equal to 8.8 m and a beam depth equal to 9 m at the centerline. The top and bottom chord has a riveted built-up Π section (see Tab. 1) while the diagonal element has a riveted built-up double C section with cross stiffeners (see Tab. 1). The cross girder, with a span equal to 8.8 m at a distance equal to 5 m, has a riveted build-up section (see Tab. 1). All rivets were 20 mm with a hole equal to 22 mm in diameter. The basic material of the structural elements was mild steel. In the numerical example, fatigue damage is supposed to be located at the edge of rivet hole in a high stressed region. In particular, a diagonal element, a bottom chord and a

Figure 4. The trestle rail bridge under investigation.

cross girder were reinforced by CFRP lamina of different width and a Young modulus in the fibers direction equal to 174 GPa. The reinforcement was bonded to the steel element by a bi-component epoxy resin with a shear stiffness equal to 270 Mpa.

4.1 Reinforcement of a diagonal element

In the diagonal element under investigation (see Fig. 5), the angles $150 \times 150 \times 18$ were fastened to a steel plate with a single line of rivets at a distance equal to 100 mm. The evaluation of the stress intensity factor was performed by the simplified model illustrated in Figure 1. In particular, the model width W was = 1.1; $C = 165$ mm with a crack length $2a = 90$ mm. The stress analysis produced a maximum and minimum applied stress in the angles equal to $\sigma_{max} = 138.22$ MPa and $\sigma_{min} = 52.55$ MPa. The relevant stress ratio was then $R = 0.38$. The effective stress intensity factor was finally computed by Equations 4–5 as

Table 1. Bridge elements reinforced by CFRP patch.

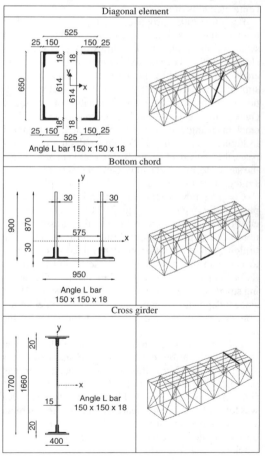

$\Delta K_{eff} = 922.55\,\text{Nmm}^{-3/2}$. The reinforced was performed by removing the rivets around the cracked hole and inserting a CFRP lamina with a width equal to 100 mm and a thickness equal to 2.4 mm (see Fig. 5). The angles were then fastened to the plate by high strength bolts. The stress intensity factor in the reinforced element was computed by the model illustrated in Section 3. The maximum and minimum applied stress were equal to $\sigma_{max} = 136.17\,\text{MPa}$ and $\sigma_{min} = 51.77\,\text{Mpa}$. As expected, the reinforcement produced a marginal reduction of the applied stress in the angles. As a result the stress ratio R was still equal to 0.38 and the effective stress intensity factor was computed by Equations 4–5 as $\Delta K_{eff} = 735.84\,\text{Nmm}^{-3/2}$ with a reduction equal to 20%.

4.2 Reinforcement of a cross girder

In the cross girder under investigation (see Fig. 6), the angles $150 \times 150 \times 18$ were fastened to the web plate with a single line of rivets at a distance equal to 100 mm. The bottom and top flanges were realized by two cover-plate fastened again to the angles by a single line of rivets (see Tab. 1) The evaluation of the stress intensity factor was performed by the simplified model illustrated in Fig. 5. In particular, the model width was $W = A + C = 300\text{mm}$ with a crack length $a = 45\,\text{mm}$. The stress analysis produced a maximum and minimum applied stress in the angles equal to

$\sigma_{max} = 49.08\,\text{MPa}$ and $\sigma_{min} = 4.27\,\text{MPa}$. The relevant stress ratio was then $R = 0.09$. The effective stress intensity factor was finally computed by Equations 4–5 as $\Delta K_{eff} = 327.20\,\text{Nmm}^{-3/2}$.

The reinforced was performed by removing the rivet around the cracked hole and inserting a CFRP lamina with a width equal to 100 mm and a thickness equal to 2.4 mm (see Fig. 6). The angles was then fastened to the plate by high strength bolts. The stress intensity factor in the reinforced element was computed by the model illustrated in Section 3. The maximum and minimum applied stress were equal to $\sigma_{max} = 48.44\,\text{MPa}$ and $\sigma_{min} = 4.22\,\text{MPa}$. As expected, the reinforcement produced a marginal reduction of the applied stress in the angles. As a result the stress ratio R was still equal to 0.09 and the effective stress intensity factor was computed by Equations 4–5 as $\Delta K_{eff} = 277.82\,\text{Nmm}^{-3/2}$ with a reduction equal to 15%.

4.3 Reinforcement of a bottom chord

The bottom chord under investigation (see Fig. 8), the angles $150 \times 150 \times 18$ was fastened to the web plate with a single line of rivets at a distance equal to 100 mm. The bottom flange was a realized cover-plate fastened again to the angles by a single line of rivets. The evaluation of the stress intensity factor was performed by the simplified model illustrated in Fig. 7. In particular, the model width was $A = 870\,\text{mm}$ with

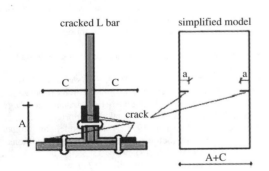

Figure 5.   Reinforcement of a an angle of a diagonal element.

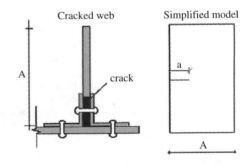

Figure 7.   Reinforcement of the cracked angles of a cross girder.

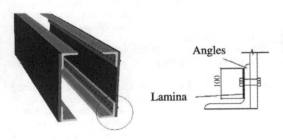

Figure 6.   Simplified model for the crack of the cross girder.

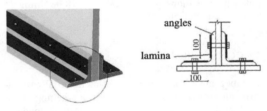

Figure 8.   Simplified model for the cracked web of the bottom chord.

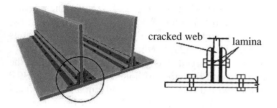

Figure 9. Reinforcement of the cracked web of the bottom chord.

a crack length $a = 100\,\text{mm}$. The stress analysis produced a maximum and minimum applied stress in the angles equal to $\sigma_{max} = 142.27\,\text{MPa}$ and $\sigma_{min} = 45.68\,\text{MPa}$. The relevant stress ratio was then $R = 0.32$. The effective stress intensity factor was finally computed by Equations 4–5 as $\Delta K_{eff} = 1408.96\,\text{Nmm}^{-3/2}$.

The reinforcement was performed by removing the rivets around the cracked hole and inserting a CFRP lamina with a width equal to $150\,\text{mm}$ (see Fig. 5). The angles was then fastened to the plate by high strength bolts. The stress intensity factor in the reinforced element was computed by the model illustrated in Section 3. The maximum and minimum applied stress were equal to $\sigma_{max} = 141.43\,\text{MPa}$ and $\sigma_{min} = 45.41\,\text{MPa}$. As expected, the reinforcement produced a marginal reduction of the applied stress in the angles. As a result the stress ratio R was still equal to 0.32 and the effective stress intensity factor was computed by Equations 4–5 as $\Delta K_{eff} = 918.06\,\text{Nmm}^{-3/2}$ with a reduction equa to 35%.

5 CONCLUSIONS

The mechanical of CFRP make this material particularly interesting for the repair and strengthening of old steel bridge members subjected to fatigue loading. High fatigue resistance of carbon fibers allows the use of bonded CFRP-plates for crack patching. Reduction of crack opening displacements produced by bonding CFRP-plates perpendicularly to the crack path, results in a significant reduction of stress intensity factors at the crack tip and, therefore, the crack growth rate.

A simplified model was proposed in order to compute the stress intensity factor of the reinforced elements, such as angles, web and flanges.

The effectiveness of the proposed repair technique was showed with reference to a rail bridge with riveted built up section. The reinforcement of the cracked elements by CFRP lamina produced a significant reduction of the effective stress intensity factor range (around 20%) and then a greater fatigue lifetime.

Finally, high tensile strength of carbon fiber makes it possible to apply compressive stresses in the cracked steel sections by prestressing the CFRP-plates, which promote crack closure phenomena and contribute to a further reduction in the crack growth rate.

ACKNOWLEDGEMENT

The Italian Ministry of Instruction, University and Research (MIUR) supported the research within the COFIN02 research project coordinated at a national level by Professor Luigi Ascione.

REFERENCES

Bassetti A. 2001. *Application de lamelles precontraintes en fibres de carbon pour le renforcement d'elements de pont rivetes endommages par fatigue* (in French). Ph.D. Thesis n. 2440, Swiss Federal Institute of Technology, EPFL.

Bassetti A., Colombi P. & Nussbaumer A. 2003. Analysis of cracked steel members reinforced by pre-stressed composite patch. *Fatigue Fract. Engng. Mater. Struct.* 26: 59–66.

Broek D. 1986. *Elementary engineering fracture mechanics*. Dordrecht: Martinius Nijhoff Publishers.

Colombi P. 2003. Stress intensity factor in notched fibre reinforced steel plate: closed form vs. numerical solution. *Composite in construction; Proc. intern. conf., Cosenza (Italy), 16–19 September 2003*, in press.

Guo Y. & Wu X. 1999. Bridging stress distribution in center-cracked fiber reinforced metal laminates: modelling and experiments. *Engng. Fract. Mech.* 63: 147–163.

Hensen W. 1992. Grundlagen für die Beurteilung der Weiterverwendung alter stahlbrucken (in German). Ph.D. thesis, Rheinisch-Westfälischen Technische Hochschule, RWTH.

Naboulsi S. & Mall S. 1996. Modelling of a cracked metallic structure with bonded composite patch using the three layer technique. *Composite Structures* 35: 295–308.

Newman J.C. Jr. 1981. A crack-closure model for predicting fatigue crack growth under aircraft spectrum loading. In J.B. Chang & C.M. Hudson (eds), *Methods and models for predicting fatigue crack growth under random loading, ASTM STP 748*: 53–84. American Society for Testing and Materials.

Owen D.R.J. & Fawkes A.J. 1983. *Engineering fracture mechanics – numerical methods and applications*. Swansea: Pineridge Press Ltd.

Suresh S. 1991. Fatigue of materials, Cambridge: Cambridge University Press.

Suzuki T. & Sakai M. 1994. A model for crack-face bridging. *Int. J. Fracture* 65: 329–344.

Tada H., Paris P. & Irwin G. 1973. *The stress analysis of cracks handbook*. Hellertown: Del Research Corporation.

Veers P.J. 1987. *Fatigue crack growth due to random loading*. SAND87-2037, Sandia National Laboratories.

Wang G.S. & Blom A.F. 1991. A strip model for fatigue crack growth predictions under general load conditions. *Engng. Fract. Mech.* 40(3): 507–533.

Wu X.R. & Carlsson A.J. 1991. *Weight functions and stress intensity factor solutions*. Oxford: Pergamon Press.

System-based Vision for Strategic and Creative Design, Bontempi (ed.)
© 2003 Swets & Zeitlinger, Lisse, ISBN 90 5809 599 1

Buckling strength evaluation of corroded flange of plate girder

T. Kaita & K. Fujii
Department of Civil and Environmental Engineering, Hiroshima University, Japan

ABSTRACT: For proper maintenance to occur, it is very important to establish a reliable strength estimation method for corroded steel structures. In this study, non-linear FEM analyses were performed parametrically for corroded compressive flanges without eccentricity. Using the results, an accurate and simple estimation method was proposed. A plate surface is generated by using the spatial auto-correlation method. The following conclusions can be drawn from the FEM analyses: (1) The ultimate strength of a corroded plate can be estimated by the representative thickness $t = t_{avg} + 2\sigma_{st}$ without concerning its irregularity, where t_{avg} = average thickness, and σ_{st} = standard deviation of plate thicknesses. (2) When the standard deviation of plate thicknesses is large, such as $\sigma_{st} = 1.0$ mm, the ultimate strength may become larger than that of a plate without corrosion.

1 INTRODUCTION

The number of technical reports on corrosion damage in steel structures is increasing gradually. However, it has not been clarified yet whether or not these corroded structures have enough margins for failure. This fact causes some uncertain problems; for example, what should be measured, or how should such structures be managed in future? Therefore, it is very important to accurately estimate the remaining strength of corroded steel structures.

There are some experimental studies concerning the remaining strength of corroded plates. Matsumoto et al. (1989) investigated tensile strength using a tensile coupon test on corroded plates. To predict the remaining tensile strength of a corroded plate, they proposed a minimum value of average thicknesses through the cross-section perpendicular to the loading axis. On the other hand, Muranaka et al. (2001) proposed a representative thickness of $t_{avg} - 0.7\sigma_{st}$ (t_{avg} = average thickness, σ_{st} = standard deviation of plate thicknesses) based on their tensile tests. Thus, we can find several investigations that try to estimate remaining strength by using representative thickness formulated by some statistic parameters.

Though the estimation method by representative thickness must be suitable and rational, it should be noted that the representative thickness changes with stress state in a corroded plate. For example, strength in tension could be determined by the cross-sectional area of a plate, but under compression it would be determined by the flexural rigidity of the plate because

of its buckling. It should be noted that, the representative thickness for a compressive stress state has not yet been clarified.

This paper proposes a simple and reliable method for estimating the remaining strength by using the representative thickness of corroded plates subjected to a compressive stress. The representative thickness is determined by non-linear FEM simulations, taking into account corroded surface irregularities made using the spatial auto-correlation method. The purpose of this is to reproduce surface irregularities analogous to their actually appearing. The corroded steel plates are assumed to be rectangular plates with three simply supported edges and the fourth free, such as a flange panel of a plate girder bridge.

2 NON-LINEAR FEM ANALYSIS OF CORRODED PLATES

2.1 Numerical model

As is shown in Figure 1, we used a constant size of plates with 200 mm × 800 mm and 20 × 80 elements in the analyses. The plate is simply supported along three edges and free along the fourth. Uniform prescribed displacements in x-direction were applied along an edge and the opposite edge, through the middle plane of the shaded elements. The axial force was calculated from reaction forces at nodal points along loading edges. A plate has surface irregularities caused by overall corrosion on both its surfaces.

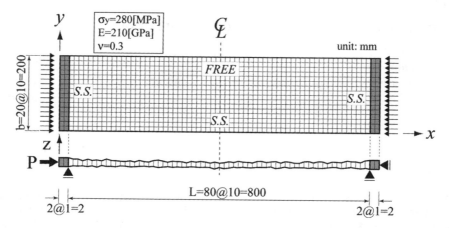

Figure 1. Numerical model.

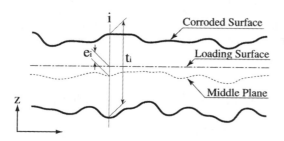

Figure 2. Eccentricity by corrosion.

Therefore, the middle plane of a corroded plate is not flat, and has eccentricities against the loading plane, as shown in Figure 2. The average eccentricity e_{avg} can be obtained by Equation 1:

$$e_{avg} = \sum_{i=1}^{N} \frac{e_i}{N}, \tag{1}$$

where N is the number of nodal points and e_i shows the eccentricity at the nodal point i. Finite element analyses were performed under the condition that a plane of average eccentricity is coincident with its loading plane, namely without eccentricity. The shaded elements with 2 mm width along the loading edges are set to meet the condition of no eccentricity.

The isoparametric shell element with four nodal points, updated Lagrangian formulation, and incremental method was adopted in the analysis. Concerning material properties, perfect elastic-plastic material, Plandtl-Reuss's flow rule, and von Mises's yield criteria were assumed.

2.2 Formation of a corrosion surface

A surface irregularity very similar to an actual corroded surface should be used in analyses in order to obtain accurate results for remaining strength of corroded plates. The spatial auto-correlation model is applied to generate the irregularities of a corrosion surface, as shown by Equations 2 and 3.

$$Z_i = \int_\Omega e^{-\beta d_{ij}} v_j \, ds, \tag{2}$$

$$Z_i = \begin{bmatrix} 1 & e^{(-\beta d_{12})} & \cdots & e^{(-\beta d_{1n})} \\ e^{(-\beta d_{21})} & 1 & \cdots & e^{(-\beta d_{2n})} \\ \vdots & \vdots & \ddots & \vdots \\ e^{(-\beta d_{n1})} & e^{(-\beta d_{n2})} & \cdots & 1 \end{bmatrix} \begin{Bmatrix} v_1 \\ v_2 \\ \vdots \\ v_n \end{Bmatrix}. \tag{3}$$

where, Z_i = depth by corrosion at point i, d_{ij} = distance between point i and point j, and v_j = corrosion factor at point i. The spatial auto-correlation model is ordinarily expressed by equation 2. In this analysis, corrosion depths on a plate surface are obtained from Equation 3, expressed by discrete style. This model represents a corrosion pattern in which corrosion is spread not only to depth-direction but also to width-direction by corrosion factor v_j. The damping parameter β and the influence radius of corrosion factor Ω used $\beta = 0.4$ and $\Omega = 50$ mm, respectively, according Okumura et al. (2001).

The corrosion factor v_j is assumed to distribute at random over the plate surface at 2 mm intervals. Also its histogram is assumed to yield to Poisson's distribution. In Equation 3, the corrosion depth Z_i is given at the grid point with 2 mm intervals.

In the FEM analysis, the element thickness is given by the average thickness on four nodal points of the element. And the eccentricity of a nodal point is given by the corresponding eccentricity at that point of corroded surface.

3 RESULTS AND DISCUSSION

3.1 *Influence of statistical parameters*

Typical examples of corroded plates generated by a spatial auto-correlation method are shown in Figure 3, assuming their initial thickness equals 8.0 mm. The feature of these plates in Figure 3 is that each plate has the same average thickness (t_{avg} = 7.0 mm) but a different standard deviation of thickness. The histogram of each plate thickness corresponding to Figure 3 is indicated in Figure 4. The ordinate of Figure 4 indicates normalized frequency F/N, where F = frequency and N = number of grid points for the corroded surface. Moreover, the load-deflection curves of them are shown in Figure 5. σ and σ_y in Figure 5 are average stress (=P/b/t_{avg}, P = axial force, b = flange width) and yield stress, respectively.

From these figures, the following facts can be pointed out:

(1) As shown in Figure 5, each ultimate strength is quite different in spite of the same average thickness.

Therefore, the ultimate compressive strength cannot be estimated only by average thickness. This fact seems to suggest the necessity of standard deviation to estimate the strength with sufficient accuracy.

(2) It is noticed that the ultimate strength becomes larger with an increase in standard deviation, as shown in Figure 5. Especially, the figure shows that the ultimate strength with large standard deviation, such as σ_{st} = 1.0 mm and 0.5 mm, becomes larger than that of an 8.0 mm thickness plate without corrosion.

(3) It is also noticed that the unevenness of a surface increases when the standard deviation becomes larger, as in Figure 3. When σ_{st} = 1.0 mm, the maximum and minimum thickness are 8.0 mm and 1.6 mm, respectively; oppositely, when σ_{st} is small (=0.2 mm), they are 7.3 mm and 5.7 mm, respectively. Thus, a corroded plate with the smaller standard deviation has a smaller maximum thickness.

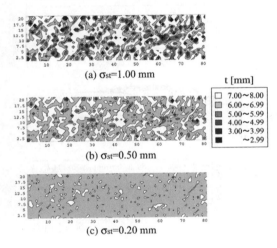

(a) σ_{st}=1.00 mm

(b) σ_{st}=0.50 mm

t [mm]

□	7.00~8.00
■	6.00~6.99
■	5.00~5.99
■	4.00~4.99
■	3.00~3.99
■	~2.99

(c) σ_{st}=0.20 mm

Figure 3.   Contour map of plate thickness.

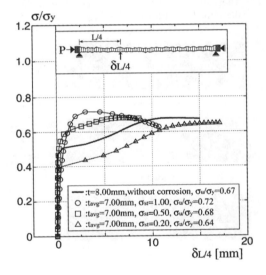

Figure 5. $\sigma/\sigma_y - \delta_{L/4}$ relation.

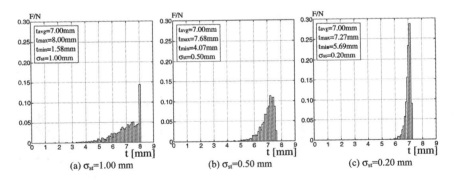

(a) σ_{st}=1.00 mm   (b) σ_{st}=0.50 mm   (c) σ_{st}=0.20 mm

Figure 4.   Histogram of plate thickness.

Assuming that the corroded thickness is formed by uniformly reduced corrosion and unevenness such as corrosion pits, the uniformly reduced corrosion must be large when the standard deviation is small, in conditions where plates have the same average thickness. By reason of this fact, the ultimate strength (buckling strength) with a smaller standard deviation would be smaller.

On the other hand, results under the condition of a constant standard deviation, as well as a constant average thickness, are indicated from Figure 6 to Figure 8. The typical characteristics of these figures which differ from Figure 3 to Figure 5 are:

(1) As shown in Figure 6, three types of corroded plates have different corroded surfaces in which three plates have respective locations of the maximum or the minimum thickness, though the maximum and minimum thickness of each plate is almost the same.
(2) Therefore, the histogram of each plate is almost the same, as is illustrated in Figure 7.

(3) From the load-deflection curves shown in Figure 8, we can find an interesting feature that the ultimate strengths of three corroded plates are almost the same when they have the same average thickness and the same standard deviation of thicknesses. However, their load-deflection curves are different from that of a plate without corrosion, and their ultimate strengths are slightly larger than one without corrosion.
(4) The above-mentioned facts suggest that the ultimate strength of a corroded plate can be estimated by using the average thickness and standard deviation of thicknesses.

3.2 Ultimate behavior of corroded flange

In the previous section, it was noted that the ultimate strength of a corroded plate increases as the standard deviation increases. In order to elucidate this

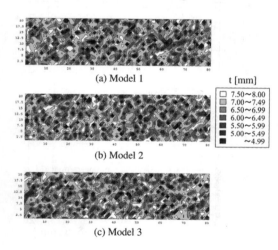

(a) Model 1

(b) Model 2

(c) Model 3

Figure 6.   Contour map of plate thickness.

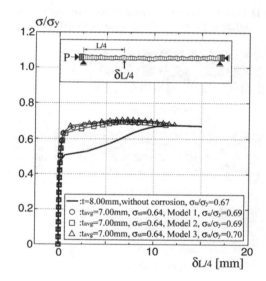

Figure 8. $\sigma/\sigma_y - \delta_{L/4}$ relation.

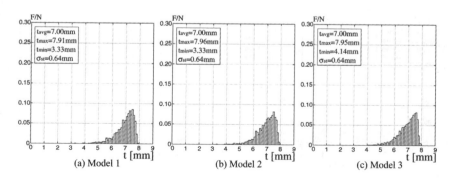

(a) Model 1   (b) Model 2   (c) Model 3

Figure 7.   Histogram of plate thickness.

phenomenon, the ultimate behavior of corroded plates subjected to compressive force is investigated.

Figure 9 and Figure 10 show load-deflection curves and deflection shapes according to some conditions, which are indicated in each figure (a) for two types of corrosion states: without corrosion, Figure 9; and with corrosion, Figure 10.

Elastic buckling occurs at $\sigma/\sigma_y = 0.5$ for the plate with no corrosion, but buckling of the corroded plate is not clear though inclination of the curve reduces rapidly at $\sigma/\sigma_y = 0.6$ (see figures (a)). For the initial yielding, both plates yield almost at the same load: $\sigma/\sigma_y = 0.65$. Also, the maximum loads (σ_u/σ_y) are almost equal in spite of their different average thicknesses. Another difference between plates with and without corrosion can be found in deflection shapes; namely, the buckling mode in Figure 9 (b) is a half of a sinusoidal wave for loading direction, but Figure 10 (b) shows one wave which is clearly caused by corrosion eccentricities. The ultimate strength of a corroded plate may be enhanced by the eccentricities that will make a different buckling mode.

Expansion of plastic regions is also shown by shaded elements in Figure 9 (b) and Figure 10 (b). In the case without corrosion, yielding occurs near the loading ends initially, then expands toward to center. At the maximum load, yielding occurs at the flange tip at the center (see Figure 9 (b)). On the other hand, the plastic region concentrates near the edge opposite to the free

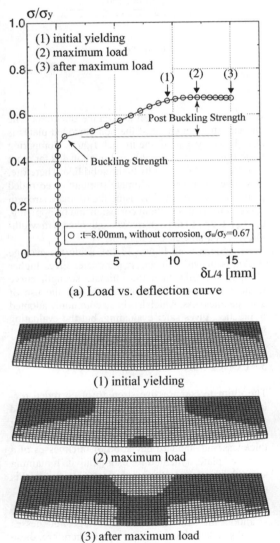

(a) Load vs. deflection curve

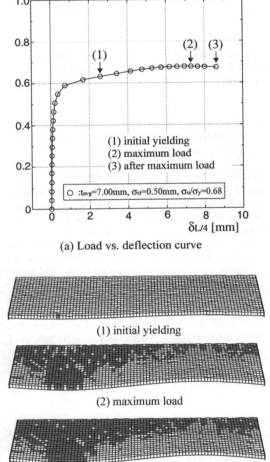

(a) Load vs. deflection curve

(1) initial yielding

(1) initial yielding

(2) maximum load

(2) maximum load

(3) after maximum load

(3) after maximum load

Figure 9. Process of bucking (without corrosion).

Figure 10. Process of buckling (with corrosion).

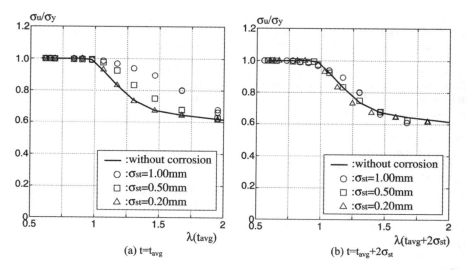

Figure 11. The ultimate strength curve for rating remaining strength.

edge because of an increase in deflection along the free edge. It seems that the maximum deflection appears at the flange tip of a cross-section severely corroded.

4 A FORMULA FOR EVALUATING THE ULTIMATE STRENGTH OF A CORRODED PLATE UNDER COMPRESSION

A formula for evaluating the ultimate strength of corroded plates would require both accuracy and simplicity. A way to simplify the estimation would be to use a representative thickness of a corroded plate. In this section, a formula for evaluating ultimate strength is proposed by using a representative thickness and the buckling strength curve of plates without corrosion.

The ultimate strengths obtained from FEM analyses are plotted in Figure 11. In the figures, the ordinate indicates ultimate strength σ_u/σ_y, where $\sigma_u = P_u/t_{avg}/b$, σ_y = yield stress, P_u = the maximum axial force, and b = flange width. The abscissa is a non-dimensionalized width-thickness parameter λ shown as:

$$\lambda = \frac{b}{t}\sqrt{\frac{\sigma_y}{E}}\sqrt{\frac{12(1-\nu^2)}{\pi^2 k}}, \qquad (4)$$

where t = representative thickness, v =Poisson's ratio, k = buckling coefficient, and E = elastic modulus. The figure (a) in Figure 11 is obtained by applying the average thickness to the representative thickness; on the other hand, for figure (b), the representative thickness t is applied as $t_{avg} + 2\sigma_{st}$, which is expressed by

standard deviation as well as average thickness. The ultimate strength curve of the non-corroded plates is also shown by a solid line in each figure. Comparing these figures, $t = t_{avg} + 2\sigma_{st}$ in Equation 4 is far more suitable to fit FEM results to the solid line. Therefore, it is concluded that the ultimate strength of corroded plates can be estimated by using the ultimate strength curve of the plates without corrosion and by applying, $t = t_{avg} + 2\sigma_{st}$ to the representative thickness in width-thickness parameter λ.

As noticed from Figure 11 (a), using the average thickness in width-thickness parameter gives higher ultimate strengths than the ultimate strength curve without corrosion. This fact shows that the use of average thickness, which has been commonly adopted in practice, gives safer evaluating, but the evaluating proposed herein would be more accurate.

5 CONCLUSIONS

The ultimate compressive strength of corroded rectangular plates with three simple supported edges and a free edge was investigated based on results using non-linear finite element simulations. Using average thickness and standard deviation of thicknesses of a corroded plate, a method for estimating its remaining strength was proposed. Conclusions obtained in this paper are as follows:

1. The ultimate strengths of corroded plates become almost the same when their average thicknesses and standard deviations are equal. Therefore, these statistical parameters are applicable to estimate reliable strengths of corroded plates.

2. As standard deviations of thicknesses increase, the ultimate strength is enhanced under the condition of the same average thickness. This is caused by the change of buckling mode due to eccentricity according to corrosion.

3. An estimation method for the remaining strength of a corroded plate is shown, using the representative thickness $t = t_{avg} + 2\sigma_{st}$ in width-thickness parameter λ and buckling strength curve of plates without corrosion.

REFERENCES

Fujii, K., Kaita, T., Hirai, K. & Okumura, M. (2002). Applicability of Spatial Auto-Correlation Model for Corroded Surface Modeling in Corroded Steel Plates. *Journal of Structural Engineering*. Vol.48A. 1031–1038. (In Japanese).

Fujii, K., Satoh, M., Minata, O., Ohmura, H. & Muranaka, A. (1995). A Proposal on Effective Thickness for Evaluation of Buckling Strength of Corroded Steel Plate. *Proc. of the 5th East Asia-Pacific Conference on Structural Engineering and Construction*. 2105–2110.

Kawai, T. (1974). The Buckling Problem Analysis. *Baifukan.* (In Japanese).

Matsumoto, M., Shirai, Y., Nakamura, I. & Shiraishi, N. (1989). A Proposal of Effective Thickness Estimation Method of Corroded Steel Member. *Bridge Found. Eng. 12.* 19–25. (In Japanese).

Muranaka, A., Minata, O. & Fujii, K. (1998). Estimation of Residual Strength and Surface Irregularity of the Corroded Steel Plates. *Journal of Structural Engineering.* Vol.44A. 1063–1071. (In Japanese).

Natori, T., Nishikawa, K., Murakoshi, J. & Ohno, T. (2001). Study on characteristics of corrosion damages in steel bridge members. *Journals of the Japan Society of Civil Engineers.* No.668/I-54. 299–311. (In Japanese).

Nukuchal, W.K. (1979). A Simple and Effective Finite Element for General Shell Analysis. *Int. J. for Numerical Method in Engineering.* Vol.4. 179–200.

Okumura, M., Fujii, K. & Tsukai, M. (2001). Statistical Model of Steel Corrosion Considering Spatial Auto-Correlation. *Journals of the Japan Society of Civil Engineers.* No.672/VI-50. 109–116. (In Japanese).

Zienkiewicz, O.C. (1977). The Finite Element Method Third Edition. *Mc Graw-Hill.*

System-based Vision for Strategic and Creative Design, Bontempi (ed.)
© 2003 Swets & Zeitlinger, Lisse, ISBN 90 5809 599 1

Testing equipment for fatigue and damage tests of steel cords

M. Kopecky, V. Cuth, I. Letko & J. Vavro
Faculty of Industrial Technologies – TnUAD, Puchov, SLOVAKIA

ABSTRACT: The contents of the paper point out the necessity of combining the theoretical and experimental approaches in the investigation of tire load in vehicles.

The models are planar and they model the cross-section of the tyre enabling the consideration of the bottom load and the internal pressure in the tyre, as well as the influence of the lateral force.

The paper presents the findings, the formulations necessary for solving the task obtained in the experimental model tests and serving as a basis for comparison with the results obtained from purely theoretical approaches, e.g. by the method of finite elements, with identical load conditions.

1 INTRODUCTION

The steel cords reinforcing motor vehicle tyres are unevenly loaded in time as the tyre is in operation and in contact with the road surface.

The conditions for conducting and evaluating experimental tests that would model the considered loading of the steel-cord-reinforced tyre have been defined as follows:

– cyclic loading of the decaying compression type with the sinusoidal functional dependence of the increase in the loading force on time, this loading being exerted in the axis of the test specimen,
– frequency of the loading force is to be controllable within the range of 10 Hz to 30 Hz,
– deformation of the specimen (compression) should be controllable up to 30% of the length of the specimen,
– the angle between the non-deformed clamped part of the specimen and the part being deformed must be constant, amounting to 15° of 20°,
– a possibility should be available of conducting the tests under different thermal conditions within the temperature range between 0°C and 100°C, and the given temperature should be constant in the entire course of a particular test,
– the testing equipment should allow for testing several test specimens at a time,
– the shape and dimensions of the test specimen should be identical to those used in tests according to the Slovak technical standard STN (Determination of rubber-to-cord adhesion after dynamic deformation by Henley method),

– the fabrication of test specimens and preparation thereof prior to the test should conform to the regulations set out in standard STN,
– the basic result of the fatigue tests conducted under the conditions set out above shall be the determination of rubber-to-cord adhesion, the relative decrease in rubber-to-cord adhesion and comparing the results obtained under the conditions described above with those obtained in tests according to standard STN.

To be able to conduct these experimental tests, it was necessary to design simple test equipment for cyclic loading of the test specimens.

2 THE DESIGN OF THE TEST SPECIMEN AND THE MANNER OF CLAMPING THEREOF

The test specimen shall be fabricated in accordance with the currently valid standard STN (Determination of rubber-to-cord adhesion after dynamic deformation by Henley method).

If the test specimen is to be loaded with cyclic loading of the decaying compression type with the sinusoidal functional dependence of the increase in the loading force on time, and this loading is to be exerted in the axis of the test specimen, then this type of loading is different from that applied in dynamic tests as set out in standard STN where the loading force is exerted upon the test specimen in the middle of its length. For this reason it was necessary to modify the method of clamping of the specimen, as well as the entire system of the loading mechanism of the test specimen.

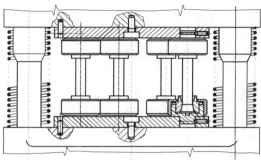

Figure 2. The complete aggregate for the loading of test specimens.

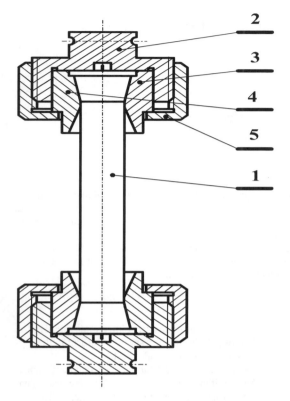

Figure 1. The design of the test specimen.

The system of clamping of the test specimen has been designed as is shown in Figure 1. Both ends of the test specimen 1 will be clamped in the designed clamp. Structurally the clamps consist of four parts, namely of the base body 2, the fixing sleeve 3 and of two identical fixing segments 4 and 5. The clamps are designed so as to enable easy clamping of the specimen, an unambiguous transfer of the load upon the specimen, and that they meet the conditions of loading. It was also kept in mind that parts of the clamp should be simple enough to fabricate without special effort.

One end of the test specimen will be inserted into the clamp throat entrance with a recess in the clamping segments 4, 5.

The segments, together with the specimen, will be inserted into the accurate cylindrical opening in the base body 2. The sleeve 5 will be slid onto the smaller external surfaces of the clamping segments, the sleeve being subsequently bolted and tightened. Thereby the clamping of an end of the specimen itself is completed. A cylindrical surface with a groove is formed in the main body, which enables to subsequently insert the specimens into the specimen-clamping device in the testing equipment. The designed clamping system ensures accuracy and axial alignment of the clamping of the specimen. It also enables to define the angle of incidence of the material between the clamped and the deformed part of the specimen, and the stem of the specimen near the clamped part may be deformed only by the angle given by the conical surface in the clamping segments. It will be possible to fabricate the clamping segments with various angles of the cone and thus to simulate different angles of incidence during the test. At the same time, the conical recess will enable that the specimen be deformed in the direction where the resistance of the tested material to deformation is the least. Moreover, the designed system of clamping enables to vary the loading of the cord itself.

As is seen in Figure 2, a cylindrical cavity is formed in the middle of the base body, whose diameter is greater than the diameter of the cord. Thus, during the compression of the specimen, the loading force will not be exerted directly upon the cord and deformation of the cord, if any will be caused indirectly, through the deformation of the rubber. If the base body is fabricated without this cylindrical cavity, the loading force will be exerted upon the cord directly, and hence it will deform the cord directly. It is assumed that these differing methods of loading will be found useful especially in steel-cord reinforced specimens.

3 THE DESIGN OF THE CLAMPING DEVICE

The following requirements must be met in the design of the clamping device:

1. High precision and sufficient rigidity of the clamping device.
2. Possibility of clamping a number of specimens in the clamping device.
3. Maximal structural simplicity.
4. Highest possible service life and reliability of the designed structure.
5. Easy fabricability of components.

With a view to meeting the conditions of experimental tests and the conditions set out above, it has been decided to use a normalised guide stand in the structure of the clamping device which can be adapted to the conditions of cyclic loading by simple modifications. The advantage of using normalised guide stands is the fact that the upper, movable part of the stand travels in the guideway made up of a sleeve and a column. The movement of the upper part is thus conducted along a precisely defined path. The precision of the movement depends on the structural type of the guideway used in the design of the stand, which can be sliding guideway or linear motion guideway. The wear of the guideway and the service life of its component parts also depend on the type of the guideway.

The guide stand conforming to standard STN has been used in the present design of the test equipment. This guide stand is equipped with circular work surfaces with the diameter of 200 mm. The upper 2 and the lower 3 faceplates must be fixed onto the work surfaces of the stand in a precisely defined position. Using pins ensures accurate positioning of the faceplates on the work surfaces of the stand. The faceplates are fastened to the work surfaces with bolt joints. Seven test specimens with the clamping heads 1 mounted will be inserted into the openings of the faceplates.

The position of the clamping heads on the test specimens will be fixed by stud bolts 4 in both the upper and the lower faceplate. The tips of the stud bolts fit in the groove formed in the base body of the clamping head. In the stage of fabrication of the faceplates and of fixing thereof onto the components of the guide stand, it is necessary to ensure that the specimens, the clamping heads and the openings for mounting of the clamping heads in the upper and the lower facelifts are axially aligned. Identical loading of all test specimens will be achieved only on meeting this condition

4 THE DESIGN OF THE LOADING MECHANISM

The function of the loading mechanism is to ensure the conditions, defined in the introduction, for conducting the experimental tests.

In order to make it possible to continuously vary the frequency of the loading force, it is advantageous to use an electrical motor with a semiconductor speed control as the drive of the loading equipment.

There are a number of mechanisms enabling transformation of rotary motion into translator's motion.

From the point of view of achieving a maximum design simplicity of the loading mechanism, cam mechanism appears to be the most advantageous. Its disadvantage, however, rests in the fact that it does not allow a continuous variation of the feed and hence it would be necessary to design and fabricate a new

cam for each degree of deformation of the specimen. On the other hand, its advantage is the fact that even in various degrees of deformation of the specimen it is not necessary to additionally set the test specimen-loading node.

This, however, will hold true only if all cams to be used in conducting testing in selected degrees of specimen deformation possess an identical radius of the non-stroke part (r = cons).

5 ANALYSIS OF DEFORMATIONS IN THE TEST SPECIMEN

An overall view of the complete aggregate for the loading of test specimens is shown in Figure 2.

The method of the application of load to the specimens by force whose magnitude varies periodically along the sine curve is shown in Figure 3.

The maximum deformation of the specimen is 30% of the functional length of the specimen (77,5 mm), which constitutes the specimen's deformation of (23,25 mm) at the maximum frequency of force variation of 30 Hz.

Loading tests are conducted on two types of specimens: on specimens with no steel cord and on specimens reinforced with steel cord with ø 1 mm which is cured in the centreline of the specimen.

Two finite-element models have been created to calculate great deformations. The model with no steel cord is shown in Figure 4 and the model with steel cord of ø 1 mm is shown in Figure 5.

The material constants for rubber and steel cord, which have been used in the calculation, are in Table 1.

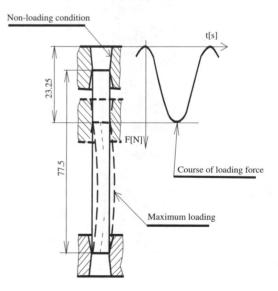

Figure 3. The design of the loading mechanism.

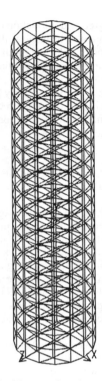

Figure 4.   Model with no steel cord.

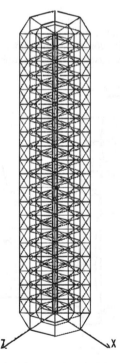

Figure 5.   Model with no steel cord of Ø 1 mm.

Table 1.

Material	ρ [kg.m⁻³]	E [MPa]	m	G [MPa]
Rubber	1255	8,2	0,488	2,8
Steel cord	7800	2,1	0,33	0,8

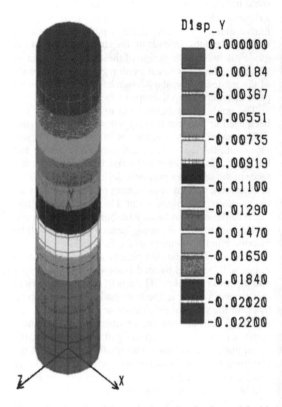

Figure 6.   Results of theoretical solution for the model with no steel cord.

Specimen no. 1 with no steel cord is substantially more flexible than the steel cord reinforced specimen no. 2.

This is corroborated by the calculation of shifts (Figs 6 and 7) at an identical loading force. In order to verify the results of calculation, it is necessary to perform experimental measurements and subsequent evaluations on a greater number of specimens and to modify the calculation accordingly.

Items involved here are the actual marginal conditions of the clamping of the specimen, properties of adhesion between steel cord and rubber, magnitude of the loading force and its frequency, the shape and diameter of the steel cord, etc.

The testing machine enables to clamp the specimen so as to allow to move the steel cord out of the

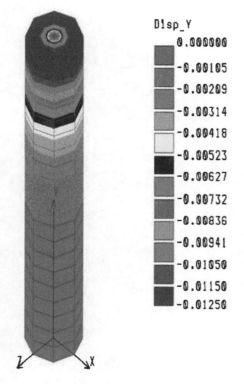

Disp_Y
- 0.000000
- -0.00105
- -0.00209
- -0.00314
- -0.00418
- -0.00523
- -0.00627
- -0.00732
- -0.00836
- -0.00941
- -0.01050
- -0.01150
- -0.01250

Figure 7. Results of theoretical solution for the model with steel cord of Ø 1 mm.

specimen or not, as necessary. The shifts in Figure 7 are calculated for such compression of the specimen, which will allow moving the cord out of the specimen. The shift is given in metres.

6 CONCLUSION

The theoretical and experimental model tests enable to select the most suitable version in solving the problem of loading the tyres of transport vehicles. The test results may be utilised in developing new models and true to shapes of tyres.

The test results may also be used in comparing the efficiency of different tests methods.

ACKNOWLEDGEMENTS

The authors expressed their thanks to Slovak Agency for Research and Science for its support of this work (grant 1/9413/02).

REFERENCES

Kopecky M. & collective 1998. Development of testing equipment for cyclic loading of the test specimen. *Scientific work* 4/98, FPT-Puchov, 12/98. *Prospect IGITUR*, s.r.o., 1998.

System-based Vision for Strategic and Creative Design, Bontempi (ed.)
© 2003 Swets & Zeitlinger, Lisse, ISBN 90 5809 599 1

Performance of bolted semi-rigid connections under cyclic loading in steel portal frames

Y.M. Kim & C.M. Yang

Faculty of Architecture and Urban Engineering, Chonbuk National University, South Korea

ABSTRACT: This report describes recent experimental results on the quasi-static behavior of a one story and one bay steel structure tested with fixed, semi-rigid, and flexible connections. The behavior of flexible can semi-rigid structures under cyclic lateral loading is studied, and their respective responses are compared to that of the fixed structure subjected to similar loading. The result of this study show that semi-rigid connection was developed about 41% of rigid connection for initial rotational stiffness, and simple connection about 10%. Also, the hysteretic energy dissipation capabilities of the connections were determined, and the mechanism of failure was identified.

1 GENERAL INSTRUCTIONS

The ability of steel frames to resist loads may be determined more by the strength and stiffness of the connections than by the properties of the members themselves. Frame design was in fact based on the simple ideal models of rigid and pinned joints. The use of these extreme cases which were ideally pinned or fully rigid for representing the connection behavior in structural analysis is due to two reasons: the low effort for dissemination of structural analysis methods that incorporate the connection flexibility, the little knowledge about the moment versus rotation curves associated with semi-rigid connections. Another reason that contributes to the continuous use of the simple and fixed solutions is related to the structural engineer's natural resistance to alter the design process (de Carvalho et al. 1998). However, its validity is questionable because most of the commonly used connection types process intermediary stiffness (Guo-Qiang & Motivo 2000). Base on this fact, steel frames are divided into the three categories of Rigid (FR, Type1), Semi-rigid (PR, Type3) and Flexible (PR, Type2) (AISC 1994). Among the connection types proposed in AISC and Eurocode 3, type3, PR and semi-rigid connections are those with high-strength bolts. Many bolt connections, often called semi-rigid connections, are considered to be much more flexible than their welded counterparts (Shen & Astaneh-Asl 1999). The issues in the bolted connection as compared with the welded connections are the stiffness, complex behavior and ductility, as well as construction cost. The earliest studies of the rotational stiffness of steel beam-to-column connections date back nearly 80 years (Wilson & Moore 1917). Recently study has covered the response to static loading of both nonsway and sway frames, dealing with topics such as end restraint and column stability (Nethercot & Chen 1988), drift of multi-story frames (Gerstle 1988), and serviceability deflection control in portals (Melchers & Yee 1983). A study in the dynamics field investigated a set of the frames with different connection types subjected to an ensemble of ground motions (Nader & Astaneh 1989). Limited work was found to study the cyclic behavior by experiments. In reality, joints do not occur in isolation but as part of a structure. In particular, it was few tests on moment capacity of the frames with different connections compared with that on connections only. It is therefore of practical importance to investigate the actual flexibility of frames with real connections with respect to some rational test.

Therefore, all tests were carried out by applying loads with double-acting hydraulic jacks to the 2-dimensional frames which consist of only one-story and one-bay appropriately mounted on fixed supports. The test reported herein consists of six unbraced portal frames tested to failure under cyclic lateral loading condition. The main objectives of the experimental studies are: (1) to compare the inelastic behavior of the portal frames with different three types of connection (simple, semi-rigid, and rigid) subjected to the cyclic loading, (2) to observe the failure modes of the portal frames under cyclic loading, and (3) to know the energy-dissipation capacity and ductility ratio of the connections in the portal frames subjected to the cyclic loading.

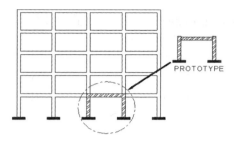

Figure 1. Moment resisting frame.

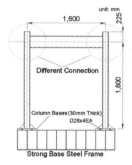

Figure 2. Detail of frame.

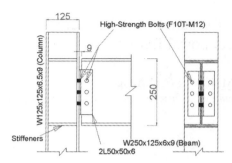

Figure 3. DWA connection.

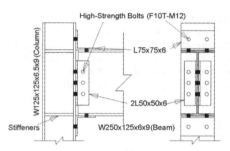

Figure 4. TSD connection.

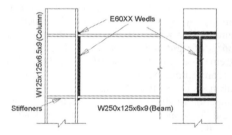

Figure 5. FW connection.

2 THE EXPERIMENTAL ANALYSIS

2.1 Descriptions of the specimens

All specimens are 2-dimensional steel portal frames which consist of one story and one bay as part of moment-resisting steel frames. Figure 1 shows the configuration of test specimens. The moment-resisting frames are widely used for low-rise buildings.

The portal frames (Fig. 2), which were used herein, were composed of three different types of connections. Each test has been performed twice to maintain reliability of tests. As a result, six tests of portal frames under cyclic lateral forces were conducted. The primary difference among the specimens is the method by which connection is consisted. Figures 3, 4 and 5 show details of flexible (DWA), semi-rigid (TSD) and the fixed (FW) beam-to-column connections, respectively.

All angles were bolted to the beam web, flange and column flanges with same size of bolts (F10T-M12). The fixed connection (FW) consisted of not the angles and high-strength bolts but welding. The flange and web of the beams were welded to the flange of the columns by the shielded-arc welding (E60XX). The column bases of each specimen are welded to a 30-mm-thick end plate and bolted to a rigid base-beam using four M24 high-strength bolts. To insure fixity of columns to the base plates, a pair of triangular rib plate was used at the base of each column (Fig. 6).

Details of the TSD and DWA connection geometries are reported in Table 1.

2.2 Material and section properties

The column and beam elements were fabricated from standard rolled shapes of steel. The column was a H125 × 125 × 6.5 × 9 and the beam was a H250 × 125 × 6 × 9. The column and beam sizes were the same for all six specimens. SS400 steel was used for the members and connection elements as well as base plates and stiffeners. The mechanical properties of SS400 are given in Table 2.

Table 3 gives section properties of the beams and columns as well as the angles used in the bolted connections.

900

Figure 6. Detail of base plate.

Table 1. Geometries of bolted connections (units: mm).

Specimens	Semi-rigid		Simple	
Angles	TSD1	TSD2	DWA1	DWA2
Bolt diameter		12		
Web Angles				
Angle		L50 × 50 × 6		
Length		168		
Gage		28		
Pitch		42		
Top and Seat Angles				
Angle		L75 × 75 × 6		
Length		125		
Gage		40.5		
Pitch		63		

Table 2. Mechanical properties of SS400.

Units: kg/cm^2

Yield strength	Tensile strength	Modulus of elasticity	Shear modulus of elasticity	Poisson's ratio
2500	4100	2.1e6	8.1e5	0.3

2.3 Test set-up and instrumentation

A sketch of test set-up and instrumentations is shown in Figure 7. The set-up consists of four major components: (1) Hydraulic double acting ram to apply the cyclic force; (2) reaction wall, which was made of steel, supporting the acting ram; (3) specimen in used this test; and (4) reaction block supporting the columns in the test specimen. To prevent out-of-plane displacements of the specimen, lateral supports were provided at the beam.

The instrumentations used in this test are the load cell and the linear variable displacement transducers (LVDT). Cyclic forces were measured using the load cell attached to the acting ram. The displacement was measured by six linear variable displacement transducers (LVDTs) for global and local response of the specimens. Control displacements of the test were measured using 200 mm linear variable differential transformer located in parallel with the acting ram. To measure local moment in the column, 100 mm LVDT was installed

Table 3. Section properties of elements.

		Beam	Column	Angle	
				Top & Seat	Web
Area (cm^2)		37.66	30.31	8.727	5.644
Unit weight (kg/m)		29.6	23.8	6.85	4.43
Moments of	Ix	4050	847	46.1	12.6
inertia (cm^4)	Iy	294	293	46.1	12.6
Radius of	Rx	10.4	5.29	2.3	1.5
gyration (cm)	Ry	2.79	3.11	2.3	1.5
Section	Zx	324	136	1.48	3.55
modulus (cm^3)	Zy	47	47	1.48	3.55

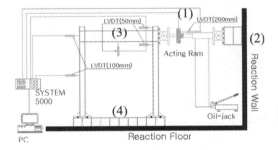

Figure 7. Sketch of test set-up and instrumentations.

at 870 mm from the column base plate. 50 mm LVDT was located in the beam flange to measure deflection of the beam. Connection rotations are measured from the relative rotation between the beam and column as shown in Figure 8.

Using measured displacements, rotation of the connection can be approximately obtained from the relative displacement divided by the length of the lever arm (Nader et al. 1989 and Thomas et al. 1986). The connection rotation is measured from the displacements ($\Delta 1$ and $\Delta 2$) obtained from the transducers as follows:

$$\Theta = \tan^{-1}\left(|\Delta 1| + |\Delta 2|\right)/428 \qquad (1)$$

where 428 is the distance between the two transducers. The rotation of the connection was calculated in several ways, which all resulted in very close values. Since both quantitative and qualitative behavior is important, every specimen should be coated with white wash prior to testing so that the locations of most significant yielding can be identified visually. All bolts in DWA and TSD connections were installed by the turn-of-nut method. Using a manual torque wrench with a dial-type torque indicator, measure the torque at this condition by applying the torque wrench in the tightening direction (Protocol for Fabrication).

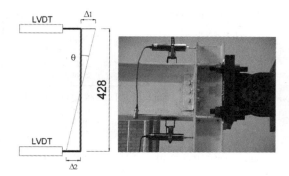

Figure 8. Method of measuring connection rotation.

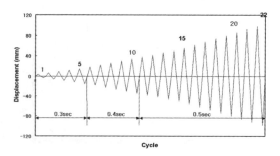

Figure 9. Test program (displacement, mm).

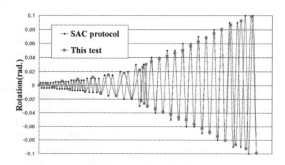

Figure 10. Comparison of test programs.

2.4 Test procedure

The quasi-static test is characterized by the applications of forces by means of hydraulic actuators with very low speed (Cosenza et al. 1994). According to the ATC-24 and SAC loading protocol recommendations, the deformation parameter to be used to control the loading history is the interstory drift angle, ϕ, defined as interstory displacement divided by story height. Therefore, the control parameter in this test is interstory displacement. The tests were carried out controlling the displacement at the end of the column as shown in Figure 7. The typical cyclic displacement history is shown in Figure 9. The displacement history consists

in a regular displacement increase at every step (linear type: one repetition). This displacement history was designed to simulate the effects of earthquakes and cause severe in elasticity in the connection area.

Providing that compare this test with SAC loading history, there are little differences relative to the number of cycles at the same level of displacement and for the increments of the cycle amplitude due to limit of the loading system. Figure 10 shows above differences.

3 THE CYCLIC TEST RESULTS

3.1 Deformation patterns

3.1.1 DWA specimens

First, since the frames with DWA connections were tested, sounds like the bolt slip occurred in the connections at 6 mm drift. As load step was increased, the sound was larger. It was found that first deformation developed in the bottom of the columns at about 18 mm draft. And then, one plastic hinge lines formed in the web angles and large deformation developed in the vicinity of the bolt holes. However bolts did not show significant deformation.

3.1.2 TSD specimens

Deformation pattern of this specimen was very similar to DWA specimen. In addition, after 4step (12 mm), it was found that top and seat angles were separated from the surface of column flange. After 20step (86 mm), all top and seat angles were perfectly fracture. Fracture line of the top and seat angles was located in distance from the angle heel to the vicinity of the toe of the fillet, as shown in Figure 11. Also, three plastic hinge lines formed in the top and seat angles. Deformation of double web angles was similar to that of DWA specimen.

The value of distance from the top angle heel to the toe of the fillet (k_a) was average 13.5 mm.

$$k_a = 0.88 \times r_a + t_a \qquad (2)$$

where t_a is the thickness of the top and seat angles (6 mm); r_a is the radius of the top and seat angle fillet (8.5 mm). Unlike specimen DWA, after 13step (46 mm drift), some yielding could be observed on the panel zone.

3.1.3 FW specimens

The first yield lines began forming in the panel zone of the columns at applied 5step (15 mm). This yield lines developed in near the stiffeners to the horizontal direction. At 7step (22 mm), it was observed that yield lines extended to vertical direction in panel zone (Fig. 12, left). The next deformation was located to the bottom of the columns at about 8step (26 mm drift). Yielding now appeared to extend through the joints

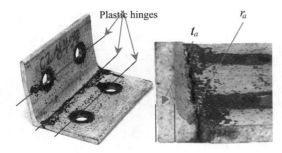

Figure 11.   Fracture of top and seat angles.

Table 4.   The load-displacement behavior of the frames.

Average values due to cyclic behavior	Specimens		
	DWA	TSD	FW
Yield			
Load (ton)	4.29	6.77	11.85
Displ. (mm)	22	22	30
Maximum			
Load (ton)	9.56	12.40	15.60
Displ. (mm)	98	92	98
Initial stiffness (ton/mm)	0.30(65%)	0.44(95%)	0.46

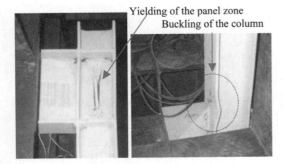

Figure 12.   Deformation of the panel zone and column.

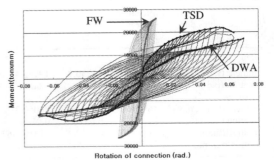

Figure 14.   Total response of moment-rotation curves.

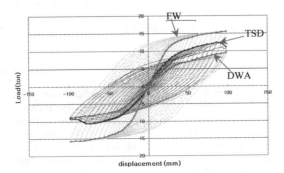

Figure 13.   Total response of load-displacement curves.

and columns. Finally, local buckling at the bottom of the column was observed (Fig. 12 right). In particular, the column end undergoes plastic deformations in the vicinity of the connection and bottom plate.

3.2   *Hysteresis behaviors*

Figure 13 shows the response of the test frames by plotting the horizontal load against the horizontal displacement measured at the column tip.

As it is shown from the corresponding experimental hysteretic loops, this figure depicts the load versus displacement relationship for both the cyclic and the skeleton curves of the specimens. In many cases the skeleton curve coincides with the monotonic loading curve (Wakabayashi & Minoru 1989). The skeleton curves well represented to the characteristic behavior of the each specimen. There is no sign of failure at the end of the test but the frame with TSD connections. However, the test was terminated at a displacement of 98 mm at the column tip due to lateral buckling, even though lateral support was set up, and limitation of the instruments. The initial stiffness, yield displacement, and lateral load at yield for the connections of specimens DWA, TSD, and FW estimated from the result of the cyclic tests are presented in Table 4.

Figure 14 shows moment-rotation hysteresis loops for all type specimens. The moment acting on connection was calculated by multiplying load measured in the load cell by the distance from the centerline of the acting ram to the face of the column base plate. This distance was 1770 mm. As mentioned earlier, using measured displacements, rotation of the connection can be approximately obtained from the relative displacement divided by the length of the lever arm, as shown in Figure 8.

In bolted specimens that were tested, pinching of hysteresis loops were related to development of gap between angles and column flange in the tension zone of connection (Ataneh 1989), as shown in Figure 15.

Figure 15. Deformation of bolted connections.

Table 5. Moment-rotation behavior of the connections.

Average values due to cyclic behavior	Specimens		
	DWA	TSD	FW
Yield			
Moment (ton × mm)	7593.3	11230.7	19142.4
Rotation (rad.)	0.0175	0.0108	0.0041
Maximum			
Moment (ton × mm)	16921.2	21948.0	26050.3
Rotation (rad.)	0.0698	0.0510	0.0100
Initial stiffness (ton × mm/rad.)	1111754 (9.7%)	4624068 (40.5%)	11410566

Table 6. Dissipated energy of the connections and frames.

	Connections			Frames		
	DWA	TSD	FW	DWA	TSD	FW
Story drift angle (rad.)						
0.01	156	215	13	78	116	49
0.02	780	1293	397	435	742	1066
0.03	2479	3523	1302	1644	2435	4408
0.04	5336	7015	2561	3853	5281	9596
0.05	9856	12132	4356	7440	9487	17476

The values of the ultimate moment and rotation of the connections reached in the connections are also given in Table 5.

3.3 Energy dissipation and ductility

The hysteresis energy of the frames was defined as the summation of the areas enclosed by cyclic load-displacement curves. Energy of the connection can be obtained from moment-rotation curve. The energy-dissipation capacity of the connections and frames is summarized in the Table 6.

It was indicated that DWA connection was about 200%, TSD connection was about 300% higher than FW connection at drift angle 0.03 radian. However, at drift angle 0.03 radian, the dissipated energy capacity

Table 7. Ductility of frames and connections.

Parameters	DWA	TSD	FW
Yield displacement of frame (mm)	22	22	30
Yield rotation of connection (rad.)	0.0175	0.0108	0.0041
0.03 radian considered (54 mm)			
Displacement ductility of frame (mm)	2.55	2.55	1.87
Rotation ductility of connection (rad.)	2.48	3.00	1.48
Maximum drift considered (98 mm)			
Displacement ductility of frame (mm)	4.45	4.18	3.27
Rotation ductility of connection (rad.)	4.00	5.17	2.46

of the frame with TSD connection was about 60%, 150% of the frame with FW connection, and with DWA connection, respectively.

Traditionally, ductility of a steel connection is measured in terms of rotational ductility. The displacement ductility of the frames are shown in Table 7 as well as the rotation ductility of the connections.

The rotation ductility of the connection at the occurrence of the ultimate criterion (0.03 radian) for each model varied between 1.48 and 3.00.

4 CONCLUDING REMARKS

A test program was conducted to evaluate the cyclic behavior of the portal frames with flexible (DWA), semi-rigid (TSD), and rigid (FW) beam-to-column connections. To maintain reliability of the tests, each test has been performed twice. Base on experimental investigation reported in this paper, the following conclusions are drawn:

1. For the frames with bolted connection (DWA and TSD), slippage of the bolt occurred in the connections. And then it was found that large deformation developed in the vicinity of the connections. However bolts did not show significant deformation. Also, it was not found to panel zone deformation for the DWA specimen whereas for the TSD specimen, some yielding could be observed on the panel zone. After all top and seat angles of the TSD specimen were perfectly fracture.
2. For the frames with fully welded connection (FW), first signs of deformation occurred in the panel zone. Deformation now appeared to extend through the joints and columns. Finally, the failure of FW specimens is attributed to local buckling of the column.

3. The response of the FW and DWA specimens was almost bilinear type and the TSD specimen was trilinear type in the load-displacement curves. The initial rotation stiffness of the DWA connection was not zero but about 10% of the FW connection, and the TSD connection was about 41%.
4. Comparison of the energy dissipation shows that DWA connections were about 200%, TSD connections were about 300% higher than FW connections at drift angle 0.03 radian.
5. Where or not drift limit 3% considered, the rotation ductility of the connections were calculated that the DWA connection and the TSD connection were higher than the FW connection, 160% and 210%, respectively.
6. The moment overstrength factors for the DWA, TSD and FW connections are 2.14, 1.74 and 1.37, respectively. However, if an drift limit of 3% is imposed, the connection overstrength would reduce to 1.8, 1.63 and 1.23, respectively. Structural overstrength factors for the DWA, TSD and FW specimens, corresponding to an assumed drift limit of 3% were 2.15, 1.77 and 1.32. Therefore, in all frames, the overstrength factor is well above the value of 1.2 suggested for moment resisting frames.

The primary purpose of this work was to verify the capacity of frames with bolted semi-rigid connection as well as with flexible connection. The experimental results provide necessary information for researchers and engineers who need to verify their analytical methods. As a result, it has to be design that considered to actual stiffness of beam-to-column connection.

ACKNOWLEDGEMENTS

This work was supported by the Research center of Industrial Technology (or RCIT), Engineering Research Institute at Chonbuk National University.

REFERENCES

de Carvalho, L. C. V, de Andrade, S. A. L and Vellasco, P. C. G. S. 1998. Experimental Analysis of Bolted Semi-Rigid Steel Connections. *J. Construct. Steel Res. Vol. 46, Nos. 1–3*: 238–240

Guo-Qiang, Li and John Motivo, 2000. Approximate estimation of the maximum load of semi-rigid steel frames. *J. Construct. Steel Res. 54*: 213–225.

Shen, J and Astaneh-Asl, A. 1999. Hysteretic Behavior of Bolted-Angle Connections. *Journal of Constructional Steel Research 51*: 201–218.

Nader, M. N and Astaneh-ASL, A. 1989. Experimental Studies of a Single Story Steel Structure with Fixed, Semi-rigid and Flexible connections. *UCB/EERC-98/15*.

Protocol for Fabrication, Inspection, Testing, and Documentation of Beam-Column Connection Tests and Other Experimental Specimens. *Report No. SAC/BD-97/02*.

Cosenza, E, Manfredi, G and De Martino, A. 1994. Experimental Testing for The Analysis of The Cyclic Behavior of Steel Elements: An Over View of The Existing Procedures. *STESSA'94, Timisora, Romania*

Wakabayashi, Minoru. 1989. *Design of Earthquake-Resistant Buildings*. McGraw-Hill Book Company.

Ataneh, A, Nader, M. N and Malik, L. 1989. Cyclic Behavior of Double angle Connections. *Journal of structural Engineering, ASCE, Vol. 115, No. 5*.

ECCS-CECM-EKS, 1986. Recommended Testing Procedure for Assessing the Behavior of Structural Steel Elements under Cyclic Loads. *Technical Working Group 1.3, Seismic Design, No. 45*.

Bernuzzi, C, Zandonini, R and Zanon, P, 1996. Experimental Analysis and Modelling of Semi-rigid Steel Joints under Cyclic Reversal Loading. *J. Construct. Steel Res. Vol. 38, No. 2*.

Mazzolani, F. M, 1988. Mathematical Model for Semi-rigid Joints under Cyclic Loads. *Connections in Steel Structures: Behaviour, Stength and Design*, London: Elsevier Applied Science.

Elnashai, A. S, Elghazouli, A. Y and Denesh-Ashtiani, F. A, 1998. Response of Semirigid Steel Frames to Cyclic and Earthquake Loads. *Journal of Structural Engineering, Vol. 124, No. 8*.

Richard Liew, J. Y, Yu, C. H, Ng, H and Shanmugam, N. E, 1997. Testing of Semi-rigid Unbraced Frames for Calibration of Second-order Inelastic Analysis. *J. Construct. Steel Res. Vol. 41, No. 2/3*: 159-195.

Kishi, N and Chen, W. F, 1990. Moment-Rotation Relations of Semirigid Connections with Angles. *Journal of Structural Engineering, Vol. 116, No. 7*.

Thomas, Stelmack, W, Marley, Mark J and Gerstle, Kurt H, 1986. Analysis and Tests of Flexibly Connected Steel Frames. *Journal of Structural Engineering, Vol. 112, No. 7*.

Sway estimation of rigid frames using equation

B. Ahmed & M. Ashraf

Department of Civil Engineering, BUET, Dhaka, Bangladesh

ABSTRACT: The lateral sway of a building is to be kept within a limit to ensure the comfort of the occupants and for the protection of mechanical and architectural systems. In case of multi-storied building frames the overall sway is of utmost importance and needs to be estimated at the preliminary stage of design. Schueller (1977) proposed an equation to estimate the sway of rigid frames based on Portal Method. The present paper investigates the level of accuracy of the proposed equation and proposes necessary modifications so that it can be readily used to estimate sway. Modifications are proposed to use this equation to estimate sway of non-regular frames.

1 INTRODUCTION

The commonly accepted range for sway is from 0.0016 to 0.0035 times the height of the building, depending on the building height and the magnitude of wind pressure. The Committee on Wind Bracing of the American Society of Civil Engineers has recommended that the maximum sway be less than 0.002 times the height of the building for normal wind pressure. The sway of a rigid frame is caused by shear wracking resulting in bending of columns and beams and by the cantilever behavior of the frame causing axial deformation of the columns. The highest stresses are imposed on the exterior columns and beams since they are the furthest from the neutral axis of the frame.

2 DEVELOPMENT OF SCHUELLER'S EQUATION

In deriving the approximate equation for calculating the lateral sway of a building frame, the stiffness provided by the adjacent frames and filler materials are neglected. Also, the reduction of rigidity due to joint slippage and deformation is not considered. The following subsections describes the required components to compute sway.

2.1 *Sway due to bending of beams and columns*

The assumptions of portal method are used to obtain an approximate solution of sway due to shear wracking. Figure 1 shows the deformed state of a typical bent

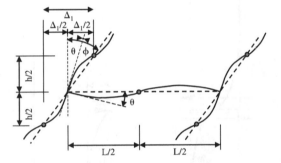

Figure 1. Deformed shape of a typical building frame.

bay with the assumed hinge location at mid-span of beams and mid-height of columns, where, ϕ = angle of rotation due to the bending of columns; θ = angle of rotation due to the bending of beams; Δ_c = deflection due to bending of columns; Δ_g = deflection due to bending of beams.

The relationship between beam rotation and deformation as obtained from Figure 2 is

$$\frac{\Delta_g/2}{L/2} = \tan\theta \approx \theta \qquad or, \quad \theta = \frac{\Delta_g}{L} \qquad (1)$$

Again, the relationship between column rotation and deformation according to Figure 3 is

$$\frac{\Delta_c/2}{h/2} = \tan\varphi \approx \varphi \qquad or, \quad \varphi = \frac{\Delta_c}{h} \qquad (2)$$

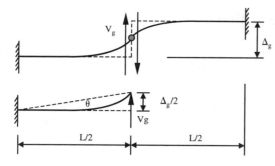

V_g

Δ_g

θ

$\Delta_g/2$

V_g

L/2

L/2

Figure 2. Deflected shape of a typical beam and the corresponding sway.

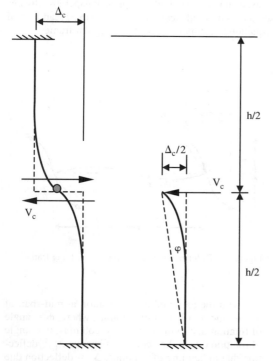

Δ_c

h/2

$\Delta_c/2$

V_c

V_c

h/2

φ

Figure 3. Deflected shape of a typical column and its corresponding sway.

The total deformation of a typical bent is

$$\frac{\Delta_1}{h} = \tan(\theta + \varphi) \approx \theta + \varphi$$

$$\Rightarrow \frac{\Delta_1}{h} = \frac{\Delta_g}{L} + \frac{\Delta_c}{h} \qquad (3)$$

The sway of columns is represented in Figure 3. The beams are assumed to be infinitely rigid. The deformation caused by the column shear acting at the assumed hinge, as based on simple cantilever, is

$$\Delta_c = 2\frac{V_c(h/2)^3}{3EI_c} = \frac{V_c h^3}{12EI_c} \qquad (4)$$

Again, assuming that the columns are infinitely rigid, the deflection of a simple cantilever caused by the beam shear at mid-span of the bay yields

$$\Delta_g = 2\frac{V_g(L/2)^3}{3EI_g} = \frac{V_g L^3}{12EI_g} \qquad (5)$$

Substituting the value Δ_g and Δ_c in Equation 3, the sway of the bent becomes

$$\frac{\Delta_1}{h} = \frac{V_g L^3}{12EI_g L} + \frac{V_c h^3}{12EI_c h} \qquad (6)$$

It is assumed that the ratio of Δ_1/h of each floor will be constant. This fact is, however, not true in the transition zone from the fixed building base to the assumed constant slope of the deflected bent. Since the result of this assumption is on the conservative side, the ratio of storey sway to storey height is equal to the ratio of the building Δ_{1max} to the building height H. Since I_g and I_c of the base floors are greater than the floors beyond the 3rd or 4th level, the ratio of V_c/I_c and V_g/I_g are taken from the upper floors. So, the total sway of the building due to bending of beams and columns only is

$$\frac{\Delta_1}{h} = \frac{\Delta_{1max}}{H} = \frac{V_g L^2}{12EI_g} + \frac{V_c h^2}{12EI_c}$$

$$\Rightarrow \Delta_{1max} = \frac{V_g L^2 H}{12EI_g} + \frac{V_c h^2 H}{12EI_c} \qquad (7)$$

2.2 *Sway due to axial deformation of columns*

Since gravity loads increase in a linear manner towards the base of the building, column areas are considered to increase proportionally in the same way.

In other words, the wind stresses in the columns may be assumed to increase linearly from zero at the top of the structure to maximum at the base. Hence the resultant wind pressure acts at the top of the building and thus causing a linear increase of axial column stress. The maximum deformation of a cantilever due to a single load is

$$\Delta_c' = \frac{(wH)H^3}{3EI_B} = \frac{wH^4}{3EI_B}\frac{M_{max}H^2}{3EI_B} \qquad (8)$$

where $M_{max} = (wH)H = wH^2$

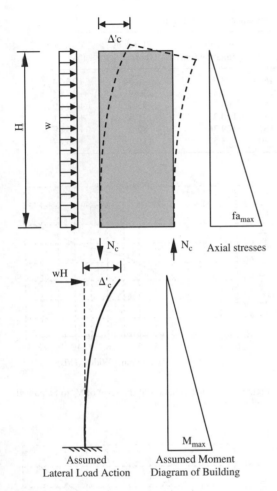

Figure 4. Cantilever action of a building due to axial stresses in columns.

Below figure labels:

Assumed Lateral Load Action

Assumed Moment Diagram of Building

The maximum wind stresses at the exterior columns for a symmetrical frame is

$$f_{max} = \frac{M_{max}(B/2)}{I_B} \qquad or, M_{max} = \frac{2f_{max}I_B}{B} \qquad (9)$$

So from Equation 8, Δ'_c can be expressed as

$$\Delta'_c = \frac{2f_{max}H^2}{3EB}$$

Again, the maximum axial column stress at the building base is, $f_{max} = N_c/A_c$. Hence lateral sway caused by column force action is given by

$$\Delta'_c = \frac{2N_cH^2}{3EA_cB} \qquad (10)$$

2.3 Total sway of a rigid frame

The approximate total sway of a rigid frame consists of the summation of deformations due to shear wracking and cantilever action. Thus:

$$\Delta_{max} = \Delta_c + \Delta_g + \Delta'_c$$

$$\Delta_{max} = \frac{HV_ch^2}{12EI_c} + \frac{HV_gL^2}{12EI_g} + \frac{2N_cH^2}{3EA_cB} \qquad (11)$$

Where,

N_c = Axial force in exterior column at the base due to wind

V_c = Shear force in exterior column due to wind above third level

I_c = Moment of inertia of column at the same level as V_c about axis of bending

A_c = Area of the exterior column at the base

V_g = Shear force in girders due to wind at the same level as V_c

I_g = Moment of inertia of girder about x-axis at the same level as V_c

H = Total height of the frame

B = Total base width of the frame

h = Typical storey height

L = Girder span

E = Modulus of elasticity

3 COMPARATIVE ANALYSIS BETWEEN THE SWAY OBTAINED FROM SCHUELLER'S EQUATION AND THOSE FROM THE "FE" ANALYSES

A number of frames are analyzed using the FE program ANSYS 5.4 and the obtained sway values are compared with those obtained using Schueller's equation. All the results are represented in Table 1 with the corresponding frame geometry. Results obtained using this equation are observed to be too conservative when compared with the FE results and as the building becomes taller the deviation becomes larger.

4 PROPOSED MODIFICATIONS TO SCHUELLER'S EQUATION

Attempts are made to make the sway results of this equation to be close to the FE analysis. In this respect the level for V_c/I_c is varied and the change in sway results are plotted to locate the exact location for V_c/I_c. From the analysis it is observed that as the H/B ratio of a frame increases the level for V_c/I_c needs to be considered at a higher level.

Table 1. Sway of rigid frames obtained from Schueller's equation and FE analysis.

Storey × bay	Beam	Column	Schueller's equation (cm)	FE result (cm)	Variation (%)
5 × 4	254 × 102UB25	203 × 203UC46	8.71	6.44	+35.24
10 × 4	254 × 102UB25	203 × 203UC71	42.53	30.9	+37.64
15 × 4	305 × 127UB37	203 × 203UC86	63.24	45.4	+39.30
20 × 4	305 × 127UB37	254 × 254UC132	120.3	75.8	+58.71
25 × 4	356 × 171UB45	254 × 254UC167	129.36	82.9	+55.99
30 × 4	356 × 171UB45	305 × 305UC240	193.57	116.0	+66.87

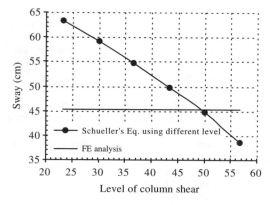

Figure 5. Variation in sway due to change in level of V_c for a 15 storey 4 bay frame.

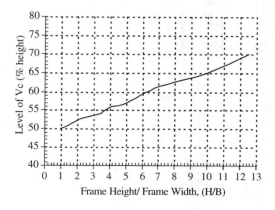

Figure 7. Actual variation of the level of V_c to be considered in Schueller's equation.

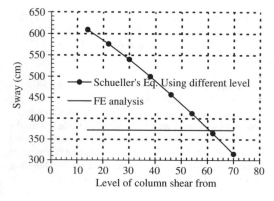

Figure 6. Variation in sway due to change in level of V_c for a 25 storey 1 bay frame.

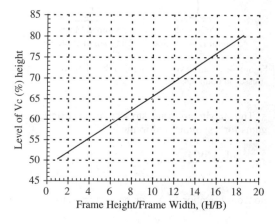

Figure 8. Proposed variation of the level of V_c to be considered in Schueller's equation.

For a 15 storey 4 bay frame, having H/B ratio to be equal to 1.875, the change in Δ_{max} due to a change in the level of V_c/I_c is reported in Figure 5. From this figure it is observed that if V_c/I_c is considered near the mid-height of the frame, 0.48 H, then the result almost coincides with that obtained from FE analysis.

Again from Figure 6 it is observed that, for a very slender 25 storey 1 bay frame (H/B =12.5) this level should be considered near 0.62 H. After studying the sway behavior of frames having slenderness ratio over quite a large range, the relation between slenderness ratio of the frame and the correct level for V_c from the base has been established as shown in Figure 7. The straight line shown in Figure 8 can closely approximate the unevenness of the previous figure and this straight line has been extended up to a slenderness ratio of 18.

From the analyses results it is proposed that while using Schueller's equation to calculate the sway of any rigid frame the ratio V_c/I_c should be taken according to Figure 8 and V_g/I_g should be considered at the level just above V_c/I_c. This modification makes the results of this equation to be close to FE results.

5 APPLICATION OF THE MODIFIED EQUATION FOR NON-REGULAR FRAMES

Non-regular frames, i.e. frames having unequal storey heights, bay size and column sections along the height or width and having different number of stories in successive bay (this particular type of frame has been termed as "stepped frame" in this paper) are very common in practice. This article studies the sway of these frames and attempts are made to calculate the sway of such frames using the modified Schueller's equation and make further modifications, if necessary.

The modified Schueller's equation can be applied directly to frames having uniform heights. But this equation cannot be applied directly for stepped frames and as such a new term "step-factor" has been introduced to estimate sway of such frames. "Step factor" is the ratio of the sway of a stepped frame to the sway of its corresponding regular frame. According to Figure 9, step-factor for frame (a) is defined as Δ_a/Δ_b; where Δ_a and Δ_b are sway of frames (a) and (b) respectively. Two other new terms- Bs and Hs as shown in Figure 9 refer to the width and height of the step respectively.

Step factors are observed to vary according to the number of stories of the step. Three different cases were studied – 10 storey steps, 5 storey steps and 2 storey steps. Following combinations are used to study the sway.

From this study it is observed that step factors increase exponentially with respect to the relative height to width ratio; $(H_s/H)/(B_s/B)$ i.e. $H_s/H \times B/B_s$. While calculating this factor, H_s refers to the height of the step rather than number of stories. The charts shown in Figures 10(a), 10(b) and 10(c) can be used for the determination of step factors for a given frame. Linear interpolations can be made regarding the number of stories as well as L_b/L_c ratio.

Thus sway for a stepped frame is to be determined by multiplying the sway of its corresponding regular rigid frame by the step factor for that specific frame.

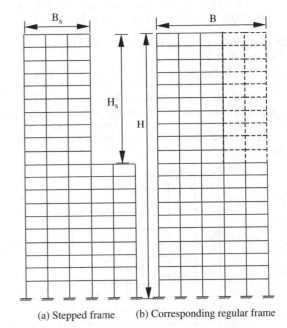

(a) Stepped frame   (b) Corresponding regular frame

Figure 9.   Relation between a stepped frame and its original regular frame.

Table 2.   Geometrical description of the stepped frames used to find step factors.

Number of stories in steps	Regular frame		Stepped frame	
	No. of storey	No. of bay	No. of stories taken off from top	No. of bay taken off
10	30	6	10	1, 2, 3, 4, 5
	25	5	10	1, 2, 3, 4
	20	5	10	1, 2, 3, 4
5	30	6	5	1, 2, 3, 4, 5
	25	5	5	1, 2, 3, 4
	20	5	5	1, 2, 3, 4
	15	4	5	1, 2, 3
2	20	5	2	1, 2, 3, 4
	15	4	2	1, 2, 3
	10	3	2	1, 2
	8	4	2	1, 2, 3

6 DESIGN PROPOSALS TO DETERMINE SWAY OF RIGID FRAMES WITH ILLUSTRATIVE EXAMPLES

Following steps are to be followed to determine sway of a rigid frame using the modified Schueller's equation.

Step 1: From the frame geometry, the ratio of frame height (H) to the frame width (B) is to be calculated.

Step 2: Using the proposed design chart as shown in Figure 8, the level for column shear (V_c) is to be determined.

Step 3: For the specified loading conditions, the column axial force at the base (N_c), Column shear force (V_c) at the predetermined level and girder shear force (V_g) are to determined using portal method.

Step 4: Using the values of the parameters as determined in Step 3, the sway of the given frame is to be calculated from the following equation:

$$\Delta_{max} = \frac{HV_c h^2}{12EI_c} + \frac{HV_g L^2}{12EI_g} + \frac{2N_c H^2}{3EA_c B}$$

Step 5: If the frame has got a "stepped" geometry, then the sway of its corresponding regular frame is to be determined first by following Step 1 to Step 4. To find the sway of the given "stepped" frame, the parameter $H_s/H \times B/B_s$ (symbols are defined in Figure 9) is to be evaluated and the step factor can be obtained from Figure 10.

Step 6: Sway of the regular frame is to be multiplied by the obtained "step factor" to get the sway of the given "stepped" frame.

7 ILLUSTRATIVE EXAMPLES

7.1 Example 1

A 12 storey 3 bay regular frame with typical storey height of 3 m and bay size of 6 m has been subjected to a gravity load of 37.5 kN/m. Wind pressure acting on the frame has an intensity of 1.5 times higher than the typical BNBC load as mentioned in Table 3. If beam and column sections represent the universal sections of 305 × 102 UB 28 and 203 × 203 UC 86 respectively, calculate the sway of this frame.

For the frame under consideration:

h = 3.0 m, H = 12 × 3.0 = 36 m
L = 6.0 m, B = 6.0 × 3 = 18.0 m
I_c = 9462 cm⁴, I_g = 5415 cm⁴, A_c = 110.1 cm²
For this frame, H/B = 36.0/18.0 = 2.00.

Now, from Figure 8, it is observed that V_c should be considered at 0.52 H from the base. Considering this fact, the following values were obtained using the portal method,

N_c = 700.39 kN, V_c = 61.28 kN, V_g = 56.63 kN

So, finally from Equation 11, Δ_{max} is obtained to be equal to 64.48 cm.

7.2 Example 2

An 18 storey 4 bay regular frame with typical storey height of 3 m and bay size of 5 m has been subjected

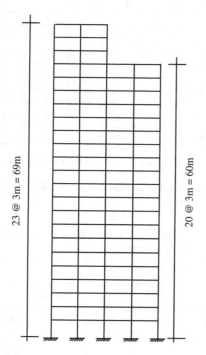

Figure 10. Relation between a stepped frame and its original regular frame.

Table 3A. Applied gravity loading.

Gravity load (kN/m²)	
Dead load	3.25
Live load	3

Table 3b. Wind load (kN/m²) intensities at different levels as par BNBC.

Storey	5	6	7	8	9	10	11	12	13
Wind load	1.84	1.96	2.06	2.15	2.23	2.31	2.39	2.47	2.52
Storey	14	15	16	17	18	19	20	21	22
Wind Load	2.58	2.65	2.72	2.77	2.82	2.87	2.92	3.08	3.08
Storey	23	24	25	26	27	28	29	30	
Wind load	3.08	3.22	3.22	3.22	3.35	3.35	3.35	3.35	

to a gravity load of 37.5 kN/m. Wind pressure acting on the frame has an intensity as mentioned in Table 3. If the beam and column sections are chosen so as to represent the universal sections of 356 ×127 UB 39 and 305 ×305 UC 97 respectively, then calculate the sway of this frame.

For the given frame:

$h = 3.0$ m, $H = 18 \times 3.0 = 54$ m
$L = 5.0$ m, $B = 5.0 \times 4 = 20.0$ m
$I_c = 22202$ cm^4, $I_g = 10054$ cm^4, $A_c = 123.3$ cm^2
For this frame, $H/B = 54.0/20.0 = 2.70$.

Now, from Figure 8, it is observed that V_c should be considered at $0.54 H$ from the base. Considering this fact, the following values were calculated using the portal method,

$N_c = 1073.12$ kN, $V_c = 41.79$ kN, $V_g = 59.56$ kN

So, finally, from Equation 11, Δ_{max} is obtained to be equal to 39.96 cm.

7.3 Example 3

The stepped frame shown in Figure 10 aside has typical storey height of 3 m and bay size of 6 m. Gravity load acting over floors is 37.5 kN/m while wind pressure acting on the frame has an intensity to be equal to the typical BNBC load as mentioned in Table 3. If beam and column sections are chosen so as to represent universal section of 305 ×127 UB 37 and 254 × 254 UC 167 then calculate the overall sway of this frame.

For the given frame:

$h = 3.0$ m, $H = 23 \times 3.0 = 69.0$ m
$L = 6.0$ m, $B = 6.0 \times 4 = 24.0$ m
$I_c = 29914$ cm^4, $I_g = 7143$ cm^4, $A_c = 212.4$ cm^2
H/B ratio for its corresponding regular frame = $69.0/24.0 = 2.875$.

So, from Figure 8, it is observed that V_c should be considered at $0.54 H$ from the base. Considering this fact, the following values were calculated using the portal method,

$N_c = 1589$ kN, $V_c = 75.49$ kN, $V_g = 67.11$ kN

Thus, from Equation 11, the sway of its corresponding regular frame is 105.035 cm.

For the determination of step factor, $H_s/H \times B/B_s = 9/69 \times 24/12 = 0.26$.

According to Figure 10(a), for 2 storey step, "step factor" = 1.01.

According to Figure 10(b), for 5 storey step, "step factor" = 1.03.

So, for 3 storey step, "step factor" = 1.017.

Thus, $\Delta_{max} = 1.017 \times 105.035 = 107.14$ cm.

8 CONCLUSION

Schueller's equation is modified using a design chart so that it can be used to estimate sway of rigid frames. The design chart can be used to identify the level of column shear to be used in the equation. The proposed modification eliminates the unavoidability of FE packages for sway calculation. Moreover, charts are proposed to estimate "step factors" in case of sway calculation of stepped frames. Use of these charts makes the equation more general so that it can be used even in case of non-regular frames.

REFERENCES

Ashraf, M. 2001. *Sway Estimation of Semi-Rigid Steel Frames*, M.Sc. Thesis, Department of Civil Engineering, Bangladesh University of Engineering and Technology, Dhaka – 1000, Bangladesh.
Bangladesh National Building Code, 1993. Housing and Building Research Institute, 1st Edition, Dhaka.
Schueller, W. 1977. *High-Rise Building Structures*, John Wiley and Sons, pp. 170–174.

System-based Vision for Strategic and Creative Design, Bontempi (ed.)
© *2003 Swets & Zeitlinger, Lisse, ISBN 90 5809 599 1*

Prestressed steel structures design: a new frontier for structural engineering

V. Nunziata
Studio Nunziata, Palma Campania, Napoli, Italy

ABSTRACT: In this paper we introduce the theoretical principles and illustrate the calculation methods when dealing with prestressed steel beams. Our aim is to make this structural typology more *widely known* and to furnish simple *calculation methods*, which in our opinion, are the real obstacle to the development of this particular structural type. Furthermore, the use of prestressed steel, compared to other typologies, offers otherwise unattainable economic and technological advantages.

1 INTRODUCTION

The main reasons why prestressed steel structures are infrequently erected is due, in our opinion, to a lack of knowledge regarding the *system* and the *calculation methods*. Once this information becomes general knowledge within the scientific and the construction community, there will be the same rapid adoption of prestressed steel (P.S.) technology as there was for similar technologies, for example, prestressed concrete (P.C.). In this respect, prestressed steel technology is the new frontier for structural engineering. The aim of this paper is to present a static analysis of significant prestressed steel structures, together with relevant results, and to compare them with other structural typologies.

2 ANALYSIS OF PRESTRESSED STEEL STRUCTURES

2.1 *General*

A prestressed system consists quite simply in "subjecting a structure to loads that produce opposing stresses to those when it is in service". Prestressing can be usefully applied to any material and, in particular to steel (Fig. 1), thus improving considerably its resistance characteristics.

In the case of P.C., the effect of prestressing enables beams to pass from being partial reagents to becoming total reagents (only compression), (Fig. 2). The increase in the characteristics of resistance are solely due to a greater use of the section. In the case of steel this is taken for granted.

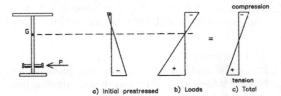

Figure 1. Prestressed steel girder: principle of function.

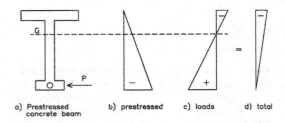

Figure 2. Prestressed concrete beam: principle of function.

The methods used for analyzing the sections are:

The static method, which in each section considers the effect of prestressing as an eccentric pressure (traditional method).

The equivalent loads method, in which the effect of prestressing is analyzed through the introduction of a system of equivalent forces of external provenance which exert pressure upon the girder and are called "equivalent loads".

2.2 *Static analysis of the section*

With reference to a simply supported prestressed steel beam, it will be necessary to assess whether in the

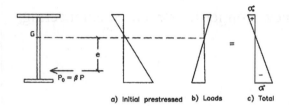

a) Initial prestressed   b) Loads   c) Total

Figure 3.   Condition at transfer.

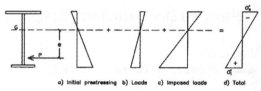

a) Initial prestressing   b) Loads   c) Imposed loads   d) Total

Figure 4.   Condition at service.

section most under stress, the tensions owing to the loads and the prestressing are lower than those allowed for by the limit state under consideration. An admissible value for *tension loss* for P.S., on account of *friction* and *steel relaxation* is 5%. The value we take into consideration is 10% (generally for P.C., *tension losses* due to friction, creep shrinkage etc are presumed to be 25%–30%). Two load conditions will be taken into account, more precisely, an initial or "at transfer" condition and a final or "at service" condition. In the first case the prestressing force P will be increased through the application of a co-efficient $\beta = 1.10$ to take account of the total (or final) tension loss.

2.2.1   *Bending*

It may be said that prestressing was invented for bending girders and it is for this state of stressing that we gain the most benefits.

In reference to Figure 3, it may be verified, at transfer:

$$\sigma_i^0 = -\frac{\gamma_p \beta P}{A} - \frac{\gamma_p \beta Pe}{W_i} + \frac{M_{min}}{W_i} \leq f_d$$

where: A and W_i are respectively the area and the lower resistant modulus of the steel girder, γ_p is the partial coefficient of safety applied to the prestressing, M_{min} is the minimum moment calculated, taking into account the partial coefficients of safety applied to the loads, e is the distance of the resulting cable from the barycentre G.

Placing an equals sign between the stresses we will obtain P for which verification at transfer is no longer necessary, or rather:

$$\sigma_i^0 = f_d \Rightarrow P$$

At service, Figure 4, will verify:

$$\begin{cases} \sigma_s^1 = -\dfrac{\gamma_p P}{A} + \dfrac{\gamma_p Pe}{W_s} - \dfrac{M_{max}}{W_s} \leq f_d \\[2ex] \sigma_i^1 = -\dfrac{\gamma_p P}{A} - \dfrac{\gamma_p Pe}{W_i} + \dfrac{M_{max}}{W_i} \leq f_d \end{cases}$$

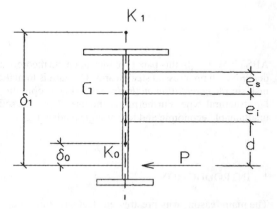

Figure 5.   Representations of kern points e_i and e_s.

where: W_s is the higher resistant modulus of the steel girder, M_{max} is the maximum moment taking into consideration the partial safety coefficients applied to the loads.

The intervention of an external moment causes the prestressing force (or rather, the center of pressure) to shift:

$$\delta_0 = \frac{M_{min}}{\beta \cdot P^*} \qquad \delta_1 = \frac{M_{max}}{P^*} \quad \text{where: } P^* = \gamma_p \cdot P$$

This allows us to make a useful, though qualitative, analysis of the prestressing of steel girders and to highlight the main differences and limitations of pre-stressed concrete. In Figure 5, given e_i and e_s the distances of the lower and higher kern points from the barycentre point, d the distance of the resulting cable from the lower kern point, we may see that the pre-stressing force shifts from point K_0 to point K_1 during the passage from the at transfer phase to the at service phase. The two points are both external to the central kern area (the section is partly compressed and partly under tension). The useful moment (M_u) in which the section will be able to absorb is:

$$M_u = M_{max} - M_{min} = P^* \delta_1 - \beta P^* \delta_0;$$
$$M_u = P^* (\delta_1 - \beta \delta_0) = P^* K_a$$

having placed $K_a = (\delta_1 - \beta \delta_0)$.

916

For P.C., we generally ignore its slight traction resistance and the section is proportioned in such a way as to obtain (Fig. 6):

$$\sigma_s^0 = 0 \; ; \; \sigma_i^1 = 0$$

which causes the prestressing force to shift in the lower kern point, at transfer, and in the higher kern point at service. In this case we obtain:

$$M_u = P^*(\delta_1 - \beta\delta_0) = P^*\left[(d + e_s + e_i) - \beta d\right] = P^* K_c$$

having placed $K_c = \left[(d + e_s + e_i) - \beta d\right]$.

The first observation that may be made on the basis of the preceding results is that in prestressed steel, the limits between which the prestressing force P shifts are wider. The second observation is that a prestressed concrete girder will have to remain compressed throughout its entire working life which constitutes a significant limitation given the extreme variety of imposed loads and the possibility that a situation could occur that was not foreseen at the design stage.

2.2.1.1 Cable zone (or Guyon zone)

We propose to determine the zone within which the plot of the resulting cable must be anticipated without going beyond the limits considered in any section of the girder. The primary operation is to ascertain the two characteristic points of the section (or limit points) E_0 and E_1, Figure 7, corresponding to the maximum

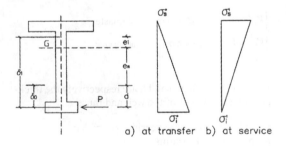

a) at transfer b) at service

Figure 6. Prestressed concrete girder.

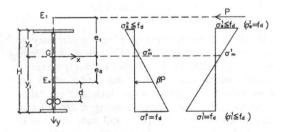

Figure 7. Limit points.

deviation that the center of pressure may tolerate at transfer and at service, without exceeding the limit state considered.

In the at transfer phase, given e_0 the deviation from the center of pressure, we have:

$$\sigma_i^0 = -\frac{\beta P^*}{A} - \frac{\beta P^* e_0}{W_i} \le f_d$$

the satisfying of the inequality, in the form of equality, permits us to find e_0, or rather:

$$\sigma_i^0 = f_d \;\Rightarrow\; e_0 = -\frac{\rho^2}{y_i}\left(1 - \frac{f_d}{\sigma_m^0}\right)$$

where:

$$\rho^2 = \frac{I}{A}; \qquad \rho_m^2 = \frac{\beta \cdot P^*}{A};$$

In the at service phase, given e_1 the deviation of the point of pressure, we have:

$$\begin{cases} \sigma_i^1 = -\dfrac{P^*}{A} + \dfrac{P^* e_1}{W_i} \le f_d \\[2mm] \sigma_s^1 = -\dfrac{P^*}{A} - \dfrac{P^* e_1}{W_s} \le f_d \end{cases}$$

the satisfying of the two inequalities, in the form of equality, allows us to find two values of e_1 the lesser of which in absolute value, will represent the higher limit point. From:

$$\sigma_i^1 = f_d \; ; \; \sigma_s^1 = f_d \; ;$$

we obtain:

$$\begin{cases} e_1' = +\dfrac{\rho^2}{y_i}\left(1 + \dfrac{f_d}{\sigma_m^1}\right) \\[3mm] e_1'' = -\dfrac{\rho^2}{y_s}\left(1 - \dfrac{f_d}{\sigma_m^1}\right) \end{cases} \Rightarrow \begin{matrix} e_1 = e_1' \;\; se \; |e_1'| < |e_1''| \\[2mm] e_1 = e_1'' \;\; se \; |e_1''| < |e_1'| \end{matrix}$$

In order to verify the section we will have to check it respectively at transfer and at service:

$$\begin{cases} M_{min} \ge \beta P^* d \\ M_{max} \le P^*(d + e_0 + e_1) \end{cases}$$

The "useful moment of the section" value is defined as:

$$M_{ut} = M_{max} - M_{min} = P^*\left[d(1 - \beta) + e_0 + e_1\right]$$

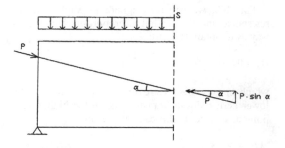

Figure 10.   Shear.

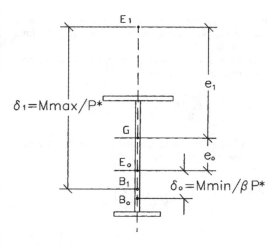

$\delta_1 = M_{max}/P^*$

$\delta_0 = M_{min}/\beta P^*$

Figure 8.   Resulting cable excursion.

a)

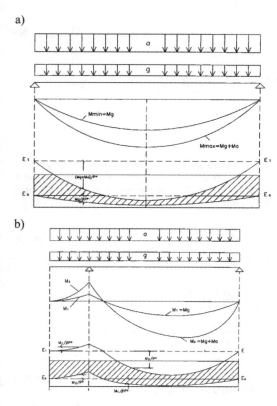

b)

Figure 9.   Cable zone.

In Figure 8 we observed before that the intervention of an external moment shifts the center of pressure upwards (positive moments) of a quantity $\delta = M/P^*$ in respect of the resulting cable. If, from limit points E_0

and E_1 we move another two points downwards B_0 and B_1 at distances of respectively $\delta_0 = M_{min}/\beta P^*$ and $\delta_1 = M_{max}/P^*$ we can state that the resulting cable will be contained between these two points. By repeating the construction, section by section, an area (or cable zone) can be singled out, within which the resulting cable along the girder must be contained.

In Figure 9, several types of cable zone are shown for different types of girder.

2.2.2   Shear

For a prestressed steel beam and generic section S, Figure 10, we have:

$$V_r = V - P\sin\alpha\,;$$

or rather:

$$\begin{cases} V_r^{\,0} = V^0 - \gamma_p\,\beta P\sin\alpha & \text{at transfer} \\ V_r^{\,1} = V^1 - \gamma_p P\sin\alpha & \text{at service} \end{cases}$$

$\tau_{\max} = V_r/t \cdot h$ where t and h are respectively the thickness and the height of the web and thus:

$\tau_{\max} \leqslant f_d/\sqrt{3}$ for pure shearing; $\sigma_{id} = \sqrt{\sigma^2 + 3\tau^2} \leqslant f_d$ for bending and shearing.

2.3   The system of equivalent loads for prestressing

The effect of prestressing on a steel girder may be analyzed by the introduction of a system of external loads (equivalent loads) which produce a series of stresses and deformations on the girder which are equivalent to its prestressing. Such stresses taken together with those produced by agent loads (dead and imposed) will give the overall state of stress to which the girder is subjected to. This must be compatible with the resistance and stability characteristics

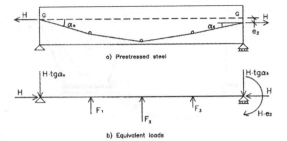

Figure 11.   Equivalent loads.

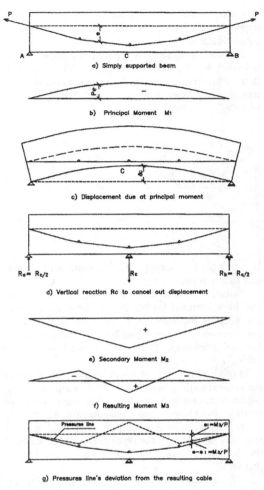

Figure 12.   Continuous girder: principle of function.

of the girder itself. A typical example of equivalent loads is shown in Figure 11.

2.4   *The continuous prestressed steel girder*

The continuous girder is the simplest of the hyperstatic type structural typologies and its use is becoming even more widespread in large structures. This presents advantages and disadvantages compared to a simply supported beam, for example, some advantages are lower flexure stresses, greater rigidity, less anchorage etc. Amongst the disadvantages are sensitivity to support failure, stress fluctuations, greater tension loss etc.

From a structural point of view, the main difference between simply supported beams and continuous beams is that, even without the presence of dead and imposed loads, the latter's prestressing means that side reactions may be generated (not always, as we shall see) which affect the state of stress. We consider a simply supported prestressed girder, Figure 12a, without external loads (and neglecting its own weight), the resulting cable represents the "successive resulting polygon" to which we give the name "*line of pressures*". This line of pressures, whilst it coincides with the resulting cable in simply supported beams, in continuous beams is generally different.

In simply supported beam, prestressing gives place to a "*principal moment*" $M_1 = P \cdot e$, Figure 12b, which upwardly deflects the beam itself, thereby causing a displacement equal to δ_c, Figure 12c. If we attach a sliding bearing to the beam in C (continuous beam) so as to cancel out displacement δ_c, this constraint will have to react with force R_c which in turn will cause reactions $R_a = R_b = P.C./2$, Figure 12d. These reactions will cause a "*secondary moment*" M_2, Figure 12e. The sum of the principal and secondary moments is termed the "*resulting moment*" $M_3 = M_1 + M_2$, Figure 12f. In each section of a continuous beam, the effect of prestressing force P and the resulting moment M_3 is equivalent to the product of force P, acting with deviation e_i in respect of the barycentre equal to

$e_i = M_3/P$. The deviation line e_i along the longitudinal section of the beam is the "*line of pressures*" Figure 12. The line of pressures deviates from the resulting cable by:

$$e - e_i = \frac{M_1}{P} - \frac{M_3}{P} = -\frac{M_2}{P}$$

therefore in an simply supported beam, being $M_2 = 0$, the line of pressures coincides with the resulting cable.

On the basis of this we can put forward a first general rule

1ª Rule: "In a continuous girder, the line of pressures is obtained from the resulting cable by lowering or raising opportunely, the profile of the intermediate supports, keeping the position of the extreme supports unchanged. This operation is called *linear transformation*".

The static regime of the continuous beam is characterized by the line of pressures. The equations derived for simply supported girders are also valid for continuous girders, provided that "e" is substituted with "e_i", or rather:

$$\sigma_i^0 = -\frac{\gamma_p \beta P}{A} - \gamma_p \frac{\beta P e_i}{W_i} + \frac{M_{min}}{W_i} \le f_d$$

$$\begin{cases} \sigma_s^1 = -\frac{\gamma_p P}{A} + \frac{\gamma_p P e_i}{W_s} - \frac{M_{max}}{W_s} \le f_d \\ \\ \sigma_i^1 = -\frac{\gamma_p P}{A} - \frac{\gamma_p P \cdot e_i}{W_i} + \frac{M_{max}}{W_i} \le f_d \end{cases}$$

By analogous reasoning, the following second general rule is demonstrated:

2ᵃ Rule: "In a continuous P.S. girder, the cables that have terminal anchorages in the same position and keeping the same form, differing only by their deviation on the intermediate supports, have the same line of pressures. These are termed *equivalent cables*".

In other terms, the equivalent cables give place to the same resulting moment M_3. This particular cable which coincides with the line of pressures which is verified by $M_2 = 0$ and consequently $R_{ip} = 0$, is termed the "*concording cable*". One final general rule may be made on the observation of the form of the diagram of moments and of that of the line of pressures.

3ᵃ Rule: "In a continuous P.S. girder, the diagram of moments in any system of forces (including the moments applied to the extremities) is the plot of the *concording cable*".

2.5 *Prestressed composite steel-concrete girders*

2.5.1 *Introduction*

The system of prestressing is particularly advantageous for composite steel-concrete sections since the positive characteristics of both materials may be better exploited. Compared to the traditional treatment of not prestressed composite sections, the introduction of prestressing as a system of equivalent loads, has no particular novelty to offer in relation to what has already been described in the preceding paragraphs, apart from the fact of having to bear in mind that concrete, being subject to so-called "slow phenomena", like viscosity and shrinkage, brings about a variation of the tension state as a function of time. Some typical prestressed composite sections are

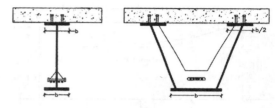

Figure 13.   Typical sections.

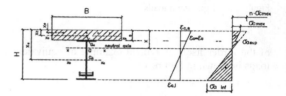

Figure 14.   Prestressed composite girder.

shown in Figure 13, where we can notice, unlike steel sections, the symmetry of the profiles.

2.5.2 *Calculation criteria*

The calculation of tensions, in reference to simply supported beams, is carried out by using the "homogenized section method". The effect of viscosity of concrete with regard to the stresses and deformations produced by permanent loads is evaluated through the introduction of an imaginary elastic modulus. The effect of shrinkage is determined by an approximate method on the basis of values of strain at infinite time. The effect of thermal differential variations is evaluated on the basis of the value of the corresponding unitary deformation with criteria analogous to the case of shrinkage.

2.5.2.1   Bending

In reference to Figure 14, we have:

$$A = A_a + A_\phi + \frac{A_c}{n}; \quad \text{dove: } n = \frac{E_a}{E_c}$$

There is nothing to say about the at transfer stage in regard to simple sections in P.C. At service, we will have to verify:

$$\sigma_{c_{max}} = \frac{1}{n} \cdot \frac{M}{I} x < f_{cd}^*$$

$$\sigma_{a_{sup}}^1 = \sigma_{a_{sup}}^0 + \frac{M}{I}(x - h_c) \le f_d$$

$$\sigma_{a_{inf}}^1 = \sigma_{a_{inf}}^0 + \frac{M}{I}(H - x) \le f_d$$

920

2.5.2.2 Shear

Resistance to shear action is only for steel girders, therefore we will have:

$$\tau_{max} = V_r/t \cdot h \quad \tau_{max} \leqslant f_d/\sqrt{3} \text{ for pure shearing}; \quad \sigma_{id} = \sqrt{\sigma^2 + 3\tau^2} \leqslant f_d \text{ for bending and shearing}.$$

3 CONCLUSIONS

Scarce knowledge of calculation methods and their potential represents, in our opinion, the main obstacle in widespread use of prestressed steel structures. This paper has pointed towards some calculation methods for P.S. structures in reference to girders, demonstrating their simplicity and possible applications.

BIBLIOGRAPHY

Nunziata, V. 1999. *Strutture in acciaio precompresso*. Palermo, Dario Flaccovio, Editore.

System-based Vision for Strategic and Creative Design, Bontempi (ed.)
© 2003 Swets & Zeitlinger, Lisse, ISBN 90 5809 599 1

Development of criteria for using of bracing and shear walls in tall buildings

S. Azizpour
Civil Engineering Department, Stanford University, California, USA

M. Mofid & M. Menshari
Civil Engineering Department, Sharif University of Technology, Tehran, Iran

ABSTRACT: This article extends a procedure in form of graphical criteria, which is utilized for different kind of multi-story steel structures. In this paper five actual ten to forty stories structures are designed, considering six kinds of lateral resisting systems; and results are compared. All results are presented in form of a few graphs, which can be used efficiently in real design conditions.

1 INTRODUCTION

The problem of the using of bracings and/or shear walls in tall buildings has been of interest to numerous engineers and structural designers for more than hundred years. Apparently, the initial impetus for the investigation was presented by engineers on nineteenth century (Figs. 1–2). Thereafter, the increasing height and weight of structure, together with different behavior of lateral frame action of structures, increased the interest in this problem. Suddenly, the problem of application of

bracings and/or shear walls with various connections and different types of eccentric/non-eccentric behavior in tall buildings gained popularity, and was confronted by many mathematicians and engineers (Grigorian 1993, Chajes & Romstol 1993, Smith & Cruvellier 1991, Nart et al. 1978).

This article presents some easily applied criteria in form of graphs for this problem and these graphs are valid for 10 to 40 multi-story structures. In general calculating the lateral deformation of highrise building involves two shear and bending components.

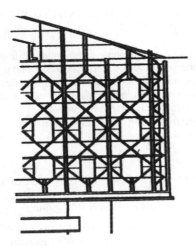

Figure 1. Noisiel–Sur-Marne Chocolate Factory, Paris, France 1872.

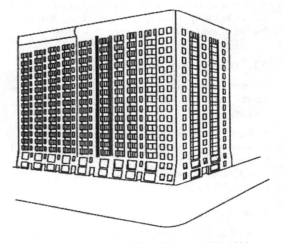

Figure 2. Monadnock Building, Chicago, USA, 1891.

These modes of deformation are studied by many researchers (Schuller 1990 & 1977, Popov 1977). What were needed, were some reliable criteria that could easily be applied to many types of multi-story buildings and be simple enough to be carried out on personal computers in form of graphs and tables. The objectives of this investigation are:

- To apply different forms of bracings and/or shear walls to some actual 10 to 40 stories steel structures; and study the maximum deflection of shear and bending modes.
- To present a simple and practical criteria in form of graphs and tables for selecting the type of lateral resisting system (bracing, moment resisting joints, ... etc.).

2 HYPOTHESIS

In general, it is assumed the behavior of a multi-story structure with moment resisting joints in shear mode and for the same structure with bracing and/or shear wall and pin beam to column joints, tends to behave in bending mode. However, it is prudent to make compatibility between these two modes, resulting into a normal distribution of deformation in different level. In this investigation, an attempt is made to evolve some criteria for the application of the different types of bracings and/or shear walls. However, no comparison between bracing systems and building with central resisting core has been made.

3 PROBLEM DEFINITION

Five different types of existing steel structural building with regular almost square shapes in plan and height in 10 to 40 stories are considered and modeled in computer. In the next stage, five different forms of lateral resisting systems are considered for these buildings in the following manner.

3.1 Different types of frame systems

As mentioned above, the following different forms of lateral resisting systems are considered for these buildings:

- Rigid frames with moment resisting joints
- Non-moment resisting joints (moment released beams) and
  - Diagonal bracing in exterior frame
  - Belt truss bracing
  - Truss tube system
- Shear wall system

In all models, P-Δ effect, accompanied by bracing stiffness effect, are taken into account. Due to space

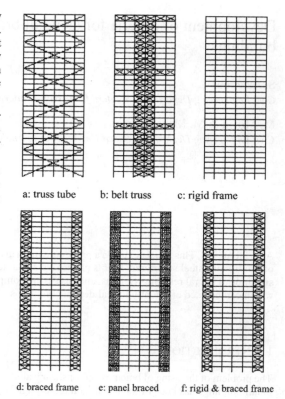

a: truss tube   b: belt truss   c: rigid frame

d: braced frame   e: panel braced   f: rigid & braced frame

Figure 3.   Different types of frame systems.

limitation, only a few types of bracings and properties of structures are shown in Figure 3.

4 PROBLEM SOLUTION AND COMPARISON OF THE RESULT

In this investigation, some commercial finite element computer programs are employed, static and dynamic analysis are performed; and maximum deflection at the top of the framing with different types of bracings, due to lateral forces are computed. These results are compared and the summary of this comparison is shown in the graphs, Figures 4–8.

5 BRIEF DISCUSSION OF THE RESULTS

5.1 Frames with moment resisting joints

Investigation of the results indicate that this type of lateral resisting system causes maximum deflection in multi-story structures up to 10 to 12 floors. However, the maximum deflection decreases and deflected shape

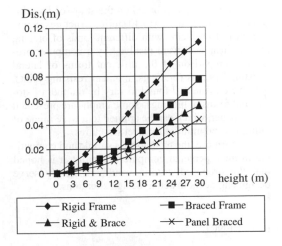

Figure 4.   Comparison of displacements, 10-story buildings.

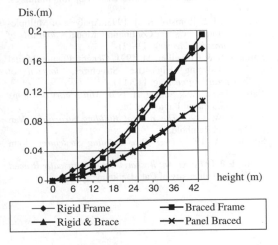

Figure 5.   Comparison of displacements, 15-story buildings.

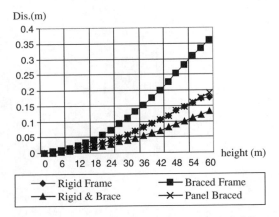

Figure 6.   Comparison of displacements, 20-story buildings.

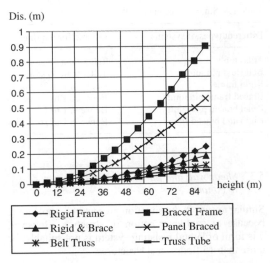

Figure 7.   Comparison of displacements, 30-story buildings.

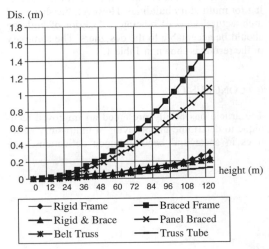

Figure 8.   Comparison of displacements, 40-story buildings.

changes to shear only rapidly, when number of floors grows to 40.

5.2   *Bracing system with pin connections of beam to column*

The maximum deflection for structures up to 12 stories with the above stated bracings is insignificant, compare to the form of lateral moment resisting system. However, because of cantilever behavior of structures this form of bracing is no longer acceptable for buildings with more than 15 floors.

Table 1. Summary of the results.

Different types of systems	Offered for buildings
Truss tube	Taller than 35 stories
Belt truss pin joints	Taller than 30 stories
Rigid frame	Between 1 to 25 stories
Braced frame pin joints	Between 1 to 15 stories
Panel braced pin joints	Between 1 to 15 stories
Rigid and braced frame	Between 1 to 30 stories

5.3 *Shear wall and pin connections of beam to column*

Similar to case 2, the situation presented is applicable, because of cantilever action of structure. However, this form of lateral resisting system is not suitable for more than 15 floors steel structures.

5.4 *Diagonal bracing in exterior face*

This is considered to be one of the best forms of bracing for multi-story buildings. However, the shape and architectural view of bracing in exterior of building should be acceptable to the designers. The summary of the results is shown in Table 1.

6 CONCLUSION

The article has briefly presented an improved technique to determine the behavior of multi-story structures in shear and bending mode deflections. The proposed technique is based on the study of five different types of actual 10 to 40 stories structures. Some special test problems with different kinds of bracing and/or shear wall were resolved by a computer program. Comparison of the different forms of lateral resisting systems (bracings, moment resisting joints, etc.) were made and found to vary by number of stories and forms of bracings. Some graphs are presented in this paper, which can be applied to a wide range of buildings and multi-story steel structures.

Furthermore, the technique is simple and compatible to most personal computers. Finally, it is hoped that the proposed criteria would efficiently serve design engineers in actual design situations.

REFERENCES

Grigorian, M. 1993. On the Lateral Response of Regular High-Rise Frames, *Structural Design of Tall Buildings*. Vol. 2.

Chajes, M.J. & Romstol, K.M. 1993. Analysis of Multiple-Bay Frames Using Continuum Model. *Journal of Structural Engineering*. 119(2).

Smith, B.S. & Cruvellier, M. 1991. General Planner Model for Analyzing High-Rise Structures, *Journal of Structural Engineering*. 117(11).

Nart, F., Henn, W. & Sontag, H. 1978. *Multi-Story buildings in Steel*. Granad Publishing Inc.

Schuller, W. 1990. *The Vertical Building Structures*. Van Nastrand Reinhold.

Schuller, W. 1977. *High Rise Building Structures*. John Wiley.

Popov, E.P. 1977. *Recent Research on Eccentrically Braced Frames*, University of Cal., Berkeley.

System-based Vision for Strategic and Creative Design, Bontempi (ed.)
© 2003 Swets & Zeitlinger, Lisse, ISBN 90 5809 599 1

Linear stability bearing capacity analysis of pin-connected steel structures

S.J. Duan, H.M. Jia, S.Y. Li & Z.Y. Liang
Research Institute of Structural Engineering, Shijiazhuang Railway Institute, Shijiazhuang, P.R.China

ABSTRACT: The pin-connected steel structure, as a kind of pre-cast structures, is widely used in structural engineering. Because of the interstice between pin and pinhole, the initial geometric displacement is generated, and then the bearing capacity of the structure is reduced. In this paper, a concept of reduced rigidity is introduced, and the stability bearing capacity of the pin-connected steel structure is studied. As the examples, the critical height of a column and the critical span of a beam assembled by the "64-Type Beam" units in China with buckling load are obtained.

1   INTRODUCTION

Pin-connected steel structures or similar structures are often applied to emergency or temporary structure engineering, because they can be easily assembled or disassembled repeatedly. As shown in Fig. 1, there is the triangle element unit of the "64 Type Beam" in China, then a structure can be assembled by such units with the pin connection. Because of the big or small interstice δ between the pin and the pinhole, the mechanical characteristic will occur, which different to the common steel structures.

Up to now, very few of studies on this problem can be found (Gralord et al. 1992; Duan & Li 1998). The designers just regard the pin connection as an ideal hinge joint, so that an assembled structure is considered as a truss be analyzed, and enlarge safety coefficient by experience to ensure the structure in safety according to the Design Code. Due to the interstice between the pin and the pinhole, the structure will generate the initial displacement towards a certain direction, which can be determined (Duan & Li 1998). The strength bearing capacity of pin-connected steel

structure is analyzed in the references (Li et al. 2001; Jia et al. 2002). In this paper, based on the previous studies (Duan & Li 1998; Li et al. 2001; Jia et al. 2002), a concept of reduced rigidity will be introduced, and an approximate calculation method to stability bearing capacity of pin-connected steel structure is proposed.

2   THE STABILITY ANALYSIS OF THE PIN-CONNECTED STEEL COLUMN

A high truss column (Fig. 2) assembled by the precut-segmental units (Fig. 1) under compression is analyzed in this section, and supposing its deformation is in the plane.

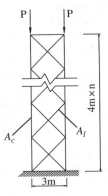

Figure 2.   Assembled steel column.

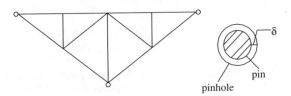

Figure 1.   Standard triangle units and pinhole.

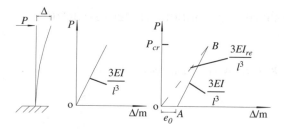

Figure 3. Reduced bending rigidity.

Table 1. The reduced rigidity and stability bearing capacity of the assembled column.

Layer	Reduced rigidity/ $\times 10^9 \mathrm{N} \cdot \mathrm{m}^2$	Stability bearing capacity/kN
6	3.488	13807
8	3.522	8111
10	3.542	5305
12	3.556	3732
14	3.566	2764
16	3.573	2128

2.1 The stability analysis for a truss under compression

For a plane truss under compression, the Euler load can be stated as (Long & Bao 1981),

$$P_c = k_1 \frac{\mathrm{p}^2 EI}{(\mu l)^2} \qquad (1)$$

similar to the elastic buckling of a solid column with a reduced coefficient k_1.

$$k_1 = \cfrac{1}{1 + \cfrac{\mathrm{p}^2}{2} (\cfrac{b}{l})^2 \cfrac{A_c}{A_i \sin\theta \cos^3\theta}}$$

Where, μ is the effective-length coefficient, A is the area of the bar. When $A_c/A_1 \to \infty$, $k_1 \to 0$; when $A_c/A_1 \to 0$, $k_1 \to 1$; For a practical structure, the critical load of a truss column is always lower than one of the solid column with same inertia moment. But if the length l is large enough, the critical load of a truss column will tend to $P_c = \mathrm{p}^2 EI/(\mu l)^2$ for a solid column.

2.2 The stability analysis for the assembled column considering the initial displacement

Due to the initial displacement, the deflection will gradually develop and additional secondary bending moment will gradually increase after pressure is carried. Buckling isn't from straight to curve according to the balanced form, while the development of distortion lead to the ultimate bearing capacity. The buckling in extreme point differs from the fork buckling of straight bar in nature, but still belongs to the problem of integral stability. The key to bearing capacity calculation is to find out the corresponding structural rigidity value.

For a perfect solid column in Fig. 3(a), the relation between load and displacement is linear, as shown in Fig. 3(b). The relation between the load and displacement of pin-connected structure is shown as curve OAB in Fig. 3(c), where the point B is determined from the yielding of material. If the initial geometric displacement (OA) is small for the whole structure and doesn't affect structural rigidity, the relation between the load after loading and the elastic displacement is still linear.

The flexural rigidity is directly applied to calculation of stability bearing capacity of the crooked column. For the assembled column by pin connections, the slope of the link between material's yielding point B in load displacement curve and the initial point O, is called reduced rigidity. Hence, the stability analysis of pin-connected steel column with initial geometric displacement is changed into a problem without initial geometric displacement, only the flexural rigidity is replaced by the reduced rigidity.

2.3 Example

An assembled column by standard triangle units of the "64-Type Beam" of Fig. 2 is taken as an example. The initial geometric displacement value can be obtained follows the reference (Li & Duan 1998). The reduced rigidity and stability bearing capacity of the structure is shown in Table 1.

The comparison about the strength bearing capacity, the stability bearing capacity considering geometric displacement and the stability bearing capacity not considering geometric displacement of the assembled column is shown in Fig. 4.

The initial geometric displacement will reduce the bearing capacity of structure. When the height of column is smaller, the bearing capacity of column is controlled by the strength; when the height of column is greater than 60 m (fifteen layers), the bearing capacity is controlled by the stability.

3 THE LATERAL STABILITY ANALYZE OF THE PIN-CONNECTED STEEL BEAM

The planar flexural rigidity of planar bending beam generally is much greater than the lateral rigidity. If the beam lacks of necessary lateral bracing, the beam may emerge balance branch of space torsional and flexural

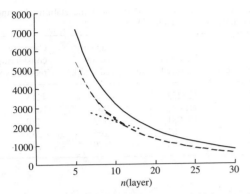

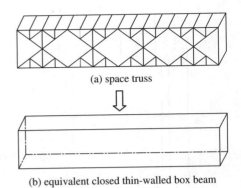

(a) space truss

(b) equivalent closed thin-walled box beam

Figure 5. Equivalent closed thin-walled beam to space truss.

- - - - Stability bearing capacity considering initial geometric displacement

——— Stability bearing capacity without considering initial geometric displacement

······ Strength bearing capacity considering initial geometric displacement

Figure 4. The comparison about the strength and the stability bearing capacity of the assembled column.

distortion when the loads reach a critical value. The beam that only bends in a plane initially begins to buckle and twist laterally, and emerges the transition of balance status at the same time. The phenomenon is called the lateral torsional-flexural buckling or lateral buckling in short. When beam is buckled, the critical bending moment M_{cr} is shown as following:

$$M_{cr} = \frac{\pi}{l}\sqrt{GI_tEI_y} \qquad (2)$$

In which, M_{cr} denotes the critical bending moment of lateral buckling, EI_y is the lateral flexural rigidity and GI_t is the torsion rigidity.

3.1 The calculation of flexural rigidity

Because the pin-connected assembled systems are similar to a truss but with the initial geometric displacement, the successful key is to obtain the factual flexural rigidity. If the system is enough long, we may approximately consider that cross section is uniform along the span. In a small distortion scale, the total displacement is assumed as the sum of the initial geometric displacement and the elastic deformation. Although the relation between the load and displacement is in multi-linear, the deduced rigidity (the factual rigidity of system) can be derived following previous section. For cantilever beam of no initial horizontal geometric displacement, we may calculate flexural rigidity according with actual situation.

3.2 The calculation of torsion rigidity

As a space truss, if the span is large enough, it can be equivalent to a closed thin-walled beam, as shown in Fig. 5, to obtain the torsion rigidity (Li 1992). The basic assumption of the method is:

(1) The plane that is vertical to the centerline of beam before distortion, still retain the plane but isn't vertical to the centerline of beam after distortion.
(2) The warping distortion of section is partial.
(3) The effect of distorted distortion and shear lag of section is not considered.
(4) Steel is ideal elastic–plastic material, and the effect of shear stress for yielding is ignored.

For calculation of the closed thin-walled beam, the section change of chord and web member is considered, every panel is regarded as a thin-walled beam unit and cross link bracing between the trusses may adopt beam unit to simulate. The assembled beam with different length has different beam units quantitatively. If assembled beam is multi-pieced, it may be equivalent to a multi-box beam or a separate beam according to the actual condition.

The thickness of thin-walled section (Fig. 6) is,

$$t_1 = \frac{\sum_{i=1}^{n} A_il_i}{lb} \qquad t_2 = \frac{\sum_{i=1}^{n} A_il_i}{lh} \qquad (3)$$

Then, the torsion inertia moment is,

$$I_t = \frac{4A^2}{2(\frac{b}{t_1} + \frac{h}{t_2})} = \frac{2(bh)^2}{(\frac{b}{t_1} + \frac{h}{t_2})} \qquad (4)$$

3.3 The reduced torsion rigidity

For a cantilever beam, the relation between torque and turn angle is linear without initial horizontal

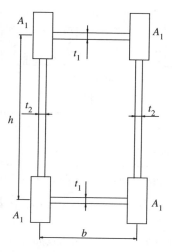

Figure 6. The cross section of closed thin-walled beam.

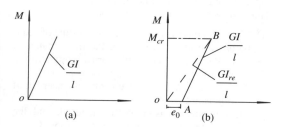

Figure 7. The reduced torsion rigidity.

displacement, which is shown in Fig. 7(a). While the relation torque and turn angle of the pin-connected steel structure is shown as curve OAB in Fig. 7(b). Following the assumptions and the proposed concept as the previous section, the reduced torsion rigidity can be obtained.

3.4 Example

In this section, a cantilever beam assembled by standard triangle units of the "64-Type Beam" is taken as an example. The critical load is

$$P_{cr} = \frac{2.123}{l^2} \sqrt{EI_y GI_t}$$

where, the flexural rigidity EI_y is $131986\,\mathrm{kN}\cdot\mathrm{m}^2$, and the torsion rigidity GI_t is $124957\,\mathrm{kN}\cdot\mathrm{m}^2$. As the results, the reduced rigidity and stability bearing capacity is shown in the Table 2.

The comparison about the strength bearing capacity, the stability bearing capacity considering the

Table 2. The reduced rigidity and the stability bearing capacity of the assembled beam.

Internode	Reduced rigidity/kN·m²	Capacity without reduced/kN	Capacity considering reduced/kN
2	122233	4260	4213
4	115497	1065	1024
6	108081	473	440
8	98567	266	236
10	88683	170	144

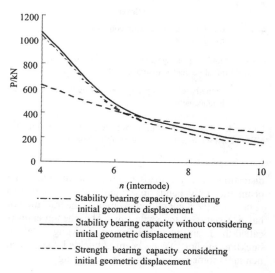

Figure 8. The comparison about the strength and stability bearing capacity of the assembled cantilever beam.

initial geometric displacement and the stability bearing capacity without regard to the initial geometric displacement of assembled cantilever beam is shown in Fig. 8. As shown in the Fig. 8, initial geometric displacement will reduce the bearing capacity of the structure. When the span of beam is smaller, the bearing capacity is controlled by the strength; when the span is greater than 26 m (6.5 internodes), the bearing capacity is controlled by the stability.

4 CONCLUSIONS

An approximate method of the stability bearing capacity of pin-connected steel structures is proposed in this paper. Duo to the affect of the initial geometric displacement, the bearing capacity of the pin-connected steel structure is lower than that of the perfect structure. For a column assembled by the "64-Type Beam", the structural safety is controlled by the strength when height is less than 60 m; or controlled by the stability when the height is more than 60 m. In fact, the collapse may occur in the out plane or the local buckling before the whole structure becomes unstable in the plane, which is not analyzed at present work. For the assembled cantilever beam, the critical length (span) is about 26 m.

REFERENCES

Gralord E. H., Gaylord C. N. & Stallmeyer. J. E. 1992. Design of Steel Structures. New York: McGraw-Hill

Duan S. J. & Li Y. F. 1998. Design and Calculation on Urgent Assembled Engineering Structures (in Chinese). *Proceedings of the Seventh National Conference on Structural Engineering.* Vol. II: 532–535.

Li S. Y., Duan S. J. & Li Y. F. 2001. Bearing Capacity of Pin-Connected Steel Structure. *Proceedings of EPMESC'VIII,* Shanghai: Triple Bookstore of Shanghai. 352–354.

Jia H. M., Duan S. J. & Li S. Y. 2002. An Approximate Method of Bearing Capacity of Pin-connected Steel Beam (in Chinese). *Journal of Shijiazhuang Railway Institute* 15 (3): 18–21.

Li G. H. 1992. Stability And Vibration of Bridge Structures (in Chinese). Beijing: China Railway Press. 6–42.

Long Y. Q. & Bao S. H. 1981. Structural Mechanics (in Chinese). Beijing: People's Education Press. 283–286.

Author index

Abdullah, A. 1567
Abdul-Malak, M.A. 229
Abendroth, R.E. 995
Abibsi, A. 1783, 1797, 1937
Abruzzese, D. 569
Abukhder, J. 85
Adajar, J.C. 2427
Adnan, A. 1207
Agostino, G. 467
Ahmed, B. 873, 907
Ahmed, S.M. 283, 1979
Ahuja, A.K. 2447
Ahuja, R. 437
Ajam, M. 229
Akgül, F. 1717
Alani, A. 223
Albertini Neto, H. 1789
Alfaiate, J. 769
Al-Gadhib, A.H. 1765
Al-Jibouri, S. 2227, 2233
Al-Jibouri, S.H. 1259,
    1263
Alptekin, G.O. 2221
Alrodan, A.K. 1435
Alshawi, M. 223
Alves, N.M. 1537
Al-Yousif, F. 419
Amanat, K.M. 1159
Amini, F. 2067
Anagnostopoulos, K.P. 2209
Anaton, J. 1863
Andrawes, B. 995
Antoniadis, D. 2179
Anumba, C.J. 343, 1567,
    2185
Anwar, H.A. 1875
Arangio, S. 701
Arets, M.J.P. 1661
Ashraf, M. 873, 907
Assaf, S. 419
Aşık, M.Z. 1269
Atchacosit, K. 515
Augusti, G. 2309
Aupérin, M. 2055
Avent, R.R. 1453
Azhar, S. 283, 1979
Azizpour, S. 923

Bártolo, H.M. 211, 1531
Bártolo, P.J. 211, 1531, 1537
Baba, K. 1655
Bajaj, A.S. 1837
Baluch, M.H. 1765
Bansal, P.K. 1991
Barberi, V. 2045, 2503
Barcala, M. 1979
Baron, D. 455
Bartoli, G. 2375
Bassotti, O. 1165
Battaglia, G. 981
Battaini, M. 2085
Bayraktar, M.E. 1607
Bel Hadj Ali, N. 481
Belfiore, N.P. 2129, 2163
Belis, J. 2275, 2281, 2285, 2293
Belletti, B. 663, 1083
Belounar, L. 645, 1273
Benmebarek, N. 1273
Benmebarek, S. 645, 1273
Berchenko, N.N. 2119
Berezovska, I.B. 2119
Bergman, L.A. 2097
Bernardi, P. 663, 1083
Bertagnoli, G. 721, 1777
Bertolini, L. 1929
Berver, E. 1459
Bhargava, R.R. 1991
Bianchi, P. 1217
Biondini, F. 533, 1177
Bodnarova, L. 1399, 1649
Bonin, G. 1297
Bontempi, F. 2495, 2511
Boothby, T.E. 1051
Borkowski, A. 475
Borner, R. 1551
Boscato, G. 1431
Boulon, M. 2393
Bracken, W.C. 753
Breccolotti, M. 2317
Brencich, A. 761, 775, 1109
Brnic, J. 639
Bärthel, J. 163
Bucciarelli-Ducci, C. 2155
Buffel, P. 2285
Busch, T.A. 349

Caballero, A. 1979
Cacace, A.G. 1771
Caicedo, J.M. 2097
Caracoglia, L. 2331
Carassale, L. 2323
Carbone, V.I. 721, 1777
Carper, K.L. 1343
Carsana, M. 1929
Casciati, F. 2085
Catallo, L. 521, 701, 1003, 2471,
    2487, 2503
Cavicchi, A. 775
Ceccoli, C. 1151, 1187
Cerioni, R. 663, 1083
Cerri, M.N. 2023
Chander, S. 2447
Chang, C.-Yu 363
Chang, W.T. 507
Charif, A. 645
Chassiakos, A.P. 2197
Chen, Y.L. 1279
Chen, Z. 1803, 1811
Cheng, C.-M. 2383
Cheng, M. 2191
Cheung, K.W. 1739
Cheung, S.O. 403, 1739
Chikh, N. 651
Chileshe, N. 1595, 1625
Cho, S.W. 597, 2063
Choi, K.M. 597
Christian, J. 1691
Christoforou, C. 137
Chung, P.W.H. 2185
Ciampoli, M. 2029, 2309
Ciani, M. 2503
Ciftcioglu, Ö. 1559
Çivici, T. 1545
Coccia, S. 803
Colaco, J.P. 1479
Colombi, P. 879
Como, M. 803
Cooper, R. 289
Corradi, C. 761
Cosma, C. 1745
Cross, J.P. 143
Csébfalvi, A. 493
Cui, Q. 1607

Cuninghame, J.R. 1035
Cuoco, D.A. 409
Cuth, V. 893
Cutting-Decelle, A.F. 481

Dainty, A.R.J. 2191
Dalmagioni, P. 1511
Daly, A.F. 1035
Danesh, F. 2067
Dantata, N. 137
de Almeida, J.R. 769
De Beule, M. 2275, 2281, 2285, 2293
De Francesco, U. 775
De Nicolo, B. 1487
de Silva, K.S.P. 1855, 2431
De Stefano, A. 1709
de Wilde, Th.S. 1009
Deasley, P.J. 289
Dehn, F. 1907
dell'Isola, F. 2023
Dessa Aguiar, S. 1803
Di Benedetto, M. 2163
Di Mella, V. 2471
Di Niro, G. 1121, 1333, 1667, 1869
Dias, J.L.M. 745
Dicleli, M. 2079
Dignan, M. 1943
Dinevski, D. 527
Diniz, S.M.C. 2353
D'Asdia, P. 2331
Dolara, E. 1121, 1333, 1667, 1869
Domaneschi, M. 2085
Donati, R. 2155
Drochytka, R. 1823
Drogemuller, R. 329
Duan, S.J. 927
Dumoulin, C. 2055
Dyke, S.J. 2097

Ebersole, D.W. 357
Edum-Fotwe, F.T. 289, 369
Eekhout, M. 549
Egbu, C.O. 343
Eibl, S.J. 299
El-Hamalawi, A. 2185
El-Kafrawy, W. 1875
Elmetwally, M.M.A. 1349
El-Rayes, K. 93
El-Shihy, A.M. 2437
Emborg, M. 1511
Endo, K. 255, 335
Era, K. 797

Fanning, P.J. 1051
Fanous, F.S. 995

Fantilli, A.P. 1443
Faraj, I. 1575
Faravelli, L. 2091
Fedele, F. 2155
Federico, F. 2401
Fellows, R.F. 11, 57, 425
Fenu, L. 389, 543, 575
Fernson, A. 2431
Ferracuti, B. 1375
Filip, M. 1399
Fischer, J. 1467
Flavigny, E. 2393
Foo, S. 329
Foraboschi, P. 781
Forbes, L.H. 283
Fowler, D.W. 1459
Francia, S. 1247
Frangopol, D.M. 3, 1717
Försterling, H. 2037
Fujii, K. 833, 885
Fujisawa, M. 2427
Furtner, P. 839
Furuta, H. 487
Furuya, N. 1285

Gago, A. 769
Gambarotta, L. 775
Gamberini, G.P. 1387
Gamisch, T. 1253
Garavaglia, E. 1211, 1789
Gastaldi, M. 1929
Gattesco, N. 1043
Geier, R. 839
Giaccu, G.F. 1387
Gianni, A. 1137
Gilbert, R.I. 1921
Gioffrè, M. 2337
Giordano, L. 721, 1777
Girmscheid, G. 157, 1253, 1523
Giudici, M. 2045
Giuliani, G.C. 2301
Giuliani, M.E. 989, 1091
Giuliano, F. 1311, 2461
Giunchi, P. 2127
Giura, P. 117
Gohnert, M. 1067
Gokhale, S. 1075
Gottfried, A. 343
Goulding, J.S. 223
Grabska, E. 475
Greco, G. 275, 1151, 1187
Gregory, M.J. 289
Grisoni, C. 2155
Guagenti, E. 1211
Guan, H. 461, 631
Guenfoud, M. 645
Guettala, A. 1783, 1797, 1937

Gukov, I. 941
Gupta, V.K. 1983
Gusella, V. 2317
Gyulaffy, M. 2123, 2171

Haddad, R.H. 811
Hadi, M.N.S. 1843, 1849
Hamada, S. 1899
Hamza, A. 1145
Hansen, L.P. 1097
Haque, M.E. 1517
Hara, T. 1023
Harada, K. 965
Hardie, M. 1973
Hardy, H.S. 1771
Harl, B. 527
Harrop, J. 651
Hartl, H. 685
Hasan, S. 1991
Hasegawa, K. 845
Hastak, M. 1607
Heathcote, P.M. 1405
Hela, R. 1399, 1649
Henderson, I. 357
Henning, T. 1495
Herbsman, Z.J. 1745
Hessing, H.W. 1319
Hewitt, C.M. 143
Hida, T. 1291
Hino, Y. 1641
Hirashima, K. 2003
Hocaoglu, M. 283
Holschemacher, K. 1393, 1907, 1913
Hoque, E. 1159
Horman, M.J. 143
Houari, H. 1797, 1937
Howorth, P.D. 357
Hristova, E.H. 1817
Hsu, T.H. 1383
Huang, C.-Mo 1967
Hunt, S. 1355
Hyari, K. 93

Iaconianni, G. 275
Ianniruberto, U. 803, 1473
Idehara, U. 797
Imbimbo, M. 1473
Iori, I. 663, 1083
Ishiyama, S. 1949
Issa, M. 1467
Ito, H. 797
Itoh, Y. 1291
Iwamatsu, J. 255

Jacoski, C.A. 383
Jaehring, A. 823

Jain, R.K. 325
Jannadi, O. 419
Jarquio, R.V. 817, 1363, 1997
Jayyousi, K. 1599
Jeary, A. 1973
Jia, H.M. 927
Jirsa, J.O. 1459
Jo, J.-S. 617
Jommi, C. 2409
Jubeer, S.K. 729
Junag, D.S. 507
Jung, H.-J. 617
Junica, M.I. 1227
Junnila, S. 1685

Kaita, T. 885
Kale, S. 1545
Kamerling, M.W. 557, 563
Kanakubo, T. 2427
Kanhawattana, Y. 69
Kanisawa, H. 335
Kanoglu, A. 2221
Karim, U.F.A. 1259, 1263
Kastner, R. 1273
Kato, Y. 669
Kawauti, Y. 797
Kayama, N. 845
Kayashima, N. 2427
Kegl, M. 527
Kelly, W.L. 413, 1589
Keskküla, T. 25
Khairy Hassan, A. 1201
Khalaf, M.K. 2437
Kim, D.H. 1303
Kim, H.C. 1303
Kim, S.C. 677
Kim, Y.M. 899
Kimura, Y. 335
Kiroff, L. 1613
Kitagawa, T. 1291
Kitoh, H. 1369
Klotz, S. 1393
Klug, Y. 1393, 1907, 1913
Knezevic, M. 237
Ko, M.G. 2063
Ko, M.-G. 617
Kocaturk, T. 557, 563
Koehn, E. 65, 303
Kolesnikov, A.O. 1235
Koo, J. 1145
Kopecky, M. 893
Korenromp, W. 2227
Kotsikas, L. 2209
König, G. 1907
Kubo, Y. 965
Kudzys, A. 31
Kulbach, V. 951

Kumar, R. 1983
Kumaraswamy, M.M. 217
Kunugi, T. 99
Kunz, C.U. 1029
Kunz, J. 823, 1217
Kupfer, H. 823
Kuroda, I. 1285
Kusama, R. 1291
Kushida, M. 1899
Kuwamura, H. 1129
Kwan, A.S.K. 309
Kwon, Y.B. 1303

Lagae, G. 2275, 2281, 2285, 2293
Lambert, P. 1817
Lamberts, R. 383
Lanc, D. 639
Langford, D. 85
Lawanwisut, W. 1803, 1811
Lazzari, M. 1511
Lee, I.W. 597, 611, 2063
Lee, I.-W. 617
Lee, J.H. 597, 611
Lee, K.H. 1303
Lee, S.G. 677
Letko, I. 893
Levialdi, S. 2127
Lewis, T.M. 1729
Ley, J. 309
Li, C.Q. 1803, 1811, 1943
Li, H. 2105
Li, Q. 499
Li, S.Y. 927
Liang, Z.Y. 927
Lilley, D.M. 1327
Liu, A.M.M. 425, 431
Liu, B. 1291
Liu, C.-T. 2383
Liu, T. 1279
Liu, Y.W. 1383
Loo, Y.C. 631
Loreti, S. 1003, 1581, 2455
Lu, Po-C. 2383
Luciani, G. 2127
Lueprasert, K. 69

Maegawa, K. 1423
Magaia, S.J. 1067
Magonette, G. 839, 2037
Mahmoud, K.M. 947
Malerba, P.G. 17, 981
Maloney, W.F. 397
Malécot, Y. 2393
Manca, S. 575
Mancini, G. 721, 1777
Mangat, P.S. 1817

Mangin, J.C. 481
Manoliadis, O.G. 2239
Mansour, M. 2079
Mantegazza, G. 761
Marazzi, F. 839, 2037
March, A.V. 1327
Marchiondelli, A. 533
Marino Duffy, B.M. 343
Maroldi, F. 1195
Marsalova, J. 1649
Martínez, P. 1631
Masera, M. 2257
Mastroianni, G. 2401
Masullo, A. 861
Materazzi, A.L. 2317
Matrisciano, A. 2129, 2163
Matsumoto, M. 2345
Matthys, S. 2267
Mattioli, D. 2155
Mawdesley, M. 1259, 1263
Mazzotti, C. 1375
McNamara, C. 329
Mecca, S. 2257
Meda, A. 1413
Mehta, K.C. 2369
Mendis, P. 1837
Menshari, M. 923
Meszlényi, R. 2123, 2171
Mezher, T. 229
Mezzanotte, R. 2155
Mezzetti, C. 2163
Mihara, T. 797
Mine, N. 99
Minkarah, I. 1607
Minter, A.R. 357
Mitrani, J.D. 1745
Miura, K. 603
Miura, N. 99
Miyamura, A. 1709
Mofid, M. 923
Mohamed, S. 1419
Mokha, A. 2079
Mokos, V.G. 583
Moon, Y.J. 611, 677
Moonen, S.P.G. 123, 169, 449, 1621
Moore, D.R. 2191
Morbiducci, R. 1109
Morcos, S. 1145
Moriguchi, Y. 669
Moscogiuri, C. 2163
Moser, S. 1523
Motawa, I.A. 2185
Motoki, M. 1227
Muenger, F. 823
Mullins, G. 1467
Musso, A. 2417

Mustafa, S.A. 2437
Nádasdi, F. 2123, 2171
Najafi, M. 1075
Naji, K.K. 205
Nakagawa, K. 1227
Nakamura, A. 1423
Nakamura, S. 1285
Nakano, S. 1115
Nardini, M. 2137
Nart, M. 781
Neale, B. 343
Neves, L.C. 3
Newton, L. 1691
Ng, S.T. 217
Ngo, N.S. 625
Nguyen, T.H. 81
Nielsen, Y. 369
Nikodem, P. 475
Nishi, T. 487
Nishimura, T. 603, 845, 2009, 2015
Noè, S. 455, 2331
Nonogami, M. 2427
Noor, M.A. 1883, 1957
North, A.N.W. 289
Numayr, K.S. 729
Nunziata, V. 861, 915
Nurchi, A. 2267
Nuzhdin, L.V. 1235

Oblak, M.M. 527
Odeh, A.M. 181
Odoni, Z. 1487
Ogawa, Y. 833
Ohmori, K. 1423
Okabe, A. 1503
Oliveira, O.J. 75
Oliver, J. 329
Ono, H. 1891
O'Flaherty, F.J. 1817
O'hashi, A. 1709
O'Kon, J.A. 957
Ozola, L. 25

Palmisano, F. 589
Pani, L. 1487
Pankow, H. 1057
Pantouvakis, J.P. 2203, 2215, 2239
Paoluccio, J.P. 851
Pappas, P. 1495
Park, K.S. 2063
Parsons, J. 461
Patnaikuni, I. 1837, 1863, 2431
Paulotto, C. 2309
Pecora, C. 1247
Pellegrini, R. 1511
Pelonero, D. 1241

Pentelenyi, P. 2113, 2143
Pereira, T.D. 315
Petránek, V. 1823
Petrilli, F. 49, 2479
Petrini, L. 1211
Pezzuti, E. 2149
Picard, H.E. 269
Pigorini, A. 1241
Pires, N. 315
Pitacco, I. 1043
Pizzarotti, E.M. 1241, 1247
Plank, M. 357
Popov, V.N. 1235
Pospíchal, Z. 45
Potts, K. 129
Prasad, J. 2447
Prokes, J. 1399
Provenzano, P. 2417
Proverbs, D. 129
Proverbs, D.G. 321
Pulaski, M.H. 143
Punyanusornkit, J. 1759
Putcha, C.S. 195
Puz, G. 941

Radic, J. 941
Rago, A. 117, 275, 701
Rahman, M.K. 1765
Rahman, M.M. 217
Ranzo, A. 1297
Rao, V.M. 437
Raoof, M. 1405
Rassati, G.A. 455
Raum, K. 357
Recchioni, M. 2163
Reid, S.G. 37
Righi, M. 2375
Riley, G. 321
Rinaldi, Z. 1473
Rivoltini, M. 1247
Rossi, R. 2091
Roumboutsos, A. 2209
Russo, S. 1431

Saad, S. 1419
Saber, A. 969
Saha, S. 1973
Sakamoto, O. 249
Sakate, T. 2015
Sakellaropoulos, S.P. 2197
Salerno, M. 1581, 2045
Salomoni, V. 1051
Samani, B.P. 975
Samara, M.F. 195, 263
Sansom, M. 309
Sapountzakis, E.J. 583
Sariyildiz, I.S. 1559, 1751

Sarja, A. 1697, 1703
Sato, Y. 1503
Savoia, M. 1375
Scattolini, E. 1241
Sciotti, A. 2409
Scrimshaw, I.C. 2245
Selvadurai, A.P.S. 2417
Sen, R. 1467
Senaud, G. 2455
Sener, E. 1075
Senouci, A.B. 205
Sepe, V. 2029, 2331
Sereno, A. 775
Serra, S.M.B. 75
Seto, T. 2009, 2015
Setunge, S. 1863
Sgambi, L. 521, 693, 707, 981, 1789, 2487
Shalouf, F. 1017
Shannis, L.G. 811
Shehab, H.K. 2437
Shi, J. 189
Shimoyama, K. 1285
Shiomi, M. 1423
Shukla, A.P. 65
Shukla, P. 303
Sibilio, E. 2029
Silvestri, M. 2471, 2487, 2495
Silvestri, S. 1151, 1187
Silvi, S. 1003
Simic, D. 1725
Simiu, E. 2353
Simone, A. 737
Singh, A. 443
Sluys, L.J. 737
Smit, S. 2233
Sobotka, A. 199
Solari, G. 2323
Sonobe, Y. 2427
Sonoda, K. 1369
Spagnoli, P. 2159
Speranzini, E. 1165
Spinelli, P. 2359
Stephenson, P. 2245, 2251
Sterpi, E. 761
Steven, G.P. 499
Stouffs, R. 1559, 1751
Stracuzzi, A. 2257
Striagka, F. 2203, 2215
Strug, B. 475
Suen, C.H. 403, 1739
Sujjavanich, S. 1759
Sumito, H. 249
Sun, X. 855, 1103
Sutrisna, M. 129, 321
Suwanpruk, J. 1759
Taddei, D. 2461, 2511

Tahir, M.Md. 1419
Takeuchi, M. 1891
Tamura, T. 249
Tan, T.H. 855, 1103
Tanaka, H. 1899
Tanaka, S. 1949
Tanigawa, Y. 1891
Tanucci, G. 2159
Tarquini, G. 693
Tay, U.L. 789
Tayebi, A. 969
Tenah, K.A. 151, 377
Thirugnanasundaralingam, K.
  2431
Thorpe, A. 289, 2179
Tijhuis, W. 57
Tin-Loi, F. 625
Tohme, H.J. 65, 303
Tokuoka, A. 1949
Tomida, M. 1423
Tominaga, Y. 249
Tomioka, N. 1503
Toniolo, G. 1177
Toth, P. 2113, 2143
Toups, J. 969
Touran, A. 137, 245
Tracanelli, A. 1043
Tranquilli, S. 521
Trombetti, T. 1151, 1187
Tsuchida, K. 1227
Tsuda, H. 1899
Tsutsumi, T. 2003
Tunçer, B. 1559, 1751
Turk, A. 715, 867
Turk, A.A. 975
Turkalj, G. 639
Tursi, A. 569

Ueda, M. 2009, 2015
Ueno, H. 249

Ugwu, O.O. 217
Ukegawa, M. 1227
Umbertini, A. 2149
Uomoto, T. 1883, 1957
Usmen, M. 1599
Uzzi, G. 189

Vaidogas, E.R. 31
Valentini, P.P. 2149
Vallini, P. 1443
van den Adel, J. 2227, 2233
van den Adel, J.F. 1259, 1263
van den Dobbelsteen, A.A.J.F.
  1661
van der Zanden, G.C.M. 1637
Van Impe, R. 2275, 2281, 2285,
  2293
van Weeren, C. 557
Vanlaere, W. 2275, 2281, 2285,
  2293
Vavro, J. 893
Veglianti, D. 707
Veltkamp, M. 549
Verma, K.K. 1453
Vestroni, F. 2023
Videla, C. 1631
Vidoli, S. 2023
Vignoli, A. 1165
Vitone, A. 589
Vitone, C. 589
Vollum, R.L. 789

Wang, J. 1967
Wang, J.Y. 137
Wang, M.-T. 363
Wang, Y.G. 2105
Watanabe, K. 1891
Watson, P.A. 1595, 1625
Wei, T.C. 1207
Weiße, D. 1393, 1907, 1913

Wethyavivorn, B. 515
Wheat, H.G. 1459
Williams, S.R. 2097
Wong, C.Y. 1855
Wong, K.K.F. 2071
Wong, Y.M. 403
Wong, Raymond, W.M. 107
Wootton, A.B. 289
Wu, Y.T. 507

Xie, Y.M. 499

Yagi, T. 2345
Yahaya, N. 1419
Yamada, K. 1949
Yamada, T. 603
Yamaguchi, E. 965
Yamaguchi, Y. 1899
Yamamoto, S. 965
Yamaoka, S. 1369
Yang, C.M. 899
Yang, J.-B. 175
Yassin, A.Y.M. 1419
Yazdani, S. 81, 659
Yen, T. 1383
Yeoh, M.L. 2185
Ying, Y. 2251
Yiu, T.W. 403, 1739
Yonekura, A. 797
Yoshitake, I. 1227, 1899

Žabička 45
Zafar, S. 1765
Zaitsu, K. 797
Zawdie, G. 85
Zayas, V. 2079
Zhang, J.H. 2105
Zhang, S.B. 431
Zhao, D.F. 2071
Zhuge, Y. 1355